THE ORIGIN OF LIFE ON THE EARTH contains a complete record of the proceedings in English, French and German, with an English translation of the Russian - language contributions, of the first international scientific gathering on this subject, held in Moscow by the Academy of Sciences of the U.S.S.R.

For many decades scientists maintained what amounted to a conspiracy of silence about the problem of the origin of life. This was no doubt a reaction to Pasteur's detailed refutation of those of his contemporaries who claimed to be able to produce life from non-living materials. Since Pasteur's time, the understanding by physicists and chemists of the properties of matter has increased out of recognition. This, with the growth of biochemical and geo-chemical knowledge in the twentieth century, has stimulated fresh speculations on this age-old problem.

The subject matter is treated under these five headings:

1. Primary Formation of Primitive Organic Compounds on the Earth.

2. The Transformation of Primary organic Compounds on the Earth.

3. The origin of Proteins, Nucleo-proteins and Enzymes.

4. The Origin of Structure and Metabolism.

5. The Evolution of Metabolism.

The book will serve as an authoritative outline of present-day ideas and controversies surrounding the origin of life, and will have permanent historic interest as an assessment of what was achieved in the first century since Pasteur.

THE ORIGIN OF LIFE
ON THE EARTH

I.U.B. SYMPOSIUM SERIES
VOLUME 1

PROCEEDINGS OF THE
FIRST INTERNATIONAL SYMPOSIUM ON

The Origin of Life on the Earth

HELD AT MOSCOW 19-24 AUGUST 1957

EDITED FOR THE ACADEMY OF SCIENCES OF
THE U.S.S.R. BY

A. I. OPARIN   A. G. PASYNSKIĬ

A. E. BRAUNSHTEĬN   T. E. PAVLOVSKAYA

English–French–German Edition

EDITED FOR THE INTERNATIONAL UNION OF BIOCHEMISTRY
BY

F. CLARK and R. L. M. SYNGE

PERGAMON PRESS

NEW YORK · LONDON · PARIS · LOS ANGELES

1959

PERGAMON PRESS INC.
122 East 55th Street, New York 22, N.Y.
P.O. Box 47715, Los Angeles, California
PERGAMON PRESS LTD.
4 & 5 Fitzroy Square, London W.1
PERGAMON PRESS S.A.R.L.
24 Rue des Écoles, Paris Ve

Library of Congress Card No. 59-12060

*Printed in Great Britain by Adlard & Son Limited,
London and Dorking*

Contents

Foreword   ix

Introductory Note from the International Union of Biochemistry   xiii

Editors' Preface   xv

Introductory Address, by A. I. OPARIN*   I

Discours d'ouverture, by M. FLORKIN   5

First Session (Chairman: M. FLORKIN)

Primary Formation of Primitive Organic Compounds on the Earth

REPORTS

V. G. FESENKOV: Some considerations about the primaeval state of the Earth   9

H. C. UREY: Primitive planetary atmospheres and the origin of life (*read by* S. L. MILLER)   16

A. P. VINOGRADOV: The origin of the biosphere*   23

J. D. BERNAL: The problem of stages in biopoesis   38

COMMUNICATIONS

V. A. SOKOLOV: The evolution of the atmosphere of the Earth*   54

B. YU. LEVIN: The formation of the Earth from cold material and the problem of the formation of the simplest organic substances*   67

N. W. PIRIE: Chemical diversity and the origins of life   76

P. N. KROPOTKIN: The geological conditions for the appearance of life on the Earth and the problems of petroleum genesis   84

A. P. TERENT'EV and E. I. KLABUNOVSKIĬ: The role of dissymmetry in the origin of living material (*read by* A. P. TERENT'EV)   95

DISCUSSION (Chairman: L. PAULING):   106

N. H. HOROWITZ, V. I. KRASOVSKIĬ and I. S. SHKLOVSKIĬ (*read by* I. S. SHKLOVSKIĬ),* A. A. GARIBYANTS,* N. M. GALAKTIONOVA,* A. I. LEBEDINSKIĬ,* I. S. SHKLOVSKIĬ,* H. A. LYUBIMOVA,* V. V. ALPATOV,* A. S. KONIKOVA,* J. D. BERNAL, N. W. PIRIE, A. E. BRAUNSHTEĬN,* A. KRAVTSOV,* L. PAULING*

Second Session (Chairman: J. D. BERNAL)

The Transformation of Primary Organic Compounds on the Earth

REPORTS

S. L. MILLER: Formation of organic compounds on the primitive Earth   123

A. N. TERENIN: Photosynthesis in the shortest ultraviolet   136

COMMUNICATIONS

K. BAHADUR: The reactions involved in the formation of compounds preliminary to the synthesis of protoplasm and other materials of biological importance   140

T. E. PAVLOVSKAYA and A. G. PASYNSKIĬ: The original formation of amino acids under the action of ultraviolet rays and electric discharges (read by T. E. PAVLOVSKAYA)*   151

CONTENTS

E. I. Klabunovskiĭ: Absolute asymmetric synthesis and asymmetric catalysis*   158

R. L. Berg: Some conditions for the appearance of life on the Earth*   169

Discussion (Chairman I. Malek):   172

   E. I. El'piner and A. V. Sokol'skaya (*read by* E. I. El'piner),*
   M. Vol'kenshtein,* A. G. Pasynskiĭ,* E. I. Klabunovskiĭ and V. V. Patrikeev*
   (*read by* V. V. Patrikeev),* M. A. Messineva,* L. Pauling,* J. D. Bernal,*
   S. Akabori, C. Reid, D. Sapozhnikov,* S. L. Miller, S. Fox,
   A. G. Pasynskiĭ,* A. Ya. Smirnova,* A. A. Gurvich*

Third Session (Chairman: In-Khun-Chen)

The Origin of Proteins, Nucleoproteins and Enzymes

Reports

S. Akabori: On the origin of the fore-protein   189

O. Hoffmann-Ostenhof: Der Ursprung der Enzyme   197

M. Calvin: Evolution of enzymes and the photosynthetic apparatus   207

L. Pauling: The nature of the forces operating in the process of the duplication of
molecules in living organisms   215

Communications

R. L. M. Synge: The occurrence of amino acids in Nature   224

F. Šorm: Ähnlichkeit der Struktur bei Eiweißstoffen   231

K. Felix: Die Kontinuität des Eiweisses   241

S. W. Fox: A chemical theory of spontaneous generation   256

(Chairman: K. Mothes)

L. A. Nikolaev: Complex compounds and models of enzymes*   263

M. G. Kritsman and A. S. Konikova: Experimental demonstration of the occurrence of metabolic processes in simple proteins (*read by* M. G. Kritsman)*   275

F. Cedrangolo: The problem of the origin of the proteins   281

Discussion: 289

   S. E. Bresler,* A. G. Pasynskiĭ,* S. Oeriu, G. F. Gause,* E. M. Makovskiĭ,*
   A. M. Goldovskiĭ*

Fourth Session (Chairman: S. Akabori)

The Origin of Proteins, Nucleoproteins and Enzymes (*continued*)

Reports

E. Chargaff: Nucleic acids as carriers of biological information   297

H. L. Fraenkel-Conrat and B. Singer: The infective nucleic acid from tobacco
mosaic virus (*read by* H. L. Fraenkel-Conrat)   303

G. Schramm: Die Bedeutung der Virusforschung für die Erkenntnis biologischer
Vermehrungsvorgänge   307

W. M. Stanley: On the nature of viruses, genes and life   313

Communications

A. N. Belozerskiĭ: On the species specificity of the nucleic acids in bacteria   322

A. Wacker: Die Spezifizität der Desoxyribonukleinsäure   332

CONTENTS

E. Broda: Die Entstehung des dynamischen Zustandes 334

M. Grunberg-Manago: Synthèse enzymatique des ribopolynucléotides 344

A. E. Mirsky: A note on the evolution of nucleic acids 358

J. Brachet: Les acides nucléiques et l'origine des protéines 361

Discussion (Chairman: O. Hoffmann-Ostenhof) 368

A. I. Oparin,* I. Málek,* E. N. Pavlovskiĭ,* N. W. Pirie, A. A. Smorodintsev,*
H. L. Fraenkel-Conrat,* W. M. Stanley,* L. A. Zil'ber,* V. Ryzhkov,*
A. N. Belozerskiĭ,* G. Schramm,* V. S. Tongur,* S. E. Bresler,*
A. S. Konikova,* M. Grunberg-Manago, K. G. Ioffe,* N. I. Nuzhdin*

Fifth Session (Chairman: M. Grunberg-Manago)

The Origin of Structure and Metabolism

REPORTS

J. D. Bernal: The scale of structural units in biopoesis 385

N. M. Sisakyan: The part played by structural elements in the biochemical function of cells* 400

I. Prigogine: Problèmes d'évolution dans la thermodynamique des phénomènes irreversibles (read at Sixth Session) 418

COMMUNICATIONS

A. I. Oparin: Biochemical processes in the simplest structures 428

P. Mitchell: The origin of life and the formation and organizing functions of natural membranes 437

A. G. Pasynskiĭ: Enzymic reactions in stationary open systems* 444

F. B. Straub: Biosynthesis of enzymes and their origin 455

R. Khesin: Cell structure and protein synthesis 460

E. Macovschi: Some relationships between coacervates and enzymes* 466

G. A. Deborin: Protein complexes as biochemically active systems 470

Discussion (Chairman: F. B. Straub): 480

K. Mothes, O. B. Lepeshinskaya,* M. V. Vol'kenshteĭn†,*
A. G. Pasynskiĭ,*† K. S. Trincher,*† Zh. Ĭordanov,* G. M. Frank,* S. W. Fox,
P. Sokol,* T. N. Evreinova,* V. I. Vorobiev,* G. P. Kalina,* M. I. Gol'din,*
R. L. Berg,* V. S. Tongur,* B. S. Diskina,* J. D. Bernal,* I. Prigogine*†
(†Contributed at Sixth Session)

Sixth Session (Chairman: K. Felix)

The Evolution of Metabolism

REPORTS

M. Florkin: L'extension de la biosphère et l'évolution biochimique 503

V. N. Shaposhnikov: Über einige wahrscheinliche Wege der Evolution des Stoffwechsels bei den Mikroorganismen 516

A. E. Braunshteĭn: The pathways of biological assimilation and dissimilation of nitrogen and some aspects of their evolution 527

COMMUNICATIONS

V. L. Kretovich: Le rôle de l'ammoniaque dans l'assimilation autotrophe de l'azote 544

CONTENTS

M. Ishimoto and F. Egami: Meaning of nitrate and sulphate reduction in the process of metabolic evolution 555

B. A. Rubin: The comparative characters of the oxidative systems of various groups of organisms in relation to their evolution* 562

S. Oeriu: The effect of cysteine on the methionine content of the animal and plant organism 572

Discussion (Chairman: J. S. Heller): 578
   K. Mothes, A. Blagoveshchenskiĭ,* N. S. Akulov,* G. A. Kritskiĭ*

Seventh Session (Chairman: E. M. Makovskiĭ)

The Evolution of Metabolism (continued)

Reports

E. Aubel: Au sujet du passage de la vie anaérobie á la vie aerobie 585

Y. Oda: Significance of molecular hydrogen metabolism in the transitionary stage from anaerobiosis to aerobiosis 593

A. A. Krasnovskiĭ: Development of the mode of action of the photocatalytic system in organisms* 606

Communications

C. Reid: The relation between primitive and present-day photobiological processes ... 619

Yu. I. Sorokin: The evolution of chemosynthesis 626

D. J. Sapozhnikow: Entstehung und Evolution der phototrophen Ernährungsweise ... 635

T. N. Godnev: Die Grundetappen der Biogenese des Chlorophylls 642

S. Scher: Thermal factors in archaeometabolism 650

Final General Discussion (Chairman: M. Calvin):* 652
   Chairman's introductory remarks, S. Fox, S. Scher, J. D. Bernal,
   D. I. Sapozhnikov, K. Mothes, E. Chargaff, G. Schramm, K. Felix,
   A. M. Goldovskiĭ, M. Calvin, A. E. Braunshteĭn, A. G. Pasynskiĭ, S. Miller,
   L. Pauling, A. I. Oparin, Chairman's closing remarks

Author Index 657

Subject Index 674

Foreword

THE QUESTION of the origin of life is one of the fundamental problems of science. However, for almost the whole of the first half of the present century this problem has occupied only an insignificant place in the world scientific literature. It is only in recent years that there has arisen a certain turning point in this respect and a great interest in the question of the origin of life has developed in wide circles of scientists.

In this connection it has been suggested that the time is ripe for drawing up an account of our knowledge of the problem of the origin of life and to point out ways in which it can be further studied.

In 1955 the General Assembly of the International Union of Biochemistry, gathered together in Brussels, put forward the desirability of calling a special International Symposium on the subject. It was suggested that the place of this Symposium should be the Soviet Union, the scientists of which had made a considerable contribution to the solution of the problem of the origin of life.

Following up the initiative of the International Union of Biochemistry, the Academy of Sciences of the U.S.S.R. organized a Symposium devoted to the problem of the origin of life on the Earth, which was held in Moscow in August 1957.

This Symposium attracted the attention of very wide circles of scientists. More than forty scientists, representing sixteen countries, took a direct, personal part in its work. Many of them were outstanding investigators in their own fields. Their names are known all over the world.

Among the participants in the Symposium were: E. Broda and O. Hoffmann-Ostenhof (Austria), I. Prigogine and M. Florkin (Belgium), Zh. Ïordanov (Bulgaria), R. L. M. Synge, J. D. Bernal and N. W. Pirie (Great Britain), F. Straub (Hungary), K. Felix, G. Schramm and A. Wacker (Federal German Republic), K. Mothes and J. Böttger (German Democratic Republic), C. Reid (Canada), In-Khun-Chen (China), J. Heller, B. Skarzinski and W. Nemerko (Poland), S. Oeriu and E. Makovskiĭ (Rumania), L. Pauling, M. Calvin, W. M. Stanley, N. Horowitz, H. L. Fraenkel-Conrat, S. Miller, A. Mirsky and E. Chargaff (U.S.A.), E. Aubel and M. Grunberg-Manago (France), I. Málek and F. Šorm (Czechoslovakia), S. Akabori, M. Ishimoto and Y. Oda (Japan).

In addition, many well-known scientists, such as H. Urey (U.S.A.), K. Bahadur (India), F. Cedrangolo (Italy), J. Brachet (Belgium) and others who could not, for one reason or another, come to Moscow themselves, sent the texts of their papers and contributions with the request that they be presented to a session of the Symposium or included in its printed works. Soviet scientific circles also took a great interest in the Symposium. A number of Soviet astronomers, physicists, geologists, chemists and biologists took part in it. About 500 visitors, in addition to the members, attended the sessions of the Symposium and they sometimes took part in the general discussions.

The very fact of there being such a representative gathering of scientists showed not only the great interest taken in the problem under consideration by the Symposium, but also that the previous negative attitude of scientists to the problem has now finally ceased to exist and the question of the origin of life has become a field of intensive experimental work.

At the basis of the programme for the work of the Symposium, which had previously been discussed and adopted unanimously, lay the principle of the evolutionary origin of life. This principle was shared by all the participants in the conference, a fact which greatly facilitated the extremely friendly and intensive work of the Symposium. It was very characteristic of this work that, in the process of discussing the different stages in the evolutionary development of matter in the Symposium, a number of new facts came to light, giving a foundation and experimental confirmation to a number of suggestions which had hitherto only been speculative in nature. Of course, although participants in the Symposium were all essentially in agreement about the evolutionary principle in the solution of the problem of the origin of life, nevertheless, on particular questions there were considerable differences between them which led to very heated and fruitful discussions.

However, the very nature of the discussions showed how far we have progressed along the path of scientific elucidation of the problem of the origin of life. For instance, even comparatively recently, the opinion was widely held among scientists that, under natural conditions and in inorganic Nature, even the simplest organic substances could not arise primarily. It was held that these substances could only be formed biogenically. In the Symposium it was shown to be completely possible that hydrocarbons and their derivatives could be formed on the surface of the Earth even before the emergence of life. This could have occurred in many different ways and the argument now was only concerned with which of these ways was the dominant one in the process of formation of our planet and in the earliest stages of its existence.

In just the same way, there was a time when it was considered that the asymmetry of organic materials, which is characteristic of protoplasm, was the exclusive prerogative of living things and it was maintained that it could not arise at any place or time in the inorganic world.

In the Symposium there were reported many asymmetrical syntheses under the influence of circularly-polarized ultraviolet light, by catalytic reactions occurring on the surface of quartz crystals, spontaneously by slow crystallization from solutions etc. The argument is now not concerned with whether or not the asymmetry of the first organic substances could have arisen abiogenically, but with which of the numerous possible ways was actually used on the surface of our planet, even long before the appearance of living materials on it.

Similarly, there lay before the Symposium the question of the possible means of abiogenic formation of amino acids, porphyrins, protein-like polymers, polynucleotides and other high-molecular organic compounds.

The large amount of experimental material put before the Symposium was a clear demonstration of the complete possibility of the primary formation of these compounds on the surface of the Earth even before life was present on it.   An extremely large amount of attention was given, at the Symposium, to nucleic acids, nucleoproteins and viruses.

The question of what stage of the evolutionary elaboration of organic material we should associate with the beginning of life is one which has aroused much argument. Can life be attributed to individual molecules, even if they are very complex, or only to the multimolecular systems which served as a basis for the emergence of life?

Numerous facts were laid before the Symposium, showing ways in which complex organic molecules could combine into multimolecular systems, the development of which could give rise to the emergence of the most primitive organisms.

The last sessions of the Symposium were devoted to general biochemical problems connected with the further development of metabolism. Although, at first glance, such problems might seem to be outside the scope of the problem of the origin of life, yet the comparative study of metabolism will certainly contribute a very great deal to our understanding of the laws which governed the emergence of metabolism, i.e. the emergence of the form of the motion of matter which is essentially characteristic of life.

One very valuable result of the Symposium was that it presented, to any scientist in the world, an extensive front of questions in the solution of which physicists, astronomers, geologists, chemists and biologists of all specialities can play a part. Each of these, if he is seriously interested in the solution of the problem of the origin of life, will find his part in the work, in which progress will contribute to a general scientific solution of the problem which concerns us all.

Furthermore, the Symposium was important, not only on account of its scientific results, but also because this gathering was a new and successful step in fruitful international co-operation between scientists of many countries.

The present collected volume is intended to bring the results of the work of the Symposium before wider circles of scientists and to enable more rapid progress to be made in the solution of the problem of the origin of life on the Earth.

A. I. OPARIN

Introductory Note from the International Union of Biochemistry

THE appearance of this book in both Russian and English marks the occasion of the first international symposium organized under the auspices of the International Union of Biochemistry. The arrangements for the Symposium were made by the Academy of Sciences of the U.S.S.R. and the meeting was held in Moscow from 19 to 24 August 1957.

The topic which was chosen, 'The Origin of Life on the Earth', covers one of the basic questions of natural science, and the participation of a large group of biochemists in this Conference indicates both the interest that is now taken by biochemists in this biological question and also the progress that is being made in an approach to its solution in terms of the formation and origin of the structural components and metabolic systems of living matter.

We are indebted to Mrs. Ann Synge for undertaking the translation of the Russian contributions to the Symposium, and to Dr. R. L. M. Synge, F.R.S., and Mr. F. Clark for editing the English edition. Finally, our thanks are due to the Pergamon Press, who have undertaken to publish this book as the first of a numbered series of publications from the International Union of Biochemistry.

M. FLORKIN
E. H. STOTZ
R. H. S. THOMPSON

Editors' Preface

THE INTERNATIONAL UNION OF BIOCHEMISTRY asked us to act as Editors of this English–French–German Edition of the entire Proceedings of the Symposium, which is being published in parallel with a Russian Edition. The Committee acting for the Academy of Sciences of the U.S.S.R. as Editors of the latter have supplied us with texts, which are here published with minor editorial changes for the sake of uniformity. Texts received in Russian have been translated into English by Mrs. Ann Synge, and these are indicated by asterisks in the Contents List.

Some of the contributions to the Symposium were preprinted as uncorrected proofs in English, French and German for the use of participants in the Symposium. As these contributions were bound, they could be confused with the present definitive publication. Unfortunately, they received notice in *Chemical Abstracts* (**52**, 1331, 1958).

A multilingual publication presents special difficulties in the transliteration of Russian names. We have followed as far as possible the system used in *Chemical Abstracts*, but this could not be done rigorously, especially in the French and German papers. To restore non-Russian proper names from Russian texts to their original spellings demands superhuman qualities, and mistakes are certainly present. For these and other errors we apologize.

Abbreviations for periodicals are as far as possible those used in the *World List of Scientific Periodicals published in the Years* 1900–1950 (Butterworths Scientific Publications, London, 1952) or in *Chemical Abstracts*. Other abbreviations follow in general the practice of the *Biochemical Journal*. The Indexes have been compiled by Mr. W. Hill.

F. CLARK

R. L. M. SYNGE

Introductory Address

A. I. OPARIN

Academy of Sciences of the U.S.S.R., Moscow

Esteemed colleagues, dear friends,

In opening the International Symposium which is to consider the problems of the origin of life on the Earth, I wish, first of all, to extend a warm welcome to our visitors, outstanding scientists of various specialities, who have come to Moscow from seventeen countries to take part in the work of the Symposium.

The very fact that the company, which is gathered here to discuss the problems of the origin of life, is so widely representative in its composition is, in itself, most significant and encouraging.

A few years ago our friend Mr Pirie, who is present to-day, asked me what really new and significant facts have been found out in the field of the discovery of the origin of life since the time of Huxley and Tyndall. It seems to me that our Symposium is a very important event in the field of enquiry in which we are interested.

Nevertheless, twenty or thirty years ago, even the calling of such a Symposium would have been completely impossible in that, until quite recently, experimental scientists had not paid sufficient attention to this problem.

During almost the whole of the first half of this century it was only possible to find, in the world literature, a very few isolated attempts to advance towards a scientific solution of the question of the origin of life.

This state of affairs was by no means fortuitous. It arose from the fact that, until the end of last century and the beginning of this one, the ideas of most scientists were governed, almost exclusively, by the principle of spontaneous generation, the conviction that living things (though only the most primitive ones) could arise directly from the inorganic materials of the natural world. However, very carefully conducted experiments showed convincingly that, in every case where spontaneous generation was stated to have been observed, the findings were the results of faults in the experimental methods. This took away the ground from under the feet of those scientists who saw, in spontaneous generation, a scientifically credible way in which life could have originated. They were, thus, without any possibility of an experimental approach to the problem, which led them to a very pessimistic conclusion, namely, to the belief that the problem of the origin of life was 'proscribed', that it was an insoluble problem and that to work on it was unworthy of any serious investigator and was a pure waste of time.

It is now quite obvious that the reason for this negative attitude towards the problem under consideration lay, not in the nature of the problem itself, but in an incorrect approach to its solution.

The problem of the origin of life cannot be solved in isolation from a study of the whole course of the development of matter which preceded this origin. Life is not separated from the inorganic world by an impassable gulf—it arose as a new quality during the process of the development of that world. An evolutionary approach to the study of our problem will, therefore, open up a wider vista of possibilities for its solution.

The advances in present-day science, the rich store of facts which are now at the disposal of astronomers, physicists, geologists, chemists and biologists, enable us to draw, with some degree of verisimilitude, a picture of the evolutionary development of matter which took place at some time on our planet, and to point out the possible stages through which this development could have passed on the way to the emergence of life.

We must suppose that, as the first stage, there were present, on the still lifeless Earth, the simplest organic compounds, the hydrocarbons and their closest derivatives. The succeeding increase in complexity of these compounds, which occurred abiogenically in the lithosphere, atmosphere and hydrosphere of our planet, in accordance with the general laws of physics and chemistry, may be regarded as the second stage in this development. This process resulted in the appearance of very complicated organic substances of high molecular weight, in particular, substances resembling proteins, nucleic acids and other compounds characteristic of contemporary protoplasm. Further, one may postulate the emergence of some sort of primary systems, based on these substances, which changed under the influence of the external medium and which could undergo selection. The evolutionary development of these systems may be regarded as the third stage which led, finally, to the emergence of the simplest primary organisms.

It is, of course, a very involved and extremely difficult undertaking, not only to give a theoretical explanation of the most important events which occurred in the past, but also to obtain proof of the correctness of this explanation.

We have, as yet, no single satisfactory account of the phenomena which occurred at some time on our planet. We want to verify our assumptions, either by observations of natural phenomena which are taking place at present, or by experimental reproduction of the separate stages of the development of matter which we have postulated.

This sort of approach to the question opens up wide possibilities for practical work by scientists on the problem of the origin of life. This work, however, does not consist in hopeless attempts to produce the sudden spontaneous generation of organisms (as was the case earlier), but in the study and experimental reproduction of phenomena which are not only quite possible, but which follow laws and which arise successively during the evolutionary development of matter.

It is quite obvious that an undertaking of this sort is not within the powers of any single investigator, or narrowly specialized scientific team, for the development of matter leading to the origin of life takes place by means of phenomena which are studied by workers in different scientific fields and requires, for its understanding, and even more for its reproduction, the mastery of many different techniques of investigation. Furthermore, it is essential that the investigations carried out should be made into a whole by the common acceptance of certain general ideas, particularly as concerns the sequence and interdependence of the phenomena being studied.

Naturally the numerous facts which have recently been brought to light in various fields of science without any direct relation to the question of the origin of life are also of great importance for the solution of our problem. It may, however, be felt that the time has come for the undertaking of work directly aimed at the solution of our problem. I believe that our present gathering provides the opportunity for the methods of investigation employed in various branches of science to be used, not only to provide a general opinion on the problem in question, but also to indicate practical ways of working towards its solution.

Of course, even the ways of approaching the work may be very various. On the Organizing Committee which called this Symposium the question arose as to whether, in view of the large amount of material for presentation, the conference ought not to be split into specialized sections. However, we decided that it would be better to limit, to some extent, the number of papers read and to provide, throughout, possibilities of general discussion in which the representatives of the various sciences and branches of learning could participate.

In opening our Symposium, allow me to express the hope that it will really be a landmark in the history of the study of the problem with which we are concerned and that its work will serve as a great stimulus to the extension of studies in this field, enabling rapid advances to be made towards the solution of the problem of the origin of life.

I think I am voicing the general wish in proposing, as chairman of our present session, the esteemed President of the International Union of Biochemistry, Professor Florkin.

Discours d'ouverture

M. FLORKIN

Président de l'Union Internationale de Biochimie

Mes chers collègues,

Je sui très reconnaissant à Messieurs les membres du Comité organisateurs de ce Symposium, de bien vouloir m'appeler à la présidence de cette séance d'ouverture.

Cet honneur, dont je sens tout le prix, ne s'adresse pas à ma modeste personne, mais à la fonction de Président de l'Union Internationale de Biochimie, à laquelle m'a appellé la confiance de mes collègues biochimistes, et que j'ai essayé d'accomplir dans la mesure de mes capacités depuis plusieurs années.

Lors de la première réunion du Conseil de l'Union, tenue à Londres à 1954, mes collègues Engel'gardt et Oparine ont bien voulu proposer l'organisation à Moscou par les soins de l'Académie des Sciences de l'URSS et sous l'égide de l'Union Internationale de Biochimie, d'un Colloque International sur l'origine de la vie.

A cette époque l'Union Internationale de Biochimie était encore dans les difficultés de la petite enfance.

Elle n'avait pas reçu la consécration de l'admission au sein du Conseil International des Unions Scientifiques et il faut bien dire qu'elle avait plus d'ennemis que d'amis.

La proposition de nos collègues de l'URSS était une précieuse marque de confiance et d'amitié, qui a été accueillie avec gratitude par le Conseil de l'Union Internationale de Biochimie.

Cette proposition venait au moment où les études sur les origines des mécanismes de la vie qui sont des objets des études biochimiques, entraient dans la phase expérimentale.

Il était particulièrement indiqué de réunir ce Symposium dans la ville même du pionnier incontesté des études sur l'origine de la vie—le professeur Aleksander Ivanovitch Oparine.

La brillante participation d'une pléiade de savants de premier plan est le gage du succès de ce Symposium de caractère véritablement et authentiquement international. Aussi ne voudrais-je pas retarder d'avantage le plaisir que nous désirons tout prendre à leurs exposés.

Primary Formation of Primitive Organic Compounds on the Earth

Some Considerations about the Primaeval State of the Earth

V. G. FESENKOV

Institute of Astrophysics, the Academy of Sciences Kazakh SSR, Alma-Ata, U.S.S.R.

THE SOLUTION of many problems of geology, geochemistry, biology, and particularly the basic problem of the origin and development of life, requires a knowledge of the conditions that characterized the physical state of the Earth during the earliest periods following its formation. To describe these conditions in the light of a definite cosmogonic hypothesis would be misleading, since the problem of cosmogony cannot be as yet considered as fully solved. On the contrary, the solution of this problem should follow from a consideration of all relevant facts that are capable of receiving, as far as possible, a unique interpretation.

From a consideration of such facts one may draw certain conclusions relating to the process of formation and development of the Earth.

The first conclusion is that during its formation the Earth lost a considerable part of its initial mass. It may be assumed that the Earth of to-day is but a nucleus of the primary protoplanetary condensation that consists of the heavier elements and their oxygen compounds [1]. This conclusion is supported by the fact that the elements most frequently met with in the Universe, in the stars and in the sun, and which for this reason should also be abundant in the primaeval medium that gave birth to the planets, are nearly totally absent in the present-day atmosphere of the Earth. Conspicuous is the negligible quantity of the inert gases (including xenon and crypton) in our atmosphere, whereas their abundance in the universe is many times greater [2].

The question may arise as to the process that could promote the escape of the primordial atmosphere of the Earth, including even such heavy gases as krypton and xenon. It is quite evident that if each gas escaped individually in accordance with its atomic weight, these very abundant heavy gases would have remained on the Earth in practically their original abundance. It must therefore be concluded that this process of dissipation is determined chiefly by the most abundant and the lightest element, namely by hydrogen which constituted the greater part of the primitive Earth's mass. As hydrogen escapes into space it takes with it all the insignificant impurities, excessively high temperatures not being required for this purpose. If we assume that the initial abundance of hydrogen corresponded, to a certain extent, to its abundance in the Universe, the inevitable conclusion is that there remains from the primitive Earth only a small percentage of its original mass. A further proof of the primitive Earth's losing a considerable portion of its mass is the very fact of the existence of the Moon. There can be no doubt that the Earth–Moon system occupies a special place in our solar

9

system. At present, the rotational moment of the Moon in its orbital motion is nearly 75% of the total rotational moment of the whole system. This indicates the importance of the role of the Moon in the dynamics of the Earth–Moon system. Nothing resembling this can be found in the systems of the other planets. For example, if we calculate the total rotational moment of Jupiter from the internal distribution of densities and the known period of rotation, and if we compare it with the sum of rotational moments of all of Jupiter's satellites, we shall find that the latter does not exceed 1·5% of that of the planet. The very great importance of the orbital rotational moment of the Moon in the case of the Earth is cogent proof that the Earth, in contrast to the other planets of the solar system, originated as a double planet and therefore the process of its formation should be very similar to the process of formation of double stars in general.

A binary star is formed from two closely situated centres of condensation in one and the same primary gaseous-dust nebula whose total rotational moment, as is usually the case, is too large for a single stable nucleus to develop. For this reason the rotational moment must necessarily be distributed between two, or, in some cases, among even a larger number of individual condensations.

A similar assumption should be made with respect to the Earth. Thus, the presence of our satellite signifies that by coming into existence the Moon took upon itself the greater part of the total rotational moment of the whole primary system, thus giving stability to the Earth. Without this the protoplanet of the Earth would never have been able to solidify as a single body.

However, the subsequent evolution of the Earth–Moon system evidently proceeded in the direction of a sharp reduction of its reserve of rotational moment, since at present it is already possible to add to the Earth the total rotational moment connected with the orbital movement of the Moon without disturbing the stability of the Earth. Indeed, the rotation period of the Earth would then reach 4·4 hours whereas approximately 1·3 hours is sufficient to disrupt the stability. However, a decrease in the rotational moment can take place only in the case of a decrease in the mass.

To sum up, the conclusion may be drawn on the basis of the above-considered facts that during its formation the Earth lost a substantial part of the original mass. This explains the discrepancy between the Earth and the Sun in the abundance of various elements in them despite the fact that both bodies must have come from one and the same medium. Hence, the conclusion may be drawn that the Earth's first atmosphere was entirely lost and that the present-day gaseous shell is a secondary phenomenon.

The chief factors responsible for this loss of mass of the protoplanet are its temperature and initial mass. This immediately becomes clear if we compare the different planets. In the biggest planet, Jupiter, with its mass 318 times that of the Earth, the atmosphere is composed of 80% of hydrogen, 15% of helium and approximately 5% of the other heavy gases [3], thus bearing the closest resemblance to the Sun. In the atmosphere of Uranus, hydrogen is second to helium in abundance; in the surface layers of the Earth it occupies the eighth to the tenth place, but is still present in sufficient quantities to form oceanic waters;

and, finally, on Mars, whose mass is one order less than that of the Earth, the content of hydrogen is so small that this planet has no water and in all probability never had any appreciable quantities of it (at the present time an equivalent layer of water on the surface and in the atmosphere of Mars is equal to approximately 0·1 mm).

In this connection, of special interest is the phenomenon of vulcanism connected with the generation of water vapours on the Moon, a body with a mass two orders less than that of the Earth. At the present time, the mechanism of lunar formative processes is attributed by certain authors [4, 5] (Baldwin, Urey, and others) solely to external forces, namely the falling of meteorites and asteroids up to hundreds of kilometres in diameter. However, most if not all geologists and others attribute this origin to internal forces, that is tectonic and vulcanic processes [6]. Without entering into a discussion of this problem, we may at least point out that there exist on the Moon a large number of formations and peculiarities of relief which could in no way originate from falling meteorites. Such are the lunar domes noted in certain numbers by P. Puiseux [7] when compiling the lunar atlas of the Paris Observatory some fifty years ago, and more recently by Wilkens & Moore; the table mountain Margentin; the polygonal forms on the Moon that are especially developed near the north pole (in the district of Mare Frigoris) and represent hexagons of vertical walls placed directly on the surface of the Moon; the systematic distribution of small craters, especially those located along the ridges of huge circular mountains; the existence of close chains of tiny craters situated mostly on rills or clefts in the lunar soil (the well known hill of Hyginus near the centre of the lunar discs strewn with twenty-three small craters); the tendency of the large craters to form twins; the general conformity between the structure of the craters or the circular mountains and the tectonic peculiarities of the surrounding territory, the orientation of gorges, and the like; (one of the best known of such faulted formations and one oriented parallel to the general direction of the gorges in the region of Ptolemy is a vertical wall situated to the northeast of Arzahel;) the existence of bright haloes around some of the smaller craters, especially those situated in clefts and whose origin is apparently due to various gases escaping from the interior of the Moon. One of the most convincing proofs in favour of earlier vulcanism is the existence of orifices at the summits of the central cones of craters which were recently discovered in considerable number by Wilkens & Moore using the 33-in. refractor of the Meudon Observatory [8].

All these peculiarities of lunar forms cannot be brought into agreement with the meteorite hypothesis but are in natural accordance with the conception of their tectonic origin.

On 3 November 1958 N. A. Kozyrev, of the Pulkowa Observatory, U.S.S.R., observed the eruption on the Moon produced by the central mountain of Alphonsus nearly in the centre of the lunar disc. This eruption was followed by emission of carbon compounds registered spectroscopically.

If it is recognized (and this follows from the above-mentioned facts) that the Moon is capable of exhibiting vulcanism and tectonic phenomena of internal forces associated with the escaping of gases, including water vapours, which must have been widespread chiefly in the distant past, it is all the more reasonable that similar phenomena should have occurred on planets with a greater mass, such as Mars and the Earth. As observations show [9], an atmosphere on the Moon should be non-existent due to the very small force of gravity on its surface and to the comparatively high temperature, which exceeds 100 °C at the centre of the lunar disc during full Moon. On Mars water vapour may easily escape into interplanetary space at a temperature of approximately 200 °C (according to Spitzer). This temperature might easily have been attained in the past during the first stages of the existence of this planet. On the Earth, water vapour escaped only during the period of dissipation of the mass of the original proto-planet, but later eruptions from the interior were totally retained because of various tectonic processes. The production of water vapour presupposes a considerable temperature in the interior of the Earth, and this requires an explanation.

In this connection, it is essential to dwell on the problem of the early thermal history of the Earth. Speaking generally, one should presuppose the existence of four different sources of heat during the formation of our planet: the conversion of potential energy into kinetic energy, in other words, the release of the energy of condensation as is the case in the gravitational compression of any gaseous-dust nebula; the origin of different mineral compounds, for example olivine and others, that is the transition of the chemically comparatively simple protoplanetary medium into complex compounds, all of which take place chiefly in conditions where oxygen is insufficient. These geochemical reactions should, in the main, also be of the exothermic type. Then there develop processes of a more protracted character, those that take place throughout the whole existence of the planet, namely radioactive heating that depends essentially on the distribution of radioactive substances within the mass of the Earth, and the redistribution of the internal masses of the planet according to molecular weight. Both processes depend on the intensity of the first two. If even during the very first stage of its existence the planetary mass reaches a sufficiently high temperature, then, owing to the convective currents that arise, radioactive substances are quite rapidly transported to the surface layers, in which case radioactive heating is confined essentially to these surface layers and does not in general attain any great magnitude. If, however, the planetary mass remained in the cold state from the very beginning, the distribution of radioactivity may be considered as being even throughout its whole mass in the course of the greater part of all past history, in which case radioactive heating might be very considerable though not capable of causing the Earth to become liquid. The detailed calculations of the radioactive heating were made by E. A. Lyubimova, J. A. Jacobs, and others for different models of the Earth [9, 10, 11]. To avoid these uncertainties in our discussion of the early thermal history of the Earth, we must consider the most indicative facts as a whole. As may be supposed, of greatest importance in this respect are the data of seismology and terrestrial magnetism, according to which the central core of the Earth (at least in its external part) is in a liquid state and does not transmit transverse waves. Consequently, the temperature of the central parts of the Earth should be at least several thousand degrees. The sharp jump in density when passing to the crust indicates apparently that the core of the Earth consists chiefly of iron and nickel [11].

A fact pointing to the thermal state of the surface layers of the Earth is that the continents are composed chiefly of granite, which consists of three basic minerals: quartz, felspar and mica. It is generally recognized that granite must have formed through the cooling of hot magma at a temperature not less than 1000 °C. The continental granite massif has been growing in volume and area since the very earliest stages of the development of the Earth [12].

The dynamics of continent formation is far from clear, but in general it should have consisted in the escape of huge quantities of molten silicate from the interior of the Earth, which was accompanied by the development of platforms, a gradual diminution of geosynclines, which was a certain irreversible and gradually relaxing process.

This process was also accompanied by a gradual decrease in the intensity of volcanic activity. A. P. Pavlov [13] has given us a very vivid picture of how enormous basaltic fields occupying many millions of square kilometres on the Yenisei, the Tungusk, in Greenland, India, the United States and in other parts of the world were formed in the past as a result of volcanic activity.

At the present time, the only active zones of vulcanism left are those in the Kamchatka region and the Kurile islands, and also in the Mediterranean. This process of the extrusion of masses of silicate to the surface, the process of formation of a sialitic Earth crust through gradual differentiation, was inevitably accompanied by the production of water vapour that fed the oceans. And this is not all. It may, apparently, be considered that the water of the oceans of to-day must have come from the interior of the Earth chiefly during the cooling period there. According to Grayton [14] the water vapour content in erupted magma of volcanoes may reach 10% in weight. Moreover, Geranson has shown that the granite magma under pressures that correspond to a depth of 10 to 20 km is capable of retaining huge quantities of water in solution that make up as much as 10% of the total weight. The ability to hold water falls with the pressure, and the water escapes in the form of vapour. Consequently, any extrusion of sialitic material to the surface must inevitably lead to the escape of enormous quantities of water that remains on the quickly cooling Earth and fills the depression between the slightly raised continents. If we consider for a moment that the average depth of the oceans spread evenly over the whole surface of the Earth amounts to approximately 3–4 km, then all that is required for an explanation of the production of this quantity of water from the interior of the Earth is an analogous extrusion of material within the limits of a thin 20–30-km layer, which exactly corresponds to the external thickness of the Earth's crust.

All these geological facts are in good agreement with the theory of H. Jeffreys [15] who postulates that the Earth was originally in a gaseous state, but that in roughly 5000 years it could be reduced to a liquid state due to convection currents. And the total energy of condensation to the present radius would be 10,000 cal/g. Later, when our planet passed to the solid state, the cooling time was considerably extended until the temperature of the surface at last reached 300° from absolute zero. According to Goldschmidt [16], the atoms of uranium and thorium cannot (due to their excessive volume) enter into any silicate lattice in the process of crystallization. Therefore, when the deeper parts of the Earth began to solidify, these atoms must have gradually been pushed to the outside and enriched the external layers. In the same way, Holmes [17] assumed that volatile material, extruded from the Earth's interior during cooling, also takes with it radioactive matter. Hence it follows that the radioactive layer during the very first stages of the solidified Earth was extremely thin, and the degree of radioactivity fell sharply with the depth. Thus, radioactivity could never have played a marked role in the thermal history of the Earth.

The formation of the Earth as a heated cosmic body leads inevitably to the loss of enormous quantities of the original gaseous elements, and all the more so of the entire primordial atmosphere.

The water of the oceans of to-day must have escaped from the Earth's interior during its cooling stage. The same must be said of the atmosphere which was also formed of gases that accompanied tectonic and volcanic processes. To a great extent, this was water vapour, carbon dioxide, methane, sulphides and also nitrogen, which even to-day is found escaping in certain localities.

It is known that oxygen in the free state cannot escape from the interior of the Earth. However, a certain quantity of this gas can form gradually by decomposition of water vapour under the action of electric discharges and in the upper layers of the atmosphere due to hard wavelengths of solar radiation. In the lower layers, this gas can exist only in negligible quantities.

The juvenile water that made up the primaeval waters of the oceans was poorly provided with various mineral salts. Its enrichment with the most diverse elements took place gradually as a result of an irreversible process, an example of which is the water cycle in nature, the constant erosion of the continents by rivers which carry their sediment back to the sea. To a certain extent, a similar process of erosion might take place also at the bottom of the ocean due to the peculiar interaction with the continents, all this leading to the formation of deep, submarine canyons in places that never reached sea level.

Resulting from the processes of this so-called geological preparation there was gradually formed a water medium enriched with all possible elements that were in a state of easy migration with respect to each other. A medium of this kind can promote the generation of life. Without such a medium organic life could not have arisen.

Thus, in order that life should appear there must be not only a sufficient amount of solar radiation, a water medium, but also an abundance of all possible elements capable of forming all possible compounds. An essential condition for this is that the surface of the planet must be only partially covered by continents and partially by oceans and that here the waters of the oceans might in the course of thousands of millions of years enrich themselves with the products of erosion of the continents. The medium required for the beginning of organic life could not have formed on a planet like Mars which has never had any open basins of water.

REFERENCES

1. G. KUIPER, *J. R. astr. Soc. Can.*, **50**, 158, 1956.
2. H. BROWN, Rare gases and the formation of the Earth's atmosphere; In *The Atmospheres of the Earth and Planets* (Ed. by G. KUIPER). Univ. Chicago Press, 1947.
3. V. G. FESENKOV & A. G. MASEVICH, *Astr. Zh. S.S.S.R.*, **28**, 317, 1951.
4. K. B. BALDWIN, *The Face of the Moon.* Chicago, 1949.
5. H. UREY, *The Planets, their Origin and Development.* Yale Univ. Press, New Haven, 1954.
6. J. SPURR, *Geology Applied to Selenology.* Science Press, Lancaster, 1945.
7. P. PUISEUX, *La terre et la lune.* Gauthier-Villars, Paris, 1908.
8. H. WILKENS & P. MOORE, *The Moon.* London, 1955.
9. J. A. JACOBS & D. W. ALLAN, *Nature, Lond.*, **177**, 155, 1956.
10. E. A. LYUBIMOVA, *Dokl. Akad. Nauk S.S.S.R.*, **107**, 55, 1956.
    E. A. LYUBIMOVA, *Izv. Akad. Nauk S.S.S.R.*, Ser. Geophys., No. 5, 416, 1955.
11. E. ÖPIK, *Irish astr. J.* **3**, No. 7, 1955.
12. V. A. OBRUCHEV, *The Principles of Geology.* Akad. Nauk S.S.S.R., Moscow, 1956.
    O. FR. TUTTLE, *Sci. Amer.*, **192**, 77, 1955.
    P. N. KROPOTKIN, *Priroda, Leningr.*, No. 4, 31, 1956.
13. A. P. PAVLOV, *Volcanoes, Earthquakes, Seas, Rivers.* Moscow, 1948.
14. L. K. GRAYTON, Conjectures regarding volcanic heat. *Amer. J. Sci.*, **243-A**, 1945.
15. H. JEFFREYS, *The Earth.* Cambridge Univ. Press, 1952.
16. V. GOLDSCHMIDT, *Naturwissenschaften*, **18**, 999, 1930.
17. E. HOLMES, *Geol. Mag.*, **2**, 322, 1915.

Primitive Planetary Atmospheres and the Origin of Life

HAROLD C. UREY

University of Chicago, Urbana, Illinois

HALDANE [1] pointed out that life probably originated under anaerobic conditions. He argued that the fermentative metabolic processes of living organisms of widely different structure are very similar while the oxidative reactions are very different, thus indicating that the anaerobic metabolism is the most primitive. He suggested that the source of energy for the metabolism was metastable molecules produced by ultraviolet light from the sun. Oparin [2] in an interesting book comes to very similar conclusions. He has discussed in some detail the possible ways by which organic substances of inorganic origin may combine to produce the most primitive organisms. These arguments as well as others by Pirie [3] and Bernal [4] seem to me to be more conclusive evidence for the primitive conditions on the Earth than any that can be drawn from geochemical and cosmochemical studies. However, studies of the latter kind confirm the biochemical conclusions.

The most remarkable feature of the Earth's atmosphere is its content of elementary oxygen, and it is the only planet on which free oxygen has been detected. It has been recognized, ever since Jeans derived formulae for the escape of gases from atmospheres, that hydrogen would escape more readily than other gases and that this must result in an increased state of oxidation of the atmosphere and perhaps in the presence of free oxygen [5, 6]. To-day we have much more information in regard to the Earth's atmosphere than previously and hence are in a better position to discuss its probable history. From the ages of the meteorites as determined from the lead isotopic abundances and from the ^{87}Rb–^{87}Sr and ^{40}K–^{40}A dating methods, we know that some very involved physical and chemical processes took place 4.5×10^9 years ago. Presumably this occurred at the time the solar system originated and we can take this as the age of the system. Also, we now know more about the temperature distribution and convection in the terrestrial atmosphere and hence are able to supplement the theory of Jeans for the escape of atmospheres. These studies make possible a better estimate of the history of planetary atmospheres generally.

HISTORY OF THE EARTH'S ATMOSPHERE

We do not know the temperature at which the Earth's surface was formed, but it can be stated firmly that the only feasible source of heat for producing a high-temperature primitive earth was its own gravitational energy of accumulation [7]. If it accumulated so rapidly that this energy could not be radiated into space, it could have originated in a melted condition. However, in view of our present great difficulty in understanding how a planet could accumulate without retaining certain gaseous constituents, e.g. krypton and xenon, it seems most likely that the accumulation process required tens or hundreds of millions of years and hence that the general temperature of the earth during its formation was low. (The writer no longer accepts Kuiper's proto-planetary model at least for the terrestrial planets [8] and in fact always had great difficulty in fitting the great amount of chemical evidence into that theory.) The arrival of objects containing metallic iron and water on the earth's surface would result in the production of hydrogen gas, from the reaction $Fe + H_2O = FeO + H_2$, which is strongly displaced to the right at high temperatures. At low temperatures reactions to form methane from carbon and hydrogen, and ammonia from nitrogen and hydrogen should occur and these substances should have been present temporarily at least*.

Thus a reducing atmosphere must surely have existed for a short period of time at least.

The escape of gases from planetary atmospheres is determined at the escape layer by the formula of Jeans,

$$L_i = M_c c_i \sqrt{\frac{RT_c}{2\pi\,\mu_i}}\,(1 + x_i)\,e^{-x_i}, x_i = \frac{GM\mu_i}{RT_c\,a_c}$$

In this formula, L_i is the rate of escape of molecules of the ith kind in molecules per sec and cm^2, M_c is the number of molecules per cm^3 at the escape layer, c_i is the fraction of these molecules at the escape layer which are of the ith kind, μ_i is the molecular weight of the escaping molecule, T_c is the temperature at the escape layer, a_c is the radius of the planet at the escape layer, M is the mass of the planet, and G the gravitational constant. The quantities in this formula can be estimated approximately with the exception of c_i and this depends particularly on the mixing in the atmosphere. Convection must stop at a high level where diffusional separation becomes high. This level is estimated to be at about 160 km above the Earth's surface and the rate of escape may be limited by diffusion to the escape layer which for the Earth is some 300–500 km above the Earth's surface. Also, condensible substances such as water will be kept below the tropopause at 8–17 km above the Earth's surface. Finally, condensible substances may be decomposed by ultraviolet light into non-condensible substances which can then escape through a low temperature layer to the higher atmosphere. In a recent paper, the writer [10] has reviewed this problem for the Earth, Venus and Mars. The escape of planetary atmospheres when these factors are considered is a very complicated problem. The results will be briefly summarized here.

At the present time escape of hydrogen from the Earth is limited by condensation of water at about 187 °K at the tropical tropopause and by diffusion from the 160 km level to the escape layer, the temperature of which must be high, i.e. some 2000–4000 °K. The calculated rate of escape is 10^7 atoms/cm^2/sec, though this is uncertain by an order of magnitude probably. The escape rate

---

* When these arguments were advanced some years ago [9] the brilliant work of Miller had not been done and hence modifications of the discussion are necessary.

2

corresponds to the decomposition of 20 g of water per cm^2 during 4.5×10^9 years. This would not account for the elementary oxygen of the Earth's atmosphere, but the calculated loss may be in error sufficiently to make agreement possible, as has often been done in the past. However, hydrogen, methane, ammonia, carbon monoxide and hydrogen sulphide escape from the interior of the Earth in unknown amounts. These are oxidized and this can occur without decrease in atmospheric oxygen only by the escape of hydrogen from the Earth. Also, unknown amounts of ferrous iron of the Earth's crust have been oxidized to ferric iron. In order to have oxidized the carbon, sulphur, nitrogen and ferrous iron observed in the crust of the Earth, water to the extent of about 10% of the oceans must have been decomposed and the hydrogen lost from the Earth. We do not know how extensive the loss of hydrogen has been, but it seems most likely that the rate of loss has been much greater for much of geologic time than the calculated rate given above.

For the purposes of the calculation of the rate of loss of hydrogen mentioned above, the concentration of hydrogen as water or molecular hydrogen above the tropopause was taken as 2 ppm. Light of the Schumann region cannot penetrate to the tropopause and below because molecular oxygen absorbs in this region. In the absence of molecular oxygen only carbon dioxide will absorb in this region and this gas is removed in a high degree from the Earth's atmosphere by reaction with silicate rocks ([9], p. 148 ff.). Hence, at the present time, water below the tropopause is not decomposed photochemically and hence excess amounts of hydrogen do not escape above the tropopause and thus to the escape layer and away from the Earth. However, before oxygen appeared in the atmosphere this must have occurred and hence far more hydrogen escaped to the high atmosphere and the rate of escape from the Earth was far greater than it is now. Thus there are good reasons to suppose that the rate of escape during the early history of the Earth was very large.

We outline the history of the atmosphere approximately as follows. Molecular hydrogen escaped so rapidly that this occurred essentially during the period of accumulation of the Earth. Methane and ammonia were decomposed rapidly, but carbon compounds soluble in water were formed which dissolved rapidly in the oceans. Some volatile hydrogen compounds, e.g. CH_4, C_2H_2 etc., remained in the atmosphere and were decomposed by light and the hydrogen escaped. If these were absent, water below the tropopause was decomposed and the hydrogen escaped. When carbon dioxide appeared, it reacted with the silicate rocks to form limestone. Only when oxygen appeared did the rapid escape of hydrogen cease due to the absorption of the Schumann region by molecular oxygen and the present low rate of escape begin. There is no difficulty in understanding some very large rate of escape in the past and a very small rate at the present time.

When did free oxygen first appear in the Earth's atmosphere? An attempt was made to answer this question some years ago [9]. Unfortunately, no additional evidence has come to light during the past years. (1) Thode, MacNamara & Fleming [11] have observed that ^{34}S is concentrated in sulphates relative to the sulphides and they present evidence that this began some 10^9 years ago. This may mark the time at which free oxygen first appeared in the atmosphere.

(2) The enormous iron deposit of the pre-Cambrian some 2×10^9 years ago may mark the time of transition from a reducing to an oxidizing atmosphere, as MacGregor [12] suggested.

Attempts have been made in the writer's laboratories to find primitive sources of hydrogen and to determine the relative abundance of deuterium in such hydrogen. It was thought that fractionation of the hydrogen isotopes during escape would occur and hence that primitive hydrogen would have less deuterium than the hydrogen of the present oceans and that the difference in deuterium content would give an indication of the total loss of hydrogen. No conclusive decision in regard to this question has been deduced.

THE ATMOSPHERE OF VENUS

The atmosphere of Venus contains large amounts of carbon dioxide above the cloud layer estimated by Herzberg [13] as some 10^5 cm atmospheres. No water or oxygen has been detected. Some evidence has been found by Kozyrev [14] for the presence of nitrogen and carbon monoxide.

Recent data of Pettit & Nicholson [15] on the intensity of light reflected and absorbed in the 8–14 cm region indicate that the temperatures of the light and dark hemispheres are 233 °K and 238 °K respectively. Adel [16] has given reasons for believing that this radiation comes partly at least from higher transitions of the CO_2 molecule and since this radiation is absorbed by great thicknesses of this gas, the radiation in this region probably originates fairly high in the atmosphere and not at the cloud level. From the distribution of intensity in the P & R branches of the 7820 and 8689 Å bands of CO_2 Chamberlain & Kuiper [17] estimate a temperature of 285 °K. Their measurements refer to regions well away from the mid solar point. Since these bands are partly absorbed by the atmosphere the temperature must be some average for all the gas above the clouds at the positions investigated. Mayer, Stoanaker & McCollough [18] have reported a temperature greater than 350 °K by observations on the 3·15 cm radiation. Possibly this radiation comes from the surface of the planet, though this point is uncertain.

From the standpoint of the question as to whether life exists on the planet, the problem of the presence of water on the planet is of paramount importance for no life as we know it exists in the absence of condensed water, and though many terrestrial plants grow in very dry places and conserve their liquid water, it is very difficult to believe that life could have evolved in the absence of copious amounts of liquid water.

The planet is covered with clouds of a slightly yellow colour which show marked absorption in the blue and near ultraviolet [14]. These clouds clear slightly and permanent surface markings have been observed by Danjon [19] and Dollfus [20]. If conditions were similar to those of the Earth, nearly all carbon dioxide would have reacted with the silicate rocks and form limestone, dolomite and sand [9]. Whipple & Menzel [21] suggest that the planet is completely covered by oceans so that no effective contact between rocks and carbon dioxide exists. Urey assumed that no water existed and hence erosion was ineffective in making contact between carbon dioxide and the rocks. Danjon's and Dollfus' observations require that some permanent surface features exist. These might be continents awash with the oceans so that erosion is not effective. Or, water clouds may exist in the high atmosphere but no liquid water is now present in its surface.

It has been suggested that the clouds are due to dust, but in this case the dust must be remarkably white. No abundant white solids are present on the Earth and no method for their production on Venus has been suggested. Moreover, the partial clearing indicates the presence of phenomena such as rain or evaporation. Dust clouds would indicate the presence of strong convection and of very small particles. Settling of dust during a short period of time would be impossible under these conditions.

Water and carbon dioxide appear to be the only stable substances likely to be present on a planet having an oxidation state such as that of Venus. Lyot [22] observed the polarization of the light from the clouds and found it to be very similar to that produced by small droplets of water. Altogether it seems most likely that the clouds are due to water, as Menzel and Whipple have argued, but it is not certain that the surface is covered with oceans.

Since Venus is nearer the sun and had a smaller mass, the escape of hydrogen from its surface should be greater than that from the Earth on the basis of Jeans' formula. However, the escape of hydrogen from the Earth is limited by condensation of water at the tropopause and the diffusion of hydrogen in the high atmosphere and not by the conditions imposed by Jeans' escape equation. We can make only very uncertain estimates in regard to detailed structure of the atmosphere of Venus. Since the planet probably rotates only once in its year, a rising current at the mid solar point probably exists similar to the rising current at the Earth's equator. For purposes of approximate calculation we estimate this temperature as 225 °K as compared with 187 °K for the temperature of the Earth's equatorial tropopause. If the atmosphere of Venus above this point is saturated with water at this temperature, the concentration of hydrogen above the tropopause will be about 145 times as great as that above the Earth and, other conditions being similar, the rate of loss of hydrogen will be about $1 \cdot 45 \times 10^9$ atoms/sec/cm². This is equivalent to 3000 g of water/cm² during $4 \cdot 5 \times 10^9$ years. This would be sufficient to oxidize 1000 g of carbon/cm² from the zero oxidation state to carbon dioxide. This estimate has no great certainty at all.

The decomposition of water below the tropopause cannot occur because of the absorption of light in the Schumann region by carbon dioxide. This absorption will be substantially complete if 100 cm atmospheres of carbon dioxide is present above the tropopause. Thus, the history of the atmospheres of Venus and the Earth must have been different because the carbon dioxide remains in the atmosphere of Venus and not in that of the Earth. As soon as 100 cm atmospheres of carbon dioxide remained above the tropopause of Venus the rapid loss of hydrogen ceased, but in the case of the Earth this occurred only when some 2 cm atmospheres of oxygen gas appeared above its tropopause. Hence, the oxidation of the Earth has probably progressed to a much more advanced stage than did that of Venus. The general course of chemical change should have been similar to that outlined for the Earth.

There is no certain evidence that life exists on Venus. The conditions most likely to prevent life are (1) the absence of water and (2) prohibitively high temperatures on its surface. So far as we know the conditions on that planet do not exclude its existence.

THE ATMOSPHERE OF MARS

The only constituent of the atmosphere of Mars that has been definitely identified is carbon dioxide. From Kuiper's [23] observations on the intensities of absorption of the 1·6 band in the Martian and terrestrial atmospheres, Grandjean & Goody [24] estimate that the CO_2 content of the Martian atmosphere per cm^2 is thirteen times that of the earth. The remainder of the atmosphere is probably nitrogen with some admixture of radiogenic argon. The total amount of atmosphere is about 230 g/cm^2 according to the measurements of Dollfus [25].

Very small amounts of water are present on Mars. The polarization of the polar caps is similar to that of ice at liquid-air temperatures [25] and Kuiper [23] reports that the reflection spectrum of the caps is similar to that of frost at low temperatures. Also, the morning haze is probably water. Dunham [26] estimated the water as less than 5 cm atmospheres. Oxygen has not been detected.

The maximum equatorial daytime temperature is reported to be as high as 30 °C but the night temperature falls to −70 °C. It is evident that there is no liquid water on the planet at the present time.

The escape of gases from Mars presents quite different problems from those met in the cases of the Earth and Venus, because the mass of the planet is so very much smaller. Hydrogen will escape readily from the planet if the temperature of the high atmosphere is only moderate. The interesting question is whether oxygen will escape also. A recent study by Urey [10] in which condensation at the equatorial tropopause and diffusion in the high atmosphere are considered comes to the following conclusions. If the temperature of the high atmosphere, i.e. the escape layer, is at 2000 °K oxygen will escape from the planet at appreciable rates and the net effect is the removal of water. (A temperature of 2000 °K for the high atmosphere of Mars is not unreasonable in view of the indications that high temperatures exist in the high terrestrial atmosphere.) Water remains near the surface but carbon dioxide is transported by oxygen to the high atmosphere. Photochemical decomposition gives atomic oxygen and carbon monoxide. The latter reacts with water at low levels to produce carbon dioxide and hydrogen. Both the oxygen and hydrogen escape. On the other hand nitrogen will not be lost at catastrophic rates because it is not appreciably dissociated at the escape layer and remains mostly as molecular nitrogen, whereas oxygen is mostly dissociated. Thus very large amounts of water may have been present in the past. If life is present on Mars, such oceans must have existed in the past and only the escape of oxygen and hydrogen from the planet could have removed large quantities of water from the planet.

If large amounts of water were present on Mars in the past, a more extensive cloud layer must have been present, the albedo was higher and glaciers must have covered the poles and most of the surface. These glaciers must have transported glacial drift toward the equator. Since much of the surface was covered with ice, carbon dioxide could not have reacted with the surface rocks and must have remained in the atmosphere. Hence, high concentrations of carbon dioxide would have reached the high atmosphere and the escape of atomic oxygen must have been very rapid. When most of the water was lost, the carbon dioxide could have reacted with the rocks and disappeared and the present situation with little water and carbon dioxide would have developed.

The evidence in regard to the development of the Martian atmosphere does not preclude the existence of life on the planet providing oxygen in large amounts has escaped from the planet. It is likely that this is the case. The general chemical development should have been similar to that occurring on the Earth during its early history.

CONCLUSION

It is probable that the three planets, Venus, Earth and Mars, all originated with substantial amounts of water on their surfaces. The estimated temperatures are such as not to be prohibitive for the evolution and maintenance of life.

This paper is a brief summary of certain parts of a much more detailed survey of the problem of atmospheres which will appear in the *Handbuch der Physik*, where detailed arguments for many points mentioned will be given and where more detailed references will appear.

REFERENCES

1. J. B. S. Haldane, *The Origin of Life*. Rationalist Annual, 1929.
2. A. I. Oparin, *The Origin of Life*. Macmillan, New York, 1938.
3. N. W. Pirie, *New Biol.*, **16**, 41, 1954.
4. J. D. Bernal, *The Physical Basis of Life*. Routledge & Kegan Paul, London, 1951.
5. S. Arrhenius, *Ann. Nat.-(u.Kultur)phil.*, **9**, 22, 1910.
6. J. H. J. Poole, *Sci. Proc. R. Dublin Soc.*, **22**, 345, 1941.
7, 8. H. C. Urey, *Chapter in Physics and Chemistry of the Earth*, Vol. 2. Pergamon Press, London, 1956.
9. H. C. Urey, *The Planets*. Yale Univ. Press, 1952.
10. H. C. Urey, *Handbuch der Physik*. In the press.
11. H. G. Thode, J. MacNamara & W. H. Fleming, *Geochim. et cosmoch. Acta*, **3**, 235, 1953.
12. A. MacGregor, *S. Afr. J. Sci.*, **24**, 155, 1927.
13. G. Herzberg, *Atmospheres of the Earth and Planets* (Ed. by G. P. Kuiper). Univ. of Chicago Press, 1949.
14. N. A. Kozyrev, *Publ. Crimean astrophys. Obs.*, **12**, 169, 1954.
15. E. Pettit & S. B. Nicholson, *Publ. astr. Soc. Pacif.*, **67**, 293, 1955.
16. A. Adel, *Astrophys. J.*, **93**, 397, 1941.
17. J. W. Chamberlain & G. P. Kuiper, *Astrophys. J.*, **124**, 399, 1956.
18. C. H. Mayer, R. M. Stoanaker & T. P. McCollough. As reported in *Sky & Telesc.*, **15**, 435, 1956.
19. A. Danjon, *Astronomie*, **57**, 161, 1943.
20. A. Dollfus, *Mém. Soc. Sci. Liége*, 4e série, **18**, 141, 1956.
21. F. H. Whipple & D. H. Menzel, *Publ. astr. Soc. Pacif.*, **67**, 161, 1955.
22. B. Lyot, *Ann. Obs. Paris (Meudon)*, **8**, 1929.
23. G. P. Kuiper, *Atmospheres of the Earth and Planets* (Ed. by G. P. Kuiper). Univ. of Chicago Press, 2nd ed., 1952.
24. J. Grandjean & R. M. Goody, *Astrophys. J.*, **121**, 548, 1955.
25. A. Dollfus, *C. R. Acad. Sci., Paris*, **233**, 467, 1066, 1951.
26. T. Dunham, *Atmospheres of the Earth and Planets* (Ed. by G. P. Kuiper). Univ. of Chicago Press, 1949.

The Origin of the Biosphere

A. P. VINOGRADOV

V.I. Vernadskiĭ Institute of Geochemistry and Analytical Chemistry of the Academy of Sciences of the U.S.S.R., Moscow

IN REVIEWING this little-studied question, I have naturally tried to assemble the best-authenticated data. However, as there are not many such, I have tried to fill the gaps by means of scientific reasoning. I know that I shall often repeat what has been said by others before me.

As I was not able to give a direct or unequivocal answer to the question of when and under what conditions the biosphere came into being, I was obliged to follow the whole course of geochemical events on the Earth before I could convince myself that I had found out the place and time of its appearance.

The fundamental propositions concerning the biosphere were, undoubtedly, established by E. Süss. He introduced into science the concept of the biosphere as an envelope of the Earth comprised of living things. V. I. Vernadskiĭ, with his characteristic deep insight, showed the full significance of this envelope in regard to the geochemical processes of the Earth. He said that 'from the geological and geochemical point of view the problem is not that of the synthesis of an individual organism, but that of the emergence of the biosphere.' Nearly a hundred years earlier the happy thought occurred to Daubrée that there is a similarity between the composition of meteorites and that of the layers of the Earth. This idea was, scientifically, extremely fruitful. Bowen, Daly, Goldschmidt, Urey, O. Y. Shmidt and many others followed it up. I am in complete agreement with this point of view. Thanks to isotopic analyses of lead and other researches using radioactivity it has been possible to establish that the age of the substance of which the Earth is composed and that of the substance of meteorites is very similar, namely about 5×10^9 years [20].

THE CRUST OF THE EARTH AT PRESENT

The crust of the Earth as we know it consists of basaltic and granitic shells overlaid by a covering of sedimentary deposits. The crust of the Earth is classified both according to its chemical composition and to its seismic properties. The superficial part is separated from the rock of the mantle by the Mohorovičič discontinuity, which lies at a depth of about 40 km beneath the continents. Lower down there lie the ultrabasic rocks which are even poorer in SiO_2 and richer in Mg and Fe. Of these ultrabasic formations, some, the dunites, sometimes emerge on to the surface of the Earth, filling up cracks and deep fractures of its crust.

The basaltic shell covers the whole of the globe. The granitic shell covers about half the Earth's surface and is most highly developed on the continents. It is absent from the floor of the Pacific Ocean. Borings made on the Pacific atolls

(Marshall Islands and others) have not shown any granite, the bore passing straight into a basic olivine rock. The floors of the Atlantic and Indian Oceans (except in their deep rifts) seem to have a granitic layer. The basaltic layer in the beds of the oceans seems to be at least 10–15 km thick. There is, thus, no gradual transition between the oceanic and continental parts of the crust of the Earth.

The view was put forward a long time ago that there was a certain uniformity of composition of the shells of the Earth—the granitic, the basaltic and any other—throughout its whole extent.

Undoubtedly the structure of the crust of the Earth, its thickness and composition, give an indication of the way in which it could have been formed. The formation of the crust of the Earth is related to the differentiation of the substances of the Earth when hot.

THE HEAT OF THE EARTH

The course of the thermal balance of the Earth over 5×10^9 years is a very complicated problem. It is generally considered that there were two possible sources of the heat of the Earth. (1) That it was the result of the radioactive decay of U, Th and ^{40}K and (2) that it was caused by the energy liberated as a result of the compression of the Earth. Even as concerns radiogenic heat there has been no agreement among scientists during recent years, mainly owing to the absence of sufficiently accurate data concerning the amounts of U, Th and K in meteorites and in the depths of the Earth, and to the inaccuracy of determinations of the constants of decay. If we assume that, at the present, the mean content of radioactive substances in the silicate phase of the Earth is the same as that of the stony meteorites or chondrites, i.e. $U \sim 3 \times 10^{-6}\%$, $Th \sim 1 \times 10^{-5}\%$ and $K \sim 8 \cdot 5 \times 10^{-20}\%$, then elementary calculations will show that 5×10^9 years ago the radiogenic heat was enough to melt the material of which the Earth is composed. I must add, though, that the mean values assumed for the content of U, Th and K in meteorites are minimum ones.*

There is even more room for doubt in the second question, namely, the extent to which the mean values of the content of radioactive elements in chondrites is a permissible means of calculating the thermal effect on the Earth. Unfortunately, however, we have no other means of doing so. Even in the case of dunites, those ultrabasic rocks of the mantle of the Earth which sometimes reach its surface, we have no reliable data as to their content of U, Th and K or other elements, let alone mean values. I must point out that the obtaining of such data is quite a difficult task. Our comparative estimate of the contents of U, Th, K and a number of other elements in chondrites and dunites indicates that the latter contain considerably less of radioactive and some other elements than do the stony meteorites or chondrites. As we shall see later, there is, from our standpoint, an explanation for this. We can also agree that the singularly good and definite determinations of K in dunites carried out by Holyk and Ahrens are correct. They give extremely low values for the K content of dunites, namely $\sim 1 \times 10^{-3}\%$.

* Even when analysing the same stony meteorites different workers have made estimates of U content ranging between 3×10^{-6} and $3 \times 10^{-5}\%$ [8, 14, 17].

In a few words, if we assume that the crust of the Earth was formed as a slag from the mantle of the Earth and that, overall, it removed into itself from the mantle from $\frac{1}{3}$ to $\frac{1}{2}$ of all the radioactive elements of the Earth, then the analogy between the chondrites, so far as concerns their U, Th and K contents, and the mean composition of the silicate phase of the Earth at least, is unshakeable at present. Nor do the data which Birch has just obtained, showing an identical heat flow per unit area of surface of the continents and ocean beds, contradict this view [1, 3].

The role of gravitational heat, particularly in the earliest phases of the development of the Earth, is not clear.

However, by far most important event in the history of the development of the thermal balance of our planet was the formation of the crust of the Earth with its alteration of the distribution of radioactive and other elements and of heat within the terrestrial globe, and its disturbance of thermal equilibrium.

THE FORMATION OF THE CRUST OF THE EARTH

The interdependence of the formation of the crust of the Earth, the hydrosphere and the atmosphere is widely accepted and would appear to be an incontestable truth.

TABLE I

Possible modes of formation of the crust of the Earth

From the hot material of the protoplanet	From the cold material of the Earth
Differentiation of substances into phases at temperatures above 2000°A. Loss of light gases (H_2, He). Formation of the permanent nucleus of the Earth.	Cold, solid heterogeneous material (Fe and silicates) losing chemically inert and volatile compounds. Absence of gas pressure.
Formation of the thick crust of the Earth (during 10^6–10^7 years) and possibilities of differentiation of basaltic and granitic layers.	Heating with the formation of a thin, growing crust of the Earth by melting out. (Temp. 1000°A).* Growth of the Fe-nucleus of the earth.
Absence of volcanism.	Earthly and later underwater volcanism. Degassing. Formation of the primitive atmosphere (without inert gases), vapours, H_2O, CO_2, HF etc.
Primary density of the atmosphere containing H_2O, CO_2, H_2 etc. and also inert gases in cosmic abundance.	Cooling of the significant surface of the Earth. Weathering. Water condensation. Formation of the ocean. Formation of continents with ancient nuclei of formations which developed as a result of plutonic activity (granitic envelope).
Cooling of the surface of the Earth. Great weathering processes. Condensation of all the water to form the primary 'acid' ocean. Formation of continents. Formation of the secondary oxygen-containing atmosphere as we know it today (by precipitation of $CaCO_3$ and by photosynthesis).	Contemporary, secondary, oxygen-containing atmosphere resulting from precipitation of $CaCO_3$ and photosynthesis.

* The presence of H_2O, CO_2, HF etc. may have lowered the temperature.

The available data as to the amounts of H_2O, CO_2, HF, HCl, S, HBO_3 and a number of other elements or compounds in the crust of the Earth, have led to the unanimous opinion that they cannot be products of rock weathering of the crust of the Earth. Some other source must be found.

If we leave aside details of minor importance we may take it that two different sets of ideas prevail as to how the crust of the Earth and oceans and the atmosphere could have been formed. The first is that the crust of the Earth was formed during the primary process of differentiation of the substance of the Earth from the hot material of the protoplanet. The second is that they were formed from the cold material of the earth by melting. They are directly opposed.

I have presented these two sets of ideas in the form of comparative tables (Table 1). I do not pretend that I have been perfectly objective in constructing them. It seemed to me that, on both schemes, the formation of the crust of the Earth should show some sort of logic.

THE 'HOT' THEORY OF THE FORMATION OF THE CRUST OF THE EARTH

If we assume that the crust of the Earth was formed from hot material of the protoplanet, the phenomena which are most difficult to explain are (1) the absence from the Earth of all inert cosmic gases while H_2O, CO_2 and other light, volatile chemical compounds were retained; (2) the absence of a thick crust of the Earth and (3) the appearance of intense volcanic activity, especially at the beginning of the geological history of the Earth.

On the stars and the nebular aggregations of matter in space there is a very considerable amount of the heavy inert gases Ne, A, Kr, Xe. For example, the amount of Ne and A is of the same order as that of O_2. In our atmosphere, on the other hand, the concentration of the light and heavy inert gases is negligibly small and constitutes some thousandths or tens of thousandths of their relative concentration in the universe as a whole. The inert gases which are found to the greatest extent in the atmosphere of the Earth, viz. ^{40}A and ^4He are of secondary origin, arising from the radioactive decay of ^{40}K and U and Th either by the spontaneous fission of U and Th, or as a result of secondary nuclear reactions occurring on a modest scale on the Earth. The isotopic composition of these inert gases in the atmosphere of the Earth is different from the isotopic composition of the stars and cloud-like aggregates. If we do not make the assumption that these inert gases were absent from the protoplanetary cloud, then it is hard, on the basis of the 'hot' theory of the formation of the Earth, to explain why N_2, CO_2, H_2O, and other gases and vapours were retained on the surface of the Earth while the heavier Ne, A, Kr and Xe disappeared.

Now for a few words about the thickness of the crust of the Earth. If the siliceous material of the Earth became differentiated at a high temperature, there must have occurred a complete and far-reaching melting out heating those parts of it which fuse most difficultly. Calculations and actual fusion of the ultrabasic rocks (dunites) have shown that, in them, this process is not finished. From the relevant data it might be expected that from a substance having a composition similar to that of stony meteorites some amount of a lighter fraction could be melted out. In fact, the thickness of the crust of the Earth is extremely small, about $1/100$ of that of the mantle. This question, however, requires separate discussion. We will leave it on one side for the moment. Finally, we will consider the reasons for the intense volcanic activity which occurred at the beginning of the formation of the crust of the Earth. The fact that this phenomenon took place in the remote past is beyond question and is geologically well documented. It is enough to point out that, at present, there are more than 500 active volcanoes on the Earth. Naturally, the mechanism of volcanic activity cannot be considered apart from the mechanism of the differentiation of the Earth into layers. According to the views of the very high-standing specialists who have concerned themselves with this question from the point of view of the 'hot' theory, such as Chamberlin, Buddington, Bullen, Jeffreys and others, the crust of the Earth was formed during a, geologically speaking, very short period of about 10^6–10^7 years. Further thermodynamic changes tended towards the loss of heat and the cooling of both the Earth as a whole and its crust. During this process the liquid magma retained the cosmic gases and vapours which had been in equilibrium with it at the temperature of solidification, and became solid. By far the greater part of the gases and vapours of volatile substances were present, according to this hypothesis, at the periphery of the planet, forming its primary heavy atmosphere which, only later, came down to the cooling surface of the Earth. Naturally, the question arises as to why, at that time, the process of formation of the solid crust of the Earth should have been accompanied by volcanic activity which continued, though less strongly, throughout the whole later history of the Earth. To explain this effect one would have to postulate, not a fall but a rise of temperature within the Earth, or else to admit that there was a secondary melting of the substance of the Earth, a fresh rise of temperature within the planet. According to the 'hot' theory, however, such a supposition is manifestly absurd.

THE HYPOTHESIS OF THE MELTING OUT OF THE CRUST FROM A COLD EARTH

The hypothesis that the crust of the Earth was formed from cold material involves difficulties of its own. *The solid, cold, heterogeneous material of which the planet was formed did not retain any gases or other compounds which were not chemically bound in it.* This helpful concept first occurred to H. Brown [2]. This plausible assumption provides a general answer to the question of the reasons why all the inert gases in the Earth fall far short of their cosmic abundance.

When the Earth reached a certain size there took place an adiabatic process in which its substance became heated owing to the accumulation of radiogenic heat generated by the radioactive breakdown of U, Th and K, and perhaps also, to some extent, owing to gravitational compression. Under the influence of this heat the substance of the Earth differentiated and the light and low-melting fractions separated outwards to the surface. It is very hard to explain this process in physico-chemical terms. I will therefore allow myself a digression which seems to be suggestive. I drew attention to the fact that the chemical composition of stony meteorites or chondrites differs considerably from that of the ultra-basic formations within the Earth, exemplified by dunites, in having a high content of chemical elements which would appear to be easily mobile in molten silicates (Table 2).

TABLE 2

The contents of some chemical elements in chondrites, dunites, basalts and granites (% %)

Element	Silicate phase of meteorites	Dunites	Basalts	Granitics	Depth of core drawn upon (km)
Li	$2 \cdot 7 \times 10^{-4}$	3×10^{-5}	$1 \cdot 5 \times 10^{-3}$	7×10^{-3}	~ 600
Na	$0 \cdot 67$	$0 \cdot 23$	$1 \cdot 94$	$2 \cdot 77$	~ 300
K	$8 \cdot 5 \times 10^{-2}$	1×10^{-3}	$0 \cdot 83$	$3 \cdot 34$	~ 1000
Rb	8×10^{-4}	2×10^{-4}	$4 \cdot 5 \times 10^{-3}$	4×10^{-2}	~ 1000
Sr	1×10^{-3}	2×10^{-4}	$4 \cdot 4 \times 10^{-2}$	3×10^{-2}	~ 1500
Al	$1 \cdot 74$	$0 \cdot 44$	$8 \cdot 76$	$7 \cdot 70$	~ 400
U	3×10^{-6}	$(1 \cdot 10^{-6})$	8×10^{-5}	$3 \cdot 5 \times 10^{-4}$	~ 1500
Ti	1×10^{-1}	$6 \cdot 10^{-2}$	9×10^{-1}	$2 \cdot 3 \times 10^{-1}$	~ 500

Consider what happens when you heat a bar made of the material of a stony meteorite towards its melting point in such a way that only a very narrow zone of it is actually melted and that you then move the source of heat gradually along the whole length of the bar. This can be repeated many times. You will then have a liquid fraction which will travel repeatedly through the bar of chondrite being so treated. As a result of this zone melting you will get, collected at one end of the bar, those substances which lower the temperature of crystallization, while at the other end there will be those which raise the temperature of crystallization of the silicate melt. I have carried out this experiment with chondrite and convinced myself that there actually does occur a process of enrichment in a definite direction (the direction, as it were, of driving out of alkalis and other elements). This method will obviously permit us, in future, to obtain a large number of relevant quantitative data. It seems to me that it also provides us with the possibility of giving an experimental explanation of the mechanism of the differentiation of the substance of the Earth. These experiments have enabled me, though only speculatively, to take a first step and to suggest that the *dunites forming the mantle of the Earth are the residues left by melting out the terrestrial material which had a composition similar to that of the chondrites.* If this is true, an estimation of the amount of the easily transferred elements in dunites, the crust of the Earth and chondrites should give us a measure of the thickness of the mantle of the Earth which was involved in the formation of its crust (Table 2). As yet we have no accurate extraction coefficients for the behaviour of each element mentioned in the Table. However, if we use for our calculation the figures for chondrites as representing the original composition and those for dunites as representing the residues and consider the accumulation in the crust of the Earth (granites and basalts separately) of such elements as the alkali metals, U, Th and other elements, then we find that the thickness of the mantle of the Earth involved for this purpose will be hundreds of kilometres, in some cases more than a thousand*. It follows from this that in order to achieve a considerable concentration of many of the chemical elements in the rocks of the crust of the Earth a very great thickness of the mantle would have to have been involved. This makes it obvious why the crust of the Earth is so thin.

If we assume that the crust of the Earth has been growing at a steady rate for 5×10^9 years, then its thickness has increased by 1×10^{-3} cm/year. If it has been growing for 5×10^6 years it has grown 1 cm thicker each year, and only if the process was completed within 5×10^2 years would the rate of growth have been 10 m/year.

THE PRIMARY ATMOSPHERE

From what has just been said it may be seen that I support the hypothesis of the heating of the cold substance of the Earth and of the formation of the primary atmosphere as a result of the liberation, during the melting of the material of the Earth, of volatile compounds which had been chemically bound to it until that time.

The composition of the volcanic gases of the present day gives a general indication of the nature of this primary atmosphere. The main bulk of it consisted of H_2O, next in amount come CO_2, CO, HCl, HF, H_2S, N_2, NH_4Cl and maybe CH_4. No great concentration of inert gases has been observed. The high concentrations of ^{40}A which are sometimes observed in volcanic gases, like the relatively high concentration of it in the atmosphere, is mainly to be attributed to the radioactive decay of $^{40}K \rightarrow {}^{40}A$. The time which would have been required for the accumulation in this way of the amount of ^{40}A which is now present in the atmosphere if it arose from the amount of formations exposed to superficial weathering would seem to be about 5×10^9 years, i.e. it corresponds to the age of the Earth as estimated by the lead isotope method.†

The amount of ^4He, another inert gas which is present in the atmosphere and which seems to be a product of the radioactive decay of U and Th, is less than would be expected from the available data as to the amounts of U and Th in the crust of the Earth. This indicates that He, and, of course, H which is still lighter, are continually leaving the Earth. The loss of H by this means is greater than that of D. The idea which we have accepted about the formation of the primary atmosphere does not account for the preservation of gaseous N_2. N_2 is present in volcanic gases but its source is unknown. It is very likely that N_2 was present in the form of compounds, the general view being that these were nitrides of Fe, Ti and other metals or ammonium salts. The nitride Fe_5N_2 has been found as an efflorescence on the lavas of Etna and Vesuvius, while osbornite,

* In making this calculation I have assumed that the basalts are 20 km thick and that the average thickness of the granites over the whole surface of the Earth is 10 km [21].

† I shall deal in detail with the isotopic composition of the gases of the atmosphere in another place [24, 13].

TiN, has once been observed in the form of very small crystals in the Bustee meteorite. The great rarity of these compounds does not exclude the possibility that they might have been, in part at least, the sources of N_2. On reacting with water they yield NH_4^+. The process of emission of NH_4Cl and other ammonium compounds by volcanoes, and especially fumaroles, seems to be of greater extent. It is sufficient to recall, as an example, the exhalations of Tuscany. In the loose rocks of Kamchatka, a very long way from any volcanoes, we have found that $10^{-2} - 10^{-3}$ % of NH_4Cl is constantly present. In determining gases in rocks Rayleigh [10] has shown that nitrogen may be present in them in a combined state. According to recent determinations on igneous rocks, their nitrogen content is about 0·001 cc/g of rock. That of stony meteorites is about 0·0008 cc/g while it is interesting to record that the amount in dunites is minimal, i.e. about 0·0004 cc/g. Is the NH_4Cl of volcanoes, then, a juvenile product, or is it synthesized on the incandescent lava from the N_2 of the air? We have tried to synthesize NH_4Cl on incandescent lava from H_2 and N_2 but the synthesis only occurs in the absence of atmospheric O_2. All this together drives one to the conclusion that the NH_4Cl of volcanoes is a juvenile product and that the N_2 of the atmosphere was formed by outgassing of the Earth. It is relevant to mention that the ratios $^{14}N/^{15}N$ in the rocks and in the atmosphere are almost the same. The primary atmosphere, like the primary ocean, contained NH_4^+ ions which were not of biogenic origin.

As concerns the question of CH_4 in the primary atmosphere, it must be pointed out that the amount present in volcanic gases is extremely small and it may be supposed that this methane always arises from the reaction of carbon, dispersed in the rocks, with hydrogen, $C + 2H_2 \rightarrow CH_4$, or in accordance with the reactions $CO + 3H_2 \rightarrow CH_4 + H_2O$ or $CO_2 + 4H_2 \rightarrow CH_4 + 2H_2O$ on the incandescent lava. In any case Poole [9] has retracted his concept of a primary methane-containing atmosphere.

Finally, we must consider sulphur and its compounds in the primary atmosphere. In volcanic gases sulphur is found in the form of H_2S and S and is later converted to SO_2 and oxidized further. The bulk of the sulphur is, however, fixed in the form of sulphides of iron and other heavy metals below the surface of the Earth. It has been suggested that the S of volcanoes is of secondary origin, that is to say, it is derived from sedimentary formations, e.g. marine sulphates. One may convince oneself beyond question that the sulphur of volcanoes is juvenile in nature. It is accompanied by selenium. More important, however, is the fact that the ratio $^{34}S/^{32}S$ in volcanic sulphur is markedly different from that in sulphates and corresponds with the isotopic composition of the S in stony and iron meteorites [23, 24].

A very rough calculation shows that the amount of gas produced on the surface of the Earth must have emanated from the whole thickness of the mantle of the Earth. The outgassing of the Earth did not proceed at a constant rate but its intensity was probably determined by the general tectonic rhythm of the Earth. The bulk of it was ejected at the beginning of the geological history of the Earth. However, a dense, heavy atmosphere was not formed. Rubey [12] has suggested provisionally that the primary atmosphere contained about 1% of CO_2 (instead of the 30 atmospheres of CO_2 required by the 'hot' theory). One may well add that, inasmuch as there is not firm basis for this view, the interesting problem of the kinetics of the formation of the shells of the Earth is still awaiting investigation.

THE PRIMARY OCEAN

The sources of the more important anions (carbonate, fluoride, chloride, sulphate, borate, etc.) present in the waters of the oceans, like that of the water itself, were the products of outgassing of the internal rocks of the mantle of the Earth, while the sources of the more important cations (Na, K, Mg, Ca, Sr, etc.) were the weathered products of the rocky formations of the surface of the Earth. The main supply of gases was maintained by volcanic and intrusive activity and they also emerged along with lava. Clearly, the heating of the surface of the Earth and the large amount of gases in the atmosphere entailed by it must, at some time, having reached a maximum. This was followed by slow cooling of the surface of the Earth and condensation of the products of outgassing. These events, it can only be supposed, must have occurred during the first hundreds of millions of years of the life of the planet. There is, however, no factual basis for this figure.

The processes of thickening of the crust of the Earth, increase in the amount of CO_2 and other gases in the atmosphere and increase in volume of the oceans, occurred synchronously. They first reached a maximal rate of development, later declined and are not yet complete.

Acid vapours were neutralized by the rocks. The gases of the atmosphere were in equilibrium with the waters of the oceans and, in particular, HF, HCl and other acids were quickly removed from the atmosphere. As concerns CO_2, the more of it there was in the air the more $CaCO_3$ was dissolved in the water and the formation of calcareous deposits was generally impossible under these conditions [18]. The composition of the gases emanating from the interior of the Earth has probably changed very little. The chemical composition of the oceans has, therefore, not been submitted to any abrupt changes in regard to the salts present. These changes very quickly became as insignificant as the changes which we may observe in the other shells of the Earth (basaltic and granitic). A more significant alteration in the composition of the salts of the oceans occurred in many places when deposits of $CaCO_3$ or dolomite were laid down. What were the reasons for the deposition of $CaCO_3$? Essentially they were two: (1) The dissociation of $Ca(HCO_3)_2$ by the evaporation of the water in shallow seas and (2) The biological fixation of CO_2 in the skeletons of organisms ($CaCO_3$) and by photosynthesis.

The evaporation from shallow waters occurred on the greatest scale at the time when the epeirogenic, or shallow continental seas were formed. These seas, as we shall see later, became important at the time of the appearance of the broad platforms of the continents, i.e. about $2 \cdot 5 \times 10^9$ years ago or somewhat earlier. In fact, we find that the percentage of carbonates in the deposits of these platforms where there were shallow seas is 50 as compared with 15% which is the average for all the sedimentary formations of the Earth [19].

As part of the overall change in the composition of the ocean we must also take into account the appearance of a considerable amount of SO_4^{--} in the water. In the primary atmosphere sulphur was present, for the greater part, as H_2S or S and, although these could have been oxidized photochemically on the surface of the Earth in the presence of water, the process of oxidation probably did not take place to any great extent until a considerable amount of O_2 had appeared.

The most ancient and the primary ocean seems to be the depression in the Pacific ocean, the bed of which is not covered by the granitic envelope. The beds of the Atlantic and Indian oceans are covered by the granitic shell (except, possibly, in their deepest parts) and, in the opinion of most geologists, they were formed in the palaeozoic, or perhaps even the mesozoic, age owing to the subsidence of the crust of the Earth and the consequent submergence of the granitic shell beneath the waters.

INDICATIONS OF THE EARLY BIOSPHERE

Among these indications may be considered the skeletons of organisms, imprints and other morphological structures preserved in the geological formations, biogenic rocks themselves and, finally, the character of the weathering of rocks and their composition. As we can see from Fig. 1, none of these indications very rapidly disappear in time.

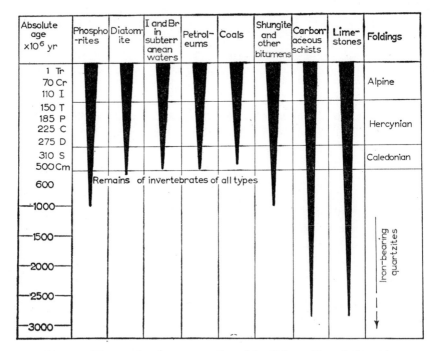

Fig. 1.   Diagram showing conservation of the different biogenic formations through the ages.

PLATE I

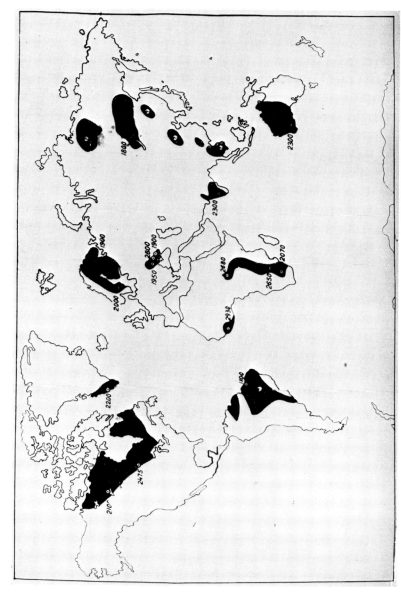

FIG. 2. The black areas represent roughly the areas in which contemporary outcrops of the most ancient rocks have been demonstrated.

A. P. VINOGRADOV

The evolution of the ancient crust of the Earth 3×10^9 years ago and earlier was characterized by intensive tectonic and volcanic activity such as has not taken place since. The whole world comprised a single geosynclinal area. Limitless fields of effusive material and enormous streams of lava built up the basaltic shell of the Earth. Tremendous weathering processes involving the destruction of the erupted materials gave rise to mighty deposits, mainly of clastic material, which, as it were, acted in some places as a filter for the hot gases and magma rising from the depths of the Earth. In addition, the intrusive activity became even stronger at that time. Enormous masses of so-called anatectic granitic batholiths are scattered through these extremely ancient sedimentary strata. Granitic material penetrates so profusely through these ancient sedimentary formations of gneiss that it is hard to define the boundary between the true granite and the host rocks. Thus the early Archaean granites, which are charac-terized by a high content of potassium felspar, arose from the earliest sedimentary deposits by their becoming molten again under the influence of heat and emana-tions. Eighty per cent of all granites arose in the Archaean. The growth of the granitic shell, showing an extraordinarily vast scale, was virtually finished by the end of the Archaean or beginning of the Proterozoic, i.e. about $1 \cdot 5$ or maybe 2×10^9 years ago.

With the further development of intrusive activity in the crust of the Earth, small islands of solid land appeared in the upsurge of the Archaean surface of the Earth. These constituted ancient nuclei of geological formations which can be shown by methods of dating based on radioactivity to be $2 - 2 \cdot 5 \times 10^9$ years old or more. These nuclei of continents are known to occur on almost all the main land masses of the present day. These nuclei of continents have, as their foundations, the earliest effusive formations (see Fig. 2).

A turning point occurred in the history of the surface of the Earth when more stable and undisturbed areas first came into being in its geosynclinal surface. These gradually extended to form platforms.

A particularly marked contraction of the geosynclinals and intensive growth of the platforms may be noted at the very end of the Archaean or beginning of the Proterozoic, i.e. about $1 \cdot 5 - 2 \times 10^9$ years ago. The crust of the Earth entered into a new stage of development with the contraction of the geosynclinals and the growth of the platforms with their sedimentary coverings. The biosphere and organic beings are closely associated with sedimentary formations. The earliest sedimentary formations were now laid down on the basis of the persistent nuclei of ancient rocks. The schists of the Keewatin formations of the American continent are estimated to be more than $2 \cdot 5 \times 10^9$ years old. Schists of the same type, found in Kambove in West Africa are credited with an age of more than $2 \cdot 2 \times 10^9$ years. The Svinion gneisses of Karelia are thought to be more than $2 \cdot 1 \times 10^9$ years old. The Saxagan gneisses of the Ukraine are over 2×10^9 years old. The Shamva granites of Africa are $2 \cdot 8 \times 10^9$ years old and so on [7, 22]. In these, and even in more recent formations of the end of the Archaean and beginning of the Proterozoic, one may find most suggestive evidence for the presence of an oxygen-containing atmosphere in the Archaean in the form of sedimentary iron ores, iron-containing quartzites (the so-called jaspilites) containing haematite and magnetite, which is a product of its metamorphosis; that is to say, they contain oxidized iron. We may mention the iron-containing quartzites of Krivoĭ Rog, of the Kursk magnetic anomaly, of Canada, Sweden (Kiruna and other places), Africa and other places. When studying the breccia of Suodeniemi in comparison with the primaeval formation of Finland (age 2×10^9 years), Rankama [11] did not find any excess of Fe^{III} in the breccia. Geijer [4] denied this and found haematite in the breccias. These ores of the Archaean and Proterozoic are many times greater in amount than all the iron ores of later dates. About the same age is assigned to the universal appearance of calcareous rocks in the form of marbles and crystalline dolomites. These crystalline carbonates originally formed part of the composition of conglomerates and breccias. They were gradually transformed, especially during the Proterozoic, into enormous strata on the platforms. In parallel with this, traces of the most ancient organisms have been found in the Proterozoic and lower down in the Archaean limestones etc. The first such find was that of the well known *Collenia walcotta*, an alga from the limestone bed of the Grand Canyon, from the Grenville limestones of the Great Lakes which are about 1.5×10^9 years old. Grant and his fellow-workers described an organic structure, similar to *Collenia* in the Huron formations which are of about the same age. In the Lower Huron sediments of Minnesota, Grüner found the alga *Inactis*. In the Jatulian formations of Karelia (about 1.6×10^9 years old) *Carelozoon jatulica* has been described. Tyler and Barghoorn found the remains of blue-green algae and flagellates in the formations of the Canadian shield (the formations are about 2×10^9 years old). MacGregor found traces of algae in the limestones of Rhodesia, the age of which is estimated at about 2.7×10^9 years. Other similar finds have been made. Thus we have direct evidence that at least as long as about 2×10^9 years ago O_2 was present in the atmosphere. In as much as the primary atmosphere contained H_2O and CO_2 and other oxygen-containing compounds there is absolutely no reason to suppose that some part, at least, of the O_2 in the Archaean atmosphere was of abiogenic origin, being formed by photochemical dissociation of these compounds in the upper layers of the atmosphere. This process is very slow and the intense volcanic activity did not permit the accumulation of O_2 in the primary atmosphere. Moreover, the absence of O_2 did not prevent the development of anerobic life. Even if there were no ozone screen, which is supposed to have shielded the organisms from the harmful effects of ultraviolet irradiation, the waters of the seas, even when quite shallow, would have provided an excellent screen.

Carbonaceous schists and graphite are associated with all these finds. Shungite is also found at the time of the transition from the Archaean to the Proterozoic ages (1.6×10^9 years ago).

Although Thode *et al.* [15] thought, on the basis of determination of the ratio $^{32}S/^{34}S$ in sulphides of sedimentary origin, that the earliest limit for life is somewhere about 700–800 million years ago, we have proved experimentally that this is not true, by determining the isotopic composition of the S in similar sulphides. From this we see that, as I have already said, there is a more or less determinate limit somewhere between 2.5×10^9 and 2.0×10^9 years ago and the correct figure is probably nearer to the longer than to the shorter period.

At this time, not only do the morphological signs of organisms disappear, but even the sedimentary deposits themselves have vanished owing to assimilation. As a result of this the physical and chemical aspects of our investigations assume particular importance.

CONCLUSIONS

If we can observe signs of a biosphere in geological strata dating from more than 2×10^9 years ago, then, naturally, the origins of the biosphere must have been earlier than this. In considering what conditions were peculiar to these

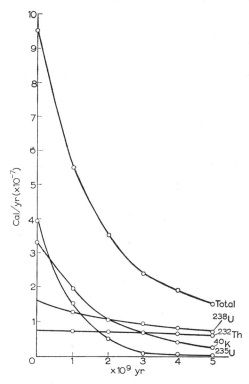

FIG. 3.   Radiogenic heat formed in the Earth by U, Th and ^{40}K separately and together plotted against time.

times and are not now present, we may also mention some, of which, perhaps, I have not spoken in sufficient detail. It is impossible to make any, even remotely plausible hypothesis as to the amount of change which has taken place in, for example, the intensity of ultraviolet or cosmic radiation, etc. It may be that the most important factor limiting the development of living things was the temperature of the rocks, waters and gases on the surface of the Earth. From the graph shown in Fig. 3 it may be seen that, as early as 3×10^9 years after the origin of the Earth, the total heat derived from the decomposition of radioactive elements had begun to abate at a less catastrophic rate than it had done previously. From that time until the present it diminished by less than a factor of 2. The same tendency is found, to a certain extent, in the temperature of the surface of the Earth. I would suggest that the peculiarity of the time when the Archaean biosphere came into existence was just this considerable amount of heat at the surface of the Earth. It manifested itself in numerous volcanic and post-volcanic phenomena in the form of hot gases, hot springs and so forth. This could have led to intensive catalytic synthesis of numerous organic substances on the surface of the Earth from CO_2, CO, H_2S, S, NH_4, CH_4, HCl, HF and other compounds on a scale which has been unparalleled since that time. From the time of the inception of the biosphere to the Cambrian period, in the strata of which palaeontologists have found highly organized organisms including all forms of invertebrate animals, at least $1·5–2·0 \times 10^9$ years must have elapsed. In the course of this time there must obviously have developed all sorts of methods of oxidation of H_2S and other analogous processes and, later, the dehydrogenation of H_2O by means of chloroplasts as well as other reactions. Any conceivable process of photodissociation of H_2O would have taken 10^8 years to form the oxygen of the atmosphere. The photosynthetic O_2 in the atmosphere is produced during 5000 years, forming a sound basis for the development of aerobic life. Many other geochemical cycles of elements and molecules in which organisms were an essential link were also set up and consolidated. Thus, the phosphates of the bones later provided a basis for the development of the neuromuscular tissue in vertebrates. Many other molecules were drawn into these cycles and became involved in the evolution of organisms. $CaCO_3$, $CaHPO_2$, chitin, cellulose, porphyrins and many other, even more complicated compounds were among them. This, however, is a long way outside the province of the geochemical history of the biosphere.

Thus, we may conclude that the mechanism by which the light basaltic formations were melted out from the whole thickness of the mantle of the Earth under the influence of radiogenic heat, was associated with the outgassing of H_2O, CO_2 and other gases and vapours on to the surface of the Earth. This determined the composition of the primary Archaean atmosphere and ocean. In the course of time the composition of the salts of the ocean and that of the atmosphere may have undergone some change owing to the irregular accession of vapours and gases to the surface of the Earth. The Archaean atmosphere contained, among other vapours and gases, NH_4Cl, H_2S and S of abiogenic origin and, possibly also CH_4 and some O_2, which provided the necessary conditions for the catalytic synthesis of complicated organic compounds if the temperature was raised. The last marked changes in the composition of the oceans and atmosphere took place between 3×10^9 and 2×10^9 years ago when the temperature of the surface of the Earth became much what it now is. The ancient nuclei of the continents persisted and provide evidence of magmatic phenomena which took place in the remote past, being locally completed 3×10^9 years ago. We have no reason to exclude the possibility of the existence of anaerobic forms of life at that time. At the same time as, or slightly later than the alteration in the geosynclinal condition of the surface of the Earth there appeared the first platform-like structures which were submerged in the shallow seas. These seas were associated with the intensive precipitation of $CaCO_3$ and the removal of CO_2 from the atmosphere. The even more powerful process of photosynthetic formation of free oxygen made its appearance. It is just at this time that one can also observe traces of plants and other organisms, as well as oxidized iron ores which provide direct evidence of an oxygenous atmosphere. Associated with the formation of an oxygen-containing atmosphere, there was intensive oxidation of H_2S and S and an increase in the amount of sulphates in the oceans, as well as oxidation of NH_4 and an increase in the amount of N_2 in the atmosphere. During the later periods of the Proterozoic and in the Cambrian, there occurred no noteworthy change in the composition of the oceans or atmosphere.

Having been brought into existence by the whole course of geological history, the biosphere made its appearance when the Earth was between two and three thousand million years old.

REFERENCES

1. F. BIRCH, *Geophysics*, **19**, 645, 1954.
2. H. BROWN, Rare gases and the formation of the Earth's atmosphere. In *The Atmospheres of the Earth and Planets* (Ed. by G. P. KUIPER), 1947.
3. E. C. BULLARD, *Proc. Roy. Soc.* A, **222**, 408, 1954.
4. P. GEIJER, *Geochim. et cosmoch. Acta*, **10**, 304, 1956.
5. V. M. GOLDSCHMIDT, *Geochemistry* (Ed. by ALEX. MUIR). Clarendon Press, Oxford, 1954.
6. B. GUTENBERG, *Internal Constitution of the Earth*, 1951.
7. A. HOLMES & LUCIEN CAHEN, *Colon. Geol. Min. Resour.*, p. 3, 1954.
8. E. A. LYUBIMOVA, On thermal régime of the Earth. *Trud. geofiz. Inst., Mosk.*, No. 26, p. 39, 1955.
9. J. H. J. POOLE, *Proc. R. Dubl. Soc. Sci.*, **25**, n.s. 201, 1951.
10. RAYLEIGH (LORD), *Nature, Lond.*, **141**, 970, 1938.
11. K. RANKAMA, *Spec. Pap. geol. Soc. Amer.*, No. 62, 650, 1955.
12. W. W. RUBEY, *Bull. geol. Soc. Amer.*, **62**, 1111, 1951.
13. H. A. SHILLIBEER & R. D. RUSSELL, *Geochim. et cosmoch. Acta* (8), **2**, 16, 1955.
14. L. B. SLICHTER, *Bull. geol. Soc. Amer.*, 52 (4), 1941.
15. H. G. THODE, J. MACNAMARA & W. H. FLEMING, *Geochim. et cosmoch. Acta*, **3**, 235, 1953.
16. H. C. UREY, *The planets*. Yale Univ. Press, New Haven, 1952.
17. H. C. UREY, *Proc. nat. Acad. Sci., Wash.*, **41**, 3, 1955.
18. A. P. VINOGRADOV, *Dokl. Akad. Nauk S.S.S.R.*, **27**, No. 3, 1940.
19. A. P. VINOGRADOV, A. B. RONOV & V. M. RATYNSKII, Evolution of the chemical composition of carbonaceus rocks, *Soveshchaniya po osadochnym poradom*, **1**, 104, 1952.
20. A. P VINOGRADOV, I. ZADOROZHNYĬ & S. I. ZYKOV, *Dokl. Akad. Nauk S.S.S.R.*, **35**, No. 5, 1107, 1952.
21. A. P. VINOGRADOV, *Geokhimiya*, No. 1, 1956.
22. A. P. VINOGRADOV, *Geokhimiya*, No. 5, p. 3, 1956.
23. A. P. VINOGRADOV, S^{32}/S^{34} Isotopic composition of meteorites and of the Earth, *Radioisotopes in Scientific Research* (Proc. Int. Conf. held in Paris, 1957), Pergamon Press, 1958.
24. A. P. VINOGRADOV, The isotopic composition of rocks of the Earth and of meteorites, *Radioisotopes in Scientific Research* (Proc. Int. Conf. held in Paris, 1957), Pergamon Press, 1958.

The Problem of Stages in Biopoesis

J. D. BERNAL

Birkbeck College, University of London, England

As THE very calling of this Symposium indicates, the question of the origin of life can only be investigated by a combined effort in which experts in many fields co-operate. Every solution put forward by an individual, however well-read or brilliant, is bound to be a partial one and open to criticism because of its reliance on ideas or supposed facts drawn from regions of knowledge with which that individual is not directly acquainted. These failings can in the course of time be removed by mutual criticism, but the process is very slow and one of our hopes is that the present Congress will act like a catalyst and speed it up. However, with multiplicity of counsel there is another danger arising from different scientific formation of the participants and different ideas of the nature of the problem to be solved. By dealing separately with different aspects of the Origin of Life their sequence and inter-relatedness may be overlooked. It is on this last point that I would like, in this paper, to put forward some suggestions as to the general pattern of the Origin of Life, and in particular to try to block out some formal account of the stages in which it may be deemed, provisionally, to have taken place, in order to focus attention on the problems that may occur at each stage. I am not suggesting that my pattern is the correct one or that it may not require drastic modification, but I do urge that it is better in such a Congress to have before it some pattern than none. At any rate it has helped me to construct one, and my ideas may be useful even if they only provoke contradiction.

In general the pattern I propose is one of stages of increasing inner complexity, following one another in order of time, each one including in itself structures and processes evolved at the lower levels. The division into stages is not in my opinion an arbitrary one. Although the evolution of life was continuous, for no stage could have been completely static, it cannot have been uniform. Discontinuities which occurred at later stages of organic evolution, such as the emergence of air-breathing forms, are likely to have been paralleled at the earlier biochemical stages at such jumps as the genesis of sugars, nucleic acids and fats. One of our major problems is to establish the correct order of the steps inferred from existing metabolism as well as the postulating and checking of other steps which have been subsequently effaced by the success of more efficient biochemical mechanisms.

Before considering these transitions in detail I would like to recall certain general principles which may serve to guide the lines of speculation without themselves furnishing decisive arguments for or against any particular solution. The first of these is the principle of Lyell which tells us to search in the present world for processes which may have occurred in the past. In its particular application to the origin of life, it is to search in the inorganic world for the origin of the processes, as well as the materials, of the organic world. This implies more than the condition that the process of the organic world must not be contrary to chemical laws or Henderson's principle of the *fitness of the environment*. It requires, in addition, that just as the elements used in building up living structures are a selection from those found in the inorganic atmosphere, hydrosphere, and lithosphere, so also are the basic reactions of oxidation-reduction, hydrolysis-condensation likely to have an unbroken continuity with those occurring on the surface of the Earth. It is, indeed, a fact of observation that some soluble simple ions like those of potassium and magnesium and the labile atoms of sulphur, phosphorus and iron, which undergo the greatest transformations in the mineral world, have a key importance in biochemistry, while the stable atoms, such as silicon, aluminium, or sodium, which constitute a far larger part of the Earth's crust, are either absent or play a subsidiary role.

The one limitation to our study of *biopoesis* or life-making is that it is a special and not a general problem. We are limited, and necessarily so in the first place, to the origin of the *one* form of life that we can observe now on this Earth. There may have been other radically incompatible forms on this Earth at earlier times and these or others we succeed in making artificially. Where life exists on other planets it is most likely that it will be radically incompatible with ours, though we may suspect that it will show striking parallels, biochemically as well as structurally. However, pending the advent of practical biopoesis or trips in space to acquire the basis of comparative biopoesis, we must restrict ourselves to tracing the genealogical tree of life as we know it right back to its origin or origins, for they may be multiple, in the inorganic world. The biochemical genealogy of the terrestrial life, though uniquely determined working backwards, is by no means unique working forwards. This is what makes the biochemical approach to biopoesis more likely to give results than the purely geochemical, except at the very outset. Starting from any initial inorganic origins there are too many possible lines to be followed up. At a number of occasions in biopoesis there must have been alternative arrangements with little to choose between them—even trivial ones such as right- or left-hand configurations of molecules. There may well be potential biochemical cycles that would have solved the problems of the formation of life and reproduction of organism as well as, and even better than, those actually evolved. But biochemical evolution differs from that of organisms in that variant forms, if not actually incorporated in the common biochemical pattern, became absolutely extinct. There is only one *dominant* chemical pattern of life. If more than one exist the others must be obscure, as are some of the red algae, and unnecessary to the survival of the dominant. It is as if in the subsequent evolution of species only man and a few of his pets were to survive.

One of the major reasons for assuming that, in tracing the origin of life on this planet, we are dealing with a very particular form and have not exhausted the biochemical potentialities of life, is the extreme chemical and structural conservatism or inertia of once established patterns of structure or activities. At and above the level of the protozoa there is no essential change in structure

and metabolism of the nucleated cell. A common pattern underlies all modifications. Not only was life on this Earth one at that level, but also it has not divided
into branches ever since. It cannot be just because all living organisms are part
of the food chains of others that they are biochemically compatible. For green
plants that do not depend on complex molecules made by other organisms it
would be a great biological advantage to be inedible and resistant to fungal
and bacterial decay. Yet no plant has achieved this isolation from the rest of the
living world. It is precisely because of this biochemical and structural inertia,
that we have some reasonable hope of being able to trace back origins by the
comparative methods used by Darwin and his followers for gross morphological
features in the latter stages of evolution. We may expect patterns of reactions
as well as structures to accumulate with modifications and subsequent fusion
into more complicated ones and so on until and beyond those found in living
things today. The unravelling of protein structure, discussed in my later paper,
has shown evidence of several stages of such reduplications and complications or
foldings in the most literal sense. Formally the chemical evolutionary process
may be likened to the evolution of a drainage for newly emerged lands. Comparatively trivial variations may determine the location of bends but once the
main pattern is cut it deepens and fixes itself only to be changed by the effects of
its own actions. A too successful utilization of some component can, as Horowitz
[13] has pointed out, lead to the holding up of some activity and the employment
of an alternative source. An increase of efficiency in another part may render
certain earlier steps unnecessary, but in the main the original pattern will be
preserved. We should, as time goes on, be able to trace it even more accurately.

We may define life, for the sake of this discussion only, as *the embodiment
within a certain volume of self-maintaining chemical processes.* Our central problem
is not here to explain how such a system works but how it can establish itself
starting from available inorganic materials and subsequently reproduce and
evolve *de novo.* This can be divided into four inter-related but distinct problems:

    (1) the problem of the external source of free energy to keep the system going;

    (2) the problem of the facilitation of the energy interchanges within the system,
where an isothermal condition implies some catalysis;

    (3) the problems of the means of holding the system together and in the more
complicated cases, such as bacterial and nucleated cells, of how all parts of the
organism can maintain their individuality while being in constant chemical
relation with each other;

    (4) the problems of reproduction with its almost, but never quite exact,
duplication of organisms as shown in evolving species, pose the further problem
of the normal transference, with occasional modification, of specific guiding
patterns.

All these problems are being discussed in various sections of this Symposium.
I list them here simply to provide a general background for a tentative establishment of stages in biopoesis. Although they overlap, the four conditions for life
listed above form a natural order. The energy source must come first, there must
be some reactions or mere coherence would not imply life and there can be no
reproduction without something to reproduce. An analysis of biopoesis can be

made in accordance with these major conditions by considering first the essential reactions on an atomic or micromolecular scale in their thermodynamic and kinetic aspects; next the sequence of structures starting from atoms and building up to polymers of colloidal dimensions; and finally the way the mutual arrangements of these impose a pattern of linked reactions which can be reproduced.

On the first steps of emergence of simple organic molecules in the hydrosphere there is still no agreement, but as this question will be largely debated here I will not pursue it at any length. All I would like to say is that following Lyell's principle it seems preferable to start by supposing substances and reactions that still occur even though now modified by the action of life. It is not strictly necessary to postulate the character of the original atmosphere of the Earth because of the continual contributions which must have occurred from volcanic sources. The character of these seems largely independent of organic sources and to consist mainly of steam, carbon dioxide, ammonia, and hydrogen sulphide. With regard to the supply of carbon dioxide I suspect it is derived from lower layers of the crust where it may exist in the high pressure form of orthocarbonate in such a mineral as fayalite $Fe_2 (C, Si)O_4$. Ammonia is already known to exist as ammonium felspar $\{K,(NH_4)\}$ $AlSi_3O_8$. Both CO_2 and NH_3 in the form of NH_4Cl are known to be liberated in volcanic gases, fumaroles etc. Probably a far larger amount reaches the hydrosphere through the weathering of carbonate- or ammonia-containing igneous rocks. The weathering of 100 km of igneous rock already largely depleted of ammonia would provide all the nitrogen at present in the atmosphere.

The question as to whether primary or secondary inorganic hydrocarbons were ever found in the primitive atmosphere is still an open one. They are hardly ever detected in volcanic gases and their presence in carbonaceous meteorites in my opinion points to the origin of these meteorites in a region further from the sun than the Earth. In any case oxidation of methane at the top of the atmosphere would relatively soon reproduce the condition in which carbon dioxide would be the chief carbon compound in the atmosphere.

It has been argued that CO_2, the most oxidized form of carbon, is most unlikely in the primitive atmosphere. If it was all derived from the oxidation of the postulated earlier CH_4 I would agree for, in that case, intermediates in the forms of alcohols and carboxy acids would first have been formed. The situation would be different if atmospheric CO_2 is a product of the lithosphere as the existence, admittedly rare, of carbonates of deep origin would seem to indicate. In any case if CO_2 was not a precursor of life it must have been one of its earliest products, as witnessed by the universal presence of limestone even in the early pre-Cambrian rocks. Perhaps a study of carbon isotopes, in carbonatites and limestones of various ages would resolve this problem.

The major exergonic reactions occurring in the primitive hydrosphere would be

$$2NH_3 \rightarrow N_2 + 3H_2 \text{ or } N_2 + 2H_2 + 2H \text{ etc.}$$
$$8SH_2 \rightarrow S_8 + 8H_2$$

both of which, in the absence of free oxygen, would yield molecular hydrogen which would diffuse out of the atmosphere. Nitrogen would steadily be built up in the atmosphere and elementary sulphur or iron sulphide would be deposited. The other main oxidizing reaction is strongly endergonic

$$2H_2O \rightarrow O_2 + 2H_2 \text{ or } O_2 + 4H \text{ etc.}$$

but the energy to effect it can be provided by short-wave radiation at the top of the atmosphere. The concentration of molecular oxygen would tend to rise until it sufficed to oxidize the hydrogen emitted by the dehydrogenation of NH_3 and SH_2 and also the ferrous iron derived from weathering of rocks. Free energy available for biochemical reactions may also have been available from this source. What this equilibrium concentration of oxygen would be is still a moot point but it would seem on biochemical evidence alone that oxidation reactions, though now furnishing most of metabolic free energy, are not primitive. In any case the high concentration of atmospheric oxygen now observed in the atmosphere is now derived from photosynthesis, the mechanism of which, at least using visible sunlight, seems to have a fairly elaborate biochemical history. The type of endergonic reaction which could lead to organic compounds is, however, now part of the photosynthetic cycle of reactions.

$$CO_2 + 2H \rightarrow HCOOH \text{ formic acid}$$
$$\text{or } CO_2 + 4H \rightarrow H_2CO \quad \text{formaldehyde} + H_2O$$

None of the actual reactions which occurred in the primitive ocean are likely to be as simple as those indicated above. More probable variants and intermediates will certainly be discussed at this Symposium. I only cite them to show firstly that the major features of current metabolism were already present in the primitive hydrosphere and secondly that the actual basic compounds which make up living organisms can be most easily envisaged as constructed mainly of carbon dioxide and ammonia by not implausible processes which do not involve unsupported hypotheses about the constitution of the primitive atmosphere. They are moreover thermodynamically sound even without the assumption of the utilization of free energy derived from the sun. The free energy supplied on this hypothesis would be simply due to the greater reduction potential of the surface lithosphere with respect to an atmosphere from which hydrogen can escape.

Life, geologically speaking, consists of the interference with secondary lithosphere–atmosphere reactions so as to produce a small but ever-renewed stock of organic molecules.

One of the major tasks of biopoesis is to establish the nature and the *order of formation* of the simpler molecular species out of which the more complex compounds and polymers now found in living organisms were derived. I have no competence in this field, but to complete the picture, I am indicating on the diagram, Fig. 1, the kind of molecular genealogical table that needs to be drawn up. Both the lines of derivation and the order need to be examined. Indeed this table is less a statement of probabilities than a setting of problems which may be solved ultimately by a critical use of present-day biosynthetic changes (for it does not follow that the present derivations were the same at the outset) and a series of tentative pictures of biopoesis. Particularly important is the problem of the origin of the sugars, whether anteriorly or posteriorly, as I have imagined, to that of the amino acids. Another associated problem is the stage at which photosynthesis and oxidation enter the picture. I have tentatively put it after the appearance of the porphyrins.

I am inclined now, especially after looking at the results of the synthetic experiments of Miller, Terenin, Pavlovskaya and Pasynskiï, to think that sugar production must have come rather earlier in biopoesis. Our preoccupation with proteins, quite rightly as the essential biochemical molecule most difficult to synthesize, has led us to pay particular attention to amino acid synthesis.

However, in the actual synthesis non-nitrogenous substances, mostly vegetable acids, were in fact the main products. Although in these experiments no sugars were produced, this may have been due to the absence of suitable inorganic catalysts.

As important, but much more characteristic of living systems than the molecules they contain, is the mode in which the chemical reactions between them are carried out. This mode we now observe in living organisms is that of reactions arranged in cycles and operated by means of specific enzymes. This cannot have been the original mechanism, if for no more compelling reason than that the enzymes themselves are produced by the system and are particularly complex bodies even for the simplest reactions. The problem here is to trace the evolution of such facilitating agents for increasing efficiency and speed of action in relation to the kind of substances available at the corresponding stage of molecular evolution. We have to examine the possible nature of proto-enzymes and proto-co-enzymes. The relation between the reactions and the facilitators is a complementary one. Suitable enzymes must exist at every stage for all the essential reactions at that stage. However, a newly evolved or modified enzyme may in turn modify the reaction or produce new molecules. To some extent every enzyme system will select its own substrates and thus, by reciprocal interaction, biochemical evolution will advance. The modal elements of all organic and biochemical reactions are extremely simple, they all involve the juxtaposition of two particular atoms at hardly more than the sum of their atomic distances apart, the making or breaking of a bond and usually the insertion or removal of a proton. To secure any reaction at all the two components must be present in the appropriate quantum state; to secure that the reaction is only of one kind the molecules of the reagents must come together in the same configuration; to secure rapid reaction that configuration must be easily made and broken. The actions can be direct or mediated by other molecules with reactive groups of which sulphydryl, phosphate and iron ions are the commonest both in the inorganic and biochemical world.

The efficiency of the primary inorganic catalysts was probably extremely low, but this was of little importance as there could have been at the start no competition. Increase in efficiency and speed of reaction must have run in parallel with increasing complexity and size of structure. Two factors intervene in this evolutionary process: greater specificity of the reaction, implying the production of more stable attachment bases suitable for one particular reaction; and greater efficiency of the reaction, implying an adjusted set of quantum states for the more active agent in the transformation, and minimizing the activation energy. These functions we know today as those of enzyme and co-enzyme respectively. The first of these are now provided by the proteins, the second by nucleotides, flavones and some transition-metal compounds. It is most significant that, while the enzymes are so far innumerable, each responsible for one or two reactions only, the co-enzymes are few and each can function in many different reactions. Specificity in quantum level of the active partner would seem to be less important than specificity in spatial configuration in the passive partner.

The prevalence of nucleotides among co-enzymes is particularly noteworthy. The active group here is the terminal phosphate which can add one or two further phosphate groups that are easily detachable by a process of energy exchange, long known to biochemists as the energy-rich phosphate bond. In existing life and probably in life as far back as we can trace it the sugar-purine complex has been attached to the phosphate group. But this probably indicates a limiting stage of efficient modification of quantum levels. At an earlier stage, before sugars or purines had been synthesized, the basic phosphate-hydrogen exchange mechanisms had probably been active first as oligo- or poly-meta-phosphate and then with phosphate linked with some simple carbon-nitrogen derivative such as cyanate. Indeed, as Lipmann claims [14], carbamyl phosphate $(OC \cdot NH_2 \cdot OPO_3)$ derived from the cyanate and phosphate ions can reasonably be regarded as the first living molecule, or at least as the first step in the evolution of biochemistry.

The association of phosphate with the fixing of carbon dioxide may be related to the basic anabolic process, the formation of amino acids and sugars at first in the triose glyceraldehyde form. The energy required for this came in the first place from dehydrogenation reactions, but at some stage it came to be derived from sunlight by photochemical reactions. The present highly efficient mechanism of photosynthesis is too complicated to have been an early one, but its place may have been filled first by some other and less efficient organo-metallic light trap, perhaps a clathrate compound of iron. The origin of the first effective photosynthesis, and with it the first production of molecular oxygen and its concentration in the atmosphere, may also be linked with that of the bulk production of pentose and hexose sugars. The earlier this occurred in biopoesis the earlier can have been the origin of the new omnipresent nucleosides.

Papers presented at the Symposium, notably those of Calvin, Krasnovskiĭ, Reid and Sorokin, have enlightened me on the evolution of photosynthesis by emphasizing the separation of at least three factors existing in the photosynthesis of green plants: carbon dioxide fixation, light energy utilization, and oxygen production. These may well have originated separately. Carbon dioxide fixation using some other source of free energy I had already postulated as preceding photosynthesis. However, I had not considered the intermediate stage, which I now feel fits much better into the picture of photosynthetic decomposition, of SH groups giving molecular sulphur as now carried out by the sulphur bacteria.

This would have had the first effect of photosynthesis in biopoesis in providing a secure source of organic materials, perhaps even too much in the absence of oxidation mechanisms, leading to a hydrogen shortage which was only relieved by the evolution of a means of extracting it from water with an improved chlorophyll photocatalyst. Only after this stage had been reached and oxygen began to accumulate in the atmosphere did its pressure rise sufficiently to initiate the more complicated oxidative processes supplementing those of fermentation. Some oxidations of the sulphide to sulphur type may have preceded this stage, but the energy gain would have been much lower. In the overall picture of the evolution of the chemistry of life what we notice is not so much an improvement in the total energy changes—except in so far as solar energy is used—but rather in the effecting of a speedier turnover, in increase in power of assimilation or energy production.

With the other element in catalysis, the specific fixed base, similar considerations apply. It is clear that the present profusion of protein enzymes cannot have been primitive. A major problem is the discovery of what preceded them in this role. The degree of polymerization of amino acids and the complexity of their sequences which would be required before a protein could function as an enzyme is very great. Protein enzymes must therefore have come relatively late in biopoesis. What preceded them? Even simpler amino acid polymers cannot have been primitive and it would appear that the choice lies between postulating an inorganic crystal-clay or quartz as the primary catalyst or assuming that in the early stages there was no heterocatalysis and that reactions proceeded through the diffusion of active radicals as Pringle [1] has proposed.

The discussion of the first stages of biopoesis, the formation of what Pirie [2] has called probiotic soups, involves not only the chemical problems of the formation of the particular organic molecules they contained and of the reaction chains that link them, but also the physico-chemical problem of how these molecular concentrations were built up and maintained. It is conceivable, though I think unlikely, that no such stage of solution of monomers or oligomers such as amino acids, simple peptides, or sugar molecules, ever existed and the formation of such molecules went *pari passu* with their polymerization. If, however, free molecules ever existed or even more so, if there was a stage where these were the only molecules there were, the problem of how their diffusion was restricted is a real one that bears closely on the locus of the origin of life. All conditions counter-indicate the primary synthesis of anything but the very simple molecules, of say three to six atoms, in large volumes of water where the dilution is so great that the probability of chance encounters leading to more complex compounds would be negligible. The possibilities of small volumes of water such as occur in drying pools are rather greater as far as concentration go, but not the maintenance and propagation of the resulting substances and reactions, for the chances of drying up or washing out would be too great.

What is required is a medium free from turbulence and under constant conditions for long periods in which the diffusion of small molecules, though never stopped, would be so restricted that considerable concentrations could be built up and maintained. Such conditions are only likely to be found on an azoic Earth—in mud beds; under water; on dry land; or alternatively wet and dry as in tidal estuaries. From the purely physical point of view it is unimportant whether this layer is referred to as clay [3], or soil [4] or even the steady concentration gradient [1] for this could only be maintained in a medium weighed down by solids and the only solid that stays put under water is clay. It is a separate question to ask whether the small first-formed molecules were actually absorbed on the mineral particles or merely lay in their interstices and still another whether these particles also assisted in catalysing reactions between organic molecules. I suspect that such catalysis did occur on particles of montmorillonite, quartz and iron hydroxide, but this can only be proved by experiment. The argument that such structures or even their elements such as silicon or aluminium are not found extensively in living systems to-day is beside the point. There was no need for primitive life to synthesize crystals of materials that were amply available in its environment and when substitutes in the form of polymerized organic enzymes were formed there was no need to retain the original minerals.

As long as only small molecules formed from the condensation of carbon dioxide and ammonia were available, nothing in the nature of a separate organism was possible, only patches of fairly constant composition in which metabolism was maintained for various periods and which were more like cold flames than organisms as we know them. All such *sub vital* units would be broadly similar but not identical, and would have indefinite and shifting boundaries and could in general merge and fuse with one another. Where two were incompatible, one or both would be destroyed; where compatible, their range of biochemical activities would be increased by fusion. In the long run this would lead by a kind of natural selection to improved performance and uniformity within the areas in which interchange could take place, which may over extensive mud flats have been many square miles in extent.

The first crucial step which enabled life to get beyond this stage and to emancipate itself from mineral support was the production of polymers. These must not be imagined to have had in the first place the perfection of those we know in living things. The active polymers, the proteins and nucleic acids, are characterized by high degree of specific order in the arrangements of their various monomers. The passive polymers silk fibroin or cellulose seem to be simple regular polymers of a better quality than those produced artificially by most radical-activated polymerization processes.

It is not to be expected that the first natural polymers would have such a high degree of regularity or specificity. This, however, would not be required in the first place simply to provide the colloidal properties necessary to permit the existence of globules or proto-cells independent of mineral support and, owing to their lightness, able to float away and be distributed over larger areas. These proto-cells, which lacked membranes, would be formed by the loose coherence of neutral hydrated particles of dimensions of the order of 150–300 Å. Owing to long-range ionic forces, whose precise mechanism has not yet been explained, such particles cohere in quite dilute solutions. They form, as Barbu & Joly [5] have shown, *coacervate* drops when they are approximately spherical and *tactoids* or spindle-shaped drops when the particles are markedly elongated or flattened. The spontaneous formation of such coacervate drops, varying in size from sub-microscopic to a few millimetres, offers considerable justification for the hypothesis of Oparin [6] that the formation of coacervates formed one stage in the development of life. They would appear as a natural consequence of the formation of even irregular and polydisperse polymer molecules of protein. In so far as each coacervate drop contained most or all of the reactants and enzymes necessary for mutually supporting chemical reactions and could carry them out in the dilute medium from which it was precipitated, it qualifies as a self-subsisting system. However, as it was indefinitely divisible or miscible with other drops and possessed no mechanism for ensuring its reproduction it hardly qualifies as an organism and might well, following Pirie [2], be termed an *eobiont*.

If the physical consequences of polymerization made possible the existence of long-lived independent aggregates, its chemical consequences can have given rise to a more advanced characteristic of life, the regularization and fixing of reaction chains in the eobiont. Here evidence is accumulating that the key role was played by the polynucleotides or nucleic acids or perhaps by their possible precursors the polymetaphosphates or organo phosphates—phosphate groups linked by some polyalcohol, possibly as simple as glycerol and phosphoglyceraldehyde. The essential feature of any such system of linking is that the energy-transferring power of the phosphate group is not lost. As Bresler [15] has shown, nucleic acid can be diphosphatized reversibly just as can a single nucleotide. At the same time a new formal element is introduced when two different nucleotides or proto-nucleotides are coupled—the possibility of a topochemical reaction specifically dependent on the order of linking of the nucleotides. This is the germ of the evolution of order and reproducibility in living systems. The degree of reproducible order we see now is very great; it cannot have been so at the outset. But further elucidation of the reciprocal relations of synthesis between proteins and nucleic acids should help to show how such a high degree of order could be built up step by step, from lower degrees.

Polymers, and especially ordered polymers, can acquire another form of regularity over and above that of the sequence of their monomers. According to the geometrical and chemical character of the identical repeating unit and its various residues, the polymer chain assumes one or many *configurations* determined sterically and through internal hydrogen bonding. In this way discrete spirals such as the Pauling [7] α-helix of fibrous proteins can be built up as well as the more complex two- or three-strand twining of deoxyribose nucleic acid (DNA) and collagen. Further coiled-coiling or folding can lead to discrete quasispherical molecules like those of the globular proteins with their potential enzyme activities. These in turn can become reduplicated and aggregated to form larger molecules and intracellular structures in a way discussed in more detail in my second paper. Here it is is sufficient to recall that the small globular proteins can aggregate almost as do separate atoms with different valencies. Univalent associations lead to doubled molecules as in the haemoglobins, bivalent association to chains and rings as in insulin, tervalent association to sheets or basket-like forms as found in viruses, multivalent association to clumps such as occur in haemocyanin. The associations can be of various degrees of stability, dependent on the nature of the surrounding medium, or they can become virtually permanent by the formation of covalent links, as in the production of fibrinogen. The most important is the so-called globular fibrous (g ⇌ f) transformation by which small protein molecules can be rapidly and reversibly aggregated into fibres, a phenomenon most carefully studied in the case of insulin. Such transformations seem to play a considerable part in intracellular mechanics, notably in the formation and disappearance of the mitotic spindle (tactoid).

The achievement of higher degrees of regular configuration must have depended to a certain extent on geometrical accidents, that is, it was a secondary consequence of a polymerization process involving primarily only the individual in the chain. For steric reasons any polynucleotide would tend to adopt a quasi-spiral structure with the flat purine and pyrimidine groups piled on top of each other, but nothing in the monomers could have preconditioned the possibility of the snug fitting of two identical polymers into a double spiral. Indeed out of many possible nucleosides produced by variations in their biosynthesis, those containing desoxyribose may have been selected on account of the close fitting and consequently low energy of their association in pairs. How important is this low energy is shown by the work of Rich [8] in which two complementary synthetic polyribose nucleotides, one with purine and the other with pyrimidine groups, each separately irregularly coiled, came together *in vitro* out of the quasi-infinity of possible configurations into a close double spiral similar to that of natural DNA. The stability and specificity of this fit we may well imagine led, though possibly somewhat late in biopoesis, to its use as the chief carrier of specificity in sexual reproduction.

The complementary, but not symmetrical, relation of proteins and nucleic acids probably belongs to this stage of biopoesis. A particular nucleic acid can promote the synthesis of *one specific* protein molecule, as is shown in the behaviour *in vivo* of viruses of both ribonucleic acid (RNA) and DNA type, and as Straub [9] has shown also in the production of the enzyme amylase *in vitro* using liver nucleic acid. On the other hand a specific protein enzyme can promote the syntheses of many if not all nucleic acids, as has been shown by Ochoa [10]. Which particular nucleic acid is formed may depend on the nature of the nucleic acid model already present. The story is only beginning to be unfolded and we shall no doubt hear more about it at this Symposium; however, enough seems to be established already to mark out the first appearance of the *nucleic acid-protein, mutual synthesis relation* as a decisive stage in biopoesis. Subsequent stages would involve the coming together of a set of different systems of this character to provide a comprehensive self-regenerating metabolic system.

The association of protein and nucleic acid also provides a new type of physical body in which a core of nucleic acid or nucleoprotein is surrounded by a shell of protein molecule synthesized by the core itself. This was first described for the plant (RNA) viruses by Franklin [11] and Caspar [12] and probably also holds for the RNA-containing microsomes in the cytoplasm. Though it has not been so convincingly demonstrated, it also holds for the DNA-containing chromatin bodies in bacteria and for the chromosomes in higher organisms. It does not follow, however, that the actual production of protein or nucleic acids occurs in these bodies in the condition in which these have been observed. Rather then would it seem to mark a resting stage of a process which in full activity does not, and perhaps could not, occur in such an enclosed state. This we cannot know until their mechanism of reproduction has been observed.

However that may be, these small bodies 100–300 Å in dimensions appear as the simplest macromolecular sub-units or organelles which form the population of cells or existing organisms. It would seem not unreasonable to imagine that they antedate cells themselves and may have first appeared as inhabitants of either the diffuse pools of metabolizing material or the coacervate drops already described. The protein-covered resting stage that we observe to-day in viruses may indeed in the first place have served to protect them when the rest of the system dried up. However, neither the nucleoprotein organelles nor the viruses can be considered as organisms in the full sense, or even by themselves as proto-organisms, because of their extremely limited and specialized metabolisms.

More elaborate organelles such as plastids, mitochondria and Golgi bodies, as well as some DNA viruses, possess another element which seems to mark them off as later in biopoesis. This is the presence of membranes, seeming to consist of phospholipid, usually appearing in double or multiple layers containing hydrocarbon chains of 16–20 atoms long. The present biosynthesis of lipids is much too complicated for it to have been their original synthesis.

Nevertheless they probably originated, then as now, from a condensation of two-carbon acids which in turn may be derived from sugars. I am still inclined to put their first appearance as somewhat late, but convincing evidence for this is lacking and this gap in our knowledge seriously hinders the building of a consistent scheme of biopoesis.

Because a hydrocarbon chain of more than a few atoms is hydrophobic, with the first synthesis of lipids there appears a foreign element in an aggregate of water-soluble molecules. Such lipid molecules are driven together to form *micelles* which if they are long and uniform take the shape of bimolecular ribbons or sheets. Though such micelles are not polymers in the chemical sense of being held together by covalent links, they play the same role in two dimensions as linear polymers do in one, though they are far more easily disaggregated and reaggregated. The function of lipid sheets in cells seems to be twofold: first as divisions between parts of a cell; and second as the basis of attachment of other molecules, either active enzymes as lipoproteins or passive lipid-based protein membranes. This first function is an intrinsic consequence of the packing of long-chain hydrophobic molecules. Such sheets will automatically set themselves across concentration gradients and make it possible by closing up to maintain *vesicles* with a different chemical composition from their surroundings. The membrane-limited drop differs from the coacervate drop in holding up the diffusion of molecules and thus allows for much more intra-organismal specialization.

Double lipid membranes, such as those of soap bubble but with the hydrophilic side out, are intrinsically stable. They have been demonstrated in the electron microscope round such elementary structures as animal (DNA) viruses and bacteriophages and, although its structure seems more complicated, the cell

4

nuclear membrane is also double. The association with DNA in all these cases may be significant, indicating the relatively later arrival of this form of nucleic acid. The disappearance of the nuclear membrane at the outset of mitosis may also be significant as a reversion to an earlier state of affairs. That most DNA-containing structures are found within such membranes may also be an indication of the relative lateness of DNA over RNA in biopoesis.

One consequence of closed vesicles whose membranes offer a differential resistance to the diffusion of molecules of different size or character is the appearance of osmotic pressure and the need to equalize it by ionic mechanisms or periodic expulsions of liquid to secure any permanence for the enclosed system. The simple membrane-covered drop has a minimum surface for its volume. Where active molecules, such as enzymes, are attached to it greater effective surface can be obtained by pushing in the surface to form invaginations or cisternae leading to the kind of complexity found in mitochondria, plastids, Golgi apparatus, or endoplastic reticulum. At some such degree of complexity and interdependence of biochemically specialized parts we approach the first possibility of a self-subsistent enclosed cell, an *organism* rather than an organelle. How far the evolution was one single process, and how far it represents a fusion of partially competent but chemically interdependent sub-organisms still remains as a major problem in biopoesis. I am inclined to favour the latter alternative and even to postulate something like an organization of this fusion through the dominance of the more reliably self-reproducing DNA-protein mechanism. It would seem from the study of plant viruses that RNA-protein reproduction, precise as it is, can only take place in the presence of DNA and we as yet know of no independent organisms which only contain RNA.

It is perhaps best to leave the problem of physico-chemical biopoesis at this point and refer the study of further development to the older established disciplines of morphological evolution. Even the development of the nucleated cell of the protozoa and all higher organisms does not seem to depend on any radically new biochemical factor. The specialization of parts of cells and ultimately of whole cells for secretory, muscular, receptor or neural functions, seems to have been achieved by the setting apart and modifying of the chemical and structural elements already present in the generalized cell.

The general picture of biopoesis described above seems to fall into seven distinguishable stages set out in Table 1. This provisional division is based essentially on the degree of coherence and organisation of the effective sub-vital or vital unit. In the first stage there is no degree of coherence. The whole or part of the hydrosphere—oceans or lakes—is the seat of the essential micromolecular prevital process. In the second stage further biochemical evolution occurs in concentrations determined by more or less fixed mineral aggregates forming extensive sub-vital units. In the third stage, thanks to polymerization, coacervate drops are formed liberating life from mineral dependence and constituting separate but indefinitely divisible and fusible eobionts. The fourth stage, which I admit is more hypothetical than the others, is that of nucleoprotein organelles similar to the viruses incapable of independent metabolism but set apart from the remainder of the uniform protobiont. The fifth and later stages are characterized by the presence of lipoprotein membranes giving rise to other types of organelles—mitochondria, plastids etc. The sixth stage envisages the formation of a membrane-enclosed cell, the first organism of the type of the present day bacteria. The seventh stage is that of the appearance of the nucleated cell of the protozoa, which is the basis of all the later evolution of species both plant and animal.

In the other columns of the Table 1 have put down hypothetical sequences of biochemical evolution running in parallel with the structural evolution outlined above which is shown in more detail in Fig. 1. Here there is, on account of the greater complexity, no such clear sequence. The evolution of the main metabolites—amino acids, sugars, fats, enzyme systems, proteins and co-enzyme systems, nucleotides—must have proceeded in close interaction with each other but the pattern is still difficult to unravel. Nor are the correlations with the stages in the evolution of structure by any means as yet verifiable. Indeed some of the correlations suggested have been inserted only to provide the elements of a plausible detailed account. For instance, the origin of pentose sugars has been referred to the third or eobiont stage while that of the nucleic acids only occurs in the fourth stage. Good arguments could be adduced for referring them indeed to the second and third stages but that of the sugars must in all cases precede the nucleoside of which it is part. A similar doubt affects the position in the sequence of photosynthesis, which by providing abundant new energy must have led to a great break-out of vital evolution. It may, however, as I have earlier maintained, have occurred in a more primitive form from the very beginning, using ultraviolet light in the first place. I have abandoned this view because I now think that the essential anabolic step—the reduction of carbon dioxide to carbohydrate—can have been effected in the dark with hydrogen and free energy supplied by the oxidation of ammonia to nitrogen.

I realize that this is still a most debatable point, but the picture of an enlarged table in which every alternative suggestion finds some place is one I could not contemplate at this stage, though it might be well worth while to appoint a committee to draw one up as a provisional working hypothesis after this Symposium. The major problems of biopoesis, as I have seen them, are difficult enough to solve and no doubt others have found or will find many more before a generally accepted scheme can be drawn up. However, I list nine of them here in what I think may have been chronological order, and it is to be hoped that some of them will receive elucidation in the course of our present discussions.

1. What was the constitution of the original atmosphere? Was it oxidative or reductive in character? Did the carbon dioxide come from the lithosphere or from oxidation of hydrocarbons?

2. What was the nature of the first simple organic compounds? Had they a carbohydrate or amino character? Or were both formed simultaneously?

3. At what stages were triose and cyclic (pentose) sugars formed? At what stages were pyrimidines formed? When were purines formed from them?

4. What was the precursor of porphyrins as the molecule trap for photosynthesis?

5. What was the first coherent metabolism of the sub-vital (mineral supported?) indefinite areas?

6. What polymerized compounds stabilized the eobionts (coacervate drops)?

7. What were the first nucleoproteins? Did RNA precede DNA in the biopoesis?

8. What is the origin of long-chain lipids? What was contained in the first lipid-covered vesicles (organelles)?

9. What is the history of the nucleated cell?

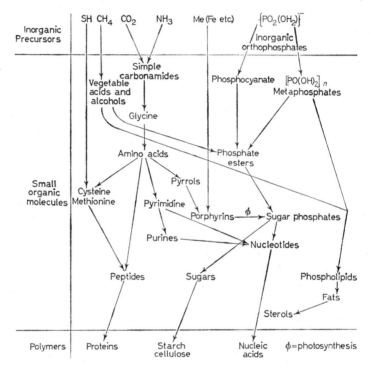

FIG. 1.   Scheme of organic molecular evolution

Of these questions 1, 2, 3, 4, 5, and 7 form a sequence in biochemical history to which I have suggested answers in Fig. 1. Questions 6, 8, and 9 form a sequence in the history of intracellular structure. The relation of the two sequences need not however be as indicated here or in Table 1.

To conclude, the purpose of this paper has been throughout not one of providing solutions to the problems of biopoesis but rather of formulating these problems themselves and putting them in some framework of order. The two chief tasks in the elaboration by many workers of a complete scheme of biopoesis are first the establishment of more or less plausible connected areas of development, those for instance of the origins of proteins or of photosynthesis, and secondly the reasonable linking of these areas of knowledge into a coherent whole. The first of these tasks has been much advanced in recent years, as witness the many valuable contributions to this Symposium, but the second is only just

TABLE 1.—*Stages in biopoesis*

		Main new constituents			Primary free-energy source	Developments in Biosphere				Catalyst or enzymes	Coherence mechanism	Reproduction mechanism
	Stage	Surface of Lithosphere	Hydrosphere	Atmosphere		Free-energy sink	Leading types of metabolism	Main metabolites	Coenzymes			
1	Production and concentration of simple molecules	SiO_2 Sand, $AlSiO(OH)$, $Fe(OH)_2$ Clay, $CaCO_3$ Precipitated limestone	NH_4HCO_3, H_2S, $NaCl$, KCl, KH_2PO_4 } Low concentrations	CO_2 (or CH_4), N_2, NH_3, H_2S, H_2O } Very little	$2NH_3 \rightarrow N_2 + 3H_3$ / $N_2 + 2H_2 + 2H$ / $8SH_2 \rightarrow S_8 + 8H_2$	$CO_2 + 4H = H_2CO + H_2O$ / Fixation of CO_2	CO_2, NH_3 condensation	NH_4^+, $CO_2(OH)^-$, CO_2NH_2, HS^-	$PO_2(OH)_2^-$, $\{PO(OH)_2\}_n$ Polymetaphosphoric acid	SiO_2?	Non-turbulent areas, Sea bottoms, Sand banks	None
2	Dehydrogenation and condensation. SUB-VITAL AREAS	Same with FeS	NH_4HCO_3, H_2S, KCl } Decreasing concentration, $NaCl$ Increasing concentration	Increasing N_2, Decreasing CO_2, CH_4, NH_3 and SH_2 disappear	Short-wave sunlight ?	The same	Dehydrogenation	Amino acids, Trioses	$NH_2CO\ PO_2(OH)$	Clay, Iron hydroxides	Adsorption on clay	Continuity of sub-vital areas
3	Polymerization and coacervate formation EOBIONTS	Organically formed $FeO(OH)$ and $CaCO_3$	K ions and inorganic PO_4 ions decreasing	Very low concentration of CO_2	Visible sunlight, Metal clathrate photosynthesis?	Primitive photosynthesis $2H_2S \rightarrow 4H + S_2$	Anaerobic fermentation	Peptides, Pyrimidines, Purines, Pentoses	Proto nucleotides, Flavones	Peptide proto-enzymes	Coacervate drops of large peptide molecules	Simple division, Evolution and reproduction not distinct
4	Nucleoprotein organelles	Organically formed accelerated weathering	Composition approximating to present but less $NaCl$	Rapidly increasing O_2	Activated porphyrin PHOTOSYNTHESIS	$2H_2O \rightarrow 4H + O_2$ Photosynthesis liberation of oxygen	Formation and fermentation of carbohydrates	Proteins, Nucleic acids, Starch	ATP, RNA	Protein enzymes	Protein-covered organelles in coacervates	Precise copying of nucleo-proteins
5	Lipid-covered organelles	The same	The same with increasing $NaCl$	Atmosphere approximating to present composition	Lipid plastids with chlorophyll for photothesis	$(n+1)CH_3COOH \rightarrow CH_3(C_2H_4)_nCOOH$ Lipid formation	Oxidation of carbohydrates	Lipids, Sterols	DNA	The same	Lipid-covered vesicles, spherical and laminar	The same
6	Membrane-enclosed cells. Protobacteria ORGANISMS	Organic soils on land areas	,, ,,	The same	Oxidation of S and Fe with atmospheric oxygen	Maintenance of ionic concentrations	—	Cellulose	The same	,, ,,	Lipid-based cell membrane	Fission and conjugation of nucleo-proteins
7	Nucleated cells PROTOZOA	Trapped organic matter in sediments Oil	,, ,,	,, ,,	Separation of photosynthetic plants from organiphagic animals	—	—	Fibrous protein, Myosin, Collagen		,, ,,	Nuclear membrane Protein-covered cell wall	Mitosis and sexual reproduction

To face page 52.

beginning and I hope that the suggestions I have made here may do something to rouse interest in it.

REFERENCES

1. J. W. S. PRINGLE, *New Biol.*, **16**, 54, 1954.
2. N. W. PIRIE, *New Biol.*, **16**, 41, 1954.
3. J. D. BERNAL, *Proc. phys. Soc. Lond.*, **52**, 537, 1949.
4. J. B. S. HALDANE, *New Biol.*, **16**, 12, 1954.
5. E. BARBU & M. JOLY, *Discuss. Faraday Soc.*, **13**, 77, 1953.
6. A. OPARIN, *Proiskhozhdenie zhisny.* Moscow, 1924.
7. L. PAULING, *Proc. nat. Acad. Sci., Wash.*, **37**, 205, 1951.
8. J. RICH, *J. Amer. chem. Soc.*, **78**, 3548, 1956.
9. F. B. STRAUB, *Acta physiol. hung.*, **10**, 137, 1956.
10. S. OCHOA, *Science*, **122**, 907, 1955.
11. R. FRANKLIN, *Nature, Lond.*, **177**, 928, 1956.
12. D. L. D. CASPAR, *Nature, Lond.*, **177**, 475, 1956.
13. N. H. HOROWITZ, *Proc. nat. Acad. Sci., Wash.*, **31**, 153, 1945.
14. M. E. JONES, L. SPECTOR & F. LIPMANN, *J. Amer. chem. Soc.*, **77**, 819, 1955.
15. S. E. BRESLER (private communication).

The Evolution of the Atmosphere of the Earth

V. A. SOKOLOV

Petroleum Institute of the Academy of Sciences of the U.S.S.R., Moscow

THE PROBLEM of the evolution of the atmosphere of the Earth has attracted much attention in recent years both in connection with the new cosmogonic hypotheses concerning the formation of the Earth [1, 2] and in connection with the problem of the origin of life [3–5].

From contemporary scientific evidence one may, it seems, draw the most generally accepted conclusion, that the Earth, like the other planets, was derived from a cloud of dust and gas which lay in an equatorial plane round the Sun. The substance of the Earth, like that of the other planets, is closely associated with the substance of the primitive Sun. The age of the substance of the Earth is estimated at 5000–7000 million years.

Assuming that this view is correct, the composition of the gas in the cloud of dust and gas must have corresponded with the composition of the outer layers of the Sun at the time when it was formed by condensation.

The interstellar medium itself is well known to contain a very rarified gas (10^{-24} g/cm^3) composed mainly of hydrogen (about 90%) and helium (about 9%). The quantity of such elements as oxygen, carbon, nitrogen and neon in the gas amounts, in all, to about 1%, while all the other elements together, mainly iron, silicon, magnesium, sulphur, etc., account for only about 0·2–0·3%. The interstellar gas contains not only elements, but also their compounds.

Hydrogen and helium predominate in the atmosphere of the Sun at present. All the rest of the elements only constitute about 1–2% of it and among these, according to the evidence of spectrographic analysis, O, Mg, N, Si, C, S and Fe are present in by far the greatest concentrations. A high concentration of light gases, e.g. H_2, CH_4 and NH_3, may be observed in the atmospheres of the large planets of the solar system.

During the condensation of the cloud of dust and gas there took place a differentiation of its substance, with the formation of the denser, heavier nuclei of the incipient planets and their somewhat lighter surrounding envelopes. This is the period at which we may properly consider the history of the Earth to have started. The primary atmosphere undoubtedly contained H and He. As to other elements and compounds, their presence in the atmosphere depended on the temperature.

Different opinions have been expressed as to the temperature of the Earth at the time of its formation. Some investigators have thought that its temperature was very low, others that it was so high that the Earth was, so to speak, in a molten state.

This question is very important in consideration of the history of the atmosphere of the Earth and it is of the utmost complexity. The accumulation of new scientific data and generalizations from them have forced people to change the ideas which were originally put forward.

One must reckon that at the earliest period of the formation of the Earth the amount of radioactive substances and, therefore, the intensity of their radiations and the amount of heat dissipated by them was considerably greater than it is now, mainly owing to the higher concentrations of actinouranium (^{235}U) and ^{40}K. The calculations made by some workers show that, 3000–4000 million years ago, the amount of radioactive heat given off was so great as to have caused the whole Earth to be molten [6]. Such calculations are, however, only of suggestive value, the more so since the question of the amount and distribution of radioactive elements in the crust of the Earth has, as yet, been insufficiently studied. It has been stated that the amounts of radioactive elements in the Earth are considerably less than those assumed in the calculations mentioned above.

It would appear that the original temperature of the protoplanetary cloud of dust and gas was low. The lowest calculated value is 10–20 °K [5]. The heat given out by the radioactive elements in this dispersed material was well dissipated. When the Earth was formed, as an aggregation of this cloud of dust and gas, heat was given off on account of its condensation. Furthermore, during the whole course of its history radiogenic heat was being given off at a gradually declining rate corresponding to the rate of decay of the radioactive elements as well as heat derived from chemical reactions.

The general trend of the mean temperature of the Earth may be supposed to have followed a curve, the first part of which corresponds to the low temperature already mentioned. It then rose gradually, reached a maximum and later declined.

The thermal conditions of the crust of the Earth and the inner parts of the terrestrial globe were not, however, uniform, and it must not be thought that they were in thermal equilibrium. There can be no doubt that the temperature of the outer layers of the Earth must have been far lower than those of the deeper layers. At present the mean temperature of the surface of the Earth is about 0 °C. As one goes deeper the temperature rises (1 °C for every 20–50 m) till, at some depth, it reaches 1000 °C or higher, as is evident from volcanic eruptions.

The question as to what was the temperature of the surface of the Earth in earlier epochs, e.g. 2000–3000 million years ago, remains unsolved. There is reason to suppose that the temperature was higher then than it is now. However, since the temperature of the surface of the Earth has not changed significantly during the last several hundred million years, it may be supposed that 2000–3000 million years ago it can scarcely have exceeded 100–200 °C, more likely it was below 100 °C. This was the time of the extensive development of volcanic activity. Large masses of magma were erupted on to the surface of the Earth at that time. The problem of the mean maximal temperature of the surface of the Earth at an even earlier period—3000–4000 million years ago—remains obscure.

Temperatures of the order of 1000 °C prevailed in the deep zones of the Earth in earlier epochs too. Heat was lost from these deep zones by the emission of hot gases, lava and water during volcanic activity, and by thermal conduction by the crust of the Earth.

From the point of view of those who hold that the Earth was formed at low temperatures, conditions on it were favourable to the retention of numerous substances which, when the temperature rose, provided the necessary conditions for the formation of an atmosphere and a hydrosphere. If we assume that the Earth existed for a long time in a completely molten state at a temperature of some thousands of degrees, then, it is clear that light gaseous substances, and even water, would have been almost completely lost and thus there could not have occurred the emission of vapours and gases from volcanoes, such as is seen now and occurred in earlier times.

Thus, a number of different considerations tell against the idea that the atmosphere and hydrosphere of the Earth were formed as a result of its complete melting with a subsequent condensation of water. It would seem more satisfactory to suppose that there was a gradual emission of gases and water vapour during the whole course of the history of the Earth.

Let us consider the history of the atmosphere of the Earth starting from the hypothesis that the temperature of its surface was low.

At low temperatures (10–20 °K) such as may have prevailed in the protoplanetary envelope of the Earth, only hydrogen and helium can exist in the gaseous state. All the other elements and their compounds are solids at such temperatures.

As is well known, the speed for escape of gases amounts, in the case of the Earth, to about 11·3 km/sec and the root-mean-square speed of gaseous molecules at different temperatures changes in proportion to $\sqrt{T}$. According to the calculation of Jeans, the retention of the atmosphere of a planet is assured under conditions in which the root-mean-square speed of the molecules does not exceed 0·2 × the speed for escape.

However, the actual conditions for the dissipation of gases from the atmosphere seem to be more complicated in that, at great heights, owing to the rarification of the atmosphere, the atomic state of the gases and the action of the rays of the Sun, the molecules and atoms of these gases can attain considerable speeds, corresponding to a temperature of some hundreds of degrees or perhaps even more.

A study of the composition of the present-day atmosphere shows a minute, insignificant concentration of such inert gases as Ne, Kr and Xe. According to the hypothesis which we have discussed these gases were lost from the primary atmosphere. It has been shown by V. G. Fesenkov that, during its escape, hydrogen may carry other gases away from the atmosphere with it. The conditions for the loss of gases would seem to be determined by other factors as well as their temperature [7–10]. In this connection it has been held that, during the formation of the Earth, the primary atmosphere was lost and that later, owing to the heating of the Earth and the consequent formation of gases, a new, secondary atmosphere made its appearance.

Various opinions have been advanced as to the nature of this secondary atmosphere and the changes undergone by it [3, 11–17].

One of the earliest hypotheses (that of Kelvin) was that the main gases of this secondary atmosphere were CO_2, N_2 and H_2S. According to another hypothesis the main gases of the secondary atmosphere were CH_4 and NH_3 (Oparin, Urey and others). The view has been expressed, however, that oxygen was present to a greater or lesser extent in this secondary atmosphere.

From the point of view of the possibility of the formation of the organic compounds which served as starting materials for the development of living substance, the most favourable circumstance, according to A. I. Oparin, was the reducing conditions and their later transition to oxidizing conditions.

Recently Poole and Rubey have accepted the idea that the main gases of the atmosphere were CO_2 and N_2. Starting from the idea of an abundance of such substances as H_2O, CO_2, N_2 etc. on the superficial zone of the Earth, and considering all these substances as an equilibrium mixture, Rubey arrived at the conclusion that if one excludes water vapour, the atmosphere contained about 91% CO_2 and $6\cdot4\%$ N_2.

In order to discuss these very complicated problems one must make a more detailed survey of both the process of the formation of gases and the process of their chemical alteration and dispersal as they have occurred ever since the formation of the Earth as a planet.

Among the processes of gas formation which were taking place in the pre-biological stage of the existence of the Earth one must take note of:

Radioactive processes involving the formation of He and A as well as Kr and Xe;

Radiochemical and photochemical processes occurring as a result of the action of radiations on various substances;

The chemical processes of breakdown and synthesis.

For a long time during the pre-biological stage of the existence of the Earth, radioactive processes undoubtedly had a great effect on the composition and abundance of the gases of the atmosphere.

The giving off of α-particles during the radioactive breakdown of U, Th, and other elements provided the conditions required for the appearance of considerable amounts of helium, while the transformation of K (k-capture) led to the formation of A.

We shall reckon, in accord with the views of many workers, that the outer envelope of the Earth contains 4 ppm of U, $11\cdot5$ ppm of Th and $2\cdot5\%$ of K [18]. After the passage of 3000 million years the amounts of these elements present in the layers of rocky formations of a thickness of, say, 40 km formed 5×10^{13} metric tons of He and 8×10^{13} metric tons of ^{40}A.

The amount of helium formed in this way was even greater on account of the breakdown of actinouranium and perhaps neptunium and other previously existent radioactive elements.

The amount of He contained in the atmosphere at present (about $3\cdot5 \times 10^9$

metric tons) constitutes only a very small fraction of the quantity which has been formed in the superficial parts of the lithosphere. As to argon there is about 6.5×10^{13} metric tons of it in the atmosphere and hydrosphere at present, i.e. about 80% of the amount mentioned above.

The opinion has been expressed, however, that the mean amount of K in the crust of the Earth is considerably less than that suggested above. Urey has therefore put forward the suggestion that part of the argon was left over from the earlier periods of the history of the Earth.

The proportion of He retained by the different rocky formations varies very widely, from 2% (when almost all has been lost) up to 95% (when almost all has been retained). The mean value of the retention of He would seem to be about 33% [18]. Owing to escape through crevices in the rocks, emission by volcanoes, by diffusion, by being carried away in water and by other processes of migration, some part of the helium which has been formed must have been given off into the atmosphere. The fraction of helium given off into the atmosphere must have been greater than that of argon, owing to the higher molecular weight of argon and its slower rate of migration.

The insignificant concentration of helium present suggests that it has been lost from the atmosphere. There may also have been some loss of argon, though this will have been small in comparison with that of helium.

Thus, the radioactive breakdown of U and Th, and the transformation of K would provide for the appearance of helium and argon in the atmosphere, although the overwhelming bulk of the helium was lost again.

The radiochemical processes of gas formation were mostly effected by the action of α-radiations in that these account for about 90% of the radiant energy given off by the radioactive elements. Each α-particle disrupts a large number of the molecules of the compounds which it encounters in its path. For example, during the action of one curie of radium emanation (and its breakdown products) on water, tens of cm^3 of oxyhydrogen gas ($2H_2 + O_2$) are formed every 24 hours. One α-particle can, on the average, disrupt tens of thousands of molecules of water. Similarly, α-particles can also act on other compounds.

The α-particles (in the form of helium) mentioned above, therefore, gave rise to chemical actions, disrupting considerable amounts of various compounds in the crust of the Earth and thus providing the necessary conditions for the occurrence of different synthetic processes.

If we allow that the greater part of the crust of the Earth affected by α-radiations consists of compounds and not of elements, we may calculate roughly that the amount of material subjected to chemical changes of this kind is about 10^{18} — 10^{19} metric tons, reckoning the thickness of the crust as 40 km. To put it otherwise, no less than 10–20% of the molecules of the material of the lithosphere, and maybe even more, underwent changes as a result of radiochemical processes. No doubt the fragments of the disrupted molecules (individual atoms and ions) entered into combination with one another so that the original compounds were, in part, formed again. Nevertheless, some fraction of the gases formed left the lithosphere and hydrosphere and entered the atmosphere of the Earth.

Among the gases formed by the action of α-rays we must include oxygen, as there is so much of it in the crust of the Earth and a considerable proportion of the α-particles must have struck oxygen-containing compounds such as SiO_2, Al_2O_3, H_2O, Fe_2O_3 and others.

However, the oxygen liberated during radiochemical reactions will have entered into combination again, owing to its chemical activity, and various oxides will have been formed. In this way many gaseous oxides must also have been formed, e.g. CO, CO_2, SO_2, SO_3, NO, N_2O, NO_2 etc. Such oxides as SO_2, SO_3, NO and NO_2 would be retained in the rock formations in the presence of water, and would take part in various reactions, while CO and CO_2 would, to a considerable extent, be given off into the atmosphere. Hydrogen, which does not take part in any reactions, would also be given off into the atmosphere. The gas which is emitted into the atmosphere during the radiochemical breakdown of water in the rocky formations is enriched in hydrogen because the oxygen oxidizes various substances in the course of its migrations. Part of the hydrogen reacts with the oxygen to form water again. As a result of reactions between hydrogen and CO or CO_2 a certain quantity of hydrocarbons is formed. As a result of radiochemical reactions, nitrogen is given off partly in the free form and partly in the form of compounds such as N_2O and NH_3.

Thus radiochemical processes provided for the accession to the atmosphere of such gases as N_2, H_2, CO_2, CO, CH_4 and heavier hydrocarbons and also N_2O, NH_3 etc. There was also some accession of oxygen although its chemical activity and its oxidation of the superficial layers of the rocky formations seem to have led to a marked lowering of its concentration in comparison with that of the other gases of the atmosphere. The oxygen which entered the atmosphere was used up in the oxidation of some of the CO, H_2 and CH_4. Photochemical reactions played a definite part in the oxidative and other processes which took place in the atmosphere (splitting of H_2O, etc.). The only gases which could persist in the atmosphere were such as were very stable chemically and would not enter into combination with one another.

Passing on to the question of chemical processes of gas formation, we must note their limited importance in view of the low temperatures which prevailed in the protoplanetary envelope and during the first period of the formation of the Earth as an aggregate within this envelope. At that time hydrogen predominated in the atmosphere. Hydrogen and other gases were lost from the atmosphere by dissipation but, at the same time, in proportion to the compaction, aggregation and heating of the Earth during its formation, there also occurred at first, an emission of those gases which, at the low temperature prevailing earlier, existed in the solid state.

The amounts of these gases given off were directly proportional to their boiling points and vapour pressures. In the first place such gases as Ne, N_2, CO, A, CH_4 and Kr were given off (with boiling points of from -152.9 °C for Kr to -245.9 °C for Ne). Fluorine and oxygen must also have been given off in this range of temperature, but, very likely they were present in the form of compounds in the primary envelope. It must be noted that the rate of some oxidative reactions at very low temperatures may even be greater than it is at, for example, o °C. For example, the reaction between NO and O_2 to form NO_2 goes 100 times faster at -184 °C than at o °C [17].

To the next group of gases, which are given off proportionately to the rise in temperature, belong CF_4, Xe, C_2H_4, C_2H_6, N_2O (boiling points of from -83.6 °C for N_2O to -128 °C for CF_4). Within this range of temperature a number of other compounds also go over to the gaseous state but they are not very stable chemically.

With a further rise in temperature CO_2, H_2S, C_3H_8, CO, NH_3 etc. will have been given off. Later still, when the temperature rose still further, water vapour was given off and underwent various chemical reactions.

Among these reactions we may mention the formation of hydrogen by the action of water on rock formations and, in particular, on the more reduced compounds of iron and other metals. The reactions whereby the hydrocarbons, C_1–C_4 and higher, are synthesized by the interaction of hydrogen with CO_2 and CO are extremely important.

The interaction between CO_2 and the silicates, which leads to the formation of carbonates, has played a great part in the history of the CO_2 in the atmosphere.

Like the temperatures, so the conditions under which gases were given off, were different for the crust of the Earth and the deeper layers. At the time when gases which had previously been condensed were being given off from the superficial layers, the temperature was so high in the deep layers that water vapour was already under considerable pressure. However, if there was to be any large-scale migration of gases from such great depths, suitable vents had to be formed in the crust of the Earth to serve as paths for this migration. This could only occur after heating of the deeper-lying layers had allowed the development of tectonic processes.

Volcanic gases provide visible evidence of the way in which chemical processes of gas formation in the deep zones of the crust of the Earth are going on at present. Apart from water vapour, the main substances composing these and other gases given off by magmatic formations are CO_2, N_2, CO, H_2 and CH_4 as well as other gases (H_2S, SO_2, Cl_2, HCl, NH_3 etc.).

Study of the composition of gases contained in cooling magmatic formations, without heating them, has shown that they contain mainly CO_2 and N_2. In some cases, however, CH_4 and heavier hydrocarbons have been found, and also H_2 and other gases. In this connection, considerable interest attaches to the emissions of gas recently discovered in the Khibin massif in the Kola peninsula. Studies of the composition and distribution of the eruptive formations found here (by A. Kravtsov, V. A. Sokolov, M. G. Gurevich, M. M. Elinson, I. A. Petersilé, A. S. Fridman, workers in the apatite mines and others), have demonstrated the presence of methane and heavier hydrocarbons and also hydrogen. The emission of jets of hot gases (CH_4, H_2, etc.) is sometimes observed in these parts. CH_4, C_2H_6, C_3H_8 and H_2 are also very often met with in low concentrations in the eruptive formations of the neighbourhood. In some specimens small quantities of bituminous substances were observed. A consideration of the physico-chemical and geochemical conditions prevailing argues in favour of the magmatic origin of these gases.

It must be pointed out that the problem of the formation and migration of gases in very deep zones of the Earth is extremely complicated. It has been suggested that at very high pressure, processes of decomposition of various compounds may take place, and that these processes lead to a diminution in total volume.

It has been calculated by Parson that, at a pressure of $570,000$ kg/cm², Fe_2O_3 will dissociate, giving off oxygen. This could occur at a depth of about 1400 km from the surface of the Earth. The later fate of the oxygen thus liberated, and the possibility of its migration to the superficial parts of the terrestrial globe, involve the consideration of many properties of matter at high pressure which are as yet obscure, owing to the subject having been little studied.

Thus, the evaporation of condensed gases and chemical processes which took place in the prebiogenic stages of the existence of the Earth provided for the appearance in the atmosphere, in the first place, of CO, CH_4 and N_2 as well as the rare gases (Ne, A, Kr, Xe). At the same time, radiochemical processes led to the appearance in the atmosphere of N_2, H_2, CO, CH_4, NH_3 and N_2O at temperatures which were still low. The presence of all these gases, in addition to the remains of the original hydrogen, gave rise to reducing conditions on the surface of the Earth. Synthesis of ammonia could have taken place at high pressures. Later on, as the temperature rose, there was a greater accession of CO_2 and O_2 to the atmosphere, gases dissolved in the water, NH_3 and H_2S reacted with other substances and hydrogen was dissipated. All this led to a gradual change from reducing to oxidizing conditions.

The oxygen, which was being liberated as a result of radiochemical reactions, would seem to have migrated within the crust of the Earth towards its more superficial parts (towards a place where the pressure was lower), oxidizing various substances on its way. Such oxygen as managed to reach the atmosphere came into contact with the superficial layers of the crust of the Earth and oxidized them. Later on, the appearance of O_2 in the biogenic stage markedly accentuated this oxidative process. Under present-day conditions, therefore, the superficial layers of the crust of the Earth are more highly saturated with oxygen in the form of its various compounds than arc the formations which lic more deeply. Not until there had been a considerable degree of oxidation of the material of the crust of the Earth could some of the oxygen, so to speak, force its way out into the atmosphere. In other words, the oxygen which was first formed did not reach the atmosphere and this remained in a reducing state.

These conditions were suitable for the formation of those compounds which, in the later development of matter, served for the building of living material. A. I. Oparin and other workers [3, 4] have discussed the possibility of the formation of these original substances by abiogenic means. The formation of amino acids by the action of electric discharges on a mixture of CH_4 (or CO), H_2, H_2O and NH_3 has been confirmed by the experiments of S. Miller [19]. One may therefore take it for granted that such organic compounds could have been formed as a result of radiochemical reactions.

The appearance of living organisms on the Earth had a great influence on the composition of the atmosphere. The development of living organisms, which mainly took place on the surface of the Earth, gave rise to the process of photo-synthesis, i.e. the process by which plants extract CO_2 from the atmosphere. In plants CO_2 enters into a reaction whereby the carbon is used for the building of organic substances while the oxygen is given off into the atmosphere. Another extremely important process is that of the decay and oxidation of dead organisms owing to the action of bacteria and various chemical factors (the action of O_2, H_2O, etc.). The products of this decay are given off into the atmosphere, mainly in the form of CO_2.

A small part of the carbon of organisms is transformed into stable compounds which are not susceptible to bacterial action and these compounds are buried in sedimentary deposits. The total mass of carbon which has left the atmosphere in this way to be laid down in sedimentary formations amounts to 1–2×10^{16} metric tons. The amount of O_2 thus liberated amounts to $2 \cdot 6$–$5 \cdot 2 \times 10^{16}$ metric tons. The amount of O_2 which has been given off is many times greater than that in the atmosphere at present (about 1×10^{15} metric tons).

The supplies of CO_2 in the atmosphere were replenished by the continual emission of it from magmatic formations through volcanoes and by other routes. Study of this problem shows that the total amount of CO_2 reaching the atmos-phere from magmatic formations during the last 500 million years alone is very great and would account for all the organic carbon contained in sedimentary formations.

Study of the gases of soils and bogs indicates that such gases, apart from oxygen, have been formed and given off into the atmosphere as a result of bio-chemical processes. The air in the soil contains, on an average 1–2% of CO_2 which passes, by gaseous exchange, into the atmosphere. Gas surveys have shown that the air of the soil contains, in addition to CO_2, methane in concentrations of $10^{-3} - 10^{-4}\%$. In the same work (1937–9) dinitrogen monoxide (N_2O) was found to be ubiquitous in the air of soils in concentrations of $10^{-3} - 10^{-4}\%$ [20]. The gases of bogs are mainly composed of CH_4, CO_2 and N_2. Heavier hydrocarbons than methane are practically absent [14, 21]. As a result of the vital activities of organisms there reach the atmosphere small quantities of other volatile substances (H_2, CO, NH_3, H_2S, ethers, terpenes etc.) as well as the gases mentioned above. In regions where there are oil- and gas-bearing formations one may often observe the emission of gaseous hydrocarbons (CH_4, etc.) in the form of jets. Such jets of CH_4 may also be observed emanating from coal seams.

Whether or not CO, H, CH_4 and other hydrocarbons remain in the atmos-phere depends on the absence or presence of oxygen. The presence of oxygen and of ozone formed from it (by the action of solar radiation and electrical dis-charges in the atmosphere), leads to the oxidation of hydrocarbons, CO and H_2, as ozone acts on them at room temperature and even lower. The amount of hydrocarbons given off during these processes is very great and, if there were no oxidation of them in the atmosphere, they would be present there in considerable concentrations [14]. The absence of methane from the contemporary atmosphere can hardly be attributed to its dissipation from the outer layers, for, in that case the heavier hydrocarbons (C_2–C_4) would remain in the atmosphere. Careful studies have demonstrated the absence of any noteworthy concentration of hydrocarbons. Such concentrations must be less than 10^{-5} % [14].

As a result of all these processes the atmosphere assumed its present aspect. According to G. P. Kuiper [17] the percentage of N_2 in the contemporary atmosphere is 78·09, that of O_2 20·95, of A 0·93, of CO_2 0·03 of Ne 0·0018, of He 0·00052, of Kr 0·0001, of H_2 0·00005 and of Xe 0·000008.

In considering the evolution of the atmosphere of the Earth, we may divide it into several stages (cf. Table 1). The first stage began from the period of the formation of the Earth from the cloud of dust and gas.

TABLE 1

Evolution of the atmosphere of the Earth

	I Stage of formation of the Earth	II Stage of heating	III Transitional stage	IV Biogenic stage
Main components	H_2, He	CH_4, H_2, CO, N_2	N_2, CO_2 CO	N_2, O_2
Important admixtures	Ne	CO_2 Rare gases	CH_4 [O_2] Rare gases	A, CO_2 Rare gases

At this period the atmosphere contained only hydrogen and helium with a small admixture of other gases, mainly neon. There was a gradual dissipation of the atmosphere, especially of the hydrogen in it.

The second stage was associated with the gradual heating of the planet undergoing formation, owing to compression and radioactive and other exothermic processes.

Various gases were given off into the atmosphere from the interior of the Earth owing to their evaporation with the rising temperature and their formation in the coarse of radioactive, radiochemical and chemical processes.

The abundance of hydrogen in the primary atmosphere must have influenced its later composition. Even after the loss of hydrogen from the atmosphere, compounds of hydrogen must have remained on the Earth, in the first place compounds with those elements which have the greatest cosmic abundance and which were present in the original cloud of dust and gas. This was the origin of such compounds as H_2O, CH_4, NH_3, H_2S, etc. The emission of water vapour and the formation of the hydrosphere led to a lowering of the concentration of the easily soluble and chemically active gases.

Although the Earth lost nearly all its hydrogen in the early stage of its development it, so to speak, inherited a reducing nature passed on by the remains of the hydrogen and compounds formed from it. These compounds were formed both in the atmosphere and in the crust of the Earth. A loss of the atmosphere occurred but, at the same time, there occurred a continual replenishment of it caused by the formation in, and migration from, the interior of the Earth of, in the first place, CH_4, N_2, CO and the rare gases, and later CO_2 and small quantities of H_2S and NH_3. Such gases as NH_3, H_2S and, to a considerable extent, CO_2, took part in chemical reactions during their migration within the crust of the Earth and dissolved in water, so their concentrations in the atmosphere were small.

The next, or third stage may be referred to as transitional, in reference to the transition from the reducing to the oxidizing state of the atmosphere.

Through volcanoes and in other ways, such gases as CO_2, CO, N_2, CH_4, H_2, NH_3, H_2S and the rare gases continued to be given off into the atmosphere. During both this and the preceding stage, radiochemical and chemical processes led to the formation of oxygen from those oxides of which the crust of the Earth essentially consists. The chemical activity of the oxygen, however, hindered its emission into the atmosphere. During its migration within the crust of the Earth the oxygen oxidized those substances which it encountered there. Such oxygen as reached the atmosphere there oxidized hydrogen and its compounds (CH_4 etc.). The presence of hydrogen and some of its compounds in the first and second stage thus precluded any considerable accumulation of oxygen in the atmosphere.

During the course of the third stage the N_2, CO_2 and CO given off from the interior of the Earth accumulated in the atmosphere owing to the preferential loss from it of the light gases such as H_2 and CH_4. As the solution of CO_2 in the waters of the surface of the Earth and its reaction with silicates lowered its concentration in the atmosphere, the main components of the atmosphere came to be the chemically inert nitrogen, with a greater or less admixture of carbon dioxide and a small admixture of methane and other gases. It may also be that small amounts of oxygen made their appearance in excess of the amounts used in oxidizing carbon monoxide and methane.

The fourth, or biogenic stage in the evolution of the atmosphere of the Earth is associated with the appearance and development of plant-like organisms. The biochemical taking up of CO_2 and giving out of O_2 led to a considerable accumulation of O_2 in the atmosphere. The continued emission of CO_2, N_2, the rare gases and others from the interior of the Earth gave the atmosphere its present characteristics. The taking up of CO_2 by plants and the laying down of organic residues in sedimentary formations has led to a transfer of the carbon of CO_2 from the atmosphere to these sedimentary formations.

Only a very small amount (2–4%) of the oxygen given off during this process is present in the present-day atmosphere. The remainder would appear to have been put out of circulation by the oxidation of the minerals of the superficial layers of the crust of the Earth, and possibly part of it was lost. Such gases as CO, H_2, CH_4 and hydrocarbons containing two or more carbon atoms were oxidized by oxygen in the atmosphere. CO_2 and H_2O were thus formed. The carbon of the atmosphere (in the form of CO_2) and also the nitrogen, took part in cyclic processes associated with living material. The gases given off from the interior of the Earth (H_2S, SO_2, NH_3, Cl, HCl, etc.) underwent oxidation and entered into various chemical combinations.

In the scheme of the evolution of the atmosphere just enunciated, the primary atmosphere consisted of hydrogen and helium and existed at the time of the formation of the Earth from a cold cloud of dust and gas.

If we assume that the Earth was formed from an accumulation of cosmic dust (hydrogen being absent or only present in small amounts) or if we assume its origin from a cloud of hot gas which would have permitted the rapid loss of hydrogen, then the atmosphere of the Earth in its earliest stages would not have had the reducing character which has been described in our scheme.

The formation of hydrocarbons and some of their derivatives seems to have taken place at all stages of the existence of the Earth. In zones where the temperature is high these compounds are destroyed. However, on cooling to temperatures at which these compounds are stable, they are formed again by means of chemical and radiochemical processes.

The formation of hydrocarbons and their derivatives certainly occurs in magmatic formations. The water contained in these formations provides a source of hydrogen thanks to which reducing processes take place with the formation of hydrocarbons.

The finding of hydrocarbons in the Khibin massif is suggestive in this connection. Methane and hydrogen are found there. The methane is usually accompanied by ethane, propane and heavier hydrocarbons.

Organic residues laid down in sedimentary deposits from another source for the formation of hydrocarbons, which have come into being since the development of life on the Earth. The further evolution of the atmosphere will surely involve an increase in the amount of argon in it and possibly also of oxygen and nitrogen since CO_2 and N_2 predominate in the composition of the gases which are given off from the interior of the Earth and which replenish the atmosphere. However, further changes in the concentration of gases in the atmosphere, and in the total amount of them, will depend on the intensity of the escape of gases into space and on processes of chemical binding of O_2, N_2 and CO_2 with the materials of the crust of the Earth. Neither of these has received much study.

REFERENCES

1. *Trudy pervogo Soveshchaniya po voprosam kosmogonii.* Communication of O. Y. SCHMIDT & V. G. FESENKOV. Izd. Akad. Nauk, S.S.S.R., Moscow, 1951.
2. V. G. FESENKOV, *Proiskhozhdenie i razvitie nebesnykh tel po covremennym dannym.* Izd. Akad. Nauk S.S.S.R., Moscow, 1953.
3. A. I. OPARIN, *Vozniknovenie zhizni na Zemle.* Izd. Akad. Nauk S.S.S.R., Moscow and Leningrad, 1941.
4. A. I. OPARIN, *Proiskhozhdenie zhizni.* Voenizdat, Moscow, 1948.
5. A. I. OPARIN & V. G. FESENKOV, *Zhizni vo Vselennoi.* Izd. Akad. Nauk S.S.S.R., Moscow, 1956.
6. V. G. KHLOPIN, *Izv. Akad. Nauk S.S.S.R. Ser. geogr. i geofiz.*, **2**, 207, 1937.
7. S. K. MITRA, *The Upper Atmosphere.* Royal Asiatic Society of Bengal, India.
8. V. G. FESENKOV, *Astr. Zhur.*, **28**, 221, 1951.
9. V. G. FESENKOV, *Dokl. Akad. Nauk S.S.S.R.*, **20**, 785, 1950.
10. I. S. SHKLOVSKIĬ, **76**, 173, 1951 ; *Astr. Zhur.*, **28**, 234, 1951.
11. H. C. UREY, *The Planets: Their Origin and Development.* Yale Univ. Press, New Haven, 1952.
12. H. C. UREY, *Geochim. et cosmoch. Acta*, **1**, 209, 1951 ; *Proc. Roy. Soc.*, A, **219**, 281, 1953.

5

13. J. H. J. POOLE, *Sci. Proc. R. Dublin Soc.*, **25**, 201. 1951.
14. V. A. SOKOLOV, *Ocherki genezisa nefti*. Gostoptekhizdat, Moscow, 1948.
15. R. T. CHAMBERLIN, chapter in *The Atmospheres of the Earth and Planets* (Ed. by G. P. KUIPER) (revised edition). Chicago, 1952.
16. W. W. RUBEY, *Spec. Pap. geol. Soc. Amer.*, **62**, 631, 1955.
17. G. P. KUIPER (ed.), *The Atmospheres of the Earth and Planets* (revised edition). Chicago, 1952.
18. K. RANKAMA, *Isotope Geology*. Pergamon Press, 1954.
19. S. L. MILLER, *Science*, **117**, 528, 1953.
20. V. A. SOKOLOV, *Neft. Promyshl. S.S.S.R.*, **2**, 46, 1940.
21. V. A. SOKOLOV, *Migratsiya gaza i nefti*, Izd. Akad. Nauk S.S.S.R., Moscow, 1956.

The Formation of the Earth from Cold Material and the Problem of the Formation of the Simplest Organic Substances

B. Yu. LEVIN

*O. Shmidt Institute of Geophysics
of the Academy of Sciences of the U.S.S.R.,
Moscow*

ONE ASPECT of the problem of the origin of life may be formulated as the following question: How, and under what conditions did the abiogenic synthesis of organic compounds take place and lead to the appearance on our Earth of organisms, which later became the major synthesizers of these compounds? To obtain an answer to this question it is necessary to survey the history of the whole substance of our planet, as this history determines how far abiogenic synthesis could proceed and what was the state of the Earth at the time when life came into being.

1. Let us begin with the question of the time and place of the original formation of the organic compounds which is most closely asssociated with the question of the formation of the Earth. For a long time there prevailed, among those who studied the formation of planets, hypotheses according to which the Earth and other planets were formed from aggregations of incandescent gaseous material. At temperatures of several thousands of degrees C organic compounds cannot exist. These hypotheses therefore led to the assumption that organic compounds were only formed after the formation and sufficient cooling of the Earth.

At present there prevails, among students of the origin of planets, a different opinion as to the 'original' state of the planetary material. Almost all contemporary hypotheses concerning the origin of the planets regard them as having been formed from a cold cloud of gas and dust which at one time encircled the Sun. In such a cloud the simplest organic compounds must have been present, just as they are present elsewhere in the interstellar gases.

However, the unanimity with which those who study the origin of the planets agree about the 'original' state of the planetary material does not mean that the authors of theories about this subject are unanimous in their ideas about its further evolution, the actual process of formation of planets. In particular, and this is very important in connection with the problem we are considering, different workers have different views as to the later thermal history of the original material of dust and gas. Thus Kuiper [1, 2] considers that very massive protoplanets composed of dust and gas must have been formed within the cloud of dust and gas. He claims that their compression, in the course of their transformation into the planets of the present, was accompanied by strong heating on account of the gravitational energy thus released. A similar idea is now advocated by V. G. Fesenkov [3, 4]*. If this idea of Fesenkov were correct it would mean that the simplest organic compounds which existed in the pre-planetary cloud must have disintegrated during the hot stage and only after the Earth had become sufficiently cool could their formation begin again. In this case the compounds which existed in the cloud cease to interest us and the problem of the original formation of the simplest organic compounds is exactly the same as it was at the time when the hypotheses of Jeans and his associates prevailed.

The other extreme case, in which there is supposed to be minimal heating of the Earth during the process of its formation, is that envisaged in the theory of O. Yu. Shmidt [6–8]. According to this theory the Earth was formed by the gradual accumulation of dust particles of the protoplanetary cloud taking place at low temperatures. An essential intermediate stage in this process was the formation of a multitude of bodies of the size of asteroids. The collision of these bodies naturally led to heating, but this was localized. As well as the non-volatile stony materials which constituted the main part of the mass of the Earth, there must have entered into it various gases, both in the sorbed state and in the form of frozen bodies formed in cold parts of the cloud far away from the Sun and entering the zone where the Earth was being formed. In this way organic compounds existing in the preplanetary cloud could perfectly well enter the Earth and be present throughout the whole depth of its substance. Contemporary organic substances on the Earth are, if one may put it so, the direct descendants of the organic compounds of the protoplanetary cloud.

The ideas of Urey [9–14] are, to some extent, intermediate between those of Fesenkov and Shmidt. According to Urey, the main process consisted in the accumulation of cold solid particles, but he considers that, at some stage, there was strong superficial heating of the asteroid-like bodies. We shall return later to the question as to why Urey needed to postulate this heating. In the mean-while it is important for us to note that, according to Urey, the composition of the internal parts of the asteroidal bodies remained unchanged during heating. According to Urey, therefore, as well as to Shmidt, organic compounds from the preplanetary cloud must have entered into the composition of the Earth.

Without entering into detailed criticism of Kuiper's and Fesenkov's hypothesis from the astronomical point of view we will only point out the implausibility and baselessness of their supposition that, when gravitational instability developed within the preplanetary cloud and it began to disintegrate into separate aggregates, there was formed just one protoplanet for each planet. In fact, gravitational instability must have led to the development of many aggregates (protoplanets),

* Recently, in a book written in collaboration with A. I. Oparin [5], V. G. Fesenkov has expressed ideas which are essentially similar to those of O. Shmidt. In particular, he considered that the Earth was formed by gradual growth and that, in the first place, it was relatively cold. Nevertheless, he postulated a large original mass, 'the proto-Earth', with a high hydrogen content. This involved an internal inconsistency. In the address which he presented to the present symposium, V. G. Fesenkov has reverted to his earlier views which are similar to those of Kuiper.

the later fate of which must, on account of their collision with one another, have been far more involved and complicated than that indicated by Kuiper.

A more important criticism of Kuiper's and Fesenkov's hypotheses for us to-day is based, not on astronomical, but on physical and chemical considerations. Data as to the chemical composition of the Earth and meteorites contradict the idea that the Earth was formed from a hot, massive protoplanet [9–17]. We must emphasize that the contradiction only becomes manifest when one considers all the mutual implications of the chemical data. There is some chemical evidence which does not contradict the idea that the Earth was formed by such a process as Kuiper and Fesenkov postulate. This is the part of the evidence which has been surveyed in the works of, for instance, Eucken and Latimer, who therefore arrived at a wrong conclusion [12]. Furthermore, I. S. Shklovskiĭ [18, 19] had shown that the process of thermal dissipation of gaseous aggregates takes place extremely slowly. It would be impossible, within the period allowed by cosmogonic theory, for the protoplanet to have got rid, by this means, of the tremendous amount of hydrogen which supposedly entered into its composition.

Thus, Kuiper's hypothesis is open to most serious objections of an astronomical, physical and chemical nature. Objections of almost the same kind could be made to the views of V. G. Fesenkov. The replacement of the idea of the separation of hot gaseous bodies from the Sun, by the idea of their formation from a cold cloud of gas and dust was unsuccessful.

I am glad to notice that A. P. Vinogradov who, some years ago, subscribed to the view of the formation of the Earth from hot material, now supports the idea that it was formed from cold material, as may be seen from his paper (p. 23).

2. Inasmuch as I am taking part in the working out of O. Shmidt's theory, it seems to me that this is the theory which gives the clearest and most logical explanation of the essential features of the planetary system, both astronomical and chemical. It must, however, be mentioned that Urey's theory, to which I shall refer later, agrees, in many respects, with that of Shmidt. This agreement, which is increasing as both the theories are further developed, is very significant for two reasons. In the first place, Urey developed his theory independently of Shmidt. In the second, Urey was, primarily, basing himself only on chemical data and only secondarily on astronomical evidence, while the development of Shmidt's theory began (1943–44) with the explanation of the fundamental astronomical characteristics of the planetary system and only later (1949–50) embraced the chemical aspects. It must be added that Urey, being a chemist, made a detailed and penetrating analysis of the chemical evidence.

The process of evolution of the protoplanetary cloud and the formation of the planets as envisaged by Shmidt's theory, may be conventionally divided into two stages. The first comprises the formation of numerous bodies with diameters of several hundreds of kilometres (we shall call these bodies of an asteroidal type or simply asteroidal bodies). The dust component of the cloud must have settled comparatively quickly into its central plane, i.e. it became collected into a very flat disc. The breakdown of this disc into separate aggregates owing to the onset of gravitational instability would seem to have been the chief way in which the asteroidal bodies were formed. If the properties of the dust particles were such that they stuck together when they hit one another, then the formation of asteroidal bodies may have happened in this way too.

Owing to the opacity of the disc of dust, its outer zone was extremely cold (at a temperature of about $3°K$) and even volatile compounds condensed there. Only a small inner zone was heated by the Sun and there only solid particles and bodies made of compounds of high melting point could exist [20, 21]. Thus, there developed a markedly zonal differentiation in the abundance and composition of solid material, in particular, of the asteroidal bodies which had accumulated by the end of this first stage.

The second stage of evolution, which began even before completion of the first, consisted in the formation of planets from the swarm of asteroidal bodies (and also from the fragments which were formed when they collided). The original circular orbits of these bodies gradually became elliptical owing to their gravitational attraction and this provided a wide 'feeding zone' for each planet. The natural averaging out of the pecularities of movement of the separate bodies, which occurred when they amalgamated, led to the orbits of the planets being almost circular. Zonal differences in the characteristics and composition of solid matter caused, as we have said, by differences in temperature, are now reflected in differences in mass and composition between the two groups of planets, those belonging to the same group as the Earth and the giant planets.

According to this concept, the planets of the same group as the Earth, and also the Moon, should be of essentially the same composition. We have no direct evidence of the composition of these bodies and are therefore obliged to judge their composition by their mean densities, in the case of the Earth $5·5$ g/cm^3, in that of the Moon $3·3$ g/cm^3. It would seem that, to solve the problem, it is necessary to adopt one view or another as to the nature of the dense core of the Earth.

For more than a century it was held that the core of the Earth consisted of nickel–iron. At present, however, most geophysicists believe that the core of the Earth may be explained by a discontinuity in the increase in density owing to the effects of high pressure. This idea was first put forward in a general form by V. N. Lodochnikov [22]. In 1948 the English physicist Ramsey [23–24] developed the same hypothesis independently and it soon obtained recognition. Working on the basis of the Lodochnikov-Ramsey hypothesis, it may be shown that the Earth, Venus, Mars and the Moon are of the same composition and only Mercury is made of denser material. This is obviously due to specially strong heating by the Sun's radiation of those parts of the preplanetary cloud from which Mercury was formed [17, 25–28].

Urey supports the earlier hypothesis, that the core of the Earth is largely made of iron. In this case the differences in density between the planets belonging to the same group as the Earth have to be interpreted as being a result of their differing contents of metallic iron. This leads one to look for processes which might have led to variation in the iron : silicate ratio. Superficial heating of the asteroidal bodies so that some of the silicates were vaporized without changing the internal composition seems to Urey [12, 13] the most likely, although the astronomical and physical aspects of this process remain extremely obscure [29].

However, as we have already said, Urey insists that the internal parts of the asteroidal bodies did not undergo any change. They should therefore bring into the composition of the Earth all those organic compounds from the protoplanetary cloud which had been incorporated in them when they accumulated at low temperatures.

Thus we see that, according to the theories of both Shmidt and Urey the simplest organic compounds must have entered into the composition of the Earth even during the process of its formation. The English astrophysicist Hoyle, who also believes that the Earth accumulated from solid particles, assigns to the organic compounds derived from the protoplanetary cloud, the determining role in the origin of life and the formation of petroleum beds [30].

Let us see what evidence astronomy provides about these simplest organic compounds.

3. Spectroscopic observations have shown that the simplest organic compounds exist both within our planetary system and far beyond its bounds. For example, it has been established that the gas–dust medium which occupies the whole of interstellar space contains molecules of CH and CN. These molecules and also molecules of C_2 are present in the atmospheres of relatively cold stars.

The giant planets, Jupiter, Saturn, Uranus and Neptune, contain large amounts of methane (CH_4) and ammonia (NH_3) which are undoubtedly of abiogenic origin.

Spectroscopic observations have revealed the presence of molecules of C_2, C_3, CN, CH, OH, CO and N_2 in the heads and tails of comets. Until recently it was believed that these chemically unstable radicals made their appearance as a result of the photodissociation of chemically stable parent molecules which were given off as vapours (desorbed) from the nuclei of the comets. It was supposed that CH_4, NH_3, CO_2 and H_2O acted as such parent molecules. Recently, however, Donn & Urey [31] basing themselves on the laboratory experiments which have been carried out during recent years by various workers, have put forward the hypothesis that frozen, unsaturated radicals are present in the nuclei of comets.

Turning to the planets belonging to the same group as the Earth we must note that CO_2 is present in the atmospheres of Venus and Mars. The amount of CO_2 present on Venus is equivalent to a layer 1 km thick (at normal temperature and pressure) and that on Mars to one 440 cm thick, i.e. twice as thick as that on the Earth.

Among the bodies formed in the inner zone of the planetary system must be included the meteorites which fall on the Earth. In the regions of the planetary system which are far from the Sun there are probably meteorites made of the 'ices' of various gases, i.e. bodies related to the nuclei of comets. However, the meteoric bodies which move through the same region as the Earth, that is, those near to the Sun, are composed of materials of high melting point, silicates and nickel-iron. Among the gases which are present in a sorbed form in all meteorites, without exception, are organic compounds. The gases given off by meteorites when they are heated contain CO_2, CO, CH_4, H_2, N_2, H_2S and SO_2. The presence of hydrocarbons on some meteorites has been well known for a long time. It was just this fact which served as a basis for N. V. Sokolov when, in 1890, he put forward the hypothesis that organic substances entered into the composition of the Earth at the time of its formation [31a].

Extremely interesting evidence about the organic compounds of the planetary system is provided by the study of one type of meteorites, namely the carbonaceous chondrites. They are called carbonaceous because they contain amorphous carbon, and possibly also graphite, as well as various hydrocarbons. Some years ago Mueller [32] undertook a study of such compounds in one such meteorite in the British Museum. This work is so far the most comprehensive.

The British Museum contains specimens from all the 20 carbonaceous chondrites which are known from all over the world. It has been shown that nineteen of these give no fluorescence with ultraviolet rays. This indicates the absence of free hydrocarbons having a H/C ratio greater than 1·4.

The hydrocarbons contained in the Cold Bokevelt meteorite have been submitted to detailed analysis. Extraction with numerous solvents (methyl alcohol, ethyl alcohol, chloroform, benzene) applied in various orders has shown the extracted material to amount to 1·1%, the greatest part being extracted with ethyl alcohol and benzene. The extracted material after deduction of ash (18%) and crystals of sulphur (11–12%) had the following composition: C, 24·26; H, 8·12; N, 4·00; S, 8·78; Cl, 5·89; O etc., 48·95%.

The presence of chlorine in organic compounds is of particular interest since halogens are absent from terrestrial bitumens.

A study of thermal breakdown at temperatures up to 350 °C showed that the substances extracted lost 55% of their weight while the powdered meteorite lost only 8·85% (mainly due to the loss of combined water which is present in all carbonaceous chondrites).

By comparing the carbon compounds present in the Cold Bokevelt meteorite with the bituminous substances found in terrestrial sedimentary deposits, Mueller noticed the following two important differences. In the first place, on heating the meteorite lost water, but it did not give off liquid hydrocarbons. In the second place, terrestrial carbonaceous substances are not, as a rule, extracted by solvents. The first of these assertions requires confirmation as Boato [33] found that, on heating powdered specimens of some carbonaceous chondrites. to 250–300 °C, oily sublimates made their appearance in a number of cases. Nevertheless, there is a difference between the carbonaceous compounds in meteorites and the terrestrial bituminous substances, and, in particular, the abiogenic origin of the meteoritic compounds is not open to the least doubt. Terrestrial minerals of biological origin always give optical rotation while the extracts of meteorites studied by Mueller were optically inactive. He therefore made special mention of a fallacy which is often met with in popular literature, namely that the presence of organic compounds in meteorites may be interpreted as indicating the presence of life on those bodies from which they originated. Mueller believes that the meteoritic organic material consists of complicated organic acids which arose abiogenically by a process of polymerization in a gaseous medium containing nitrogen, chlorine and sulphur. Judging from the difficulty of dissolving silicates, this material envelopes the stony particles.

Unfortunately we lack any more accurate data about the composition of meteoritic organic material. One can only add that the composition of these carbonaceous compounds must reflect the equilibrium between carbon on the one hand and hydrogen, oxygen, nitrogen and sulphur on the other, which was established at the time when the substance of the meteorite attained its highest temperature.

While studying the isotopic composition of the carbon and hydrogen from twelve carbonaceous meteorites, Boato [33] found a notable difference between the different meteorites and, in some cases, between different parts of the same meteorite. This is due to a process of fractionation or to chemical reactions taking place at different stages of the formation of the meteorites and the whole planetary system. Data as to the isotopic composition of the carbon and hydrogen will be very valuable in later investigations of these processes and, in particular for a study of the original organic compounds.

4. Let us come back, at last, to our own Earth. As we have already said, various gases and vapours, as well as organic compounds, must have entered into the composition of the whole thickness of the substance of the Earth during its formation. During the gradual heating of the interior of the Earth owing to the accumulation of heat generated by the decay of radioactive elements, gases and vapours began to seep towards the surface and were given off, forming the atmosphere and hydrosphere [15]. This same process of internal heating led to the gradual development of the crust of the Earth starting about 3000 million years ago when the temperature became high enough for the partial melting of silicates. We must note that A. P. Vinogradov (p. 23) makes a great mistake in assuming that the temperature of the superficial layers of the Earth changed according to a curve corresponding approximately with that for the amount of heat generated, and that at some time it was high. The mean temperature of the surface of the Earth was always low and was always determined by the heat reaching it from the Sun. The temperature of the interior, however, had in general risen throughout the long history of the Earth.

At present all astronomers, geologists, geophysicists and geochemists are agreed that the contemporary atmosphere and hydrosphere of the Earth are not the residues of some very extensive primary atmosphere, but are of 'secondary' origin, i.e. they have arisen owing to the gradual giving off of gases and vapours from the interior [34–39 and Sokolov, p. 54]. Among other evidence indicating that the hydrosphere and atmosphere arose in this way, an important piece is that concerning the absence of any great fluctuations in the CO_2 content of the atmosphere during the course of the whole of geological history. As the amount of carbon laid down in carbonaceous deposits increased in the course of time, there must have been a continual accession of CO_2 to the atmosphere.

The emergence of gases and vapours from the interior into the atmosphere—during volcanic eruptions, through gas springs and by the general 'breathing' of the planet—continued until the present, though, unfortunately to what extent these gases and vapours are juvenile and to what extent they are taking part in cycles involving only the outer layers of the Earth we do not know. Thus, for example, we cannot tell what part of the methane which is present in the atmosphere or that which is given off by sources of natural gas, is of abiogenic origin.

The presence of such abiogenic, cosmic methane, though perhaps only in the distant past, perhaps in the first stages of the emission of gases from the interior of the Earth, may be inferred from its presence on the other planets, in meteorites and from what are now known to be the essential features of the process of formation of the Earth. From the fact that methane is present in eruptive formations it also follows that abiogenic methane must, up till now, have been given off from the interior to a greater or lesser extent.

It is hard to estimate the overall quantity of hydrocarbons and abiogenic organic compounds in general which was present in the whole volume of the Earth in the past and the quantity it now contains. It is, however, clear, from the evidence adduced already, that this quantity may be very large. This circumstance is one of the incentives to a search for ways in which petroleum could have been formed abiogenically. The main stimulus to such a search is the fact that analysis of geological data concerning the conditions under which petroleum has been laid down and concerning the distribution of natural gases in the Earth suggests that petroleums are of purely abiogenic origin [40, 41].

The ironic way in which Hoyle [30] referred to the organic theory of the formation of petroleum and the absence from his book of serious discussion of the possibility of its inorganic origin evoked a protest from Link, the president of the American Association of Petroleum Geologists [42]. That there is a serious basis for working out a non-organic theory of the formation of petroleum is evident from, for example, the fact that that eminent specialist on the question of the formation of petroleum, Prof. V. D. Porfir'ev has changed his earlier opinion and now embraces the non-organic theory [43]. At the same time we must draw attention to the perfectly correct appeal by Link for a reconciliation between the views of representatives of related scientific disciplines.

As Mueller pointed out, even before the formation of meteorites, that is to say, in the very earliest stages of the evolution of the dust–gas cloud, hydrocarbons could polymerize, forming the hydrocarbon compounds which are present now in the carbonaceous chondrites. Thus, it was not only methane, but also these more complicated compounds which entered into the composition of the Earth from the very beginning. Such of these compounds as are not now present in the interior of the Earth probably broke down long ago into simpler ones owing to the high temperatures which now prevail there. However, such of them as managed to move outwards towards the surface while the temperature was still moderate could have undergone further complication and polymerization during their journey towards the surface.

Finally, when they emerged on to the surface of the Earth they were exposed to new possibilities. According to Süss, the photodissociation of methane in the presence of water vapour indicates a possible mode of synthesis of the most diverse organic substances. Evaluation of these complicated questions of organic chemistry is outside the sphere of competence of astronomers and geophysicists. Chemists must play the main part here.

Nevertheless, the evidence of contemporary astronomy and geophysics leads to two conclusions which seem to me important for the problem of the origin of life. In the first place, organic compounds of varying degrees of complexity existed in the preplanetary material and, with it, entered into the composition of the Earth through its whole depth. In the second place, the emission of gases and vapours from the interior, leading to the formation of the hydrosphere and atmosphere, was accompanied by the carrying out of organic compounds which underwent further changes in the course of it.

Such then, is the astronomical and geophysical background which must be borne in mind when considering the problem of the origin of life on the Earth.

REFERENCES

1. G. P. KUIPER, *Astrophys. J.*, **109**, 308, 1949.
2. G. P. KUIPER, in *Astrophysics* (Ed. by J. A. HYNEK). McGraw-Hill, New York, 1951
3. V. G. FESENKOV, *Sovremennye predstavleniya o proiskhozhdenii nebesnykh tel.* Akad. Nauk S.S.S.R., Moscow, 1953.
4. V. G. FESENKOV, p. 9.
5. A. I. OPARIN & V. G. FESENKOV, *Zhizni vo vseleno'.* Izd. Akad. Nauk S.S.S.R., Moscow, 1956.
6. O. YU. SHMIDT, *Dokl. Akad. Nauk S.S.S.R.*, **45**, 245, 1944.
7. O. YU. SHMIDT, *Chetyre lektsii o teorii proiskhozhdeniya Zemli.* 3rd ed., Moscow, 1958.
8. O. J. SHMIDT, *Mem. Soc. Sci. Liège* (Liège symposium, 1954), **15**, 638, 1955.
9. H. C. UREY, *Geochim. et cosmoch. Acta*, **1**, 209, 1951.
10. H. C. UREY, *The Planets.* Yale Univ. Press, 1952.
11. H. C. UREY, *XIIIth Int. Congr. pure appl. Chem.*, 1953, p. 188, Uppsala, 1954.
12. H. C. UREY, *Astrophys. J.* Suppl., **1**, 147, 1954.
13. H. C. UREY, Chapter 10 in *Nuclear Geology* (Ed. by H. FAUL). John Wiley, New York, p. 355, 1954.
14. H. C. UREY, *Astrophys. J.*, **124**, 623, 1956.
15. B. YU. LEVIN, *Priroda*, Leningr. **10**, 3, 1949.
16. B. YU. LEVIN, *Izv. Akad. Nauk S.S.S.R.*, Ser. Geofiz., **4**, 289, 1953.
17. B. YU. LEVIN, *Trudy geofizich. Instituta Akad. Nauk S.S.S.R.*, **26** (153), 11, 38, 1955.
18. I. S. SHKLOVSKII, *Dokl. Akad. Nauk S.S.S.R.*, **76**, 193, 1951.
19. I. S. SHKLOVSKII, *Astr. zhur.*, **28**, 234, 1951.
20. L. E. GUREVICH & A. I. LEBEDINSKII, *Dokl. Akad. Nauk S.S.S.R.*, **74**, 905, 1950.
21. L. E. GUREVICH & A. I. LEBEDINSKII, *Izv. Akad. Nauk S.S.S.R.*, Ser. Fiz., **14**, 790, 1950.
22. V. N. LODOCHNIKOV, *Zap. Min. Obshchestva*, 2 Ser., **64**, 207, 1939.
23. W. H. RAMSEY, *Mon. Not. R. Astr. Soc.*, **108**, 406, 1948.
24. W. H. RAMSEY, *Mon. Not. R. Astr. Soc.*, Geophys. suppl., **5**, 409, 1949.
25. K. E. BULLEN, *Nature, Lond.*, **170**, 363, 1952.
26. K. E. BULLEN, *Seismology.* Methuen, London, 1954.
27. K. E. BULLEN, *Ann. Géophys.*, **11**, 53, 1955.
28. S. V. KOZLOVSKAYA, *Dokl. Akad. Nauk S.S.S.R.*, **92**, 903, 1953.
29. B. J. LEVIN, *Mem. Soc. Sci. Liège* (Liège symposium, 1956), **18**, 186, 1957.
30. F. HOYLE, *Frontiers of Astronomy.* London, 1955.
31. B. DONN & H. C. UREY, *Astrophys. J.*, **123**, 339, 1956.
31a. N. V. SOKOLOV, *Byull. Mosk. O-va Ispyt. Prirody*, **3**, 720, 1890.
32. G. MUELLER, *Geochim. et cosmoch. Acta*, **4**, 1, 1953.
33. G. BOATO, *Geochim. et cosmoch. Acta*, **6**, 209, 1954.
34. G. P. KUIPER, *Astrophys. J.*, **100**, 378, 1944.
35. H. BROWN, in *The Atmospheres of the Earth and Planets* (Ed. by G. P. KUIPER). Univ. Chicago Press, 1949.
36. R. T. CHAMBERLIN, *ibid.*
37. J. L. KULP, *Bull. geol. Soc. Amer.*, **62**, 326, 1951.
38. W. W. RUBEY, *Bull. geol. Soc. Amer.*, **62**, 326, 1951.
39. B. MASON, *Principles of geochemistry*, N.Y. – London, 1952.
40. P. N. KROPOTKIN, *Sov. Geol.*, Moscow, **47**, 104, 1955.
41. P. N. KROPOTKIN, P. 84.
42. T. A. LINK, *Bull. Amer. Ass. Petrol. geol.*, **41**, 1387, 1957.
43. V. D. PORFIR'EV, *Tezisy dokladov na yubileĭnoĭ nauchno-tekhnich. konfer.* L'vovskogo Politekhn. Inst., 1957.

Chemical Diversity and the Origins of Life

N. W. PIRIE

Rothamsted Experimental Station, Harpenden, Great Britain

CONTEMPORARY discussions about the origin of life start with the simplifying assumption that no occult phenomena are involved and no forces or principles operated to bring life into being in the past that do not operate now. This assumption is sometimes called the 'uniformitarian' principle. The chemistry and physics with which biology is and has been concerned is the ordinary chemistry and physics of the period at issue but we know very little even of the chemistry and physics of to-day and the little we know is not necessarily the most relevant part. Furthermore, Haldane argues [1, 2] that chemistry and physics may have been significantly different in the Pre-Cambrian. That would complicate detailed interpretation but would not affect the principle.

This basic assumption has been made by most scientists and philosophers who have considered the problem. They have not disagreed about whether life could originate from non-living matter but only about how often it did so. The 2500 year history of this dispute has often been surveyed (e.g. Huxley, Tyndall, Oparin). On the one side we have such men as Redi, Spallanzani, Pasteur and Tyndall who regarded the event as so infrequent that it could be disregarded in the course of ordinary work; on the other such men as van Helmont, Needham, Pouchet and Bastian who looked on it as an easy and regular transition. Although the dispute did not always proceed along strictly objective lines it was extremely valuable both in integrating knowledge and in uncovering new phenomena. In this respect it contrasts with the idea that 'Life' is something quite different from anything else and that it either comes to us from space or is the consequence of special activity by a deity or demiurge. Though sterile, this conclusion has been common among physicists and engineers and has been come to by a few biologists such as Linnaeus and Wallace.

The 'uniformitarian' principle takes us to the limit of simplicity. Before we can frame a theory of the origin of life we should know the nature of the environment in which it originated and we should know, or be able to define, the criteria by which we would define or recognize it. Unfortunately we know neither. During the nineteenth century it was generally assumed that Earth had cooled from an incandescent mass so that if any form of life had been carried over from an earlier phase in its history it must have been carried by silicates or some such thermostable material. The discovery of radioactivity made the idea tenable that Earth originated by the accretion of cold interstellar detritus and so made the old 'cosmozoic' idea a little more attractive. But this idea merely moves our problem to a different environment [3] and does nothing to solve it. At present there are advocates for both a hot and a cold origin of Earth so that it would seem wise not to make our theory of the origin of life depend exclusively on either.

On the conventional theory that Earth was originally incandescent with approximately its present mass, the oceans can only have formed after there was a solid crust and its components come from those parts of the total mass that later came near enough to the surface to be washed. Similarly the atmosphere consists of those original volatile components that were heavy enough to be retained by gravitation, together with subsequent exhalations. On the accretional theory, on the other hand, it is probable that a much larger proportion of the whole mass was exposed to liquid water during the process of condensation. It is already difficult, on the conventional theory, to account for the low salt content of the ocean; present-day rivers would bring down that amount in a fraction of the time for which the ocean is thought to have existed. On the accretional theory, the problem of what materials were initially present in solution is raised in an even more acute form and a recognition of this may keep us from being dogmatic about the composition of the pools that first formed on Earth.

It is unlikely, on either theory, that the probiotic atmosphere contained O_2 because of the immense preponderance of Fe^{++} over Fe^{+++} in rock. O_2 is now produced by photosynthesis at such a rate that each molecule of it in the atmosphere has a 'half-life' of only a few thousand years before returning to CO_2 or H_2O. It is tempting to assume that O_2 had this origin initially but that assumption cannot account for the immense deposits of sedimentary Fe^{+++} and sulphate. If, as seems certain, these are made by atmospheric oxidation of Fe^{++} and S or H_2S, it is hard to see where all the C or other reducing material that is simultaneously produced during photosynthesis has gone to. As Herbert Spencer first pointed out, the C in shale, coal and oil is approximately equivalent to the O_2 in the atmosphere now. A probiotic origin for O_2 must be sought and one is readily available in photolysis of H_2O in the upper atmosphere followed by loss of H_2 into space. The atmosphere is a system through which the CO_2 now present in limestone and dolomite, and the O_2 now present in sulphates or instrumental in making Fe^{+++}, has flowed. The quantities present in, or represented by, these 'fossil' forms of CO_2 and O_2 are very much greater than the quantities in the atmosphere or ocean now. This, taken in conjunction with the fact that rates of production and sequestration are uncertain by factors of at least 10, makes it legitimate to conclude that dogmatism about the composition of the atmosphere at any stage in Earth history before perhaps the Jurassic is out of place. Very large amounts of O_2 and CO_2 have passed through it and the concentration of either at any phase of history is still a matter of assumption. If a certain type of atmosphere is necessary for a certain type of biopoesis (see p. 78, footnote) it is reasonable to postulate that atmosphere for argument but it is not reasonable, on existing information, to try to exclude some other type of atmosphere or mode of biopoesis. The fact that amino acids and related substances are made when electrical discharges pass through a mixture of CH_4, NH_3, H_2O and H_2 [4] is sometimes quoted as evidence that that was the composition of the probiotic atmosphere. This would be logical only if it were demonstrated that similar substances are not formed in other gas mixtures and if we know that these substances were the substrate from which the first life grew. There are geochemical reasons [5] for thinking that the probiotic atmosphere was mainly CO_2 and N_2.

As knowledge grows the range of possible compositions for Earth's surface will be narrowed. It could be argued that discussions about biopoesis might well wait till this narrowing had taken place. There are two important reasons for disagreeing with this idea. The urge to solve the problem of the origin of life is an important stimulus for the accumulation of evidence about the original environment. Reciprocally, if biochemical research could define unequivocally the necessary qualities and composition of an original organism, or eobiont*, this would define the conditions in at least part of the primitive environment. It would be analogous to the use of the morphology of fossils to define whether the region in which they lived was dry land, marsh or water.

There are many difficulties here. I have already argued [7] that, even with existing organisms and systems a rigid division into the living and the non-living is not possible. Every criterion that has been suggested will both exclude something that, for aesthetic reasons, we wish to call living and include something that we do not. Something more satisfactory could be achieved by saying that a living organism had to show some arbitrary number out of a group of qualities but in practice this would be almost as clumsy as a catalogue of the things we intend to call living and it would operate particularly badly among the simpler systems where the issue becomes of most interest. It seems better to recognize that life is not a definable quality but a statement of our attitude of mind towards a system. This makes life a fallible guide through geochemistry.

Even if it is not possible to say that a system with certain activities is alive it may yet be possible to say that certain chemical substances or processes are peculiar to life and essential for it. A cursory study of present-day organisms shows many uniformities in their use of proteins, fats, carbohydrates, phosphoric esters etc. At one time particular attention was attached to the proteins, now there is a tendency to use the phosphoric esters as the fundamental criterion of life. It is of course perfectly legitimate to say that you do not propose to call any system alive unless it contains protein. That establishes a simple linguistic rule and it is essentially what Engels did in his celebrated dictum. But it is not a very useful point to make because not all systems containing protein or phosphoric esters are alive and to say that whatever else a system may be doing, it cannot be called alive if it does not contain the chosen substance, seems to be as arbitrary as the erection of a colour bar among people.

All present-day forms of life that have been examined contain protein. The number examined is only a small proportion of the whole but protein-based mechanisms seem to be so efficient that it is likely that most or even all the other forms of life also use proteins now. If this turns out to be so it will have no more relevance for a discussion about the origins of life than the now almost universal use of paper has for the origin of writing or the use of matches for the original making of fire. The first metal frying pan was probably made of gold because that metal was available and usable though later ousted. The point is worth

---

* I have proposed elsewhere [6] the words *biopoesis* and *eobiont* for the origination of life and for the first organisms originated and argued the advantages of the new words.

labouring because very many people have written as if the problem of the origin of life was the same as the problem of the spontaneous synthesis of proteins and some, having realized that the latter involves difficulties, have concluded that God or some similar agency must be involved.

Proteins, so far as we know, are mainly useful to an organism because they are enzymes that catalyse metabolic actions very efficiently. But there are innumerable non-protein catalysts of similar actions. Oxidations can be catalysed by many metals and by thiourea, some of the rare earth elements are esterases and so on. An organism using such systems might be sluggish but it would be conceivable. If *Corycium* is indeed the fossil of an organism it was enigmatic in more ways than the paleontologists have thought of and probably organized its metabolism with the help of molecules that would not fit neatly into our systems of classification. Proteins, built economically out of about twenty-five amino acids, are probably a late development selected from a more chaotic group of primitive chemical experiments. Evolution operates to give us morphological structures that are relatively simple and efficient without being by any means the only possible structures; it is only reasonable to conclude that it also operated on chemical structure to make the efficient enzymes with which we are familiar.

The evidence for evolution, and the Linnaean system of classification, both make it appear that the number of species in existence at any time has been getting larger. Projecting this principle back it seems reasonable to think that all sprang from one or a few common ancestors [8]. This is logical enough but it is illogical to think that this ancestor was the original organism. It seems much more probable that this, the beginning of morphological complexity, was nearly the limit of biochemical complexity. With this idea in mind we may consider some aspects of biochemical complexity to see what hints they give us about the mechanisms that may have been made use of initially, and about the manner in which selection may have operated on them.

The origins of life were probably local phenomena. It is an illusion to think that rare events necessarily happen and prosper to an extent proportional to the amount of material to which they could happen. Thus, although human genius may arise unrecognized with a predictable frequency, it has flourished and become effective most often in specialized and often small communities. Similarly Vavilov showed that new plant species often arise in the isolated and slightly adverse environments at the edge of the main areas of growth. I am therefore perfectly willing to postulate an effective environment less extensive rhan the whole probiotic hydrosphere. At different stages in Earth's history either the whole environment of parts of it probably ranged from being alkaline with NH_3 to acid because of the oxidation of S and H_2S. Two thousand million years of leaching, precipitation and rearrangement have considerably diminished the complexity of the mineral surfaces at which relevant actions may have gone on so that, besides the elements commonly present in large bodies of water now, it is reasonable to think about actions involving such elements as V, Ba, Cr, Se, Ge etc. either in solution or, as Goldschmidt [9] suggested, at the reactive edges of crystals.

Oil and bitumen regularly contain vanadium; this suggests that it was once

used commonly as it is still used by some tunicates. It is interesting that it is
the primitive species of tunicate that have blood corpuscles containing large
amounts of V and also normal, or stronger, H_2SO_4. An existence that depends
on a strongly acid solution of an element as rare as V is obviously both hazardous
and precarious so that more highly evolved species, able to do the same job with
a commoner element, such as iron, have an advantage. Dependence on the use
of V in quantity seems to have been disappearing and we see now only the last
remnant of it. But selection does not operate in the same way against the use of
traces of V and, in traces, the element is present in many organisms. It is essential
for some moulds and algae [10] and probably for other plants as well. Much the
same can be said for aluminium. It is essential for the growth of some plants and
is widely distributed, particularly in the more primitive types such as tea [11]
and lycopodium. It is not so easy here as with V to see what kind of reaction may
be involved. In many species there is barium in the choroid and chromium in
the blood corpuscles but there is no evidence whether these occurrences are the
relics of ancient metabolic paths or the beginnings of new ones.

Selenium is widely distributed in rocks so that dependence on it would rarely
be a serious disadvantage and yet it is seldom used and is poisonous to most
species. A few plants however grow better in the presence of Se and it is built
into their proteins in place of sulphur so that the protein is poisonous to animals.
The phenomenon, if not the interpretation, was known to Marco Polo and a
close study of it would be most illuminating.

The relationship between S and Se leads naturally to a consideration of the
possibility of a similar relationship between carbon and germanium. There is
no evidence that Ge is essential for any present-day organism but the Hartley
coal seam in Northumberland is rich in it and it is present in workable amounts
in many other coal seams. This could be the result of adsorption of Ge by coal
or its precursors but it is just as likely that coal-forming organisms used Ge.
If they did, some may do so still, and a search might be rewarding both biochemically and commercially. The presence in fossils of some other elements, for
example caesium, thallium and titanium suggests a biological role for them also,
but secondary specific absorption, during the process of fossilization, confuses
the interpretation of all evidence of this type. Argument about these elements
may seem to be too nebulous to merit serious attention. There are two reasons
for setting it out; it is important to keep all the possibilities to some extent in
mind, and until the possible significance of this type of evidence is appreciated
not much effort is likely to be put into finding or co-ordinating the facts.

Halogen metabolism offers some other hints about the early course of evolution.
Halide ions have probably been available ever since liquid water formed, there
may have been free chlorine, and chlorinated hydrocarbons are present in
bitumens both of terrestrial and meteoric [12] origin. The ability to handle the
halogen-to-carbon bond may therefore have been useful to an eobiont. Sponges
still make extensive use of bromine compounds, so do the various species of
mollusc that make Tyrian purple; there is at least one group of plants,
Dichapetalum, that makes fluoroacetic acid and several of the moulds make a
range of chlorine compounds. But the vertebrates have nearly given up this type

of metabolic expertise. Not completely however; we still use iodine in the thyroid and normal life depends on this otherwise exceptional synthesis. There is no reason to think that this use of iodine is new; it is found in present-day amphibia and fish and may well be ancient. I suggest that it is a relic of an initially more catholic approach to metabolism and that evolution has not eliminated it because there are few regions where the amount of iodine in rock is so small as to make this dependence a disadvantage. The only logical alternative is to look on the thyroid as the remains of a commensal sponge that lodged in the gill arches of a primitive vertebrate giving rise ultimately to symbiosis as intimate and essential as that in the lichens.

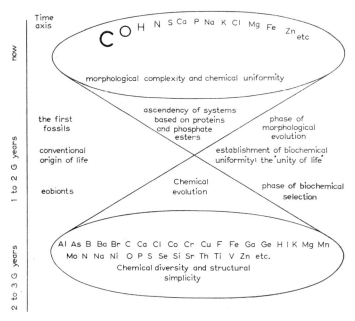

FIG. 1. At each level of time the width of the cone represents the number of ways in which living or lifelike systems worked. The size of the atomic symbol is an indication of the contribution that element may have made to the process at the time.

The evidence that much of evolution is accompanied by the selective loss rather than gain in capacity was marshalled by Lwoff [13]. This leads to the conclusion that present-day organisms are descended from one or a few super-organisms with more extensive capacities than those now found. It is necessary to conclude that these super-organisms were far removed from eobionts and were perhaps built up by symbiosis among several of them. The same type of selection that Lwoff has called attention to probably then operated so that the final organism would be derived as much by discarding or minimizing capacities as by acquiring new ones. The metabolic processes used by present-day organisms were probably present in some of the early forms of life but there is no reason

6

to think that they were all present, that they were present in all forms, or that when present they were quantitatively important. Life now is the result of two quite independent processes; the random appearance of capacities in small atypical regions, and the integration of these capacities into a mechanism adapted to survival in the environment that exists more generally. The former may have been concerned predominantly with reactions that are now unusual but they are the processes that should be taken as the origins of life. This point of view is roughly illustrated in the diagram (Fig. 1). Two cones are set apex to apex and the number of processes used by all the forms of life at any time is indicated by the width of the cone at that time. The broad base thus shows the original biochemical complexity, the broad top the present morphological complexity, and the narrow middle is the conventional 'origin of life'.

At each stage of science there has been a tendency to associate life with a recently discovered type of phenomenon. At one time it was magnetism. Then Pasteur overstressed the relevance of optical activity* and pointed out the analogy with crystallization. Proteins and adenosine triphosphate have had their turn and now there is a tendency to overstress isotopic fractionation. Living systems, like all other systems with a series of stages of adsorption, diffusion, or phase equilibrium, may differentiate between isotopes. They pack the regions of separation into smaller compass than an isotope separation factory but they only perform the same fractionation that a long enough column of suitable mineral adsorbent would. An unusually high ratio of ^{12}C to ^{13}C in a structure is *prima facie* evidence that C was once part of an organism, but other systems can fractionate C isotopes and living systems do not at all times fractionate them in the same way [14]. The Universe contains a vast range of processes and types of compound. It is probable that none of these appear exclusively in living systems but it is equally probable that many more have appeared or still appear in them than is generally assumed.

The argument has been presented here in terms of the elements because they make it easy to put diversity on to a quantitative basis. Somewhat similar conclusions can be drawn from other aspects of chemistry. The more primitive animal species have the most complex fats [15], this may be a consequence of their failure to fractionate food fats [16, 17] but that in itself is evidence of versatility. Some insects use substances such as formic acid and the oxides of nitrogen that seem to fall outside the range of normal biochemistry and they may well have been doing this for 100,000,000 years. The simpler organisms such as moulds and bacteria handle a more diverse group of metabolites and make a more diverse group of excretory products than any other organisms but there is no evidence about the antiquity of the species. In summary: the development of morphological complexity has been associated with some biochemical simplification, in the process many originally vital activities have probably been lost and the relative importance of others has probably altered. This Symposium will have demonstrated that there is no basis for dogmatism about the processes involved in the origins of life; my contention is that there is not yet even a basis

* This point has been elaborated elsewhere (N. W. PIRIE, *Trans. Bose Res. Inst.*, **22**, 111, 1958).

for dogmatism about the materials undergoing these processes. A quotation from Louis MacNeice may serve as a summary:

World is suddener than we fancy it.
World is crazier and more of it than we think,
Incorrigibly plural.

REFERENCES

1. J. B. S. HALDANE, *Nature, Lond.*, **153**, 555, 1944.
2. J. B. S. HALDANE, *New Biol.*, **16**, 12, 1954.
3. N. W. PIRIE, *Modern Quarterly*, **3**, NS 82, 1948.
4. S. L. MILLER, *Science*, **117**, 528, 1953.
5. W. W. RUBEY, *Spec. Pap. geol. Soc. Amer.*, **62**, 631, 1955.
6. N. W. PIRIE, *Discovery*, **14**, 238, 1953.
7. N. W. PIRIE, *Perspectives in Biochemistry.* Cambridge Univ. Press, 1937.
8. N. W. PIRIE, *New Biol.*, **16**, 41, 1954.
9. V. M. GOLDSCHMIDT, *New Biol.*, **12**, 97, 1952.
10. D. I. ARNON & G. WESSEL, *Nature, Lond.*, **172**, 1039, 1953.
11. E. M. CHENERY, *Plant & Soil*, **6**, 174, 1955.
12. G. MUELLER, *Geochim. et cosmoch. Acta*, **4**, 1, 1953.
13. A. LWOFF, *L'évolution physiologique: études des pertes des fonctions chez les micro-organismes.* Paris, 1943.
14. H. CRAIG, *Science*, **119**, 141, 1954.
15. T. P. HILDITCH & J. A. LOVERN, *Nature, Lond.*, **137**, 478, 1936.
16. F. B. SHORLAND, *Nature, Lond.*, **170**, 924, 1952.
17. T. P. HILDITCH, *Nature, Lond.*, **170**, 925, 1952.

The Geological Conditions for the Appearance of Life on the Earth, and the Problems of Petroleum Genesis

P. N. KROPOTKIN

Geological Institute, U.S.S.R. Academy of Sciences

THE GEOLOGICAL CONDITIONS AT THE SURFACE OF THE EARTH IN THE EARLY STAGES OF ITS DEVELOPMENT AND THE PROBLEM OF THE ORIGIN OF LIFE

ALL THE modern investigations on the origin of life lead to the conclusion that the source of the primary, most primitive forms of life on the Earth was abiogenic organic compounds of the complex hydrocarbon type [1–4].

Among the organic material widely distributed in the Earth's crust that could be considered as a source of the primary forms of life, is petroleum or complex hydrocarbons, similar to it in composition.

Most investigators assume that the Earth's atmosphere originally had no oxygen. Free oxygen appeared later, as a result of the life activity of plants [5]. Evidently, reducing chemical conditions were predominant in the atmosphere at that time. Besides a certain amount of methane, there were probably carbon dioxide, nitrogen, and aqueous vapour in the atmosphere, similar in composition to the present atmosphere of Venus. (It consists of CO_2, N_2 according to Kozyrev, and H_2O—according to Lyot, and judging by the reflection of the sun's rays, penetrating the cloud layer of this planet to the reflective surface, which is most probably an ocean surface.) The important, and perhaps even predominant, rôle of carbon dioxide in the atmosphere's composition at the early stages of the Earth's development has been shown by the numerous calculations, made by different authors, of the amount of CO_2, which is equivalent to the total amount of carbon in mineral coal and in the diffused carbonaceous matter buried in sedimentary rocks.

Developing in such conditions at the surface of dry land or water basins, the primary living organisms evidently could neither make use of solar energy (not yet having acquired chlorophyll) nor of the energy which under present conditions is freed through oxidation of organic compounds in the atmosphere or in water containing molecular oxygen (for instance, in processes of putrefaction). It would appear that chemical processes, at that time, were of the type now effected by anaerobic bacteria.

Two types of exothermic reaction accompanied by the emission may be con-

84

sidered as a prototype of the processes on the basis of which the vital activity of the primary organisms could have taken place:

$$\text{1. } C_nH_m = a\,(H_{n'},\,C_{m'}) + CH_4 \uparrow,\ \text{with } n' = \frac{n - 1}{a},\ m' = \frac{m - 4}{a}$$

$$\text{2. } SO_4'' + 2C + 2H_2O = 2HCO_3' + H_2S \uparrow$$

The first type of reaction is carried on by anaerobic bacteria during the decomposition of organic matter in water basins in conditions of a reducing chemical medium, methane (CH_4) being formed at the expense of more complex organic compounds.

The second type of reaction, i.e. desulphatization, is brought about by desulphurizing petroleum bacteria in the presence of petroleum and water containing SO_4'' ions. Petroleum bacteria, discovered by T. L. Ginzburg-Karagicheva in the petroleum of the Apsheron Peninsula, and by Bastin in the Pennsylvania oil (U.S.A.), are found in wells from 750 to 2760 metres deep. They breed most abundantly near the under interface, where the petroleum comes in contact with the waters underlying it, these waters usually being of the sulphate-chloride type. It is known that the sulphates in these waters are of inorganic origin and are derived partly from the salt residue in the marine sedimentary strata, and partly, possibly, from mineralized waters of more abyssal genesis. The course of both mentioned reactions from left to right is favoured by the fact that the gaseous products (CH_4, H_2S) gradually rise.

Similar conditions, in principle, could have arisen in the Archaean era at the surface of lagoons or other water basins, if they were covered with a film of oil. It should be noted that the oxidation of oil, which now rapidly leads to the formation of resin, polymerization of bitumens, and to the transformation of petroleum into asphalt, at that time did not as yet take place because of the lack of oxygen. Consequently, conditions favourable for the reduction of sulphates in sea or lake waters, with petroleum present, could have been maintained for a considerable time.

THE PRESENT STATE OF RESEARCH ON THE INORGANIC ORIGIN OF PETROLEUM

The pattern of the origin and development of life, outlined above, could only be considered sufficiently if the sources of the large quantities of petroleum or abiogenic hydrocarbons, similar to oil in chemical composition, were known. The origin of petroleum has been debated for 100 years and is one of geology's most controversial problems. The hypothesis of inorganic origin of petroleum was highly popular in the second half of the nineteenth century, when it was developed by D. I. Mendeleev, M. Berthelot, H. Moissan, E. Coste, and others. But later, it seemed to have been completely abandoned. This was especially so during the 1920's and 30's, when there appeared the investigations of C. D. White, P. D. Trask, and others in the U.S.A., of I. M. Gubkin, G. L. Stadnikov, and A. D. Arkhangelskiĭ in the U.S.S.R., and so on [6].

But geologists have lately again become interested in the inorganic hypothesis. This interest was roused owing to the fact that explorations in any well-studied petroleum- and gas-bearing district have shown, first of all, that the petroleum- and gas-bearing sources descend vertically to great depths, down to the folded basement, consisting of metamorphic or igneous rocks, and, secondly, that in an overwhelming number of cases, the distribution of petroleum is not connected with the distribution (in area) of sedimentary formations rich in organic matter (such, for instance, as coal and bituminous shales).

That the problem is of great importance is shown by the fact that in 1954 it was discussed at the Lvov conference dedicated to the problems of the origin and migration of oil where two reports in favour of the inorganic origin hypothesis were submitted [7–9, 11, 15]. Earlier still, in 1951, N. A. Kudryavtsev had criticized the organic theory and put forward serious arguments in favour of the inorganic origin of petroleum [10, 11]. In the United States, the inorganic (cosmic) hypothesis was supported by Macdermott [12]. Moreover, such well known specialists as Van Tuyl & Parker and Van Orstrand [13, 14] also pointed out some facts confirming this theory.

At the same time, the ideas connected with the organic hypothesis were developing in such a way, that they began to contradict one another (the hypotheses of V. A. Sokolov, V. A. Uspenskiĭ, and others), none of them being universally accepted. In our mind, these contradictions are not accidental and reveal a profound crisis, or an impasse, into which the organic theory has come.

SPACE DISTRIBUTION OF OIL AND GAS DEPOSITS AND THEIR RELATION TO THE TECTONIC STRUCTURE

Oil fields are usually found in the regions which possess natural gas deposits (methane, with a certain amount of ethane and heavier hydrocarbons), sometimes in mixed oil and gas deposits, forming together definite oil and gas provinces (petroliferous provinces). Geological investigation of these districts shows that both their general outline and the location of separate deposits of petroleum and gas occurring in the above-mentioned provinces, are determined not by the presence or absence of sedimentary rocks rich in biogenic organic substances (for instance, coal, carbonaceous and bituminous shales), but by purely tectonic factors, i.e. by dislocations of the strata in the Earth's crust. Frequently, the localization of oil is determined by deep faults, cutting both the sedimentary cover and the crystalline basement under it, consisting of granite and gneiss. Such are the petroleum fields of Egypt along the faults of the Earth's crust bordering the Red Sea graben, the large gas fields of eastern Brazil, and the oil appearing in the Lake Baikal graben in Siberia and in the Lake Albert graben in Africa. The connection with the deep faults and flexures of the crystalline basement is manifested, although in a somewhat masked form, in the location of many oil and gas fields on tectonic platforms, for instance, the Volga River fields, connected with the flexure of the Zhiguly Hills, in Eldorado field (Kansas, U.S.A.) and others. (See Fig. 1); [15–17]. This connection with the tectonic disturbances indicates the compliance of the oil and gas deposits to the zones where, owing to faults, flexures and tension of Earth's crust, the basement becomes more penetrable to fluids rising from the depths of the Earth.

The absence of any connection between the localization of petroleum and the distribution of biogenic organic substances is evidenced by the fact that the coal basins and large deposits of bituminous rocks of the combustible shale type (Scotland, Tasmania, Sweden, Estonia, and others) are, in the overwhelming majority of cases, not oil-bearing districts of industrial importance. And if in some of such districts, like the Urals and Pennsylvania, petroleum is met, its distribution in the vertical direction is traced much lower than the layers rich in organic substances, and, consequently, must have another source.

THE VERTICAL RANGE
OF HYDROCARBON MIGRATION

The vertical distribution of petroleum and gas also indicates a much wider range of hydrocarbon migration than accepted in different variations of the

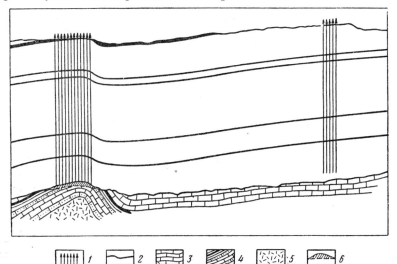

FIG. I. An example of the connections between oil deposits and dislocations of the basement and sedimentary cover of the tectonic platform: oil field of El Dorado, Kansas, U.S.A.

Vertical section: the vertical scale is considerably more than the horizontal (cited by Moore from Ver Viebe, 1950). *1*—drill holes; *2*—Pennsylvanian rocks (C_3); *3*—Mississippian sediments (limestone C_1); *4*—Ordovician sediments (S); *5*—granites of the pre-Cambrian crystalline basement; *6*—Stapleton oil zone in the lower Palaeozoic rocks.

organic theory. The secondary nature of oil pools usually does not raise any doubt.

I. O. Brod pointed out that 'if we are to understand as primary deposits those which originated *in situ*, then we must state that such deposits do not exist at all' [18]. Obvious structural geological and lithological evidence is always found to show that these hydrocarbons came to the reservoir rocks not only after the formation of the rocks bearing them, but after the rocks have undergone the action of tectonic forces (fractured, flexed and folded). Asphalts and asphaltites often lie in veins, which prove the vertical migration of hydrocarbons of the deep oil type (Sadki deposits, Buguruslan district, and some pyrobitumen dikes on pre-Cambrian crystalline shields).

The vertical distribution of petroleum does not show any connection with the distribution of organic matter in the Earth's crust layers. The achievements in the technique of prospect drilling to a depth of 4·8 km in the U.S.S.R. and 6·3 km in the U.S.A., have furnished much new data on the extent of the vertical migration of hydrocarbons. It turned out that petroleum and gas are met in large quantities below the layers rich in organic matter (for instance, the dark clays of the Maikop series in the Caucasus), which only recently were considered the mother formations (i.e. primary source rocks) of oil. With the increase of drilling depth, in oil districts all over the world are discovered new oil-bearing horizons in rocks having satisfactory porosity, down to the base of the non-metamorphized sedimentary cover.

The early Palaeozoic sedimentary rocks (Cambrian, Ordovician) at the base of the sedimentary layers are oil bearing in the Mid-Continent, Appalachian, and so-called Permian Basin of western Texas on the North American platform, in Wyoming, U.S.A., on the Chinese platform, and in the southern Siberian platform. The Devonian series, comprising the lower part of the sedimentary cover, are oil-bearing in the Timan and Volga-Urals provinces on the Russian platform.

If the igneous and metamorphic rocks of the folding basement are sufficiently crushed by faults and cracks and may serve as oil collectors, these rocks some-times contain commercial reserves of oil (Kansas, the Edison oil field and others in California; Mara-La Paz field in Venezuela) [19]. Traces of petroleum have been met in fractured granites or gneisses of the pre-Cambrian basement in Wyoming, on the shores of Lake Baikal and the Red Sea, and in the pre-Cambrian Ural–Volga oil-bearing districts (Shugurovo, Vyatskaya Polyana) [11, 20]. In some Volga districts the impregnation of oil bitumens has been discovered in cores of granite-gneissic rocks of the pre-Cambrian crystalline basement extracted from boring wells. Bores in the metamorphic shales of the folding basement in Timan have revealed oil and combustible gas to a depth of 400 m below the roof (upper surface) of basement [21].

In the part of the Canadian pre-Cambrian shield bordering on the Michigan and Appalachian petroleum- and gas-bearing provinces, combustible gases appear directly from the pre-Cambrian granite-gneiss basement (the region of the Lakes Superior and Huron, the Edwards Mine in the Adirondack pre-Cambrian uplift). At Fort William, for instance, combustible gas was obtained by drilling in the pre-Cambrian basement at a depth of 335–400 m below its surface [22].

Combustible gas comes from a considerable depth from the pre-Cambrian rock of the Baltic (Fennoskandian) shield (Kola Peninsula, some Swedish mines) and Australia (methane gases at the Kalgoorlie Mines; gases containing 70% of hydrogen and 7% of methane from a depth of 260 m on the York Peninsula) [23]. This list is enough to convince us that the sources of petroleum and gas are deep down in the pre-Cambrian basement, corresponding to what the geo-

PLATE II

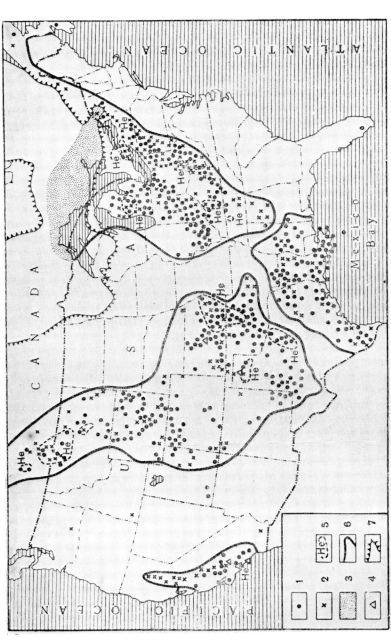

Fig. 2. The distribution of petroleum and natural gases in the U.S.A. and Canada. 1—petroleum; 2—combustible natural gases; 3—region of emersion of combustible and nitrogen gases on the pre-Cambrian shield (contours shown approximately); 4—region of extraction of pre-Cambrian oil; in California, extraction from metamorphic rocks of the pre-Cretaceous period; 5—regions of location of natural gases, rich in nitrogen and helium; 6—contours of the oil-bearing provinces; 7—contours of Pre-Cambrian crystalline shield.

P. N. KROPOTKIN

physicists call the granite layer of the Earth's crust. The presence of free hydrogen and methane in volcanic gases, and the discovery of liquid hydrocarbons and solid paraffins in the basalt lava of Mt. Etna and in products of volcanic eruptions on the Island of Java indicate that hydrocarbons are met in the magma of the basic (basaltic) and ultra-basic (peridotitic) composition, forming in still deeper layers of the Earth. Stony meteorites, which are considered as analogues of the Sima layer ultra-basic rocks, contain gases with $4 \cdot 2\%$ of CH_4 and $17 \cdot 6\%$ of H_2. In the carbonaceous varieties of stony meteorites, paraffin matter is found, composed of carbon ($80–84 \cdot 9\%$) and hydrogen ($15–20\%$). Some meteorites have the specific odour of heavy remains of crude oil [24–27].

Thus, various facts indicate that the vertical range of migration of hydrocarbons is very great. Not only methane, but more complex hydrocarbons too can rise to the upper layers of the Earth's crust from the crystalline basement and the deeper subcrustal layers of the solid mantle of the Earth, formed of ultrabasic material. The peculiar gas deposits of so-called condensate pools, found during the last decades at the deepest levels of oil deposits ($2 \cdot 8$ to 4 km deep), may be samples of these deep fluids. A condensation of such fluids at a decreasing pressure produces liquid methane, oil and combustible gases.

THE GEOCHEMICAL ASSOCIATES OF PETROLEUM: METHANE, HYDROGEN, NITROGEN, AND HELIUM

Gaseous hydrocarbons, free hydrogen, nitrogen, and helium, i.e. gases the deep origin of which becomes more and more evident (Fig. 2), are the characteristic geochemical associates of petroleum. The gas pressure at the deep horizons is so great (combustible gases up to 880 atm, nitrogen up to 20 atm and more) that it cannot be explained by biochemical processes or by the capture of atmospheric gases. The high pressure of subterranean gases shows that they come from the depths. V. I. Vernadskiĭ, who long ago considered the Earth as a cold and solid cosmic body with scatterings of separate nidi of magmatic melts, was the first to note the grandiose scale at which the deep juvenile gases (nitrogen, methane, and others) discharge. Their ascent from the depths of the Earth's crust he figuratively called 'the breathing of the Earth'. V. I. Vernadskiĭ also noted the connection of these gases with faults, stressing that all the large helium pools (Amarillo, Texas, and others) were connected with the outflows of 'tectonic gas streams: nitrogen, methane-nitrogen gases, and methane' [28]. In some methane-nitrogen gas streams the concentrations of helium exceed by several thousand times those of helium in the atmosphere. The source of this helium is the crystalline basement, where it gradually accumulates, due to the decay of radioactive elements. 'Nitrogen', V. I. Vernadskiĭ pointed out, 'unlike oxygen, constantly enters the Earth's atmosphere from the deep sections of the Earth's crust ... In many places, gas streams are known to consist of almost pure nitrogen, always containing noble gases. Besides these emissions, nitrogen in the shape of unnoticeable emanation, undoubtedly, continuously penetrates everywhere into the Earth's crust, and into the biosphere' ([28] p. 226). He ascribed the same deep origin to free hydrogen, which now, thanks to improved methods of analysis, is constantly being found in small amounts (sometimes to 10%) in combustible gases [29, 30]. 'By no means always',—wrote V. I. Vernadskiĭ, 'are hydrocarbons connected with life. There exists methane, which rises from the deeper sections of the Earth's crust ... It is in regard to methane, in particular, that the exclusive connection with life is doubtful, since this light gas has properties similar to those of hydrogen. Its known syntheses in the laboratory are extraordinarily varied and often independent of organic compounds. There must be analogous processes in magmas'. ([31], p. 133).

Lately, thanks to the investigations carried on by V. A. Sokolov, the magnitude of incessant addition of methane from the depths of the Earth into the atmosphere has become known. V. A. Sokolov has estimated the annual addition of methane to the atmosphere from oil and gas deposits and volcanoes to be about 100 million tons [32]. Even if we were to take a figure ten times less, it would appear that, during a very short geological period of 100,000 years, the atmosphere has received an amount of hydrocarbons many times more than the known and estimated oil resources on the Earth. In this aspect, the accumulation of oil appears to be a secondary resulting effect of the grandiose process of ascension of gaseous hydrocarbons, together with other gases, from the depths of the Earth.

THE THERMAL CONDITIONS FOR THE FORMATION OF OIL AND THE CHANGE IN ITS COMPOSITION IN THE EARTH'S CRUST

Thus, the tectonic regularities of oil and gas distribution (in area) in the Earth's crust, the wide vertical range of hydrocarbon migration, and, finally, the geochemical association of petroleum with gaseous hydrocarbons, hydrogen, nitrogen and helium, throw light on the origin of oil and gas. The hydrocarbons rising up out of the depths of the Earth are of a primary inorganic origin. Together with methane, the hydrocarbon stream contains heavier, compositionally more complex hydrocarbons which are detained in the porous rock of the sedimentary cover, accumulating in the form of the peculiar gas mixture of the so-called condensate pools (see above) and in the form of methane petroleum, i.e., petroleum composed almost exclusively of saturated hydrocarbons. Judging by the physical-chemical equilibrium of hydrocarbons studied by S. P. Obryadchikov and A. V. Frost, methane petroleum forms at a temperature of 200–350° [33, 34]. The further change in the composition of petroleum in the Earth's crust consists chiefly in the differentiation of hydrocarbons and removal of the lightest fractions, which are the richest in hydrogen; correspondingly, the petroleum is enriched with naphthenes, isoparaffins, and heavy components. Together with the differentiation, a certain oxidation of the petroleum takes place (the appearance of naphthene acids, bases, resin), and also its sulphuration in connection with the life activity of bacteria and the dissolution in petroleum of the products, mostly of plant origin (such as porphyrins and phytosterol), contained in petroliferous rocks [35]. Porphyrins, to which such great importance was attached by the advocates of the biogenic origin of petroleum, are practically absent in some of the clear light oils. Porphyrin enrichment is found especially in the heavy, resinous, and sulphurous oils. According to available data, the same refers to the dissolution in oil of admixture of organic matter of biogenic origin exhibiting optical rotation.

In discussing the deposits of petroleum and combustible gases as the results of ascension of hydrocarbons rising from the deep layers of the Earth's crust, we would like to emphasize that available facts agree with the hypothesis that hydrocarbons are of inorganic origin, though not connected with magma. Disintegrating at high temperatures (especially when there is an acidic, i.e., granite magma, comparatively richer in oxygen) in conditions when methane CH_4 can be split off or oxidized, the petroleum hydrocarbons are preserved at a lower temperature, in reducing conditions. This is in harmony with the fact that in regions of the acidic or mediosilicic (andesitic) vulcanism, carbon compounds in gases are represented chiefly by carbon dioxide CO_2, and outside these regions by CH_4 (the Caucasus, the zones of mud-vulcanism, etc.).

These conclusions about the abyssal but magma-independent origin of petroleum and gas are in agreement with the modern conceptions of deep faults, of the solid state of the Earth's mantle and the formation of the planet from cold cosmic dust and gas (the hypotheses of O. Yu. Shmidt, H. Urey and others [36, 37]). Judging by the relative abundance of hydrocarbons in the cosmos, there was a sufficient amount of these compounds in the original gas-and-dust nebula from which the Earth and other planets of the solar system have arisen. The idea of primary (cosmic) origin of petroleum hydrocarbons was first put forward by V. Sokolov [38].

THE BIOGENIC (ORGANIC) THEORY OF ORIGIN OF PETROLEUM. CHANGES IN THE COMPOSITION OF ORGANIC MATTER IN THE EARTH'S CRUST

Although the number of facts in favour of the inorganic origin of petroleum increases every year, most specialists still adhere to the biogenic conception of its origin (see, for instance, the review [39]). Different variations of the organic theory can be divided into two groups. One trend proceeds from the idea that petroleum hydrocarbons were formed under the 'least severe' pressure and temperature conditions, i.e. under conditions which exist in sediments immediately after their deposition in a water basin or at the early stages of their genesis [40, 41]. From this point of view it proves impossible to explain the secondary nature of the petroleum occurrence in most of the petroleum beds, and the absence, outside the oil fields, of any signs of petroleum in sedimentary rocks; in other respects these rocks may have exactly the same lithological composition and geological age as those developed in the oil-field districts, or may even be richer in biogenic organic matter, in comparison with them. Discoveries of oil in the crystalline basement mentioned here also exclude the possibility of the origin of petroleum according to this scheme.

The second trend is represented by the hypothesis held by V. A. Sokolov, V. B. Porfiriev, J. Roberts and others. These authors clearly demonstrate the complete unsoundness of the hypothesis of 'least severe' conditions for the formation of oil as far as hydrocarbon chemistry is concerned. Instead, they offer a scheme for the formation of oil and gas as a result of changes in biogenic organic matter under 'the most severe' conditions, i.e., at temperatures of 150–500° and at a considerable depth [42, 43]. But the fact that a number of rich oil deposits have been found in the sedimentary cover of the shields lying on the pre-Cambrian crystalline basement, has proved fatal for all these variations. The thickness of that covering strata often does not exceed 1·5 km, while the temperature at its base, corresponding to the geothermal gradient of the tectonic platforms, could not rise above 40–60°, i.e. certainly could not reach the limits necessary for the formation of petroleum according to these schemes (the Ural–Volga region, Kansas and Oklahoma, Egypt). The pre-Cambrian basement itself, with its insignificant graphitized fossils of plant and animal organic matter could not, of course, produce later a noticeable amount of biogenic hydrocarbons when the sedimentary layers had been formed above it.

Examination of a large number of analyses of the chemical composition of bitumens and caustobiolites clearly reveals the rules governing the changes of organic matter in the Earth's crust. The triangular baricentric diagram (Fig. 3) shows two independent centres of primary organic matter. One of these centres corresponds to the compositions of cellulose, wood, peat, and sapropel. The figurative points of the composition of the changed organics of the coal series (lignite and coal, anthracites, and other) and of the sapropelite series (sapropel coals, combustible or bituminous shales, shungites) stretch in a narrow strip from this centre to the pure carbon (graphite). Changes in the organics are bound with losses of carbon dioxide, water, methane, and inevitably lead to their dehydration rather than to hydrogenization. In this case, the ratio of the number of hydrogen atoms to carbon atoms decreases from 1·67 to 0·2–0·5 receding more and more from the high ratio of H : C (1·7–2·1) characteristic of petroleum. Another centre, being quite separate, located in the upper part of the diagram, is formed by methane and other combustible gases, a complex mixture of condensate pool hydrocarbons and methane oil. The diagram shows that all the other oil bitumens are formed at the expense of dehydration and oxidation of these compounds, forming naphthene and resin oils, oxyasphalts, and others.

Thus it is clear that changes in biogenic organic matter in the layers of the Earth's crust, chiefly consisting in carbonization and elimination of hydrogen and oxygen, cannot lead to the formation of petroleum from animal and plant organic substances, since petroleum consists of compounds almost completely saturated with hydrogen [44].

According to some conceptions, the source of oil is volatile derivatives, separating when the change in the organic substances takes place, for example, methane, which is formed together with CO_2, CO, and H_2O during the metamorphism of biogenic organic matter [45]. But as the study of the composition of coal-mine gases shows, these gases, as a rule, do not contain any heavy hydro-

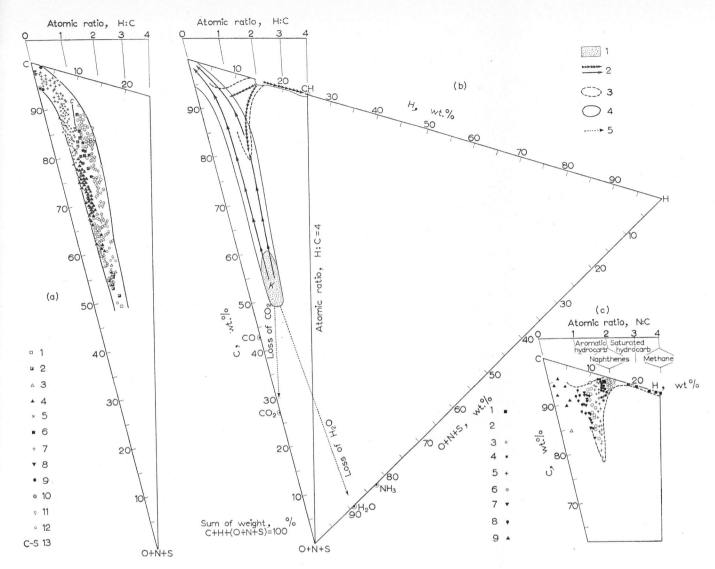

FIG. 3. The chemical composition of fossil organic substances.
(a) Composition of caustobiolites of the coal—sapropelite series: *1*—cellulose; *2*—wood; *3*—peat; *4*—lignites; *5*—coal; *6*—striped coals and others; *7*—anthracites; *8*—bedded graphites; *9*—shungites: *10*—sapropel coals; *11*—combustible bituminous shales; *12*—sapropels; *13*—carbonified saproponites.

(b) Demonstrated processes of change of organic substances in the earth crust: *1*—composition of the caustobiolites of the coal sapropelite series (*K*) and bitumens of the oil series; *2*—demonstrated processes of change of organic substances; *3*—composition of gaseous hydrocarbons and bitumens of the oil series; *4*—composition of caustobiolites of the coal—sapropelite series: *5*—Loss of CO_2, H_2O and others.

(c) Composition of bitumens of the oil series: *1*—Average composition of hydrocarbons of combustible gas; *2*—average composition of methane oil; *3*—normal type oils; *4*—resinous oils; *5*—asphalts and malthas; *6*—gilsonites; *7*—grahamites; *8*—impsonites; *9*—anthraxolites.

The sum of three perpendiculars dropped from any point of the diagram to the sides of the equilateral triangle is a constant value; it is 100% and corresponds to the sum of the contents in weight (C) + (H) + (O + N + S) in the composition of the organic substance. The weight percentages of carbon, hydrogen, and the sums of oxygen, nitrogen, and sulphur correspond to each of the three perpendiculars dropped to the sides of the triangle.

To face p. 92.

carbons (ethane, propane, butane, and others), and, therefore, cannot be considered as a primary source of the formation of petroleum.

Thus, the available data reveal the insolvency of different variants of the organic (biogenic) hypothesis, and favour the hypothesis of abyssal inorganic origin of petroleum and gas not connected, however, with magmas.

REFERENCES

1. A. I. OPARIN, *The Origin of Life on the Earth.* Izd. Akad. Nauk S.S.S.R. Moscow, Leningrad, 2nd ed., 1941.
2. A. I. OPARIN, *Vop. Filos.* No. 1, 1953.
3. D. V. BELIKHOV, *Zap. Kazan Ped. Inst., Fak. estestv. Nauk,* **9**, 1950.
4. A. I. OPARIN & V. G. FESENKOV, *Life in the Universe.* Izd. Akad. Nauk S.S.S.R., Moscow, 1956.
5. W. RUBEY & K. RANKAMA, *Spec. Pap. geol. Soc. Amer.,* No. 62, 1955.
6. I. M. GUBKIN, *Petroleum Research Science.* Gosnauchnotekhneftizdat, Moscow, 1932.
7. N. A. KUDRYAVTSEV, *Materials of a Discussion on Problems of the Origin and Migration of Petroleum.* Izd. Ukr. Akad. Nauk, Kiev, 1955.
8. P. N. KROPOTKIN, *Material of a Discussion on Problems of the Origin and Migration of Petroleum.* Izd. Ukr. Akad. Nauk, Kiev, 1955.
9. P. N. KROPOTKIN, *Soviet. Geol., Moscow,* No. 47, 1955.
10. N. A. KUDRYAVTSEV, *Neft. Khoz.,* No. 9, 1951.
11. N. A. KUDRYAVTSEV, *Izv. Akad. Nauk S.S.S.R., Ser. Geol.,* No. 4, 1955.
12. E. MACDERMOTT, *Geophysics,* **4**, 195, 1939.
13. F. M. VAN TUYL & B. N. PARKER, *Bull. Amer. Ass. Petrol. Geol.,* **19**, 1547, 1935.
14. C. E. VAN ORSTRAND, *World Oil,* **128**, 150, 1948.
15. I. O. BROD & N. A. YEREMENKO, *Principles of the Geology of Petroleum and Gas.* Izd. MGU, Moscow, 1953.
16. K. L. LANDES, *Petroleum Geology.* Wiley: Chapman & Hall; New York: London, 1951.
17. W. A. VER VIEBE, *North American and Middle East Oil Fields.* Wichita, Kansas, 1950.
18. I. O. BROD, N. A. YEREMENKO & V. A. KLUBOV, *Vestnik Mosk. Univ.,* **10**, 1948.
19. R. F. WALTERS, *Bull. Amer. Ass. Petrol. Geol.,* **37**, 201, 1953.
20. S. POWERS & F. G. CLAPP, *Bull. Amer. Ass. Petrol. Geol.,* **16**, No. 8, 1932.
21. A. Y. KREMS, *Neft. Khoz.,* No. 1, 1947.
22. F. M. VAN TUYL & B. N. PARKER, *Col. Sch. Min. Quart.,* **36**, No. 2, 1941.
23. W. G. WOOLNOUGH, *Bull. Amer. Ass. Petrol. Geol.,* **18**, 226, 549, 1934.
24. R. PRENDEL, *Ezhegodn. po geol. miner. Rossii,* v. 2, 1898.
25. E. COHEN, *Meteoritenkunde,* Heft I. Stuttgart, 1894.
26. G. MUELER, *Geochim. et cosmoch. Acta,* **4**, No. 1–2, 1953.
27. R. W. PIKE, *Bull. Amer. Ass. Petrol. Geol.,* **24**, 496, 1940.
28. V. I. VERNADSKIĬ, *The History of the Minerals of the Earth's Crust,* vol. I. Leningrad, 1927.
29. I. V. VYSOTSKIĬ, *Principles of the Geology of Natural Gas.* Gostoptekhizdat, Moscow, 1954.
30. L. V. KHMELEVSKAYA, *Izv. Akad. Nauk S.S.S.R., Ser. Geol.,* No. 4, 107, 1947.
31. V. I. VERNADSKIĬ, *The History of the Minerals of the Earth's Crust.,* vol. II, *The History of Natural Waters.* Part I. Leningrad, 1933.
32. V. A. SOKOLOV. In a symposium: *In Memory of Acad. I. M. Gubkin.* Izd. Akad. Nauk S.S.S.R., Moscow, 1951.
33. S. N. OBRYADSHIKOV, in *The Origin of Petroleum and Natural Gas,* a symposium, Moscow, 1947.
34. A. V. FROST & L. K. OSNITSKAYA, in a symposium: *In Memory of Acad. I. M. Gubkin.* Izd. Akad. Nauk. S.S.S.R., Moscow, 1951.
35. O. A. RADCHENKO & L. S. SHESHINA. *Dokl. Akad. Nauk S.S.S.R.,* **105**, 1285, 1955.
36. P. N. KROPOTKIN, *Izv. Akad. Nauk S.S.S.R., Ser. Geogr. Geophys.,* No. 1, 1950.
37. A. V. PEIVE, *Izv. Akad. Nauk S.S.S.R., Ser. Geol.,* No. 1, 1956.
38. V. SOKOLOV, *Bull. Soc. Nat. Moscou,* nouv. sér., **13**, 720, 1890.

39. I. O. BROD & V. G. LEVINSON, *The Origin of Petroleum and Problem of Petroleum and Gas Accumulation (A Review of Foreign Literature for* 1940–1954). Gostopte-khizdat, Moscow, 1955.

40. V. A. USPENSKIĬ & O. A. RADCHENKO. *Izv. Akad. Nauk S.S.S.R., Ser. Geol.,* No. 6, 121, 1952.

41. P. W. SMITH, *Bull. Amer. Ass. Petrol. Geol.,* **38**, 377, 1954.

42. V. A. SOKOLOV, *Notes on the Petroleum Genesis.* Gostoptekhizdat, Moscow, 1948.

43. V. B. PORFIRIEV & I. V. GRINBERG. *Nauch. Zap. Lvov. polytechn. Inst.,* **16**, No. 4., Lvov, 1949.

44. O. A. RADCHENKO, in a symposium: *In Memory of Acad. I. M. Gubkin.* Izd. Akad. Nauk S.S.S.R., Moscow, 1951.

45. I. I. POTAPOV. *Neft.Khoz., Azerbaijdszchan,* No. 9, 1951.

The Role of Dissymmetry in the Origin of Living Material

A. P. TERENT'EV & E. I. KLABUNOVSKIĬ

Moscow State University (M.V. Lomonosov) and Institute of Organic Chemistry of the Academy of Sciences of the U.S.S.R., Moscow

ALMOST 100 years ago Pasteur noticed a characteristic peculiarity of the chemical processes of living nature, namely that they are optically selective. Pasteur stated that this was perhaps the only sharp boundary which can be discerned between the chemistry of dead and living nature.

TWO FORMULATIONS OF THE QUESTION

How did there arise, in living protoplasm as it exists to-day, living enzymic systems, with dissymmetrical molecules subserving the optical selectivity of chemical processes? Many authors hold that the proteins which first came into existence were optically symmetrical and that it was only during the process of evolution that they gradually assumed an optical dissymmetry which was useful in some way, for it is easier to imagine the process of formation of symmetrical proteins than of dissymmetrical ones. This assumes that life can exist without dissymmetry and that symmetrical proteins, being alive, developed dissymmetry, i.e. dissymmetry developed out of symmetry.

Another view is possible and we will try to substantiate it. We will start from the assumption that *life cannot and never could exist without molecular dissymmetry.* This means that it is necessary to find an answer, based on some experimental evidence, to two main questions:

1. What is the biochemical role of molecular dissymmetry?

2. How could the molecular dissymmetry of the original protoplasm, which led to the development of the living protein-enzymes, have arisen without the intervention of life?

THE ESSENTIAL PROPERTIES OF OPTICALLY ACTIVE SUBSTANCES: THE PASTEUR EFFECT

The optical activity of organic substances is only one of the manifestations of molecular and crystalline dissymmetry. Many other manifestations of dissymmetry may be cited: the piezo effect, triboluminescence, polarized fluorescence. Finally, there are known to exist a large number of crystals which are dissymmetrical in form but do not contain centres of dissymmetry. Among these are

95

$K_2Cr_2O_7$, Cu_2O, $Ba(NO_3)_2$ and $Pb(NO_3)_2$ [1]. Antipodes differ from racemates in the form of their crystals, their solubility and their melting points. The presence of several centres of dissymmetry in one structure is the reason for the existence of many diastereoisomers with different physical and chemical properties. It has been shown, e.g. that the polymerization of the amino acid derivatives, (—)-propylene oxide [2] and (—)-a-methylbenzyl methacrylate [3] leads to the formation of polymers which differ in their properties according to whether they were made from a pure antipode or a racemate.

These special properties of optically active compounds provide the necessary conditions for some other factors which are not present in substances with symmetrically constructed molecules. These peculiarities and the behaviour of optically active substances may be termed the 'Pasteur effect' since Pasteur first drew attention to them.

The reasons for this effect are primarily determined by the configurations and conformations of the molecules. When they interact with one another, dissymmetrical molecules form crystalline or colloidal solid bodies with different 'packings' depending on the nature of the dissymmetry. Not surprisingly, the bonds between the molecules, which are responsible for the Pasteur effect, are extremely labile.

There can be no doubt that, in biochemical processes involving complicated molecules with many centres of dissymmetry, the Pasteur effect must be very important. Maybe the first protein manifested the characteristics of life owing to the presence of a definite sequence in the arrangement of residues of dissymmetrical molecules of amino acids.

THE ORIGIN OF DISSYMMETRY IN PRIMAEVAL PROTOPLASM

Let us try to answer the second question: How could dissymmetry have arisen in the primaeval protoplasm?

Various ways by which optically active substances may be obtained abiogenically are known.

In the first place: the resolution of a racemate by the spontaneous crystallization of one antipode from a solution of the racemate. This method need hardly be taken into account in connection with the complicated substances of colloidal structure which undoubtedly played the essential part in the building up of the primaeval protoplasm.

In the second place: the chemical action of circularly polarized ultraviolet light. By this means Kuhn and other authors have succeeded in bringing about a number of absolute asymmetric syntheses with appreciable optical activity.

In spite of the insignificant predominance of the right circularly polarized component in the scattered light falling on the surface of the Earth, this action must surely have made itself felt during the long years of the evolution of the living world.

We consider that this factor must be taken into account in connection with the problem under discussion and more will be said about this later.

In the third place: asymmetric catalysis with the help of dissymmetrical crystals of minerals. Schwab and his colleagues were the first (1932–34) to bring about the asymmetric destruction of butan-2-ol using, as catalysts, finely divided metals on crystals of *dextro-* and *laevo-*quartz. Later (1950–53) [3] we extended this method considerably, bringing about a number of asymmetric syntheses with different catalysts on quartz crystals under many variable conditions. In addition syntheses were brought about in solution at ordinary temperatures using a layer of alkali on crystalline quartz.

This gives us reason to suppose that, under natural conditions, quite complicated syntheses could have taken place on the surface of dissymmetric crystals of minerals with the formation of optically active compounds of high molecular weight.

The only objection to the supposition that the first dissymmetrical compounds could have arisen in this way is the fact that, in nature, there is no predominance of optically active crystals of one sign. One antipode is always accompanied by an equal amount of the other in the formations in which it occurs as found by G. G. Lemmlein in the case of quartz.

If we assume that the sole causes determining the dissymmetry of the primaeval protoplasm were minerals then, in order to arrive at an explanation for the one-sided dissymmetry of the natural amino acids, we should have to postulate a one-sided dissymmetry of the crystals of geological formations. We have no basis for doing so. Thus, there must be some dissymmetrical, natural factors which would make it possible for one form of complicated organic molecule to come into being and become predominant.

It is possible that these were the right circularly polarized light which, in the view of physicists, is present in the scattered sunlight.

In the coastal zone of the primaeval ocean where life probably arose, amino acids could form complex compounds with iron, copper, vanadium, magnesium and other metals. This led to a considerable, selective absorption of light owing to the circular dichroism of such complexes. The preferential destruction of D-amino acids by light could have led to the development of the L-forms and their products.

In this connection it is possible to approach the problem of the formation of petroleums from a new standpoint. Until now the presence of optically active substances in petroleums has been considered as an incontrovertible proof of their biogenic origin. Nevertheless, petroleum has undoubtedly undergone a number of chemical transformations in the depths of the Earth involving the catalytic activity of various silicates and other formations. Among these there might have been some in which crystals of one particular sign predominated. The optical activity of petroleum might thus have arisen purely abiogenically.

By using the method of asymmetric catalysis it has been possible to discover the dissymmetrical structure of minerals and formations with which the ordinary crystallographic methods have been ineffective. For this the asymmetric synthesis of an organic compound by catalysis based on the mineral under investigation must be realized. The appearance of optical activity in the catalysate serves as indisputable proof of the dissymmetry of the catalyst.

The experimental evidence concerning the spontaneous resolution of racemates and photochemical asymmetric synthesis will be considered below. The part played by asymmetric catalysis and asymmetric adsorption in producing the dissymmetry of living material will be considered separately.

SELECTIVE SPONTANEOUS CRYSTALLIZATION
OF ANTIPODES

The self-propagating separation of enantiomorphs, commonly called spontaneous crystallization, may occur under various conditions: from optically active solvents; by seeding with a crystal of one or other antipode of the same compound or one isomorphous with it; or by spontaneous crystallization.

These cases of selective crystallization are due to differences in the nature of racemates. The spontaneous crystallization of true racemic compounds containing equal amounts of (+)- and (−)-enantiomorphs in the crystal lattice of the molecules is a comparatively rare phenomenon [4].

Crystallization under the influence of isomorphic crystals, or those of one antipode of the crystallizing racemate, is possible when the racemate crystallizes as a conglomerate in which each of the antipodes crystallizes in its own lattice. True spontaneous crystallization occurs when mixed crystals are formed, the antipodes entering into a common lattice in any proportions. In specially favourable cases the crystalline deposit contains a great excess of one antipode [5].

1. *Crystallization in an optically active solvent.* When crystallizing sodium or ammonium tartrate from a solution of D-glucose, Kipping & Pope [6] usually obtained an excess of one enantiomorph in the deposit. McKenzie [7] separated out (+)-ammonium tartrate by crystallizing ammonium tartrate from a solution of (−)-ammonium malate. Crystallization from a solution of (+)-ammonium malate led to the separation of the (−)-tartrate [8].

This case is of great interest as being the first example of the isolation of one antipode of a racemic acid by the action of another optically active acid instead of by a base as ordinarily used.

2. *Crystallization initiated by a crystal of one antipode or by an isomorphous crystal.* A considerable amount of work has been devoted to the study of the selective crystallization of optical antipodes, or crystalline enantiomorphs, by insertion, into a supersaturated solution, of a crystal of one antipode of the same substance, or some other crystal isomorphous with it.

On the basis of Pasteur's work Gernez [9] proposed a method of isolation of one antipode under the influence of crystals of the (+)- or (−)-antipode [10]. Kipping & Pope [11] were inclined to ascribe such separation to the action of seeds of crystallization reaching the solutions in the dust of the air of the laboratory. In fact, when a compound crystallizes as a conglomerate of (+)- and (−)-crystals, crystallization with free access of air leads to an equal probability of the separation of either (+)- or (−)-isomer.

This is confirmed by the observations of Anderson & Hill [12] on the crystallization of synthetic atropine sulphate. Read [13] also inclines towards this view.

Soret [14] observed that crystallization of sodium chlorate in the air led to the formation, mainly, of the (−)-enantiomorph while, when the crystallization took place in sealed tubes the (+)-form separated in 433 cases, the (−)-form in 411 cases while in 43 cases a mixed form was produced. However, if the necessary precautions are taken, this method gives satisfactory results.

Thus, by priming with crystals of one antipode it has been possible to separate the racemic forms of zinc and ammonium lactates [15], phenylbenzylhydrazone of erythrose [16] and Co- and Cr-oxalatobisethylenediamine [17].

In 1934, Calzavara [18, 19] took out a patent on the separation into antipodes of racemic adrenaline and other alkaloids. This was the method by which Velluz *et al.* [20] resolved racemic *threo*-1-*N*-nitrophenyl-2-aminopropane-1 : 3-diol.

The selective crystallization brought about by the introduction into a super-saturated solution of racemate of crystals of one antipode or other crystals iso-morphous with it has been studied in detail by Ostromyslenskiĭ [21]. It was found that, from a supersaturated solution of sodium ammonium tartrate one antipode would crystallize out in the presence of not only the (+)- or (−)-tartrate but also when isomorphous or isodimorphous crystals were added. Thus. the introduction of L-asparagine evoked the crystallization of (+)-tartrate. Even such compounds as glycine, which are not composed of dissymmetrical molecules but form enantiomorphic crystals can evoke the crystallization of one isomer from a solution of racemate of asparagine or sodium ammonium tartrate. In the presence of crystals of sodium nitrate one enantiomorph always crystallizes out from aqueous solutions of sodium periodate [22] sodium silicotungstate [23] or guanidine carbonate [24]. Zelinskiĭ [24] achieved the separation of enantio-morphs during the crystallization of dimethyldihydroxyglutaric acid.

Enantiomorphic substances in nature are almost always found in the separate crystalline state, their crystalline racemates are extremely rare. It is thus quite possible that localized asymmetric synthesis could take place on such inorganic and organic dissymmetrical crystals.

3. *Spontaneous crystallization.* On evaporation, concentrated solutions of acid ammonium malate deposit crystals which show optical acitivity. Van't Hoff & Dawson [25] showed that these crystals consist of three parts of the (+)- and one part of the (−)-salt. Malic acid may be obtained in an optically active form by the spontaneous crystallization of a salt of composition $C_4H_6O_5,2MoO_3,2NH_3$ [26].

The spontaneous crystallization of sodium tartrate and sodium ammonium tartrate has been thoroughly studied. Other known cases of spontaneous reso-lution of racemates concern asparagine [27], methoxy-4-methyldeoxybenzoin [28], dibenzalpentaerythritol [29] and erythritol [30], dilactylamide [31], the lactone of gulonic acid [32], camphoric [33] and glutamic acids [10, 36], complex salts of cobalt and rhodium [34], β-decalol [35] and *iso*hydrobenzoin [36].

Neuberg [37] found that, when it has been kept for a long while in a solution of potassium salts, β-methylvaleric acid deposits crystals of the (+)-acid of a high degree of purity. After keeping a solution of methylethylallylphenyl-ammonium iodide in a sealed ampoule for some months, Havinga [38] observed that resolution had taken place, the crystals, dissolved in chloroform, had a rotation of $+27°$ while that of the mother liquor was $-0·15°$.

On crystallization of racemic histidine hydrochloride Duschinsky [39] obtained the (+)-isomer while Vogler & Kofer [40] were the first to resolve 2 : 4-dioxo-3-diethyl-5-methylpiperidine into its antipodes.

Recently Darmois [41] has proposed a general method for the resolution of racemic bases, based on the artificial forcing of spontaneous crystallization.

By this method Ferreira [42] made a partial resolution of the racemic alkaloids narcotine and laudanosine which are not soluble in water. He converted them to hydrochlorides and caused pyridine to react slowly with the solution. The resolution of synthetic adrenaline was considerably more successful. After four crystallizations the alkaloid was almost completely resolved [41].

It is obvious from the material which has been surveyed, that it is essentially compounds of comparatively simple structure which can be submitted to spontaneous separation. Therefore, as has been shown above, it seems hardly likely that the primaeval colloidal organic substances became dissymmetrical in this way. On the contrary, the belief that the only factors playing a part in bringing about the primary asymmetry of the organic world were asymmetric adsorption and catalysis [43] and circularly polarized light, polarized mainly in one direction, meets with no such difficulties and agrees with the experimental evidence [44].

PHOTOCHEMICAL ASYMMETRIC SYNTHESIS

Interest in the question of the ways in which the primary dissymmetrical substances could have arisen has increased rapidly since the discovery of the optical isomer by reducing phenylglyoxylic acid, by adding bromine to stilbene and esters of fumaric or cinnamic acids [46–49].

Pasteur [45] saw physical processes as the source of the optical activity of the substances important for life.

To test this idea he tried to bring about an absolute asymmetric synthesis by crystallizing the antipodes out of a racemate in powerful magnetic fields or in rapidly rotating tubes.

Under similar conditions attempts have been made to obtain an excess of one optical isomer by reducing phenylglyoxylic acid, by adding bromine to stilbene and esters of fumaric or cinnamic acids [46–49].

Similarly, electrolysis of salts of iron with substituted malonic acids in a magnetic field did not lead to the formation of optically active products [50], although the influence of a magnetic field in orienting crystals of complex salts of cobalt, nickel [51, 52] etc. has been noticed.

The attempts by Ostromyslenskiĭ [53] to find differences in the rates of crystallization of antipodes were unsuccessful. So were those of Rosenthaler [54] to hydrolyse polysaccharides asymmetrically in a magnetic field.

All these unsuccessful attempts were based on the false assumption that a magnetic field, or mechanical movement, were factors of such a nature that their involvement in reactions might evoke the formation of optically active compounds. This mistake became obvious after 1894 when P. Curie [55] formulated the requirements which must be fulfilled by a dissymmetrical agent if it is to be able to lead to the formation of asymmetry by influencing reactions; elliptically or circularly polarized light could constitute such an agent.

Another reason for the lack of success in achieving asymmetric syntheses was the choice of agents which had no effect on the reaction in question [56].

Thus, the dissymmetrical agent must not only be able to evoke dissymmetry but must also be able to initiate the reaction [57].

These two requirements were met in experimental work devoted to the photochemical asymmetric resolution of racemates and the asymmetric synthesis of optically active compounds, when the agent evoking the dissymmetry was circularly polarized light. Both the necessary conditions were satisfactorily fulfilled.

ABSOLUTE ASYMMETRIC SYNTHESIS UNDER THE INFLUENCE OF CIRCULARLY POLARIZED LIGHT

1. *Asymmetric decomposition of racemates.* Scattered sunlight, when reflected from the surface of the Earth under the influence of its magnetic field, becomes partly circularly polarized with a slight preponderance of the right-handed component [58–61]. The suggestion has been made that, owing to the effect of this component being in excess, there occurred, during the course of the long years of evolution of the living world, a regular biosynthesis of optically active organic compounds [62–64].

This hypothesis, which was first put forward by Van't Hoff, seemed very attractive and provided a stimulus for researches into the experimental conditions required for the accomplishment of absolute asymmetric synthesis under the influence of circularly polarized light in which one component preponderated.

The photochemical effect of linearly polarized light on organic compounds was discovered in 1841 but statements about its selective effect on optical antipodes were mistaken [65]. A selective action on antipodes can only be expected from circularly polarized light [66, 67].

The first attempts to demonstrate this effect experimentally were unsuccessful [68] and only Cotton [69] succeeded in discovering circular dichroism—different degrees of absorption of circularly polarized light by the optical antipodes of the racemic tartrates of chromium or cobalt—a phenomenon which has been called the Cotton effect [70]. It should be noted that McKenzie [71] had already tried to carry out the asymmetric decomposition of salts of racemic lactic acid under the influence of circularly polarized light.

After it has been established that optical antipodes have different capacities for the selective absorption of light which is circularly polarized in one direction, many attempts were made to use this dissymmetric factor for the selective decomposition of racemates.

Thus the photochemical asymmetric decomposition of camphor and lactic acid [72] and the decarboxylation of acids having the formulae

$$
\begin{array}{c}
CH_3 \\
| \\
C_2H_5-C-COOH \\
| \\
CN
\end{array}
$$

and

$$
\begin{array}{c}
HOOC \qquad\qquad COOH \\
\diagdown \qquad\qquad \diagup \\
Cl-C - C-Cl \\
\diagup \qquad\qquad \diagdown \\
CH_3 \qquad\qquad CH_3
\end{array}
$$

were undertaken.

The negative results of these attempts are explained by the absence of any circular dichroism or any photochemical dissociation in those parts of the absorption spectrum which were being studied. An asymmetric effect may, accordingly, be expected in substances which are highly susceptible to photochemical decomposition taking place under the influence of light with waves of the same length as those which manifest dichroism. Under these conditions selective absorption of one component of circularly polarized light occurs and this should lead to asymmetric synthesis when the reaction proceeds with the activation (or leads to the appearance) of centres of dissymmetry.

In 1929, Kuhn & Braun [74], bearing this in mind, submitted the ethyl ester of α-bromopropionic acid to photochemical decomposition by the action of circularly polarized light.

The major component of the light brought about a greater decomposition of the antipode of the opposite sign. The product contained an excess of the (+)-ester with $a = +0.05°$ when right circularly polarized light was used.

A relatively high degree of asymmetric resolution was obtained (rotation, $a = 1.04°$, degree of resolution 0.5%) by the use of the dimethylamide of α-azidopropionic acid (Kuhn & Knopf, 1930 [75]).

As in the previous case, the right-handed component of the light brought about greater decomposition of the (−)-antipode.

The optical activation ($a = \pm 0.21°$) of the nitrosite of humulene (α-caryophyllene [76]) by the action of circularly polarized light was carried out by Mitchell [77]; left-handed light brought about decomposition of the (+)-antipode.

Special hopes were entertained of being able to carry out asymmetric photochemical decomposition of the light-sensitive salts of cobalt and rhodium which, in the optically active form, have a high specific rotation [78]. However, only the racemic complex $K_3\{Co(C_2O_4)_4\}$ could be optically activated by the selective decomposition, under the influence of right circularly polarized light, of the (−)-antipode [79].

All the cases which have been discussed are not really cases of asymmetric synthesis, but they were the first examples of the photochemical resolution of racemates.

Far greater theoretical interest attaches to the experiments aimed at carrying out absolute asymmetric syntheses of optically active compounds from substances which had a symmetrical structure. As a result of a reaction of this sort, an asymmetric carbon atom appears in the product and the compound shows optical activity.

2. *Photochemical, absolute, asymmetric synthesis.* Genuine, absolute, asymmetric synthesis, as distinct from the resolution of racemates, in the course of which new centres of asymmetry came into being, was accomplished very soon after Kuhn's experiments.

The first attempts to carry out photochemical absolute asymmetric syntheses by the bromination of substituted cinnamic acids [80] angelic acid [81] or by adding HCN to acetaldehyde [82] were unsuccessful.

Not until 1933–34 did Karagunis & Drikos [83] first bring about an absolute asymmetric synthesis by adding chlorine to a free triarylmethyl radical under the influence of circularly polarized light:

$$R_1R_2R_3C— + \tfrac{1}{2}\,Cl_2 \rightarrow R_1R_2R_3C—Cl$$

During the reaction the magnitude of the rotation passed through a maximum, reaching $0.08°$.

In the following year Tenney & Heggie [84] obtained optically active products under the same conditions, adding bromine to 2 : 4 : 6-trinitrostilbene, while Betti & Lucchi [85] found a small asymmetric effect on chlorinating propylene, butylene and butadiene.

Special interest attaches to the first absolute asymmetric synthesis of a natural compound, carried out in 1945 by Tenney & Ackerman [86].

At first they obtained an optically active substance, (+)-tartaric acid, by the action of circularly polarized light, and it was in the very form in which it occurs in living Nature. The synthesis was completed by the hydroxylation with hydrogen peroxide of diethyl fumarate by illumination with circularly polarized light. The rotation of the product passed through a maximum, reaching $+0.073°$ which corresponds to a degree of asymmetric synthesis of 2.5%.

It should be added that (+)-tartaric acid is obtained by the action of the right-handed component of circularly polarized light and this is the component which is present in slight excess in scattered light on the surface of the Earth as we noted earlier. This fact provides strong support for the hypothesis that the optical asymmetry of the molecular constituents of living organisms was brought into being by the action of circularly polarized light.

A DISSYMMETRIC SEQUENCE AS A FACTOR IN LIFE

In conclusion we will give some consideration to the significance of those factors which we termed the Pasteur effect.

Recent investigations have shown that polymers and polycondensates in which the molecules are composed of unsymmetrical links of a single type have special properties, different from the properties of irregular polymers. This is caused by the different and closer packing of regular chains [87].

The same idea should be applied to enzymic systems with a definite sequence in the arrangement of their links of dissymmetric L-amino acids. This gives rise to a definite, and always uniform, orientation of the molecules taking part. Out of the chaos of different molecules of the surrounding solution, the enzyme-catalyst strings together an appropriate molecule in a definite order. Weakly associated with the molecule of the enzyme by the Pasteur effect, the molecular system, which has been built up in this way, is imprinted by the molecule which propagated it, just as a stereotype or a page of text is printed by the matrix of a printing machine.

REFERENCES

1. V. S. Podisko A. V. Shubnikov, *Trudy Instituta Krist.*, No. 11, 212, 1955.
2. C. C. Price & M. Osgan, *J. Amer. chem. Soc.*, **78**, 690, 1956.
3. N. Beredjik, *J. Amer. chem. Soc.*, **78**, 2646, 1956.
4. V. Grignard, *Traité de Chimie Organique*, Vol. 1, p. 935, Paris, 1935.
5. A. V. Ingersoll, in *Organic reactions*, **2**, 401, 1950.
6. F. S. Kipping & W. J. Pope, *J. chem. Soc.*, **73**, 606, 1898; *Z.Kristallogr.*, **30**, 472, 1899
7. A. McKenzie, *J. chem. Soc.*, **107**, 440, 1915.
8. A. McKenzie, *J. chem. Soc.*, **121**, 349, 1922; **123**, 2875, 1923.
9. Gernez, *C. R. Acad. Sci.*, Paris, **63**, 843, 1866.
10. E. Jungfleisch, *Bull. Soc. chim. Fr.* (2), **41**, 225, 1884.
11. F. S. Kipping & W. J. Pope, *J. chem. Soc.*, **95**, 103, 1909.
12. L. Anderson & D. W. Hill, *J. chem. Soc.*, p. 993, 1928.
13. J. Read, *Nature, Lond.*, **171**, 843, 1953.
14. C. Soret, *Chem. Zbl. II*, 905, 1901; *Z.Kristallogr.*, **34**, 630, 1900.
15. T. Purdie, *J. chem. Soc.*, **63**, 1143, 1893.
16. O. Ruff, *Ber. dtsch. chem. Ges.*, **34**, 1362, 1901.
17. A. Werner, *Ber. dtsch. chem. Ges.*, **47**, 2171, 1914.
18. E. Calzavara, *Chem. Zbl. II*, 2134, 1934; Fr. Pat.,763374, 23.1., 1933.
19. A. P. Terent'ev & V. M. Potapov, *Priroda, Leningr.*, **5**, 37, 1955.
20. L. Velluz, G. Ammiard & R. Joly, *Bull. Soc. chim. Fr.*, **3**, 342, 1953; *Chem. Abstr.*, 2470, 4216, 1956.
21. I. Ostromyslenskiĭ, *Ber. dtsch. chem. Ges.*, **41**, 3035, 1908; *C.R. Acad. Sci.*, Paris, **176**, 391, 1923.
22. A. S. Eacle, *Chem. Zbl.*, 649, 1896; *Z.Kristallogr.*, **26**, 562, 1896.
23. G. Wyrouboff, *Chem. Zbl.*, **2**, 90, 1898.
24. N. D. Zelinskiĭ, *Ber. dtsch. chem. Ges.*, **24**, 4006, 1891.
25. J. H. Van't Hoff & H. M. Dawson, *Ber. dtsch. chem. Ges.*, **31**, 528, 1898.
26. G. Wyrouboff, *Bull. Soc. chim. Fr.* (2), **41**, 212, 1884; **45**, 52, 1886; *Liebigs Ann.*, (6), **9**, 221, 1886; *Z. phys. Chem.*, **5**, 118, 1890; K. Freudenberg, *Stereochemie*, **1**, 565, 1933.
27. A. Puitti, *C.R. Acad. Sci.*, Paris, **103**, 134, 1886; W. Körner & A. Menozzi, *Ber. dtsch. chem. Ges.*, **21**, 87, 1888.
28. M. Bruzau, *C.R. Acad. Sci.*, Paris., **196**, 122, 1933.
29. J. Böeseken & B. Felix, *Ber. dtsch. chem. Ges.*, **61**, 787, 1928.
30. M. Godchot & P. Vieles, *Bull. Soc. chim. Fr.* (4), **51**, 589, 1932.
31. L. Marquenne & G. Bertrand, *C.R. Acad. Sci.*, Paris, **132**, 1565, 1901.
32. E. Fischer & R. Curtiss, *Ber. dtsch. chem. Ges.*, **25**, 1025, 1892.
33. E. Jungfleisch, *C.R. Acad. Sci.*, Paris, **110**, 792, 1890; **108**, 982, 1889.
34. F. Jaeger, *Rec. trav. chim. Pays-Bas*, **38**, 250, 1919; *Z. anorg. Chem.*, **175**, 211, 1928.
35. W. Hückel & C. Kuhn, *Ber. dtsch. chem. Ges.*, **70**, 2479, 1937.
36. E. Erlenmeyer, *Ber. dtsch. chem. Ges.*, **30**, 1531, 1897; see also *J. chem. Soc.*, p. 912, 1927; *J. chem. Soc.*, p. 2305, 1929; *Z. angew. Chem.*, **188**, 47, 1930; *Z. Kristallogr.* **69**, 69, 1928.
37. C. Neuberg, *Biokhimiya*, **2**, 383, 1937.
38. E. Havinga, *Chem. Weekbl.* ;**38**, 642, 1941; *Biochem. biophys. Acta*, **13**, 171, 1954.

39. R. DUSCHINSKY, *J. Soc. chem. Ind., Lond.*, **53**, 10, 1934.
40. K. VOGLER & M. KOFLER, *Helv. chim. acta*, **39**, 1387, 1956.
41. E. DARMOIS, *C. R. Acad. Sci., Paris*, **237**, 124, 1953.
42. R. C. FERREIRA, *Nature, Lond.*, **171**, 39, 1953.
43. E. I. KLABUNOVSKIĬ & V. V. PATRIKEEV, *Priroda, Leningr.*, **7**, 89, 1954. *Vestnik Moskov. Gosndarst. Univ.*, **5**, 53, 1953.
44. E. I. KLABUNOVSKIĬ, *Origin of Life*, p. 158.
45. L. PASTEUR, *Oeuvres de Pasteur* (Ed. par VALLÉRY-RADOT), Vol. I, p. 375. Masson et Cie, Paris, 1922.
46. A. P. TERENT'EV & E. I. KLABUNOVSKIĬ, *Uchennye Zapiski Moskov. Gosudarst. Univ.*, **151**, 145, 1951.
47. J. P. MATHIEU, *La synthèse asymmetrique*, Paris, 1934.
48. P. D. RITCHIE, *Advanc. Enzymol.*, **7**, 65, 1947.
49. P. GUYS & G. DROUGININE, *J. Chim. Phys.*, **7**, 97, 1909.
50. P. D. RITCHIE, *Asymmetric Synthesis and Asymmetric Induction.* O.U.P., London, 1933.
51. L. W. STOCK, *Z. phys. Chem.*, (B), **23**, 236, 1923.
52. G. ROASIO, *Z. Kristallogr.*, **59**, 88, 1924.
53. I. OSTROMYSLENSKIĬ, *Ber. dtsch. chem. Ges.*, **41**, 3035, 1908.
54. J. ROSENTHALER, *S.B. preuss. Akad. Wiss.*, **1**, 20, 1908.
55. P. CURIE, *J. Phys. Chim. Hist. nat.* (III), **3**, 403, 1894.
56. J. MEYER, *ChemZtg*, **1**, 41, 1904.
57. F. M. JAEGER, *Optical activity*, p. 76. New York, 1930.
58. JAMIN, *C. R. Acad. Sci., Paris*, **31**, 696, 1850.
59. H. BECQUEREL, *C. R. Acad. Sci., Paris*, **108**, 997, 1899.
60. L. TENNEY & R. HEGGIE, *J. Amer. chem. Soc.*, **57**, 1622, 1935.
61. A. BYK, *Ber. dtsch. chem. Ges.*, **37**, 4696, 1904; **42**, 141, 1909; *Arch. Pharm., Berl.*, **269**, 356, 1931; *Z. phys. Chem.*, **49**, 641, 1904.
62. E. I. KLABUNOVSKIĬ & V. V. PATRIKEEV, *Vestnik MGU* (5), 53, 1953.
63. K. D. TODOROV, *Kristalicheskata antisimmetria i zhivot"t na bel'tsite.* State University, Stalin, Bulgaria, 1951. Reviewed by E. I. KLABUNOVSKIĬ, *Biokhimiya*, **19**, 638, 1954.
64. A. I. OPARIN, *Proiskhozhdenie zhizni Zemle.* Izd. Akad. Nauk S.S.S.R., Moscow 1957; *The Origin of Life on the Earth.* Oliver & Boyd, Edinburgh, 1957.
65. D. J. MACHT & W. T. ANDERSON, *J. Amer. chem. Soc.*, **49**, 201, 1927.
66. L. PASTEUR, *Rev. Sci., Paris* (III), **7**, 3, 1884.
67. SUTHERLAND, *Phil. Mag.*, **19**, 52, 1841.
68. J. A. LE BEL, *Ann. Chim. Phys.* (III), **8**, 373, 1896.
69. A. COTTON, *Liebigs Ann.*, **8**, 360, 1896.
70. *C.R. Acad. Sci., Paris*, **189**, 1260, 1929; *J. Chim. phys.*, **7**, 81, 1909; *J. chem. Soc.*, p. 3258, 1928.
71. A. McKENZIE, *Z. angew. Chem.*, **45**, 59, 1932.
72. G. BREDIG, *Z. angew. chem.*, **36**, 456, 1923.
73. F. HENLE & H. HAAKH, *Ber. dtsch. chem. Ges.*, **41**, 4261, 1908; **42**, 141, 1909.
74. W. KUHN & E. BRAUN, *Naturwissenschaften*, **17**, 227, 1929.
75. W. KUHN & E. KNOPF, *Naturwissenschaften*, **18**, 183, 1930; *Z. phys. Chem.* (B), **7**, 292, 1930.
76. G. R. CLEMO & J. O. HARRIES, *Chem. & Ind.*, p. 50, 1951; *J. chem. Soc.*, p. 665, 1952.
77. S. MITCHELL, *J. chem. Soc.*, p. 1829, 1930.
78. R. LUTHER & A. NIKOPULOS, *Z. phys. Chem.*, **82**, 361, 1913.
79. R. TSUCHIDA, *J. chem. Soc. Japan*, **59**, 1339, 1935.
80. J. FREUNDLER, *Bull. Soc. Chim. Fr.*, **1**, 657, 1907.
81. M. PADOA, *R. C. Accad. Lincei*, **18**, 390, 1909.
82. J. PIRAK, *Biochem. Z.*, **130**, 76, 1922.
83. G. KARAGUNIS & G. DRIKOS, *Naturwissenschaften*, **21**, 607, 1933; *Nature, Lond.*, **132**, 354, 1933; *Z. phys. Chem.* (B), **26**, 428, 1934; *Prakt. Akad. Athen*, **9**, 177, 1934.
84. L. TENNEY, D. HEGGIE & R. HEGGIE, *J. Amer. chem. Soc.*, **57**, 377, 1935.
85. M. BETTI & E. LUCCHI, *Chem. Abstr.*, 7273, 1939.
86. L. TENNEY, D. ACKERMAN & J. ACKERMAN, *J. Amer. chem. Soc.*, **67**, 486, 1945.
87. G. NATTA, *Chim. nell' Industr.*, **38**, 124, 1956.

N. H. HOROWITZ:

On Defining 'Life'

Several speakers at this Symposium have brought up the question of how life is to be defined. As a biologist, I am interested in this question, because it is a test of our understanding of the nature of living matter, and because at a symposium on the Origin of Life it seems important to try to reach a common understanding on this basic concept. I would like to consider the problem first in rather general terms and later narrow it to the forms of life that we know. I shall first ask: What are the minimum properties of a living system? And then: What is the simplest chemical system known to exhibit these properties? I do not claim any special originality for the ideas I shall present; in one form or another, they have been current among geneticists for some time.

Some biologists and biochemists tend to regard the question of the definition of life as essentially meaningless. They view living and non-living matter as forming a continuum, and the drawing of a line between them as arbitrary. Life, on this view, is associated with the complicated chemical apparatus of the cell—with enzymes, membranes, metabolic cycles, etc.—and it is said to be impossible to decide at what point in its evolution such a system becomes alive. I do not accept this point of view, because I have not been convinced that the postulated continuum actually exists.

Others define life in terms of metabolism and energy flux, or in terms of the ability to reproduce. Such definitions fall short of the mark. A steam-engine has metabolism, and many simple examples of self-reproduction are known; the hydrogen ion, for example, can catalyse its own production from many substances (e.g., ethyl acetate). That familiar analogy of a living system, a flame, shows both metabolism and the ability to grow and perpetuate itself.

Self-duplication and metabolism of a sort are important in the definition of life I shall propose, but they are not sufficient. In addition, we must provide our system with the impulse to evolve. This is essential, because in specifying the minimal properties of a primitive living system, or eobiont, we must include the potentiality of evolving into the countless forms that we recognize as alive. To the property of self-duplication, I therefore add the ability to *mutate randomly and to reproduce in the new form*. This property of mutability implies that the reproductive process in living things involves much more than the simple autocatalysis we find in ordinary chemical systems. It involves a *copying* mechanism which insures that mutations occurring in the parents will be faithfully reproduced in the offspring.

With the ability to mutate and to reproduce by copying, evolution becomes inevitable, and our system is almost alive. It is necessary to add a final element, however, and that is the ability to *influence the environment* in such a way as to *insure a supply of the materials necessary for the perpetuation of the system*. I suggest that these three properties— mutability, self-duplication, and heterocatalysis—comprise a necessary and sufficient definition of living matter. Any system endowed with these properties must, given the right conditions, evolve under the pressures of random mutation and natural selection. In time, all the complexity of structure and function that we associate with living things might conceivably develop by a kind of logical necessity. Some years ago, I attempted to show how the synthesis of biochemically important substances might evolve in such a system [1].

I am familiar with the argument that since not all living things can reproduce themselves—the mule is often cited as an example—it is not permissible to include self-reproduction in a definition of life. It is true that mules rarely reproduce, but this is for trivial reasons having to do with the mechanics of gamete formation. That the cells of which the mule is composed are capable of reproducing is evident from the fact that they are products of the division of one original cell and are undoubtedly capable of

106

indefinite growth in tissue culture. Furthermore, there is no reason to doubt that the mule itself is capable of reproducing asexually, as are most animals, by division of the early embryo, giving rise to monozygotic twins. This mechanism is no different in principle than that by which bacteria and other asexual organisms multiply.

The next step in our inquiry is to attempt to define a living system chemically. What is the minimal chemical system that exhibits the essential properties of living matter? It is not possible to give a complete answer to this question at the present time, but from the study of chemical genetics we have obtained an important fragment of the answer. It will be noticed that the essential properties of living matter as I have defined them are precisely the properties of the genes, as shown by experiment. Genes are mutable; they reproduce by copying, as shown by the fact that mutant genes are exactly duplicated; and they induce the formation of specific catalysts in their environment, as shown by many examples in which gene mutation has been found to result in the permanent hereditary loss of specific enzymes, or in the production of structurally novel kinds of enzymes [2]. It is as if the genes were the only living components of the cell, everything else being—directly or indirectly—the products of genic activity.

We are thus led to the problem of the chemical nature of genes. I cannot take up here the many lines of evidence that point toward the nucleic acids as the ultimate genetic material. The evidence for the genetic role of deoxyribonucleic acid has been reviewed recently [3]. The question we are concerned with is whether a molecule of nucleic acid could have been the first living thing on the Earth. It is tempting to believe that this was so. Even if true, however, this would not solve all our problems, because we recognize that no living thing can function in a vacuum. Until very recently nucleic acids were known to function only within living cells. If life can be manifested only in such complex systems as cells, then the problem of its origin becomes truly formidable. The recent work of Kornberg [4], however, suggests that deoxyribonucleic acid reproduction may occur in a rather simple system. Likewise, the synthesis of proteins in isolated systems, which has been accomplished in several laboratories, suggests that the heterocatalytic activity of the genes may also proceed under relatively simple conditions. If these inferences are correct, then the question raised by Professor Oparin—namely, did life arise as individual molecules or in the form of complex polymolecular systems—can be answered in the following way: Life arose as individual molecules in a polymolecular environment.

California Institute of Technology,
Pasadena, California, U.S.A.

REFERENCES

1. N. H. HOROWITZ, *Proc. nat. Acad. Sci., Wash.*, **31**, 153, 1945.
2. N. H. HOROWITZ, *Fed. Proc.*, **15**, 818, 1956.
3. R. L. SINSHEIMER, *Science*, **125**, 1123, 1957.
4. A. KORNBERG, In: *The Chemical Basis of Heredity* (Ed. by MCELROY & GLASS). The Johns Hopkins Press, Baltimore, p. 579, 1957.

V. I. KRASOVSKIĬ & I. S. SHKLOVSKIĬ (U.S.S.R.):

The Possible Influence of Cosmic Rays on the Origin and Evolution of Life on the Earth

It has now been proved that both the radio waves and the light rays (with a continuous spectrum) of the Crab nebula were brought into being by relativistic electrons moving in magnetic fields [1, 2]. This being so, we must reckon with the fact that this nebula—the residue of the supernova of A.D. 1054—contains a tremendous number of relativistic particles, i.e., primary cosmic rays. The same may be said of the other nebulae which are residues of supernovae. In fact the residue of the supernova of 1572 and that of the supernova of 1604 are sources of radio waves [3, 4]. Recently it has been discovered that radio waves are also emitted by the loop nebulae in *Cygnus* which are undoubtedly residues of a supernova which burst out several thousand years ago [5]. In the Crab nebula [6], the mean concentration of relativistic electrons with energies $E > 10^9$ eV, $N(E > 10^9) \sim 3 \times 10^{-7}$ cm^{-3}. It might be expected that the concentration of relativistic protons would be of the same order. When the radius of the Crab nebula in its expansion reaches 5 parsecs the concentration of relativistic particles will reach 3×10^{-9} cm^{-3}, i.e., it will still be about 30 times as great as the concentration of primary cosmic rays in the neighbourhood of the Earth.

The question arises as to whether the Sun, moving within the Galaxy, with the planets revolving round it, might have entered a region in which the abundance of cosmic rays was tens, or even hundreds of times greater than it is now. We can answer this question in the affirmative. It happened when supernovae burst out in the immediate vicinity of the Sun.

The frequency with which supernovae burst out in the Galaxy was, until recently, estimated by means of indirect evidence from other galaxies. It has been shown [6] that this does not give a correct estimate, such outbursts being of at least one order higher in our own Galaxy. In this respect our Galaxy resembles the galaxies NGC 3184, 6946 and 4321, in which the frequencies of outbursts of supernovae are anomalously large. In fact, during the past thousand years, at least 5 outbursts of supernovae have been observed in our Galaxy (in 1006, 1054, 1572, 1604 and 1843); the last being *Nova Carinae* [7]. These were all very bright so they cannot have been more than 2000–2500 parsecs away, especially if we allow for interstellar absorption of light. Hence it follows that about once in every thousand years there occurs an outburst of a supernova at a distance of not more than 1000 parsecs from us. Assuming that the supernovae form a very flattened system within the Galaxy, being 100 parsecs thick, we find that in each 500 million years a supernova will burst out at a distance of less than 5 parsecs from the Sun. This means that during the existence of the Earth stars near to the Sun have burst out into supernovae on several occasions (about 10).

What sort of things could have happened under such unusual circumstances? The brightness of the stars bursting could hardly exceed -20^m, i.e. the amount of radiation reaching the Earth from the star was 1000 times less than that from the Sun. That, however, does not necessarily mean that the amount of hard radiation (e.g., X-rays) reaching the Earth from the star and from the nebula in the very earliest stage of its development, could not be considerably greater than that from the Sun. This could have had serious consequences (see below). The gaseous envelope formed by the flare-up of the supernova, which was expanding at 10^8 cm/sec, passed through the solar system. However, considering the negligible density of the gas in this envelope (about 10^{-22} g/cm^3) this would hardly have left any traces.

What is important is that at such times the amount of cosmic radiation reaching the Earth must have been several tens of times greater than the normal value for a period of some thousands of years. It should also be noted that the relativistic particles in the expanding nebula were very irregularly distributed. Thus there might be periods, lasting many hundreds of years when the amount of cosmic radiation reaching the Earth was hundreds of times what it is now.

This could well have entailed serious biological, and above all, genetical consequences. Until recently it was held that the process of evolution of living things was brought about by the influence of natural selection and the various physical conditions of the surrounding medium. Among these, however, no consideration has ever been given to the important factor of the general level of hard radiations. On the strength of what has just been said, we must recognize that, at some stages of evolution, this latter factor must have been of great, if not of decisive significance.

According to the evidence available (e.g., 8), the amount of irradiation due to cosmic rays in the lowest layer of the atmosphere is now 0·04 r/yr, i.e. about one-third of the general level of natural radiation. Nevertheless, an increase in the dose of radiation to as little as twice the normal level may have serious genetical consequences [8]. Hence it is clear that if the intensity of cosmic radiation were increased ten- to a hundredfold for thousands of years, this might have catastrophic results for many forms of animals and plants. For example, one may put forward the hypothesis that the reptiles of the Mesozoic age might have become extinct within a relatively short period for this reason. On the other hand, speaking generally, it is quite possible that for other forms, this factor might have favoured their further evolution.

While we are considering the catastrophic consequences of a significant increase in the intensity of cosmic radiation in bygone periods in the development of the Earth, we must mention that this factor could have stimulated the formation, from primitive organic compounds, of those complicated complexes from which life could have originated on the Earth.

REFERENCES

1. I. S. SHKLOVSKIĬ, *Dokl. Akad. Nauk S.S.S.R.*, **90**, 983, 1953.
2. J. OORT & T. WALRAVEN, *Bull. astr. Insts Netherlds*, **12** (462), 285, 1956.
3. R. HANBURY BROWN & C. HAZARD, *Nature, Lond.*, **170**, 364, 1952.
4. J. SHAKESHAFT, M. RYLE, J. BALDWIN, B. ELSMORE & J. THOMSON, *Mem. R. Astr. Soc.*, **67** (3), 106, 1955.
5. D. WALSH & R. HANBURY BROWN, *Nature, Lond.*, **175**, 808, 1956.
6. I. S. SHKLOVSKIĬ, *Kosmicheskoe radioizluchenie*. Moscow (Gostekhizdat), 1956.
7. J. THANEREY, *Observatory*, **76**, 311, 1956.
8. N. P. DUBININ, *Vestnik Akad. Nauk S.S.S.R.* (8), 22, 1956.

A. A. GARIBYANTS (U.S.S.R.):

The Question of the Primary Synthesis of Organic Substances on the Earth

According to a widely held view, 3000–4000 million years ago, when the transition from the magmatic stage of development of the Earth to the present geological stage was completed, the temperature on the surface of the planet was so high that all organic substances, if any were present by that time, must have been given off into the atmosphere. We must therefore reckon that absence of free oxygen in the atmosphere of the planet was a necessary condition for the occurrence of the primary synthesis of organic compounds and for their continuing to exist and being transformed.

In picturing the protoplanetary system, investigators have argued that the mass of hydrogen in the protoplanetary cloud was greater than that of oxygen. However, it is far from being proved that after the long period of development of the planet preceding the stage of magmatic cooling, there was the same lack of free oxygen as there had been earlier.

An attempt will be made here to show that the ratio between the amounts of hydrogen and oxygen in the atmosphere changed in favour of hydrogen soon after the formation of the crust of the Earth, so that conditions became favourable for the occurrence of the primary synthesis and retention of its products.

Judging from the temperature of crystallization of magmatic formations the temperature of the surface of the Earth must, at some time, have been not less than 1600 °C. The liquid incandescent surface of the magma was, at that time, surrounded by a very large atmosphere. Exchange of gases between the magma and the atmosphere took place comparatively easily. However, with the appearance of the solid crust of the Earth, the exchange of gases between the planet and its atmosphere became considerably more difficult. From the moment of its formation, the crust of the Earth constituted a barrier and a bed for the substances which condensed and were deposited on the surface of the planet during its later cooling. Basing ourselves on the mass of the lowest-boiling components of the crust of the Earth we may calculate the approximate composition of the atmosphere at the end of the stage of magmatic cooling of the planet. Such a calculation gives the probable percentage composition of the atmosphere as: water 80–90, carbon dioxide 12–15, phosphorous anhydride 0·5–1·0, nitrogen 0·05–0·1 and other components 0·01–0·02.

The gases of the atmosphere were dissolved in the magma in considerable amounts determined by their partial pressures and solubilities. It is important to note that water vapour, being the main component of the atmosphere, was contained in large amounts in the magma.

In the process of cooling of the planet the molten magma began to crystallize. The transition from the liquid to the solid state was associated with a lowering of solubility as a result of which a large quantity of gases was emitted and rushed outwards.

At the same time there were taking place, within the solidifying magma, reactions between hydrogen, carbon and oxygen and also between oxygen and some of the other elements of the magma. Free oxygen is, as a rule, absent from the gases contained in magmatic formations. During the slow cooling of the molten magma, part of the oxygen of the water which had originally been dissolved in the magma, was used in the oxidation of the elements of the magma. Among these were, in the first place, iron, which passed from a lower to a higher state of oxidation, and calcium, which arose from the natural radioactive decay of potassium. As a result, part of the oxygen of the water remained for ever within the magma, while hydrogen, the inert gases, methane, carbon dioxide and carbon monoxide passed outwards into the atmosphere.

As the temperature fell, the differences in rate of permeation between the light and heavy gases increased markedly. Thus, as concerned permeability by diffusion, under the conditions which prevailed during the cooling of the crust of the Earth, the migration of hydrogen from the interior to the surface was on an exceptionally large scale, out of all proportion, from a quantitative point of view, to the relatively small-scale translocation by diffusion of the other elements and compounds.

Similar ideas about the flow of hydrogen out from the deeper parts of the Earth were put forward by L. V. Khmelevskaya as early as 1947.

To get an idea of the amount of hydrogen which could have reached the atmosphere from the interior of the Earth, we may consider the crust of the Earth as being like a membrane in air-free interplanetary space, which can only lose the gas dissolved in it through one surface into the vacuum. Owing to our lack of factual data, we have to use an arbitrary, probable figure for the original concentration. If we take it as being 1 vol. of hydrogen (at NTP) per 10 vol. of formation, then, with a coefficient of diffusion of 1×10^{-6} cm²/sec, it is easy to calculate the mass of hydrogen which will be given off into the atmosphere from a layer of the crust of the Earth 50 km thick in relation to time.

Such an approximate, indicative calculation shows that after 1000 million years from the time when the process began 10^{13} to 10^{14} tons of hydrogen could have entered the atmosphere. However, the hydrogen and carbon dioxide entering the atmosphere from the depths of the Earth were not the sole sources of the starting products for the primaeval synthesis of organic substances. The beginning of crystallization of the magma was accompanied by the differentiation of its components. The denser components of the molten magma sank, while the less dense, acidic components rose towards the surface. In the course of this, masses of elementary carbon were thrown out on to the surface along with the lighter acidic components of the magma. The appearance of elementary carbon on the surface of the Earth and its contact with the heated water vapour of the atmosphere must have led to the formation of water gas. Unfortunately, we have no way of gauging the scale on which this process occurred, but it is important to note that such a process did occur, making possible the accumulation in the atmosphere of the starting materials for the primary syntheses.

In all probability it was just these two processes: the giving off of hydrogen from the depths of the Earth and the formation of carbon dioxide on its surface, which accounted for the accumulation in the atmosphere of the starting products for the primary synthesis of organic substances and which prevented free oxygen from existing in the atmosphere. Under these conditions it was possible for hydrocarbons, a certain amount of oxygen-containing compounds as well as ammonia and hydrogen sulphide, to be formed and to remain as such in the atmosphere.

The primary synthesis must have occurred, for the most part, in the atmosphere in contact with the surface of the crust of the Earth which contained substances with catalytic properties.

A relatively small quantity of organic substances, mostly methane, may have been formed within the solidifying magma. But, as the crust of the Earth cooled, so its permeability decreased substantially and the accession to the atmosphere of organic substances from within it almost ceased.

As the planet cooled further, water settled down on its surface and, later, also the products of primary synthesis, which were distributed in the waters of the oceans where further transformations occurred. One result of these was the formation of proteins.

N. M. GALAKTIONOVA (U.S.S.R.):

The Content of Bituminous Material in Sedimentary and Metamorphic Rocks of the Crystalline Foundation

(Based on the results of a study of the cores of test borings in the central regions of the Russian platform)

The theory of the origin of life on the Earth, postulates that, for a long time before the appearance of life on the surface of the planet there accumulated a large quantity of organic substances which had been formed abiogenically.

This hypothesis is based on the well-known syntheses of organic from inorganic substances effected under technological conditions, the presence of hydrocarbon compounds in some meteorites (which have been formed under conditions unsuitable to life), the frequently observed presence of hydrocarbon radicals in the spectra of stars and the existence of hydrocarbons in the atmospheres of some planets. From these facts it follows that the abiogenic synthesis of organic compounds is widely distributed in nature.

In this connection it would be very significant if we could find, on our own planet, organic substances of abiogenic origin formed a long time ago, before the appearance of life on the Earth.

Hydrocarbons of various origins have now been found in the crust of the Earth both in rocks of the sedimentary complex, starting with the most ancient Precambrian rocks and ending with recent deposits, and also in the rocks of the crystalline foundation.

The elucidation of the origin of the hydrocarbons found in the crust of the Earth is sometimes extremely complicated and requires special precautions to avoid confusion of products of abiogenic synthesis with those of more recent biogenic origin.

The solution of such problems has been substantially helped by the new geochemical data which have been obtained by the systematic and many-sided investigation of the cores of test borings.

The study of the section made by a bore, beginning with the superficial layers of the sedimentary complex and ending with the formations of the crystalline foundation, provides the possibility of using geological and geochemical methods to clarify the origin of the bituminous substances found in the cores.

With this object we shall consider some new material which has been obtained by studying the cores of 40 test bores which were driven into the extensive territory of the central regions of the Russian platform, occupying an area of about 1000 km longitudinally and 1200 km latitudinally. As a result of studying the sections brought up by the test bores, the following facts have been established.

1. The depth at which the foundation lies is not the same in all parts of the Russian platform (minimum observation 845 m, maximum 1950 m).

2. Bituminous substances were found both in rocks of the sedimentary Palaeozoic complex, and in plagioclase gneisses—rocks of the crystalline foundation, untouched by superficial weathering processes. It has been shown that the relief of the crystalline foundation is complicated by intensive, tectonic disturbances expressed as cleavages of the foundation into blocks which are displaced in relation to one another. The constitution of the sections, seen as a whole, gives an intelligible picture of lack of uniformity in both the qualitative and quantitative distribution of bituminous substances horizontally and vertically. Thus, in the metamorphic rocks of the crystalline foundation, composed mainly of gneisses, the concentration of bituminous substances varies from nothing to some thousandths of 1%. It is very important to note that the qualitative composition of the bituminous substances of the rocks of the foundation differs from that of the bituminous substances contained in formations of the sedimentary strata covering the foundation.

As concerns the sandstones and clays of the Precambrian sedimentary strata which lie directly upon the crystalline foundation, it would seem that bituminous substances are, as a rule, absent from them.

In the dolomites and anhydrites of the Devonian beds which cover the Precambrian rocks, bituminous substances are present in concentrations which may reach as high as some tenths of 1%.

Tracing the distribution of bituminous substances further in the rocks of the Devonian period, we notice that the content of bituminous substances corresponding to a particular geochemical facies sometimes diminishes and sometimes increases, at times reaching more than 1%, as for example, in the rocks of the Rudkinsk horizon of the Frasnian.

At the same time the qualitative composition of the bituminous substances syngenetic with the sedimentary rocks is determined mainly by geochemical conditions and also changes vertically though they are continuous throughout the territory. As analysis of the palaeogeographic conditions has shown, the rocks of the Morsovo and Dankovo-Lebedyan horizons of the middle and upper Devonian, which were mainly laid down under the conditions of saline lagoons in reducing circumstances favourable to the laying down and transformation of organic substances, are characterized essentially by a reduced type of bituminous substances.

In the rocks of the Upper Givetian of the middle Devonian, which were laid down under shallow-water conditions, i.e. under conditions which were not favourable for the accumulation and transformation of organic substances, we find either a complete absence of bituminous substances, or bituminosities of an acid character.

The factual material which has been brought forward concerning the study of the present distribution of bituminous substances is evidence that the bituminous material found in a scattered form in sedimentary deposits is found in the very deposits (or in their immediate vicinity) where the geochemical conditions were favourable for the laying down and transformation of organic compounds of animal and vegetable origin. The bituminous substances in the scattered form which are contained in the rocks of the sedimentary complex which was studied are therefore, in the first place, syngenetic with the deposits in which they lie and, in the second place, they are undoubtedly of biogenic origin. This is indicated by the numerous finds of remains of animal and plant life in these rocks.

As concerns the more ancient rocks of the crystalline foundation, it must be stated that no traces of vital activity have been found in them.

The question arises as to the source of the bituminous substances which have been found in the rocks of the foundation.

One hypothesis, based on the possibility that bitumens of biogenic origin might have migrated downwards from the overlying sedimentary strata into the foundation, seems untenable in that it is inconsistent with the possible rate of their migration from the less dense sedimentary deposits into the denser igneous rocks of the foundation. Furthermore, if this were correct, it would be impossible to explain those cases in which the distribution of bituminous substances is such that their concentration in the rocks of the foundation is greater than in the sedimentary rocks immediately overlying it, for migration from areas of low concentration to areas of higher concentration cannot occur.

All this suggests that the bituminous substances found in the metamorphic rocks of the foundation were either formed in the metamorphic rocks themselves, or else that they migrated into these formations from the magmatic focus by cracks and fissures.

Both of these suggestions imply that the bituminous substances found in the crystalline foundation were of completely abiogenic origin.

As concerns the view that bituminous substances migrated out of the foundation into the sedimentary rocks, this idea does not receive any confirmation in the territory under discussion, as there are places in it where bituminous substances are completely absent from the foundation while being present in considerable amounts in the sedimentary layers immediately overlying it.

In conclusion, it must be remarked that the material produced is evidence of the extensive distribution in the crust of the Earth of bituminous substances in the dispersed form, which also contain a certain amount of hydrocarbons. They are found both in the strata of the sedimentary complex, and sometimes in the metamorphic rocks of the crystalline foundation. However, analysis of the geochemical and palaeogeographical circumstances demonstrates, absolutely convincingly, the independent and separate formation of the bituminous substances which have been discovered in the sedimentary strata and the hydrocarbon compounds of the metamorphic rocks of the foundation.

The demonstration, over an enormous territory, of bituminous substances in only very minute amounts in the rocks of the crystalline foundation, the impossibility of their migrating upwards to any considerable extent, and also the absence of any appreciable quantity of them, not to speak of the absence of petroleum deposits in the graben of the Vyatsk uplift and on the Tokmovo uplift which are broken into by a large number of deep fractures of the foundation, constitute serious objections to the hypothesis of the inorganic origin of petroleum.

A. I. LEBEDINSKIĬ (U.S.S.R.):

The successful solution of the problem of the origin of life on the Earth may be made far easier by a study of the conditions under which life exists on Mars.

The hypothesis that life exists on Mars rests quite firmly on the fact that we can observe seasonal changes in the colouring of the various parts of the planet which we call seas and canals.

The form in which life exists on Mars is undoubtedly very different from that of life on the Earth and is probably essentially anaerobic as there is no appreciable amount of free oxygen on Mars. A marked shortage of water must also be considered as a definite peculiarity of the Martian biosphere.

Both the Earth and Mars were undoubtedly formed by the gradual acquisition, over a long period, of cold bodies falling on their surfaces.

The possibility of the so-called 'hot' origin of the planets is open to the most crushing criticism but this, of course, falls outside the scope of such a short communication. In the course of the 'cold' formation of planets, both the Earth and Mars were made up of particles from which all gaseous components had been given off by prolonged vacuum distillation at temperatures close to o ° C. Water and gaseous products could be given off from such particles when they had fallen on to the Earth either by heating them strongly or under the action of high pressure.

This giving off of water and gases could occur, in part, owing to the effect of meteoritic bodies falling on the surface of the planet; but it probably took place, for the most part, under the influence of high pressure in the interior with a gradual migration to the surface of the Earth of water and gases, along with the products of volcanic eruptions.

All these cosmogenic considerations lead to a belief in a great similarity in composition between the eruptive products on the Earth and those on Mars. Probably the conditions for dissipation of the atmosphere were also very similar on both planets, for the rate of dissipation is determined by the temperature of the superficial layers of the ionosphere which are in radiative equilibrium with the ultraviolet radiations of the sun responsible for ionizing them.

We may, therefore, postulate the presence, on the surface of Mars, of enough water to fill the oceans to the same depth as those of the Earth or, at least, to half that depth.

The differences between the atmosphere and oceans of the Earth and those of Mars must have been mainly caused by the different climate and different results of the activity of the biosphere.

In the cold Martian climate the mean temperature of the soil at all latitudes is below o ° C and therefore water can exist there only in the solid phase, in the form of underground deposits of ice and everlastingly frozen soils, in which the ice cannot be observed.

What can be observed is a small amount of water on the polar caps and this is the water which takes part in the seasonal cycle.

The biosphere which has developed on Mars during the short hours of diurnal thawing must have evolved far more slowly than that on the Earth and has probably not yet succeeded in creating an oxygen-rich atmosphere.

It is even more surprising that on Mars we find practically the same partial density of carbon dioxide as on the Earth. It is hard to explain this coincidence in any other way than by the activity of the biosphere.

The impermeability of the contemporary Martian atmosphere to ultraviolet rays is due not to absorption by oxygen, as on the Earth, but to absorption by carbon dioxide. Thus the limit of the wavelength of light which can pass through is about 1900 Å and, surprisingly, this corresponds with the short-wave limit of the band of mitogenic rays. The idea suggests itself that the ability of organisms to reflect and absorb mitogenic rays is a relic from the time when there was neither oxygen nor ozone in the atmosphere of the Earth.

I. S. SHKLOVSKIĬ (U.S.S.R.):

I cannot agree with the point of view of Academician V. G. Fesenkov that the mass of the primaeval Earth was far greater than the mass of the Earth today because it was

8

mainly composed of hydrogen (according to Fesenkov the hydrogen departed into interplanetary space owing to thermal dissipation).

As early as 1951 we proved in a strictly mathematical way that this was impossible [1].

Of course, at particular stages in the evolution of the atmosphere of the Earth, it may have contained some, perhaps even a considerable amount of hydrogen, but the mass of this hydrogen was always small compared with that of the Earth at any given time.

The presence of ammonia and methane in the primaeval atmosphere of the Earth, though only in small amounts (some mm at NTP) led to the atmosphere being impermeable to ultraviolet rays of 2200 Å.

In considering the hypothesis that the primaeval organic compounds were synthesized under the influence of the nearer ultraviolet part of the spectrum, we must make due allowance for the absorption of ultraviolet rays by the various components of the atmosphere of that time.

The agent which, together with V. I. Krasovskiĭ, I suggested might have stimulated the development of life, namely a high level of cosmic radiation during particular epochs in the history of the Earth, has a definite advantage as against such mechanisms as ultraviolet radiations from the sun or electrical discharges.

Cosmic rays do not depend on the haphazard permeability of the atmosphere, they act uninterruptedly and they penetrate water. The disturbances and changes brought about in the structures of organic molecules by high-energy particles considerably surpass the effects of ultraviolet photons with energies of some volts.

We may note the possibilities for asymmetric synthesis of organic compounds by the action of cosmic rays while pointing out that a circularly polarized component in solar radiation has not been discovered.

Developments in physics and chemistry lead to the conclusion that there must certainly have been epochs in the past when the intensity of cosmic rays was hundreds of times greater than it is today. Advances in radiation biology show that this factor can hardly have failed to produce an effect on organic substances.

The object of this contribution is to direct the attention of specialized biochemists to this important fact.

REFERENCE

1. I. S. SHKLOVSKIĬ, *Astron. Zh.*, **28**, 234, 1951.

H. A. LYUBIMOVA (U.S.S.R.):

(I want to make a few remarks about the original temperature conditions on the Earth.) From the preceding papers it is clear that there are, at present, two different opinions as to the original state of our planet. One postulates that the Earth was originally molten (Fesenkov) while, according to the other, the Earth was relatively cold, or, more accurately, its original temperature was not above that of its melting point (Urey, Shmidt). Both hypotheses postulate the agglomeration of the planet from a dispersed medium. The second opinion is increasingly supplanting the first. It must be emphasized that, from the point of view of the question here being discussed, that of the origin of life on the Earth, we should be mainly interested in the conditions prevailing on its surface. Such being the case the following facts are of interest.

The temperature of the surface of the Earth is now determined exclusively by the activity of the Sun. Astronomical evidence about the evolution of the Earth shows that the luminosity of the Sun has not greatly altered during the time life has existed on the Earth and, thus, the action of the sun on the surface of the Earth has been relatively uniform.

These facts, in themselves, suggest that the conditions on the surface of the Earth which led up to the birth of life, existed for millions of years in the past.

A knowledge of the temperature of the internal depths of the Earth makes it possible to explain other factors without which the formation of life would have been impossible, namely the oxygen-containing atmosphere and the origin of water.

V. G. Fesenkov has formulated the requirements which must be met by a cosmogonic theory describing the thermal history of the Earth but, to satisfy these conditions, it is not necessary to proceed from the assumption that the Earth began by being molten. One may proceed on the basis of a theory that the Earth was not molten and was relatively cold, e.g. that of Schmidt.

Let us return to the facts. The question of natural radioactivity has now been fairly well studied by physicists. There are methods whereby the presence of radioactivity may be measured with extreme accuracy. Many measurements of radioactivity, both of terrestrial formations and of meteorites arriving from space, show that, as a rule, radioactivity is present in all formations. Radioactive elements are dispersed. The amount of radioactive material is extremely small, from 1 to 0·01 ppm. However, if these fractions of a gram are considered over thousands of millions of years, they could have heated the depths of the interior of the Earth to some thousands of degrees.

Goldschmidt's concepts that the atoms of uranium and thorium have too great a volume to enter into any silicate lattice during crystallization should, it seems, now be reconsidered. Studies of the structure of olivine, a basic component of the Earth show that its structure contains a sufficient number of large holes to accommodate foreign atoms. [This work was carried out by Belov and his colleagues at the Institute of Crystallography of the Academy of Sciences of the U.S.S.R.] Therefore we cannot believe that the radioactive atoms are concentrated in the Earth's crust only. They may be widespread over the silicate mantle of the Earth.

Furthermore, the radioactivity of ^{40}K has been investigated during the last decade. This is known not to be a rare element but to be widely distributed in nature. The heat given out by the breakdown of potassium played a considerable part in the history of the Earth. Most contemporary students of the thermal history of the Earth (Verhogen, Birch, Jacobs, Allan) consider that there is no reason to suppose that radioactive sources of heat are completely absent at a great depth within the Earth and believe them to be one of the main sources of its heat. They gradually heated the deepest parts of the interior of the Earth without making any associated change in the mean annual temperature of the surface. Our calculations, based on the assumption that the mean composition of the Earth corresponds with the mean composition of stony and iron meteorites, show that the Earth as a whole has never been molten. However, beneath the crust of the Earth the conditions are suitable for the formation of molten foci which might be associated with volcanic activity. In the past the layer in which molten foci could be formed was considerably nearer the surface than it is now and volcanic activity was greater.

Outflows of lava enabled the continents to extend. This concept is confirmed by the works of Rubey, Wilson, Magnitskiĭ and Vinogradov. The vapours given off during eruptions condensed to water.

While this was happening the mean temperature of the surface remained much what it is now and this, it would seem, must have been more favourable for the emergence of life than the extremely high temperatures entailed by the hypothesis that the Earth was originally molten.

V. V. ALPATOV (U.S.S.R.):

I should like to draw special attention to the problem of the optical activity of protoplasm and its components in connection with the origin of life on the Earth. Pasteur made one of the most outstanding discoveries of the last century in the biological field. He demonstrated a fundamental molecular difference between living and non-living matter, namely, the inequality of the number of molecules of the *dextro* and *laevo* forms in materials derived from organisms. This dissymmetry of life is not only expressed at the molecular level, it also manifests itself in the structure of the bodies of plants and animals. My experiments, published over the past decade in *Dokl. Akad. Nauk S.S.S.R.*, give reason for the belief that the dissymmetry of the form of the bodies of organisms is closely associated with the dissymmetry of the molecules of which they are composed. It is interesting to consider the distribution over the surface of the globe of populations of right-handed and left-handed organisms. I shall adduce only two examples from my own personal experiments. Among the colonies of the bacterium *Bacillus mycoides*, which resemble spiral nebulae, there are some which are right-handed and other which are left-handed. My colleague O. K. Rossolimo (1948) has shown that the whole territory of the Soviet Union is inhabited by colonies of one type, and only in the Caucasus, in the Ussuriĭ region and in Tyan-Shan, where there are relicts of ancient floras and faunas of the Tertiary period, estimated as being more than a million years old, and also in the tropics, do mixed populations, forming left-handed and right-handed colonies, predominate. In many hundreds of species of higher plants I have investigated the direction of the spiral vascular bundles. It was found that the great majority of species of the flora of the Soviet Union (about 93%) have only left-handed vascular bundles. In about 2% of species they were right-handed and in about 4% of species they were of both sorts, i.e. they were racemic. Tropical families of plants—Begoniaceae, Balsaminaceae and Orchidaceae—are either right-handed or racemic. From these two examples it follows that the nearer we get to the equator the greater is the prevalence of racemic populations. This distribution suggests that either the racemic form is characteristic of more ancient types, the tropical flora and fauna being more ancient than those of higher latitudes, or else that at the equator some other factors are constantly at work, for example, the passage of the Sun through the zenith, which maintains the incidence of left and right forms better than at higher latitudes. It would be desirable to collect more material on this subject in both the northern and southern hemispheres. This would require the co-ordinated participation, in the work, of biologists of all countries of the world.

A. S. Konikova (U.S.S.R.):

Prof. Bernal's address is of great interest to this conference.

He put forward hypotheses which are extremely important for working out the problem of life but they are not all incontrovertible. I shall permit myself to dwell on some which seem to me to require further clarification.

With regard to the scheme of biopoesis presented for our attention, I should like to say the following: this is rather a scheme of the development of Nature in general than a scheme of the origin of life. It shows the progressive motion of nature but the specific transition from non-living to living nature is not shown in it.

The whole scheme contains no reference to the appearance of the phenomenon of self-development in some compounds and, therefore, nowhere in it is a boundary drawn between that which is still not living and that which is already living. Even when there developed an eobiont-nucleoproteid, which is capable of self-reproduction, according to the scheme it could only reproduce exactly the same nucleoproteid: the eobiont is not capable of self-development as well as the other complicated forms of matter set forth in the scheme up to the point of the appearance of the organism.

I suggest that the absence of the specific elements of life from Prof. Bernal's scheme of biopoiesis is due to an inaccurate definition of the concept of life by this speaker.

According to this definition, the concept of life is 'the embodiment within a certain volume of self-maintaining chemical processes'. But any reversible chemical reaction in non-living nature would come within that definition.

I suggest that this is not the most adequate and authentic definition of life which we can give on the basis of the contemporary level of studies of the subject. A more correct definition would seem to be one which does not reflect the factor of the self-maintaining properties of particular substances but, rather, the factor of their self-development, which does not appear outside living nature. Of course, with the emergence of life, the factor of self-development of matter does not manifest itself in the material world in general in the form of a process of creation of more and more new substances, but within the confines of particular chemical substances.

A living thing is a chemical substance or complex which, by a process of chemical reactions with the substances of its surroundings, accomplishes its reproduction and development, i.e. it remains itself while yet changing (not only in the direction of decay).

Life is the attainment, by a chemical substance, of the ability to rebuild itself by interacting with other chemical substances, remaining like itself and beginning to be different from itself. This factor of a qualitative break in Nature associated with the emergence of a chemical substance of such a kind that, in reproducing itself, it developed, is not to be seen in the whole of the suggested scheme of biopoesis, starting with the simplest organic molecules and finishing with cells.

The scheme provides a correct and consistent materialist picture of the form of development of nature but does not disclose the main point of these stages of development: it does not reflect the transition from chemistry to biology. In other words, it does not reflect the essential dissimilarity—the boundary between these two forms of the motion of matter, one of which obviously precedes the other.

It would also have been desirable for the scheme of biopoesis to have shown the specific characteristics of life.

J. D. Bernal (Great Britain):

The concept of organic evolution cannot be applied logically to early stages of biopoesis because it implies the prior setting up of a system of quasi-perfect reproduction. This is now maintained by a genetic mechanism based on deoxyribonucleic acid. Before this mechanism existed offspring could only have a rough resemblance to their parents and every act of reproduction was a measurable step in evolution. The evolutionary staircase, which consists of long runs of unaltered reproduction separated at intervals by sudden mutations, must in its early stages have been more like an irregular ramp.

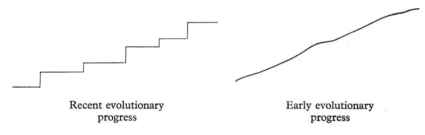

Recent evolutionary
progress

Early evolutionary
progress

N. H. Horowitz (U.S.A.):

Prof. Bernal and I appear to differ in our definitions of life. He considers as alive chemical systems which I do not. I do not have time to elaborate on this difference of opinion, but my reasons for preferring my own view were stated in my paper.

N. W. Pirie (Great Britain):

Like some painters, Dr Horowitz seems to see life in the strong primary colours—or even in black and white. I see more shades and so disagree with almost all his simplifications.

First he says he does not believe in a continuous transition between living and non-living because he has not seen it. Nor has anyone else, because our idea is not that it still exists but that it once did. As Darwin, Tyndall and others pointed out many years ago, any eobiont that appeared now would be promptly eaten.

To demand that a living system should mutate is a purely linguistic restriction and it leads to absurdities. Only a tiny fraction of the organisms that are universally accepted as living have been shown to mutate though many of them probably do. But some very ancient species do not seem to mutate very much.

It is important to distinguish more clearly than Horowitz does between at least three types of multiplication: Multiplication in many-celled organisms where the process can fail, as in worker bees and mules, although the organism is obviously still alive. Multiplication in single cells of an organism, or in single-celled organisms, which can be absent as in the brain, although the tissue is obviously still alive. And the multiplication of cell components such as genes, microsomes and mitochondria. Here there is absolutely no reason to postulate any form of autosynthesis—it is probably the system that makes another gene rather than the gene that makes a copy of itself. If we accept all these different types of reproduction, it is unlikely that the ability to reproduce could be used as an adequate criterion of life.

A. E. Braunshteĭn (U.S.S.R.):

Prof. Horowitz has put forward the view that single molecules might be alive. He refers to the molecules of deoxyribonucleic acid of genes, which have the power of self-reproduction and self-development (variability). In this sense viral nucleic acids could also be said to be alive.

Attacking the viewpoint that a multimolecular system is necessary for the development of qualities of life, at the end of his paper Prof. Horowitz ingeniously defined the minimal living unit as 'a living molecule in a multimolecular environment'.

However, if this definition is to describe the position accurately *one word* must be added, so that it reads ' . . . in a multimolecular *living* environment'. By doing this, however, the idea contained in Prof. Horowitz's definition is negated.

A. Kravtsov (U.S.S.R.):

The Non-organic Origin of Methane and Its Homologues in Igneous Formations

Many years of investigation by the Department of Combustible Minerals at the Moscow Geological-Prospecting Institute have enabled us to draw the conclusion that the fuel gases, hydrogen, methane and its homologues, which are contained in the formations of the Khibinsk alkaline massif, were formed within those formations.

Methane and the heavier hydrocarbons and hydrogen can be produced as a result of the formation of igneous rocks from magma. Furthermore, owing to the action of radioactive radiations, such gases as H_2, O_2, CH_4, CO and CO_2 may be formed.

We have shown that H_2 and CO were the starting materials for the formation of hydrocarbons, the reaction being, for example, as follows: $4CO + 2H_2O \rightarrow CH_4 + 3CO_2$ (the water is present as vapour). Hydrogen is formed by the action of aqueous vapours on the iron-containing silicates which enter into the composition of rock formations, at temperatures of 600–800 ° C, according to the equation $2FeO + H_2O \rightarrow Fe_2O_3 + H_2$.

Various hydrocarbons are formed by the action of hydrogen on CO or CO_2.

The inflammable gaseous components referred to are formed at great depths and then migrate (are translocated) to the surface. We suppose that this whole process occurs according to the following scheme: At great depths there is migration (translocation) of the separate gaseous components (H_2, CO, CO_2, etc.). The hydrogen, being the most easily diffusible gas, reaches the surface more quickly than the rest. The diffusion of hydrogen occurs, not only through crevices, but also through the crystalline lattices of the minerals of which rocky formations are composed (the Khibinsk massif in particular). Later, in order of diminishing rates of migration to the surface, there appear methane, and to a lesser extent, its homologues.

Methane and its homologues leave the magmatic formations and enter a stratum of sedimentary deposit where, if the thermodynamic conditions and hydrostatic pressure are suitable, they cease to be gaseous and become liquid. This seems to us to be the way in which condensation petroleum is formed.

We have no basis for explaining the presence of inflammable gases in the igneous formations of the Kola peninsula as being derived from organic substances of sedimentary formations.

We must not be held prisoner by the deeply rooted ideas of some very highly authoritative scientists, that methane and its homologues (the heavier hydrocarbons) are formed in any considerable amount only as a result of the transformation of organic material. All this is a result of the fact that many workers dogmatically repeat the theory of petroleum formation put forward by I. M. Gubkin in his own time. It is now time to make a radical revision of our ideas about the nature of the inflammable gases in petroleum. We do not wish, in the least, to belittle the tremendous part played by that outstanding scientist I. M. Gubkin in the development of petroleum geology in our country. All the same, we must boldly eradicate incorrect explanations of any natural phenomena if this is required by the facts. This must be done in the matter of the origin of the combustible gases and of petroleum. The demonstration of the inorganic origin of considerable amounts of methane and heavier hydrocarbons in igneous formations is of great significance in the deliberations of this present session about the question of the origin of life on the Earth, based, as they are, on the ideas which have been developed in recent years by A. I. Oparin & V. G. Fesenkov.

The question of hydrocarbons and other carbon-containing substances in igneous formations, therefore, requires special and deep study. In the course of this, methods must be worked out for the more detailed analysis of gases and a series of such determinations must be made on types of igneous formations of different geological ages. In this connection we shall watch with great interest the investigations of formations of the fundament (pre-Cambrian) of the Ural–Volga region, the Ukrainian crystalline massif, Kamchatka, Elbruz and other places.

L. PAULING (U.S.A.):

In connection with the origin of life, I should like to say that it is sometimes easier to study a subject than to define it.

For many years I have been studying the nature of the chemical bond and I have even written a book about it, which has since been criticized. However, when I discussed this question with Prof. N. D. Sokolov, we found that it is extremely difficult to define a chemical bond.

The Transformation of
Primary Organic Compounds on the Earth

Formation of Organic Compounds on the Primitive Earth

STANLEY L. MILLER

Department of Biochemistry, College of Physicians and Surgeons, Columbia University, U.S.A.

ONE OF the most fundamental problems of biology is posed by the question, 'How did life arise on the Earth'. The Theory of Evolution offers an explanation for the development of complex multi-celled living organisms from single-celled organisms, but this theory does not explain the development of the first organism. To assume that life arose from inorganic matter presents overwhelming difficulties. Not only would a self-duplicating organism have to be made from the inorganic matter, but the organism would have to contain the complex apparatus to synthesize all its components and energy requirements from carbon dioxide, water and light.

Oparin [1] in his book *The Origin of Life* proposed that spontaneous generation of life would be less difficult if the ocean contained a large amount of complex organic compounds similar to those present in living organisms. These compounds would serve both as structural components and as the energy source for the first organisms. Oparin also proposed that the Earth had a reducing atmosphere of methane, ammonia, water and hydrogen in its early stages, and that organic compounds might be formed under these conditions. Bernal [2] has given a similar discussion.

Urey [3, 4] based his arguments for the reducing atmosphere on the thermodynamic properties of the gases in a cosmic dust cloud from which the solar system was formed. The equilibrium constants at 25 °C. for the reactions of the gaseous species are given in Table I.

TABLE I

	$K_{25}°$
$CO_2 + 4H_2 = CH_4 + 2H_2O$	7×10^{22}
$CO + 3H_2 = CH_4 + H_2O$	3×10^{26}
$C + 2H_2 = CH_4$	8×10^{8}
$N_2 + 3H_2 = 2NH_3$	7×10^{5}
$H_2 + \frac{1}{2}O_2 = H_2O$	4×10^{41}
$S + H_2 = H_2S$	6×10^{5}

These equilibria show that in the presence of hydrogen the carbon will be as methane, the nitrogen as ammonia and the oxygen as water. Urey proposed

123

that organic compounds might be synthesized by ultraviolet light and by electric discharges in the proposed reducing atmosphere.

Experimental support for these theories came from studies of the action of electric discharges on these gases [5–7]. The experimental results will be summarized, and some of their implications will be discussed.

As a basis for discussion the following model of the primitive Earth is proposed. The atmosphere was reducing and the oceans covered an appreciable fraction of the surface of the Earth. The temperature is assumed to have been less than 100°. The sources of energy for the production of the initial organic compounds were ultraviolet light, electric discharge and high temperatures (under local conditions such as volcanoes). Although the level of radioactivity was higher than at present, the energy available was still quite small, and there is no evidence that the cosmic ray intensity was ever large enough to compare with the energy from the sun.

The energy from ultraviolet light would probably be greater than that from electric discharges. Because of the difficulties of working with ultraviolet light in the region where the reduced gases would absorb (<2000 Å), electric discharges were used in the first experiments.

SPARK DISCHARGE—RUN 1

An approximation of the proposed model is shown in Fig. 1. The apparatus is made of Pyrex with tungsten electrodes. The water in the small flask is boiled to promote circulation and to bring water to the region of the spark. The products of the discharge are condensed and flow through the U-tube, which prevents circulation in the wrong direction. The non-volatile compounds accumulate in the small flask. The spark discharge is produced by a high frequency Tesla coil having a peak of 60,000 volts.

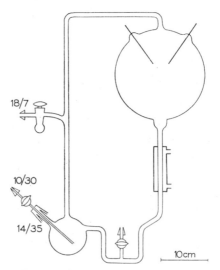

FIG. 1.   Spark-discharge apparatus

The pressures of hydrogen, methane, and ammonia were 10, 20 and 20 cm of Hg, respectively. During a run the water was boiled and the spark operated continuously. Colloidal silica, originating from the action of ammonia on glass, formed in the boiling flask during the run together with a yellow polymer. The yellow polymers have a strong ultraviolet absorption but no peaks above 230 mμ. The non-dialysable compounds were hydrolysed and chromatographed. Only a very small amount of amino acid was present in this fraction.

A red colour was formed with the spark discharge in some of the experiments. The synthesis of the colour seems to depend on the presence of trace metals. The colour is an organic compound and has absorption maxima at 390 and 540 mμ. It is not a porphyrin.

Analysis of Products

Analysis of the gases remaining at the end of a run showed carbon monoxide, carbon dioxide and nitrogen present in addition to the initial gases. The organic compounds were separated into acidic, basic, and ampholytic fractions by various ion-exchange resins. The different acids were separated by chromatography on silica [8] and the amino acids by chromatography on Dowex 50 [9]. The compounds were identified by R_F values on ion-exchange resins, silica, and on paper. Some of the compounds were further characterized by preparation of derivatives and comparing the melting point and mixed melting point with an authentic sample of the derivative.

TABLE 2

Yields of compounds (moles $\times$ 10^5)

	Spark Run 1	Silent discharge Run 3	N$_2$ Run Run 6
Glycine	63 (2·1)*	80 (0·46)*	14·2 (0·48)*
Alanine	34	9	1·0
Sarcosine	5	86	1·5
β-Alanine	15	4	7·0
α-Aminobutyric acid . . .	5	1	—
N-Methylalanine	1	12·5	—
Aspartic acid	0·4	0·2	0·3
Glutamic acid	0·6	0·5	0·5
Iminodiacetic acid . . .	5·5	0·3	3·9
Imino-acetic-propionic acid . .	1·5	—	—
Formic acid	233	149	135
Acetic acid	15·2	135	41
Propionic acid	12·6	19	22
Glycolic acid	56	28	32
Lactic acid	31	4·3	1·5
α-Hydroxybutyric acid . . .	5	1	—
Succinic acid	3·8	—	2
Urea	2	—	2
Methylurea	1·5	—	0·5
Sum of yields of compounds listed .	15%	3%	8%

* Percent yield of glycine, based on carbon placed in the apparatus as methane.

The optical rotation of a sample of alanine was $0.000 \pm 0.003°$. If this sample had been either pure enantiomorph, the rotation would have been $0.12°$. The yields of compounds from the various runs are shown in Table 2.

Absence of Purines and Pyrimidines

The mixture of compounds from a run similar to Run 1 was evaporated to dryness and the whole sample was chromatographed on a column of Dowex 50 (H^+) [10]. The eluent showed no 260 mμ absorption maximum where the naturally occurring purines and pyrimidines would have been eluted, and paper chromatography of the evaporated fractions showed no spots with an ultraviolet lamp. It is concluded that the presence of any purine was less than 0.2×10^{-5} moles and of any pyrimidine was less than 0.1×10^{-5} moles.

The Effect of Adding Ferrous Ammonium Sulphate

Since iron is one of the more abundant elements on the Earth, and would be present as both the metal and ferrous compounds, an experiment was performed to compare the organic compounds synthesized by a spark discharge in the system with and without added ferrous ammonium sulphate. About 16% of the iron had been oxidized to ferric by the end of the run. The organic compounds were the same as in Run 1, and the quantitative values were only slightly different.

THE SILENT DISCHARGE—RUN 3

An experiment was performed using a silent electrical discharge (ozonizer) instead of a spark. As seen in Table 2, the yields are about one-fourth that of the spark, but the products are similar.

SPARKING A MIXTURE OF METHANE, NITROGEN, WATER AND HYDROGEN—RUN 6

The equilibrium constant for the reaction $N_2 + 3H_2 = 2NH_3$ is 7×10^5 atm^{-2}, at $25°$, which predicts that the nitrogen would remain as ammonia instead of N_2 until the partial pressure of hydrogen fell below 10^{-2} atm by escape into outer space. However, the disruptive effect of ultraviolet light and electric discharges might result in a steady-state concentration of ammonia less than the equilibrium value. To see which organic compound would be formed under these conditions, a mixture of methane, nitrogen, hydrogen, and water was sparked. The same products are formed as in Run 1, but the yields are somewhat less.

THE MECHANISM OF SYNTHESIS

There is the question of whether the compounds observed in this system were synthesized by micro-organisms. To check this point, blank runs with the same gases but no spark were made. The amino acid production was less than 10 μg. There is the possibility that the micro-organisms might synthesize amino acids from some of the products of the discharge. To check this point the apparatus was filled with water and the reduced gases, sealed, autoclaved for 18 hours at $130°$, and sparked for one week. The yield of organic compounds was the same as in runs without autoclaving. In addition the apparatus was 80–100° during the run, the alanine was racemic, and the organic compounds do not represent the distribution one would expect if produced by living organisms. For these reasons it is stated with confidence that the organic compounds in the system were synthesized without the aid of micro-organisms.

The next problem in attempting to understand the chemistry of the system is to determine which compounds are formed in the electric discharge and which reactions are taking place in the solution phase of the system. The following alternative hypotheses will be made for the synthesis of the products: (1) Hydrogen cyanide, aldehydes, acrylonitrile, aliphatic nitriles, amines and part of the polymers are synthesized in the electric discharge, and the amino, hydroxy and aliphatic acids are formed by hydrolysis of the respective nitriles in the solution. (2) All the products identified were synthesized in the gas phase from radicals and ions formed in the electric discharge.

In order to determine a few of the direct products of the electric discharge, samples were withdrawn from the U-tube during the course of a run. Hydrogen cyanide was qualitatively detected by the Prussian Blue test and estimated by titration with AgNO₃. Formaldehyde was detected qualitatively by chromotropic acid and acetaldehyde by *p*-hydroxydiphenyl [11]. The total aldehydes (and ketones) were estimated with 2:4-dinitrophenylhydrazine [12].

Figure 2 shows the concentrations of ammonia, hydrogen cyanide, and aldehydes in the U-tube and amino acids in the 500 ml flask during the sparking of a mixture of methane, ammonia, water and hydrogen. It is seen that the

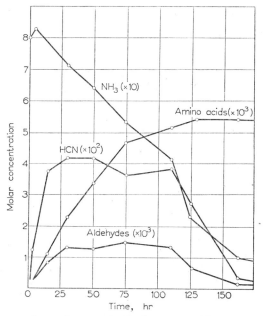

FIG. 2. Concentrations of ammonia, hydrogen cyanide and aldehydes in the U-tube, and amino acids in the 500 ml flask while sparking a mixture of methane, ammonia, water, and hydrogen in the apparatus of Fig. 1.

concentration of ammonia decreased steadily during the run, mostly due to decomposition of the ammonia to hydrogen and nitrogen in the discharge. The hydrogen cyanide concentration rose to 4×10^{-2} M, and after 120 hours apparently little more was synthesized in the spark. Thereafter the hydrogen cyanide present was hydrolysed to formic acid or decomposed in the spark. The aldehyde concentration rose to about 10^{-3} M and declined after 120 hours. The concentration of amino acids rose during the run and levelled off after about 140 hours.

Several repetitions of this experiment gave concentrations of these compounds of the same order of magnitude, but the values were not reproducible in detail. Probably the most important variable that could not be controlled was the operation of the spark.

Hydrolysis of Amino- and Hydroxynitriles—Run 4

Hydrogen cyanide, aldehydes and ammonia are known to react to give amino- and hydroxy-nitriles. There is a question of whether the conditions of this experiment will hydrolyse these nitriles to the corresponding acid. A solution of 63 m-moles NH_3 (corresponding to 25 cm Hg pressure), 20 m-moles hydrogen cyanide, 6·1 m-moles formaldehyde, 3·64 m-moles acetaldehyde and 1·16 m-moles propionaldehyde (in 325 ml H_2O) was boiled in the apparatus for a week. The glycine, glycolic acid, iminodiacetic acid and imino-aceticpropionic acid accounted for 52% of the formaldehyde; alanine, lactic acid and imino-acetic-propionic acid accounted for 58% of the acetaldehyde; α-amino-n-butyric acid and α-hydroxy-butyric acid accounted for 36% of the propionaldehyde. This experiment shows that aminonitriles and hydroxynitriles can be hydrolysed in this system, and further that the amino and hydroxy acids are formed in good yield from the aldehyde.

By titrating samples withdrawn from the U-tube for hydrogen cyanide during the course of the run, the rate constant for hydrolysis of hydrogen cyanide to formic acid is estimated to be 0·1 hr^{-1}. Similarly by determining the amino acid concentration in the 500 ml flask at various times, the rate constant for hydrolysis of the aminonitriles is estimated to be 0·2 hr^{-1}.

From these rate data and the concentrations in Fig. 2 the yield of formic acid from hydrolysis of hydrogen cyanide is calculated to be 3·6 m-moles and the yield of amino acids from hydrolysis of the aminonitriles is calculated to be 1·4 m-moles. These values agree within the experimental error with the observed yields of 2·4 m-moles of formic acid and 1·2 m-moles of amino acids. Thus in the case of the spark discharge, the rates of hydrolysis under the conditions of the experiment are sufficient to account for the total yields of formic acid and amino acids observed.

The Ratios of Products

Further evidence that the synthesis of the amino and hydroxy acids is through the corresponding nitrile can be obtained by considering the ratios of products predicted by this mechanism.

It can be shown [6] that if the reaction of the aldehyde, hydrogen cyanide, and ammonia to form the amino- and hydroxy-nitriles is a rapid and reversible equilibrium and that the hydrolysis is a first-order irreversible reaction, then the ratio of hydroxy acid to amino acid at the end of the run will be

$$R_1 = h_i H_i / k_i K_i (NH_3), \tag{1}$$

where H_i and K_i are the equilibrium constants for the formation of the hydroxy and aminonitrile from aldehydes, and h_i and k_i are the respective rates of hydrolysis. Similarly we have

$$R_2 = N\text{-methylamino acid/amino acid}$$
$$= -m_i M_i (CH_3 NH_2) / k_i K_i (NH_3),$$

where M_i and m_i are the equilibrium constant and rate constant of hydrolysis of the methylaminonitrile.

β-Alanine cannot arise from a Strecker synthesis as with the α-amino acids. A reasonable mechanism would be from a Michael addition of ammonia to acrylonitrile, acrylamide or acrylic acid. One would expect that hydrogen cyanide and methylamine would also add to give, after hydrolysis, succinic acid and N-methyl-β-alanine. N-Methyl-β-alanine was not detected during the analysis since it does not react with ninhydrin. The rate of formation of the nitrile of β-alanine and succinonitrile would be

$$K_{NH_3} (NH_3) (CH_2 = CHCN) \text{ and } K_{HCN} (CN^-) (CH_2 = CHCN),$$

respectively, where the K's are the rate constants for addition. Assuming that the addition is irreversible and that the nitriles are hydrolysed by the end of the run, then

$$(\text{Succinic acid})/(\beta\text{-Alanine}) = K_{HCN} (CN^-)/K_{NH_3} (NH_3).$$

This treatment is easily generalized to include additions to acrylonitrile and acrylic acid. The ratios of products are given in Table 3.

If the ratio hH/kK does not depend on the aldehyde, then equation 1 predicts that the ratio of the hydroxy acid to the amino acid should be the same for the different aldehydes in a given run. The agreement is good for the spark discharge and silent discharge except for hydroxybutyric/aminobutyric in the silent discharge. In Run 4 the hydrolysis of the amino- and hydroxy-nitriles was necessarily the mechanism for synthesis of the respective acids. There is less agreement of the ratios than with the electric discharges, but the agreement is within the errors of the experiment.

Similarly the ratios of methylamino acid/amino acid are nearly the same for Run 1 and 3. The succinic acid/β-alanine ratio is the same in Runs 1 and 6.

The ratios of various products are in qualitative agreement in all cases and in quantitative agreement (within the experimental error) in most of the cases. The similarity of products in Runs 1 and 4 is striking (except for the expected absence of β-alanine and succinic acid since no acrylonitrile was added), suggesting that the products were formed by the same mechanism.

9

TABLE 3

Ratios of products

	Spark Run 1	Silent Run 3	N₂ Run Run 6	Aldehydes HCN, NH₃, Run 4
Glycolic / Glycine	0·89	0·35	2·3	0·73
Lactic / Alanine	0·91	0·48	1·5	0·33
Hydroxybutyric / Aminobutyric	1	1	—	0·55
Sarcosine / Glycine	0·08	1·07	0·11	—
Methylalanine / Alanine	0·03	1·4	—	—
Succinic / β-Alanine	0·25	—	0·29	—

Since the production of aldehydes and hydrogen cyanide is sufficient to account for the observed yield of amino acid, there can be little doubt that most of the amino and hydroxy acids were formed from the nitriles in Run 1. However, these experiments do not exclude the possibility that a small percentage of the amino acids was formed directly in the spark, entirely by radical reactions*.

The synthesis of the products expected from acrylonitrile and the agreement of the ratios of these products in the different runs provides strong indirect evidence for the synthesis of β-alanine and succinic acid by β-addition, and in turn that acrylonitrile or derivatives were synthesized in the electric discharges.

If cyanate were formed in the electric discharge, then both urea and methylurea could be expected of reaction with ammonia and methylamine (Wöhler synthesis). The direct synthesis of the simple ureas in the electric discharge is also quite reasonable.

DISCUSSION

Assuming that the Earth initially had a reducing atmosphere, do the experimental results obtained in this very simple system show that amino acids or other organic compounds would be present in the ocean? The experiments on the mechanism of the electric-discharge synthesis of amino acids indicate that a special set of conditions or type of electrical discharge is not required to obtain amino acids. Any process or combination of processes that yielded both alde-

---

* The hydrogen cyanide concentration in the silent discharge case is too low to account for the yield of amino acids unless the hydrolysis of the nitriles is more rapid than in Run 1. Hydrogen peroxide catalysis is a possibility. The ratios of products in the various runs is strong evidence that the products were formed by the same mechanism.

hydes and hydrogen cyanide would have contributed to the amount of α-amino acids in the hydrosphere of the primitive Earth. Therefore, electric discharges are not critical for the synthesis of amino acids, and similar results could be expected from ultraviolet light.

The ultraviolet light emitted by the sun as black-body radiation amounts to 85 cal cm^{-2} yr^{-1} for wavelengths less than 2000 Å and 1·6 cal cm^{-2} yr^{-1} for wavelengths less than 1500 Å [4]. Superimposed on the black-body radiation is a strong Lyman α-line at 1216 Å of 1·9 cal cm^{-2} yr^{-1} [13]. This line is absorbed by CH_4, H_2O, NH_3 and CO.

Hydrogen atoms from photolysis of CH_4, NH_3 and H_2O would react with CO to give formaldehyde [14, 15]. Carbon monoxide activated by wavelengths less than 1545 Å reacts with H_2 to give formaldehyde and glyoxal [16]. Hydroxyl radicals would react with hydrocarbons to give aldehydes [17]. If any O atoms should be formed by photolysis of water or CO, they would react rapidly with H_2 to give H_2O and with hydrocarbons to give aldehydes*.

Active nitrogen, probably N atoms in the ^4S state [18, 19], reacts with methane and other hydrocarbons to give hydrogen cyanide in good yield [20]. Photo-dissociation of N_2 ($>$1100 Å) or NH radicals give N atoms. NH and NH_2 radicals from the photolysis of ammonia might react with hydrocarbons to give hydrogen cyanide, but this has not yet been demonstrated.

The reactions outlined above show that aldehydes and hydrogen cyanide would be produced photochemically, and there probably are other photochemical reactions that would also give these compounds†.

Infra-red radiation by the polyatomic molecules of the reducing atmosphere would probably result in a cool atmosphere and ocean rather than the boiling temperatures used in these experiments or the molten Earth proposed by some workers. However if there were any local areas of high temperature, hydrogen cyanide would be formed [21], and aldehydes might be synthesized from hydro-carbons and carbon monoxide by reactions analogous to the Fischer–Tropsch or hydroformalation reactions [22].

If the conditions on the Earth were cool, then the hydrolysis of the nitriles would still take place, but more slowly than in these experiments. The Strecker synthesis of amino acids will work at much lower concentrations of aldehyde and hydrogen cyanide than obtained in these experiments. At very low concentrations, however, the Strecker synthesis will not operate. The rate of synthesis of amino acid is given by

$$- d\,(HCN)/dt = kK\,(NH_3)\,(RCHO)\,(HCN)$$

* If aldehydes were synthesized from the Lyman α-radiation with a quantum yield of 1·0, then yield for the Earth would be $2 \cdot 10^{13}$ moles yr^{-1}. If the aldehydes were dissolved in the present oceans this would give a solution of $3 \cdot 10^{-8}$ M. Of course, the efficiency of the Lyman radiation would not have been 100%, but the oceans would probably have been smaller in volume, and the electric discharges and temperature reactions would contribute to the aldehyde production.

† Some preliminary experiments performed at Brookhaven National Laboratory showed that the 1850 Å mercury line will synthesize amino acids from CH_4, NH_3, and H_2O. Only NH_3 and H_2O absorb this line but apparently the radical reactions formed the active carbon intermediates. Formaldehyde was detected. The yield of amino acids was very low.

The kK (RCHO) means the sum of this term over the different aldehydes. The hydrolysis of hydrogen cyanide to formic acid is a competing reaction with the rate

$$- \,\mathrm{d}\,(\mathrm{HCN})/\mathrm{d}t = r\,(\mathrm{HCN})$$

where r is the rate constant for the hydrolysis of hydrogen cyanide. Thus if the concentrations of aldehydes are so low that $kK(\mathrm{NH_3})(\mathrm{RCHO})/r \ll 1$, then cyanide will not be available for the Strecker synthesis because of hydrolysis to formic acid. It is necessary to know the values of K, k, H, h, and r, their pH and temperature dependence for a quantitative treatment of this problem.

From a qualitative standpoint it can be seen that the Strecker synthesis will operate in very dilute solutions. The H for acetaldehyde at $25°$ is 1.4×10^4 [23] and the K is probably greater. The experiments reported here indicate that h, k, and r are of the same order of magnitude. Thus the hydrolysis of the nitriles in the hydrosphere is by the same mechanism as in these experiments (probably OH^- attack on the carbon of the nitrile) then (RCHO) can be as low as 10^{-4} or 10^{-5} M and the Strecker synthesis will still operate. If the value of k relative to r (and h) is increased by catalytic hydrolysis (e.g., SH^-, HPO_4^-) then the concentration of aldehydes could be much lower.

The ratio of hydroxy acid to amino acid is given by equation (1). If the concentration of ammonia is very low and (RCHO) and (HCN) are high enough, then hydroxy acid will be synthesized rather than amino acid or formic acid.

There are competing reactions which the aldehyde can undergo instead of a Strecker synthesis. The aldehydes can be reduced or oxidized, the latter being important if any oxygen were present. The most important competing reaction would be aldol condensations. These condensations would give products that are of biological importance such as trioses, tetroses, pentoses and hexoses. The rate of these condensations relative to the Strecker synthesis would not depend markedly on the concentrations of aldehydes, since the aldol condensations would be second-order reactions. Therefore, the competing reactions of the aldehydes would not predominate at low concentrations.

The composition of the primitive Earth atmosphere has been assumed to be reducing in the above discussion. The general geochemical argument for the reducing atmosphere, advanced by Oparin and Urey, is that the ratio of hydrogen to oxygen in the Universe is about a thousand to one, the Earth being rather anomalous. No one has shown any mechanism which, before the planets were formed, would produce oxygen in the region of the Earth but not in the region beyond Mars. The formation of oxidizing conditions on Mercury, Venus, Earth, and Mars after their formation is explained by the escape of hydrogen from these planets. Their atmospheres are hot enough and their gravitational fields weak enough so that hydrogen can escape into outer space from the atmosphere. The escape of the strong reducing agent H_2 results in oxidizing atmosphere. In the region beyond Mars, the planets are at low temperature and have a high gravitational field. These conditions prohibit the escape of hydrogen from their atmospheres, as a result of which they are still reducing.

A second argument for the existence of a reducing atmosphere on the primitive Earth is based on the assumption that for life to arise there must be present first a large number of organic compounds similar to those that would make up the first organism. Therefore, if it can be shown that the organic compounds which make up living systems cannot be synthesized under oxidizing conditions, and if it can be shown that these organic componds can be synthesized under reducing conditions, then one conclusion would be that the Earth had a reducing atmosphere in its early stages and that life arose from the sea of organic compounds formed while the Earth had this atmosphere.

From a review of the literature on electric discharges [24] and ultraviolet light [25], from the result of the experiments described in this paper, and from the first part of this discussion, one can see that organic compounds can be easily synthesized under reducing conditions.

There have been many attempts to synthesize organic compounds under oxidizing conditions, usually from carbon dioxide and water, and these attempts have almost always failed. A review of these attempts using ultraviolet light [26] shows that success was claimed by some workers, but when their experiments were repeated in other laboratories or when contaminating reducing agents were removed, no organic compounds were synthesized. The action of electric discharges on carbon dioxide and water has also resulted in failure [27]. Of course, if a strong reducing agent such as Na or Mg is used, organic compounds can be formed, but these reducing agents would not be present on the Earth with either a reducing or an oxidizing atmosphere. High-energy radiations on ammonium carbonate solutions might give organic compounds, but the presence of ammonia would imply reducing conditions.

There has been one successful synthesis of organic compounds from carbon dioxide and water using 40 million electron volt helium ions from a 60-inch cyclotron [28, 29]. Formic acid was obtained in small yield, and if ferrous ion was added to the solution as a reducing agent then a small yield of formaldehyde was obtained in addition to formic acid. In view of the absence of a strong source of high-energy particles, the small yields, and the very simple organic compounds synthesized, it would seem that instead of showing that organic compounds can be synthesized this experiment can best be interpreted to mean that organic compounds cannot be effectively synthesized under oxidizing conditions.

If any organic compounds should be synthesized under oxidizing conditions, however difficult this may be, then the question of their stability arises. In the presence of molecular oxygen the organic compounds would be oxidized rather rapidly, especially in the presence of light [30]. An important reaction of the oxygen would be the oxidative deamination of the amino acids. This reaction is catalysed by blood charcoal and probably by many iron compounds [31]. The oxidative deamination is a significant reaction even in the absence of catalysts [32]. Oxygen would also attack aromatic compounds such as the purines and pyrimidines, especially in the presence of light. These arguments make a strong case that free oxygen must have been absent when the organic compounds were formed and also absent during the development of heterotrophic organisms. Shortly after the appearance of oxygen on the Earth the autotrophic organisms would have to develop, for otherwise the nutrients would be rapidly exhausted.

If the Strecker synthesis was the principal synthesis of amino acids on the primitive Earth, then ammonia must have been present in the ocean even though N_2 could be the principal nitrogen species in the atmosphere*.

This implies that the Earth must have been rather reducing, with a pressure of H_2 of at least 10^{-4} atmospheres, unless one is to assume that the amino acids were formed in limited areas containing reducing conditions.

This argument would not be valid if there are other reasonable syntheses of amino acids. One possibility would be the reductive amination of any a-keto acids present in the ocean, although decarboxylation of the keto acid would be a competing reaction. Another reaction would be synthesis of amino acids from a-keto aldehydes and ammonia catalysed by mercaptans [33, 34]. A possible source of the a-keto aldehydes would be from the oxidation of polyhydroxyl compounds obtained from aldehyde condensations. These two syntheses require ammonia, however. It is very difficult to see how an amino group can be synthesized directly from N_2 by any reasonable process except under reducing conditions. Reasonable syntheses of amino acids involving hydroxylamine, nitrites or nitrates would require strong reducing agents to convert the nitrogen to an amino group. A direct synthesis of the amino acids in an electric discharge, if possible, would probably require reducing conditions.

On the basis of primarily geochemical arguments Rubey [35] has argued that the primitive Earth had an atmosphere of carbon dioxide, nitrogen, carbon monoxide and water. This atmosphere would come mainly from the interior of the Earth instead of being the residual gases of the cosmic dust cloud. Abelson [36] has examined the action of a spark discharge on this mixture of gases and found that good yields of amino acids could be obtained as long as some hydrogen was present†. If no hydrogen was present, then no amino acids were obtained. The amino acid production was more rapid if CO_2, H_2O and NH_3 (instead of N_2) were used. The mechanism of the reaction was not investigated, but it may well be a Strecker synthesis as in the methane, ammonia and water case.

Because of the presence of hydrogen in the gas mixtures used by Abelson, the mixtures were reducing although not as reducing as the methane, ammonia, water and hydrogen mixture. Therefore, the argument that reducing conditions are necessary to synthesize organic compounds is not altered, but whether the atmosphere was strongly reducing or only weakly reducing cannot be decided on the basis of ability to synthesize organic compounds.

As hydrogen escapes into outer space from a strongly reducing atmosphere, it becomes less reducing and finally becomes oxidizing. Thus the atmosphere proposed by Urey would be converted in the course of time to the atmosphere

---

* Ammonia is quite soluble in water. The vapour pressure in atmospheres is given by $P_{NH_3} = a\,[(NH_4OH) + (NH_4^+)]$, where the concentrations of NH_4OH and NH_4 are in moles/litre. For $25\,^{\circ}C$ a is $9 \cdot 3 \times 10^{-5}$ at pH = 7; $8 \cdot 8 \times 10^{-4}$ at pH = 8, and $6 \cdot 1 \times 10^{-3}$ at pH = 9. Thus unless the temperature of the ocean was rather high (70–100°) most of the ammonia would be in the ocean. The cyanide could be formed from the N_2 in the atmosphere (as in Run 6).

† The equilibrium constant for the reaction $CO_2 + 4H_2 = CH_4 + 2H_2O$ is 7×10^{21} at $25\,^{\circ}C$, so that the mixture of gases used by Abelson is thermodynamically unstable. Whether this equilibrium would be attained on the Earth is not predicted by thermodynamics, but carbon dioxide in the presence of hydrogen can be reduced to carbon monoxide and methane in electric discharges and probably by ultraviolet light.

proposed by Rubey. The principal question is the relative length of time that the Earth had these respective atmospheres. This question is not critical to the problem of spontaneous generation since organic compounds can be synthesized in both proposed atmospheres (provided Rubey's contains some hydrogen) and since the organic compounds would be similar in both cases.

REFERENCES

1. A. I. OPARIN, *The Origin of Life.* Macmillan, New York, 1938 (Republished by Dover Publications, 1953); (3rd ed.) *The Origin of Life on the Earth.* Oliver & Boyd, Edinburgh, 1957.
2. J. D. BERNAL, *Proc. phys. Soc. Lond.*, **62A**, 537; **62B**, 597, 1949.
3. H. C. UREY, *The Planets.* Yale Univ. Press, New Haven, 1952.
4. H. C. UREY, *Proc. nat. Acad. Sci., Wash.*, **38**, 351, 1952.
5. S. L. MILLER, *Science*, **117**, 528, 1953.
6. S. L. MILLER, *J. Amer. chem. Soc.*, **77**, 2351, 1955.
7. S. L. MILLER, *Biochim. biophys. Acta*, **23**, 480, 1957.
8. W. A. BULEN, J. E. VARNER & R. C. BURRELL, *Analyt. Chem.*, **24**, 187, 1952.
9. W. H. STEIN & S. MOORE, *Cold Spr. Harb. Symp. quant. Biol.*, **14**, 179, 1949.
10. J. S. WALL, *Analyt. Chem.*, **25**, 950, 1953.
11. B. A. NEIDIG & W. C. HESS, *Analyt. Chem.*, **24**, 1627, 1952.
12. G. R. LAPPIN & L. C. CLARK, *Analyt. Chem.*, **23**, 541, 1951.
13. W. A. RENSE, *Phys. Rev.*, **91**, 299, 1953.
14. A. CARESS & E. K. RIDEAL, *Proc. Roy. Soc.*, **A**, **120**, 370, 1928.
15. H. S. TAYLOR, *Trans. Faraday Soc.*, **21**, 560, 1926.
16. W. GROTH, *Z. phys. Chem.*, **37B**, 315, 1937.
17. N. A. MILAS, L. E. STAHL & B. B. DAYTON, *J. Amer. chem. Soc.*, **71**, 1448, 1949.
18. J. BERKOWITZ, W. A. CHUPKA & G. B. KISTIAKOWSKY, *J. chem. Phys.*, **25**, 457, 1956.
19. D. S. JACKSON & H. I. SCHIFF, *J. chem. Phys.*, **23**, 2333, 1955.
20. C. A. WINKLER & H. I. SCHIFF, *Disc. Faraday Soc.*, **14**, 63, 1953.
21. V. MIGRDICHIAN, *The Chemistry of Organic Cyanogen Compounds.* Reinhold, New York, p. 5, 1947.
22. H. H. STORCH, E. GOLUMBIC & R. B. ANDERSON, *The Fischer–Tropsch and Related Syntheses.* John Wiley, New York, 1951.
23. W. F. YATES & R. L. HEIDER, *J. Amer. chem. Soc.*, **74**, 4153, 1952.
24. G. GLOCKLER & S. C. LIND, *Electrochemistry of Gases and other Dielectrics.* John Wiley, New York, 1939.
25. W. A. NOYES, Jr., & P. A. LEIGHTON, *The Photochemistry of Gases.* Reinhold, New York, 1941.
26. E. RABINOWITCH, *Photosynthesis.* Interscience, New York, vol. I, p. 81, 1945.
27. K. A. WILDE, B. T. ZWOLINSKI & R. B. PARLIN, *Science*, **118**, 43, 1953.
28. W. M. GARRISON, D. C. MORRISON, J. G. HAMILTON, A. A. BENSON & M. CALVIN, *Science*, **114**, 416, 1951.
29. W. M. GARRISON & G. K. ROLLEFSON, *Disc. Faraday Soc.*, **12**, 155, 1952.
30. C. C. PALIT & N. R. DHAR, *J. phys. Chem.*, **34**, 993, 1930.
31. O. WARBURG, *Heavy Metal Prosthetic Groups and Enzyme Action.* Oxford Univ. Press, p. 38, 1949.
32. P. H. ABELSON, *Ann. N.Y. Acad. Sci.*, **92**, 276, 1957.
33. T. WIELAND, J. FRANZ & G. PFLEIDERER, *Ber. dtsch. chem. Ges.*, **88**, 641, 1955.
34. T. WIELAND & F. JAENICKE, *Ber. dtsch. chem. Ges.*, **88**, 1967, 1955.
35. W. W. RUBEY, *Spec. Pap. geol. Soc. Amer.*, **62**, 631, 1955.
36. P. H. ABELSON, *Science*, **124**, 935, 1956.

Photosynthesis in the Shortest Ultraviolet

A. N. TERENIN

University of Leningrad

THE PRIMITIVE atmosphere of the Earth, deprived of oxygen, was exposed to intense irradiation by the shortest ultraviolet wavelengths present in the solar radiation, but now screened off by oxygen and the ozone layer.

Investigation of the upper atmosphere with rockets equipped with spectral apparatus, and computation [1] have in fact revealed a high intensity of the solar radiation in the range of wavelengths shorter than 1850 Å, strongly absorbed by oxygen of the atmosphere and therefore not reaching the Earth's surface.

It was interesting to have some information about what kinds of organic compounds could be synthesized photochemically under the action of such a shortest ultraviolet spectral range, known as the Schuman region. The study of the photochemical dissociation of simple gas molecules under the action of light quanta in this range was started some 20 years ago by Harteck and Groth in Germany [2], by Leighton & Steiner in U.S.A. [3], and by us in U.S.S.R. [4].

In Fig. 1 are shown in a very simplified and schematic manner the spectral regions of absorption and photochemical sensitivity of some gases, which could form the primitive terrestrial atmosphere, namely ammonia, water, methane and carbon monoxide. The absorption by oxygen, beginning from 1850 Å on to the shorter wavelengths, shows that under ordinary laboratory conditions only ammonia can be subjected to photochemical change. The shorter ultraviolet wavelengths necessary to decompose water, methane and carbon monoxide are not transmitted through the air surrounding the radiation source and require either a vacuum on their path, or the substitution of the air by a gas transparent in this range, as for example hydrogen, to study their action.

In Fig. 1 alongside the wavelengths (given in Å) there is also given the scale of the energy values of the corresponding quanta, expressed, as is usual with physicists, in electron-volts. The sharp limits of the photochemically active ranges indicate approximately the thresholds, from which there begins the splitting of gas molecules into primary fragments—atoms and radicals, as shown in the figure. In addition, the dashed horizontal arrows indicate the final, stable products, formed as a result of subsequent reactions of these primary particles. The resulting quantum yield of the photolysis of CO under irradiation by λ 1295 Å is near to 1 [5]; for NH_3 and λ 1470 Å it is *ca.* 0·5 [15], and for H_2O vapour under irradiation by λ 1650 Å it can amount to 0·3, according to recent data [16]. For the photolysis of CH_4 the quantum yield is equal to 0·35–0·5 as judged from hydrogen evolution [6]. Of much help for the identification of these particles has been the photodissociation into emitting radicals, found by us in 1936 [4], which occurs at somewhat shorter thresholds, as indicated by an asterisk in Fig. 1 at the radicals concerned. The method of luminescent fragments also allows a direct observation of their further reactions, which is very important for disentangling the complicated path from the primary radicals to the stable final products. We studied recently with the aid of this method the reaction of the excited amino radical (NH_2^*) with methane by observing the quenching of its luminescence.

When a mixture of gases is present, there is in principle the possibility to activate only one component by light, for example the one possessing its threshold at the longest wavelength, e.g. ammonia, not affecting the others. In general, however, the radiation used activates more or less all the components of the gas mixture.

The strong monochromatic radiation of the xenon lamp (at 1295 Å) permitted Groth to activate the carbon monoxide molecules in mixtures with hydrogen

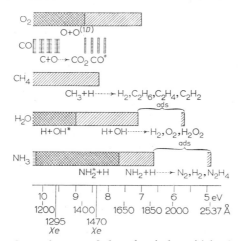

FIG. I.   Spectral ranges of photochemical sensitivity for gases

and methane [5]. In the last case however methane was also activated [6]. The final products in these cases, according to Groth, were:

$$CO + H_2 --\rightarrow CO_2, H_2O, H_2O_2, H_2CO, (HCO)_2$$
$$CO + CH_4 --\rightarrow H_2CO, (HCO)_2, \text{aldehydes}, H_2$$

Formaldehyde, glyoxal and other aldehydes are thus the products of photosynthesis from simple stable gases under the action of the shortest ultraviolet radiation. The quantum yield for the aldehydes from $CO + CH_4$ is about 0·1. Formaldehyde can also be produced by the action of the same shortest radiation upon a mixture of gaseous water with carbon dioxide [7].

Formamide can be obtained by the action of the ordinary short ultraviolet radiation ($\lambda > 1850$ Å) on a mixture of ammonia and carbon monoxide [8], only the former being activated, according to Fig. 1.

It must be mentioned that, although nitrogen is regarded as photochemically inert in this spectral range, since it is dissociated at much shorter wavelengths than the Schumann range, nevertheless metastable nitrogen molecules are here produced, as has been recently proved by Soviet scientists. They have observed in nitrogen irradiated by wavelengths in the Schumann range the emission of bands belonging to such high excited levels of the N_2 molecule, that they could be reached only by subsequent absorption of light by metastable molecules [9]. These metastable nitrogen molecules, possessing an extraordinary large amount of energy of 9·76 eV, must certainly display a definite chemical activity on collisions with H_2, CH_4, CO.

From the indicated composition of the primary, intermediary and final products of the photochemical transformation of the natural gases here considered it can be inferred that under favourable conditions from their combination not only aldehydes and amides, but amino acids can also result.

To test this possibility experimentally we—at Leningrad University, and independently Groth—at Bonn University [10], have tried to obtain the amino acids from a mixture of ammonia, water vapour and methane*. He exposed to Schumann radiation a mixture of CH_4 and NH_3 next to the surface of liquid water, and obtained a positive result: traces of glycine and of the alanines could be detected by chromatography†.

The conditions of our experiments differed from those of Groth in that respect, that he used the radiation of a krypton lamp, i.e. the two strong lines 1235 and 1165 Å, whereas we had a powerful hydrogen lamp of a type described before [4] with a many-lined and continuous spectrum in the Schumann range. The spectral distribution of energy in the latter is nearer to that of the sun than the separate monochromatic lines of the krypton source.

The various reaction cells used allowed us to irradiate not only the gaseous mixtures, but also layers of condensed gases frozen at low temperatures. This was done in order that the primarily formed radicals should remain trapped, and entered in subsequent reactions when the layer was warmed up.

On exposing a mixture of $CH_4 + NH_3 + CO$ and liquid water in contact with these gases to the radiation of the hydrogen lamp through a thin LiF (or CaF_2) window, we detected by chromatography in the product the alanines and several other amino acids, which latter could not be identified. The research is still going on.

In the presence of active adsorbents of the type of oxides there arises the possibility of photoactivation of NH_3 and H_2O to the reaction with methane by longer ultraviolet radiation ($\lambda > 1850$ Å). This follows from the photodissociation of NH_3 and H_2O molecules observed by us when these molecules are adsorbed on alumina, aluminosilicates and silicates.

Upon adsorption of gaseous ammonia on active aluminium oxide the threshold of its photolysis into nitrogen and hydrogen is shifted to considerably longer wavelengths, viz. from 1900 Å to 2700 Å [11] (Fig. 1)‡. Water molecules adsorbed

---

* The results have been reported by Groth at the last International Congress of Chemistry in Paris in July 1957.

† In his research Groth also tried the well-known photo-sensitization of the gas reactions to the longer ultraviolet, viz. to the mercury resonance line 2537 Å, which is achieved by adding mercury vapour to the gas mixture. It is the former which is the photo-active component. It was found that amino acids can also be detected in this case, not for methane as component, but for ethane only. This method has however no connection with the problem considered here.

‡ The horizontal bracket with the notation 'ads' on the figure represents this spectral shift.

on silicates are also decomposed in the range of $\lambda < 2300$ Å, rather than in the Schumann ultraviolet. The easier photolysis of water molecules in these heterogeneous conditions is explained by the fact that water forms at the surface of porous silicates, aluminosilicates and oxides superficial hydrates of the type

$$—Si—OH,$$

as observed by us in infra-red spectra [12]. The splitting of OH radicals from these hydrates requires quanta of lesser magnitude than does the photodissociation of gaseous water, as has been found by us recently [13].

This shift of the photochemically sensitive spectral range toward longer ultraviolet wavelengths, amounting to *ca.* 1 eV, or more than 20 kcal in energy, results in the accessibility of the photoreactions of these inert gases to the ordinary ultraviolet range, when they are adsorbed. This circumstance probably explains that puzzling fact that in early experiments done during the first decade of this century [14] it was found that water could be decomposed and even formaldehyde photosensitized from carbon monoxide and water in quartz vessels under irradiation by an ordinary mercury quartz lamp in which the wavelengths required to start this process (in unperturbed molecules) were cerainly lacking.

On summarizing my report, I consider it to be proved that aldehydes and amino acids could be formed from the gases of the primitive Earth atmosphere under the action of the shortest ultraviolet radiation of the sun. It is also likely that in heterogeneous environment such photosynthesis was possible in the longer ultraviolet range.

REFERENCES

1. C. DE JAGER, *Ann. Géophys.*, **11**, 330, 1955, Table 1; *Usp. fiz. Nauk*, **61**, 653, 1957.
2. P. HARTECK & F. OPPENHEIMER, *Z. phys. Chem.* B **16**, 77, 1932; W. GROTH, *Z. Elektrochem.*, **45**, 262, 1939; W. GROTH, *Z. Elektrochem.*, **58**, 752, 1954; W. GROTH & SCHARFF, *Z. phys. Chem. (Frankf. Ausg)*, **1**, 300, 1954; **2**, 142, 1954.
3. P. A. LEIGHTON & A. B. STEINER, *J. Amer. chem. Soc.*, **58**, 1823, 1936.
4. H. NEUIMIN & A. TERENIN, *Acta phys.-chim. U.R.S.S.*, **5**, 465, 1936; *Izv. Akad. Nauk S.S.S.R. (cl. sc. math., natur.)*, 529, 1936.
5. W. GROTH, *Z. phys. Chem.*, B **37**, 307, 315, 1937; K. FALTINGS, W. GROTH & P. HARTECK, *Z. phys. Chem.*, B **41**, 15, 1938; K. FALTINGS, *Ber. dtsch. chem. Ges.*, **72**, 1206, 1939.
6. W. GROTH, *Z. phys. Chem.*, B **38**, 366, 1938.
7. W. GROTH & H. SUESS, *Naturwissenschaften*, **26**, 77, 1938.
8. H. J. EMELEUS, *Trans. Faraday Soc.*, **28**, 89, 1932.
9. A. V. JAKOVLEVA, *Sow. Phys.*, **9**, 547, 1936; *Izv. Akad. Nauk S.S.S.R. (ser. fiz.)*, **4**, 59, 1940; I. I. GROMOVA, *Optics & Spectr.*, **1**, 433, 1956; *Trans. Xth Conf. on Spectroscopy, Lvov*, 1956 [Ed. Lvov Univ., 1957], p. 308.
10. W. GROTH & HAMIS v. WEYSSENHOFF, *Naturwissenschaften*, 510, 1957.
11. K. KASSPAROV & A. TERENIN, *Acta phys. chim. U.R.S.S.*, **15**, 348, 1941.
12. Cf. review: A. N. TERENIN, *Microchim. Acta*, H. **2–3**, 467, 1955.
13. Cf. review: A. N. TERENIN, in the Symposium *Problems of Kinetics and Catalysis VIII*, Ed. Acad. Sci. U.S.S.R., 1955, pp. 27–30.
14. D. BERTHELOT & H. GAUDECHON, *C.R. Acad. Sci., Paris*, **150**, 1690, 1910; M. KERNBAUM, *C.R. Acad. Sci., Paris*, **149**, 273, 1909; A. COEHN, *Ber. dtsch. chem. Ges.*, **43**, 880, 1910; A. COEHN & GROTE, *Nernst Festschr.*, S. 136, 1912; A. TIAN, *Ann. phys., Paris*, **5**, 248, 1916; J. ANDREJEW, *Z. Electrochem.*, **19**, 551, 1913.
15. H. JUCKER & E. K. RIDEAL, *J. chem. Soc.*, 1058, 1957.
16. MEI CHIO CHEN & H. A. TAYLOR, *J. chem. Phys.*, **27**, 857, 1957.

The Reactions Involved in the Formation of Compounds Preliminary to the Synthesis of Protoplasm and other Materials of Biological Importance

K. BAHADUR

Chemistry Department, Allahabad University, India

THE PROBLEM of the origin of life on Earth has always been a challenge to the thinking man. The ancient sages of India held that life originated in water. Recent scientific investigations are leading us to the same conclusion.

It is well known that light plays a prominent role in the synthesis of a number of compounds, some of which are of great biological interest [1]. In our laboratories, we have observed that, if, under sterilized condition; a mixture of paraformaldehyde, potassium nitrate, ferric chloride and water is exposed to artificial light from a 500 watt electric bulb, a number of amino acids are synthesized in the mixture [2]. It has been found that hydrogen ion concentration of the mixture has a great influence on the nature of the amino acids formed. Depending upon the pH value of the mixture and the period of exposure different amino acids are found to be present in the mixture; and what is more interesting a number of the amino acids in the beginning disappear and new ones are formed [3]. A number of photodynamic catalysts as fuchsine red etc. [4] have been observed to help in this synthesis.

These experiments lead us to conclude that free radicals are formed in the mixture owing to the effect of light from paraformaldehyde. The free radicals combine with the nitrogen from potassium nitrate giving rise to compounds which finally attain a comparatively stable state at amino acid stage.

It has been observed by us that if a mixture of paraformaldehyde, colloidal molybdenum oxide and water under sterilized conditions is exposed to artificial electric light from a 500 watts bulb, then too, a number of amino acids are synthesized in the mixture. This finding is of very great importance. It proves that for the synthesis of amino acids in addition to light only water, a carbon source and atmospheric nitrogen are essential. This can only be possible if light helps in the formation of certain free radicals which help in the subsequent synthesis of amino acids.

This startling discovery unfolds a new approach to study the origin of life. Taking the preliminary conditions in the era before the beginning of life we know that there was a vast expanse of water, plenty of carbon dioxide and numerous minerals to act as catalysts, and the sun shining intermittently to initiate the reactions involving the formation of amino acids. These reactions had been

140

taking place in those days and are still taking place though the concentrations of the different reactants have changed. Those amino acids formed the basic material for the chemical origin of life on Earth [5] which is the most relevant theory on the formation of life [6]. Once the amino acids are formed, here are possibilities that peptide linkages are also formed in the mixture. Experiments on these lines are being carried out in our laboratories.

The mechanism of these reactions can be explained in a simple manner by making use of only the fundamental reactions as hydration, dehydration, condensation, hydrogenation, etc. Such reactions have been observed in the biogenesis of different plant products and so can be considered to be taking place in these mixtures also, under suitable conditions in the presence of light [7].

A scheme on the formation of most of the amino acids from the preliminary starting materials as formaldehyde—or carbon dioxide dissolved in water which on exposure to light soon gets converted to formaldehyde [8–11] with fixed nitrogen in the presence of a suitable catalyst has been given below.

FORMATION OF MONO-AMINO MONO-CARBOXYLIC ACIDS

Glycine

$$CH_2O + 2H \rightleftharpoons CH_3OH \qquad (1)$$
$$CH_2O + O \rightleftharpoons HCOOH \qquad (2)$$
$$O + 2CH_2O \rightleftharpoons HO \cdot CH_2 \cdot COOH \qquad (3)$$
$$HO \cdot CH_2 \cdot COOH \rightleftharpoons CHO \cdot COOH + 2H \qquad (4)$$
$$CHO \cdot COOH + 2NH_3 \rightleftharpoons NH : CH \cdot COO \cdot NH_4 \qquad (5)$$
$$NH : CH \cdot COONH_4 + 2H \rightleftharpoons NH_2 \cdot CH_2 \cdot COONH_4 \qquad (6)$$
$$NH_2 \cdot CH_2 \cdot COONH_4 + H_2O \rightleftharpoons NH_2 \cdot CH_2 \cdot COOH + NH_3 \qquad (7)$$
$$\text{(Glycine)}$$

Serine

Glycine is synthesized as described in reaction (7). Glycine on condensation with formaldehyde gives serine.

$$CH_2(NH_2)COOH + CH_2O \rightleftharpoons OH \cdot CH_2CH(NH_2)COOH \qquad (8)$$
$$\text{(Serine)}$$

Homoserine

$$OH \cdot CH_2CH(NH_2)COOH + CH_2O \rightleftharpoons CHOCH_2CH(NH_2)COOH + H_2O \qquad (9)$$
$$CHOCH_2CH(NH_2)COOH + 2H \rightleftharpoons OHCH_2CH_2CH(NH_2)COOH \qquad (10)$$
$$\text{(Homoserine)}$$

Proline

Serine is synthesized as mentioned in the reaction (8). It can give rise to proline through the following series of reactions.

$$OH \cdot CH_2CH(NH_2)COOH + CH_2O \rightleftharpoons CHOCH_2CH(NH_2)COOH + H_2O \qquad (11)$$
$$CHO \cdot CH_2CH(NH_2)COOH + 2H \rightleftharpoons OHCH_2CH_2CH(NH_2)COOH + H_2O \qquad (12)$$
$$CH_2O + OHCH_2CH_2CH(NH_2)COOH$$
$$\rightleftharpoons CHOCH_2CH_2CH(NH_2)COOH + H_2O \qquad (13)$$
$$CHOCH_2CH_2CH(NH_2)COOH + 2H \rightleftharpoons OHCH_2CH_2CH_2CH(NH_2)COOH \qquad (14)$$

$$\begin{array}{c} \text{CH}_2\!\!-\!\!\text{CH}_2 \\ | \qquad\qquad \rangle\text{CHCOOH} \rightleftharpoons \\ \text{CH}_2\text{OH} \;\; \text{NH}_2 \end{array} \quad \begin{array}{c} \text{CH}_2\!\!-\!\!\text{CH}_2 \\ | \qquad\qquad \rangle\text{CH}\cdot\text{COOH} + \text{H}_2\text{O} \\ \text{CH}_2\!\!-\!\!\text{NH} \end{array} \qquad (15)$$
$$\text{(Proline)}$$

Aspartic acid

$CHOCH_2CH(NH_2)COOH$ is formed as suggested in the reaction (11).

$$CHOCH_2CH(NH_2)COOH + O \rightleftharpoons COOHCH_2CH(NH_2)COOH \qquad (16)$$
$$\text{(Aspartic acid)}$$

Glutamic acid

$CHOCH_2CH_2CH(NH_2)COOH$ is formed as described in the reaction (13).

$$CHO\cdot CH_2CH_2CH(NH_2)COOH + O \rightleftharpoons COOHCH_2CH_2CH(NH_2)COOH \qquad (17)$$
$$\text{(Glutamic acid)}$$

Hydroxyglutamic acid

Glycine is formed as described in the reaction (7).

$$CH_2O + CH_2(NH_2)COOH \rightleftharpoons CHOCH(NH_2)COOH + H_2O \qquad (18)$$
$$CH_2O + CHOCH(NH_2)COOH \rightleftharpoons CHOCH(OH)CH(NH_2)COOH \qquad (19)$$
$$CHOCH(OH)CH(NH_2)COOH + 2H \rightleftharpoons OH\cdot CH_2CH(OH)CH(NH_2)COOH \qquad (20)$$
$$CH_2O + OH\cdot CH_2CH(OH)CH(NH_2)COOH \rightleftharpoons CHOCH_2CH(OH)CH(NH_2)COOH \quad (21)$$
$$CHOCH_2CH(OH)CH(NH_2)COOH + O \rightleftharpoons COOHCH_2CH(OH)CH(NH_2)COOH \quad (22)$$
$$\text{(Hydroxyglutamic acid)}$$

Lysine

$OHCH_2\cdot CH_2CH_2CH(NH_2)COOH$ is formed as described in the reaction (14).

$$CH_2O + OHCH_2CH_2CH_2CH(NH_2)COOH \rightleftharpoons$$
$$CHOCH_2CH_2CH_2CH(NH_2)COOH + H_2O \qquad (23)$$
$$NH_3 + CHO(CH_2)_3CH(NH_2)COOH \rightleftharpoons$$
$$NH = CHCH_2CH_2CH_2CH(NH_2)COOH + H_2O \qquad (24)$$
$$2H + NH = CHCH_2CH_2CH_2CH(NH_2)COOH \rightleftharpoons$$
$$NH_2\cdot CH_2\cdot CH_2\cdot CH_2\cdot CH_2CH(NH_2)COOH \qquad (25)$$
$$\text{(Lysine)}$$

Ornithine and arginine

$$NH_3 + H_2O \rightleftharpoons NH_4OH \qquad (26)$$
$$CO_2 + H_2O \rightleftharpoons H_2CO_3 \qquad (27)$$
$$H_2CO_3 + 2NH_4OH \rightleftharpoons (NH_4)_2CO_3 + H_2O \qquad (28)$$
$$(NH_4)_2CO_3 \rightleftharpoons 2NH_2^+ + CO'' + 2H_2O \qquad (29)$$
$$2NH_2^+ + CO'' \rightleftharpoons CO(NH_2)_2 \qquad (30)$$

$CHOCH_2CH_2CH(NH_2)COOH$ is formed as described in the reaction (13).

$$NH_3 + CHOCH_2CH_2CH(NH_2)COOH \rightleftharpoons$$
$$NH = CHCH_2CH_2CH(NH_2)COOH + H_2O \qquad (31)$$
$$2H + NH = CHCH_2CH_2CH(NH_2)COOH \rightleftharpoons NH_2(CH_2)_3CH(NH_2)(COOH) \qquad (32)$$
$$\text{(Ornithine)}$$
$$\begin{array}{c} NH_2\!\!-\!\!CO + H\cdot NH(CH_2)_3CH(NH_2)COOH \rightleftharpoons \\ | \\ NH_2 \end{array}$$
$$\begin{array}{c} NH_2\!\!-\!\!C\!\!-\!\!NH(CH_2)_3CH(NH_2)COOH + H_2O \\ \| \\ NH \end{array} \qquad (33)$$
$$\text{(Arginine)}$$

Histidine

$CHOCH_2CH(NH_2)COOH$ is formed as mentioned in the reaction (11).

$$CH_2O + CHOCH_2CH(NH_2)COOH \rightleftharpoons OHCH_2 \cdot CO \cdot CH_2CH(NH_2)COOH \quad (34)$$

$$2CH_2O + H_2O \rightleftharpoons CH_3OH + HCOOH \quad (35)$$

$$HCOOH + 2NH_3 \rightleftharpoons NH_2CH = NH + 2H_2O \quad (36)$$

$$
\underset{\substack{+ \\ OHCH_2COCH_2CH(NH_2)COOH}}{\overset{CH}{\underset{NH \quad NH_2}{\diagup \diagdown}}}
\rightleftharpoons
\underset{CH_2-C-CH_2CH(NH_2)COOH}{\overset{CH}{\underset{N \quad N}{\diagup \diagdown}}}
\quad (37)
$$

$$
\underset{CH_2-C-CH_2CH(NH_2)COOH}{\overset{CH}{\underset{N \quad N}{\diagup \diagdown}}}
\rightleftharpoons
\underset{\underset{\text{(Histidine)}}{CH = C-CH_2CH(NH_2)COOH}}{\overset{CH}{\underset{N \quad NH}{\diagup \diagdown}}}
\quad (38)
$$

Alanine

The formation of aspartic acid has been described above. This can easily convert to alanine by the decarboxylation of the carboxyl group away from the amino group.

$$COOH \cdot CH_2CH(NH_2)COOH \rightleftharpoons CH_3CH(NH_2)COOH + CO_2 \quad (39)$$
$$\text{(Alanine)}$$

Threonine

Serine is formed as mentioned above. This undergoes following series of reactions to give rise to threonine.

$$OHCH_2CH(NH_2)COOH + CH_2O \rightleftharpoons OHCH_2CH(OH)CH(NH_2)COOH \quad (40)$$

$$OHCH_2CH(OH)CH(NH_2)COOH + CH_2O \rightleftharpoons$$
$$CHOCH_2CH(OH)CH(NH_2)COOH + H_2O \quad (41)$$

$$CHOCH_2CH(OH)CH(NH_2)COOH + O \rightleftharpoons COOHCH_2CH(OH)CH(NH_2)COOH \quad (42)$$

$$COOHCH_2CH(OH)CH(NH_2)COOH \rightleftharpoons CH_3CH(OH)CH(NH_2)COOH + CO_2 \quad (43)$$
$$\text{(Threonine)}$$

Leucine

Glutamic acid is formed as described before:

$$COOHCH_2CH_2CH(NH_2)COOH \rightleftharpoons CH_3CH_2CH(NH_2)COOH + CO_2 \quad (44)$$

$$2CH_3OH + CH_3CH_2CH(NH_2)COOH \rightleftharpoons (CH_3)_2CHCH_2CH(NH_2)COOH + 2H_2O \quad (45)$$
$$\text{(Leucine)}$$

Norleucine

$OHCH_2CH_2CH_2CH(NH_2)COOH$ is formed as described in reaction (14).

$$CH_2O + OHCH_2CH_2CH_2CH(NH_2)COOH \rightleftharpoons CHO(CH_2)_3CH(NH_2)COOH \quad (46)$$

$$2H + CHO(CH_2)_3CH(NH_2)COOH \rightleftharpoons CH_2(OH)(CH_2)_3CH(NH_2)COOH \quad (47)$$

$$CH_2O + CH_2(OH)(CH_2)_3CH(NH_2)COOH \rightleftharpoons CHO(CH_2)_4CH(NH_2)COOH \quad (48)$$

$$CHO(CH_2)_4CH(NH_2)COOH + O \rightleftharpoons COOH(CH_2)_4CH(NH_2)COOH \quad (49)$$

$$COOHCH_2(CH_2)_3CH(NH_2)COOH \rightleftharpoons CH_3(CH_2)_3CH(NH_2)COOH + CO_2 \quad (50)$$
$$\text{(Norleucine)}$$

Isoleucine

The formation of threonine has been described before. It can act as the starting material for formation of isoleucine as described below.

$$CH_3CH(OH)CH(NH_2)COOH + CH_2O \rightleftharpoons CHOCH(CH_3)CH(NH_2)COOH \quad (51)$$

$$2H + CHOCH(CH_3)CH(NH_2)COOH \rightleftharpoons OHCH_2CH(CH_3)CH(NH_2)COOH \quad (52)$$

$$CH_2O + OHCH_2CH(CH_3)CH(NH_2)COOH \rightleftharpoons$$
$$CHOCH_2CH(CH_3)CH(NH_2)COOH + H_2O \quad (53)$$

$$CHOCH_2CH(CH_3)CH(NH_2)COOH + 2H \rightleftharpoons$$
$$OHCH_2CH_2CH(CH_3)CH(NH_2)COOH \quad (54)$$

$$OHCH_2CH_2CH(CH_3)CH(NH_2)COOH + CH_2O \rightleftharpoons$$
$$CHO \cdot CH_2 \cdot CH_2 \cdot CH(CH_3)CH(NH_2)COOH + H_2O \quad (55)$$

$$CHO \cdot CH_2CH_2CH(CH_3)CH(NH_2)COOH + O \rightleftharpoons$$
$$COOHCH_2CH_2CH(CH_3)CH(NH_2)COOH \quad (56)$$

$$COOH \cdot CH_2CH_2CH(CH_3)CH(NH_2)COOH \rightleftharpoons$$
$$CH_3CH_2CH(CH_3)CH(NH_2)COOH + CO_2 \quad (57)$$
(Isoleucine)

Valine

Alanine can be synthesized as described above. This can act as starting material for the synthesis of valine,

$$\begin{matrix} CH_3OH & H \\ & + \\ CH_3OH & H \end{matrix} \Big\rangle CHCH(NH_2)COOH \rightleftharpoons (CH_3)_2CHCH(NH_2)COOH + 2H_2O \quad (58)$$
Valine

It should be noted that in the formation of all these amino acids, the reactions considered can easily take place under laboratory conditions with the help of light and are generally taking place in plants in the biogenesis of plant products.

The interconversion of the amino acids described is similar to that observed in the various biological tissues. In the formation of glycine and serine, $NH = CHCOOH$ is the chief initial product which on hydrogenation becomes glycine (7) and on condensation with a formaldehyde molecule becomes serine (8). A close relationship is observed between glycine and serine in biological tissues also where glycine can be utilized in the formation of serine in the presence of vitamin B_{12} [12–15].

Proline, ornithine and glutamic acid are synthesized from $CHO \cdot CH_2CH_2-CH(NH_2)COOH$ (13), (14), (15), (17), (31), (32). Shemin & Rittenberg [16] also found proline and ornithine to be interconvertible and it is probable that their interconversion involves α-aminoglutaraldehydic acid. Glutamic acid and proline have also been found to be interconvertible in liver and kidney tissues [17–19].

Aspartic acid can easily give alanine by decarboxylation (39). Kritsman [20–22], Wood & Werkman [23], Evans & Slotin [24] and Braunshteïn [25] observed the interconversion of aspartic acid and alanine through oxaloacetic and pyruvic acid stages. According to them, aspartic acid, formed by the amination of oxaloacetic acid, transaminates with pyruvic acid to form alanine and oxaloacetic acid. It is, however, quite possible that in a photochemically activated mixture, as is considered here, these amino acids are related by decarboxylation and carboxylation reactions.

α-Aminosuccinaldehydic acid is the basic compound for the formation of lysine (12), (13), (14), (23), (24) and (25), arginine (12), (13), (31), (32), (33) and histidine (34), (35), (36), (37), (38). The formation of glutamic acid can also be traced to this compound (12), (13) and (17). Interconversion of glutamic acid and lysine, arginine and histidine [25] has been observed in living tissues [16–19]. Serine on condensation with formaldehyde, (9) and (10), changes to homoserine.

On a different condensation with two molecules of formaldehyde, (40) and (41), and subsequent oxidation and decarboxylation, (42) and (43), serine forms threonine. In *Neurospora*, homoserine has been observed to go to threonine by Teas, Horowitz & Fling [26]. It is quite probable that even in this, serine is an intermediate compound.

Thus the formation of a number of amino acids can be explained through the intermediate formation of free radicals by making use of simple reactions as condensation, oxidation, reduction, intermolecular changes etc. These can be made to take place under laboratory conditions by using drastic reagents and by keeping the thermodynamic level constant. Under the influence of light, these reactions take place under normal conditions.

The chain reactions initiated by light do not stop at the amino acid stage, helping in the formation and dynamic interconversion of the amino acids as observed by us [3] but continue, resulting in the formation of compounds with peptide linkage. The different amino acids formed unite differently, forming different types of peptides. Even though the possible number of such peptides is very large, only a few stable ones remain in the mixture for an appreciable time and the others soon hydrolyse to amino acids which recombine to give newer peptides. The peptides can be of molecular weights of the order of protein, but only a few such aggregates get a chance to remain stable under the activated state of the mixture and in most of them there will be a state of continuous molecular change initiated by the irradiating electromagnetic waves. These are under investigation in our laboratories. Considering the result of our experiments and the work carried out on mitogenetic radiations [27] I have come to the following conclusions on the problem of the origin of life.

Consider a macromolecule formed by the activation of light. It is a huge molecule of indefinite shape, of numerous peptide linkages and having various groups attached to it and the molecule is in such a state that if activated or excited by light it can undergo a number of permutations and combinations with little or no change in its thermodynamic energy level, resulting in the formation of different protein molecules. This macromolecule is made by the union of different amino acids by the influence of light.

It is known that in a protein molecule, there are fluctuating electric charges [28]. Hence in this macromolecular aggregate, also, there will be fluctuating electric charges. Whenever there is a fluctuating charge, radiations of a mitogenetic order are emitted.

During the disintegration and synthesis of certain systems by electromagnetic waves, A. & L. Gurwitsch have observed that if a 3% gelatinized nucleic acid solution is irradiated with 3220–3240 Å wavelength radiation a secondary radiation of 2450–2500 Å, i.e., of shorter wavelength than the primary and even of stronger intensity than the primary radiation is emitted [29]. And Wolff & Ras [30] observed a similar effect with sterile blood serum, which produced secondary radiations similar to the above when bacteria have grown in it.

It has been observed by Gurwitsch [31] and Korosi [32] that certain molecules which are capable of enzymic cleavage can react on mitogenetic radiations and themselves become radiant. Differently charged centres of these molecules are activated differently by the irradiating light to emit mitogenetic radiations.

Latmanisowa [35], studying the secondary radiations from nerves after mitogenetic radiations, observed that the induction effect of secondary rays is very strong in the beginning, starts decreasing after five minutes and disappears after thirty minutes and does not appear any more on continuous exposure. Gurwitsch [37] observed similar loss in the power of secondary radiations of radiating cells or tissues when they themselves are exposed to mitogenetic rays. Even good radiating cultures lose their power of radiation when exposed to their own wavelength. Overdose of radiation causes retardation in the emission of secondary radiations. Gurwitsch called this phenomenon mitogenetic depression [33], Salkind observed a retardation in the secondary emission of rat blood [34]. Correlating these data we can safely conclude that the macromolecular aggregate, when exposed to certain radiations, will emit secondary radiations of different wavelength and magnitudes depending upon the nature of bonds which are decomposed or synthesized, upon the atoms taking part in the reactions, and upon the wavelength and magnitude of the initiating radiations.

It is found that the mitogenetic radiations emitted by protein molecules on irradiation cease after a certain period of irradiation [33–35]. This is due to the fact that the protein molecule has a more or less fixed structure and the irradiation can introduce only a limited possibility of further permutations and combinations, under the influence of the free radicals thus formed. On the other hand the macromolecular aggregate has infinite possibilities of permutation and combination within the same molecule and so can continue emitting mitogenetic radiations for a long time till a stable structure is achieved. The macromolecule can also combine with other molecules synthesized photochemically, giving rise to further emission of mitogenetic radiations. The resulting compound if unstable will also emit radiations, because in its attempt to attain a stable state it will of a necessity disturb the fluctuating electrostatic forces of the molecular system. A similar type of mitogenetic radiation is observed when an enzyme reacts on a substrate [31, 32].

When a mixture of paraformaldehyde and potassium nitrate in water is exposed to light in the presence of a suitable catalyst, a dynamic mixture of amino acids is formed. These amino acids are constantly changing from one to another and these combine with one another to form macromolecular aggregates. And thus the whole mixture forms a continuous source of mitogenetic radiations for a long time when irradiated.

In these molecular changes, only those changes, which involve the formation of molecules at the same thermodynamic energy level or at little energy-level difference, help in keeping up a continuous emission. If the molecular changes involve considerable changes in energy level as manifested by evolution or absorption of heat, resulting in the destruction of the macromolecules, the emission of the mitogenetic radiation is hindered temporarily.

If molecules with a fluctuating electrostatic charge, or molecules which can attain such a configuration on being irradiated, are exposed to electromagnetic radiations of certain wavelengths, they emit secondary radiations of mitogenetic order. The frequency and intensity of these radiations depend upon the nature of the atoms in the molecule and will be the net resultant of the different bonds and atoms present in it.

The macromolecular aggregate, if exposed to these secondary radiations, because it contains all the fragments to synthesize the radiating molecule, will be able to synthesize the radiating molecular system. However, if the radiating system has got some inactive portions which do not participate in the emission of the secondary radiation, then only the active portion of the radiating system will be synthesized from the macromolecule and not the whole molecule which is emitting the mitogenetic radiation.

This finds unquestionable confirmation in the autosynthesis of enzymoids as observed by A. Gurwitsch [36] who found that enzymoids can be synthesized in dilute aqueous solution of glycine, if a trace of the initiating enzyme molecule is present in the solution and the solution is irradiated. This can be easily explained if it is presumed that the active group of the enzyme contains the atomic groupings which can be synthesized by glycine on activation by irradiation. The mitogenetic radiation helps in the auto-synthesis of the radiating nucleus as it is only the reactive group in the enzyme which is capable of mitogenetic radiations. Such enzymically active molecules thus synthesized have been named Enzymoids.

In the prebiological era of the Earth there was a vast expanse of water, which contained a considerable amount of minerals and dissolved carbon dioxide. These minerals acted as catalysts in the synthesis of protein from water and carbon dioxide. The Earth was covered with heavy clouds and so light and dark phases fluctuated too often, thus producing the optimum conditions for the emission of mitogenetic radiations [37]. Reflection of the mitogenetic radiations by various reflecting surfaces, rendered them polarized [33] and the polarized radiations were extremely active in exciting the molecules for periodic fluctuations in their charges and they helped in the synthesis of asymmetric molecules. Under these conditions, a number of asymmetric molecules having peptide linkages were formed.

For the emission of secondary radiation, it is essential that the molecule must be such that its state of rest can be easily disturbed by even a slight initiation through irradiation, resulting in a dynamic state of fluctuating electrostatic charge. This initiation is accomplished by a starting stroke at an appropriate spot in the molecule. The intensity of the stroke does not have any effect on the nature of the radiation emitted, and its only function is to start the continuous emission of the radiations by setting up a fluctuating electrostatic charge in the molecule. This can be well understood from the experiments on mitogenetic radiations [33, 38]. Followed by the primary impacts, a series of fluctuations in electrostatic charge are set up in the molecules liberating mitogenetic radiations. However, these radiations cease after a certain time, following a retardation. This is also accompanied by a movement of the carbon chain of the molecule. When such chains keep on moving for some time their movability is choked. To understand this clearly, we can compare the carbon chain to a heavy metallic chain which is twisted and twisted till further twisting is not possible. At this stage the chain is not free to move much, and comes to a stand-still. If this is hung freely it will slowly untwist itself to attain its original long form at which it can again be twisted. Similarly irradiation initiates a mito-genetic radiation which after a certain lapse of time slowly becomes feebler and feebler and finally comes to an end. The radiation falling on the molecule twists the carbon chain and the twisting continues till the movement of the various chains of the molecule is nil. At this stage, the mitogenetic radiations cease. If the source of radiation is removed, the twisting also stops and the molecule recoils and reaches its original state and again becomes fit for the emission of secondary radiations on irradiations. Such results were obtained in the case of some compounds whose mitogenetic radiations were studied [34].

However, such an arrangement of the molecule chain is possible where the chain may not get twisted, but may merely oscillate during the display of fluc-tuating electrostatic charges in the molecule. In such cases, no decrease in the mitogenetic radiations will be observed for a long time. In the case of certain mitogenetic-radiation-emitting materials, no retardation or cessation has been observed even when they are exposed to radiations for a long time [34, 39].

The mitogenetic radiation is found to increase if the irradiation is intermittent. Gurwitsch observed in 1932 that when there is a regular interval between the irradiation period and the dark period when there is no irradiation, then the increase is greater than when the interval is irregular [37]. This is probably because the regularity in the exposure period provides a better chance for the molecule recoil.

So we can imagine the effect of the surroundings on the macromolecular aggregate in the prebiological era. Itself capable of forming a number of proteins, the slight initiating stroke of light set up a series of fluctuating electrostatic charges in its unstable structure giving rise to mitogenetic radiations which were best aided by the intermittent light falling on the molecule. The radiations initiated the formation of a number of proteins, stable and unstable. Under the prevailing conditions, the stable ones remained and the unstable ones broke up and formed newer compounds, which sometimes, combining with the macro-molecule itself, gave still newer compounds. The structure of the macromolecule is such that an unlimited number of reactions could have continued to take place. The stable compounds remained and the unstable compounds broke up and continued in their attempt to produce a stable structure, combining, breaking up, and recombining, and thus giving birth to protein molecules, which in due course started reacting.

It has been observed that when protein molecules are irradiated, they emit secondary radiations which are similar to those emitted when the same protein is acted on by some proteolytic enzyme [31, 40]. Hence of the various proteins synthesized, if a protein A proteolyses a protein B, it gives rise to certain mitogenetic radiations. We already know that if a certain mitogenetic radiation falls on a system which can synthesize the source of irradiation, that source is synthesized in that system. So in this dynamic system of proteins and macromolecules and various compounds, these mitogenetic radiations favour the formation of B more and more. Similarly another protein can proteolyse A, thus favouring the synthesis of A. In this way, the syntheses of many proteins were achieved.

Such reactions were possible only when the reactants were in the mitogenetic radiation zone.

As soon as they were removed from that zone, owing to physical reasons, the reactions stopped. This led to the possibility of still newer reactions, depending upon the type of reactants which were then available. The mitogenetic synthesis by polarized radiation was responsible for the synthesis of asymmetric protein molecules. Thus there was a time when, on the surface of the Earth, the various protein molecules were synthesized.

Adenylic acid and nucleic acid were also similarly formed. Of the innumerable compounds synthesized only the compounds which were stable under the then prevailing physical and chemical conditions remained and the others got decomposed into different compounds. With the new compounds thus formed or the compounds formed by the inter-reaction between the stable proteins, the probability of further reaction remained open. The reactions continued and the chemically fittest only survived.

Some of these stable compounds combined with adenosine triphosphate which is capable of liberating energy. These molecules, since they had the advantage of being associated with a source of energy, needed lesser activation energy for the commencement of the synthetic reaction as compared to other molecules without any energy source. So, the formation of such molecules has a greater probability.

But this could not continue for a long time unless these molecules were kept held up together by some force for a long time. In the beginning this type of association might have been possible because of the coacervate stage. But these types of aggregations led merely to the synthesis of molecules. Nucleic acid was also synthesized as described above. This molecule formed the support for the protein molecules. Whenever the latter came in contact with nucleic acid, the system being stable and able to be held permanently together, acquired the most favourable conditions for the synthesis of protein; for, the energy-giving adenylic acid phosphates the proteins to be synthesized and the compounds which helped in the synthesis, were all held together by nucleic acid in a systematic order arranged as the books in a library.

Thus the system became capable of synthesizing the protein not only easily but also in a systematic manner, one after the other, depending upon the arrangement of the compounds on the nucleic acid skeleton and this system capable of autosynthesis and acting as the preliminary protoplasm made its first appearance on the surface of Earth. The preliminary protoplasm thus formed combined with the various mineral atoms and gradually evolved to the present protoplasm.

Thus the fundamental five elements 'Kshiti, jala, pavak, gagan, sameera',

(Earth, water, fire, ether and air) were solely responsible for the origin of life on this Earth.

REFERENCES

1. E. C. C. BALY, *Photosynthesis.* Methuen, London, 1940.
2. K. BAHADUR, *Nature, Lond.*, **173**, 1141, 1954.
3. S. RANGANAYAKI & K. BAHADUR, *Proc. nat. Acad. Sci. India*, **23**, A, 21, 1954.
4. L. SANTAMARIA, Istituto di Patologia Generale, Milano, Italy, Personal Communication, June 11, 1954.
5. See F. DARWIN, *Life and Letters of Charles Darwin*, Vol. 3, p. 18 (footnote), London, 1887; G. HARDIN, *Sci. Mon., N.Y.*, **70**, 178, 1950.
6. A. I. OPARIN, *Origin of Life* (transl. by S. MORGULIS). Dover Publications, New York, 1953.
7. J. B. COHEN, *Organic Chemistry for Advanced Students.* Edward Arnold, London, 2nd ed., 1919.
8. A. BAEYER, *Ber. dtsch. chem. Ges.*, **3**, 63, 1870.
9. F. L. USHER & L. H. PRIESTLEY, *Proc. Roy. Soc.*, B, **84**, 101, 1011.
10. H. C. RAMSPERGER, *J. Amer. chem. Soc.*, **47**, 79, 1925.
11. N. R. DHAR & A. RAM, *Nature, Lond.*, **129**, 205, 1932.
12. J. A. STEKOL, S. WEISS & K. WEISS, *Abstr. Amer. chem. Soc.*, 120th *meeting*, 21C. New York, Sept., 1951.
13. J. A. STEKOL, K. W. WEISS & S. WEISS, *Fed. Proc.*, **10**, 252, 1951.
14. H. R. V. ARNSTEIN & A. NEUBERGER, *Biochem. J.*, **48**, ii, 1951.
15. H. R. V. ARNSTEIN & A. NEUBERGER, *Biochem. J.*, **50**, xxxviii, 1952.
16. D. SHEMIN & D. RITTENBERG, *J. biol. Chem.*, **158**, 71, 1945.
17. H. A. KREBS, *Advanc. Enzymol.*, **3**, 191, 242, 1943.
18. A. C. WALKER & C. L. A. SCHMIDT, *Arch. Biochem.*, **4**, 457, 1944.
19. M. R. STETTEN & R. SCHOENHEIMER, *J. biol. Chem.*, **153**, 113, 1944.
20. M. G. KRITSMAN, *Biokhimiya*, **9**, 379, 1944; *Chem. Abstr.*, **39**, 3315, 1945.
21. M. G. KRITSMAN, *Ann. Rev. Soviet Med.*, **2**, 349, 1945.
22. M. G. KRITSMAN & S. S. MELIK-SARKISYAN, *Biokhimiya*, **10**, 1, 1945; *Chem. Abstr.*, **39**, 3559, 1945.
23. H. G. WOOD & C. H. WERKMAN, *Biochem. J.*, **30**, 48, 1936.
24. E. A. EVANS, Jr., & L. SLOTIN, *J. biol. Chem.*, **136**, 301, 1940.
25. A. E. BRAUNSHTEĬN & R. M. AZARKH, *J. biol. Chem.*, **157**, 421, 1945.
26. H. J. TEAS, N. H. HOROWITZ & M. FLING, *J. biol. Chem.*, **172**, 651, 1948.
27. O. RAHN, *Invisible Radiations of Organisms.* Gebr. Bornträger, Berlin, 1936.
28. J. G. KIRKWOOD, *Symposium on the Mechanism of Enzyme Action.* Johns Hopkins Press, Baltimore, 4, 1954.
29. A. GURWITSCH & L. GURWITSCH, *Biochem. Z.*, **246**, 127, 1932.
30. L. K. WOLFF & R. RAS, *Zbl. Bakt.*, **1**, *Orig.*, **128**, 306, 1933.
31. A. GURWITSCH, *Int. Congr. Electro-Radio-Biology*, **1**, Venice, 1934.
32. K. DE KOROSI, *Int. Congr. Electro-Radio-Biology*, **1**, Venice, 1934.
33. O. RAHN, *Protoplasma—Monographien.* 9. *Visible Radiation of Organisms.* Gebr. Bornträger, p. 115, 1936.
34. S. SALKIND, *Roux's Arch.*, **128**, 378, 1933.
35. L. W. LATMANISOWA, *Pflüg. Arch. ges. Physiol.*, **231**, 265, 1932.
36. A. GURWITSCH, *Enzymologia*, **12**, 139, 1947.
37. A. GURWITSCH, *Die mitogenetische Strahlung.* Springer, Berlin, 1932.
38. O. RAHN, *Invisible Radiations of Organisms.* Gebr. Bornträger, Berlin, p. 122, 1936.
39. L. K. WOLFF & G. RAS, *Zbl. Bakt.*, **1**, *Orig.*, **128**, 314, 1933.
40. H. BARTH, *Arch. Sci. biol. St. Petersb.*, **35**, 29, 1934.

The Original Formation of Amino Acids under the Action of Ultraviolet Rays and Electric Discharges

T. E. PAVLOVSKAYA & A. G. PASYNSKIĬ

*A. N. Bakh Institute of Biochemistry of the Academy of Sciences
of the U.S.S.R., Moscow*

IN THE history of the formation of organic compounds on the Earth, special significance is attached to the appearance of amino acids, since they are the starting materials for the formation of peptides and protein-like compounds without which life, in its turn, could not have come into being. The original formation of amino acids from simpler compounds required an expenditure of energy to activate the starting molecules. According to Oparin [1] the most significant of the various sources of energy available in the prebiological history of the Earth was ultraviolet irradiation from the Sun, which in regard to the Earth amounted to about 10^{20} kcal/yr, a high proportion of which reached the surface of the Earth at that time. Of lesser importance (probably not more than $0 \cdot 1-1 \cdot 0\%$ of this value) were electrical discharges in the atmosphere, though these were also an important factor in activating chemical reactions.

As early as 1913, Loeb [2] observed the formation of glycine when silent electric discharges were passed through mixtures of carbon monoxide, ammonia (both obtained by the decomposition of formamide) and water vapour. In recent years the formation of amino acids by passing electrical discharges through mixtures of methane, ammonia, hydrogen and water vapour, imitating the possible composition of the primaeval reducing atmosphere of the Earth, has been studied in detail in Miller's [3] interesting work. In his experiments he obtained glycine, α-alanine, β-alanine, sarcosine, α-aminobutyric acid and other compounds.

K. Bahadur [4] has also published some interesting data concerning the production of serine, aspartic acid, valine, lysine and other amino acids by the prolonged action of sunlight on solutions of mixtures of paraformaldehyde, KNO_3 and $FeCl_3$.

In the present work, we have studied the action of ultraviolet rays, as an important source of energy under the primaeval conditions of the Earth, on solutions of mixtures of formaldehyde and ammonium chloride or nitrate, and we have demonstrated the formation of amino acids under these conditions. We have also repeated Miller's experiments using gaseous mixtures of somewhat different composition.

151

THE ACTION OF ULTRAVIOLET RAYS

The irradiation of the solution was carried out in optical cuvettes through laminae of plane-parallel quartz, using a PRK–2 lamp at 25 cm, the intensity of the irradiation being $2·7 \times 10^6$ erg/cm^2 min during 20 hours. In the main experiments we used aqueous solutions containing $2·5\%$ CH$_2$O and $1·0–1·5\%$ NH$_4$NO$_3$ or NH$_4$Cl; the volume irradiated was 20 ml. During irradiation the temperature of the solution was about 40–45 °C, in some experiments it was $+1–+2$ °C (the temperature of melting ice). The pH of the solution was $1·5–2$, or 5–6·2 when chalk was present. When the irradiation was finished the volatile amines and organic acids were distilled off in a vacuum and the concentrate (e.g. 1 ml.) was submitted to chromatography on paper (Leningrad slow) using butanol-acetic acid mixtures as solvents. Chromatography was repeated in most experiments to give better separation of the spots. The chromatograms were coloured with ninhydrin and were then fixed with solutions of copper salt; the fixed spots were of the ordinary rosy colour. Identification of the spots was, however, made more difficult by the possible presence of volatile amides and amines in the concentrate [5]. Preliminary extraction of the concentrate with ether in the modified Soxhlet apparatus for 45 hours only led to a weakening of the spots. We therefore compared the extraction of amines with ether, directly with chromatograms through which butanol and acetic acid had flowed for 77 hours (method of repeated chromatography). The dried unsprayed chromatograms were then extracted with ether for 120 and 168 hours after which they were sprayed. As a result of this we manage to bring about the disappearance of a large spot ($R_F \sim 0·4$), the identification of which with amines was confirmed with control mixtures of amino acids with diethylamine (hydrochloride).

To get rid of amides, acid hydrolysis of the eluate of the spots was carried out by refluxing with 15% HCl for 8 hours. The hydrochloric acid was then removed by evaporating six times with water.

Later we adopted another routine for analysing our experimental mixtures. The separation of the amino acids and organic bases was carried out on an ion-exchange resin, Amberlite anionite (IRA–400) with strongly basic properties.

Thus, in the beginning, volatile amines were distilled off *in vacuo* in the presence of barium hydroxide, from the mixtures we obtained, while amides were hydrolysed with 15% HCl for 8–10 hours.

To separate the amino acids from non-volatile organic bases the mixture was put through a column of anionite at a rate of 9 ml/hr. The bases passed right through this column, while the amino acids were retained in it. The elution of the amino acids was carried out with about 20 volumes of M-HCl which was put through at the same rate as the experimental solution. When the hydrochloric acid had been removed from the eluate, this was concentrated *in vacuo*. The completeness of the separation of amino acids from organic bases on the column was checked, using artificial mixtures of amines and amides. The concentrate of the eluate was further analysed for its component amino acids by paper chromatography using the following solvents: mixtures of butanol, acetic acid and water (4 : 1 : 5), phenol-water and, for the identification of valine, phenylalanine and isoleucine, mixtures of cresol with a phosphate buffer (0·067 M-KH$_2$PO$_4$ + 0·067 M-Na$_2$HPO$_4$ (I : I)).

In some experiments supplementary measurements were made on the chromatogram with a microphotometer. Fig. I shows a microphotogram of amino acids synthesized in a mixture of formaldehyde and ammonium nitrate.

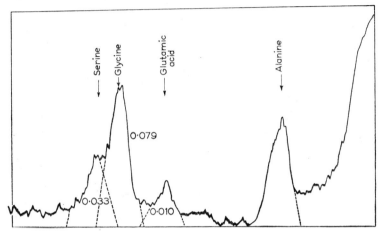

FIG. I.   Microphotogram of mixtures of amino acids.

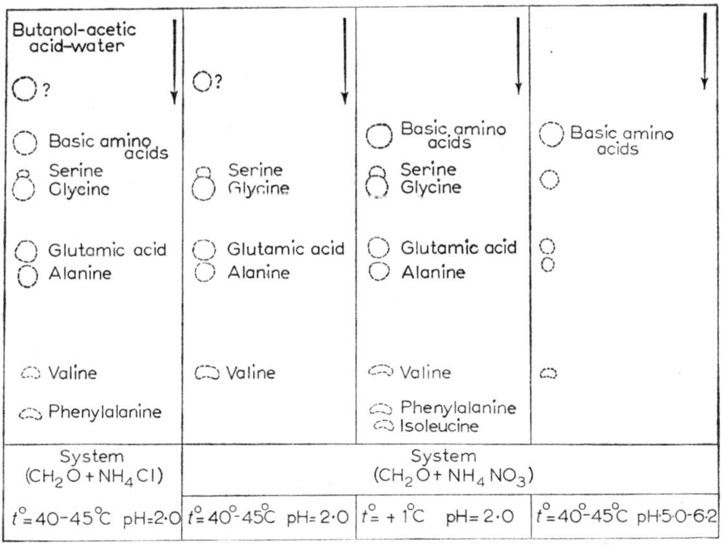

Butanol-acetic acid-water			
◯ ?	◯ ?		
◯ Basic amino acids		◯ Basic amino acids	◯ Basic amino acids
⊖ Serine	⊖ Serine	⊖ Serine	
◯ Glycine	◯ Glycine	◯ Glycine	◯
◯ Glutamic acid	◯ Glutamic acid	◯ Glutamic acid	◯
◯ Alanine	◯ Alanine	◯ Alanine	◯
� Valine	� Valine	� Valine	�
� Phenylalanine		� Phenylalanine	
		� Isoleucine	
System (CH$_2$O + NH$_4$Cl)	System (CH$_2$O + NH$_4$NO$_3$)		
$t° = 40$–$45°$C pH=2·0	$t° = 40°$–$45°$C pH= 2·0	$t° = + 1°$C pH= 2·0	$t° = 40°$–$45°$C pH 5·0-6·2

FIG. 2.   Chromatograms of amino acids synthesized by the action of ultraviolet rays.

In the formaldehyde-ammonium chloride mixture after irradiation with ultraviolet rays (at a temperature of 40–45° and pH 1·5–2) it was established that the following amino acids were present: basic amino acids, serine, glycine, glutamic acid, alanine, valine and also phenylalanine (Fig. 2).

In a solution of formaldehyde and ammonium nitrate treated in the same way, the following were identified: serine, glycine, glutamic acid, alanine and valine (Fig. 2). Lowering of the temperature of the experiment to 1–2 °C, while keeping all the other conditions unchanged and using ammonium nitrate, led to the formation of isoleucine, phenylalanine and basic amino acids as well as those just listed (Fig. 2).

If the experiments were carried out in the presence of chalk (i.e., at pH 5–6·2) the basic amino acids predominated while glutamic acid, alanine, valine and phenylalanine were only formed in negligible amounts under these conditions (Fig. 2). The amino acid content was 10^{-4} M. In control experiments, in which the mixtures were not irradiated, amino acid spots were not found.

The idea that bacterial contamination might have been a factor in the formation of amino acids is, to our minds, precluded by the conditions under which the experiments were conducted, involving the intensive exposure to ultraviolet irradiation for 20 hours of a solution containing 2·5% of formaldehyde at a pH of 1·5 and a temperature of 45 °C. Furthermore, the results of the control experiments (without irradiation) were negative. We checked this by special microbiological experiments in which the experimental solution was cultured on nutrient media: meat-peptone-agar and wort-agar. The absence of growth of colonies after 72 hours demonstrated the complete sterility of the experimental solution.

THE ACTION OF ELECTRIC DISCHARGES

In the gaseous mixtures (of methane, ammonia, hydrogen and water vapour) studied by Miller, the formation of amino acids was hindered by a deficiency of oxygen and a great excess of hydrogen such as he believed to have been present in the primaeval reducing atmosphere of the Earth. For every molecule of amino acid formed, two atoms of oxygen were needed and these could only be obtained from two molecules of water. At least one atom of nitrogen was also needed and this required a molecule of ammonia. At least two atoms of carbon were also needed and they could only be obtained from two molecules of methane. But even in the mixture $2H_2O + NH_3 + 2CH_4$ there are 15 atoms of hydrogen of which no more than half are required for the formation of the simplest amino acids (glycine and alanine), while Miller's mixtures contained, in addition, free, and obviously superfluous, hydrogen. When molecules of more complicated amino acids are formed the proportions, as one can easily see, remain unfavourable. For this reason the composition of the gaseous medium used by Miller is unsuited to the formation of amino acids. We arrive at the same conclusion by a thermodynamical calculation in respect of the overall reaction by which alanine, for example, is formed. When they take place under standard conditions there is a great increase in free energy (ΔZ_0):

$$2H_2O + 3CH_4 + NH_3 \rightarrow CH_3 \cdot CH(NH_2) \cdot COOH + 6H_2$$
$$\Delta Z_0 = + 62,040 \text{ cal/mole}$$

Naturally, in an electrical discharge the energy of the discharge will cover this increase in ΔZ_0, but even when reactions are proceeding in an electrical discharge, those which are thermodynamically capable of occurring spontaneously will be favoured. Obviously, more favourable conditions for the reaction will be present in a mixture in which carbon monoxide is exchanged for hydrogen, and this, from geochemical considerations, would appear to have been a possible component of the primaeval atmosphere of the Earth, while not destroying its reducing character. From this point of view the formation of amino acids was facilitated when the atmosphere was depleted of hydrogen and contained a certain amount of CO. In fact, in this case the formation of alanine, for example, could proceed in accordance with the overall equation:

$$CH_4 + 2CO + NH_3 \rightarrow CH_3 \cdot CH(NH_2) \cdot COOH$$
$$\Delta Z_0 = - 5900 \text{ cal/mole}$$

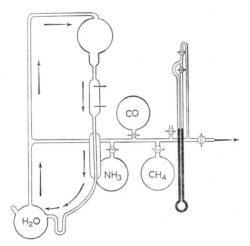

FIG. 3.   Diagram of apparatus for the synthesis of amino acids in an electric discharge.

In fact, a certain amount of CO was formed in Miller's apparatus when electric discharges were passed through mixtures of CH_4 and H_2O (1–10%), but the alteration in the composition of the starting mixture which this entailed had a somewhat damping effect on the reactions which were going on. We therefore tried Miller's experiments leaving hydrogen out of the mixture altogether and substituting CO.

We carried out our experiments in an apparatus constructed in accordance with Miller's diagram (Fig. 3) [6]. At first we repeated Miller's experiments using a gaseous mixture of the same composition as that which Miller used and we were able fully to confirm his results, obtaining identical two-dimensional chromatograms. To supplement our test of the possibility of bacterial contamination, we carried out experiments lasting 80 hours, which were the same apart from the absence of electrical discharges, and obtained wholly negative results. It is obvious that when water is continually boiling and the gas is circulating in the electrical discharge, bacterial processes can be excluded.

Experiments with mixtures containing CO were carried out in a spark discharge (using electrodes in the form of two circular plates inserted into the discharge tube at a distance of 5 cm from one another) lasting 100 hours at a potential of about 24 kV with a mixture of the following composition:

$$CH_4 \text{ and } NH_3 - 200 \text{ mm Hg}; CO - 100 \text{ mm Hg}$$

and water vapour up to atmospheric pressure. At the end of the experiment the solution was analysed in the ordinary way with preliminary vacuum distillation to remove amines and volatile organic acids and the concentrate was chromatographed [3, 6]. In this way we established (Fig. 4) the presence of a number of

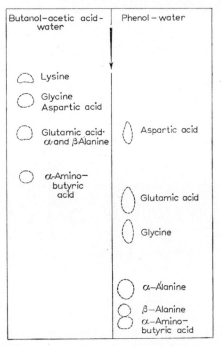

FIG. 4. Chromatograms of amino acids synthesized in an electric discharge.

amino acids: glycine, α- and β-alanine, α-aminobutyric acid and aspartic and glutamic acids. We did not study the mechanism of their formation but it would appear that the formation of cyanhydrins, as postulated by Miller, played an essential part, as HCN was found to be present in the solution after the passage of the discharge. The results of our experiments and theoretical considerations indicate that the presence of free hydrogen in the gaseous mixture is not necessary for the formation of amino acids in an electric discharge. It is possible that, during the evolutionary development of the Earth, more favourable conditions for the formation of amino acids in the atmosphere existed at the stage when a considerable part of its hydrogen had been lost and the atmosphere, while still retaining its reducing character, could have contained a relatively large quantity of CO. Under such conditions amino acids could have been formed, not only in electric discharges but also by the action of ultraviolet rays which were a far more powerful source of energy. It would seem that these processes may have some significance even now. We may suggest the possibility of the partial formation of formaldehyde by irradiation of mixtures of CO and H_2 or CO_2 and water vapour [5] with ultraviolet light. By means of further reactions of formaldehyde with ammonium salts dissolved in water, in mist particles, raindrops etc in ultraviolet rays, the formation of some amino acids, as demonstrated in our experiments, could occur, together with the formation of many other organic substances [1, 5].

The authors are deeply grateful to Academician A. I. Oparin for his continued interest in the work and for a number of valuable comments, and to A. I. Grebennikova for help in carrying out some of the experiments.

REFERENCES

1. A. OPARIN, *Vozniknovenie zhizm na Zemte (The Origin of Life on the Earth).* Izd. Akad. Nauk S.S.S.R., 1957.
2. W. LOEB, *Ber. dtsch. chem. Ges.,* **46**, 690, 1913.
3. S. MILLER, *J. Amer. chem. Soc.,* **77**, 2351, 1955.
4. K. BAHADUR, *Nature, Lond.,* **173**, 1141, 1954; K. BAKHADUR (BAHADUR) & S. RANGANAYAKI, *Zhur. obshch. Khim.,* **25**, 1629, 1955.
5. E. ORLOV, *Formal'dehid.* Moscow (ONFI), 1935; J. WALKER, *Formaldehyde.* New York, 1953.
6. S. MILLER, *Science,* **117**, 528, 1953.

Absolute Asymmetric Synthesis and Asymmetric Catalysis

E. I. KLABUNOVSKIĬ

Institute of Organic Chemistry of the Academy of Sciences of the U.S.S.R., Moscow

IT IS well known that almost all substances subserving the vital activities of organisms are optically active. In considering the process whereby the first protein bodies came into being, one must, therefore, bear in mind the way in which they became dissymmetrical, this being a necessary stage in the emergence of the functions of living substance. It is clear that, once they had developed, optically active compounds, having a greater free energy than racemates, would quickly become commoner owing to partial asymmetric synthesis or, as they act more effectively as dissymmetric catalysts, they would supplant racemates in all important vital processes. The original optically active substances did not arise by the action of other optically active compounds, but by absolute asymmetric synthesis, owing to the action of dissymmetrical physical factors, namely circularly polarized light and asymmetric adsorption.

A consideration of the experimental evidence set forth below shows convincingly the part played by the factor of dissymmetric adsorption in the production of the first optically active compounds. In view of the theoretical importance of absolute asymmetric synthesis for an understanding of the processes which led to the production of optically active substances without the participation of other optically active organic compounds we must consider both the case of absolute asymmetric synthesis of optically active compounds from substances of symmetrical structure, and examples of the resolution of asymmetrically adsorbed racemates under the influence of the structure of the crystals on which they were adsorbed.

1. THE RESOLUTION OF RACEMATES BY ASYMMETRIC ADSORPTION

Long ago, van't Hoff [1] showed the possibility of producing optical activity in racemates by bringing them into contact with optically active substances in the form of solvents, adsorbents etc.

A number of attempts to resolve racemates of mandelic and tartaric acids [2], camphor and camphorsulphonic acid and carvoxime [3] under the influence of optically active fructose, limonene and pinene, were unsuccessful. It was only when the unstable racemate of 2-acetomethylamide-5 : 4-dimethyldiphenylsul-

158

phone was crystallized from a solution of (+)-ethyl tartrate that partial optical activation was observed [4–6].

By an improvement of the method it has been possible to resolve mandelic acid (0·66°) under the action of (+)-carvone [7]. A high degree of resolution was achieved by using racemates with surface-active properties, such as camphor, terpineol and pinene, by bubbling their vapours through aqueous solutions of tannin, gelatin and leucine [8].

Better results are obtained if the resolution is carried out, not in the liquid phase, but on the surface of a solid adsorbent.

It is known that diastereoisomers can be separated on optically inactive adsorbents. On aluminium oxide one may separate the (—)-menthyl ester of DL-mandelic acid [9] and the (—)-*iso*propanolamide of DL-*iso*lysergic acid [10], and *N*-benzoyl*cyclo*heptano-2 : 3-pyrrolidine, while on glucose one may separate the brucine salt of DL-mandelic acid [11].

Similar behaviour is manifested by the superficial diastereoisomers formed by the interaction of a racemate with a layer of optically active substance carried on an inert adsorbent. Thus carbon, silica gel and aluminium oxide, when carrying a layer of optically active alkaloid, are effective agents for the resolution of mandelic acid [12].

Highly specific adsorbents of this type have recently been made [13].

Curti & Colombo [14] used silica gel, precipitated in the presence of (+)-camphorsulphonic acid. Using the artificial optically active adsorbent prepared in this way, they succeeded in obtaining a 30% resolution of camphorsulphonic acid and a 10% resolution of mandelic acid.

Grubhofer & Schleith [15] increased the efficiency of such agents considerably by using an ion-exchange resin, the carboxylic acids of which had been esterified with quinine. The quinine-containing resin (25% quinine) thus obtained would resolve racemic acids almost completely.

In this latter case, when the optically active agent is chemically associated with the carrier, the mechanism of separation is based on the asymmetric adsorption of the antipodes of the racemate; while in the previous cases, the resolution was produced by selective solution of the antipodes in a layer of optically active compound on an inert adsorbent.

Natural dissymmetric adsorbents have also been studied in connection with the resolution of racemates, for example, wool, silk, polysaccharides, colloidal adsorbents [16] and quartz.

The first attempts to demonstrate the differential adsorption of the antipodes of tropacocaine, atropine and homatropine on the protein of wool or silk were made by Willstätter [17] in 1904.

The selective adsorption of antipodes on wool was discovered in the case of racemic azo-dyes but the degree of resolution was insignificant and the findings could not always be repeated (Ingersoll, Adams, Brode, 1922–26 [18]). Slight selectivity is observed when the (+)- and (—)-forms of an acid having the formula

$$(CH_3)_2N \cdot C_6H_4 \cdot N:N \cdot C_6H_4 \cdot CO \cdot NH \cdot CH(C_6H_5) \cdot COOH$$

are adsorbed on serum protein [19], and also when strains are adsorbed on

histological preparations of tissues, a case in point being the adsorption by malig-
nant tumours of the antipodes of the stain

[20].

It would seem that only by asymmetric adsorption on a protein, genetically
associated with the spiral structure of deoxyribonucleic acids, can one explain
the selective sorption of D-alanine by the walls of the blood vessels and many
other examples of the appearance of spiral structures in natural compounds of
high molecular weight [21].

The protein of wool is very effective in resolving racemic hydroxy acids. A
considerable degree of resolution was achieved by Marthin & Kuhn [22] by
passing a continuous ribbon of wool through a solution of mandelic acid.

Bradley [23], also studying the asymmetric adsorption of mandelic acid and
its analogues on wool and casein, concluded that successful resolution was only
possible in the case of acids of which one antipode could form a superficial labile
salt by reacting with the basic groups of the protein.

For analytical purposes the asymmetric adsorbents lactose, starch and especially the cellulose of paper, have had a great application. By using lactose in
Tsvet's chromatographic method a complete separation of the antipodes of
p-phenylenebisiminocamphor was obtained (Henderson & Rule, 1938) [24].
Great efficiency of resolution was seen, both in the case of Tröger's base, containing an asymmetric atom of tervalent nitrogen, and in that of DL-chloram-
phenicol [25].

A less effective method was adsorption on starch during chromatographic
separation of complex, racemic, cobalt compounds [26]. Only in the case of cobalt
triethylenediamine did the separation amount to 10–30%.

The resolution of racemates by paper chromatography has been widely used
during the past years. Many attempts [27] to resolve racemic acids and amines on
the celluloses of paper and deacetylated chitin [28] have failed to give satisfactory
results. Only on paper treated with (+)-tartaric or (+)-camphorsulphonic acid,
at first using optically active solvents, has it been possible to separate the antipodes of β-hydroxynaphthylbenzylamine [29], phenylalanine [30] and tyrosine-
3-sulphonic acid. The separation occurs even without the use of optically active
solvents, which is explained by the asymmetric character of the adsorption on the
cellulose of the paper [31].

Many examples of the separation into antipodes of racemic amino acids and
sugars are now known and their number is steadily growing [32].

A method for the resolution of racemates of special theoretical interest has
recently been published. It is based on the selective spontaneous crystallization
of inclusion complexes, formed by the honeycomb-like spiral structure of a
complex-former, with insertion, into the spaces thus formed, of molecules of
the racemate to be resolved [33].

The adsorbent or complex-former may be optically active, racemic or inactive, but it must have a dissymmetric structure. Cases have been described in which all three forms of such complex-formers were used.

For the resolution of esters of hydroxy acids Cramer [33] used a crystalline inclusion complex with cyclodextrin. The resolution amounted to 16%. For the resolution of *sec.*-butyl bromide, Powell [34] used triorthothymotide, which crystallizes as a racemate without forming enantiomorphic crystals, but which easily gives rise to inclusion complexes.

Schlenk [35] gave an example of the use of an optically inactive adsorbent—crystals of urea—which have a spiral structure, similar to that of quartz, and which easily form inclusion complexes. When racemic 2-chloro-octane is crystallized with urea 95·6% resolution is achieved.

Quartz occupies an important position in hypotheses concerning the appearance of the first optically active substances, by virtue of its being a dissymmetric adsorbent.

Owing to its dissymmetrical lattice, quartz manifests considerable selectivity in the adsorption of compounds with molecular or crystalline dissymmetry. The selective adsorption on quartz of galactose and arabinose is well known [36]. It is found that there is epitaxy of hemihedral crystals of glycine, alanine and glutamic acid on D- and L-quartz [37].

The selective adsorption of antipodes on quartz for the purpose of resolving racemates does not show a high specificity. Thus, attempts to resolve *p*-phenylenebisiminocamphor have been unsuccessful [24] while the degree of activation of racemic butan-2-ol and the differential adsorptive capacity of D- and L-quartz for (−)-2-methylbutan-1-ol was insignificant [38].

In spite of the low selectivity of the adsorption of antipodes of a number of metallic complexes, this method has had a certain application in the establishment of their structure. A number of cases are known of the selective adsorption of one antipode of a complexes of chromium or cobalt on L-quartz [39, 40], as well as the partial resolution of racemic complexes of chromium, cobalt and platinum [41, 42].

Quartz plays an incomparably more important part as a carrier of catalysts, with the help of which one may carry out absolute asymmetric syntheses, thereby imitating enzymic activity.

2. ASYMMETRIC CATALYSIS

Enzymes and Chemical Models of Enzymes

Practically all vitally important processes are brought into being by the influence of enzymes—dissymmetric formations—the mechanism of their stereospecific action being, for the most part, still obscure. Therefore, in trying to find out the subtle ways in which these catalysts act, great interest attaches to attempts to produce dissymmetric inorganic and organic catalysts, i.e., chemical models of enzymes. This is valuable, both for the elucidation of the stereospecificity of enzymes, and for an understanding of the mechanism of asymmetric catalysis, which plays a great part in the production and development of dissymmetry in the organic world.

The multiplet theory of catalysis of A. A. Balandin [42] designates those atoms or groups of atoms in the reacting molecules, which form intermediate adsorption complexes with the catalyst, as the multiplet. The multiplet theory might be applied with advantage to the study of enzymic reactions, in that enzymes are microheterogeneous while, in a number of cases, chemical models of enzymes are also heterogeneous catalysts. Furthermore, it is easy to use the multiplet theory for the classification of reactions catalysed both by enzymes and by models of them.

All reactions of enzymic asymmetric synthesis can be divided into two groups: coupling at $C \rightleftharpoons C$ and $C \rightleftharpoons O$ bonds [43].

Table 1 shows the enzymes, the starting material and the multiplet index of the reaction.

TABLE 1

Enzymes	Starting material	Index of the reaction*
1. Oxynitrilase	Aldehyde + HCN	$\begin{array}{cc} C & \cdot & C \\ \\\| & & \| \\ O & \cdot & H \end{array} \equiv N$
2. Carboligase	Aldehydes	$\begin{array}{cc} C & \cdot & C \\ \\\| & & \| \\ O & \cdot & H \end{array}$
3. Ketoaldomutase	Aldehydes, Acids	$\begin{array}{cc} C & \cdot & H \\ \\\| & & \| \\ C & \cdot & O \end{array}$
4. Reductase	Oxo compounds	$\begin{array}{cc} C & \cdot & H \\ \\\| & & \| \\ O & \cdot & H \end{array}$

* Points are active centres of catalysts.

Optically active catalysts, even if of comparatively simple structure, exert an asymmetrizing influence on reactions, similar to that of natural enzymes.

At first, attempts were made to use optically active solvents as asymmetric influences on reactions.

It was discovered that the reaction between α-phenylethylamine and phenyl isocyanate proceeded asymmetrically in a medium of (−)-α-pinene [44] as did Grignard reactions in (+)-dimethoxybutane [45]. The extent of the asymmetry was, however, small. Only by using optically active substances as catalysts in a particular reaction, as, for example, in the decarboxylation of camphorcarboxylic acid by the action of alkaloids, was any considerable (up to 17%) difference found in the rate of decomposition of the antipodes, with the resultant production of optically active camphor.

The action of the catalyst, in this case, resembles that of carboxylase. The action of alkaloids on the asymmetric reduction of β-methyl- and β-(α-naphthyl)-cinnamic acid in the presence of hydrocinchonine [46] would appear to be analogous, as would their action in the bromination of cinchonine salts of cinnamic acid or glucosamine cinnamate [47].

There is, of course, a catalytic action by alkaloids which is even more like that of enzymes. It is seen in cases when the possibility of the formation of individual chemical compounds is ruled out. There are many such examples [48] of the formation of an excess of one antipode of esters by the catalytic action of brucine or strychnine. They are obtained by acetylation or benzoylation of racemic secondary alcohols or by the esterification of racemic chloranhydrides of acids.

The dehydration of methylphenylcarbinol [49] also belongs to this group of reactions; it occurs in the presence of 2% camphorsulphonic acid with the formation of the optically active oxide. The asymmetric dehydration of a diphenyldinaphthylallyl alcohol with the formation of a substituted allene [50] has also been reported.

The general nature of the index is such that, in spite of their variety, all these reactions belong to the group of reactions catalysed by esterases.

(+)-Camphorsulphonic acid is of special interest, being an asymmetric catalyst which, besides acting as an esterase, can also function asymmetrically as a ketoaldomutase. Asymmetric synthesis in the flavone series can be brought about by the catalytic action of (+)-bromocamphorsulphonic acid.

Optically active 4'-methoxy-5 : 6-benzoflavonone has been obtained by the method of Fujise & Sasaki [51]. (+)-7-Hydroxyflavone was obtained from 2 : 4-dihydroxychalcone, and (+)-6 : 8-dimethyl-5 : 7-diacetoxy-4'-methoxyflavone was obtained from 2' : 4' : 6'-triacetoxy-3' : 5'-dimethyl-4-methoxychalcone.

A chemical model of oxynitrilase is provided by the catalytic action of the cinchona alkaloids in the synthesis of the partially optically active nitrile of mandelic acid from benzaldehyde and HCN. This reaction extends to cover other aldehydes, including cinnamic aldehyde, anisic aldehyde, citral, piperonal and acetaldehyde [52].

Prelog & Wilhelm [53] have made a detailed study of the influence of the structure and of the configuration of the molecules of catalysts (derived from quinine and quinidine) on the efficiency of the asymmetric catalytic synthesis of the nitriles of benzallactic and mandelic acids:

$$C_6H_5 \cdot CH:CH \cdot CHO + HCN \rightarrow C_6H_5 \cdot CH:CH \cdot CH(OH) \cdot CN$$
$$C_6H_5 \cdot CHO + HCN \rightarrow C_6H_5 \cdot CH(OH) \cdot CN.$$

A definite relationship has been established between the spatial structure of the catalyst and that of the product.

Chemical models of enzymes are to be found, not only among micro-heterogeneous catalysts, but also among heterogeneous ones. The adsorption of the reacting substances on the surface of the catalyst is fundamental to any heterogeneous-catalytic process. It is, therefore, necessary to distinguish between cases in which the catalyst itself is dissymmetrical and those in which the structure of the catalyst is symmetrical but it is carried on a dissymmetrical carrier. It might be expected that, in both cases, asymmetric adsorption would lead to asymmetric catalysis.

When the $(C_2H_5)_2N$ group has been introduced into the cellulose of cotton fibres they are transformed into active catalysts which, like the alkaloids, can simulate the asymmetric activity of carboxylase in breaking down camphor-carboxylic acid, and that of oxynitrilase in catalysing the synthesis of the (−)-nitrile of mandelic acid. A catalyst of this sort was obtained in 1932 by Bredig & Gerstner [54]. Although these authors regard the example they give as the first case of heterogeneous asymmetric catalysis, namely that in which the optically selective activity of the catalyst itself is the determining factor rather than that of the carrier, nevertheless, the mechanism of the dissymmetric action of a catalyst of this sort is, in fact, dependent on asymmetric adsorption on the optically active cellulose with ordinary, optically non-specific catalysis.

The mechanism of action is the same in the case of the catalyst palladium on silk fibroin (Akabori [55]) in reactions of asymmetric reduction of $C = N$ bonds. In support of this explanation we have the facts of asymmetric adsorption on cellulose, which has had extensive application recently in the chromatographic resolution of racemic amino acids on paper [31, 32].

Attempts by Ghosh [56] to bring about asymmetric catalysis on asymmetric, dichroic, thin layers of metals (silver, platinum and palladium), which have a high optical rotation, were unsuccessful. We therefore have, for the present, no evidence for the existence of dissymmetric catalysts which are not associated with a dissymmetric carrier.

More successful experiments in the field of the optically selective activity of catalysts have been done with optically non-specific catalysts carried on a dissymmetric carrier.

Schwab and his colleagues [57] used, as their catalyst, copper, platinum or nickel, deposited in a thin layer on optically active crystals of quartz. They achieved optically selective decomposition of racemic butan-2-ol at 400–500 °C. In this reaction the optical antipodes of the racemate are dehydrated at unequal rates and an excess of one optical antipode gradually accumulates in the remaining alcohol:

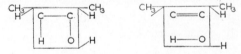

These effects have been successfully reproduced in the dehydration of other alcohols, namely menthol and methylethylbutylcarbinol [58].

Terent'ev & Klabunovskiĭ [59] have made a detailed study of the dehydration and dehydrogenation of butan-2-ol using various metal-quartz catalysts and extended their application to the absolute asymmetric synthesis of α-β-diphenyl-propionic acid by liquid-phase hydrogenation of α-phenylcinammic acid, and that of optically active pinane from α-pinene.

Ponomarev & Zelenkova [60] used nickel on quartz for the asymmetric syn-thesis of a number of derivatives of furane. The reactions occurred under pressure at 120 °C. From 1-(α-furyl)-propan-3-ol they obtained optically active 1-tetrahydrofuryl-propan-3-ol and 1 : 6-dioxa*spiro*(4 : 4)nonane; while from 1-(α-furyl)-butan-3-ol they obtained optically active 1-tetrahydrofurylbutan-3-ol and 2-methyl-1 : 6-dioxa*spiro*(4 : 4)nonane.

The action of the catalyst in evoking dissymmetry in these cases resembles that of reductase.

Using a catalyst (alkali on quartz) it has been possible to bring about the asymmetric, liquid-phase cyanethylation of 2-methyl*cyclo*hexanone. This differs essentially from the reactions previously considered in that it does not require a high temperature but takes place at 20–30 °C, i.e. under the same conditions as enzymic syntheses in nature [61, 43]:

From what has been said it is seen that much material has been collected with reference to the imitation of the asymmetric action of enzymes.

Chemical models of enzymes have an interesting peculiarity: the range of their actions is incomparably greater than that of the enzymes while they are not so stereospecific. If a particular enzyme is capable of carrying out the re-actions described under one heading in the index, then the corresponding organic catalyst will be able to bring about reactions of a completely different type with a fair degree of specificity.

Table 2 shows the enzymes, the index of their reactions and their chemical counterparts which have a comparable action.

Clearly, if the model of the enzyme has a relatively simple structure (deri-vatives of camphor), it will be hard to distinguish the parts of the molecule corresponding with the coenzyme or apoenzyme. Even in the case of the quinine alkaloids it has been possible to show that, for example, in the cyanhydrin syn-thesis, it is only the C-9 configuration in the molecule which determines the asymmetric synthesis of the oxynitrile [53]. In the case of heterogeneous catalysts it is easier to distinguish the evocation of dissymmetry from the act of catalysis since dissymmetry is evoked by asymmetric adsorption.

The results obtained by the use of catalysts, and, in particular, quartz catalysts, as chemical models of enzymes are of great theoretical interest in that they reveal the possibility of creating a new type of heterogeneous model of enzymes. Further-more, the bringing about of absolute asymmetric syntheses and asymmetric de-composition of racemates, by the use of metals deposited on optically active quartz crystals, enables a new approach to be made to an understanding of the origin of the first asymmetric substances in nature.

TABLE 2

Enzyme	Reaction index	Chemical model
1. Oxynitrilase . . Carboligase . .	$\begin{array}{ccc} C & \cdot & C \\ \| & & \| \\ O & \cdot & H \end{array}$	Alkaloids Ethylamine on cellulose
2. Reductase . .	$\begin{array}{ccc} C & \cdot & H \\ \| & & \| \\ O & \cdot & H \end{array}$	Alkaloids
3. Esterase . .	$\begin{array}{ccc} O & \cdot & C \\ \| & & \| \\ H & \cdot & X \end{array}$ X = OH or Cl	Alkaloids Camphor derivatives
4. Ketoaldomutase .	$\begin{array}{ccc} C & \cdot & H \\ \| & & \| \\ C & \cdot & O \end{array}$	Camphor derivatives Metal on quartz
5. Decarboxylase .	$\begin{array}{ccc} C & \cdot & H \\ \| & & \| \\ C & \dot{-} & O \end{array}$	Alkaloids Ethylamine on cellulose

6. No analogue. Action
     the reverse of that
     of   glutamino-
     dehydrase
	$\begin{array}{ccc} C\rceil & \cdot & H \\ \| & & \| \\ N & \cdot & H \end{array}$	Palladium on silk

7. No analogue .	$\begin{array}{ccc} C & \dot{-} & C \\ \| & & \| \\ H & \cdot & O \end{array}$	Metals and oxides on quartz
8. No analogue .	$\begin{array}{ccc} C & \cdot & H \\ \| & & \| \\ C & \cdot & H \end{array}$	Metals on quartz
9. No analogue .	$\begin{array}{ccc} C & \cdot & C \\ \| & & \| \\ C & \cdot & H \end{array}$	Alkali on quartz

REFERENCES

1. J. H. VAN'T HOFF, *Die Lagerung der Atome im Raume*, 3 Aufl. Braunschweig, 1908.
2. Cf. *J. phys. Chem.*, **20**, 412, 1896; *J. Amer. chem. Soc.*, **23**, 255, 1900; *Ber. dtsch. chem. Ges.*, **64**, 342, 1931.
3. S. GOLDSCHMIDT & H. C. COOPER, *Z. phys. Chem.*, **26**, 714, 1898.
4. T. S. PATTERSON & C. BUCHANAN, *J. chem. Soc.*, p. 290, 1940.
5. T. S. PATTERSON & A. H. LAMBERTON, *J. chem. Soc.*, p. 1453, 1937.
6. C. BUCHANAN & S. H. GRAHAM, *J. chem. Soc.*, p. 500, 1950.
7. E. SCHRÖER, *Ber. dtsch. chem. Ges.*, **65**, 966, 1932.
8. G. KARAGUNIS & P. NIKOLAIDIS, *Koll. Z.*, **106**, 112, 1944; *Z. angew. Chem.*, **48**, 74, 276, 1935.
9. M. JAMISON & E. TURNER, *J. chem. Soc.*, p. 611, 1942.
10. A. STOLL & A. HOFFMANN, *Hoppe-Seyl. Z.*, **251**, 155, 1938.
11. V. PRELOG & V. GEYER, *Helv. chim. Acta*, **28**, 576, 1945; L. ZECHMEISTER, *Ann. N.Y. Acad. Sci.*, **49**, 220, 1948. H. B. HASS, T. DE VRIES & H. H. JAFFE, *J. Amer. chem. Soc.*, **65**, 1486, 1943.
12. H. FISCHGOLD & K. AMMON, *Biochem. Z.*, **234**, 39, 1931.
13. R. G. HALDEMAN & P. H. EMMETT, *J. phys. Chem.*, **59**, 1039, 1955.
14. R. CURTI & U. COLOMBO, *J. Amer. chem. Soc.*, **74**, 3961, 1952; A. P. TERENT'EV & V. M. POTAPOV, *Priroda*, **5**, 37, 1955.
15. W. GRUBHOFER & L. SCHLEITH, *Naturwissenschaften*, **40**, 508, 1953.
16. M. JOHNSON, *The selective adsorption of the various types of aminoacids on several colloidal adsorbents.* Diss., Washington, Catholic Univ. of Amer. Press, 1938.
17. R. WILLSTÄTTER, *Ber. dtsch. chem. Ges.*, **37**, 3758, 1904.
18. Cf. *J. Amer. chem. Soc.*, **41**, 1264, 1919; **44**, 2930, 1922; **45**, 1990, 1923; **46**, 2032, 1924; **63**, 923, 1941; *J. chem. Soc.*, **127**, 1731, 1925; p. 1568, 1939; *Nature, Lond.*, **141**, 917, 1938; **142**, 163, 1938.
19. F. KÖGL, J. G. FABER & Z. C. DEBOER, *Rec. Trav. chim. Pays-Bas*, **69**. 482, 1950; *Expos. ann. Biochim. med.*, **11**, 19, 1950.
20. F. KARUSH, *J. phys. Chem.*, **56**, 70, 1952.
21. F. KRIK (CRICK), *Khimicheskaya Nauka i Promyshlennost'*, **1** (4), 472, 1956; D. M. MATTHEWS & D. H. SMYTH, *J. Physiol.*, **116**, 20P, 1952.
22. H. MARTHIN & W. KUHN, *Z. Elektrochem.*, **47**, 216, 1941.
23. W. BRADLEY & G. C. EASTY, *J. chem. Soc.*, p. 499, 1951; p. 1513, 1953; *Nature, Lond.*, **173**, 312, 1954; *Disc. Faraday Soc.*, **16**, 152, 1954. *Chem. & Ind.*, p. 574, 1954.
24. G. M. HENDERSON & H. G. RULE, *J. chem. Soc.*, p. 1568, 1939; *Nature, Lond.*, **141**, 917, 1938; **142**, 163, 1938.
25. V. PRELOG & P. WIELAND, *Helv. chim. acta*, **27**, 1127, 1944; *Referativnyǐ Zhurnal (Khimiya)*, 71826, 1956.
26. H. KREBS & R. RASCHE, *Naturwissenschaften*, **41**, 63, 1954; *Z. anorg. chem.*, **276**, 236, 1954.
27. C. E. DENT, *Biochem. J.*, **43**, 169, 1948; *J. chem. Soc.*, p. 1679, 1948.
28. A. SANTORO, *Chem. Abstr.*, **48**, 4448i, 1954.
29. G. B. BONINO & V. CARASSITI, *Nature, Lond.*, **167**, 569, 1951; *R.C. Accad. Lincei*, **9**, 229, 1950.
30. S. BERLINGOZZI, G. SERCHI & G. ADEMBRI, *Sperimentale (Ser. Chim. biol.)*, **2**, 89. 1951; *Chem. Abstr.*, **46**, 9070g, 1952.
31. H. KOTAKE, T. SAKAN, N. NAKAMURA & S. SENOH, *J. Amer. chem. Soc.*, **73**, 7973, 1951; *J. chem. Soc. Japan*, **72**, 795, 1951; *J. Inst. Polyt., Osaka*, Ser. C, **2**, 29, 1951; *Chem. Abstr.*, 7075, 1953; E. I. KLABUNOVSKIĬ, *Priroda* (2), 88, 1955; S. K. YATKAR & D. S. SASTRY, *J. Univ. Poona Sci. Technol.*, **4**, 69, 1953; *Chem. Abstr.*, **78**, 1240i, 1954.
32. P. BURMA & B. BANERJEE, *Sci. & Cult.*, **15**, 363, 1950; *Chem. Abstr.*, **45**, 3753, 1951; R. WEICHERT, *Acta chem. scand.*, **8**, 1542, 1954; **9**, 547, 1955; *Z. Naturforsch.*, **7b**, 677, 1952; *Ark. Kemi*, **5**, 523, 553, 1953; *Hoppe-Seyl. Z.*, **279**, 27, 1943; **281**, 120, 1944; C. E. DALGLIESH, *J. chem. Soc.*, p. 137, 3940, 1952; *Biochem. J.*, **52**, 3, 1952; K. CLOSS, *Chem. & Ind.*, p. 103, 1953; Y. J. FUJISAWA, *Chem. Abstr.*, **48**, 13550c, 1954; M. MASON, *J. biol. Chem.*, **195**, 515, 1952; J. P. LAMBOOY, *J. Amer.*

chem. Soc., **76**, 133, 1954; N. NAKAMURA, *J. chem. Soc. Japan*, **72**, 789, 1951; E. I. KLABUNOVSKIĬ, *Priroda*, **11**, 86, 1955; *Chem. Abstr.*, **50**, 11961g, 1956.

33. F. CRAMER, *Z. angew. Chem.*, **64**, 136, 1952; **68**, 115, 1956.
34. H. M. POWELL, *Nature, Lond.*, **170**, 155, 1952; *Endeavour*, **15**, 20, 1956; *J. chem. Soc.*, p. 3747, 1952; W. BAKER & J. F. MC OMIE, *Chem. & Ind.*, p. 256, 1955; *J. chem. Soc.*, p. 61, 1948; p. 1443, 1952; *Angew. Chem.*, **68**, 115, 1956.
35. W. SCHLENK, *Experientia*, **5**, 200, 1949; **8**, 337, 1952; *Angew. Chem.*, **67**, 762, 1955; *Svensk kem. Tidskr.*, **67**, 435, 1955.
36. L. HOLZAPFEL, *Z. Elektrochem.*, **55**, 577, 1951.
37. H. SEIFERT, *Naturwissenschaften*, **42**, 13, 1955; *Z. Elektrochem.*, **59**, 409, 1955.
38. E. I. KLABUNOVSKIĬ & V. V. PATRIKEEV, *Dokl. Akad. Nauk S.S.S.R.*, **78** (3), 485, 1951; N. I. SHUĬKIN, V. V. PATRIKEEV & E. I. KLABUNOVSKIĬ, Avt. Svid., No. 95526, 30/Mai, 1953.
39. R. TSUCHIDA & M. KOBAYASHI, *Bull. Chem. Soc. Japan*, **6**, 342, 1936.
40. G. K. SCHWEITZER & C. K. TALBOTT, *Chem. Abstr.*, **46**, 11004, 1952.
41. I. R. KUEBLER & J. C. BAILAR, *J. Amer. chem. Soc.*, **74**, 3535, 1952; **75**, 4574, 1953; *Nature, Lond.*, **142**, 162, 1938.
42. A. A. BALANDIN, *Zhur. russ. fiz. Khim. Obshch.*, **61**, 900, 1929; *Izv. Akad. Nauk S.S.S.R.*, **4**, 624, 1955.
43. E. I. KLABUNOVSKIĬ, *Khimicheskaya Nauka i Promyshlennost'*, **2**, No. 2, 197, 1957.
44. R. WEGLER, *Leibigs Ann.*, **498**, 62, 1932.
45. H. L. COHEN & G. F. WRIGHT, *J. org. Chem.*, **18**, 432, 1953.
46. D. L. LIPKIN & T. D. STEWART, *J. Amer. chem. Soc.*, **61**, 3295, 3297, 1939.
47. H. ERLENMEYER, *Helv. chim. Acta*, **13**, 731, 1930.
48. R. WEGLER, *Liebigs Ann.*, **498**, 62, 1932; **506**, 77, 1933; **510**, 72, 1934.
49. H. WUITS, *Bull. Soc. chim. Belg.*, **30**, 30, 1921.
50. P. MAITLAND & W. H. MILLS, *J. chem. Soc.*, p. 987, 1936.
51. S. FUJISE & H. SASAKI, *Ber. dtsch. chem. Ges.*, **71**, 341, 1938; *J. chem. Soc. Japan*, **72**, 1073, 1951.
52. G. BREDIG & P. S. FISKE, *Biochem. Z.*, **46**, 7, 1918; G. BREDIG & M. MINAEFF, *Biochem. Z.*, **249**, 241, 1932.
53. V. PRELOG & M. WILHELM, *Helv. chim. Acta*, **37**, 1634, 1954.
54. G. BREDIG & F. GERSTNER, *Biochem. Z.*, **250**, 414, 1932.
55. S. AKABORI, *Nature, Lond.*, **178**, 323, 1956; *Kagaku*, **45** (2), 54, 1955; *Biokhimiya*, **22** (1-2), 154, 1957.
56. J. G. GHOSH, *J. Indian chem. Soc.*, **16**, 51, 1939.
57. G. M. SCHWAB, F. ROST & L. RUDOLPH, *Kolloidzschr.*, **68**, 157, 1934; *Naturwissenschaften*, **12**, 237, 1932.
58. A. STANKJEWIECZ, Diss. Königsberg, 1938.
59. A. P. TERENT'EV, E. I. KLABUNOVSKIĬ, *Sbornik Stateĭ po obshcheĭ Khimii*, Vol. 2, p. 1521, 1598, 1953; *Uchen. Zapiski. Moskov. Gos. Univ.*, **151**, 145, 1951.
60. A. A. PONOMAREV & V. V. ZELENKOVA, *Zhur. obshch. Khim.*, **23**, 1543, 1953; *Dokl. Akad. Nauk S.S.S.R.*, **87**, 423, 1952.
61. A. P. TERENT'EV, E. I. KLABUNOVSKIĬ & E. I. BUDOVSKIĬ, *Sbornik Stateĭ po obshcheĭ Khimii*, Vol. 2, p. 1612, 1953.

Some Conditions for the Appearance of Life on the Earth

R. L. BERG

Biological Faculty, Leningrad State University, Leningrad

IN MY communication discussion will be focused on the conditions that could have favoured the origin of the orderly organization of matter which we call life.

Thanks to the work of Bernal, Haldane, Terenin and Pirie, it has become clearer and clearer in recent years that life could only have developed in the presence of a solid substrate or, as Terenin has just said, the presence of a solid substrate made possible the origin of life. In the triphasic system of a porous solid substrate permeated by air and water, we have the necessary, specific condition without which life could not have come into being.

If we are going to adopt a geophysical, rather than a physico-chemical approach to the subject, the gas, liquid and solid substrate must be taken as being the atmosphere, hydrosphere and lithosphere respectively. The solid substrate might be represented by dry land or the bottom or margin of an area of water or it might be suspended in water. The liquid and gaseous substrates might be just as varied in nature.

Where then did life arise on our planet—on land or in the ocean? There are, at present, two contradictory ideas on this question. On the one hand there is the very widely supported hypothesis that life originated in the ocean, and, on the other, the suggestion of Vil'yams, Kholodnyĭ and L. S. Berg, that the dry land was the cradle of life. This old argument was started by the ancient Greeks. Vernadskiĭ put forward a peculiar point of view on this question. 'The first manifestation of life during the creation of the biosphere must have arisen, not in the form of the appearance of any one type of organism but in the form of associations corresponding to the geochemical functions of life' says Vernadskiĭ. In other words, there was a multiple origin of life, it developed under various conditions in various forms. I shall bring forward a number of arguments in favour of the theory of the multiple biopoiesis.

Both the supporters of the theory that life arose in the ocean and those of the theory that it arose on dry land put forward a number of arguments in defence of their positions. Taken together, the arguments of both sides serve to substantiate the idea of the multiple origin of life. In fact, I shall dispute the hypotheses that life could have arisen only in water or only on land.

The most important arguments in favour of the hypothesis that life originated exclusively in the ocean are: (1) the similarity between the salt composition of the body fluids of land animals and that of the waters of the ocean; (2) the indispensability of water for processes of fertilization and for the occurrence of the early stages of embryonic life in land animals and some plants, also the adaptation of gametes to movement through an aqueous medium and (3) the marine nature of the earliest sedimentary deposits of biogenic origin.

The similarity in the salt composition of the waters of the ocean and that of the body fluids of land animals could be accounted for, as Vernadskiĭ explained in 1921, by a parallel accumulation of salts in the organism and in the sea water, although the mechanism of this accumulation and regulation is completely different in the two cases.

The indispensability of water for the processes of fertilization shows, at most, that the ancestors of the group of animals or plants in question lived in an aqueous medium, but this fact must not be regarded as proof that life originated in the ocean. In most plants the pollen cannot even endure moistening. The nuclei of the pollen tube making their own ways into the ovarian sac of angiosperms do not constitute a locomotor apparatus like the locomotor apparatus of sper-matozoa. As Gerassimova-Navashina has shown, the forces which repel these nuclei from one another are similar to those which act in every mitotic division of a cell.

The presence of the external skeletons which make up the strata of sedimentary formations demonstrate the secondary nature of the creatures which gave rise to these formations. The exoskeleton is, in essence, a screen. The first inhabi-tants of the Earth are supposed to have had no exoskeletons. We must also remember that land organisms leave less recognizable remains than do marine organisms. Clearly, not one of the arguments used in favour of the exclusively marine origin of life will withstand criticism.

The most serious consideration which excludes, not merely all open waters, but also the whole surface of the land, from having been the seat of biopoiesis was put forward by L. S. Berg in 1947. He stated that, at present, life is protected from the harmful effects of ultraviolet radiation by the so-called 'ozone screen'. Free oxygen serves as a shield for living things. However, there was no oxygen in the primaeval atmosphere. Living things are the only sources which could bring about a constant oxygen content in the atmosphere. L. S. Berg poses the question: What protected living things from short-wave radiation during their development?

The idea of something which served the purpose of the ozone screen thus came forward. According to L. S. Berg, life came into being 'in the solid substrate of the dry land, within the superficial layers of mechanically shattered rocky formations, and there it existed, concealed from the destructive ultraviolet rays while, at the same time, being accessible to the external world and to the heat radiation of the Sun.'

It was living organisms that produced the free oxygen of the atmosphere and only then did they colonize the dry land and open water.

At present we have some reason to believe that there is a constant source of free oxygen in the atmosphere itself and that there are, or once were, analogues of the ozone screen, not only in the lithosphere, but also in the hydrosphere and atmosphere.

According to Urey, short-wave radiation played a decisive part in the evolution of the atmosphere. By causing the dissociation of water it enabled free oxygen and hydrogen to be formed. The oxygen liberated from the water of the air enabled further evolution of the atmosphere to occur. It took part in the formation of organic compounds and served as a screen. Radiations and, in particular, short-wave radiations, while making possible the synthesis of organic compounds (as is mentioned in the communications of Miller, Bahadur, Pavlovskaya and Pasynskiǐ to this Symposium), liberated, at the same time, free oxygen and thus gave rise to a carrier to their own action, which carrier absorbs the excess of ultraviolet radiations that might otherwise have set a limit to the further evolution of organic substances.

However, other substances in the hydrosphere and atmosphere could also act as a screen. As a number of workers have shown, nitrogen, as well as oxygen, has absorption bands in the ultraviolet part of the spectrum. Compounds of nitrogen and oxygen and carbon dioxide can be decomposed by irradiation.

At my request K. S. Shifrin calculated the thickness of a layer of carbon dioxide and that of a layer of water sufficient to prevent the passage of the short-wave radiations which are absorbed by ozone if it is present in the atmosphere in an amount equivalent to a layer 3 mm thick at N.T.P. The thickness of such a layer of CO_2 is just 500 m and that of a corresponding layer of clear water is 10 m. If the water is turbid the thickness might be less.

According to Urey the transition from the reducing to the oxidizing atmosphere was accompanied in particular by the formation of CO_2. Chamberlin maintains that the aggregate of CO_2 laid down in sedimentary deposits, used up in the production of coal, peat, bitumen, humus, etc., and now present in the living material of the biosphere, is about 400 times greater than that now contained in the atmosphere and oceans. If this is true, then, of course, this carbon dioxide could have acted as a screen.

Water is an unsatisfactory screen, for its superficial layer is constantly being mixed. The turbulent hydrosphere could not serve as a screen for plankton.

Water could only act as a screen for deep-living forms of life.

Shifrin's calculation shows that living things attached to the floor of shallow basins would have been shielded from ultraviolet radiations even in the absence of any atmospheric 'protoscreen'. This calculation is further confirmation of Markov's hypothesis that life originated on the bottoms of shallow lagoons. However, an atmospheric 'protoscreen' did, in fact, exist.

The Earth is an open system. The energy of the Sun is the cause of the migration of matter which, at first, can only have been a hindrance to the origin of life. In the course of time, owing to the grinding up of rock formations and the appearance of a triphasic system on the surface of the Earth, there arose obstacles to the turbulent movement of the air and water. This created the conditions required for the origin of life. The surface of the land, the weathered superficial layers of the crust of the Earth, shallow continental basins and lagoons of the ocean, were the arenas in which life came into being on our planet in the form of a multifarious host of germs.

Session II.   DISCUSSION

I. E. EL'PINER & A. V. SOKOL'SKAYA (U.S.S.R.):

The Part Played by Acoustic Energy in the Initiation of Chemical Processes under Natural Conditions

The experimental data brought forward at this meeting encourage us to express some considerations which indicate that sonic and supersonic vibrations, as well as other physical agents (ultraviolet radiations, electric discharges and radioactive decay—Miller, Pasynskiĭ and Pavlovskaya) may have served as a source of energy for the synthesis of the fundamental products which served as material for the building up of living organisms in the earliest period of the existence of our planet.

As long ago as 1950, one of us (El'piner, 1950) carried out special experiments which showed that reduction of iodine occurs when water, saturated with gaseous hydrogen and molecular iodine, is submitted to the action of supersonic vibrations. It would appear that this process takes place in cavitational spaces into which molecules of iodine, as well as gaseous hydrogen, diffuse. The ionization (or dissociation) of iodine is closely associated with ionization (or dissociation) of hydrogen. Later Henglin (1956) also observed the reduction of iodine in water saturated with hydrogen and molecular iodine when submitted to supersonic vibrations.

Recently we have succeeded in demonstrating that other gases are also activated (dissociated) when acted on by supersonic vibrations in water. For example, it was found that ammonia is formed when hydrogen and nitrogen in water are submitted to sonic vibrations.

The action of the vibrations was applied to water, nitrogen and hydrogen in glass vessels, the intensity of the supersonic vibrations was 6–7 watts/cm^2 of the emitting surface (the frequency was 380 and 750 kilocycles). The volume of water submitted to the vibrations was 10 ml. In preliminary studies the water was saturated simultaneously with gaseous nitrogen and hydrogen. These gases had been carefully freed from any admixture of oxygen.

The amount of ammonia in the water before and after the action of the vibrations was determined by Nessler's method (Table 1).

As may be seen from the table, the amount of ammonia formed increases as the action of the vibrations is prolonged. If the water is saturated with nitrogen alone, ammonia does not appear until the vibrations have been applied for a long time (120 minutes) and then only in extremely small amounts. Similarly, only very small amounts of ammonia are found when water is submitted to the action of supersonic vibrations for a long time in the presence of nitrogen and oxygen. This agrees with some findings reported in the literature (Beuthe, 1933 and Polotskiĭ, 1947). The main compounds formed when supersonic vibrations act on water saturated with nitrogen in the presence of oxygen are oxides of nitrogen.

The presence of carbon monoxide in gaseous mixtures of nitrogen and hydrogen does not hinder the formation of ammonia when they are acted on by supersonic vibrations in water. Carbon monoxide was produced by the decomposition of oxalic and formic acids by sulphuric acid on gentle warming.

Later it became clear that, in addition to ammonia, hydrogen cyanide was to be found in water containing a gaseous mixture of nitrogen and hydrogen if carbon monoxide was also present. We used Gin''yar's method for determining this hydrogen cyanide. The method is based on the reaction of transformation of pikrinic acid into purpuric acid in the presence of hydrocyanic acid.

Numerous experiments have shown that when 4 ml. of water is exposed to ultrasonic vibrations for 3 hours in the presence of N_2, CO and H_2, 15 μg of HCN is formed per ml of water.

TABLE I

Amount of ammonia synthesized when distilled water saturated with various gases is exposed to supersonic vibrations

Duration of exposure (min.)	Amount of ammonia in μg/ml water exposed to supersonic vibrations in the presence of the following gases				
	Hydrogen H_2	Nitrogen N_2	Hydrogen and nitrogen $(H_2 + N_2)$	Hydrogen nitrogen and carbon monoxide $(H_2 + N_2 + CO)$	Air
50	—	—	0·85	—	—
60	0	0	1·25	—	0·04
120	—	0·62	2·6	—	—
180	—	—	8·7	—	0·62
180	—	—	—	7·8	—
180	—	—	—	7·1	—
180	—	—	—	8·5*	—
180	—	—	9·0†	6·5†	—
360	—	—	12·5	—	—

* The exposure to supersonic vibration was carried out in 0·1 N-HCl.
† The exposure to supersonic vibration was carried out in 1% succinic acid.

Hydrocyanic acid was not found in water exposed to supersonic vibrations in the presence of oxygen or of nitrogen alone, or in that of gaseous mixtures of nitrogen and hydrogen. As a control we also used water containing ammonia or nitrous acid in view of the possibility that these substances might be formed in water exposed to supersonic vibrations.

A similar amount of hydrocyanic acid was also found when methane was substituted for carbon monoxide in the gaseous mixtures used.

The formation of hydrocyanic acid in our experiments is, most probably, to be attributed to an interaction between activated nitrogen and aldehydes or other carbon-containing compounds. As our investigations have shown formaldehyde is, in fact, found in water exposed to supersonic vibrations if this water contains hydrogen, nitrogen and carbon monoxide (Table 2).

TABLE 2

Amount of formaldehyde formed related to the nature of the gases with which the water is saturated and to the duration of exposure to supersonic vibrations

Reacting mixture	Duration of exposure (min.)	Amount of formaldehyde formed (μg/ml)
10 ml distilled water with CO + H_2 + N_2 .	—	0
,, ,, ,, .	60	1·8
,, ,, ,, .	120	6·0
,, ,, ,, .	180	12·6
10 ml distilled water + air . . .	180	0·4

In conclusion, it must be pointed out that there must have been sources of acoustic energy of comparatively great intensity at some time, in the form of a number of phenomena which took place at various periods in the history of the Earth (earthquakes, upheavals of the sea, waterfalls, etc.). It would be valuable to make a quantitative calculation of the acoustic energy which has been produced and which is now being produced under natural conditions.

M. Vol'kenshtein (U.S.S.R):

In connection with Prof. Terent'ev's contribution I should like to make the following remarks.

The role of asymmetry, i.e. the stereochemical fixity of macromolecular structures in biology, is extremely important. Asymmetry ensures more accurate and richer methods of recording information and passing it on in the process of self-reproduction. Life, as we know it now, has no other methods. Racemic life may be considered to be no more than a speculative idea.

The problem may be broken down into the following questions:

1. What possible causes could there have been for the formation of pure optical antipodes on the surface of the Earth? Were these causes biogenic or abiogenic?

2. What were the causes for the accumulation in the biosphere of particular antipodes of the original vitally important substances?

I believe that pure antipodes can be produced without biogenesis and that therefore, for biological problems it is only necessary to answer the second question. Let us, however, begin by considering the first for a while.

Local asymmetry of chance origin is commonly found in inorganic nature, for example, in beds of quartz. The reasons for this are quite obvious.

I agree with Prof Terent'ev that catalysis on the surface of asymmetric crystals might lead to the appearance of pure antipodes of simple organic molecules, in particular, amino acids. Their formation can, however, hardly be attributed to the phenomenon of circular dichroism. As concerns this phenomenon, the position of inorganic and living nature should be the same in principle. However, asymmetry is only produced in the latter. On the other hand the degree of circular polarization in scattered and reflected light on the surface of the Earth is very slight and such circular polarization could hardly be the cause of the asymmetry which we can observe.

To my mind we must include among the sources of asymmetry thermodynamic fluctuations in the concentrations of pure antipodes. How did they accumulate in the biosphere?

One can give a number of reasons why life should, in principle, make use of large rather than small molecules—polymers rather than monomers. In this connection stress should be laid on the great importance of recent work by the Italian chemist Natta on the synthesis of so-called isotactic and syndiatactic polymers, which are chain-like macromolecules with stereochemically fixed structures. Stereospecific catalytic synthesis probably also forms the basis of life.

Originally life also developed in alternative ways at random, probably being righthanded in some parts of the world and left-handed in others. Later, evolution led to the disappearance of one of these forms. Why? Probably because the evolutionary process, which could originally follow either the *dextro* or *laevo* path, when once started in a particular course could not stop and did not alter its course. There is thus no difficulty in imagining the existence of life, exactly equivalent to our own, but based on the opposite antipodes.

In conclusion, it must be pointed out that any proper scientific study of the problem of the accumulation of asymmetry during the process of evolution should begin with the study of irreversible processes using thermodynamic methods. Professor Prigogine's address will be devoted to this field of physics and the application of such ideas to biology.

A. G. Pasynskiĭ (U.S.S.R.):

The Asymmetry of Organic Substances

As A. I. Oparin maintained, one of the fundamental problems with which the Symposium is concerned is that of the emergence of asymmetry among organic compounds. The interesting papers of Terent'ev & Klabunovskiĭ, to which we listened yesterday and to-day and also the contributions of Akabori and others to come, deal with this subject. From their evidence it is clear that a considerable degree of asymmetric synthesis and resolution of racemates occurs under the influence of previously existing optically active substances such as solvents, etc.; while absolute asymmetric synthesis takes place also in the presence of previously existing optically active catalysts or enzymes, alkaloids, optical isomorphs of quartz etc., on the surfaces of which one antipode is adsorbed or reacts more quickly than the other. The action of circularly polarized light is also very important. In my own contribution I wished to draw attention to the importance, in this connection, of recent achievements in the production of stereospecific or so-called isotactic polymers having a determinate spatial arrangement of their side groups. In his interesting work with Ziegler's catalyst $[Al(C_2H_5)_3 + TiCl_4]$ Professor Natta has shown that, on this catalyst, which is not itself optically active, one may, owing to the oriented adsorption of phenyl groups, obtain molecules of polystyrene with a strictly regular spatial disposition of side groups Alongside the ordinary vinyl polymer, in which the L- and D-configurations are arranged at random, there are formed long series of L-forms alternating with series of D-forms. In the work of Akabori and his colleagues, as Oparin stated in his recent book, aldehydes react with polyglycine adsorbed on the surface of kaolin in its *cis*-form. This should lead to all the amino acid residues which are synthesized into any one chain having the same spatial configuration. The oriented adsorption of monomers may not in itself have been significant, but the arrangement of the links of the chain of the polymer relative to one another was fixed and the conditions of maximal saturation of the bonds between the side groups and the closeness of the packing may have led to a specific type of twisting of the polymeric chains (e.g., the spiral configuration proposed by Pauling and Corey), and this might have been an important step on the way to pure asymmetric synthesis. In the presence of catalytic substances structures of this kind which themselves possessed catalytic properties, might act as primitive enzymes evoking asymmetry like those, for example, of which Klabunovskiĭ spoke in his paper. Thus it is possible that asymmetry did not arise because optically active monomers were first formed and optically active polymers were then formed from them but, on the contrary, stereospecific polymerization led to the formation of catalysts of high molecular weight which evoked asymmetry. Later, on account of these catalysts, optically active substances of low molecular weight began to be prevalent. Thus these latter would be, essentially, of secondary origin. As Klabunovskiĭ has already stated, the appearance of optical asymmetry in an organism was important in that it hastened reactions within that organism and thus favoured its evolution.

E. I. KLABUNOVSKIĬ & V. V. PATRIKEEV (U.S.S.R.):

Some Questions of Symmetry and Asymmetry in the Animal and Plant Worlds

Bilateral symmetry of the body is very prevalent among higher animals. This means that the right and left halves of their bodies are mirror images of one another. The internal organs of these animals are, however, often arranged asymmetrically, and this is undoubtedly determined by the history of the development of the living world [1]. The bilateral symmetry of the form of the body of animal organisms is a result of the adaptation of relatively highly organized beings to their conditions of life, requiring directed participation in the inorganic natural world around them which is, on the whole, symmetrical [2, 3]. However, as well as these, there are organisms which, for the most part, lead a sessile life, and which have asymmetrical bodies; among these are, for example, shrubs and trees among plants and gastropod molluscs among animals. Such organisms manifest so-called enantiomorphism so that they can exist in two independent dissymmetric forms. A large collection of factual material concerning the extensive prevalence of dissymmetry in the animal and vegetable kingdoms has been assembled in his book by the zoologist Ludwig [4].

The conditions for the existence in nature of either the one or the other of two dissymmetric forms are identical and one would therefore expect that both forms would be equally distributed in nature. In many cases, however, only one form is prevalent. What is the reason for this? It is known that the molecules of proteins and carbohydrates, which are the essential components of the protoplasm of the cells of animal and vegetable organisms, are dissymmetrical in structure. It would therefore be natural to suppose that this 'microdissymmetry' of the molecules would also manifest itself, to some extent, in the shape of the body. Such a conclusion would, however, be too hasty, we have no experimental proof that such is the case. Such a mechanistic concept of the relationship between the dissymmetry of the molecules which compose the protoplasm and dissymmetry of the external form of the body or its separate organs will always lead to failure, as, for example, the attempt [5] to establish a difference in the effect of powdered L- or D-quartz on the right and left lungs of animals, although these did not show spiral dissymmetry.

Let us first consider the phenomenon of dissymmetry in inorganic nature which must have preceded the organic world. The inorganic world differs fundamentally from the organic in that one optical isomer does not predominate in it; as G. G. Lemmleïn [6] has shown in the case of quartz, optically active crystals always form closely associated twins or both enantiomorphs are found together in equal amounts in the mineral formation where they occur. Nevertheless, the dissymmetry of such minerals probably played some part in the development of organic living material on the Earth [7, 8]. It is known that optically active crystals of quartz may serve as a dissymmetric factor in catalytic reactions which take place under conditions similar to those under which natural syntheses occur, and this is experimental proof that the dissymmetric lattices of crystals could play a part in the creation of living material [9]. In nature, however, such reactions occurring on the surfaces of crystals could not lead to a preponderance of one optical isomer because the amounts of D- and L-crystals are equal in the inorganic world. We must therefore look for some other cause for the occurrence of dissymmetric organic substances. Photosynthesis might constitute such a factor.

The possibility of producing such an effect when an asymmetric reaction occurs under the photosynthetic influence of circularly polarized light, even when the preponderance of one sign is only very small, has been confirmed by the well-known experiments of Kuhn, Tenney et al. [10]. Their results are convincing testimony of the selective action of circularly polarized light on the vital activities of living material. The predominance of one structural isomer of amino acids in the proteins of protoplasm is, therefore, not a chance occurrence. It is explained by the action of the right circularly polarized component of scattered sunlight throughout the long years of the evolution of the living world. This component has been shown to exist by many experiments [11]. The amount of circularly polarized light in relation to the total radiation is greater at higher latitudes than close to the equator. In view of this one would expect a corresponding picture of the geographic distribution on the Earth of animals having a dissymmetric form of body; in the equatorial zone there should be an equal prevalence of right and left forms, while in higher latitudes one form should predominate. Not only latitude, but height above sea level also sometimes determines the prevalence of one or other spiral form of the body and this must surely be related to the amount of polarized light falling on the particular portion of the surface of the Earth. As concerns the vegetable kingdom, here the arrangement of the leaves is characteristically spiral or alternate but the preponderance of one form in association with geographical distribution has never been observed anywhere [12]. The plant world would appear to be a kind of bridge between the molecular-racemic world of inorganic nature and the animal kingdom with its clearly expressed dissymmetry of the macromolecules of proteins of protoplasm. It would appear that the relatively small proportion of optically active constituents in comparison with the total mass of racemic compounds is not enough for it to be manifested as morphological dissymmetry of the body. It is, however, manifest in the configuration of the elements of the detailed structure of plants: according to the observations of Alpatov [13] the thickenings in the walls of the conducting vessels are always in the form of a left-handed spiral, regardless of the arrangement of the leaves of the plant.

There is another type of living organism, the soil bacterium Bacillus mycoides, which has a colony reminding one of a spiral nebula, the direction of growth being counterclockwise (left-handed form). Investigations by Nastyukova [14] have shown that all soils in the U.S.S.R. are inhabited by this left-handed form alone, with the exception of the Transcaucasus, Central Asia and the Ussuriï region where the right-handed form predominates. This form also predominates in some of the mountainous regions of South America while the left-handed form is widely distributed on the plains. A similar specificity of geographical distribution is also seen among widely distributed marine molluscs, the *Prosobranchia* (Orders *Archeogastropoda* and *Mesogastropoda* and sub-order *Steno-glossa*) which inhabit all warm seas. Among these the dextrotropic form predominates, the shell being twisted like a right-handed screw [15]. The laevotropic form is extremely rare, representing no more than 0·01–0·0005% of individuals. The preponderance of the dextrotropic form in molluscs would seem to have become more widespread in relatively recent times. Thus, shells of molluscs of the species *Fusus antiquus* dug up from lower Permian formations and the protoconchs of some molluscs are of the laevo-tropic configuration, while contemporary forms are of the dextrotropic configuration.

Bearing in mind the special conditions of the equatorial zone, which enable more ancient forms of organism to be preserved, we should remember that the optical activity of petroleum is undoubtedly of organic origin. In this connection it is worth calling attention to the fact that metamorphosed petroleums are distributed everywhere, the exception being just the laevorotatory petroleums of the equatorial belt, from Java, Borneo and South America.

The salient evidence concerning the geographical distribution of *dextro* and *laevo* forms of organism (and also petroleums) derived from the scanty literature is collected in Table I. The signs D and L denote right-handed and left-handed (or, in the case of petroleums, dextrorotatory and laevorotatory) forms respectively.

TABLE I

Geographical distribution of dissymmetric forms

Contemporary forms	High latitudes	Found in the equatorial zone and areas of slight polarization
Colonies of *B. mycoides* . .	L	L and D
Molluscs—*Prosobranchia* . .	D	D and L
Lonistes, Planorbis .	D	D and L
Partula saturnalis . . .	—	D and L
Achatinella mustelina . . .	—	D and L
Ancient forms		
Molluscs—*Fusus antiquus* . .	—	L and (D ?)
Gastropoda (protoconch)	—	L and (D ?)
Petroleums	D	D and L

As may be seen from the table the inverse, or less widely distributed organisms (molluscs or bacteria) which have retained their form since ancient times, are to be found in those places where radiation is even now considerable, namely, in the equatorial zone and in mountainous regions. In northern regions the inverse forms are extremely rare. How can this be explained? All the facts which have been enumerated are hard to understand if we start from the natural assumption that a great part was played in the setting up of the dissymmetric body-form of organisms by the right-handed component of circularly polarized light, acting incessantly throughout the millions of years of the evolution of organisms, to produce, predominantly, one dissymmetric form.

In acting as a selective factor the right-handed component of circularly polarized light may have had a double action. When there was excessive solar radiation in the Archaeozoic and Palaeozoic it permitted the survival of those forms of very simple organism which were less able to sustain the effects of the solar radiation which, at that period was very hard. Under these conditions the form of an organism which was more susceptible to the effects of radiation could not extend its habitat and must have either been destroyed or, as L. S. Berg [17] maintains, have hidden itself in the deep layers of the soil or water. As the intensity of the irradiation decreased at the end of the Palaeozoic, the form of the organism which was able to extend its range and develop was just the very one on which the powerful radiation had earlier had a destructive effect owing to its relatively great susceptibility.

12

Almost all the original types of the more viable organisms were formed during the Tertiary and superseded the earlier forms which could only persist in areas where the intensity of the radiation remained relatively high enough. We must thus consider the reason for the emergence of new forms of organism as being changes in the intensity and nature of solar radiation.

The facts we have been discussing give an indirect indication of a possible connection between the dissymmetry of molecules and that of the body-form of many organisms, the existence of which was postulated by V. I. Vernadskiĭ. We have no direct evidence for this at present. Thus, polarimetric analysis of amino acids obtained by hydrolysis of the conchiolin from the shells of right-handed and left-handed molluscs (*Fruticicola lantzi* Lindh., *Aplexa hypnorum* and *Limnaea stagnalis*) have not, so far, given any indication of a connection between dissymmetry of body-form and the optical isomerism of the amino acids of which the protein is composed [18]. A negative result was also obtained in a study of the amino acids of the proteins of the tissues of the foot of left-handed and right-handed specimens of the mollusc *Fruticicola lantzi* Lindh. It is true that neither of these results can be considered to be conclusive in that the solutions studied were not very transparent and could, only with difficulty, be studied polarimetrically. It would be very desirable to repeat these investigations using modern methods.

It may be assumed that the formation of organisms having a dissymmetrical body-form is determined by the action of dissymmetric factors on specially sensitive receiving centres—optically active receptors in the protoplasm which, it would seem, are also sensitive to circularly polarized light [19, 20]. This is shown by the studies of Alpatov [21] and others which established that there is, in fact, a receptor in the bodies of right-handed and left-handed organisms on which optically active poisons act selectively. Furthermore, even in organisms which do not have a dissymmetric body form the laevorotatory (natural) isomers of optically active substances (e.g. nicotine and adrenaline) are usually the more toxic. Their effect on the more widely distributed forms of organisms having a dissymmetric body-form is also of this nature. In addition, in molluscs the widespread right-handed form is also more susceptible to the action of laevorotatory acriquine than to that of its optical isomer. The inverse forms of these molluscs are, however, more sensitive to dextrorotatory acriquine. The opposite picture is seen among the soil bacteria *B. mycoides* with a right-handed spiral colony; a greater proportion of them survive in a medium to which dextrorotatory acriquine has been added than in a medium containing laevorotatory acriquine, that is to say, they behave like the left-handed forms of the molluscs. Studies have also been made of the effect on dextrotropic molluscs of (+) and racemic tartaric acids and also of (+)- and (−)-cinchonine and (+)-tartaric acid, i.e., just those natural compounds which are most toxic to other organisms. In left-handed molluscs, on the other hand, these compounds were the less toxic.

These facts are certainly indicative of a definite connection between the dissymmetry of the molecules of optically active reagents and the dissymmetrically constructed receptors in protoplasm (but not the protoplasm itself). The dissymmetry of these receptors then, in some way, affects the external dissymmetrical features of the organisms.

The examples which have been adduced demonstrate the complexity of the phenomenon of interaction of dissymmetric factors with living organisms even in cases where one is dealing with receptors for dissymmetric reagents and not with the protoplasm as a whole. A collection of statistical material will show how far such an idea is correct.

REFERENCES

1. B. V. OGNEV, *Vestnik Akad. Med. Nauk S.S.S.R.*, No. 4, 26, 1948.
   Cf. also *Nature, Lond.*, **169**, 232, 1952; **134**, 275, 1934; *Health Education*, No. 3, 1951.
2. A. V. SHUBNIKOV, *Simmetriya i antisymmetrya konechnykh figur.* Moscow: Izd. Akad. Nauk S.S.S.R., 1951.
3. R. DREIDING, *Chimia*, **11**, No. 6, 152, 1957.
4. W. LUDWIG, *Das Rechts-Linksproblem im Tierreich und beim Menschen.* Berlin, 1932; *Verhandl. dtsch. zool. Ges.*, B., 1937.
   Cf. also V. I. VERNADSKIĬ, *Biogeokhimicheskie ocherki.* Leningrad, Izd. Akad. Nauk S.S.S.R., 1940; K. A. BRODSKIĬ, *Dokl. Akad. Nauk S.S.S.R.*, **63**, 451, 1948.
5. E. J. KING et al., *J. Path. Bact.*, **57**, 491, 1945.
6. G. G. LEMMLEĬN, *Trudy biogeokhim. Lab. Akad. Nauk S.S.S.R.*, **5**, 225, 1939.
   V. V. ALPATOV, *Byull. Mosk. Obshch. Isp. Prirody*, **58**, No. 5, 51, 1953.
   V. I. VERNADSKIĬ, *Ocherki Geokhimii.* Moscow: Gorgeonefteizdat, 1934, p. 327.

7. A. P. Terent'ev, E. I. Klabunovskiĭ & V. V. Patrikeev, *Dokl. Akad. Nauk S.S.S.R.*, **74**, No. 5, 947, 1950.
8. A. P. Terent'ev & E. I. Klabunovskiĭ, this book, p. 95; E. I. Klabunovskiĭ, this book, p. 158.
9. A. P. Terent'ev, E. I. Klabunovskiĭ & E. I. Budovskiĭ, *Sbornik statei po obshchei Khimii*, vol. 2, p. 1612, 1953.
10. Cf. *Uchennye Zapiski Moskovskogo Gosudarstvennogo Universiteta*, **151**, no. 8, p. 145, 1951.
11 Cf. *Ber. dtsch. chem. Ges.*, **37**, 4696, 1904; **42**, 141, 1908; *J. Amer. chem. Soc.*, **57**, 377, 1935; C. Dorno, *Physik der Sonnen- und Himmelstrahlung*, 1919; *Nature, Lond.*, **134**, 275, 1934.
12. L. A. Smirnov, *Bot. Zh.*, **35**, No. 4, 394, 1950.
13. V. V. Alpatov, *Priroda*, No. 11, 59, 1951.
14. O. K. Nastyukova, *Dokl. Akad. Nauk S.S.S.R.*, **59**, No. 9, 1647, 1948.
15. V. I. Vernadskiĭ, *Biogeokhimicheskie ocherki.* Leningrad, Izd. Akad. Nauk S.S.S.R., 1940.
16. *Opredelitel Faunai Flora Morei S.S.S.R.* Moscow, 1948, p. 359, cf. Ref. [15], p. 195; *Nature, Lond.*, **132**, 287, 1933.
    I. L. Korobkov, *Vvedenie v izuchenie iskopaemykh Mollyuskov.* Izdate'l'stvo Leningradskogo Gosudarstvennogo Universiteta, 1950, p. 101.
17. L. S. Berg, *Priroda*, No. 2, 43, 1949.
18. A. R. Kizel' *et al.*, *Dokl. Akad. Nauk S.S.S.R.*, **31**, No. 6, 602, 1941; **25**, No. 6, 481, 1939.
19. G. F. Gauze, *Asimmetriya Protoplazmy.* Moscow, 1940; *Biologicheskii Zh.* No. 6, 2011, 1936.
20. E. I. Klabunovskiĭ & V. V. Patrikeev, *Vestnik Moskovskogo Gesudarstvennogo Universiteta*, No. 5, 53, 1953.
21. V. V. Alpatov, *Dokl. Akad. Nauk S.S.S.R.*, **59**, No. 7, 1365, 1948.

M. A. Messineva (U.S.S.R.) :

The organization of the present Symposium shows how necessary it is for specialists of the most various departments of science to collaborate if the problem of the origin of life on the Earth is to be solved and also if they are to discover what are the specific properties of living material.

However there has not, until now, been enough co-ordination of the work on this problem, so some of the investigations have been wrongly directed. For example, there has been a tendency for more than 10 years to identify some of the questions concerning the possible ways in which life could have arisen with those concerning the origin of petroleum [1, 2, 3]. At this Symposium we have listened to a paper by Prof. P. N. Kropotkin (p. 84).

Such an identification is quite wrong. The conditions necessary for the origin and development of life are quite different from those required for the production of petroleum and the geological formations from which it comes. According to the very accurate definition of V. I. Vernadskiĭ [4]: 'From a geochemical point of view living material *means oxygen-containing material* rich in carbon; only on some occasions does it manifest itself as carbonaceous organism, containing more than 10% by weight of carbon (p. 147, Vernadskiĭ's italics).

The composition and energy content of the components of petroleums is of quite the opposite nature. All petroleums which have so far been studied have a very strict limit as regards the two main elements carbon and hydrogen. The hydrocarbons which enter into the composition of petroleums show great resistance to external influences, even to the action of bacteria.

There are only a few types of bacteria which can use petroleum and for this they must also have scarce nitrogenous and phosphorus-containing nutrients. As yet there is no definitive agreement about the possibility of the development of obligate anaerobes depending on petroleum. And, even more significant, recent experimental studies have shown that the presence of oxygen is necessary for the first phases in the development of anaerobes. Even if it is correct to suppose that life originated on the Earth under reducing conditions, still its development, the origin of the biosphere on the Earth and the further evolution of living forms is, of necessity, associated with an oxidoreductive complex of reactions. The biosphere, as a whole, forms a frontier between the lithosphere and hydrosphere, on one side, and the atmosphere on the other.

As for petroleum, accumulations of it could only be formed and preserved until the present in the enclosed structures of the lithosphere, in formations which could act as reservoirs.

From this it follows that the thermodynamic conditions and whole geochemical state required for the appearance of living material and those required for the mass formation of the hydrocarbons of petroleum were not merely opposite in character, but were mutually exclusive. On those planets where there is a large amount of hydrocarbons (Saturn and Jupiter) there is no life. It is much to be regretted that Prof. P. N. Kropotkin's paper not only does not help towards a solution of the problem of the conditions necessary for the origin of life, but is even misleading about a problem which is outside the programme of this Symposium, namely that of whether the origin of petroleums was organic or inorganic.

The views of Prof. P. N. Kropotkin on this subject are in contradiction to the evidence of observation and to the scientific ideas of most Soviet scientists who are working on the problem of the origin of petroleums. It is incorrect to believe, as P. N. Kropotkin does, that there are industrially worth-while deposits of petroleum in the rocks of the foundation and that there is no connection between the production of petroleum and the sedimentary rocks The best proof of the organic origin of petroleum is given by its regional distribution and the association of petroleum formation with dispersed organic material in sedimentary rocks. These latter contain the same sort of hydrocarbons as petroleum and often the components found on chemical analysis of 'dispersed' bitumen show that its composition is very similar to that of one fraction or another of petroleum.

The mechanism of the formation of petroleum from organic material is being more and more clearly revealed in numerous works by Soviet scientists [7, 8, 9].

During the last 20–25 years work has been going on concerning organic catalysis in sedimentary formations [5, 6, 9]. Fresh-water and marine deposits and sedimentary formations from a depth of 2 km (Upper Devonian) have been studied.

The results of these experiments, which were carried out under conditions similar to those occurring naturally, were to show that ancient sedimentary formations, containing dispersed organic material, have enzymic properties [6].

The enzymic properties of the sedimentary formations are revealed by the fact that they bring about many reactions which cannot be caused by the action of inorganic catalysts, whether they be clayey minerals or compounds of such multivalent elements as vanadium, nickel or chromium. Among such reactions are included the hydrolysis of proteins and polysaccharides. Many ancient sedimentary formations can act as catalases and reductases.

Furthermore, the conditions under which the enzymic properties of the sedimentary formations manifest themselves are markedly different from those necessary for inorganic catalysis; all the processes which we have studied take place in the presence of natural moisture and at temperatures no higher than 50 °C.

The enzymic activity of the formations is independent of the depth from which they are obtained and of their age.

What is the cause of the enzymic activity of the formations ? Do they contain molecules of the enzymes with which we are familiar or only fragments of such molecules which retain some activity ? Is there, maybe, new formation of enzymes occurring after diagenesis ? All these questons still require answering and may be important in connection with the early period of the emergence of life on the Earth.

It seems to me to be necessary to direct the attention of biochemists and geochemists to the study of these 'fossil enzymes.'

The results which I have described have, however, been obtained by the investigation of more than a thousand different specimens of rock. They demonstrate the lack of uniformity of the properties of the different parts of the lithosphere, one part having clearly defined enzymic properties while other formations are inactive.

The enzymic properties of sedimentary formations bring about various transformations of the organic substances contained in them. We have obtained very clear-cut results in experiments using formations from the Upper Tertiary (Kolkhida) and Tertiary sediments from the Stavropol region to Maïkop inclusive.

The catalytic action of the formations (enzymic properties) is related to the granulometric and chemical composition of the deposit and is not the same in clays, aleurites and sandstones. A remarkable case of the sharp differentiation of catalytic activities is provided by thin layers of clay-aleurite deposits. Enzymic activity took place with the formation of new, light bitumens during the course of the experiments which lasted one year.

I therefore take the liberty to contradict categorically the conclusions of P. N. Kropotkin that primary inorganic synthesis provides the single correct explanation of the origin of industrially important formations of petroleum, that life developed from petroleum and under the same thermodynamic conditions as petroleum, and also that desulphatizing bacteria were the 'pioneers' of life on the Earth.

On the contrary, it must be held that these two processes occurred at separate times and they must, undoubtedly, have occurred at separate places. Life developed at a boundary between phases, both in respect of its material components and in respect of energetic factors. The indispensable conditions for the development of life were maximal heterogeneity of the surrounding medium and the possibility of using various sources of energy whether from chemical sources, light or in other forms. This is because the energy content of each quantum had to correspond exactly with that required for some particular process going on with the living organism. The products of the vital activities of organisms and, especially, the products of their autolysis might, when given off under reducing circumstances, have served as a source of material for the formation of all caustobiolites including petroleums.

It is very possible that what served as a source of carbon for the emergence of the first 'living' molecule was the small amount of hydrocarbons which were present at an early stage of the development of the planet, or it may have been other compounds of carbon, the existence of which at that time is so probable. However, life did not develop from accumulations of petroleum; the living material of the biosphere provided that remarkable mechanism for the accumulation of energy in the lithosphere as a result of which industrial collections of petroleum were formed. In ancient formations one must look for 'traces of life' not only in the shape of remains of highly organized forms (shells, impressions, etc.), but also in the shape of remains of organic molecules, in particular such as are capable of acting catalytically, that is, such as have the properties of enzymes.

REFERENCES

1. A. V. KOZHEVNIKOV, *Voprosy Filosofii*, no. 2, 1954.
2. N. A. KUDRYAVTSEV, *Neftyanoe Khozyaïstvo*, no. 9, 1951.
3. N. A. KUDRYAVTSEVA, *Voprosy Filosofii*, no. 2, 1954.
4. V. I. VERNADSKIĬ, *Izbrannye Sochineniya*, Vol. 1. Moscow (Izd. Akad. Nauk S.S.S.R.), 1954.
5. M. A. MESSINEVA, Fermentativnye svoĭstva presnovdnykh ilov, *Byulleten MOIP, Otdel Biologii*, **49**, issue 5–6, 1940.
6. M. A. MESSINEVA, Bzaimosvyaz' razlichnykh faktorov preobrazovaniya organicheskogo veshchestra pri genezise nefti: energeticheskiĭ balans etogo protessa. *Trudy VNIGNI*, Issie 12 (Gostoptekhizsat), 1957.
7. Collected publication, *Proiskhozdenie nefti i prirodnogo gaza*, BTEI ('Tsimtneft'), 1947.
8. Collected publication, *Materialy diskussii po probleme proiskhozhdeniya i migratsii nefi*. Kiev (Ukrainizdat), 1955.
9. Collected publication, *Proiskhozhdenie nefti*. Gostoptekhizdat, Moscow, 1955.

L. PAULING (U.S.A.):

It is easy to understand why organisms are built up of optically active molecules. The more complicated molecules are asymmetrical, they exist in both laevorotatory and dextrorotatory forms. Living organisms have the ability to create specific molecules with the help of matrices. In doing so the matrix for a L-molecule cannot possibly be used for the synthesis of a D-molecule. Thus, if we wished to have a racemic organism which would produce both L-organs, i.e. L-molecules, and D-molecules, it would have to contain two collections of matrices, two collections of genes—one dextrorotatory and one laevo-rotatory. The course of events depends, however, to a considerable extent on chance. In living organisms chance separates these two collections. They are completely independent of one another and it would not be logical to expect that both should have developed in exactly parallel ways side by side giving rise to corresponding organisms, i.e. duplicating the mechanism with which L-organisms and D-organisms would each, separately, be endowed.

J. D. BERNAL (Great Britain):

I should like to make an observation about the paper to which I listened this morning concerning the action of radiation in the extreme ultraviolet on the synthesis of small molecules, as this paper throws new light on the hypothesis as to the important part played by clays and other mineral substances in the emergence of life.

When I postulated the implication of these mineral substances in the scheme of bio-genesis I was thinking of their adsorptive powers, which would lead to an accumulation of organic substances on their surfaces. Later on, though I had no proof at that time, I put forward the suggestion that they might have a catalytic action about which Prof. Akabori will speak later. Today we have heard of yet another phenomenon, namely the extension of the limits of absorption towards the long-wave ultraviolet range, for those molecules which are adsorbed on such surfaces. I should like to make it clear here how I envisage the action of such substances on the surface of the Earth.

I imagine that adsorption, for the most part, took place on minerals of secondary origin. The clayey minerals which we meet in the soil do not appear to be the direct products of weathering; they are formed by precipitation of solutions of alumina and silica. This has been demonstrated by experiment. In this way we get aluminosilicates and their porous polyhydrates, which were certainly produced abiogenically in the early stages of the formation of the crust of the Earth, in association with the circulation of water. Together with them we also find iron hydroxides. The places where they were formed were beds of mud.

Beds of mud have two important properties. In the first place, considered vertically they form columns, that is to say they allow dissolved material to pass through them, as through a chromatographic column, they modify various reactions and separate the reagents into different zones. In the second place, the way in which beds of mud are formed is such that they are periodically covered by new layers, perhaps daily, perhaps whenever it rains.

This means that a reaction which leads to the formation of many substances is diverted towards the production of substances which are sorbed. The adsorbed material is removed from the sphere of the reaction and the reaction is diverted towards its synthesis. In other words, beds of mud constitute an apparatus for the utilization of material. However, if this were the whole story, it would not lead to the formation of substances but to their disappearance. In this connection I believe that a great part was played by the second factor, i.e. the fact that beds of mud are continually accumulating layer by layer and that the accumulated material again enters into circulation through stream erosion.

It seems attractive, at first sight, to suppose that the original synthesis occurs at great depths in pure water. On beds of mud, synthesis occurs only in the superficial layer, i.e. in a layer less than 1 mm thick. This layer is constantly being renewed and seems very likely to provide suitable conditions for polymerization.

In conclusion, I should like to make a general comment. From the physical aspect, the process of biogenesis is very like the colloidal process of synaeresis, in which the original watery medium separates out from the colloids. In the early stages this process may have been purely physical, making use of colloidal mineral substances, but later it became the very complicated synaeresis which we see in the evolution of biological forms.

S. Akabori (Osaka, Japan):

A Comment to the Paper of Prof. Klabunovskiĭ

Asymmetric catalysis is important not only from the standpoint of biochemistry but from that of synthetic organic chemistry. As it is well known, many enzymes are metallo-proteins and, on the other hand, metallic palladium is a good catalyst for the hydrogenation of organic compounds. Based on these facts we devised a hydrogenase model which was prepared as follows. When silk fibroin was warmed in an aqueous solution of palladium chloride, the former absorbed effectively palladium ion. Brown-coloured Pd-silk-fibroin thus formed was shaken under hydrogen at 50°, whereby black coloured Pd-silk-fibroin was obtained. This Pd-silk is capable of catalysing asymmetrical hydrogenation as applied to various unsaturated compounds. The experimental results are represented in the Bakh memorial volume of *Biokhimiya* [1].

It is interesting that natural silk fibroin produces asymmetric catalyst, but if silk fibroin was once dissolved in copper-ammonia solution and reprecipitated, it loses this specific character. It seems, therefore, the asymmetric property of an enzyme depends not only on the asymmetric structure of individual component amino acids but also on the asymmetric structure of the whole enzyme-protein molecule.

REFERENCE

1. S. Akabori, S. Sakurai, Y. Izumi & Y. Fujii, *Biokhimiya*, **22**, 154, 1957.

C. Reid (Canada):

I believe that we have paid insufficient attention to small molecules, other than amino acids, which may have appeared under the supposed early atmospheric conditions.

If we accept Dr Miller's view of a sea containing comparatively high concentration of ammonia, and also the view that formaldehyde may have appeared either from CO_2 or from methane, it implies that hexamethylenetetramine must have formed in large quantities, since this substance is formed exothermically and in high yield even without light under all conditions in aqueous solutions, except at unreasonably low pH. The formation of large quantities of this substance would provide a 'pre-coacervation' concentration stage on subsequent evaporation of water.

That such a step might be a useful one towards amino acids, we have tested by long irradiation of hot hexamethylenetetramine solutions with Hg 1850 Å light. Glycine and alanine have been identified in the products, and a third substance of uncertain identity is also formed.

A second molecule which may have appeared as the ammonia atmosphere slowly became oxidized is hydroxylamine. This is an interesting molecule, since its absorption of light extends to considerably longer wavelengths than does that of H_2O or NH_3. We have found that the ultraviolet synthesis of amino acids using the Hg 1850 Å line is, in fact, more efficient when hydroxylamine rather than ammonia is used as the source of nitrogen.

D. Sapozhnikov (U.S.S.R.):

The Screening of Ultraviolet Rays before the formation
of the Ozone Layer

We believe that the products of gaseous dissociation brought about by ultraviolet radiation might have acted as a screen against short-wave ultraviolet rays. Near ultraviolet rays are absorbed by the products of dissociation of compounds of low molecular weight. Thus, at some particular depth, suitable conditions might be produced for the synthesis of compounds of high molecular weight.

S. L. Miller (U.S.A.):

In regard to the experiments of Pavlovskaya & Pasynskiĭ I would like to comment that their mixture of methane, carbon monoxide, water and ammonia is quite reducing. Under geological conditions this mixture of gases would be stable only in the presence of an appreciable pressure of hydrogen. In the experiments of Pavlovskaya & Pasynskiĭ, it is quite probable that some hydrogen was produced during the sparking.

There is a question of the stability of carbon monoxide in a primitive atmosphere. Carbon monoxide reacts at a significant rate with water in the presence of base to give formate. Therefore, the carbon monoxide that was produced on the Earth would dissolve in the ocean and the steady-state concentration would have been small.

There have been several comments about the importance of sugars for the formation of life. I should point out that polyhydroxy compounds, probably sugars, were produced in my electric discharge experiments. This is reasonable since it is well known that formaldehyde, which was produced in the spark, condenses in weakly basic solutions to give 4-, 5- and 6-carbon sugars. We can expect that similar condensations would have taken place in the primitive ocean.

S. Fox (U.S.A.)

Comments on the Origin of Optical Activity

Many concepts of origin of optical activity have been considered. Many others from the literature have not. One may particularly deserve serious consideration. If a compound which occurs early in generalized biosynthetic pathways happens to crystallize in D and L forms and then be separated by chance, then precipitation of one form by seeding can occur. If this happens to be D-aspartic acid, for example, L-aspartic acid is left behind in the primordial soup or paste. The primitive conversion of aspartic acid to other compounds, e.g. alanine, would thus give L-alanine and a monoconfigurational biochemical world would be triggered.

This is more fully explained in a recent paper [1].

REFERENCE

1. S. W. Fox, J. E. Johnson & A. Vegotsky, Science, **124**, 923, 1956.

A. G. Pasynskiĭ (U.S.S.R.):

In connection with Dr Miller's remarks I should like to state that the point is not that the formation of amino acids could occur only in a hydrogen-containing atmosphere or only in one containing CO; it probably took place under both conditions. Under the actual experimental conditions used by Miller and ourselves the presence of free hydrogen certainly was not necessary.

A. Ya. Smirnova (U.S.S.R.):

The Relationship between the Mineral and Organic Worlds

It seems to me that in studying the pre-proteinaceous substances and their later transformation into proteins with vital functions, more attention should have been paid to certain supplementary factors.

I am thinking of the similarity of many of the properties of complex compounds which are not proteinaceous in nature, with the properties of proteins and other organic compounds.

I am referring, in the first place, to their high molecular weight, optical activity, viscosity, stability, 5- and 6-membered rings and great sensitivity to changes in pH and temperature of the surrounding medium. It has already been shown that some complex compounds of mineral nature have an activating effect similar to that of enzymes.

To supplement this generally known fact I may add a more concrete example which has not yet been published, I am referring to complex compounds of Fe^{III} with pyrophosphates.

As concerns pyrophosphates, much has been said about their application to the synthesis of enzymic proteins and nucleoproteins. It seems to me that the possible uses of pyrophosphate residues are far from being exhausted by the studies mentioned.

In the first place, there is no acidic residue which gives rise to such a multiplicity of complex compounds as $P_2O_7^{4-}$ which, even under conditions which are almost like those in nature, will mask the specific properties of about 15 cations. In doing so the reaction with each cation is 'multivariant' with the simultaneous separation of mixtures of reaction products. This fact reminds one of the biochemical process which Prof. Gol'dovskiĭ found to be multivariant.

The nature of the reaction products is reminiscent of some organic substances. For example, the pyrophosphate complexes of Fe^{III} which I have isolated have the general properties of organic substances. One of them is very viscous and, when dried in a thin layer, it reminds one of gelatin; it swells on wetting. Another substance occurs in the form of glistening colourless crystals which refract light strongly. In my work, which is still not complete, I demonstrate the similarity between these mineral complexes and organic materials.

In this present communication I want to speak about the possibility that mineral complex compounds may have taken part in the production of complicated organic compounds. It is a perfectly admissible idea that mineral complex compounds were probably formed before organic ones for, in accordance with the laws of thermodynamics and electrostatics, they could come into being directly from those materials which were available on the Earth and in its atmosphere at the time, while complicated organic compounds were probably formed on the basis of these complex compounds with the participation of hydrocarbons, the radicals of organic acids, carbon dioxide and ammonia.

A. A. GURVICH (U.S.S.R.):

I work on the problem of mitogenetic radiations and shall, therefore, allow myself to make some observations in connection with Dr Bahadur's very interesting paper.

It seems to me that the facts set out by Dr Bahadur in the first part of his paper, to show the possibility that when solutions of simple compounds of carbon and nitrogen are activated by light a whole series of amino acids may be formed, are of great theoretical interest.

Dr Bahadur's suggestion that mitogenetic radiation develops when this occurs and that the actual process takes place by means of free radicals seems very probable and the application of mitogenetic spectral analysis, which both we and he have already considered, might turn this probability into fact, for, owing to the great sensitivity of the mitogenetic method, the detection of small concentrations of compounds which disappear quickly is perfectly possible.

In connection with mitogenetic radiations, Dr Bahadur recalled the process of auto-synthesis of the active groups of enzymes at the expense of simple amino acids. This phenomenon, which was noticed long ago in our laboratory, has been studied for many years, and it has been established that the power of autosynthesis, or autocatalysis as we call it, is also possessed by comparatively simple organic compounds containing cyclic groupings, for example tyrosine in a solution of glycine.

As Dr Bahadur said, the necessary energetic factor is provided by the mitogenetic radiations developing in the system during the formation of the cyclic compound. This latter behaves like a very small hole, serving as a matrix, similar to the radicals into which the radicals of glycine are split and which form the new cyclical systems.

The radicals were discovered by mitogenetic spectral analysis. The process of auto-catalysis of tyrosine itself has also been confirmed by a number of other methods.

I was greatly interested by Dr Bahadur's ideas given in the second part of his paper, though I must emphasize that both earlier and now, in our experimental work and in our analysis of the data, we are far from having reached ideas of such a general nature.

The Origin of Proteins, Nucleoproteins and Enzymes

On the Origin of the Fore-protein

SHIRO AKABORI

Institute for Protein Research, Osaka University, Osaka

IF PROTEIN is absolutely essential for all living things, the very beginning of life must have been a spontaneous formation of protein at a certain age of the Earth.

In 1936 Oparin [1] postulated that α-amino acids could have been formed non-biologically from hydrocarbons, ammonia and hydrogen cyanide at the age of the Earth when the atmosphere contained these substances in high concentrations. Bernal [2] emphasized the role played by ultraviolet light in the formation of organic compounds at a certain stage of the evolution of the Earth. He also suggested that life might have originated on the surface of clay which accumulated large amounts of organic substances. Oparin's hypothesis has received strong experimental support from the recent work of Miller [3].

It has generally been believed that the first proteins or fore-proteins were non-biologically formed by the polycondensation of preformed free amino acids. This belief is solely based on the fact that proteins in present-day organisms are synthesized via free amino acids. Such non-biological formation of polypeptides and proteins, however, seems to be very difficult owing to the requirement of free energy, though Bresler [4] reported the reconversion of tryptic hydrolysates to the original proteins under an extremely high pressure.

In 1955 I proposed [5] a hypothesis concerning the origin of the fore-protein and speculated that it must have been produced through reactions consisting of the following three steps.

The first step is the formation of aminoacetonitrile from formaldehyde, ammonia and hydrogen cyanide.

$$CH_2O + NH_3 + HCN \longrightarrow H_2N-CH_2-CN$$

The second is the polymerization of aminoacetonitrile on a solid surface, probably in the state adsorbed on clay, followed by the hydrolysis of the polymer to polyglycine and ammonia.

$$x\, H_2N-CH_2-CN \longrightarrow (-NH-CH_2-\underset{\underset{NH}{\|}}{C}-)_x \xrightarrow{+\, x\, H_2O} (-NH-CH_2-CO-)_x + x\, NH_3$$

and the third step is the introduction of side chains into polyglycine by the reaction with aldehydes or with unsaturated hydrocarbons.

I have also pointed out that the formation of amino acid residues possessing the same configuration throughout one single peptide chain could be expected from this mechanism, assuming that the configuration adsorbed on the solid surface is the *cis*-form, as shown in Fig. 1.

189

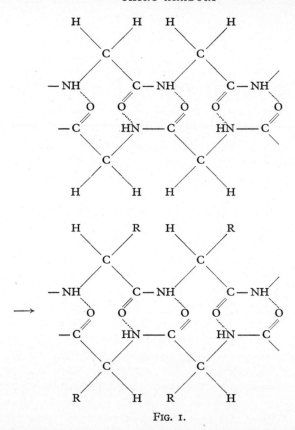

FIG. 1.

If polyglycine adsorbed on a solid surface had the configuration as indicated in the above figure, the plane including one carbon atom and two hydrogen atoms of the methylene group must be perpendicular to the solid surface. The reacting molecule must have come from outside, and, therefore, only one hydrogen atom directed to outside must have reacted, giving rise to amino acid residues of the same stereochemical configuration throughout one single peptide chain.

The validity of the second step in the above hypothesis was tested in the following model experiments, which were carried out by Hanafusa in my laboratory. Aminoacetonitrile was prepared by the condensation of formaldehyde, ammonia and hydrogen cyanide and was obtained in the form of its hydrogen sulphate. This was mixed with 20 parts of kaolinite and heated at 130–135° for 5 hours. The product was extracted with dilute sodium hydroxide solution. The presence of glycylglycine and glycylglycylglycine in the extract was confirmed by paper and column chromatography.

The present paper deals mainly with experiments concerning the last step in the formation of the fore-protein, that is the introduction of side chains into polyglycine structure. Polyglycine used in the present work was prepared not from aminoacetonitrile but from glycine N-carboxylic anhydride or from glycine ester, by polycondensation with or without supporter. Polyglycine spread on the surface of kaolinite was suspended in water and treated with formaldehyde or acetaldehyde in the presence of a basic catalyst. The reaction product was washed with alcohol, dried and hydrolysed with 6N-hydrochloric acid. The hydrolysate was dinitrophenylated and analysed by silica gel chromatography. The results of these experiments are shown in Table 1.

TABLE 1

| Sample | Aldehyde | Catalyst | Reaction | | Hydroxy-amino acid |
			Temp. (°C)	Time (hr)	Glycine
PGK	HCHO	K_2CO_3	80	7	0·031
,,	,,	$NaHCO_3$	80	7	0·030
,,	,,	TEA	100	2·5	0·004
,,	CH_3CHO	K_2CO_3	60	50	0·015
,,	,,	$NaHCO_3$	60	50	0·014
PG	HCHO	TEA	100	3	0
,,	,,	K_2CO_3	80	7	0

Abbreviations: PGK: Polyglycine-kaolinite.
PG: Polyglycine.
TEA: Triethylamine.

In the reaction with formaldehyde, 2–3% of glycyl residues of polyglycine were converted to seryl residues and in the case of acetaldehyde the rate of the conversion of glycyl to threonyl residues was about 1·5%. The degree of polymerization of polyglycine dispersed on kaolinite was from 140 to 170. It is, therefore, clear that not only the N-terminal residue but other glycyl residues reacted with the aldehydes. When polyglycine without supporter was used, practically no side chains were introduced into polyglycine under the same reaction conditions.

The conversion of seryl residue to cysteinyl or cystinyl residue in the fore-protein could have taken place as follows.

$$\underset{\overset{|}{CO}}{\overset{\overset{|}{NH}}{\underset{|}{CH_2}}} \xrightarrow{+ CH_2O} \underset{\overset{|}{CO}}{\overset{\overset{|}{NH}}{CH-CH_2OH}} \longrightarrow \underset{\overset{|}{CO}}{\overset{\overset{|}{NH}}{C = CH_2}} \xrightarrow{+ H_2S} \underset{\overset{|}{CO}}{\overset{\overset{|}{NH}}{CH-CH_2-SH}}$$

This hypothesis was then experimentally tested. For the purpose of experimental convenience we used polyserine synthesized by Okawa [6], one of my associates, according to the method shown in Fig. 2. The formation of cystinyl and cysteinyl residue has not yet definitely been confirmed, but when polyserine was treated with benzyl mercaptan in an alkaline solution, the presence of S-benzylcysteine in the hydrolysate of the reaction product was clearly demonstrated.

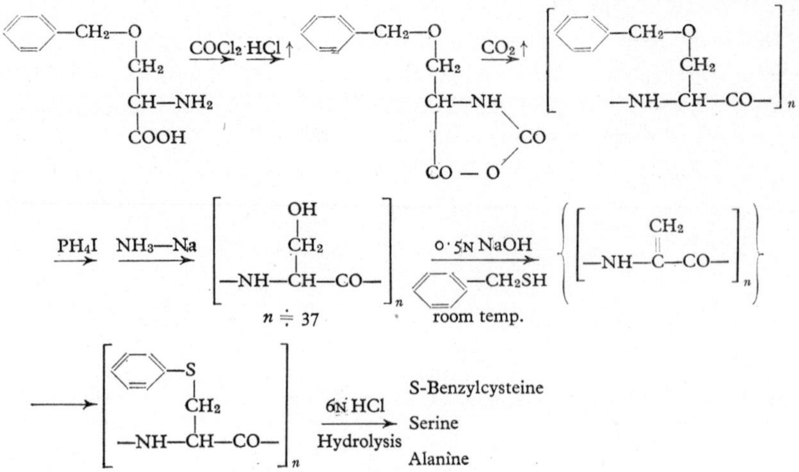

FIG. 2.

The formation of aspartyl residue in the fore-protein is also most likely to have occurred by a series of reactions shown in Fig. 3. The experiment to test this possibility was carried out by employing polydehydroalanine synthesized by Sakakibara from carbobenzoxy-dehydroalanine as shown in the figure.

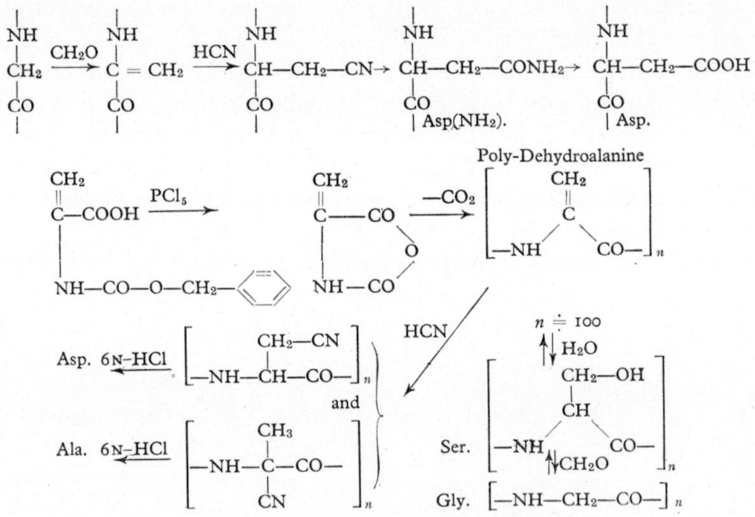

FIG. 3.   Formation of aspartic acid.

Polydehydroalanine is a light-brown, amorphous powder, which is soluble in water and formic acid but not in alcohols. This polymer was dissolved in water with potassium cyanide and kept at 20–25° for 20 hours in a sealed tube and then hydrolysed by hydrochloric acid. The hydrolysate was chromatographed on Dowex 50 × 8 with citrate buffer (pH 3·42) as elution agent (Fig. 4). The presence of aspartic acid, glycine and alanine was very clearly demonstrated. These amino acids were further identified by two-dimensional chromatography after they were converted to dinitrophenylamino acids (Fig. 5).

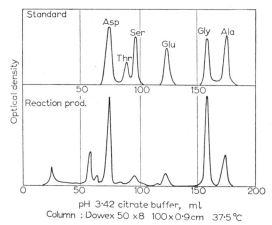

FIG. 4.   Hydrolysate of reaction product of HCN with poly-dehydroalanine.

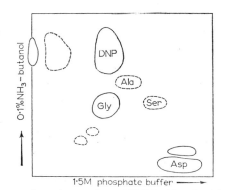

FIG. 5.   Hydrolysate of reaction product of HCN with poly-dehydroalanine. Paper chromatogram of DNP-derivatives.

The formation of aromatic and heterocyclic amino acids in the fore-protein could have occurred by the condensation of methylene group of glycyl residue followed by hydrogenation (Fig. 6). The chemical structure of phenylalanine, tyrosine, tryptophan and histidine, in which one methylene group is situated between an aromatic or heterocyclic nucleus and a glycine group might support the above-mentioned mechanism of their formation in the fore-protein.

The formation of valine, leucine and isoleucine might have resulted from the direct addition of propylene, *iso*butene and but-2-ene respectively as shown in Fig. 6. Experimental evidence for such a mechanism is not yet sufficient. Every attempt to introduce a *sec.*-butyl group to polyglycine chain with basic catalysts has failed. When, however, polyglycine dispersed on Japanese acid clay was

13

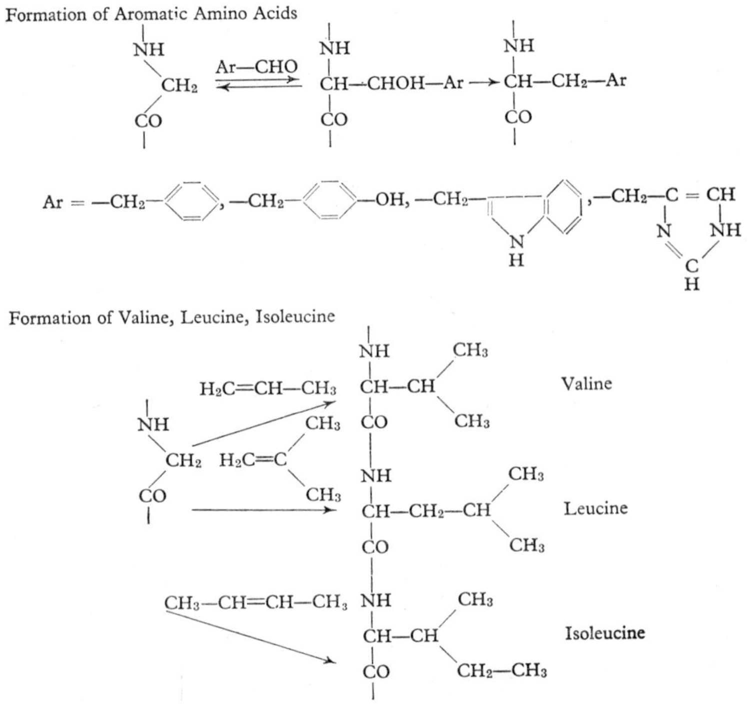

Formation of Aromatic Amino Acids

$$\underset{\underset{\text{CO}}{|}}{\overset{\underset{|}{\text{NH}}}{\underset{|}{\diagdown}}} \text{CH}_2 \quad \underset{\xrightarrow{\text{Ar—CHO}}}{\rightleftharpoons} \quad \underset{\underset{\text{CO}}{|}}{\overset{\underset{|}{\text{NH}}}{\underset{|}{}}} \text{CH—CHOH—Ar} \longrightarrow \underset{\underset{\text{CO}}{|}}{\overset{\underset{|}{\text{NH}}}{\underset{|}{}}} \text{CH—CH}_2\text{—Ar}$$

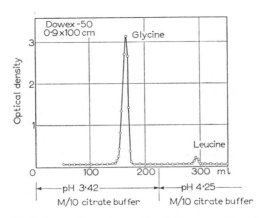

Formation of Valine, Leucine, Isoleucine

Valine

Leucine

Isoleucine

FIG. 6.

heated to 130° for 5 hours with an excess of but-2-ene (probably containing a certain amount of *iso*butene) in the presence of 0·1% but-2-ene ozonide, the formation of a small quantity of leucine (or isoleucine) was observed by paper and column chromatography after hydrolysing the reaction product. Fig. 7 shows a column-chromatographic elution curve of the hydrolysate.

FIG. 7.   Hydrolysate of reaction product of butene with polyglycine.

We could not determine whether the amino acid corresponding to the small peak was leucine or isoleucine.

As is well known in synthetic organic chemistry, in the presence of a certain catalyst, acetylene readily reacts with hydrogen cyanide to form acrylonitrile; the presence of the latter substance in the fore-atmosphere is quite conceivable. The formation of glutamine, glutamic acid, ornithine and arginine could thus be formulated as shown in Fig. 8.

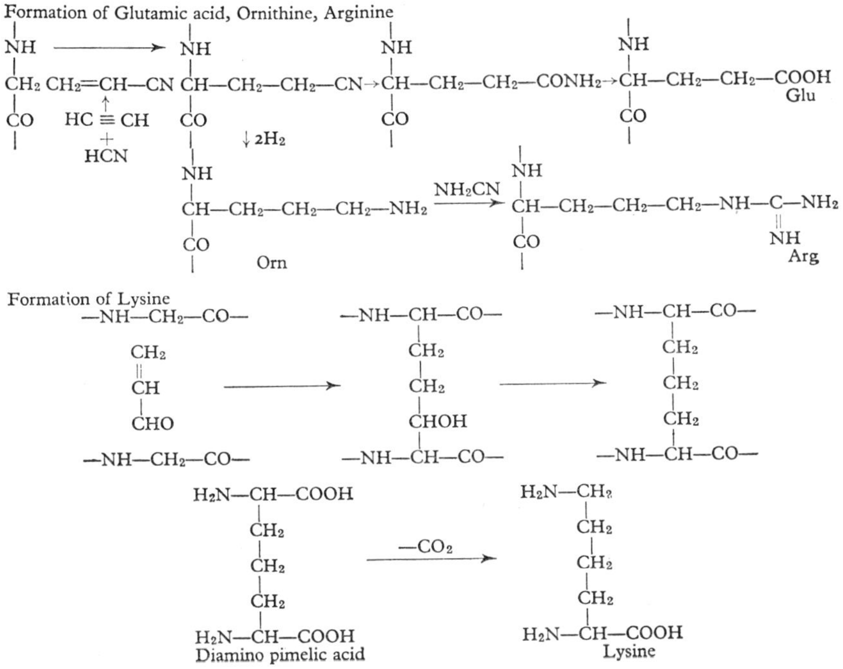

Formation of Glutamic acid, Ornithine, Arginine

$$
\begin{array}{c}
\text{NH} \longrightarrow \text{NH} \qquad \text{NH} \qquad\qquad \text{NH} \\
| \qquad\qquad | \qquad\qquad | \qquad\qquad\qquad | \\
\text{CH}_2 \;\; \text{CH}_2{=}\text{CH—CN} \;\; \text{CH—CH}_2\text{—CH}_2\text{—CN} \to \text{CH—CH}_2\text{—CH}_2\text{—CONH}_2 \to \text{CH—CH}_2\text{—CH}_2\text{—COOH} \\
| \qquad \text{HC}\equiv\text{CH} \qquad | \qquad\qquad\qquad | \qquad\qquad\qquad\qquad | \qquad\qquad\qquad \text{Glu} \\
\text{CO} \qquad + \qquad \text{CO} \;\;\downarrow 2\text{H}_2 \qquad \text{CO} \qquad\qquad\qquad \text{CO} \\
| \qquad \text{HCN} \qquad | \qquad\qquad\qquad | \qquad\qquad\qquad\qquad |
\end{array}
$$

$$
\begin{array}{c}
\text{NH} \qquad\qquad\qquad\qquad \text{NH} \\
| \qquad\qquad\qquad\qquad\qquad | \\
\text{CH—CH}_2\text{—CH}_2\text{—CH}_2\text{—NH}_2 \xrightarrow{\;\text{NH}_2\text{CN}\;} \text{CH—CH}_2\text{—CH}_2\text{—CH}_2\text{—NH—C—NH}_2 \\
| \qquad\qquad\qquad\qquad\qquad | \qquad\qquad\qquad\qquad\qquad \| \\
\text{CO} \qquad\qquad\qquad\qquad\qquad \text{CO} \qquad\qquad\qquad\qquad\qquad \text{NH} \\
| \quad\text{Orn} \qquad\qquad\qquad\qquad | \qquad\qquad\qquad\qquad\qquad \text{Arg}
\end{array}
$$

Formation of Lysine

$$
\begin{array}{ccc}
\text{—NH—CH}_2\text{—CO—} & \text{—NH—CH—CO—} & \text{—NH—CH—CO—} \\
| & | & | \\
\text{CH}_2 & \text{CH}_2 & \text{CH}_2 \\
\| & | & | \\
\text{CH} \longrightarrow & \text{CH}_2 \longrightarrow & \text{CH}_2 \\
| & | & | \\
\text{CHO} & \text{CHOH} & \text{CH}_2 \\
| & | & | \\
\text{—NH—CH}_2\text{—CO—} & \text{—NH—CH—CO—} & \text{—NH—CH—CO—}
\end{array}
$$

$$
\begin{array}{cc}
\text{H}_2\text{N—CH—COOH} & \text{H}_2\text{N—CH}_2 \\
| & | \\
\text{CH}_2 & \text{CH}_2 \\
| \qquad \xrightarrow{\;-\text{CO}_2\;} & | \\
\text{CH}_2 & \text{CH}_2 \\
| & | \\
\text{CH}_2 & \text{CH}_2 \\
| & | \\
\text{H}_2\text{N—CH—COOH} & \text{H}_2\text{N—CH—COOH} \\
\text{Diamino pimelic acid} & \text{Lysine}
\end{array}
$$

FIG. 8.

If I am allowed to make a more extended speculation, I could formulate the mechanism of the formation of lysine as shown in Fig. 8. The first step is a cross-linked condensation of one molecule of acrolein with two polyglycine chains, giving rise to a β-hydroxy-$\alpha\alpha'$-diaminopimelic acid residue. This hydroxydiaminopimelic acid could have been reduced to diaminopimelic acid which was shown by Dewey & Work [7] and also by B. D. Davis [8] to be the precursor of lysine in *Escherichia coli*. It is very important that, according to E. Work [9], diaminopimelic acid is widely distributed among various micro-organisms. These findings might support the proposed mechanism on the formation of lysine.

Although I am afraid I went too far with my speculation, I would like to emphasize that it seems not too difficult to test the theory on experimental bases. Further work along this theory is now in progress in the Laboratory for Protein Research of Osaka University.

REFERENCES

1. A. I. OPARIN, *The Origin of Life.* Macmillan, New York, 1936.
2. J. D. BERNAL, *Physical Basis of Life.* London, 1951.
3. S. L. MILLER, *Science,* **177**, 528, 1953; *J. Amer. chem. Soc.,* **77**, 2351, 1955; *Biochim. biophys. Acta,* **23**, 480, 1957.
4. E. S. BRESLER *et al., Izv. Akad. Nauk S.S.S.R., Ser. Biol.,* **13**, 392, 1949.
5. S. AKABORI, *Kagaku (Science,* in Japan), **25**, 54, 1955.
6. K. OKAWA, *J. chem. Soc. Japan* (in Japanese), **75**, 1199, 1954.
7. D. L. DEWEY & E. WORK, *Nature, Lond.,* **169**, 533, 1953.
8. B. D. DAVIS, *Nature, Lond.,* **169**, 534, 1953.
9. E. WORK, *Biochem. J.,* **49**, 17, 1951; *J. gen. Microbiol.,* **9**, 394, 1953.

Der Ursprung der Enzyme

O. HOFFMANN-OSTENHOF

Erstes Chemisches Institut der Universität Wien, Österreich

EINLEITUNG

Es IST offensichtlich, daß Leben ohne die Wirkung der spezifischen Katalysatoren, die wir als Enzyme bezeichnen, unvorstellbar ist. Weitaus die meisten chemischen Umsetzungen, welche in den Organismen vor sich gehen und deren Gesamtheit als Stoffwechsel bezeichnet wird, können nur unter dem Einfluß von Enzymen stattfinden. Somit ist die Frage nach dem Ursprung der Enzyme—und damit auch die Frage nach dem Übergang von der bereits in präbiontischen Zeiträumen vorhandenen unspezifischen Katalyse zur spezifischen Katalyse—eines der wichtigsten Teilprobleme bei der Untersuchung, auf welche Weise das Leben auf der Erde entstehen konnte. Diese Zusammenhänge wurden von Oparin [1] bereits frühzeitig erkannt und in seinem klassischen Werk in einer dem damaligen Stand des Wissens entsprechenden Weise behandelt.

Es mag nützlich sein, uns zur Einführung in die Problemstellung hier kurz in Erinnerung zu rufen, was wir unter Enzymen verstehen. Wir definieren Enzyme als 'hochmolekulare Substanzen, die von lebenden Zellen produziert werden, innerhalb oder außerhalb der Zellen vorkommen und als spezifische Katalysatoren chemischer Vorgänge in allen Organismen fungieren' [2].

Der Definition entsprechend sind somit die Enzyme Produkte von Lebensvorgängen; ohne belebte Materie kann es keine Enzyme geben. Anderseits finden wir auch bereits in den uns am primitivsten erscheinenden Organismen zahlreiche sinnreich zusammenarbeitende Enzyme*. Wir müssen also annehmen, daß die Entstehung der ersten Enzyme in einer relativ frühen Phase erfolgt ist.

Es wäre nun denkbar, daß wir durch eine eingehende Untersuchung von Enzymen aus sehr einfachen Organismenarten gewisse Hinweise zur frühesten Entwicklungsgeschichte der Enzyme gewinnen könnten. Dies scheint aber nicht der Fall zu sein; so weit derartige Untersuchungen bereits durchgeführt wurden, ergaben sie, daß sich die Enzyme primitiver Organismen in ihrem Spezifitätsgrad und in ihrer Wirksamkeit von denjenigen höherer Arten nur wenig unterscheiden.

Da wir von dieser Seite her kaum irgendwelche wesentlichen Aufschlüsse zu unserem Problem erhalten können, sind wir gezwungen, unsere Betrachtungen

---

* Es gibt allerdings zahlreiche Viren, welche über keine Enzym-Ausrüstung verfügen. Man scheint aber heute darüber einig zu sein, daß die Viren keineswegs eine besonders ursprüngliche Form des Lebens darstellen. Es wird vielmehr entweder angenommen, daß sie entsprechend ihrem Parasitismus Rückbildungsprodukte höherer Lebensformen sind, oder auch, daß sie sich aus Zellbestandteilen ableiten und nicht selbständige Lebewesen darstellen. Die Stoffwechselvorgänge, die zur Vermehrung der Viren führen, werden übrigens auch von Enzymen katalysiert; die Viren bedienen sich dazu der Enzymausrüstung der Wirtszelle.

von einem anderen Blickpunkt aus zu beginnen, nämlich der Frage, welches die Vorläufer der Enzyme in der Welt vor der Entstehung des Lebens waren.

VORSTUFEN DER ENZYME

Bereits in der unbelebten Welt existierten zahlreiche Stoffe, welche die Funktion von Katalysatoren erfüllen konnten: Wasserstoffionen, Hydroxylionen, Schwermetallionen, Metalle und Metalloxyde, kolloide Metallösungen etc.; es besteht kein Zweifel darüber, daß alle diese Katalysatoren schon in Zeiträumen, welche lange vor der Entstehung des Lebens lagen, chemische Vorgänge beeinflußt haben. Die von den genannten anorganischen Katalysatoren bewirkte Reaktionsbeeinflussung ist allerdings meist recht unspezifisch, d. h. ein und derselbe Katalysator kann zahlreiche, sehr verschiedene Vorgänge beschleunigen. Eine gewisse Erhöhung des Spezifitätsgrades, die auch gewöhnlich mit einer Steigerung der Aktivität verbunden ist, kann allerdings häufig durch Komplexbildung erzielt werden.

Neben diesen anorganischen Katalysatoren können aber auch bestimmte niedermolekulare organische Substanzen, von denen man unter Umständen annehmen könnte, daß sie bereits vor der Entstehung des Lebens existiert haben, deutliche katalytische Wirkungen entfalten, die vor allen von Langenbeck [3, 4] eingehend untersucht wurden. In einzelnen Fällen sind die Effekte der organischen Katalysatoren denjenigen der Enzyme weitgehend analog, obgleich weder deren Aktivität noch deren Spezifitätsgrad erreicht wird. So können bestimmte primäre Amine die Decarboxylierung von α-Ketosäuren in ähnlicher Weise katalysieren wie die für diese Leistung spezifischen Enzyme; manche Chinone oxydieren Aminosäuren; Isatin wirkt ähnlich wie eine Dehydrogenase, etc.

Um die Frage, welche von den gennanten Katalysatoren als Vorläufer der Enzyme aufgefaßt werden könnten, zu entscheiden, müssen wir uns zuerst mit der chemischen Konstitution der Enzyme, soweit uns diese zur Zeit bekannt ist, beschäftigen und untersuchen, ob irgendwelche Zusammenhänge zwischen den früher aufgezählten Stoffen und den Enzymen offenbar werden.

In der eingangs gegebenen Definition werden die Enzyme als hochmolekulare Substanzen bezeichnet. Bisher konnte aber bei jedem Enzym, das genauer auf seine chemische Zusammensetzung untersucht wurde, ein Protein als wesentlichster Bestandteil nachgewiesen werden. Man ginge vielleicht mit der Behauptung zu weit, daß nur Proteine Enzyme sein können, doch sprechen die zahlreichen vorliegenden Befunde deutlich dafür, daß zumindest die große Mehrzahl der Enzyme Proteincharakter aufweist.

Trotz dieser anscheinenden Gleichartigkeit der Enzyme, was ihre Eiweißnatur betrifft, können wir in bezug auf die Konstitution doch gewisse Klassen unterscheiden. Neben zahlreichen Enzymen, die offenbar ausschließlich aus Protein bestehen, kennen wir nämlich viele andere Enzymtypen, welche nur in Anwesenheit bestimmter niedermolekularer Substanzen ihre Wirksamkeit ausüben können, weshalb wir—zumindest funktionell—diese Stoffe als integrale Bestandteile der Enzyme auffassen müssen. Wir wollen hier, ohne auf die

Wirkungsweise der Substanzen näher einzugehen, diese als prosthetische Gruppe der Enzyme bezeichnen.

Wenn wir nun die chemische Natur der prosthetischen Gruppe in Betracht ziehen, so kommen wir zu einer Einteilung der Enzyme in fünf Klassen:

1. Enzyme, die anscheinend reine Eiweißkörper sind und keine proteinfremde Komponente enthalten.

2. Enzyme, die in ihrem Molekül ein Metallion enthalten: hierher können wir auch diejenigen Enzyme rechnen, bei denen das Metallion so leicht dissoziabel ist, daß es wohl kaum mehr als Bestandteil des Enzymmoleküls angesehen wird, obwohl es für die Wirksamkeit des Enzyms unbedingt erforderlich ist.

3. Enzyme die eine niedermolekulare organische Verbindung als prosthetische Gruppe enthalten; in Analogie zur vorhergehenden Klasse können wir auch diejenigen Enzyme hier einordnen, deren prosthetische Gruppen ('Coenzyme') wohl leicht dissoziabel, aber für die Wirksamkeit unbedingt erforderlich sind.

4. Enzyme, welche als prosthetische Gruppe eine niedermolekulare organische Verbindung aufweisen, die ein anorganisches Ion Komplex gebunden enthält, wie das bei den Eisen-Porphyrin-Enzymen der Fall ist.

5. Enzyme, welche als prosthetische Gruppe eine niedermolekulare organische Verbindung und daneben ein anorganisches Ion, das mit dieser offenbar nicht komplexartig verbunden ist, enthalten. In diese Klasse gehören die erst vor kurzem in bezug auf ihre Konstitution aufgeklärten Metallflavoproteine [5].

Bei den zuletzt genannten vier Klassen ist es allerdings nicht immer der Fall, daß bereits der niedermolekulare Bestandteil allein Reaktionen desselben Typus katalysiert, welche vom Gesamtenzym bewirkt werden; der Effekt der Proteinkomponente ist somit nicht immer lediglich als Steigerung der Aktivität und Erhöhung des Spezifitätsgrades zu werten. Dies ist nur manchmal der Fall: Manganionen können z. B. Decarboxylierungen verursachen [6] und sind auch für die Wirksamkeit mancher Decarboxylasen erforderlich; Kupferionen können als Oxydationskatalysatoren fungieren und sind auch Bestandteile mancher oxydierender Fermente; die Eisenporphyrin-Komponente der Katalasen und Peroxydasen kann—allerdings in einem weitaus geringeren Grade—dieselben Reaktionen bewirken wie die genannten Enzyme [7]. Anderseits sind zahlreiche Beispiele dafür bekannt, daß prosthetische Gruppen von Enzymen in Abwesenheit der Proteinkomponente anscheinend keine katalytischen Fähigkeiten besitzen. So mag angeführt werden, daß Zink einen integralen Bestandteil der Carbonatanhydratasen darstellt, für sich allein aber keinen meßbaren Einfluß auf die Einstellung des Gleichgewichtes zwischen CO_2 und Carbonat ausübt. Es sind zahlreiche Fälle ähnlichen Verhaltens beschrieben worden.

Trotz dieser Divergenzen sind wir aber wohl zur Annahme berechtigt, daß die Enzyme zumindest in vielen Fällan eine Fortentwicklung der ursprünglichen, d. h. vor der Entstehung des Lebens vereits vorhandenen Katalysatoren darstellen. So kann in vielen Fällen, wo ein Metallion ein integraler Bestandteil des Enzyms ist, dieses als die Vorstufe des Enzyms aufgefaßt werden; ebenso dürften die niedermolekularen prosthetischen Gruppen mancher Enzyme, obwohl sie selbst vielleicht nicht die ursprünglichen Katalysatoren waren, die als Vorstufe des Enzyms dienten, doch zumindest durch Modifikation aus diesen hervorgegangen sein. Dasselbe sollte auch bei denjenigen Enzymen zutreffen, die eine niedermolekulare organische Verbindung zusammen mit einem—komplexartig oder nicht komplexartig gebundenen—Metallion als prosthetische Gruppe enthalten.

Einer Schwierigkeit begegnen wir allerdings bei jenen Enzymen, bei welchen gezeigt werden konnte, daß für ihre Wirksamkeit die Anwesenheit einer prosthetischen Gruppe bzw. eines Metallions überhaupt nicht erforderlich ist. Doch auch diese Komplikation ist gedanklich überbrückar. Wenn man nämlich die Enzyme dieser Art auf ihre Wirkungsweise hin betrachtet, so findet man, daß die meisten under ihnen—es gibt allerdings auch Ausnahmen—Hydrolysen, Umlagerungen oder Abspaltungen verursachen, also Reaktionstypen, die allgemein auch durch Wasserstoff- oder Hydroxylionen katalysiert werden können. Wir glauben deshalb, daß wir uns keiner allzu formalistischen Betrachtungsweise schuldig machen, wenn wir diese Enzyme als Fortentwicklung der Wasserstoffionen- bzw. Hydroxylionenkatalyse auffassen.

DIE ENTSTEHUNG DER ENZYME AUS IHREN VORSTUFEN

Wie im letzten Abschnitt ausgeführt, kann man also die Enzyme als Fortentwicklung ursprünglicher, bereits in den Zeiträumen vor der Entstehung des Lebens vorhandener Katalysatoren auffassen. Die Enzyme unterscheiden sich aber von ihren Vorstufen vor allem dadurch, daß sie eine Proteinkomponente enthalten, welche sowohl den Spezifitätsgrad erhöht, d.h. die Spezifität einschränkt, als auch die Aktivität um Größenordnungen vermehrt. Der Zusammentritt von Protein oder Proteinvorstufen mit den ursprünglichen Katalysatoren —Wasserstoffionen, Hydroxylionen, Metallionen, niedermolekulare organische Verbindungen—muß als der Zeitpunkt der Entstehung der Enzyme angesehen werden.

Damit fällt unser Problem zum Teil mit demjenigen der Entstehung der Proteine zusammen, das in diesem Symposium von anderer Seite behandelt wird. Wir können uns hier mit der Feststellung begnügen, daß für den wesentlichen Schritt der Enzymentstehung aus den ursprünglichen Katalysatoren bereits zumindest Vorstufen der heutigen Proteine, vielleicht niedrigere Polypeptide, vorhanden sein mußten. Bei Zusammentreten mit den ursprünglichen Katalysatoren ergaben diese die ersten Enzyme, die im Vergleich zu der späteren Entwicklung wahrscheinlich noch ziemlich primitiv waren, aber gegenüber den Vorstufen sowohl in bezug auf die Spezifität als auch auf die Aktivität eine wesentliche Verbesserung darstellten.

Unsere derzeitigen Kenntnisse erlauben noch nicht, über die Natur dieser proteinartigen Verbindungen weitergehende Aussagen zu machen. Man hat aber guten Grund zur Annahme, daß innerhalb der Enzymproteine allgemein bestimmte Gruppierungen (aktive Bezirke oder Wirkgruppen), die aus in definierter Weise peptidartig verbundenen Aminosäuren bestehen müssen, für die katalytischen Wirkungen vor allem verantwortlich sind, während andere

Teile des Enzymprotein-Moleküls für die Aktivität weniger wichtig sind. Über die Natur der Wirkgruppen ist man noch ungenügend informiert; unsere Kenntnisse darüber stammen vornehmlich aus Versuchsanordnungen, die uns nur indirekte Hinweise geben können. Man kann aber mit gutem Grund annehmen, daß diese aktiven Bezirke der Enzyme aus einer verhältnismäßig kleinen Anzahl von Aminosäuren in ganz bestimmten Anordnungen zusammengesetzt sind.

Wir können uns nun vorstellen, daß die ursprünglichsten Enzymmoleküle Polypeptide waren, deren Hauptbestandteil aktive Bezirke der beschriebenen Art waren. Es wird wohl einer späteren Zeit vorbehalten bleiben, experimentell zu überprüfen, inwieweit diese Vorstellung richtig ist, weil dazu sowohl Kenntnisse über die Zusammensetzung der aktiven Bezirke als auch eine Technik der Synthese spezifisch zusammengesetzter Polypeptide erforderlich sind, über die wir noch nicht verfügen.

Es muß zugegeben werden, daß die hier entwickelten Vorstellungen über den Übergang von den ursprünglichen Katalysatoren zu den ersten Enzymen, d. h. im wesentlichen also von der unspezifischen zur spezifischen Katalyse, recht schematisch wirken und—zumindest auf den ersten Blick—den Eindruck eines sehr sprunghaften und dadurch wenig wahrscheinlichen Geschehens vermitteln. Wir dürfen dabei aber nicht vergessen, wie lange Zeit für diesen schrittweisen Prozeß zur Verfügung stand, der fortwährend durch Variation und Selektion gesteuert wurde. Nur ein enzymartiger Katalysator, der für die Existenz der frühesten lebenden Einheiten von Nutzen war, etwa dadurch, daß er den Stoffwechsel oder die Energiegewinnung rationeller gestaltete, vergrößerte deren Chancen zu überleben, während jede Fehlbildung, d.h. jeder Katalysator, der in irgendeiner Weise keinen Nutzen oder sogar Schaden brachte, das Aussterben der lebenden Einheit, in der er entstanden war, zur Folge hatte.

Weiters darf man nicht vergessen, daß allgemein katalytische Fähigkeiten und auch eine gewiße Flexibilität inhärente Eigenschaften der Proteine—und wahrscheinlich auch ihrer als Polypeptide vorstellbaren Vorstufen—sind, wobei den Substanzen, die verändert werden sollen, also den Substraten, eine Art formender Wirkung auf die Proteine eigen zu sein scheint. Diese Flexibilität der Proteine und Polypeptide dürfte durch die relative Instabilität der innermolekularen Brückenbindungen, vor allem der Wasserstoffbindungen in diesen Substanzen, den sogenannten sekundären und tertiären Strukturen, bedingt sein.

So könnte angenommen werden, daß bei gleichzeitiger Anwesenheit eines organischen oxydierbaren Stoffes, ausreichender Mengen von Sauerstoff, eines ursprünglichen Katalysators (etwa eines Schwermetallions) und von Polypeptiden die oxydierbare Substanz durch Eingehen einer lockeren Bindung mit einer Polypeptidkette diese derart verändert, daß sie in Zusammenwirken mit dem Schwermetallion eine beschleunigte Oxydation dieser Substanz bewirkt, die also imstande wäre, einen Katalysator zu ihrer eigenen Veränderung zu induzieren. In gleicher Weise kann man sich vorstellen, daß ein Ester mit einer Polypeptidkette in Wechselwirkung tritt; dabei könnte das Substrat auf die Polypeptidkette einen formenden Einfluß der Art ausüben, daß diese mit ihm eine Bindung eingeht. Diese müßte einerseits recht locker sein, andererseits aber die Resonanzverhältnisse innerhalb des Estermoleküls in der Weise verändern, daß die Esterbindung gelockert wird und leicht unter dem Einfluß eines ursprünglichen Katalysators—in diesem Falle Wasserstoff- oder Hydroxylionen —gespalten wird.

Diese Vorstellung wirkt zunächst recht spekulativ; es gibt aber auch heute noch Vorgänge, die mit einer solchen 'Urzeugung der Enzyme' gewisse Analogien aufweisen und deshalb hier als Illustration herangezogen werden können. Wir kennen einige Enzymtypen, deren Wirkung sich anscheinend ausschließlich gegen Substrate richtet, welche entweder in der Natur nicht vorkommen oder von denen es schwer vorstellbar ist, daß die Organismenart, die das Enzym produziert, mit ihnen in ihrer Entwicklungsgeschichte jemals in Kontakt gekommen ist. So kann man aus den Geweben der meisten höheren Tiere und auch des Menschen einen Enzymtypus isolieren, welcher die Hydrolyse von Diisopropylfluorphosphat, einer Substanz, deren Existenz in der Natur wohl sehr unwahrscheinlich ist, katalysiert [8, 9]. Trotz eingehender Untersuchungen konnte bisher noch kein natürlich vorkommendes Substrat aufgefunden werden, welches von derartigen Enzymen hydrolysiert wird.

Nun muß es doch als recht wenig wahrscheinlich angesehen werden, daß die Organismen tatsächlich Enzyme produzieren, welche spezifisch auf Substrate einwirken sollen, die in der Natur nicht vorkommen. Weitaus plausibler erscheint uns jedenfalls die Deutung, daß die Organismen einen bestimmten Proteintypus synthetisieren, der an sich eine andere—vielleicht nicht einmal katalytische— Funktion innehat, aber in Anwesenheit von Diisopropylfluorphosphat und ähnlichen Verbindungen als Katalysator für die Hydrolyse dieser Substanzen fungieren kann. Bei diesem Beispiel ist es allerdings nicht klar, ob das Substrat auf das Protein auch einen formenden Einfluß ausübt, oder ob dieses zufällig gerade jene Konstitution aufweist, die dazu notwendig ist, um als Katalysator des Vorganges zu wirken.

Ähnliche Verhältnisse finden wir relativ häufig; es sollen noch einige wenige Beispiele angeführt werden. Manche Insekten sind imstande, Enzyme zu produzieren, welche das Insektizid DDT [1, 1, 1-Trichlor-2, 2-bis-(p-chlorphenyl)-äthan] durch Abspaltung von Chlorwasserstoff unwirksam machen [10, 11]. Auch hier liegt eine Substanz vor, welche vor ihrer synthetischen Darstellung durch den Menschen wohl kaum in der Natur vorkam. Eine analoge Situation haben wir bei den Fermenten aus tierischen Geweben vor uns, die Procain hydrolysieren [12], und auch bei Enzymen, welche das synthetische Analgeticum Dolantin oder Meperidin (1-Methyl-4-phenyl-4-carbäthoxypiperidin) durch Hydrolyse zerstören [13].

Wie bereits erwähnt wurde, ist es in allen diesen Fällen höchst unwahrscheinlich, daß die Organismen, welche Enzyme zum Umsatz der genannten Substrate produzieren, mit diesen in ihrer Entwicklungsgeschichte jemals in Berührung gekommen sind. Die Möglichkeit kann zwar nicht abgestritten werden, daß die eine oder andere der hier aufgezählten Enzymwirkungen nur Nebeneffekte irgendwelcher Enzyme, deren Hauptsubstrate eine physiologische Bedeutung für die betreffenden Organismen haben, sind; alle bisher angestellten Versuche,

die Wirkungen bereits bekannten Enzymen zuzuordnen oder für diese Enzymtypen physiologische Substrate aufzufinden, verliefen allerdings ergebnislos.

Es könnte sogar sein, daß die hier geschilderte Erscheinung, also die Fähigkeit
mancher Eiweißstoffe, als Katalysatoren für den Umsatz offenbar unphysio-
logischer Substrate zu fungieren, eine weitaus größere Bedeutung hat, als ihr
bisher zugeschrieben wurde. Verschiedene Befunde sprechen dafür, daß viele
Resistenzerscheinungen von Mikroorganismen gegenüber synthetischen Chemo-
therapeutica durch eine Neubildung von Enzymen in den pathogenen Keimen
bedingt sind wie es auch vorstellbar ist, daß die Gewöhnung an bestimmte
Drogen und Medikamente manchmal auf diese Weise erklärt werden
kann.

Inwieweit in den beschriebenen Fällen das Substrat auf das Protein eine
formende Wirkung ausübt, d. h. es erst in dem Sinne modifiziert, daß es als
Katalysator zu seinem Umsatz dienen kann, kann noch nicht entschieden
werden. Die Beispiele zeigen aber recht deutlich die Fähigkeit mancher Proteine,
gegenüber ihnen neu entgegentretenden Substanzen katalytische Wirkungen
zu entfalten.

Was aber die postulierte formende Wirkung der Substrate auf Proteine
betrifft, verfügen wir ebenfalls über Phänomene, die wir auch noch heute beobachten und untersuchen können und die deshalb als Illustration angeführt
werden können. Es handelt sich hier um die Erscheinung der sogenannten
induzierten Enzymbildung (früher als adaptive Enzymbildung bezeichnet). Wir
verstehen darunter die Entstehung von Enzymen einer in dem betreffenden
Organismus bisher nicht vorhandenen Spezifität unter dem Einfluß ihres
Substrates oder einer diesem nahe verwandten Substanz. Da zahlreiche, ausge-
zeichnete Darstellungen dieses interessanten Gebietes vorliegen (z. B. 14–16),
ist es an dieser Stelle wohl nicht erforderlich, das Phänomen der induzierten
Enzymbildung eingehender zu behandeln; es soll hier nur festgehalten werden,
daß die Proteinsynthese dabei offenbar unter dem Einfluß bestimmter Substanzen, der sogenannten Enzyminduktoren (zur Nomenklatur vgl. [17]), in
einer bestimmten Weise verändert wird. Es entsteht nämlich eine neue katalytische Fähigkeit, d. h. ein neues, bisher in dem betreffenden Organismus nicht
nachweisbares Enzym, dessen Wirkung sich gegen den Enzyminduktor oder
gegen Substanzen, die diesem nahe verwandt sind, richtet. Das klassische
Beispiel für ein solches Verhalten ist das schon seit mehr als 50 Jahren bekannte
Phänomen, daß bestimmte Hefesorten Galactose nur dann vergären können,
wenn sie auf einem Nährboden gewachsen sind, der Galactose enthält. Unter
dem Einfluß der Galactose im Medium wird also ein sonst nicht vorhandenes
Enzym gebildet, das für die Vergärung dieses Zuckers erforderlich ist. Galactose
ist hier somit eindeutig imstande, bei der Proteinbildung eine formende Wirkung
in der Weise auszuüben, daß ein Enzym zu ihrem Abbau entsteht.

In den letzten Jahrzehnten sind zahlreiche ähnlich gelagerte Fälle in Mikroorganismen, aber auch in tierischem Gewebe bekannt geworden: es wird heute
angenommen, daß dem Phänomen der Enzyminduktion eine weitaus größere
biologische Bedeutung u. a. für die Differentiation zukommt, als ihm bisher
zugemessen wurde. Wir glauben jedenfalls berechtigt zu sein, einen analogen

Mechanismus als möglichen Weg zur ursprünglichen Bildung der Enzyme vorzuschlagen.

DAS PROBLEM DER GENETISCHEN FIXIERUNG DER URSPRÜNGLICH ENTSTANDENEN ENZYME

Im Zusammenhang mit unserer Fragestellung ist aber auch noch ein weiteres sehr wichtiges Problem zu berücksichtigen. Enzyme sind im allgemeinen nicht autokatalytisch wirksam, sie sind nicht imstande, ihre eigene identische Reproduktion zu bewirken. Eine zufällige Entstehung eines Enzyms auf dem skizzierten Wege—Zusammentreten eines ursprünglichen Katalysators mit einem eventuell durch das Substrat erst geformten Protein oder Polypeptid—hätte im Rahmen der Evolution so lange, als dieser Vorgang nicht durch einen entsprechenden Mechanismus für die Zukunft fixiert wird, keinerlei Bedeutung.

Dies gilt selbstverständlich ebenso für die im vorhergehenden Abschnitt als Modelle eines möglichen Weges der ursprünglichen Enzymbildung angegebenen Vorgänge. So ist die Fähigkeit zur katalytischen Veränderung von Substanzen, mit welchen der betreffende Organismus in seiner Entwicklungsgeschichte vorher niemals in Berührung gekommen ist, nur dann gegeben, wenn der Organismus —genetisch bedingt—Proteine produziert, die entweder zufällig gegenüber diesen Substanzen eine Katalysatorwirkung ausüben können, oder die durch den Einfluß der Stoffe zu Enzymen, deren Wirkung sich gegen diese selbst richtet, geformt werden. Auch die Fähigkeit zur induzierten Enzymbildung ist genetisch bedingt; so kennen wir Heferassen, die, auch wenn sie ständig auf einem galactosehaltigen Nährboden wachsen, niemals Enzyme zum Abbau der Galactose produzieren. Eine formende Wirkung des Induktors ist nur dann möglich, wenn die Vorbedingungen für die Enzyminduktion genetisch festgelegt sind.

Unter Berücksichtigung dieser Tatsachen müssen wir nunmehr postulieren, daß auch Enzyme des primitivsten Typus, die als Vorläufer der heute in den Organismen vorhandenen Enzyme angesehen werden dürfen, erst dann entstehen konnten, als bereits zumindest ein rudimentärer genetischer Apparat existierte, der die Entstehung von Proteinen bzw. ihrer Vorstufen (Polypeptide) im Sinne einer identischen Reproduktion eines einmal festgelegten Musters sichern konnte.

Wir brauchen uns hier nicht mit der Frage der Entstehung des genetischen Apparates bzw. seiner stofflichen Grundlagen befassen, da dieses Thema im Rahmen eines anderen Referats unseres Symposiums ausführlicher behandelt werden soll. Es muß aber an dieser Stelle auf einen sehr wesentlichen Faktor hingewiesen werden, der einen großen Einfluß auf unsere Vorstellungen über die Entstehung der ursprünglichen Enzyme haben muß. Die Genetiker nehmen heute zumindest in ihrer Mehrzahl an, daß sogenannte Mutationen, d. h. Veränderungen im genetischen Apparat, welche entsprechende Veränderungen in den Eigenschaften und Fähigkeiten des Organismus zur Folge haben, in Richtung und Auswirkung nur dem Zufall unterworfen sind und keinesfalls als eine gezielte Adaption an die Bedingungen der Umwelt aufgefaßt werden dürfen. Wohl ist es möglich, durch verschiedene physikalische oder chemische Einflüsse (Strahlen, Wärme, mutagene Substanzen) die Häufigkeit der Mutationen wesentlich zu erhöhen, doch sei es ausgeschlossen, durch äußere Faktoren eine gerichtete Beeinflussung des genetischen Apparatus zu erzielen. Der Referent ist sich dessen wohl bewußt, daß von verschiedener Seite Einwände gegen eine solche strenge Formulierung erhoben wurden; er muß aber zugestehen, daß ihn die vorliegenden Befunde eher von der Richtigkeit dieser Vorstellungen überzeugen.

Wir gelangen aber in gedankliche Schwierigkeiten, wenn wir annehmen, daß diese Starrheit auch bereits dem rudimentären genetischen Apparat in der Zeit der Urentstehung der Enzyme eigen war. So hätte eine Enzymbildung in der hier postulierten Art der Formung der Polypeptidketten durch die Substrate ja dann einen biologischen Sinn nur unter der Bedingung gehabt, daß gleichzeitig spontan eine Mutation im genetischen Apparat erfolgt wäre, die zufällig die Fixierung der entstandenen Enzyme zur Folge hätte. Eine solche Koinzidenz zweier an sich nicht sehr wahrscheinlicher Ereignisse als Grundlage für die Urentstehung eines Enzyms, die sich ja für die Neuentstehung eines jeden Enzymtypus wiederholen müßte, ist aber auch, wenn wir noch so lange Zeiträume für diese Vorgänge annehmen, eine wenig plausible Grundannahme.

Ich glaube aber, daß wir durchaus nicht dazu gezwungen sind anzunehmen, daß auch bereits der für die Zeit der Urentstehung zu postulierende genetische Apparat denselben strengen Gesetzen gehorchte, die für die heutigen Mechanismen gelten sollen; es wäre vielmehr ohne weiteres vorstellbar, daß diese Starrheit in bezug auf Einflüsse der Umwelt erst eine spätere Entwicklung darstellt. Die Annahme eines flexibleren genetischen Apparats bei der ursprünglichen Enzymentstehung erleichtert uns wesentlich den Weg zum Verständnis dieser Vorgänge. Sie ist, wie zugegeben werden muß, in keiner Art beweisbar, doch ist sie weniger unwahrscheinlich, als die Genetiker vielleicht annehmen; wir müssen uns ja vorstellen, daß die stoffliche Grundlage des damaligen genetischen Apparates von derjenigen der heute existierenden genetischen Mechanismen wohl stark verschieden war.

SCHLUSSBEMERKUNGEN

Im Vorhergegangenen wurde versucht, auf Grund unserer heutigen Kenntnisse einen möglichen Weg für die Urentstehung der Enzyme zu entwickeln; unter der Annahme, daß zu der Zeit dieses Vorgangs einige zwar nicht beweisbare, aber an sich nicht unwahrscheinliche Vorbedingungen gegeben waren, konnten wir einen plausiblen Übergang von der unspezifischen zur spezifischen Katalyse darstellen. Wie wohl in den meisten Abhandlungen unseres Symposiums ist es auch hier natürlich nicht möglich, irgendwelche bindende Aussagen zu machen; wir müssen uns damit begnügen, zu sagen, daß der geschilderte Weg an sich möglich ist und nicht mit irgendwelchen Naturgesetzen in Widerspruch steht.

Es wäre nun im Anschluß daran verlockend, die Frage der Weiterentwicklung der ursprünglich enstandenen primitiven Enzyme zu den heutigen Formen zu behandeln. Wir befinden uns hier auf einem weitaus sichereren Boden als bisher. Sowohl die Entstehung immer wirkungsvollerer und spezifischerer Biokataly-

satoren als auch das Zusammentreten mehrerer Enzyme zu sinnreich funk-
tionierenden Enzymsystemen, welche für die heutigen Organismen so charakteristisch sind, lassen sich durch die Faktoren Variation und Selektion leicht
verständlich machen. Ebenso wie alle übrigen Proteine sind ja auch die Enzyme
im Verlauf der Evolution ständigen Veränderungen unterworfen; einen Hinweis
auf diese Variabilität der Enzyme stellt die bemerkenswerte Tatsache dar, daß
die chemische Konstitution, so besonders die Aminosäurezusammensetzung,
von Enzymen gleicher Spezifität aus selbst nahe verwandten Arten meist
nicht identisch ist.

Da aber dieses Gebiet bereits den Rahmen unseres Referates überschreitet
und die Entwicklung der Enzymsysteme in unserem Symposium von anderer
Seite behandelt werden soll, wollen wir uns hier auf diese Hinweise beschränken.

LITERATUR

1. A. I. OPARIN, *Die Entstehung des Lebens auf der Erde.* Übersetzung nach der 2.
   vermehrten Auflage. Berlin–Leipzig, 1949.
2. O. HOFFMANN-OSTENHOF, *Enzymologie.* Wien, 1954.
3. W. LANGENBECK, *Die organischen Katalysatoren und ihre Beziehungen zu den Fermenten.*
   2. Auflage, Berlin–Göttingen–Heidelberg, 1949.
4. W. LANGENBECK, *Advanc. Enzymol.,* **14**, 163, 1953.
5. H. R. MAHLER, *Proc. 3rd int. Congr. Biochem., Brussels,* 1955 (Ed. by C. LIÉBECQ)
   p. 252, 1956.
6. H. A. KREBS, *Biochem. J.,* **36**, 303, 1942.
7. R. KUHN & I. BRANN, *Ber. dtsch. chem. Ges.,* **59**, 2370, 1926.
8. A. MAZUR, *J. biol. Chem.,* **164**, 271, 1946.
9. L. A. MOUNTER, C. S. FLOYD & A. CHANUTIN, *J. biol. Chem.,* **204**, 221, 1953.
10. J. STERNBURG, E. VINSON & C. W. KEARNS, *J. econ. Ent.,* **46**, 513, 1953.
11. J. STERNBURG, C. W. KEARNS & H. MORREFIELD, *J. agric. Food Chem.,* **2**, 1125, 1954.
12. B. KISCH, H. KOSTER & E. STRAUSS, *Exp. Med. Surg.,* **1**, 51, 1943.
13. F. BERNHEIM & M. L. C. BERNHEIM, *J. Pharmacol.,* **85**, 74, 1945.
14. J. MONOD & M. COHN, *Advanc. Enzymol.,* **13**, 67, 1952.
15. R. Y. STANIER, *Annu. Rev. Microbiol.,* **5**, 36, 1951.
16. S. SPIEGELMAN, in *Enzymes: Units of Biological Structure and Function* (Ed. by O. H.
    GAEBLER), p. 67, New York, 1956.
17. M. COHN, J. MONOD, M. R. POLLOCK, S. SPIEGELMAN & R. Y. STANIER, *Nature,
    Lond.,* **172**, 1095, 1953.

Evolution of Enzymes and the Photosynthetic Apparatus

MELVIN CALVIN

Department of Chemistry, University of California,
Berkeley, California, U.S.A.

MR CHAIRMAN, members and guests, I would like to express my thanks to the Organizing Committee for the opportunity to be here, and to congratulate them on the thoroughness and care with which this Symposium has been arranged.

Time does not allow, nor does this audience require, a summary, or introduction to the present-day conception of various stages which must have occurred in the origin of life on Earth as we know it. The appearance of organic material on the surface of the Earth has already been adequately discussed, and the discussion on the development of cellular organisms will come later. It seemed wiser for me not to attempt even a summary of the paper which appears in the publication of the proceedings of this conference, but rather to select two particular points which I thought might add something to the basic pattern as it has been developed by Oparin. The first of these might be termed the development of catalysts, that is, enzymes and rudimentary synthetic sequences. The second will be a discussion of the possible mode of the development of what we now know as the photosynthetic apparatus.

With regard to the first point, the development of catalysts and rudimentary synthetic sequences: Even the most cursory examination of what is now known about the nature of present-day enzymatic mechanisms cannot fail to impress one with the apparent identity between the enzymatic reactions and the reactions as they are known to the organic chemist in the laboratory. For example, glyoxylase, by which methylglyoxal is converted to lactic acid, is nothing more or less than an internal Cannizzaro reaction which is catalysed by bases. Almost all of the hydrolytic enzyme reactions—esterases, proteases, phosphatases— have their non-enzymatic counterpart in the form of generalized acid or base catalysts, or more specialized catalysis by metal salts. For example, again in the case of the phosphatases, the freshly precipitated trivalent metal hydroxides are extremely effective, or manganese ion as a rudimentary phosphotransferase.

One particular group of catalysts which is widely dispersed in present-day biological systems is that centred around the element iron, particularly catalase, peroxidase and cytochrome. Here, a rather quantitative comparison can be made between the ability of the bare iron atom to perform some catalytic function and the ability of the iron atom to perform the same catalytic function as it has been developed in biological systems. Thus, in Fig. 1 one sees a comparison of the hydrated iron ion, the iron ion surrounded by a porphyrin as it is in haem, and

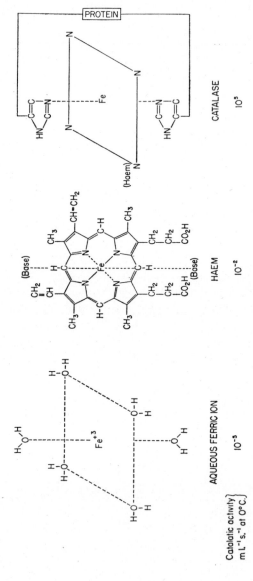

FIG. I. Evolution of a catalyst for $H_2O_2 \rightarrow H_2O + \frac{1}{2}O_2$.

iron porphyrin, or haem, as it is incorporated into a protein, surrounded by two more co-ordinating groups of the protein to form catalase. The progressive increase in catalytic ability is from 10^{-5} for the aqueous ferric ion to 10^{-2} for the haem to 10^5 for the complete enzyme. These are definitions of the catalytic function of the iron for the reaction involving the decomposition of hydrogen peroxide. However, we know that the iron has other functions, as well, most of which involve oxidation or reduction. For example, even catalase itself can function as a peroxidase, using hydrogen peroxide to oxidize organic substrates, provided the hydrogen peroxide is sufficiently dilute. Undoubtedly, the iron is also involved in what we now recognize as oxidative phosphorylation, that is, the conversion of the energy liberated upon the passage of an electron from a highly reducing potential to an oxidizing agent, such as oxygen or other material, with the concomitant storage of some of that energy in the form of unstable (pyrophosphate) linkages which may later be used for other purposes.

In order to convert the rudimentary catalytic functions which exist in all the elements and their simple compounds into the highly efficient ones that we now recognize as enzymes, we must introduce two additional ideas, one from the realm of chemistry and the other from the realm of genetics, both of which, however, could be considered as manifestations of exactly the same phenomenon. The first of these, from the realm of chemistry, is the idea of autocatalysis, that is, the basic notion that the product of a reaction may itself be a catalyst for the conversion of precursors into itself. This is a very common phenomenon in chemistry and perhaps is best illustrated in one of the simplest cases, namely, the reaction of molecular hydrogen with cupric ion. This reaction leads thermodynamically to the formation of cuprous ion and water. It so happens that the reaction of molecular hydrogen with cupric ion, although thermodynamically possible, is an extremely slow one without catalysis. However, the product of this reaction, that is, cuprous ion, is an extremely good catalyst for the reaction between hydrogen and cupric ion. Therefore, one can imagine, and indeed we have experimentally realized this long ago, a system consisting of molecular hydrogen and cupric ion which remain in this form for some period of time. However, should either a very slow noncatalytic reduction lead to cuprous ion, or should some random electron transfer lead to the formation of an appreciable number of cuprous ions in the mixture, then immediately the entire reaction mixture goes over to the more stable system consisting of cuprous ion.

The other notion which we would like to introduce is the one developed by the geneticist Horowitz. He suggested that the very complex series of reactions which we are now finding to be responsible for the synthesis of most of our existing biological material could have developed in a backward manner, beginning with the completely heterotrophic organism. He postulated that the first living things, complete heterotrophs, had available to them all possible precursors for their own duplication, and that their only function was to bring these together to produce themselves. One can then visualize a process in which at first one essential constituent of the mixture is depleted. Then, the particular organizational unit which found a way of manufacturing the depleted item from remaining molecules will, of course, survive, whereas those units which are unable to

14

do so will disappear, since they can no longer reproduce themselves. Such a process of gradual depletion of available substrates with the evolution of continually longer and longer chains of synthesis would then constitute the origin of the synthetic sequences which we are now finding in present-day living orgaismns.

With these two ideas we can see how an enzyme, or, I should say, a highly efficient catalyst, could be built. It is worthwhile to trace such a development in a specific instance with which we might be familiar, for example the iron porphyrin. Fortunately, the essential steps in the present-day biosynthetic route to porphyrin have been unravelled for us. One could begin with succinic acid and glycine, two compounds which we already know can be made by the various random methods which have been discussed earlier, such as gaseous discharge or ionizing radiation or ultraviolet light. From these (succinic acid and glycine) an α-amino-β-keto acid is formed, followed by decarboxylation to δ-aminolaevulinic acid, two of which then condense to form a pyrrole nucleus, porphobilinogen. This molecule then passes through a series of steps, involving a number of oxidations, leading finally to protoporphyrin 9. The skeleton of this sequence is shown in Fig. 2.

With the introduction of iron into the protoporphyrin, or perhaps a better way to view it would be, the surrounding of iron by the protoporphyrin grouping, the iron becomes a better oxidation catalyst, and, as you can see, there are several oxidation steps along the biosynthetic route as we now know it. Thus, one has only to suppose that one or more of the sequences of steps leading to protoporphyrin is dependent upon an iron-catalysed oxidation, and this is almost certainly so, to arrive at the conclusion that once such an iron protoporphyrin is manufactured it will itself accelerate its own synthesis from such precursors as succinic acid and glycine and thus tend to build up the supply of the material and improve the iron catalyst that will be available for a variety of other functions as well.

The second point that I would like to make concerns how the development of the photosynthetic apparatus as we now know it might have occurred: In order to do this we review briefly what our present state of knowledge might appear to be with respect to the existing mechanism by which the photosynthetic apparatus in the green plants and in the lower organisms can convert electromagnetic energy into chemical potential as reduced carbon and molecular oxygen. One need hardly do more than point out the essential features of the process to recognize its present-day separation into several rather distinct parts. The reduction of carbon dioxide, we now have every reason to suppose, occurs in a series of reactions which can take place entirely in the dark. In fact, all of the enzyme systems which we now know to participate in the conversion of CO_2 to carbohydrate have been found in a wide variety of organisms, many of which are not photosynthetic. For example, the *Thiobacillus* contains very nearly all of the necessary enzymes and *Escherichia coli* grown in xylose will contain not only 'carboxydismutase' but a number of other enzymes involved in the carbon reduction cycle. The final step was indeed taken when Racker was able to make a mixture of all the requisite enzymes and the energy-storing compounds [reduced triphosphopyridine nucleotide and adenosine triphosphate (ATP)] which produced hexose phosphate from carbon dioxide, all in the dark.

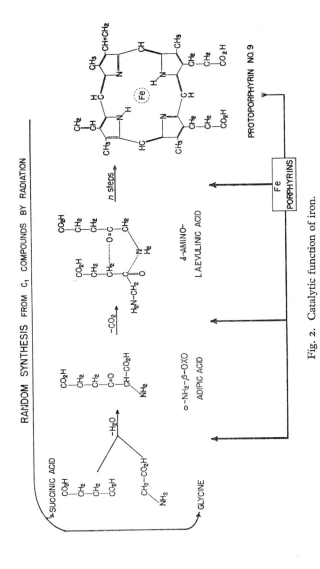

Fig. 2. Catalytic function of iron.

We can therefore follow van Niel and reaffirm the suggestion that the photo-chemical apparatus in the green plants is primarily concerned with the splitting of the water molecule and the generation of reducing agent and intermediate oxidant. The latter (intermediate oxidant) will eventually find its way into molecular oxygen. The former (reducing agent) will be used to reduce the compounds formed by combination of carbon dioxide with suitable intermediates in the cell. From our knowledge of the nature of the carbon cycle it is already clear that ATP is also required for this latter process, and this ATP may either be generated by oxidative phosphorylation or by a recombination of the 'intermediate oxidant' with some 'intermediate reductant' that has been formed by direct photolysis. Thus, we can suppose that the reaction sequence which is now used by green plants for the reduction of carbon dioxide was developed independently of the photosynthetic apparatus, and presumably *later* coupled to the energy-capturing and transforming mechanism which the photosynthetic apparatus represents.

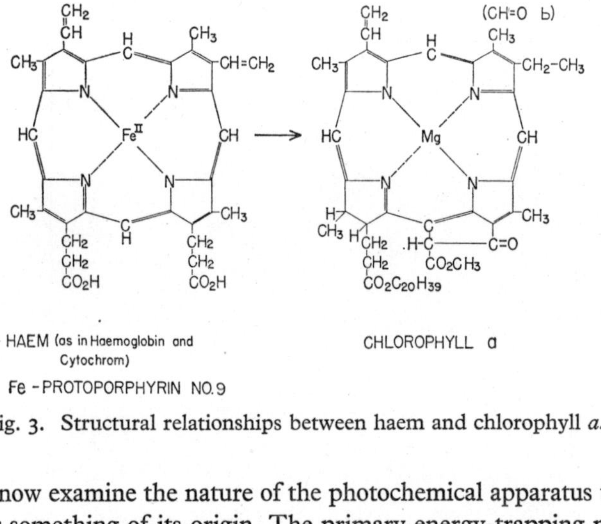

HAEM (as in Haemoglobin and Cytochrom)

Fe - PROTOPORPHYRIN NO.9

CHLOROPHYLL a

Fig. 3. Structural relationships between haem and chlorophyll *a*.

We must now examine the nature of the photochemical apparatus to see if we can discover something of its origin. The primary energy-trapping molecule is, of course, a porphyrin, chlorophyll. In recent years, the work of Granick has clearly indicated, if not conclusively demonstrated, that present-day synthesis of chlorophyll is a branch in the synthetic sequence leading also to the haems. This branch seems to occur just before the insertion of the iron into the porphyrin ring (Fig. 3).

We can thus see that the most likely course for the evolution of the photosynthetic apparatus involved the prior existence of the porphyrin type of catalytic structure. This catalytic structure was evolved not in response to the existence of sunlight, but rather in reponse to the other evolutionary driving force, which we have already seen operative in the development of the porphyrin nucleus, namely, the oxidative catalysis at which the iron compounds of the porphyrins are so efficient. This leads to the suggestion that the development of the porphyrin either was *not* directly dependent upon the existence of oxygen

PLATE III

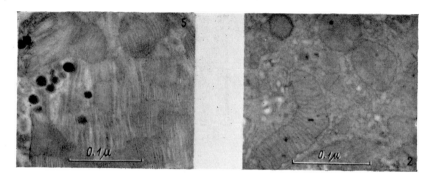

Fig. 4. Comparison of structure of mitochondria and chloroplasts
(from 'Sjöstrand').

in the primordial atmosphere but occurred in response to its function in other oxidative dismutations not involving molecular oxygen, or that there was some molecular oxygen in the Earth's atmosphere prior to the advent of the photosynthetic apparatus which now produces it.

The development of such highly organized structures as are now found in the organelles of the cells, such as the chloroplasts and mitochondria, seems to be incompatible with the penetration of very much of the ultraviolet radiation from the sun in the wavelength around 2500 Å which would have occurred had there been no oxygen in the atmosphere. To-day, of course, the oxygen in the upper atmosphere is photodissociated by this very ultraviolet light and is thus converted into quantities of ozone which, in turn, strongly absorbs in the region between 2200 Å and 3000 Å. While it is possible to conceive of the development of heterotrophic organisms in the shelter of deep water and thus not exposed to the destructive ultraviolet, it is difficult to conceive of the evolution of a photosynthetic apparatus, even a primitive one, also in the same environment, since there would be little visible light available either for the evolutionary selective mechanism.

Thus we are constrained to believe not only was the evolution of higher organisms delayed until the appearance of appreciable amounts of oxygen in the atmosphere, but also the evolution of the porphyrin catalysis itself and some of the more complex structural elements in living cells had to await this protection. Presumably, it came about by virtue of the photodissociation of water into hydrogen and oxygen followed by the escape of the hydrogen from the gravitational field of the Earth, leaving behind an appreciable quantity of oxygen, even though it is now entirely photosynthetic in origin. We can thus envisage the development of the highly organized structural units which we see to-day in the form of mitochondria prior to the development of the chloroplasts and of the photochemical apparatus. The similarity in the structure of these two organelles is very striking, and it is not unreasonable to suppose that the latter had its origin in the former (Fig. 4).

Thus, the porphyrin molecule and the structural unit into which it is built had independent evolutions. Only at a much later time did the coupling of the optical properties of the porphyrin molecule to the energy demands of the carbon-reduction cycle take place. This presumably occurred at a time when there may have already been a rudimentary photosynthetic energy-yielding apparatus in the near ultraviolet, perhaps using sulphur compounds as direct absorbers. The more efficient energy-capturing molecule, which the porphyrin is, could not be used in energy conversion until it was divested of the iron atom which was its principal reason for being. The reason for this is that the requirement for an efficient energy conversion carries with it the requirement for a long-lived excited state after the capture of the quantum. The iron porphyrin, although absorbing a good deal of visible light, cannot have a very long life in the excited state because of the presence of the magnetic iron atom in the molecule. The inhomogeneous magnetic field surrounding the iron atom breaks down the triplet–singlet selection prohibition and does not allow a long-lived triplet state of porphyrin. However, if the iron is replaced by magnesium, or some other diamagnetic, bivalent cation such as zinc, then this molecule can have a long-lived triplet state, which is essential for the energy-migration and conversion with any high degree of efficiency.

I suspect that the rudimentary beginnings of a chlorophyll-type of photosynthesis may have occurred in the precellular period, in a period in which one had already seen the appearance of lipid-type coacervates and in which the disc-like molecules of chlorophyll could assume a pseudo-crystalline arrangement, facilitating the energy transport and conversion. In all probability, it was at this point, or very near this point, that the cellular habit of life took shape. Finally, the generation of the oxygen-evolving mechanism, perhaps requiring the participation of the carotenoids and other such materials, occurred, leading to the higher plants, and to the whole potential of oxidative evolution.

The Nature of the Forces Operating in the Process of the Duplication of Molecules in Living Organisms

LINUS PAULING

California Institute of Technology, Pasadena, Calif., U.S.A.

EACH FORM of life has the power of manufacturing molecules characteristic of that form. A human being manufactures kinds of molecules, including probably some tens of thousands of different kinds of proteins, which are characteristic of him. He passes on to his child the power of manufacturing many of the same molecules. A virus particle, with the collaboration of a suitable host, may have as immediate progeny hundreds or thousands of virus particles that are made in its own image.

It may be that life originated on Earth when, in the 'hot, thin soup' containing thousands and thousands of different kinds of molecules that had been formed by more or less random chemical reactions, there was, by chance, formed a molecule with the power of catalysing the synthesis of replicas of itself.

Whatever the details of the process of duplication are, it is characteristic of living organisms that they contain molecules with the power of manufacturing duplicates of themselves. A human being has molecules of haemoglobin in his red cells; his children have molecules of haemoglobin in their red cells, usually identical with those in the red cells of the parent. A human being has molecules of deoxyribonucleic acid in the nuclei of his cells; his children have molecules of deoxyribonucleic acid in the nuclei of their cells; and it is believed that many of these molecules are identical in structure with those of the parent.

In order to understand the nature of life and the origin of life we need to know what the process is by which molecules are able to duplicate themselves, what the forces are that are operating during the process.

It is my belief that the process of duplication of molecules and the other processes that show biological specificity involve not only the interatomic forces comprised under the name of chemical bonds but also the weak forces that operate between atoms—the forces of van der Waals attraction, electrostatic attraction between charged groups, and the formation of hydrogen bonds; and that in general biological specificity is the result of the especially strong interaction, involving collaboration of these weak forces, that can occur between molecules that are complementary in structure. It is this thesis that will be presented in the following paragraphs.

Let us ask how a molecule A, which we may call a gene, could produce a replica of itself. One conceivable way is that some special stabilizing force of interaction occurs between two identical molecules, A and A, such that one molecule A is able to influence its environment so as to lead to the production directly of the second molecule A. This possibility is appealing because of its simplicity. The suggestion was made by Jordan [1] that the quantum-mechanical resonance phenomenon might lead to a special stability of an aggregate of two identical molecules, AA, relative to an aggregate of two similar but non-identical molecules, AB. A simple analogy is with a system of one electron and two identical nuclei, in which there is a strong interaction (formation of a one-electron bond) as compared with a system of one electron and two non-identical nuclei, in which there is only a weak interaction, the electron remaining attached preferentially to one of the nuclei. It was pointed out by Pauling & Delbrück [2], however, that the special quantum-mechanical interaction energy between large identical molecules, such as protein molecules, is negligible in comparison with the interaction energy of either identical or non-identical large molecules, and that this mechanism could not lead by a direct process to the synthesis of replicas of a molecule. Instead, Pauling & Delbrück suggested that the process of duplication is a two-step process, involving the use of molecule A as a template for the synthesis of the complementary molecule, A^{-1}, and then the use of A^{-1} as a template for the synthesis of a molecule complementary to it, and identical with A.

The idea of complementariness in structure as the cause of biological specificity is an old one. The principal evidence for the theory comes from the field of immunochemistry, and the first, rather vague, suggestion of complementariness was contained in Ehrlich's lock-and-key explanation of immunological specificity. The idea that antigen molecules and the homologous antibody molecules have complementary molecular structures was suggested by Breinl & Haurowitz [3], Alexander [4], and Mudd [5], in the period 1930 to 1932, and a detailed theory of the structure and process of formation of antibodies based upon the principles of molecular structure was formulated in 1940 [6].

Already in 1940 there was available a considerable amount of evidence in support of the theory of complementariness in structure of antigen and antibody, in the experimental results obtained by Landsteiner and collaborators through the study of the serological properties of azoproteins containing haptenic groups of known simple structure. A great amount of additional evidence in support of the theory was then gathered by the execution of experiments designed specifically to test the theory [7]. For example, it was found that the introduction of a methyl group in place of a *meta* hydrogen atom in the benzene ring of the benzoate ion decreases the combining power of the hapten with antibody molecules homologous to p-azobenzoic acid azoprotein to about one-fifth of the combining power of the benzoate ion itself. This fact is explained in a simple way as the result of a resistance to fitting the larger methyl group, which has an effective radius of about 2·0 Å, into the region of the antibody which in the process of its synthesis was occupied by a hydrogen atom of the haptenic group of the immunizing azoprotein, this hydrogen atom having an effective radius of about 1·2 Å. The only conclusion that can be drawn from this experiment is that the antibody is closely complementary in structure to the haptenic group of the azoprotein, and that the fit between the complementary structures is a close one, to within less than 0·8 Å, a small fraction of an atomic diameter. It has also been shown that a negatively charged group is present in the antibody at very nearly the minimum distance of approach to a positively charged group in the haptenic group (the trimethylphenylammonium cationic group) of an azoprotein used in producing the antiserum. Many observed ratios of combining powers of different haptens could be explained only in terms of the formation of specific hydrogen bonds between antigen and antibody.

The theory that the process of duplication of the gene is a two-step process involving at each stage the formation of a structure complementary to that of the molecule acting as a template has been given strong support through the formulation of the Watson-Crick structure of deoxyribonucleic acid [8]. Evidence that genes are molecules of nucleic acid rather than molecules of protein has been gathered from several sources in recent years. The efforts to determine the molecular structure of fibres of deoxyribonucleic acid culminated in the formulation by Watson & Crick of their structure, which involves two complementary molecules twisted about one another to form a double helix. At any level in one of the molecules there may be a nucleotide with any one of the four nitrogen bases adenine, thymine, guanine, or cytosine. The sequence of nitrogen bases in one of the polynucleotide chains may be, so far as we know now, completely arbitrary. However, according to the Watson-Crick structure the nature of the second polynucleotide chain is completely determined by that of the first; the second chain must be complementary to the first, with thymine wherever the first chain has adenine, adenine wherever the first chain has thymine, cytosine wherever the first chain has guanine, and guanine wherever the first chain has cytosine. This complementariness in structure is the result of the ability of adenine and thymine to form two hydrogen bonds with one another, and of guanine and cytosine to form three hydrogen bonds with one another. (Watson & Crick proposed that guanine and cytosine form only two hydrogen bonds with one another, of a nature, however, somewhat different from those in the adenine-thymine pair; it was then pointed out by Pauling & Corey [9] that there are three hydrogen bonds in the guanine-cytosine complex.) With Watson & Crick [10], we may accept as a reasonable molecular mechanism for the duplication of the double polynucleotide chain of deoxyribonucleic acid a process that involves the separation of the two chains, each of which then serves as the template for the synthesis of the other. In the nomenclature used above, we may describe the Watson-Crick double helix as AA^{-1}; its process of duplication would involve the separation into A and A^{-1}, each of which would then serve for the synthesis of a complementary structure, giving AA^{-1} and $A^{-1}A$, two double molecules identical with the original one, and each containing one-half of the original double molecule.

We may ask whether it might not be possible that the two chains A and A^{-1} of the Watson-Crick double helix are really a single chain, A and A^{-1} being attached to one another at one end. An argument has been presented to show that this suggestion is to be rejected [11]. If A and A^{-1} were separate chains, the process of duplication of AA^{-1} would be as described above. If they were the same chain, the process of duplication would consist in untwisting the double helix, to form the extended chain A—A^{-1}, with length twice as long. This would then serve to produce a compound helix

$$\frac{A\text{---}A^{-1}}{A^{-1}\text{---}A},$$

with the same total length. This long double helix would then have to be untwined, and each of the halves A—A^{-1} and A^{-1}—A would coil to form the original complex and its duplicate. There would thus be two processes of untwining involved, rather than a single one. If the second process of untwining did not occur, we might be satisfied to accept the long double chain as a complex of a molecule A—A^{-1} and its self-complementary duplicate, A^{-1}—A. This process cannot, however, be accepted, because there is no mechanism for ensuring the retention of complementariness of one end of the chain and the other end. Mutation might occur, changing the nature of one end or the other end, and if the chain in the process of duplication did not fold at some stage into the configuration of the short double helix, the lack of complementariness of the two ends of the chain would not interfere at all with the process of duplication, and this property of self-complementariness would be lost.

There is a significant difference between the manufacture of antibodies and the duplication of genes. The antiserum that is produced in response to the injection of an antigen is highly heterogeneous (the heterogeneity may correspond to the range of a factor of ten thousand in the equilibrium constant for combination of antibody and homologous antigen) [12], whereas the duplication of genes seems to be perfect, or nearly perfect. The manufacture of an antibody molecule is a process that occurs only once, so far as that molecule is concerned, and the molecule is not itself then used as a template. If the conditions within the cell in which the antibody molecule is being manufactured happen to favour the formation of a good molecule with large complementariness to the antigen molecule, the combining constant will have a large value, whereas if the conditions are unfavourable the combining constant for the antibody molecule that is formed will have a small value. There is no process of trial and error, such that the system can improve in the manufacture of antibodies against the injected antigen. The process of duplication of genes is different. A gene that had undergone mutation —for example, that has been damaged as the result of the absorption of a quantum of radiation—may serve as a template for the manufacture of a complementary molecule; we may call the mutated gene A_1^{-1}. The complementary molecule will then serve as a template, in the next cell division, for the manufacture of a molecule complementary to it, which we may call A_2. In general we would not expect A_2 to be an exact duplicate of A_1. The process of two-stage duplication would then continue: A_2^{-1}, A_3, A_3^{-1}, A_4, A_4^{-1}, ... If after any number of duplications of this sort a molecule, A_n, happens to be formed that is especially well suited to serving as a template for the manufacture of a duplicate of itself, the process of duplication from then on would be a reliable one. The mechanism of heredity thus permits the ultimate discovery of a mutated gene that undergoes true duplication; but the mutated gene may, and in general will, not be the original gene that has been damaged by X-radiation or produced in some other way by a primary process, but will be a product obtained after many steps of two-stage duplication.

The details of the process by means of which specific molecules of protein are manufactured by molecules of nucleic acid, which serve as the templates for their manufacture, are not yet known, but there is no reason to doubt that this process takes place. There are two aspects of the structure of proteins that may be differentiated. One is the ordering of amino-acid residues into the proper sequence in the polypeptide chain, and the other is the folding of the polypeptide chain into the configuration characteristic of the native protein molecule. It is likely that the principal function of the gene in the process of manufacture of a protein molecule is to select the right amino acid molecules and to order their residues into the right sequence in the polypeptide chain. The experiments of Anson and Mirsky, showing that some proteins (haemoglobin and trypsin) that have been subjected to alkali denaturation, causing some unfolding of the poly-peptide chains, can, by proper treatment, be brought back to essentially the native configuration, suggest that the process of folding of the polypeptide chains into the correct configuration may occur automatically, without the help of a template, after the polypeptide chains have been synthesized.

We may ask whether or not it is possible for the genic template to function perfectly in ordering amino-acid residues during the process of synthesis of polypeptide chains. An analysis of the forces operating between the amino acids and the genic template [13] has led to the prediction that the process must involve occasional errors, and that some protein molecules that are manufactured should have a sequence of amino acid residues slightly different from that in other molecules of the same protein. It is possible to make some predictions about the nature of the errors. For example, it may be predicted that it is highly unlikely that any amino acid residue other than a residue of glycine would occupy a glycine locus in the polypeptide chain; the selection of glycine by the template must involve the fitting of the hydrogen atom that serves as the side chain in glycine into a cavity in the template that is just large enough to accommodate a hydrogen atom, and is accordingly too small to accommodate the methyl group of alanine or any other side chain, and the van der Waals repulsion energy be-comes so great when atoms are brought into contact at a distance even 0.5 Å less than the normal van der Waals contact distance that the selectivity of this template for glycine can be expected to be essentially perfect. On the other hand, a part of the template that is complementary to alanine would have a cavity for the methyl group that would be small enough to reject all amino acids except alanine and the smaller one, glycine, and the selection of alanine rather than glycine would have to be made through the operation of the greater van der Waals attraction (London electronic dispersion energy) of the template for the methyl group than that for the hydrogen atom; the estimated magnitude of the energy difference leading to the selection of alanine rather than glycine has led to the prediction that the probability of an error involving the introduction of glycine in an alanine locus should be as much as 5%. It may well be that the calculation of the energy difference has been made with too much caution, and that the predicted probability of an error of this sort is no more than 1%.

The careful search for errors in the synthesis of protein molecules should lead to information that would either support or discredit the template theory of biological specificity. One careful study of this sort has already been made. D. Allen & W. A. Schroeder [unpublished observation] have analysed haemoglobin from normal adult human beings and from patients with phenylpyruvic oligophrenia, who have in their plasma and cerebral-spinal fluid a concentration of phenylalanine 25 or 50 times greater than that in normal individuals. They found no difference in the phenylalanine content of the two haemoglobins, to within their experimental error, which was less than 3% (one residue per haemoglobin molecule—the molecule contains about 32 residues of phenylalanine). There are about twelve residues of tyrosine per molecule in that haemoglobin, and this result shows that the probability that a phenylalanine residue will be introduced in place of tyrosine (this is the most likely sort of error involving phenylalanine) as a result of the increased concentration of phenylalanine in the body fluids of the patients with phenylpyruvic oligophrenia is smaller than 8%. at is possible, of course, that the introduction of the phenylalanine residue at I tyrosine locus would change the properties of the haemoglobin molecule enough to cause it to be rejected by the red cell.

The extent to which the properties of a molecule are determined by the folding of the polypeptide chains is suggested by the available information about the difference in structure of normal adult human haemoglobin (haemoglobin A) and sickle-cell-anaemia haemoglobin (haemoglobin S) [14]. The difference in electrophoretic mobilities of these two forms of haemoglobin corresponds to a difference in electric charge per molecule of about three electronic units. The analyses that have been made of amino acid composition show no difference in composition within experimental error; in particular, there is no difference in acidic groups or basic groups great enough to explain the difference in charge of three electronic units. Moreover, the change in electrophoretic mobility of the globins obtained from these haemoglobins on slight denaturation, which causes the molecules to acquire essentially the same electrophoretic mobility shows clearly that the electric charge is determined in considerable part by the way in which the polypeptide chains are folded.

There is now available a great deal of information about possible configurations of polypeptide chains. Precise determinations of the structure of crystals of amino acids, simple peptides, and other substances closely related to proteins have been made by Professor Robert B. Corey, Dr E. W. Hughes, and their collaborators, as well as, in recent years, by other investigators. It has been found that the interatomic distances and bond angles are essentially constant in this group of substances. The distances found are $\alpha C—C' = 1.53$ Å, $\alpha C—N = 1.47$ Å, $C'—N = 1.32$ Å, $C'—O = 1.24$ Å, angles $N—\alpha C—C' = 110°$, $\alpha C—C'—N = 114°$, $C'—N—\alpha C = 123°$, $O—C'—N = 125°$. The principal degrees of freedom of the polypeptide chain, not determined by these parameters, are the azimuthal angles about the two single bonds $\alpha C—C'$ and $\alpha C—N$. The stable configurations of polypeptide chains that have been reliably recognized so far (the α helix, the parallel-chain pleated sheet, the antiparallel-chain pleated sheet, and the polyglycine-II structure) all involve azimuthal orientations around these bonds such that N—H . . . O hydrogen bonds are formed, with the nitrogen-oxygen distance approximately 2·79 Å.

In all of these configurations of polypeptide chains and in all of the structures for simple peptides and amides that have been reliably determined there is one structural feature that would not be predicted by the classical structure theory of organic chemistry. This is the planarity of the amide group. It is found by experiment that the planarity of the group consisting of the C' atom, the N atom, and the four atoms bonded to them is preserved to within a mean deviation less than 0·05 Å from the median plane. This structural feature was predicted in a straightforward way [15] by use of the theory of resonance, which is an extension of the classical chemical structure theory. According to the theory of resonance the structure of the amide group, as of other molecules for which a single distri-bution of chemical valence bonds does not provide a satisfactory representation, can be described in terms of two distributions (in some cases more) of the valence bonds. For the amide groups we write the two following electronic structures:

$$I \qquad\qquad II$$

The group may be described as having a structure that represents the superposi-tion of these two electronic structures: it may be described as a hybrid of these structures, with the C'—N bond a bond with partial double-bond character. The observed distance C'—N, 1·32 Å (0·15 Å less than the distance αC—N), indicates about 40% double-bond character for this bond, so that the two struc-tures I and II shown above are described as contributing in the ratio about 60% to 40% to the structure of the amide group. With 40% double-bond charac-ter for the C'—N bond, the group can be expected to have the property of coplanarity to an extent that can be described quantitatively as about 40% of that of a molecule containing the carbon-carbon double bond.

The theory of resonance has been subjected to severe criticism; as I under-stand the criticism, it is based largely upon the fact that the theory involves the use of structures (such as the structures I and II given above for the amide group, or the two Kekulé structures for benzene) that do not have independent existence in reality. It is true that these structures, use of which is made in the theory of resonance, are idealizations, and do not have existence in reality. However, if the argument were to be accepted as a valid argument against the theory of resonance and the theory were in consequence to be abandoned, it would be necessary also, for the sake of consistency, to abandon the whole structure theory of organic chemistry, because the structural elements that are used in classical structure theory—the carbon-carbon single bond, the carbon-carbon double bond, etc.—also are idealizations, having no existence in reality [16, 17]. There is no rigorous way of showing by experiment that two of the carbon atoms in the *cyclo*hexene molecule, for example, are connected by a double bond. Every molecule has a structure, as was pointed out for the first time by Butlerow, and the properties of the substance consisting of these molecules are determined by their structure: we may say that the *cyclo*hexene molecule is a system that can be shown experimentally to be resolvable into six carbon nuclei, ten hydrogen nuclei, and forty-six electrons, and that can be shown to have certain other structural properties, such as values 1·33 Å, 1·54 Å, etc., for the average distances between nuclei in the molecule in its normal state; but it is not resolvable by any experimental technique into one carbon-carbon double bond, five carbon-carbon single bonds, and ten carbon-hydrogen bonds—these bonds are theoretical constructs, idealizations, with the aid of which the chemist during the past one hundred years has developed a convenient and extremely valuable theory. The theory of resonance constitutes an extension of this classical structure theory of organic chemistry; it is based upon the same idealizations, the bonds between atoms, as classical structure theory, with the important extension that in describing the benzene molecule or the amide group two arrangements of these bonds are used, rather than only one. The theory of resonance in chemistry is an essentially qualitative theory, which, like the classical structure theory, depends for its successful application largely upon a chemical feeling that is developed through practice; the theory is a part of chemical structure theory, which has an essentially empirical (inductive) basis; it is not just a branch of quantum mechanics.

The pyrimidine and purine groups of nucleic acids provide another interesting application of the theory of resonance. The molecules of adenine, guanine, thymine and cytosine, and of other pyrimidines and purines, have their carbon, nitrogen and oxygen atoms in a single plane, as is predicted for molecules with structures that can be described as involving resonance among valence-bond structures in which the double bonds occupy a number of different positions, so that the property of planarity characteristic of the atoms adjacent to a double bond becomes associated with nearly all of the bonds in the molecule. The observed inter-atomic distances in these pyrimidines and purines [9] are also found to correspond not to 0% or 100% double-bond character, but to intermediate amounts of double-bond character.

I think that it is likely that, as further investigations of haemoglobins A and S are carried out, it will be found that the apparently very small difference in amino-acid composition of these two haemoglobins, amounting to perhaps a difference in only two residues per molecule, leads to a large difference in the way in which the polypeptide chains are folded, and that this difference in folding changes the properties of the molecules significantly, in particular the ionization constants of some acidic or basic groups.

The discovery of the abnormal varieties of human haemoglobin has led to some quantitative information about the rate of evolution of human beings. It was shown by Allison that the sickle-cell heterozygotes, with a mixture of haemoglobins A and S in their red cells, are protected against malaria. We may imagine that in a highly malarial region a mutation that converted the gene for A into the gene for S occurred, that after some generations there were a number of heterozygotes AS in the population, and that of the progeny of two hetero-zygotes the 25% of type AA would die of malaria, the 25% of type SS would die of sickle-cell anaemia, and the 50% of type AS would be protected against malaria and would not have the disease sickle-cell anaemia. Under these cir-cumstances the heterozygotes would rapidly replace the original type AA. In some highly malarial regions in Africa the incidence of heterozygotes AS is as great as 50%. If the assumption is made that all of the sickle-cell homozygotes SS die without progeny, we may calculate from this incidence of the hetero-zygotes that the advantage that the heterozygotes have over the normal individuals AA is 50%—there will be an increase by the factor 1·5 in the ration of hetero-zygotes to normal individuals in each generation. This is a very great increase, such that within one thousand or two thousand years the mutant type of human being, carrying a sickle-cell gene, would be found to have largely displaced the wild type, without the mutant gene. So far as I know, this is the only quantitative information that is available about the rate of evolution in man. The information shows that the process of evolution can, under favourable circumstances, be a very rapid one, and we may understand how it is that the process of selection of a pool of favourable genes, such as is now represented in the germ plasm of the human race, could have taken place so effectively during the period as short as 10^9 years since the origin of life on Earth.

REFERENCES

1. P. JORDAN, *Phys. Z.*, **39**, 711, 1938; *Z. Phys.*, **113**, 431, 1939; *Fundam. radiol.*, **5**, 43, 1939; *Z. ImmunForsch.*, **97**, 330, 1940.
2. L. PAULING & M. DELBRÜCK, *Science*, **92**, 77, 1940.
3. F. BREINL & F. HAUROWITZ, *Hoppe-Seyl. Z.*, **192**, 45, 1930.
4. J. ALEXANDER, *Protoplasma*, **14**, 296, 1931.
5. STUART MUDD, *J. Immunol.*, **23**, 423, 1932.
6. L. PAULING, *J. Amer. chem. Soc.*, **62**, 2643, 1940.
7. L. PAULING, D. PRESSMAN, D. H. CAMPBELL, C. IKEDA & M. IKAWA, *J. Amer. chem. Soc.*, **64**, 2994, 1942, and later papers.
8. J. D. WATSON & F. H. C. CRICK, *Nature, Lond.*, **171**, 737, 1953; F. H. C. CRICK & J. D. WATSON, *Proc. Roy. Soc.*, **223A**, 80, 1954.
9. L. PAULING & R. B. COREY, *Arch. Biochem. Biophys.*, **65**, 164, 1956.
10. J. D. WATSON & F. H. C. CRICK, *Nature, Lond.*, **171**, 964, 1953.
11. L. PAULING, in *Aspects of Synthesis and Order in Growth.* Princeton University Press, p. 3, 1955.
12. L. PAULING, D. PRESSMAN & A. L. GROSSBERG, *J. Amer. chem. Soc.*, **66**, 784, 1944.
13. L. PAULING, *Festschrift Prof. Dr. Arthur Stoll.* Birkhaüser, Basel, p. 597, 1957.
14. L. PAULING, H. A. ITANO, S. J. SINGER & I. C. WELLS, *Science*, **110**, 543, 1949.
15. L. PAULING, *Proc. nat. Acad. Sci., Wash.*, **18**, 293, 1932.
16. L. PAULING, *Les Prix Nobel en 1954.* Norstedt & Söner, Stockholm, p. 91, 1955.
17. L. PAULING, in *Perspectives in Organic Chemistry*, p. 1. Interscience, New York and London, 1956.

Contribution No. 2207 from the Gates and Crellin Laboratories of Chemistry, California Institute of Technology, Pasadena, California, U.S.A.

The Occurrence of Amino Acids in Nature

R. L. M. SYNGE

The Rowett Research Institute, Bucksburn, Aberdeenshire, Scotland

THESE ARE the first two sentences from *The Specificity of Serological Reactions* by Karl Landsteiner [1]. 'The morphological characteristics of plant and animal species form the chief subject of the descriptive natural sciences and are the criteria for their classification. But not until recently has it been recognized that in living organisms, as in the realm of crystals, chemical differences parallel the variation in structure.'

Since this was written, we have seen great advances in our understanding of proteins and amino acids, and especially in the range of the living organisms which have been studied chemically in this respect. My purpose is to try to extract from the mass of scattered observations, made with a variety of motives, such generalizations as appear relevant to the subject of the Symposium.

It is convenient to consider amino acids as occurring in living organisms: (*a*) chemically combined in proteins; (*b*) chemically combined in peptides and other compounds of relatively low molecular weight; (*c*) free.

The distinction between (*a*) and (*b*) is somewhat arbitrary. It has been convenient to draw the line at about mol. wt. 10,000, but the less well-defined materials have often been placed in one class or the other on the basis of solubility in hot water, in aqueous trichloroacetic acid or of some other easily observed property. Compounds having a specially simple amino acid composition have often been placed in class (*b*) while having obviously high molecular weight.

Despite the arbitrary and empirical nature of this distinction, it is nevertheless possible to make a generalization about class (*a*), the true proteins. These are often found to be 'conjugated' with 'prosthetic groups' varying very widely in chemical nature. However, the amino acid residues are nearly always the L-isomers of the following: glycine, alanine, valine, leucine, isoleucine, serine, threonine, cyst(e)ine, methionine, aspartic acid, asparagine, glutamic acid, glutamine, proline, phenylalanine, tyrosine, tryptophan, lysine, arginine and histidine. It is not twenty years since the last of these twenty amino acids, threonine, was proved to be a protein constituent. Since then, despite intensive search in proteins from a wide variety of living organisms, with use of methods of analysis much better than those previously available, no new amino acid has been found that is generally distributed and a number of the better-studied protein preparations have had all their components accounted for quantitatively from among these twenty common amino acids. Moreover, it is unusual to find more than

224

one or two of these twenty amino acids to be absent from a protein preparation. These facts are the more striking when taken together with the fact that in classes (*b*) and (*c*) many new species of amino acid have been discovered, as is briefly discussed below.

Of course there are other amino acids which occur only in protein of a particular type, or only in proteins of a limited range of organisms or have some other peculiarity of distribution. Of these, the better-authenticated examples are so few that they may conveniently be mentioned here.

Derivatives resulting from substitution of tyrosine or thyronine with iodine occur in the proteins of the thyroid gland, and have been studied in considerable detail in recent years. Similar compounds, including bromine-substituted derivatives, occur in the proteins of a number of marine organisms, including seaweeds, sponges and corals.

L-Hydroxyproline, in animals, seems characteristically to be present only in connective-tissue proteins of the collagen and elastin groups. Some claims have been made for its occurrence in other proteins but these require verification by isolation, the more so because Radhakrishnan & Giri [2] found by isolation that L-*allo*hydroxyproline occurs free in sandal leaves (cf. [3]). These authors have listed some of the claims that chemically bound hydroxyproline occurs in nature other than in connective-tissue protein. Besides these, may be mentioned claims in respect of seaweeds [4], diatoms [5], sponges [6], fungi and bacteria [7–12], maple-sap peptides [13] and hydrolysates of soil [14–15]. A dehydrogenated form of hydroxyproline, 'oxyminaline', was stated by Minagawa [16] to be a component of fungal pectases. The only proteins in which hydroxylysine has so far been found are connective-tissue proteins which also contain hydroxyproline [17]. α-Aminoadipic acid has been reported to occur in the seed proteins of maize [18] and sarcosine in those of the groundnut [19]. Lanthionine was reported as a constituent of locust muscle by Stein [20]. Here there was no ground, as in other cases, for suspecting that it had arisen by degradation of cystine. α-Amino*iso*butyric acid has been claimed as a constituent of casein hydrolysates by Oshima, Yoshihara & Sakamoto [21].

There is evidence that Se can take the place of S in the proteins of plants grown on Se-rich soil and of animals feeding on these plants [22–24]. This is the only known natural example of incorporation of foreign amino acids into protein which parallels such observations as the incorporation of artificially administered ethionine.

αε-Diaminopimelic acid has particular interest since it appears to be confined to bacteria and blue-green algae, among which it has a wide distribution, although it is absent from some groups [12]. (Fujiwara & Akabori [25] claim to have detected it in hydrolysates of *Chlorella ellipsoidea*.) As well as occurring in various non-protein extracts of bacteria, diaminopimelic acid occurs in a combined form in the extraction residues. It now seems definitely established that it can be a constituent of the peculiar cell-wall material, which is further discussed below. What does not seem well established is whether or not diaminopimelic acid is a constituent of the 'true proteins' of bacteria (cf. [12, 26, 27]). The amino acid described as cystine from alkali-soluble proteins of *Coryne-*

bacterium diphtheriae [28] seems more likely to be diaminopimelic acid. Likewise the unknown amino acid [17] found by Samarina et al. [29] in acid hydrolysates of *Vibrio* spp. which had been extracted with hot saline was probably diaminopimelic acid. Hoare & Work [30] have described the distribution among bacteria of the different stereoisomers of diaminopimelic acid. The chemically related dipicolinic acid occurs in the spores of *Bacillus* spp., but it does not seem established whether or not it is chemically bound [31, 32]. A diaminosuberic acid isomer has been isolated from Actinomycetales by Work [33].

The above seem to be all the less common amino acids which may at present be regarded as occurring in proteins. However, the occurrence of D-forms of the common amino acids must also be considered. It is difficult to assess the significance of the occurrence of D-forms in protein hydrolysates, since the hydrolysis itself may bring about racemization. The racemic phenylalanine found by Martin & Synge [34] in hydrolysates of wool and by Galaev [28] in bacterial hydrolysates may exemplify this. Even actual inversion during hydrolysis may occur (cf. [35]). These possibilities have helped to complicate still further the long and inconclusive controversy that has raged around the alleged occurrence of D-amino acids in the proteins of cancerous tissues. Nevertheless, it is now clear that D-amino acids occur in protein-like components of some bacteria. The classic instance is the capsular 'polypeptide' of *Bacillus* spp., whose chemical nature was discovered by Ivanovics & Bruckner. This has in recent years been studied in great detail both by its discoverers and by many other workers. It seems generally agreed that this polymeric substance is the product of condensing together residues of D-glutamic acid by peptide linkages involving almost exclusively the γ-carboxyl groups [36, 37]. It seems also to be established that diaminopimelic acid most commonly occurs in the *meso* form, having the D-configuration at one end of the molecule and the L-configuration at the other [30]. Such examples have led several workers to examine systematically the configuration of amino acids obtained by the hydrolysis of bacteria. In general L-amino acids predominate, as in other living organisms. D-Amino acids have, however, been found as follows. In *Bac. brevis*, Konikova & Dobbert [38] found substantial amounts of D-amino acids. Somewhat smaller amounts were found by Stevens, Halpern & Gigger [39], who showed that D-aspartic acid contributed substantially to the total. Later Stevens, Gigger & Bowne [40] showed that the D-amino acids were predominantly D-aspartic acid and D-phenylalanine, and were in a form which could largely be extracted from the bacteria by hot aqueous ethanol; this resembles more closely the antibiotic peptides produced by this organism than 'true protein'. In agreement with this, Vyshepan [41] found very little D-amino acid in hydrolysates of cells of *Bac. brevis* or of *Bac. mycoides* which had been exhaustively extracted with ethanol. Jenkins & Ciereszko [42] found L-glutamic acid to predominate in cells of *Bac. subtilis* despite the exclusive presence of D-glutamic acid in the capsular substance. Lawrence & Halvorson [43] found small amounts of D-amino acids, including D-glutamic acid, in vegetative cells and in spores of *Bac. terminalis*. Dunn et al. [44, 45] found D-glutamic acid in *Lactobacillus* spp. Holden & Snell [46] found D-alanine in *Lactobacillus*, *Leuconostoc*, and *Streptococcus*. Camien [47, 48] found D-aspartic acid in organisms of the same genera. Stevens *et al.* [39] further found significant amounts of D-amino acids in *Bacillus subtilis* and *Torulopsis utilis*. The cell-wall material of Gram-positive bacteria has in recent years been shown to yield on hydrolysis sugars, hexosamines and characteristic mixtures of only a few amino acids; the mixtures found have proved of some value to the systematist. These amino acids belong chiefly to the group glycine, alanine, aspartic acid, glutamic acid, lysine and diaminopimelic acid (for references see [49, 50]). It is particularly interesting that the greater part of the D-alanine present in lactic acid bacteria was present in the cell wall [51]. By adding D-α-aminobutyric acid to the media in which the bacteria were grown, it was to some extent incorporated in the cell-wall material. There is thus no reason as yet for supposing that D-amino acid residues occur in the 'typical proteins' of bacteria— they have only so far been unequivocally demonstrated in 'peptide' fractions soluble in organic solvents and in capsular and cell-wall materials that are not in any sense 'typical proteins'.

Thus it seems that proteins, which are found in substantial amount in every living organism so far studied, form a remarkably compact chemical grouping. When this chemical uniformity is seen in relation to the diversity of important functions which are carried out by proteins in the living organism, it seems very reasonable to postulate a common evolutionary origin for all the organisms at present living on Earth. The observations at least cover a wide range of animals, higher plants, algae, fungi, heterotrophic bacteria and viruses. They are deficient in respect of autotrophic bacteria. Dr Howard Lees tells me that the only evidence of which he is aware relating to the amino acids present in such organisms is for *Thiobacillus thio-oxidans* [52] and for *Nitrosomonas* [53]. In both these instances most of the common amino acids and no unusual ones were observed. Fossils have in general proved unsuitable for amino acid analysis*, but it is of interest that a very incomplete amino acid analysis of haemoglobin from a Crossopterygian fish [54] did not give figures much outside the range already observed among Vertebrata.

I have elsewhere engaged in speculation [55, 56] as to why these particular twenty amino acids came to make up the proteins of living organisms, and at the Symposium itself no doubt further speculation will take place.

As concerns amino acid residues in substances of class (*b*), it is important to remember how few substances belonging to this class have been known until recent years. Such substances tend to be thrown away when proteins are prepared by the traditional methods. Systematic searches for such substances have been few, although they are becoming more frequent. The great majority of the substances in this class have been found in the course of trying to purify materials possessing some striking biological activity. Substances in this class have been listed by Bricas & Fromageot [36]; cf. [57, 58]. The number known is at present increasing very rapidly. It is striking that amino acid residues or related chemical groupings of novel structure or steric configuration occur in a large proportion of those substances possessing specific toxic activities which have been isolated from bacteria and fungi. Many of these amino acids have

* [*Note added in proof.*] But see P. H. ABELSON, *Ann. N.Y. Acad. Sci.*, **69**, 276, 1957.

been listed by Bricas & Fromageot. The conclusion seems inescapable that the toxic properties are directly related to the 'abnormal' features of chemical structure, and the student of evolution is tempted to see here a specialized adaptation which does not throw much light on the evolution of protein structure or of the common amino acids. All twenty of these last have been found in compounds of class (*b*), but of course their lower molecular weights preclude the simultaneous presence of such a wide variety of amino acid residues as is usually present in a protein.

As concerns group (*c*)—free amino acids—all the twenty common amino acids have been found free in all living organisms where thorough analysis has been made, although often the concentrations in the tissue juices may be very low. There is much evidence that free amino acids are directly involved in the anabolism and catabolism of proteins. However, the common amino acids seem to have many other biochemical functions. Increasingly many amino acids which do not occur in proteins have been found free in living organisms in recent years. The variety seems particularly abundant in higher plants, where a particular amino acid may characterize a particular genus or natural order. Lists have been given by Grobbelaar, Pollard & Steward [59], Synge [58] and Virtanen [60] but the number increases almost weekly nowadays. It is particularly great for leguminous plants. The evolutionary problem seems somewhat similar to that presented by the alkaloids.

This survey of the natural occurrence of free and combined amino acids in nature serves to emphasize the chemical similarity of all living organisms on the Earth, and thus agrees on the whole with the results of chemical and biochemical studies of other classes of substance. The information will be of great interest when the biochemistry of Mars and of planets in other planetary systems becomes accessible. As concerns the terrestrial origin of life, it seems rather to block the progress of studies, suggesting that most of the chemical evolution of proteins occurred in a remote past from which have survived only organisms which had already arrived at a very standardized chemical structure.

However, the study of amino acids and amino acid composition is only the most elementary part of protein chemistry. Recent progress towards the understanding of the structure and function of proteins opens a fascinating prospect for comparative terrestrial biochemistry in the not too far distant future. The possibility of observing species differences in the structural chemistry of proteins was suggested by early serological work with animal and plant products [1], especially if this is considered together with Landsteiner's own work on the serological specificity of synthetic and natural peptides [61]. Differences in Fe and S contents of haemoglobins from different species have long been known. We now have a number of examples of species differences between proteins and peptides which have been verified in full chemical detail. Thus, Brown, Sanger & Kitai [62] have shown that sheep insulin differs from bovine insulin at only one amino acid locus in the whole molecule, while pig insulin differs from both these at two, different loci. The vasopressin from the pituitary gland of the pig has a lysine residue where bovine vasopressin has an arginine residue [63]. Tyrocidines A and B, produced by one strain of *Bacillus brevis*, are cyclic decapeptides [64, 65] incorporating a pentapeptide sequence which also occurs, repeated twice, in the cyclic decapeptide gramicidin S [66] which is produced by a different strain of *Bacillus brevis*. In all these cases there is variation in chemical structure without much change in biological activity. Thus study of the interplay of form and function in living organisms, which led up to Darwin's formulation of evolution, is now being extended, as chemical study, to the ultramicroscopic aspects of living organisms. It seems likely that this study, which is bound to be extremely laborious, will throw light on many of the problems of systematics which are still obscure, and particularly on the systematics of micro-organisms. It is likely also that, as we begin to understand something about mechanism as well as structure, we shall be able to deduce much that is relevant concerning the problem of the origin of life.

REFERENCES

1. K. LANDSTEINER, *The Specificity of Serological Reactions.* Thomas, Springfield, Ill., 1936.
2. A. N. RADHAKRISHNAN & K. V. GIRI, *Biochem. J.*, **58**, 57, 1954.
3. A. S. RAMASWAMY, *J. Indian Inst. Sci.*, **38A**, 62, 1956; *Chem. Abstr.*, **50**, 8861, 1956.
4. A. MAZUR & H. T. CLARKE, *J. biol. Chem.*, **123**, 729, 1938.
5. E. M. LOW, *J. Mar. Res.*, **14**, 199, 1955.
6. S. AKABORI, K. SATAKE & H. ONO, *Science* (Japan), **20**, 132, 1950; *Chem. Abstr.*, **45**, 10271, 1951.
7. K. FELIX & I. PENDL, *Hoppe-Seyl. Z.*, **283**, 128, 1948.
8. E. WORK, *Biochim. biophys. Acta*, **3**, 400, 1949.
9. E. BOURLAND, M. ROUYER & J. MATHÉ, *Congr. int. Biochim. Paris, Résumés*, p. 384, 1952; *Chem. Abstr.*, **50**, 8774, 1956.
10. W. KELLNER & H. MARTIN, *Naturwissenschaften*, **41**, 164, 1954.
11. D. K. ROY, *Naturwissenschaften*, **42**, 181, 1955.
12. E. WORK & D. L. DEWEY, *J. gen. Microbiol.*, **9**, 394, 1953.
13. J. K. POLLARD & T. SPROSTON, *Plant. Physiol.*, **29**, 360, 1954.
14. J. M. BREMNER, *Biochem. J.*, **47**, 538, 1950.
15. D. I. PARKER, F. J. SOWDEN & H. J. ATKINSON, *Sci. Agric.*, **32**, 163, 1952.
16. T. MINAGAWA, *Proc. imp. Acad. Japan*, **21**, 33, 37, 1945; *Chem. Abstr.*, **47**, 151, 1953.
17. P. B. HAMILTON & R. A. ANDERSON, *J. Amer. chem. Soc.*, **77**, 2892, 1955.
18. E. WINDSOR, *J. biol. Chem.*, **192**, 595, 1951.
19. R. D. HAWORTH, R. MACGILLIVRAY & D. H. PEACOCK, *Nature, Lond.*, **167**, 1068, 1951.
20. J. M. STEIN, *Chem. & Ind.*, p. 774, 1955.
21. Y. OSHIMA, S. YOSHIHARA & Y. SAKAMOTO, *J. agric. chem. Soc. Japan*, **27**, 102, 1953; *Chem. Abstr.*, **49**, 14860, 1955.
22. M. J. HORN & D. B. JONES, *J. biol. Chem.*, **139**, 649, 1941.
23. G. S. WEISSMAN & S. F. TRELEASE, *Amer. J. Bot.*, **42**, 489, 1955.
24. R. O. LEONARD & R. H. BURNS, *J. Anim. Sci.*, **14**, 446, 1955.
25. T. FUJIWARA & S. AKABORI, *J. chem. Soc., Japan, Pure Chem. Sect.*, **75**, 990, 1954; *Chem. Abstr.*, **49**, 3325, 1955.
26. E. S. HOLDSWORTH, *Biochim. biophys. Acta*, **9**, 19, 1952.
27. G. K. SHIPITSYNA. *Dokl. Akad. Nauk S.S.S.R.*, **105**, 315, 1955; *Chem. Abstr.*, **50**, 7940, 1956.
28. Yu. V. GALAEV, *Biokhimiya*, **20**, 673, 1955.
29. O. P. SAMARINA, M. G. KRITSMAN, L. M. YAKOBSON & A. S. KONIKOVA, *Biokhimiya*, **15**, 287, 1950.
30. D. S. HOARE & E. WORK, *Biochem. J.*, **61**, 562, 1955.
31. J. F. POWELL, *Biochem. J.*, **54**, 210, 1953.
32. J. J. PERRY & J. W. FOSTER, *J. Bact.*, **69**, 337, 1955.
33. E. WORK, *J. gen. Microbiol.*, **9**, ii, 1953.

34. A. J. P. Martin & R. L. M. Synge, *Biochem. J.*, **35**, 91, 1941.
35. A. Stoll, A. Hofmann & T. Petrzilka, *Helv. chim. Acta*, **34**, 1544, 1951.
36. E. Bricas & C. Fromageot, *Advanc. Protein Chem.*, **8**, 1, 1953.
37. S. G. Waley, *J. chem. Soc.*, p. 517, 1955.
38. A. S. Konikova & N. N. Dobbert, *Biokhimiya*, **13**, 115, 1948.
39. C. M. Stevens, P. E. Halpern & R. P. Gigger, *J. biol. Chem.*, **190**, 705, 1951.
40. C. M. Stevens, R. P. Gigger & S. W. Bowne, *J. biol. Chem.*, **212**, 461, 1955.
41. E. D. Vyshepan, *Biokhimiya*, **19**, 490, 1954.
42. L. T. Jenkins & L. S. Ciereszko, *J. biol. Chem.*, **191**, 305, 1951.
43. N. L. Lawrence & H. O. Halvorson, *J. Bact.*, **67**, 585, 1954.
44. M. S. Dunn, M. N. Camien, S. Shankman & H. Block, *J. biol. Chem.*, **168**, 43. 1947.
45. M. N. Camien, A. J. Salle & M. S. Dunn, *Arch. Biochem.*, **8**, 67, 1945.
46. J. T. Holden & E. E. Snell, *J. biol. Chem.*, **178**, 799, 1949.
47. M. N. Camien, *Proc. Soc. exp. Biol.*, *N.Y.*, **77**, 578, 1951.
48. M. N. Camien, *J. biol. Chem.*, **197**, 687, 1952.
49. C. S. Cummins & H. Harris, *J. gen. Microbiol.*, **14**, 583, 1956.
50. S. Guex-Holzer & J. Tomcsik, *J. gen. Microbiol.*, **14**, 14, 1956.
51. E. E. Snell, N. S. Radin & M. Ikawa, *J. biol. Chem.*, **217**, 803, 1955.
52. I. D. Frantz, H. Feigelman, A. S. Werner & M. P. Smythe, *J. biol. Chem.*, **195**, 423, 1952.
53. T. Hofman, *Biochem. J.*, **54**, 293, 1953.
54. S. de Prailaune, *C.R. Soc. Biol.*, *Paris*, **149**, 655, 1955.
55. R. L. M. Synge, *Biokhimiya*, **10**, 179, 1945.
56. R. L. M. Synge, *Lect. Inst. Chem.*, **1**, 1952.
57. R. L. M. Synge, *The Chemical Structure of Proteins* (Ed by G. E. W. Wolstenholme, & M. P. Cameron), p. 43. Churchill, London, 1953.
58. R. L. M. Synge, in *Moderne Methoden der Pflanzenanalyse*, Vol. 4, p. 1, Berlin, 1955.
59. N. Grobbelaar, J. K. Pollard & F. C. Steward, *Nature, Lond.*, **175**, 703, 1955.
60. A. I. Virtanen, *Angew. Chem.*, **67**, 381, 1955.
61. K. Landsteiner, *The Specificity of Serological Reactions*, rev. ed. Harvard University Press, Cambridge, Mass., 1947.
62. H. Brown, F. Sanger & R. Kitai, *Biochem. J.*, **60**, 556, 1955.
63. V. du Vigneaud, D. T. Gish & P. G. Katsoyannis, *J. Amer. chem. Soc.*, **76**, 4751, 1954.
64. A. Paladini & L. C. Craig, *J. Amer. chem. Soc.*, **76**, 688, 1954.
65. T. P. King & L. C. Craig, *J. Amer. chem. Soc.*, **77**, 6624, 6627, 1955.
66. R. Schwyzer & P. Sieber, *Helv. chim. acta*, **40**, 624, 1957.

Ähnlichkeitder Struktur bei Eiweißstoffen*

F. ŠORM

Chemisches Institut, der Tschechoslowakischen Akademie der Wissenschaften, Prag

DIE außerordentliche Kompliziertheit und Vielfältigkeit der sich ständig in Bewegung und Entwicklung befindenden lebenden Materie ist durch die Variabilität der Struktur von Eiweißmolekülen, insbesondere durch die Vielzahl der Kombinationsmöglichkeiten, die sich für die Aminosäuren in den Peptidketten bietet, bedingt. Deswegen ist die Kenntnis der allgemeinen Gesetzmäßigkeiten in der Struktur von Eiweißstoffen für das Verständnis der Gesetzmäßigkeiten in der Entwicklung des lebenden Organismus und dessen Funktionen überhaupt von principieller Bedeutung.

Die in letzter Zeit von einer Reihe von Forschungsschulen unternommenen Arbeiten auf dem Gebiet des Studiums der Mikrostruktur der Eiweißstoffe und höheren natürlichen Peptide haben in erster Linie die völlige Klärung des Aufbaues biologisch höchst wirksamer Stoffe mit möglichst kleincm Molekulargewicht zum Ziele. Diese Richtung führte zu einer Reihe bedeutender Entdeckungen, anfangend mit der Entzifferung der Struktur des Insulins durch F. Sanger und seine Schule [1-13]. Ferner gelang es, den Aufbau einer Reihe anderer biologisch aktiver Peptide, ebenso wie einiger höherer Polypeptide und einfacher Eiweißstoffe festzustellen; es wird nunmehr auf dem Gebiet der Untersuchung der Struktur höherer Eiweißstoffe gearbeitet.

Der Hauptmangel einiger vorhergehender Theorien über die Mikrostruktur der Eiweißstoffe (z. B. Theorien von Bergmann & Niemann [14, 15], Gawrilow [16, 17]) bestand darin, daß diese Theorien sich nicht aur tatsächlich festgestellte Anordnungen der Aminosäuren in den Peptidketten stützten. Obgleich das bis jetzt in der Literatur angehäufte Material nur über die Struktur eines unbedeutenden Teiles in der Natur vorkommender Eiweißstoffe urteilen läßt, kann man trotzdem heute schon eine ganze Reihe gemeinsamer Züge objektiven Charakters feststellen. Vor allem wurde festgestellt, daß Stoffe, die funktionelle Ahnlichkeit haben, auch bei verschiedenen Tierarten einen analogen inneren Aufbau aufweisen.

Außer diesen markanten strukturellen Analogien, wurden bis jetzt keinerlei allgemeinere Gesetzmäßigkeiten gefunden; wahrscheinlich ist dies auf die zur Lösung dieser Probleme beschrittenen Wege und Mittel zurückzuführen, die sich in erster Linie die Klärung der Struktur einfacherer Stoffe mit verschiedenen biologischen Funktionen zum Ziele setzen und den Beziehungen zwischen den ermittelten Strukturen weniger Aufmerksamkeit schenken.

---

* Gekürzter Text eines auf dem Int. Symposium über das Eiweißproblem am 4. Oktober 1956 in Liblice gehaltenen Vortrages.

Bei der Beurteilung der gegenwärtigen Kenntnisse über den Aufbau des Eiweißes und der höheren Peptide wurde von uns die Vermutung ausgesprochen, daß es bestimmte Gesetzmäßigkeiten in dem Bau der Peptidketten gibt [18], nach denen wir in erster Linie in dem selektiven Charakter der Bindungen zwischen den Aminosäuren, in der Wiederholung elementarer Peptidstrikturen im Molekül ein- und desselben Eiweißes oder aber auch in verschiedenen Eiweißstoffen, in der Existenz von Gesetzmäßigkeiten in der Struktur der Peptidketten (wie z. B. die regelmässige Kombination bestimmter Aminosäuren) fahndeten.

Augenscheinlich können diese einfachen Gesetzmäßigkeiten (die keineswegs die einzig möglichen sind) in bedeutendem Masse durch gegenseitige Ersetzbarkeit der einzelnen Aminosäuren in den Peptidketter kompliziert werden.

Um einen Vergleich bekannter Eiweiß- und Peptidstrukturen durchführen zu können, haben wir vor allem sämtliche Angaben über die Bindungsformen einzelner Aminosäuren in den Peptidketten zusammengetragen. Zur Vollständigkeit haben wir alle beschriebenen Strukturen vermerkt einschließlich solcher in funktionell verwandten Eiweißstoffen und Peptiden (z. B. in den Insulinen verschiedener Tierarten), bei denen umfangreiche Teile der Mikrostruktur identisch sind. Die Bindung Val-Leu kommt 14 Mal vor, obgleich es sich in 13 Fällen um das gleiche in verschiedenen Hämoglobinen vorkommende Peptid handelt. Damit dieser Faktor nicht die tatsächliche Frequenz des Vorkommens der Bindungen in verschiedenen Eiweißstoffen verdeckt, wurde Tabelle 1 komponiert, welche die Gesamtzahl der Bindungen in funktionell unterschiedlichen Eiweißstoffen zeigt.

Man kann bei dem Studium der Tabellen 1 und 2 bestimmte Gesetzmäßigkeiten feststellen. So ist z. B. an Hand der Tabelle 1 sehr gut zu ersehen, daß manche Peptidbindungen in den Eiweißstoffen sehr oft vorkommen, andere dagegen seltener, während manche Kombinationen bis jetzt noch gar nicht vorgefunden worden sind. Auf Grund der Wahrscheinlichkeitstheorie, müßte die Zahl der *AB*-Bindungen der Zahl der *BA*-Bindungen gleich sein. Die relative Quantität der Komponenten *A* und *B* ist für diese Erwägung ohne Belang. Wenn auch für eine Reihe von Bindungen dieses Verhältnis zutrifft, so finden wir in anderen Fällen bedeutende Abweichungen von dieser Regel vor, die man kaum als eine zufällige Begebenheit ansehen kann:

Ala. Gly	11x	Gly. Ala	10x	Val. Glu	10x	Glu. Val	1x
Ala. Ser	4x	Ser. Ala	4x	Ser. Arg	12x	Arg. Ser	1x
Asp. Glu	10x	Glu. Asp	9x	Cys. Ala	7x	Ala. Cys	1x
Gly. Pro	6x	Pro. Gly	6x	Ileu. Val	4x	Val. Ileu	0
				Thr. Pro	4x	Pro. Thr	0
				Pro. Val	6x	Val. Pro	0

In ähnlicher Weise können erhebliche Unterschiede in der Zahl der Bindungen zwischen Aminosäuren gefunden werden, die ungefähr in gleicher Menge in den Eiweißstoffen vertreten sind. So läßt sich z. B. in dem Fall einer Bindung zwischen einer Oxyaminosäure und einer basischen Aminosäure der Unterschied in der Frequenz der Bindungen Ser.Arg und Arg.Ser nur teilweise durch die relative Stabilität dieser Bindungen erklären, da sich der überwiegende Teil des zum Vergleich herangezogenen Materials auf unversehrt bekannten

TABELLE I

Die relative Anzahl von Peptidbindungen in bekannten Eiweißstrukturen

	Ala	Arg	Asp	Cys	Glu	Gly	His	Hypro	Ileu	Leu	Lys	Met	Phe	Pro	Ser	Thr	Try	Tyr	Val
Ala	8(6)	3	2	1	7(5)	15(6)	3	1	1	4	4(3)	2(1)	1	1	6(5)	1	1	1	1
Arg	2	9(5)	2	3(2)	2(1)	6(5)	1	—	2	3(2)	1	—	1	2	1	—	2	—	3
Asp	5(4)	7(4)	7(5)	8(6)	8(7)	5(4)	1	—	2(1)	4(3)	2(1)	—	1	—	5(4)	2	—	3	3(2)
Cys	6(5)	2(1)	5(4)	1	3	5(4)	3	—	1	1	4(3)	—	1	2	2	2	—	2	2
Glu	9(5)	3	3	4	3	4	—	1	1	5	—	—	2	—	3(4)	1	1	3(2)	—
Gly	12(4)	2	5	2	4	4(3)	—	—	1	3	—	1	2	6(3)	7(4)	1	—	—	4
His	1	—	6	2	1	—	—	—	1	3(2)	—	—	3	1	1	—	—	—	—
Hypro	—	—	—	—	—	4(1)	—	—	—	—	—	—	—	—	—	—	1	—	—
Ileu	1	3(2)	1	1	3	—	1	—	—	1	1	—	1	2	—	2	—	2(1)	4
Leu	5	2	3	3	4	3	1	—	—	1	1	1	1	1	4(2)	—	—	1	5(4)
Lys	1	—	3(2)	3	1	4(3)	2	—	—	2	3	1	2	2	1	1	—	—	4(3)
Met	—	—	2	—	2	1	—	—	—	—	—	—	—	—	—	1	—	—	—
Phe	—	3	2(1)	2	5(4)	3(2)	2	—	2	—	3	—	3(2)	2	—	1	—	1	2
Pro	3	2	1	3	2	7(3)	—	1	2	2	—	—	—	1	2	1	—	1	4(3)
Ser	5	15(9)	7(5)	3	7	7(4)	1	1	—	3	2	—	1	3	2	—	—	3	5(4)
Thr	3	—	4(3)	2	1	4(3)	2	—	2	1	—	1	2(1)	4(3)	5	—	—	—	1
Try	—	1	—	—	—	2	—	—	2	—	—	—	1	—	—	—	—	—	—
Tyr	1	2	1	1	5	3(2)	1	—	—	2	2	—	1	1	2	1	—	—	1
Val	3	5(4)	7(6)	5(4)	8(6)	6	1	—	—	2	1	—	3(1)	—	3	2	—	2	—

Die erste Ziffer bezeichnet die Gesamtzahl der entsprechenden Bindungen (die Zahl der sich in demselben Eiweißstoff wiederholenden Bindungen miteinbezogen), die Ziffer in Klammern bezeichnet die Zahl der Eiweißstoffe, in denen die entsprechende Bindung vorkommt.

Strukturen bezeiht. Andereseits ist es interessant, daß die Bindung Thr.Arg zum Unterschied von der Bindung Ser.Arg bisher in Eiweißstoffen überhaupt nicht vorgefunden worden ist.

Die Vermutung, da ßbestimmte Peptidgruppierungen wiederholt in ein und demselben Eiweiß auftreten, findet in gewissem Maße bei den Eiweißstoffen Bestätigung, deren Bau schon fast völlig geklärt werden konnte (z. B. die sich wiederholenden Gruppierungen Cys.Gly und His.Leu in der *B*-Kette des Insulins). Das mehrmalige Auftreten bestimmter Peptidstrukturen in dem Molekül des Lysozyms ist bemerkenswert, hierbei ist auch die Ersetzbarkeit einiger Aminosäuren (siehe Tab. 3) gut zu sehen. Im Lysozym wurden Di- und Tripeptidstrukturen festgestellt, die auch in anderen Eiweißstoffen vorkommen. Aus Tabelle 3 ist zu ersehen, daß Ribonuclease dasselbe Tetrapeptid wie Lysozym enthält und daß β-Corticotropin vom Schaf, β-Corticotropin vom Schwein (2x) und Corticotropin A, Tyrocidin, Vasopressin und Insulin (2x) ein- und dasselbe Tripeptid enthalten; dies berechtigt uns, eine prinzipielle

TABELLE 2

Wiederholung der Peptide im Lysozym

Verwandschaft des Lysozyms mit den anderen Eiweißstoffen zu vermuten. Interessant ist außerdem, daß diese Tripeptide sich gerade in denjenigen Abschnitten der Kette befinden, wo sich Corticotropin und Insulin im Typ unterscheiden.

In der Peptidkette des Corticotropins kann eine gewiße Gesetzmäßigkeit festgestellt werden, die in der Wiederholung einer Tetrapeptidkombination mit Einschluß einer Gruppierung dreier basischer Aminosäuren besteht. Dies ist das Tetrapeptid Gly.Lys.Pro.Val (Stellung 10–13), welches unmittelbar mit dem Peptid Gly.Lys.Lys.Arg.Pro.Val in Verbindung steht (Stellung 14–20).

Peptidgruppierungen bestimmten Typs kommen auch in Eiweißstoffen ganz verschiedener Art vor. In Tabelle 3 werden Gruppierungen verschiedener Tripeptide und höherer Peptide angeführt, die für eine Reihe verschiedener Eiweißstoffe analog sind. Bei der Aufstellung dieser Tabelle fiel uns eine interessante Gesetzmäßigket auf, die darin besteht, daß in Nachbarschaft mit diesen Tripeptiden wiederholt die gleichen Aminosäuren vorzufinden sind (bei verschiedenen Proteinen verschiedene); andererseits besteht eine strukturelle Ähnlichkeit dieser benachbarten Aminosäuren (Austausch von Asparaginsäure gegen Glutaminsäure, des Phenylalanins gegen Tyrosin, Leucins gegen Isoleucin). In Tripeptiden, die für gänzlich verschiedene Eiweißstoffe analog sind, wurde in 17 von 19 Fällen Alanin vorgefunden, Glyzin in 10 Fällen, Dicarbonsäuren dagegen bedeutend seltener. Andere Säuren sind in diesen Gruppierungen in bedeutend kleineren Mengen anwesend. Es ist natürlich möglich, daß dieses ins Auge springende oftmalige Auftreten des Alanins mit der Beschränktheit der uns zur Verfügung stehender Angaben zusammenhängt.

TABELLE 3

Ähnliche Peptide in Eiweißstoffen und natürlichen Peptiden

Asp. Gly. Ala. Asp.	Lysozym
Pro. *Asp. Gly. Ala.* Glu.	β-Corticotropin vom Schwein
Asp. Glu. Ala.	Lysozym
Asp. *Asp. Glu. Ala.* Ser.	α-Corticotropin vom Schaf
Ileu. *Glu. Leu. Ala.* Leu.	Lysozym
Asp. *Glu. Leu. Ala.* Glu.	Corticotropin A vom Schwein
	β-Corticotropin vom Schwein
Thr. *Pro. Gly. Ala.*	Lysozym
Tyr. *Pro. Gly. Ala.* Glu.	Corticotropin A vom Schwein
Ala. Lys. Phe. Glu. Gly.	Lysozym
Ala. *Ala. Lys. Phe. Glu.* Arg.	Ribonuclease
Ser. *Phe. Asp. Glu.*	Lysozym
Phe. *Phe. Asp. Glu.* Tyr.	Tyrocidin A
Tyr. *Phe. Asp. Glu.* Tyr.	Tyrocidin B
Gly. *Phe. Glu. Asp.* Ileu.	Lysozym
Tyr. *Phe. Glu. Asp.* Cys.	Vasopressin
Ser. Val. Cys. Ala.	Lysozym
Ala. *Ser. Val. Cys.* Ser.	Insulin vom Rind
Asp. *Val. Glu. Ala.*	Lysozym
Leu. *Val. Glu. Ala.* Leu.	Insulin vom Rind, Schaf, Schwein

TABELLE 3 (*Forts.*)

|Gly. *Ala. Glu. Asp.* Glu.|	β-Corticotropin vom Schwein
|Gly. *Ala. Glu. Asp.* Asp.|	Corticotropin A vom Schwein
Arg. *Ala. Glu. Asp.* Phe.	Glucagon
|Phe. *Arg. Try. Gly.* Lys.	Corticotropin
|Phe. *Arg. Try. Gly.* Ser.	Melanophoren-Hormon
|Glu. *Asp. Glu. Leu.* Ala.|	β-Corticotropin vom Schwein
|Asp. *Asp. Glu. Leu.* Ala.|	Corticotropin A vom Schwein
Arg. *Glu. His. Phe. Arg. Try.*|	β-Corticotropin vom Schwein
|Met. *Glu. His. Phe. Arg. Try.*|	α-Corticotropin vom Schaf
|Met. *Glu. His. Phe. Arg. Try.*|	Corticotropin B vom Schwein
|Met. *Glu. His. Phe. Arg. Try.*|	Melanophoren-Hormon
|Thr. *Ala. Ala. Ala.* Lys.	Ribonuclease
|Ser. *Ala. Ala. Ala.* Ala.	Fibroin
Cys. *Ala. Ser. Val.* Cys.	Insulin vom Rind
Asp. *Ala. Ser. Val.* OH	Ribonuclease
Cys. *Ala. Gly. Val.* Cys.	Insulin vom Schaf
Gly. *Ala. Gly. Val.* Gly.	Fibroin
Ala. Gly. Val. Asp.	Ovalbumin
Cys. *Thr. Ser. Ileu.* Cys.	Insulin vom Schwein
Met. *Thr. Ser. Ileu.* OH	Tropomyosin
Phen. *Val. Asp. Glu.* His.	Insulin vom Rind, Schaf, Schwein
Leu. *Val. Asp. Glu.*	γ-Globulin
|Tyr. *Gly. Ala. Gly.* Ala.|	Fibroin
|Ser. *Gly. Ala. Gly.* Ala.|	Fibroin
|Ser. *Gly. Ala. Gly.* Tyr.|	Protofibroin
|Ala. *Gly. Ala. Gly.* Tyr.|	Fibroin
|Ala. *Gly. Ala. Gly.* Ser.|	Fibroin
|Ala. *Gly. Ala. Gly.* Val.|	Fibroin
Gly. *Ala. Gly. Ala.* Gly.	Fibroin
Ala. Gly. Ala.	Kollagen
Arg. Gly. Gly. Arg.	Salmin
Arg. Gly. Gly.	Gelatin, Kollagen
Ser. *Gly. Pro. Ala.* Thr.	Tabakmosaikvirus
Gly. Pro. Ala.	Gelatin, Kollagen
Ileu. *Glu. Asp. Cys. Pro.* Leu.	Oxytocin
Phe. *Glu. Asp. Cys. Pro.* Arg.	Vasopressin
|Tyr. *Val. Orn. Leu. Phe.* Pro.	Tyrocidin A
|Tyr. *Val. Orn. Leu. Phe. Pro.* Try.	Tyrocidin B
Pro. *Val. Orn. Leu. Phe. Pro.* Val.	Gramicidin S

Eine vertikale Linie bedeutet identische oder ähnliche Aminosäuren, welche analoge Tripeptide in verschiedenen Eiweißstoffen umgeben.

Eine horizontale Linie bedeutet identische oder ähliche Aminosäuren, die das gegebene Tripeptid in ein- und demselben Eiweißstoff umgeben.

In den Peptidketten einer Reihe von Eiweißstoffen können auch gewisse Gesetzmäßigkeiten festgestellt werden, welche auf eine tieferliegende Folgeordnung hinweisen, die allen Anscheinens nach mit der Spiralanordnung der Peptidkette und der Ausbildung einer Makrostruktur in Verbindung stehen. Die Verteilung der Peptidketten einiger fibrillarer Eiweißstoffe lenkt hier Aufmerksamkeit auf sich; z. *B*. des Fibroins, in dem sich die Stellung des Glycins gesetzmäßig in der Regelmäßigkeit 333333 ... und des Alanins in der Regelmaßigkeit 535353 ... wiederholt. Dementsprechend sind im Salmin zwei neutrale Aminosäuren von zwei Molekülen Arginin umgeben. Ähnliche Gesetzmäßigkeiten können ebenfalls auch für die Moleküle einer Reihe von Hormonen festgestellt werden. So wurden z. *B*. im Molekül des Glukagons die Stellungen saurer Aminosäuren (Asparagin- und Glutaminsäure) in der Reihenfolge 77655, und der Oxysäuren (Serin, Threonin) in der Reihenfolge 4446 vorgefunden; im Bacitracin ist die Reihenfolge für Leucin ebenfalls regelmäßig (334). Ähnlich dem Obenangeführten folgt aus den neuesten Arbeiten über die Struktur der Ribonuclease [19], daß Lysin 3 Mal in der Stellung 7 und einmal in der Stellung 6 vorzufinden ist.

Aus Tabelle 2 folgt, daß in den verschiedensten Eiweißstoffen sehr oft analoge Dipeptid-Gruppierungen vorkommen. Das Vorhandensein ähnlicher Tripeptide zum mindesten einmal im Molekül konnte ungefähr in der Hälfte der bekannten Strukturen höherer Peptide und Eiweißstoffe beobachtet werden. Das Vorkommen ein- und desselben Tetrapeptides bei verschiedenen Eiweißstoffen haben wir nur in dem Fall von Lysozym und Ribonuclease vorgefunden. Wir nehmen hierbei natürlich äußerst ähnliche Eiweißstoffe mit gleicher Funktion nicht in Betracht, in denen sich nur an einzelnen Abschnitten Unterschiede in der Aminosäurenzusammensetzung beobachten lassen.

Vor einigen Jahren unternahmen wir vergleichende Untersuchungen bei dem Aufbau von Eiweißstoffen, bei denen man auf Grund der Analogie ihrer Funktion im Organismus oder der Ähnlichkeit ihrer Herkunft auch eine gewisse Ähnlichkeit der inneren chemischen Struktur vermuten konnte. Die Grundlage für die vorgeschlagene Methode bildet ein Vergleich der Zusammensetzung und Struktur von Peptid-Fraktionen, die aus den Produkten einer partiellen chemischen oder enzymatischen Hydrolyse der Eiweißstoffe isoliert werden und zwar von Derivaten solcher Aminosäuren, die es gestatten, bestimmte Gruppenfraktionen von Peptiden auszusondern [18].

Die Arbeiten auf dem Gebiete des Vergleichs der Peptid-Fraktionen aus Eiweißstoffen begannen wir an zwei proteolytischen Fermenten, die einander in ihren biochemischen und physikalisch-chemischen Eigenschaften sehr ähnlich sind, und in ein- und denselben Zellen der Pancreasdrüse gebildet werden, und zwar des Chymotrypsinogens und des Trypsinogens (oder Trypsins). Günstig war auch der Umstand, daß beide erwähnten Proteine in sehr reinem Kristallzustande gewonnen werden konnten [19].

Trotz ihrer bedeutenden chemischen und physikalischen Ähnlichkeit, unterscheiden sich beide Eiweißstoffe etwas durch ihren Aminosäuren-Bestand. Jedoch finden wir bei der Gegenüberstellung der Produkte vollständiger Hydrolyse der Peptid-Derivate des Cysteins, die aus partiellen chemischen Hydrolysaten beider Eiweißstoffe gewonnen wurden, eine gewisse Ähnlichkeit in ihrem Aminosäurengehalt [20]. In letzter Zeit hat B. Keil in unserem Institut einen ausführlicheren Vergleich der aus Chymotrypsinogen und Trypsin gewonnenen Cysteinpeptide durchgeführt [21]. Es gelang ihm, eine große Anzahl individueller Peptide auszusondern. Zwar ist diese Arbeit noch nicht vollendet, man kann aber an Hand der vorliegenden Ergebnisse (Tab. 4) ersehen, daß die aus beiden Proteinen gewonnenen Peptide in vielen Fällen die gleiche Zusammensetzung haben.

TABELLE 4

Peptide der Cysteinsäure im Chymotrypsinogen und Trypsin

Chymotrypsinogen	Trypsin
Ser. Cys	Ser. Cys
Gly. Cys	Gly. Cys
Val. Cys	Val. Cys
Leu. Cys	Leu. Cys
Thr. Cys	Thr. Cys
Phe. Cys	Phe. Cys
Lys. Cys	Cys. Ala
Cys. Ser. Ala	Cys. Ser. Ala
Ala. Cys	Ala. Cys
Ileu. Cys	Ileu. Cys
His. Cys	His. Cys

Die Peptide des Cysteins sind für den Zweck eines Vergleichs zwischen den beiden Proteasen nicht sehr vorteilhaft; sie wurden jedoch aus methodischen Ursachen gewählt, da die Möglichkeit besteht, sie bequem in der Form stark saurer Peptide der Cysteinsäure zu gewinnen. Aus diesem Grunde haben wir für den Vergleich beider Proteine auch solche Peptidfraktionen verwendet, die Derivate einiger basischer Aminosäuren enthalten, insbesondere des Arginins

TABELLE 5

Basische Peptide im Chymotrypsinogen und Trypsin

Chymotrypsinogen	Trypsin
Ser. Arg	Ser. Arg
Val. Arg	Val. Arg
(Thr. Arg)	—
(Ala. Arg)	?
Phe. His	—
His. Phe	—
Ala. His	Ala. His
His. Cys	His. Cys
	Tyr. His
—	(Pro. His)
(Lys. Leu)	(Lys. Leu)
(Lys. Ser)	(Lys. Ser)
(Lys. Glu)	(Lys. Glu)
(Lys. Cys)	(Lys. Cys)

und in letzter Zeit auch des Histidins und des Lysins. Es gelang uns eine Reihe von Peptiden basischer Aminosäuren in reiner Form zu gewinnen, insbesondere die Dipeptide, welche in Tab. 5 [22, 23] angegeben sind. Diese Tabelle zeugt davon daß zum mindesten in einem Teil der Kette der innere Aufbau von Chymotrypsin und Trypsin identisch ist, obgleich merkliche Unterschiede in ihrem Aufbau zu verzeichnen sind. Es ist möglich, daß gerade diese Unterschiede die Ursache der verschiedenen enzymatischen Aktivität der beiden Eiweißstoffe sind.

TABELLE 6

Basische Peptide im Pferde- und Schweine-Hämoglobin

Hämoglobin		Hämoglobin	
Pferd	Schwein	Pferd	Schwein
Peptide des Arginins		Peptide des Histidins	
Ala. Arg	Ala. Arg	Ala. His	Ala. His
Phe. Arg	Phe. Arg	Ser. His	Ser. His
Tyr. Arg	Tyr. Arg	His. Ala	His. Ala
Arg. Leu	Arg. Leu	Ser. (His, Lys)	Ser. (His, Lys)
Arg. Phe	Arg. Phe	(Lys. His)	(Lys. His)
(Ser. Arg)	Ser. Arg	Leu. His	(Leu. His)
Leu. Arg		(Lys. His. Ser. Thr)	(Lys. His. Ser. Thr)
Arg. Lys	Lys. Arg		
(Lys. His. Arg)			

Wir haben begonnen ein ähnliches Verfahren für den Vergleich der Struktur verschiedener Eiweißstoffe auch bei anderen Eiweißtypen anzuwenden. Wir hatten uns auch früher schon damit beschäftigt, basische Peptide aus Serum-Albuminen verschiedener Tierarten zu vergleichen; es gelang uns Unterschiede in der chemischen Zusammensetzung immunologisch unterschiedlicher Eiweißstoffe festzustellen, die die gleiche Funktion und recht ähnliche physikalische und chemische Eigenschaften besitzen. In letzter Zeit haben wir Arbeiten abgeschlossen, in denen Vergleiche der basischen Peptide des Pferde- und Schweine-Hämoglobins angestellt wurden. Die Ergebnisse der Arbeiten von Mäsiar und Mitarbeitern [24, 25] werden in Tabelle 6 angeführt, an Hand deren zu ersehen ist, daß Arginin-Peptide (in erster Linie Dipeptide) beider Hämoglobine, welche auf ein- und dieselbe Weise gewonnen wurden, bis auf zwei Peptide praktisch identisch sind.

Die in diesem Vortrage mitgeteilten Ergebnisse können nur als erster Versuch angesehen werden, die zur Zeit vorliegenden Befunde über den Bau von Eiweißstoffen synthetisch auszuwerten. Einem eingehenderen Ausbau derartiger Betrachtungen steht der äußerst enge Bereich vorliegender Angaben über den Bau der Peptidketten der Eiweißstoffe im Wege und teilweise auch der Charakter des Untersuchungsmaterials. Die Beschränktheit unserer Kenntnisse verhindert, unserer Meinung nach, auch ein exakteres Vorgehen bei der Erforschung der

Gesetzmäßigkeiten des Aufbaus der Eiweißstoffe mit Hilfe statistischer Methoden; letztere werden jedoch in Zukunft sicher eine entscheidende Rolle auf diesem Gebiete spielen.

LITERATUR

1. A. P. RYLE, F. SANGER, L. F. SMITH & R. KITAI, *Biochem. J.*, **60**, 541, 1955.
2. R. B. MERRIFIELD & D. M. WOOLLEY, *J. Amer. chem. Soc.*, **78**, 359, 1956.
3. F. SANGER, L. F. SMITH & R. KITAI, *Biochem. J.*, **58**, vi, 1954.
4. F. SANGER, *Bull. Soc. Chim. biol.*, *Paris*, **37**, 23, 1955.
5. H. TUPPY, *Mh. Chem.*, **84**, 996, 1953.
6. F. SANGER & E. O. P. THOMPSON, *Biochem. J.*, **53**, 366, 1953.
7. F. SANGER & E. O. P. THOMPSON, *Biochem. J.*, **53**, 353, 1953.
8. E. S. HAUGAARD & N. HAUGAARD, *C. R. Lab. Carlsberg*, *Sér. Chim.*, **29**, 350, 1955
9. H. BROWN, F. SANGER & R. KITAI, *Biochem. J.*, **60**, 556, 1955.
10. B. MEEDOM, *C. R. Lab. Carlsberg*, *Sér. Chim.*, **29**, 403, 1955.
11. H. BROWN, F. SANGER & R. KITAI, *Biochem. J.*, **60**, 562, 1954.
12. F. SANGER, E. O. P. THOMPSON & R. KITAI, *Biochem. J.*, **59**, 509, 1955.
13. H. FRAENKEL-CONRAT, *J. Amer. chem. Soc.*, **76**, 3606, 1954.
14. M. BERGMANN & C. NIEMANN, *J. biol. Chem.*, **115**, 77, 1936.
15. M. BERGMANN & C. NIEMANN, *J. biol. Chem.*, **118**, 301, 1937.
16. N. GAVRILOV & L. AKIMOVA, *Uspekhi Khim.*, *Moscow*, **21**, 483, 1952.
17. L. AKIMOVA, *Vestn. Moskov. Univ. Ser. Fiz. Mat. Estestven. Nauk*, No. 6, **17**, 1954.
18. F. ŠORM, *Chem. Listy*, **48**, 722, 1954; *Sborn. čsl. chim. Rabot.*, **19**, 1003, 1954.
19. C. H. W. HIRS, W. H. STEIN & S. MOORE, *Fed. Proc.*, 1956.
20. B. KEIL & F. ŠORM, *Chem. Listy*, **48**, 735, 1954; *Sborn. čsl. chim. Rabot.*, **19**, 1018, 1954.
21. B. KEIL & F. ŠORM, *Chem. Listy*, **52**, 1341, 1958; *Coll. czechoslov. chem. Commun.*, in Druck.
22. J. VANĚČEK, B. KEIL & F. ŠORM, *Chem. Listy*, **48**, 1677, 1954; *Coll. czechoslov. chem. Commun.*, **20**, 363, 1955.
23. J. VANĚČEK, B. MELOUN & F. ŠORM, *Chem. Listy*, **51**, 1367, 1957; *Coll. czechoslov. chem. Commun.*, **23**, 514, 1958.
24. P. MÄSIAR, B. KEIL & F. ŠORM, *Chem. Listy*, **51**, 352, 1957; *Coll. czechoslov. chem. Commun.*, **22**, 1203, 1957.
25. P. MÄSIAR, B. KEIL & F. ŠORM, *Chem. Listy*, **51**, 1728, 1957; *Coll. czechoslov. chem. Commun.*, **23**, 734, 1958.

Die Kontinuität des Eiweisses

KURT FELIX

Institut für vegetative Physiologie der Universität Frankfurt am Main

ANDERE Referenten berichten auf diesem Symposion, wie die ersten Aminosäuren [1] und die ersten Polypeptide [2] auf der Erde entstanden sein könnten. Wenn sie die Bedingungen, die damals wahrscheinlich geherrscht haben, im Laboratorium wieder herstellen, können sie die Synthese von Aminosäuren und von Polypeptiden reproduzieren. Vielleicht sind schon vorher Polynucleotide entstanden [2a]. Diese Polymere können nach Oparin [3] bereits polymolekulare Systeme gebildet haben, 'die jedoch unvergleichlich viel einfacher waren als das lebende Protoplasma'. Aus diesen einfachen Systemen entstanden dann im Laufe einer sehr langen und langsamen Evolution die Formen der Organismen. Wie aus den Polypeptiden, die sich aus den Aminosäuren des Ur-Ozeans gebildet haben, dann die Proteine mit einer bestimmten, durch die biologische Funktion bedingten Anordnung der Aminosäuren entstanden sind, und welchen Anteil die eventuell vorher gebildete Nucleinsäure gehabt hat, wissen wir nicht.

Von den heutigen Organismen wissen wir aber, daß sie ihren Bestand an Proteinen durch die Generationen hindurch erhalten haben. Leider können wir diesen Bestand nicht weit zurückverfolgen. Immerhin hat man in fossilen Knochen und Muscheln, die 200 Millionen und mehr Jahre alt sind, dieselben Aminosäuren gefunden wie in den heutigen Vertretern der gleichen Arten [4]; allerdings nur die Aminosäuren, welche die hohen Temperaturen überstehen konnten, denen die Gebilde in den seither verstrichenen Zeiträumen ausgesetzt waren.

1. ARTEIGENTÜMLICHKEITEN IM AUFBAU DER PROTEINE

Heute möchte ich den Mitteln und Wegen nachgehen, die ein Organismus besitzt, seinen Eiweißbestand zu wahren. Zuerst seien einige Beispiele aufgeführt, die beweisen, daß Eiweißkörper gleicher Funktion bei den einzelnen Tiergattungen nicht genau gleich zusammengesetzt sind, sondern an einigen Stellen der Peptidketten sich voneinander unterscheiden.

Im Insulin wechseln die Aminosäuren unter der Disulfidbrücke der A-kette zwischen Rind, Schwein und Schaf [5].

Im Cytochrom c fand Tuppy Unterschiede in dem Teil der Peptidkette, die mit dem Hämin verbunden ist, zwischen Pferd, Rind und Schwein auf der einen und dem Huhn auf der anderen Seite [6].

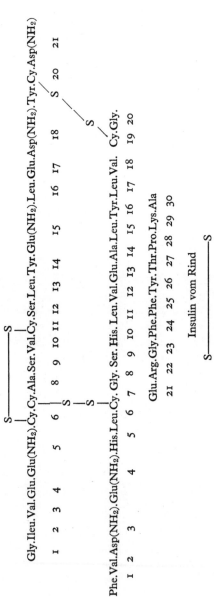

```
1    2     3  4  5     6       7  8   9   10  11  12
Val.Glu(NH₂).Lys.Cy.Ala.Glu(NH₂).Cy.His.Thr.Val.Glu.Lys
                 |                |
                 S——-hämin——S
```

Cytochrom *c* von Pferd, Rind und Schwein

```
1    2     3  4  5     6       7  8   9   10  11  12
Val.Glu(NH₂).Lys.Cy.Ser.Glu(NH₂).Cy.His.Thr.Val.Glu.Lys
                 |                |
                 S——-hämin——S
```

Cytochrom *c* vom Huhn

Die bekannten Arbeiten von V. du Vigneaud und seiner Gruppe demonstrieren uns, daß das Vasopressin des Rindes als basische Aminosäure Arginin und das des Schweins Lysin enthält [7].

```
   S————————————————S
   |                 |
H₂N.Cy.Tyr.Ileu.Glu(NH₂).Asp(NH₂).Cy.Pro.Leu.Gly(NH₂)
```

Schweine-Oxytocin

```
   S————————————————S
   |                 |
H₂N.Cy.Tyr.Phe.Glu(NH₂).Asp(NH₂).Cy.Pro.Lys.Gly(NH₂)
```

Schweine-Vasopressin

```
   S————————————————S
   |                 |
H₂N.Cy.Tyr.Phe.Glu(NH₂).Asp(NH₂).Cy.Pro.Arg.Gly(NH₂)
```

Rinder-Vasopressin

In den Corticotropinen bestehen ebenfalls Unterschiede in der Zusammensetzung zwischen Schwein und Schaf [8].

```
1   2   3   4   5   6   7   8    9   10  11  12  13  14  15  16  17  18
Ser.Tyr.Ser.Met.Glu.His.Phe.Arg.Try.Gly.Lys.Pro.Val.Gly.Lys.Lys.Arg.Arg.
```

```
19  20  21  22  23  24  25  26  27  28  29     30      31  32  33
Pro.Val.Lys.Val.Tyr.Pro.Asp.Gly.Ala.Glu.Asp.Glu(NH₂).Leu.Ala.Glu.
```

```
34  35  36  37  38  39
Ala.Phe.Pro.Leu.Glu.Phe
```

Schweine-β-Corticotropin

```
        25  26  27  28  29  30  31  32  33
. . . . . . Ala.Gly.Glu.Asp.Asp.Glu.Ala.Ser.Glu.
```

```
34  35  36  37  38  39
Ala.Phe.Pro.Leu.Glu.Phe
```

Schaf-α-Corticotropin

Anfang dieses Jahres kam heraus, daß die hypertensine, die aus Pferdeserum dargestellt werden können, etwas anders zusammengesetzt sind als die aus Rinderserum. Jene haben an 5. Stelle Isoleucin, diese Valin [9].

HYPERTENSINE

Asp. Arg. Val. Tyr. Ileu. His. Pro. Phe. His. Leu
1   2   3   4   5   6   7   8   9   10
Decapeptid aus Pferdeserum

Asp. Arg. Val. Tyr. Ileu. His. Pro. Phe
1   2   3   4   5   6   7   8
Octapeptid aus Pferdeserum

Asp. Arg. Val. Tyr. Val. His. Pro. Phe. His. Leu
1   2   3   4   5   6   7   8   9   10
Decapeptid aus Rinderserum

Asp. Arg. Val. Tyr. Val. His. Pro. Phe
1   2   3   4   5   6   7   8
Octapeptid, synthetisch dargestellt

Wenn zukünftig die Aminosäuresequenzen weiterer Proteine bekannt sein werden, können wir noch mehr Beispiele dafür anführen, wie sich Unterschiede zwischen den Tieren im Aufbau der Proteine zu erkennen geben. Die Abweichungen werden immer nur die Stellen in den Peptidketten betreffen, die für die Funktion nicht so wichtig sind. Daß nicht alle Teile eines Peptids gleich wichtig für die Funktion sind, läßt sich am deutlichsten an den Corticotropinen demonstrieren. Die Unterschiede in der Struktur zwischen dem Schaf- und Schweinecorticotropin betreffen nur den Bereich von der 26. bis zur 39. Aminosäure. Nach den Arbeiten von Bell und seiner Gruppe können vom Carboxylende her 14 Aminosäuren abgespalten werden, ohne daß die Aktivität des Hormons leidet. Diese ist somit durch die ersten 25 Aminosäuren bestimmt, von denen keine fehlen darf [9].

Die Zusammensetzung der Proteohormone und des Cytochroms c scheint genetisch festgelegt zu sein. Offenbar gibt es in einem Polypeptid und einem Eiweißkörper zwei Teile: einen, der über die Funktion entscheidet, und einen zweiten, in dem sich die Eigenarten der Tierart und -rasse auswirken kann. Der erste Teil wiederholt sich bei allen Tieren, die das Hormon bilden, so wie sich gewisse morphologische Strukturen und Zellarten wiederholen.

An den Hämoglobinen könnte man den Einfluß der Artspezifität besonders gut studieren. Überall transportieren sie den Sauerstoff, unterscheiden sich aber in der Affinität zu ihm und zum Kohlenmonoxyd, ferner in der Krystallform und in den Immunreaktionen. Die Unterschiede liegen nur in der Eiweißkomponente, da die Farbstoffkomponente überall die gleiche ist. Leider weiß man sehr wenig von ihren Aminosäuresequenzen, kennt nur bei einigen die Anzahl der Peptidketten und die Aminosäuren am Amino-Ende. Die nachfolgende Tabelle [10] gibt (S.245) darüber Auskunft.

Aus der Tabelle geht hervor, daß—wenigstens nach den Endaminosäuren zu schließen—das Hämoglobin des Pferdes mit dem des Esels und das der Rinder mit dem der Schafe verwandt ist. So reagieren Antikörper, die das Kaninchen gegen Pferdehämoglobin erzeugt hat, auch mit dem Eselhämoglobin; ferner reagieren Antikörper gegen Rinderhämoglobin auch mit dem Schafhämoglobin. Dagegen reagieren die Antikörper gegen Pferde- und Eselhämoglobin nicht mit Rinder- und Schafhämoglobin und umgekehrt.

Molekulargewichte und Endgruppen der Hämoglobine einiger Wirbeltiere

Tierart	Molekulargewicht	Endaminosäuren	Reihenfolge am Amino-Ende [11]
Pferd . .	66 000	6 Val	Val. Leu Val. Gly Val. Glu. (Leu)
Esel . . .	66 000	6 Val	—
Mensch Erwachs.	66 000	5 Val oder 4 Val	—
Mensch Foetus .	66 000	2 Val	—
Rind . . .	66 000	2 Val. 2 Met	Val. Leu Met. Gly
Schaf . .	66 000	2 Val. 2 Met	
Ziege . .	66 000	2 Val. 2 Met	
Huhn . .	(65 000)	2 Val	Val. Leu

Es ist anzunehmen, daß alle früheren Generationen von Pferden, Eseln, Rindern und Schafen die für ihre Art eigentümlichen Hämoglobine besessen haben, und daß sie auch in Zukunft die gleichen erzeugen werden. Art, Gehalt und Anordnung der Aminosäuren sind offenbar in einem Gen festgelegt.

Wie sehr das der Fall ist, zeigt sich an der Verbreitung des Sichelzellenhämoglobins, das Professor Linus Pauling in seinem Referat behandelt. Hier sei nur noch eine Besonderheit dieses Chromoproteids erwähnt, die andere Proteine nicht besitzen, wenigstens nicht nach unserer heutigen Kenntnis. Im fötalen Leben wird ein anderes Hämoglobin erzeugt als im erwachsenen. Konsequenterweise müßte man nun annehmen, daß zwei Gene hierfür existieren, eines, das im embryonalen Leben wirkt, und ein anderes, das erst nach der Geburt tätig wird. Dafür spricht, daß nach Roche beim Erwachsenen noch fötales Hämoglobin vorkommt, und umgekehrt soll auch der Embryo bereits etwas Erwachsenenhämoglobin besitzen. Damit könnte das fötale zugehörige Gen noch über die Geburt hinaus weiter wirken und umgekehrt das Erwachsenenhämoglobin schon vor der Geburt mit seiner Tätigkeit beginnen.

Es kommt vor, daß der Erwachsene noch viel fötales Hämoglobin bildet oder anfängt, wieder zu bilden. Das führt dann zu einer Anämie, an der Bewohner der Mittelmeerländer und ihre Nachkommen leiden. Da die Krankheit familiär auftritt, muß das Bestehenbleiben der fötalen Hämoglobinsynthese vererbt werden können [12].

Hier fehlt entweder das Gen für das Erwachsenenhämoglobin oder der Mechanismus, der das 'fötale Gen' ausschaltet.

Das Aminosäuremuster ist im fötalen Hämoglobin ein anderes als im erwachsenen [12]. Der Gehalt an Threonin, Serin, Methionin, Isoleucin und vielleicht auch an Glutaminsäure ist höher, der an Prolin, Valin, Tyrosin, Histidin und vielleicht auch an Alanin ist niedriger als im normalen Erwachsenenhämoglobin.

Von den Hämoglobinen, die bei den Sichelzellanämien auftreten, sei hier nur erwähnt, daß sie sich vom normalen Hämoglobin nicht in der Zusammensetzung, sondern nur im isoelektrischen Punkt und vermutlich in der Faltung der Peptidketten unterscheiden. Sollte diese Vermutung zutreffen, so würde das bedeuten, daß das zu einem Protein gehörige Gen nicht nur Art, Zahl und Anordnung der Aminosäuren, sondern auch die Weise, in der die Peptidketten gefaltet sind, bestimmt. [Nach V. M. Ingram (*Nature, Lond.*, **180**, 326, 1957) ist an einer Stelle der Peptidkette des S-Hämoglobins ein Glutaminsäurerest durch einen Valinrest ersetzt.]

Im allgemeinen vermutet man, daß die Erbfaktoren, welche die Synthese der verschiedenen Hämoglobine kontrollieren, multiple Allele sind. Dagegen soll für das fötale Hämoglobin ein besonderes Gen an einem anderen Ort existieren [13].

Inzwischen wurde wahrscheinlich gemacht, daß auch die Erzeugung anderer Proteine jeweils von bestimmten Genen abhängt. Es sind Zustände beschrieben worden, bei denen der Mangel an einem bestimmten Protein erblich ist. So beruht die Hämophilie darauf, daß eines der antihämophilen Globuline fehlt, ein Mangel, der geschlechtsgebunden vererbt wird. Bennhold hat eine gesunde Frau beobachtet, bei der das Albumin im Blut fehlte [14]. Takahara beschrieb eine japanische Familie, deren Mitglieder keine Katalase im Blut besaßen [15]. Weiter soll es vorkommen, daß die γ-Globuline fehlen. Die Krankheit tritt familiär auf und zwar bei jungen Knaben. Hier fehlt das Gen, das die Erzeugung der γ-Globuline beherrscht und vermutlich im Geschlechtschromosom lokalisiert ist [16]. Da in der γ-Globulinfraktion die Antikörper enthalten sind, erliegen solche Kinder leicht Infektionen.

Es ließen sich jetzt schon mehrere Beispiele dafür anführen, daß die Produktion bestimmter Proteine von Genen abhängt und mit dem Gen von Generation zu Generation vererbt wird. Wenn wir später in diesen Teil des Eiweißstoffwechsels tiefer eingedrungen sein werden, können wir den Schluß wahrscheinlich verallgemeinern und sagen, daß die Erzeugung aller Eiweißkörper von Genen beherrscht wird.

Kurz sei noch auf die in der Eiweißchemie allgemein bekannte Tatsache eingegangen, daß nämlich alle Proteine mit verschwindenden Ausnahmen Gemische aus einander sehr ähnlichen Komponenten sind. Die Komponenten müssen gemeinsame Stücke haben, die die Funktion bestimmen.

Andere Teile des Moleküls können variieren je nach der augenblicklichen Situation des Stoffwechsels. So ändert sich die Zusammensetzung der Proteine mit dem Alter: die basischen Aminosäuren sollen zunehmen.

Es könnte aber auch sein, daß nicht alle Zellen genau die gleichen Proteine bilden. Die γ-Globuline z.B. werden von den Plasmazellen erzeugt. Es läßt sich leicht denken, daß nicht jede Plasmazelle ihr γ-Globulin genau so aufbaut wie ihre Nachbarin. Diese Variationen dürften aber nicht das Ausmaß einnehmen wie die zwischen verschiedenen Tierarten.

Ein Beispiel dafür, daß in verschiedenen Proteinen oder Peptiden Strecken gleicher Aminosäuresequenzen vorkommen, liefern die Melanophorenhormone und die Corticotropine. Es gibt zwei Melanophorenhormone. Das α-Intermedin enthält die Aminosäuren 1 bis 13 des Corticotropins. Im β-Hormon wiederholen sich die Aminosäuren 4 bis 10 des Corticotropins und des α-Hormons. Aber links von dieser Gruppe sind mehr und andere Aminosäuren. Auch auf

der rechten Seite stehen mehr und andere Aminosäuren als im α-Intermedin
[16a].

Ser. Tyr. Ser. Met. Glu. His. Phe. Arg. Try. Gly. Lys. Pro. Val
1   2   3   4   5   6   7   8   9   10 11 12 13

α-Intermedin

Asp.Glu.Gly.Pro.Tyr.Lys.Met.Glu.His.Phe.Arg.Try.Gly.Ser.Pro.Pro.Lys.Asp
1 2 3 4 5 6 7 8 9 10 11 12 13 14 15 16 17 18

β-Intermedin

2. SYNTHESE UND UMFORMUNG VON PROTEINEN

Die Wirkung der Gene äußert sich wahrscheinlich auf zweierlei Weise; denn
ein Teil der Proteine wird direkt aus den Aminosäuren synthetisiert, ein zweiter
Teil entsteht durch Umformung aus anderen, indem Peptide oder Aminosäuren
abgespalten werden. An sich könnten auch Peptide und Aminosäuren angela-
gert werden. Aber wir können noch nicht übersehen, in welchem Umfang die
Transpeptidation tatsächlich stattfindet.

Vermutlich sind es nur wenige Proteine, die die Zelle direkt aus den Aminosäuren synthetisiert, aus denen sie dann je nach Bedarf andere bildet, die eine
bestimmte Aufgabe zu erfüllen haben. So werden wohl die Hormone der
Hypophyse aus höhermolekularen Proteinen durch proteolytische Fermente
herausmodelliert. In den primären Proteinen muß die besondere Kombination
der Aminosäuren der sekundären Proteine vorgebildet sein. Offenbar wirkt ein
Gen schon bei der Synthese des primären Proteins mit und sicherlich auch bei
der Erzeugung des Fermentes, welches das primäre in das sekundäre Protein
umwandelt.

Am einfachsten ist die Umformung zu verstehen. Das proteolytische Ferment
schält aus dem Muttereiweiß die wirksame Kombination der Aminosäuren
heraus.

Wenn die unwirksame Vorstufe eines Fermentes in die wirksame Stufe
übergeführt wird, so ist das das gleiche wie die Umformung von einem Protein
in ein anderes. In der Regel werden dabei Peptide oder Aminosäuren abgespalten.

Die Aktivierung ist ihrem Wesen nach eine begrenzte Hydrolyse. Das aktive
Ferment hat ein niedrigeres Molekulargewicht als seine Vorstufe, wenn es nicht
wie das Chymotrypsin nachträglich zu größeren Komplexen aggregiert. Das
Molekulargewicht des Pepsinogens beträgt ungefähr 42.000, das des Pepsins
38.000. Das Molekulargewicht des Trypsinogens ist nicht bekannt, aber man
weiß, daß bei der Aktivierung eine andere Aminosäure (Isoleucin) an das
Amino-Ende kommt und die bisherige (Valin) verschwindet. Im Chymotrypsin sind die Peptidketten wahrscheinlich zu einem Ring geschlossen, und
es werden mindestens zwei Peptidbindungen geöffnet, wenn es aktiviert wird
[17].

Weitere Beispiele für die Umformung von Proteinen sind die Bildung von
Paracasein aus Casein bei der Labgerinnung und die des Fibrins aus Fibrinogen
bei der Blutgerinnung.

Die Erzeugung eines Fermentes ist nach der gegenwärtigen allgemeinen

Ansicht an ein Gen gebunden. Jedem Ferment soll ein bestimmtes Gen entsprechen. Da weiter die Fermente in der Regel Eiweißkörper sind, kann an ihnen
leicht die Genabhängigkeit der Eiweißsynthese studiert werden. Wenn ein Gen
fehlt oder durch physikalische oder chemische Einwirkungen zerstört wird, wird
das zugehörige Ferment nicht mehr gebildet, und das Substrat, das von ihm
umgewandelt werden sollte, häuft sich an. Die schönsten Beweise dafür verdanken
wir Beadle [18], Tatum, Horowitz [19] und deren Mitarbeitern. Durch Strahlen
und chemische Substanzen haben sie aus der Wildform des orangegelben
Mehlpilzes (Neurospora crassa) Mutanten erzeugt, die nur am Leben erhalten
werden konnten, wenn dem Nährboden bestimmte Produkte des intermediären
Stoffwechsels zugesetzt wurden. Ohne Zugabe dieser Substanzen ist der Stoffwechsel in den Mutanten unterbrochen, und das Zwischenprodukt, das in der
Reaktionsfolge vor dem zugesetzten auftritt, häuft sich an. Es fehlt das Ferment,
welches das angehäufte in das Mangelprodukt überführt.

3. REDUPLIKATION DES EIWEISSES

Wir wissen noch wenig Präzises über den Mechanismus der Eiweißsynthese.
Nur eines ist sicher: es kommt in unseren Zeitläuften niemals vor, daß Eiweiß
aus einem Haufen loser Aminosäuren, der für sich und isoliert von anderem
lebenden Material daliegt, gebildet wird [20].

Die im Urmeer gelösten Aminosäuren dürfen wir uns nicht als etwas Bestän-
diges vorstellen. Sie sind zweifellos unter dem Einfluß der eingestrahlten
Sonnenenergie fortlaufend umgesetzt worden. Dabei könnten auch Peptide
entstanden sein [2a].

Heute wird Eiweiß immer in Gegenwart von bereits vorhandenem Eiweiß
und von Nucleinsäure erzeugt, und da liegt nichts näher als die Annahme, daß
das vorhandene Eiweiß als Muster für das neu zu bildende dient [20]. Es
könnte sein, daß die freien Aminosäuren der Zelle sich neben die entsprechenden in der Peptidkette des Mustereiweißes legen und zwar in der gleichen
Ordnung, in der sie dort aufeinander folgen. Dabei sollten sich nach Haurowitz
ähnliche Kräfte betätigen wie beim Aufbau eines Krystalls. Die Nucleinsäure
hätte nach seiner Ansicht nur die Aufgabe, die Peptidketten des Mustereiweißes
zu strecken, damit alle seine Aminosäuren zugänglich sind [21]. Nach den
Untersuchungen von Schramm an den Viren scheint die Nucleinsäure selbst
die Reihenfolge der Aminosäuren bestimmen zu können [22]. Dann werden die
freien Aminosäuren miteinander zu einer Kette vereinigt. Diese Annahme
bietet keine gedanklichen Schwierigkeiten, wenn es sich um die Neubildung in
einer einzigen Zelle handelt. Da sind offenbar alle Muster vorhanden. Weiter
läßt sich noch unschwer annehmen, daß bei der Zellteilung die Muster gleichmäßig auf die Tochterzellen übergehen.

4. WAHRUNG DER KONTINUITÄT BEI
DER FORTPFLANZUNG

Schwierigkeiten macht dagegen die Frage, wie die Kontinuität der Muster
bei der Fortpflanzung gewahrt wird. Denn hier sind die Kerne der Spermatozoen
und der Eier eingeschaltet. Sie übertragen—wenn nicht alle, so doch den weitaus

TABELLE I

Aminosäurezusammensetzung von acht Protaminen

(Molekulare Verhältnisse)

	Iridin (Salmo irideus)	Truttin (Salmo trutta)	Fontinin (Salmo fontinalis)	Lacustrin (Salmo lacustris)	Salmin (Salmo salar)	Clupein (Clupea harengus)	Sturin (Acipenser sturio)	Gallin (Gallus domesticus)
Glycin	2	2	2	2	3	+	2	1
Alanin	2	2	2	2	2	4	5	5
Serin	3	3	3	2	5	6	3	5
Threonin . . .	0	0	0	0	0	2	1	2
Valin	4	5	5	2	4	4	0	3
Prolin	5	5	5	5	5	5	0	5
Isoleucin . . .	1	0	0	1	0	1	2	1
Asparaginsäure .	0	0	0	1	0	0	0	0
Glutaminsäure .	0	0	0	1	0	0	1	1
Arginin . . .	50	50	50	40–50	55	53	35	44
Lysin	2	0	0	0	0	0	9	0
Histidin . . .	0	0	0	5–15	0	0	7	0

größten Teil—der Erbmerkmale auf die Tochtergeneration. Wenn es richtig ist, daß jedem Ferment und—wie es nach dem eingangs Gesagten wahrscheinlich ist—daß jedem Eiweißkörper ein bestimmtes Gen entspricht, dann müssen wir fragen, wie in diesen Kernen die vielen Erbmerkmale repräsentiert sind. Heute können wir diese Frage nur vorläufig beantworten, da wir die chemische Zusammensetzung der Eizellkerne überhaupt noch nicht, und die der Spermienkerne der Säugetiere nur oberflächlich kennen.

Am besten untersucht sind die Kerne der Fischspermatozoen. Sie sind auch relativ leicht zu isolieren [23].

Nach den bisherigen Analysen bestehen sie nur aus Nucleoprotamin; das heißt aus dem Salz einer Desoxyribonucleinsäure mit Protamin. Aller Phosphor, der in den Spermatozoen vorkommt, gehört der Nucleinsäure an, und neben den Aminosäuren des Protamins und neben den Purin- und Pyrimidinbasen der Nucleinsäure enthält der Spermatozoenkern der Fische keine weiteren Stickstoffverbindungen. Es könnten höchstens noch stickstofffreie organische Verbindungen in ihm vorkommen. Steroide ließen sich nicht nachweisen.

Die Kerne lösen sich vollständig in 10%iger Kochsalzlösung, und aus dieser Lösung kann ihr gesamtes Material durch destilliertes Wasser wieder in Fasern gefällt werden. Die Fasern bestehen wie die Kerne aus Nucleoprotamin. Sie haben die gleiche Zusammensetzung wie die Kerne; wenigstens, was Stickstoff, Phosphor und Arginin angeht.

Aus den Kernen und den Fasern kann das Protamin durch verdünnte Salzsäure extrahiert und über das Pikrat in das Hydrochlorid oder Methylesterhydrochlorid übergeführt werden. Wir haben auf diese Weise die Protamine aus den Spermatozoen von sieben verschiedenen Fischarten dargestellt und analysiert. Die Ergebnisse dieser Untersuchungen sind in der folgenden Tabelle enthalten. Die Zahlen in der letzten Reihe beziehen sich auf das Protamin der Hahnenspermatozoen, Gallin genannt. Sie stammen aus der Arbeit von Fischer & Kreuzer [24].

Gemeinsam ist allen Protaminen der hohe Gehalt an basischen Aminosäuren und die relativ geringe Anzahl der Monoaminosäuren. Das Verhältnis der basischen zu den Monoaminosäuren ist durchweg ungefähr 2 : 1. Unter den Monoaminosäuren fehlen Tryptophan, Phenylalanin und die schwefelhaltigen Aminosäuren. Tyrosin kommt vielleicht in einigen wenigen vor, die von uns noch nicht untersucht worden sind.

In dem Gehalt an Monoaminosäuren bestehen deutliche Unterschiede zwischen den einzelnen Fischarten, und wir glauben, daß diese Aminosäuremuster für sie charakteristisch sind. Zwei Forellenspecies haben gleich zusammengesetzte Protamine, und ihre Individuen können miteinander gekreuzt werden. Vielleicht ist die gleiche Zusammensetzung der Protamine der molekulare Ausdruck für die Kreuzbarkeit.

5. NUCLEOPROTAMINE ALS GENE

Es bestehen also zweifellos Unterschiede in der Zusammensetzung der Protamine zwischen den Tierarten. Aber unsere Frage ist: gibt es innerhalb eines einzelnen Zellkerns eine chemische Grundlage für die Vielzahl der Gene?

Wir setzen voraus, daß jedes Gen durch eine besondere Substanz repräsentiert ist. Wenn unsere Analysen richtig sind, so müssen zum mindesten in den Spermatozoen der Fische die Gene Nucleoprotamine sein. Gibt es also so viele Nucleoprotamine wie Gene?

Tatsächlich besteht eine solche Möglichkeit. Zunächst sind die Protamine keine einheitlichen Substanzen, sondern Gemische aus sehr ähnlichen Komponenten. Wir konnten z.B. Clupein, das Protamin des Heringsspermas mit der Gegenstromverteilung nach Craig in drei Fraktionen zerlegen, die sich durch ihre Zusammensetzung unterscheiden.

Die erste, am langsamsten wandernde Fraktion scheint ziemlich einheitlich zu sein und dürfte einer einzelnen Komponente entsprechen. Von den acht Aminosäuren des Clupeins enthält sie nur fünf. Es fehlen ihr Glycin, Threonin und Isoleucin. Am Amino-Ende steht Prolin. Ihr Mindestmolekulargewicht beträgt 3920. Die zweite Fraktion ist noch nicht einheitlich und ist die einzige, die Glycin enthält. Valin fehlt ihr. Alle ihre Komponenten beginnen ebenfalls mit Prolin. Die dritte Fraktion ist die am wenigsten einheitliche. In ihr kommen nur sechs Aminosäuren vor; Glycin und Isoleucin fehlen. N-terminale Aminosäuren sind Serin, Threonin und Alanin (W. Rick, nicht veröffentliche Resultate). Im nativen Clupein konnten nur Prolin und ein wenig Alanin mit der Fluordinitrobenzolmethode nachgewiesen werden. Die Komponenten des Clupeins sind vielleicht nicht regellos durcheinandergemischt, sondern irgendwie geordnet und in dieser Ordnung durch gewisse, wenn auch noch so schwache Bindungen zusammengehalten, so daß Serin und Threonin, die am Ende von Ketten der dritten Fraktion stehen, von dem Fluordinitrobenzol nicht erreicht werden.

In unseren früheren Versuchen haben wir immer nur eine N-terminale Aminosäure gefunden, nämlich Prolin; einmal allerdings noch Serin, aber da vermuteten wir, daß das Präparat bei der Aufarbeitung etwas zersetzt worden war. Ferner haben wir in den früheren Präparaten nie Glycin gefunden. Nun, die früheren Präparate waren aus Heringen der Nordsee gewonnen worden, während dieses letzte von Heringen der Ostsee stammte. Es sei daran erinnert, daß japanische Autoren ebenfalls zwei Arten von Heringen untersucht haben, die sich in der Zusammensetzung des Clupeins unterscheiden; die eine enthielt Glycin, die andere nicht [25].

Es ist also möglich, daß so kleine Unterschiede wie die zwischen zwei Heringsrassen sich in der Zusammensetzung der Protamine auswirken. Es ist nicht nur möglich, sondern muß eigentlich erwartet werden; denn auch diese kleinen Unterschiede müssen ja irgendwie in dem genetischen Apparat materiell ausgedrückt sein.

Neben den Protaminen ist auch die Desoxyribonucleinsäure (DNS) beteiligt. Ihre Analysen enttäuschen allerdings; denn die DNS aus den verschiedenen Fischspermatozoen ergeben nur sehr geringe Unterschiede, während die Zusammensetzung der Protamine in sehr deutlicher und charakteristischer Weise wechselt. Dagegen können sie sich sehr wohl in der Reihenfolge der Nucleotide unterscheiden. Rein mathematisch lassen sich sehr viele Möglichkeiten für die Anordnung der vier oder fünf Nucleotide berechnen.

Selbst wenn sich herausstellen sollte, daß die Fische nur eine Art von Desoxyribonucleinsäure enthalten, so ließe sich schon eine große Zahl von Nucleoprotaminen konstruieren, auf Grund der Tatsache, daß die Protamine nicht einheitlich, sondern Gemische aus mehreren Komponenten sind.

In den Nucleoprotaminen verhält sich die DNS zu den Protaminen etwa wie 60 : 40. Das Molekulargewicht jener beträgt ungefähr 1 Million und das durchschnittliche der Protamine rund 4000. Danach bindet ein Molekül der DNS ungefähr 100 Protaminkomponenten. Je nachdem, welche der Komponenten und in welcher Ordnung sie gebunden werden, entstehen verschiedene Nucleoprotamine.

Nach den neuesten Untersuchungen von Dr Zahn [26] kommt nun noch dazu, daß auch die Nucleinsäuren sehr wahrscheinlich ebenfalls aus mehreren Komponenten bestehen. Er befreite erst die DNS aus Heringsspermatozoen von Elektrolyten und setzte dann in steigenden Mengen Salzsäure zu. Dadurch wurde die DNS in verschiedene Fraktionen zerlegt, die sich in ihrer Zusammensetzung etwas unterschieden. Einige bestanden vorzugsweise aus Purin-, andere aus Pyrimidinbasen. Wenn diese Versuche weiter ausgebaut werden, sind wohl präzisere Resultate zu erwarten.

Wir dürfen aber jetzt schon annehmen, daß für die DNS das Gleiche gilt wie für die Protamine, und daß damit die Zahl der möglichen Kombinationen ins Ungemessene steigt, so daß jedes Gen durch ein eigenes Nucleoprotamin repräsentiert sein kann.

Mit anderen Worten: die Kontinuität der einzelnen Proteine, Hormone und Enzyme wird bei der Fortpflanzung jeweils durch ein besonderes Nucleoprotamin vermittelt. Wir können uns heute aber noch nicht vorstellen, auf welche Weise aus dem doch relativ einfachen Protamin so komplizierte Eiweißkörper wie z.B. das Insulin oder die Ribonuclease entstehen. Die fehlenden Aminosäuren könnten vielleicht aus den Proteinen des Dotters bezogen werden.

7. UMWANDLUNG VON PROTAMINEN IN HISTONE

Es ist aber höchst unwahrscheinlich, daß das komplizierte Protein direkt aus dem Protamin entwickelt wird; es muß zuvor in ein Histon, das genetische Eiweiß der somatischen Zellen, umgewandelt oder durch ein solches ersetzt werden. Wahrscheinlich geschieht das, kurz bevor die Differenzierung in der Entwicklung einsetzt. Die Histone enthalten bereits alle Aminosäuren mit Ausnahme des Tryptophans. Von ihnen ist es nicht mehr so weit bis zu den komplizierten Proteinen. Es müßten noch mehr Aminosäuren dazu kommen, und der Gehalt an basischen, der in den Histonen immer noch etwa 25% des Gesamtstickstoffs entspricht, relativ erniedrigt werden.

Wir können uns auch noch nicht vorstellen, wie das Histon aus dem Protamin entsteht, und nach welchen Regeln die fehlenden Aminosäuren ergänzt werden; denn hier dürfte ja kein Mustereiweiß vorliegen. Vermutlich enthält die DNS die Erinnerung an die Ordnung, in der die neuen Aminosäuren anzureihen sind, oder die zukünftige Erweiterung ist bereits in der Position der Aminosäuren im Protamin potentiell festgelegt; um das entscheiden zu können, verstehen wir heute noch zu wenig von der Sprache der Aminosäuren. Es ist wahrscheinlich von Bedeutung, in welcher Umgebung sich jede einzelne befindet, und welche anderen Aminosäuren links und rechts von ihr in der Kette, und oben und unten von ihr in der Spirale oder einer sonstigen Konfiguration der Ketten stehen. Die 'Wörter', die aus den Aminosäuren gebildet werden, sind wahrscheinlich nicht ein-, sondern zwei-, ja vielleicht sogar dreidimensional.

Nimmt man an, daß das Protamin einfach durch das Histon ersetzt wird, so verschiebt man das Problem nach der Stelle in der Zelle hin, wo das Histon gebildet wird.

8. MUTATIONEN

Wir haben uns bemüht, zu ergründen, wie die Organismen ihren Bestand an Eiweiß und die Konstanz seiner Zusammensetzung aufrecht erhalten, soweit es unser heutiges Wissen zuläßt.

Die zweite Frage ist die, wie die Organismen lernen, neue Proteine zu erzeugen z.B. Hämoglobin, Insulin, Hypophysenhormone oder die Fermente, die mit der Adrenalinsynthese zu tun haben, oder ob sie es überhaupt lernen können. Die vergleichende Biochemie gibt uns noch keine befriedigende Auskunft darüber, wann und wo die Hormone, Fermente usw. zum ersten Mal in der Tierreihe auftreten, weil noch viel zu wenig Organismen analysiert worden sind.

Dagegen wissen wir etwas mehr darüber, daß manche Organismen gewisse Fähigkeiten verloren haben. Eingangs erwähnte ich, daß es Menschen gibt, die kein Albumin, andere, die keine γ-Globuline, keine Katalase, keine Tyroxin-oxydase oder keine Homogentisinsäureoxydase mehr erzeugen. Es gibt eine ganze Reihe angeborener Stoffwechselstörungen, die auf dem Mangel an bestimmten Fermenten, also auf dem Mangel an bestimmten Proteinen beruhen.

Wie eine solche Fähigkeit verloren gehen kann, haben uns die Versuche, in denen künstlich Mutationen an Pilzen (vor allen *Neurospora*) ausgeführt worden sind, und die Versuche der experimentellen Erzeugung von Tumoren gezeigt. Die ultravioletten Strahlen und chemischen Substanzen, die Mutationen an Pilzen und Bakterien verursachen, sollen vorzugsweise an den Nucleinsäuren angreifen. Am wirksamsten seien die Wellenlängen, die von den Purinbasen absorbiert werden. Dort sollen auch Stickstoff- und Schwefellost angreifen, die besonders leicht Mutationen erzeugen. Letztere können natürlich auch mit dem Eiweiß reagieren. Dabei werden das Mustereiweiß und die ihm zugeordnete Nucleinsäure verändert. Infolgedessen kann auch das entsprechende Protein oder Ferment nicht mehr hergestellt werden.

Von den Versuchen der experimentellen Tumorerzeugung sind die mit dem Buttergelb (p-Dimethylaminoazobenzol) am durchsichtigsten. Man kann damit nur bei Tieren, deren Eiweiß sich mit dem Farbstoff verbindet, Lebertumoren erzeugen. Wenn dann der Tumor besteht, so enthalten seine Zellen kein Eiweiß mehr, das den Farbstoff bindet [27]. Das frühere Eiweiß wird also nicht mehr gebildet, weil das ursprüngliche Muster durch den Farbstoff verändert und damit ausgeschaltet worden ist.

9. NEUE EIGENSCHAFTEN DURCH QUANTITATIVE VERSCHIEBUNGEN

Während wir noch mehr Beispiele aufführen könnten und in Zukunft finden werden, wo durch Gen-Änderung gewisse Fähigkeiten und Eigenschaften verloren gehen, kennen wir keine, bei denen neue Eigenschaften gewonnen werden. Neue Eigenschaften müssen nicht nur dadurch gewonnen werden, daß neue Gene gebildet werden, sondern es ist manchmal nur notwendig, das quantitative Verhältnis zu verschieben. Wir dürfen nicht vergessen, daß wir einen großen Teil des intermediären Stoffwechsels an der Hefe und anderen niederen Organismen studieren und sie dann bei den höheren bestätigen. Nicht die Qualität der Einzelprozesse unterscheidet die Organismen voneinander, sondern die quantitativen Verhältnisse sowie die räumliche und zeitliche Ordnung, in der sie ablaufen.

Wenn wir diese Anschauung konsequent zurückverfolgen, müssen wir annehmen, daß von Anfang an alle Proteine und Fermente bereits existiert haben und bei der Entstehung der Organismen verschieden verteilt worden sind. Vielleicht gab es früher mehrerlei Proteine als heute, von denen manche wieder aufgegeben worden sind, weil sie sich nicht bewährt haben.

LITERATURVERZEICHNIS

1. S. MILLER, *Formation of the organic compounds on the primitive earth.* Dieses Symposium.
   T. E. PAVLOVSKAYA & A. G. PASYNSKIĬ, *The primary formation of amino acids in ultraviolet rays and electric discharges.* Dieses Symposium.
2. S. AKABORĬ, *On the origin of the fore-protein.* Dieses Symposium.
2a. L. ROKA, 6. *Colloquium Ges.. physiol. Chem.* S. 1, 1955.
3. A. I. OPARIN, *Die Enstehung des Lebens auf der Erde*, 3. Aufl. VEB Deutscher Verlag der Wissenschaften, Berlin, S.245, 1957.
4. P. A. ABELSON, *Sci. Amer.*, 1956 (also *Ann. N.Y. Acad. Sci.*, **69**, 276, 1957).
5. A. P. RYLE, F. SANGER, L. F. SMITH & R. KITAI, *Biochem. J.*, **60**, 541, 556, 1955.
6. H. TUPPY & S. PALEUS, *Acta chem. scand.*, **9**, 353, 1955.
7. V. DU VIGNEAUD, 3ème *Congrès International de Biochimie*, S. 49, 1955.
8. P. H. BELL, *J. Amer. chem. Soc.*, **76**, 5565, 1954; K. S. HOWARD, R. G. SHEPHERD, E. A. EIGNER, D. S. DAVIS & P. H. BELL, ebenda, **77**, 3419, 1955; R. G. SHEPHERD, K. S. HOWARD, P. H. BELL, A. R. CACCIOLA, R. B. CHILD, M. C. DAVIS, J. P. ENGLISH, B. M. FINN, J. H. MEISENHELDER, A. W. MAYER & J. VAN DER SCHEER, ebenda, **78**, 5051, 1956; P. H. BELL, K. S. HOWARD, R. G. SHEPHERD, B. M. FINN & J. H. MEISENHELDER, ebenda, **78**, 5059, 1956; R. G. SHEPHERD, S. D. WILSON, K. S. HOWARD, P. H. BELL, D. S. DAVIES, S. B. DAVIS, E. A. EIGNER & N. E. SHAKESPEARE, ebenda, **78**, 5076, 1956; R. A. BROWN, D. S. DAVIES, M. ENGLERT & H. R. COX, ebenda, **78**, 5077, 1956.
9. D. F. ELLIOT & W. S. PEART, *Biochem. J.*, **65**, 246, 1957; L. T. SKEGGS, J. R. KAHN & N. P. SHUMWAY, *J. exp. med.*, **104**, 193, 1956; W. RITTEL, B. ISELIN, H. KAPPELER, B. RINIKER & R. SCHWYZER, *Angew. Chem.*, **69**, 179, 1957.
10. C. B. ANFINSEN & R. R. REDFIELD, *Advanc. Protein Chem.*, **11**, 45, 1956.
11. H. OZAWA & K. SATAKE, *J. Biochem.*, Tokyo, **42**, 641, 1955.
12. J. ROCHE, Y. DERRIEN, G. DIACONO & M. ROQUES, *Rev. Hémat.*, **8**, 287, 1953; J. ROCHE & Y. DERRIEN, ebenda, **6**, 470, 1951.
13. T. H. J. HUISMAN, J. H. P. JONSEIS & P. C. VAN DER SCHAAF, *Nature, Lond.*, **175**, 902, 1955; P. C. VAN DER SCHAAF & T. H. J. HUISMAN, *Biochim. biophys. Acta*, **17**, 81, 1955.
14. H. BENNHOLD, *Klin. Wschr.*, **32**, 756, 1955.
15. S. TAKAHARA, *Lancet*, **2**, 1101, 1952.

16. O. Bruton, L. Apt, D. Gitlin & C. Janeway, *Amer. J. Dis. Child.*, **84**, 637, 1952; O. Bruton, *Pediatrics, Springfield*, **9**, 722, 1952.
16a. S. I. Harris & A. B. Lerner, *Nature, Lond.*, **179**, 1346, 1957.
17. P. Desnuelle & M. Rovery, 4. *Colloquium Ges. physiol. Chem.*, S. 133, 1953.
18. G. W. Beadle, *Sci. in Progr.*, **6**, 184, 1949.
19. N. H. Horowitz. Dieses Symposium.
20. K. Felix, *Angew. Chem.*, **60**, 231, 1948.
21. F. Haurowitz & Ch. F. Crampton, *Exp. Cell Res. Suppl.*, **2**, 45, 1957.
22. G. Schramm. Dieses Symposium.
23. K. Felix, H. Fischer & A. Krekels, *Progr. Biophys.*, **6**, 1, 1956.
24. H. Fischer & L. Kreuzer, *Hoppe-Seyl. Z.*, **293**, 176, 1951.
25. T. Ando, S. Ishii, C. Hashimoto, M. Yamasaki & K. Iwai, *Bull. chem. Soc. Japan*, **25**, 132, 1952; T. Ando, K. Iwai, M. Yamasaki, C. Hashimoto, M. Kimura, S. Ishii & T. Tamura, ebenda, **26**, 406, 1953.
26. R. K. Zahn, *Habilitationsschrift Frankfurt am Main*, 1956.
27. J. A. Miller & E. C. Miller, *Advanc. Cancer Res.*, **1**, 339, 1953; R. R. Brown, J. A. Miller & E. C. Miller, *Proc. Amer. Ass. Res.*, **1**, 7, 1953.

A Chemical Theory of Spontaneous Generation*

SIDNEY W. FOX

Oceanographic Institute, Florida State University, Tallahassee, Florida, U.S.A.

SUGGESTIONS of how life originated by natural means were offered by the Greeks [1]. Charles Darwin added to these vague concepts in 1871 [2] one paragraph of chemical prescription for the beginning of life. The details of Darwin's paragraph, although inadequate, are in agreement with the most advanced thinking today. The modern era of thought in this field received great stimulus from the book by Academician Oparin [1], whose pioneering contribution we are privileged to honour at this Symposium.

In so far as the speaker is aware, serious and informed experimentation in this field began in 1951 with studies of the effects of high-energy radiation on carbon dioxide and water by Calvin and co-workers [3]. Working with an atmosphere consisting of ammonia, methane, hydrogen and water, Miller was notably able to produce amino acids by electrical discharge [4]. Amino acids have now been synthesized in so many presumably primordial ways in different laboratories that the contention that such results are not intrinsically surprising [5] appears to be broadly supported. There is increasing evidence for the notion that no matter which simple reactants are studied, and no matter which physical conditions are tested, organic compounds in the same somewhat narrow range of possibilities will result.

The prebiochemical distance from such organic compounds as amino acids to the origin of life, however, must be quite large. Unless the first organism did not fit a Kluyverian pattern of biochemical unity [6], the amino acids and other intermediates must have yielded: proteins, nucleic acids and numerous other biochemical substances and reaction pathways, before life could emerge from its matrix. Other authors have pointed out the significance of the problem of formation of protein as a component of the problem with which we are concerned here [1, 7]. The work to be described in this paper, however, began with an attempt to understand only the prebiochemical origin of protein. The experiments yielded a succession of unexpected results and stimuli for new experiments such that a unified theory of biochemical origins is emerging.

The embarkation point for the experiments to be described was the hypothesis that peptide bonds might be formed at temperatures elevated enough to

* Aided by Grants No. H-2314 and RG-4666 of the National Institutes of Health, U.S.A., Public Health Service, and from the General Foods Corporation and the Rockefeller Foundation. Contribution No. 87 of the Oceanographic Institute of the Florida State University.

volatilize byproduct water. Huffman had shown in 1942 [8] that the production of dipeptides from amino acids at 298°K by any route, requires an input of 2000–4000 cal. per mole of dipeptide formed (Table 1).

TABLE 1

Free-energy change accompanying formation of dipeptides from amino acids

Alanine + Glycine = Alanylglycine + water
$$\Delta F°_{298} = 3730 \text{ cal.}$$

Glycine + Glycine = Glycylglycine + water
$$\Delta F°_{298} = 3230 \text{ cal.}$$

Leucine + Glycine = Leucylglycine + water
$$\Delta F°_{298} = 2960 \text{ cal.}$$

Benzoic acid + Glycine = Hippuric acid + water
$$\Delta F°_{298} = 2260 \text{ cal.}$$

(From H. M. HUFFMAN, *J. phys. Chem.*, **46**, 890, 1942)

One can calculate that the ΔF value is more favourable at higher temperatures for the dry reaction in the forward direction, but a destructively high temperature is nevertheless indicated for an energetically spontaneous reaction. One can visualize, however, an overcoming of the energetic barrier by the occurrence of a temperature sufficient to remove water in the gaseous state:

$$H_2N \cdot CHR \cdot COOH + H_2N \cdot CHR' \cdot COOH$$
$$= H_2N \cdot CHR \cdot CONH \cdot CHR' \cdot COOH + H_2O \uparrow$$

When experiments of this sort were first performed, unexpected indications of the production of more amino acids than those taken for the reactions were found. From this beginning, experimental results often paralleled by thermal experiments described in the early literature, led to a picture of thermal pathways.

Some of these results are depicted in Figs. 1 and 2.

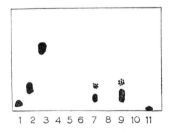

1 2 3 4 5 6 7 8 9 10 11

FIG. 1. Tracing of chromatogram of products from ammonium salts of Krebs-cycle acids.

(1) 10 μl. of aspartic acid standard; (2) 10 μl. of alanine standard; (3) 10 μl. of leucine standard, to permit comparisons of R_F; (4) 10 μl. of unheated monoammonium fumarate; (5) 10 μl. of unheated monoammonium malate; (6) 10 μl. of heated monoammonium fumarate: (7) 2 μl. of hydrolysed heated monoammonium fumarate (2 μl.); (8) 10 μl. of heated monoammonium malate; (9) 1 μl. of hydrolysed heated monoammonium malate showing faint spot with R_F of alanine; (10) 10 μl. of hydrolysed heated monoammonium succinate; (11) 10 μl. of hydrolysed heated ammonium citrate showing non-ninhydrin spot at origin. Solutions were from 1·0 g of reactant made up to 15 ml. with water. Standards contained 1·0 mg amino acid per ml. Chromatogram coloured with ninhydrin.

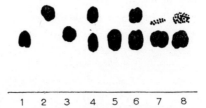

Fig. 2.   Tracing of chromatogram of products from ammonium hydrogen malate.

(1) 10 μl. of aspartic acid; (2) 10 μl. of α-alanine; (3) 10 μl. of β-alanine; (4) 10 μl. each of aspartic acid and α-alanine; (5) 10 μl. each of aspartic acid and β-alanine; (6) 10 μl. each of aspartic acid, α-alanine, and β-alanine; (7) 20 μl. of product from ammonium malate heated at 160°; (8) 20 μl. of product from ammonium malate heated at 200°. Chromatographic solvent was 7 pyridine : 3 water. Coloured with ninhydrin.

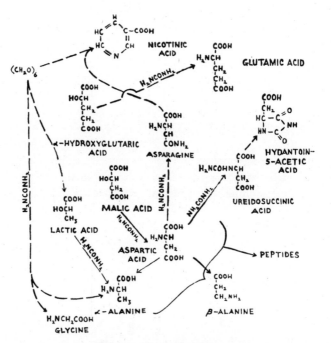

Fig. 3.   Thermal pathways.

The reactions for which detailed supporting data have been published are depicted in Fig. 3 by solid arrows. Other reactions are indicated with broken arrows.

The obtaining of conclusive evidence for the production of peptides by thermal treatment of unsubstituted amino acids revealed some striking features. Early reports on heating of amino acids show that these tend to form diketo-piperazines, amines, tars and other decomposition products [9, 10] rather than linear peptides. Even the product from aspartic acid, which appeared to be an exception, has been questioned [9]. It is now clear that a critical detail in forming peptides by heating amino acids is not to heat them singly, as in the procedures reported in virtually all of the discouraging early literature, but to heat them in concert.

For these results, the dicarboxylic acids, glutamic acid and aspartic acid, are of particular significance. Glutamic acid heated alone yields the inner lactam:

$$
\begin{array}{ccc}
\text{COOH} & & \\
| & & \\
\text{H}_2\text{NCH} & & \text{CH}_2\text{———CH}_2 \\
| & & | \quad\quad | \\
\text{CH}_2 & \longrightarrow & \text{O}=\text{C} \quad\quad \text{HC—COOH} \\
| & & \diagdown \quad\quad \diagup \\
\text{CH}_2 & & \text{NH} \\
| & & \\
\text{COOH} & &
\end{array}
$$

but when heated with glycine, which forms a linear polyglycine, it yields a polymer containing typically 20% of glutamic acid. The polymer gives rich infra-red indication of being a linear peptide and other evidence as well.

As Kovacs suggested earlier [11], polyaspartic acid is a polyimide which hydrolyses to a true peptide under alkaline conditions. This structural interpretation has been substantiated in our laboratory (A. Vegotsky, K. Harada & S. W. Fox, unpublished experiments) with the aid of infra-red studies.

These experimental results with glutamic acid and aspartic acid are significant in that they designate principles whereby one can visualize how a variegated peptide such as a protein might form under primitive thermal conditions, despite the negative indications from the literature. In view of the concept of a yet highly limited evolution of protein molecules [12, 13] the fact that most proteins are composed of at least one-fifth dicarboxylic amino acid residues is more understandable. Another feature is that these reactions need not be solid reactions inasmuch as the lactam of glutamic acid, pyrrolidonecarboxylic acid, is liquid at the temperatures employed (in the range of 160–180°). A liquid state also results from phosphoric acid, inclusion of which has been found to facilitate many of the reactions studied (K. Harada & S. W. Fox, unpublished experiments).

The thermal pathways of Fig. 3 are striking in their similarity to the sequences involved in the early stages of a generalized biosynthesis for all organisms. Obviously there are differences, but the compounds and their order of appearance in the thermal picture resemble closely the substances and sequences of anabolism. Another perspective for viewing this parallelism is provided by the *biogenetic law.* If one accepts the concept that the development of an organism reflects its evolutionary history, he should then expect that this principle would be reducible to the chemical level. In the depiction of Fig. 3, this requirement appears to be met.

Not only have the thermal pathways been found to imitate the anabolic pathways. It is now possible to point to features that were first uncovered by thermal studies, and then disclosed by more conventional biochemical experimentation.

One of these is the imide structure for aspartic acid peptides, as first proposed by Kovacs & Koenyves [11]:

$$\text{NH}_2\text{—CH—C} \overset{\displaystyle O}{\diagup} \quad \left(\quad \text{—CH—C} \overset{\displaystyle O}{\diagup} \quad \right)_n \quad \text{—CH—COOH}$$

and confirmed in studies in our laboratory (A. Vegotsky et al., unpublished experiments). This structure has been found in bacitracin hydrolysate [14] and is suggested for search in proteins (A. Vegotsky et al., unpublished experiments).

Another instance of pioneering by thermal experimentation is provided by the fact that it was possible to suggest in May of 1955 that anabolism involving the tricarboxylic acid cycle, the urea cycle, pyrimidine biosynthesis, amino acid biosynthesis, and protein biosynthesis was a joint phenomenon [12]. More recently, Reichard & Hanshoff [15] have pointed out the joint relationship of the first three of these five pathways on the basis of results from experiments employing more traditional biochemical techniques.

The unified thermal theory provides an answer for the vexing problem of how such a profusion of biochemical intermediates and processes could have originated.

The answer stresses the effect of an exponentially increasing number of biochemical substances which can result when a sustained input of energy, such as the thermal, acts upon a few simple organic compounds of the appropriate selection. The recorded and unrecorded thermal experiments indicate that increase in number of chromogenic substances in chromatograms tends to accelerate as heating is maintained. Against this background, one can visualize how an organism may emerge from its biochemical matrix, which at that moment becomes environment, with a full complement of substances. This pathway to profusion of substances is compatible with the notion, derived from the loss nature of mutants [16], that the first organism was quite fully equipped biochemically.

The biochemical inferences to this point are drawn essentially from experiments in our laboratories. If these inferences are correlated with other thinking a larger picture can be formulated. The origin of the first organism can be visualized as an extension of biochemical emergence, inasmuch as the thermal experiments suggest the appearance, in overlapping order, of reactions, protein, and nucleic acid. When translated into functional terms this sequence is anabolism-enzyme-gene and recalls the Beadle concept of control of anabolism though the hierarchy of gene-enzyme-metabolism [16]. This picture is presented in Fig. 4. The first step may be a long slow process, but once the second stage is reached the process is most easily understood as a rapid one. The first turn

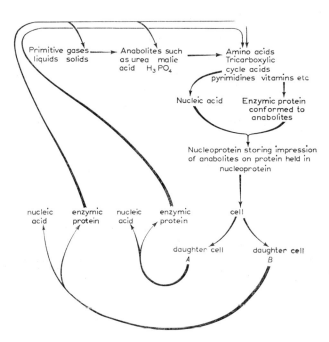

Fig. 4. Cyclical biosynthetic, enzymic, and genic process. This diagram pictures the first cell as having been formed in the first operation of the cycle.

of the cycle beginning with the appropriate intermediates is then the production of the first cell. Enzyme protein can thus be looked upon as an initiator of anabolic reactions in the life history of the new cell and nucleoprotein can be regarded as a device for memorizing the anabolic reactions. These devices can be seen to operate for the first cell in a way similar to that visualized by Beadle for current cells.

Although the entire picture presented in this paper integrates many levels and areas of biochemical activity, it is, of course, incomplete. Such problems as primordial fixation of nitrogen, origin of optical activity, membrane formation, and modulation to an aqueous state from an anhydrous one have been or will be treated elsewhere [12, 17]. Unique solutions for other component problems must also be found. As the essential validity of the main thesis is further tested, answers to the other component problems may, however, be expected to appear if the main thesis is correct. Life must have begun without the aid of such special apparatus as we can assemble or obtain today, and the thermal experiments and the interpretations of them continue to provide explanations which suggest answers to additional component problems. One may expect that a final theory will be a unified theory which will explain internally governed generation of the biochemical world, emergence of life, and the evolution of that memory mechanism of human mentality which we can reasonably anticipate will eventually solve in full the salient problems of man's curiosity about his origins.

REFERENCES

1. A. I. OPARIN, *The Origin of Life*, 2nd ed. (transl. by S. MORGULIS).　Dover Publications, New York, 1953.
2. C. DARWIN, Quoted by G. HARDIN, *Sci. Mon.*, *N.Y.*, **70**, 178, 1950.
3. W. M. GARRISON, D. C. MORRISON, J. G. HAMILTON, A. A. BENSON & M. CALVIN, *Science*, **114**, 416, 1951.
4. S. L. MILLER, *Science*, **117**, 528, 1953.
5. S. W. FOX, *Chem. Engng News*, **35**, (25), 10, 1957.
6. A. J. KLUYVER & C. B. VAN NIEL, *The Microbe's Contribution to Biology.*　Harvard University Publications, Cambridge, Mass., U.S.A., 1956.
7. H. F. BLUM, *Amer. Scient.*, **43**, 595, 1955.
8. H. M. HUFFMAN, *J. phys. Chem.*, **46**, 885, 1942.
9. E. KATCHALSKI, *Advanc. Protein Chem.*, **6**, 123, 1951.
10. A. B. MEGGY, *J. chem. Soc.*, p. 1444, 1956.
11. J. KOVACS & J. KOENYVES, *Naturwissenschaften*, **14**, 333, 1954.
12. S. W. FOX, *Amer. Scient.*, **44**, 347, 1956.
13. S. W. FOX & P. G. HOMEYER, *Amer. Nat.*, **89**, 163, 1955.
14. D. L. SWALLOW & E. P. ABRAHAM, *Biochem. J.*, **65**, 39P, 1957.
15. P. REICHARD & G. HANSHOFF, *Acta chem. scand.*, **10**, 548, 1956.
16. G. W. BEADLE, *Harvey Lect.*, **40**, 179, 1944–45.
17. S. W. FOX, J. E. JOHNSON & A. VEGOTSKY, *Science*, **124**, 923, 1956; S. W. FOX, *J. chem. Educ.*, **34**, 472, 1957.

Complex Compounds and Models of Enzymes

L. A. NIKOLAEV

Department of Chemistry, Moscow Institute of Transport Engineers

THE progress which has been attained in enzymology during the last decade is, to a considerable extent, attributable to the use of the model method. Since the time of the well known experiments of Bredig [1], in which he compared the catalytic powers of metallic salts with the properties of enzymes, and those of Warburg [2] which were concerned with studying the so-called 'charcoal models', studies have been made of model systems more similar to enzymes in their chemical nature.

The classical investigations of W. Langenbeck and also the recent work of Lautsch are typical in this respect [3, 4].

Langenbeck's fundamental idea was that one may approach an understanding of the chemical nature of enzymes by gradually increasing the complexity and changing the structure of such organic molecules as have, in some degree, the same catalytic properties as the enzyme. The brilliant success of Langenbeck's own work has shown that this method is essentially correct.

Langenbeck's models (e.g. the well known models of carboxylases and esterases) have been incomparably more helpful towards such an understanding than those in which the properties of organic substances were simulated by metals.

This certainly does not mean that one should regard 'metallic' models as being of no significance. They are systems in which the action of electronic mechanisms can be observed more directly than in complicated biocatalysts and a consideration of the part played by these mechanisms in biochemistry certainly acted as a stimulus.

However, the physical chemistry of complicated structures can obviously not be simply deduced from the properties of structures of a simpler type; many important regularities which are clearly expressed in highly organized systems are scarcely to be observed in simple molecules.

In the present paper we shall describe models of active groups of enzymes containing metals, we shall consider their thermodynamic properties and the question of adsorptive activation and, finally, we shall turn to models which do not contain metals.

As models of active groups we have chosen various complex compounds of the transition metals which have catalytic properties exactly suited to carrying out the processes brought about by catalases and oxidases.

As addenda in the complexes studied we used hydroxy acids, amino acids, esters, peptides, acid amides, heterocyclic compounds (pyridine, picoline, piperidine) and primary and secondary amines of the methane series and their hydroxyl, methoxyl and phenyl derivatives, diamines and their derivatives, biuret, triuret and several proteins. We investigated models having the functions of catalases, oxidases and dehydrases and, in the course of this, specially great attention was paid to the catalase-like function of the copper ion [5].

By studying the catalase activity of pure copper wire (with a known surface), the oxidized surface of the wire and complex copper compounds, we had the possibility of comparing the approximate degree of activity of the copper ion in the metallic and oxide latices with its activity in solution in the form of various complex ions (Table 1).

TABLE I

The catalase-like activity of copper compounds

Catalyst	No. of mols of H_2O_2 broken down during the first minute in 0·05 M solution at 18°C
Copper	10
Cupric oxide	8–10
Cuprous oxide	50
Copper ions in aqueous solution of pH 6·0	10^{-2}
Cuprammonium	10^3
Compound of copper ions with biuret .	$1·2 \times 10^3$

In spite of the approximate nature of some of the figures the table supports the idea that a considerable degree of activation is achieved by complex formation.

It must be added that, in many cases, the integration of metallic ions in crystalline salts leads to a complete loss of activity. Fig. 1 shows the course of the decomposition of hydrogen peroxide in a saturated solution of copper sulphate. Some time after the beginning of the reaction crystals of copper

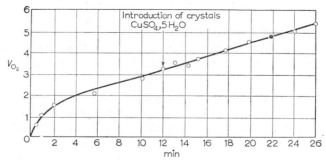

FIG. 1.   The decomposition of H_2O_2 in a saturated solution of copper sulphate. At the time indicated by the arrow crystals of $CuSO_4,5H_2O$ were added to the solution.

V_{O_2} = Volume of oxygen evolved (ml).

sulphate were added to the solution. It can be seen that the presence of the crystals did not affect the rate of the reaction, that is to say that in this case the ions in the crystal of the salt are in a state which almost completely suppresses their activity.

Thus, the transition from ions which are present in a crystalline lattice, $CuSO_4 \cdot 5H_2O$ to ions in a lattice of a semiconductor (cupric and cuprous oxides) brings about a smaller increase in activity than the transition from ions surrounded by a hydrating envelope in solution to ions surrounded by a complex envelope. In the latter case we find a sharp rise in activity which gives rise to the idea of the structural and thermodynamic peculiarity of the mechanism of catalysis by complex compounds.

The next step consisted in the elucidation of the effect of the addenda and of the complex as a whole on the magnitude of the activity. Cuprammonium was one of the most active; only the compound of copper with biuret seemed to act more efficiently as a model of catalase. Alteration in the structure of the addenda, however, has a very marked effect on the catalase-like activity.

The most important factor enhancing the catalase-like activity of 'copper' models is the presence of four nitrogen atoms in the sphere of co-ordination; if atoms of oxygen are substituted for them the activity is lessened. The part played by oxygen in the sphere of co-ordination is demonstrated in its simplest form by a comparison between the activities of methylamine (160) and α-methylhydroxylamine (80). If one decreases the number of nitrogen atoms in the sphere of co-ordination, by changing over, for example, to the internally complex compounds formed with amino acids, then there is a sharp decline in activity (Table 2).

TABLE 2

The role of oxygen in the sphere of co-ordination

Name of addendum	Relative activity
Methylamine . . .	160·0
α-Methylhydroxylamine .	80·0
Alanine	0·001
β-Aminobutyric acid .	2·5
β-Aminovaleric acid . .	0·7

On the other hand, an increase in the concentration of the addendum in the solution (a slight excess of it is necessary to prevent destruction of the complex by the hydrogen peroxide) lowers the activity owing to the formation of compounds having six as their co-ordination number. Correspondingly, cobalt complexes, of which this is the characteristic co-ordination number, have almost no catalase-like activity.

In ascending the methane series one may observe the competition of two factors. Lengthening of the chain brings about an increase in activity but lengthening, like branching of the chain, also increases steric hindrance. The activity of the complex formed with methylamine is, therefore, almost equal to that of the complex with amylamine. For the same reason the complex formed with dimethylamine, in which the copper ion is surrounded by a large number of methyl groups, has very little activity. However, when a phenyl group is introduced instead of a methyl one the activity is increased if the phenyl group is situated relatively far away from the central ion. Thus the activity of propylamine is 1·5 times that of butylamine. In this case the effect of an increase in mass is only slightly counteracted by steric hindrance.

A very important feature of the active structure is the formation of rings including the ion-complex combination. This phenomenon accounts for the activity of various chelates of which Martell & Calvin have recently followed up a whole collection of properties [6].

In 1957 the work of Courtney, Gustafson, Westerback, Hyytiainen, Chaberek & Martell was published [7]. While studying the catalytic activity of a large number of complex compounds of transition metals in the reaction of hydrolysis of substituted fluorophosphonic esters, these authors arrived at a similar conclusion concerning the part played by the formation of rings and emphasized the high activity of compounds of the 'bidentate' type. This is only one of a number of studies in which the authors were aiming at investigating the causal relation between the activity of the complex catalyst and the structure of the addendum. The fact that they drew the same conclusions as we did tends to suggest a more general applicability of the rules which we discovered for the catalase process.

The augmentation of biocatalysts with increase of their mass was remarked on by N. I. Kobozev [8] while developing the theory of 'aggravation' in which he attaches special importance to the combination of a mass, which is not in (thermodynamic) equilibrium, with a particular active group. When this occurs the activity, in the examples produced by this author, increases proportionally to the logarithm of the molecular weight. When a very active structure has been selected further, increase in its activity may be brought about, either by the addition of mass so that the added mass may contribute its share to the activity and this will increase proportionally to the logarithm of the molecular weight, or else by transformation of the structure in such a way that there is a sudden, sharp increase in activity. From our point of view the latter case is of special interest. The activation in the diamine series is a good illustration of this type.

Special attention must be paid to the fact that, in other cases, an increase in activity is associated with a decrease in the stability of the complex compound. The change from ethylenediamine to triethylenediamine is associated with an almost twenty-fold increase in activity while the stability of the compound is decreased (Fig. 2).

The activity increases even more sharply (to 800 times what it was) if di-methyltrimethylenediamine is used as an addendum. This complex serves as a good example of a highly active model structure containing very unstable rings.

Complexes with trimethylenediamine are easily destroyed by hydrogen peroxide and give results which are hard to reproduce, while hexamethylene-diamine does not form a ring, i.e. only one amino group is included in the sphere of co-ordination, and its activizing effect is correspondingly small (25). It follows that, in this field, we cannot make further progress towards the synthesis of active structures than the level of activity obtained by using dimethyltrimethylenediamine.

In the work of the American authors to which reference has already been made [7] they did not reach the conclusion that a decrease in the stability of the complexes catalysing hydrolytic processes accompanies an increase in their catalytic activity.

Maybe the rapid fall in stability as the activity increases in copper models of catalase is one reason why iron plays a more important part than copper in the genesis of biologically active structures acting like catalase. A study (Fig. 3) of the activity of complexes with heterocyclic compounds (pyridine, picoline and piperidine) revealed yet another characteristic feature of catalysts of this type.

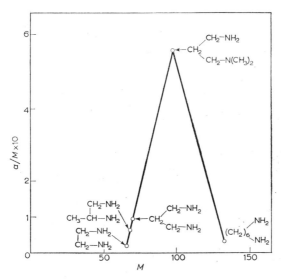

FIG. 2. The dependence of a/M on M for complex compounds of copper with different diamines.

$$a = \text{activity}$$
$$M = \text{molecular weight.}$$

A very slight change in the composition of the addendum, e.g. the substitution of pyridine for piperidine, is accompanied by a marked change in activity (the substitution of pyridine for piperidine causes the activity to drop to $1/80$ of its former value). This property can also be observed in other classes of complex compounds. Thus, in diamines, the inclusion of a methylene group increases the activity 18 times while methylation of the nitrogen increases it a further 10 times.

Among biologically active substances, such as enzymes, vitamins, hormones etc. this phenomenon of the marked variation of activity is sometimes so strongly pronounced that one can speak of the interdependence of activity and activation.

The activation of a structure is an important factor in biochemical evolutionary selection and it may be supposed that from the multitude of different compounds which developed at different periods when only the simplest forms of life were established, it was just those structures which had the greatest capacity for being activated which were of the greatest biochemical value. The process of biological evolution must have reached its greatest intensity in just those organisms in which the vitally important catalysts were composed of compounds which could be markedly activated. It is not by chance, either, that it is in those organisms which have attained a high degree of development that we find, among the catalysts which regulate their vitally important processes, complex compounds of iron and copper having a specially great activating power.

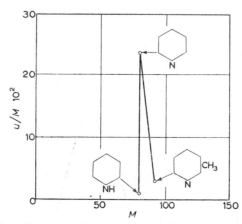

FIG. 3.   The dependence of a/M on M for complex compounds of copper with heterocyclic substances.

This phenomenon can be regarded from two points of view. In the first place, it is a reasonable assumption that when we act on a particular point of the molecule of a biologically active material and thereby alter its activity, we are interfering with the very part of the molecule which subserves its activity. In the pyridine molecule for example, the susceptible point seems to be the nitrogen atom. In the second place, one may see in the structural sensitivity of biocatalysts and 'working' models of them, the characteristic features of 'internal association' of some of their structures.

The internal association of the atoms in particular molecules or parts of molecules is a fact which it is hard to deny. Thus, the diamagnetism of phthalocyanin and its derivatives gives rise to the idea of electronic currents within the molecule joining together particular atoms.

Considerable alterations in the absorption spectra of many biologically active substances may be brought about by comparatively small changes in any single place in the molecule. These phenomena, which have been studied in detail in the chemistry of dyestuffs, are evidence for a close interaction between the electronic systems of atoms comprising a molecule.

Holland [9] has recently shown that the characteristic absorption spectra of the compound of catalase with hydrogen peroxide must be attributed to the whole complex and not to individual functional groups, for the spectra of these compounds differ from the spectrum of the enzyme owing to displacement of the energetic level brought about by complex-formation [7].

The structure formed by the addenda surrounding the central ion must obviously, in itself, play an important part in determining the catalytic functions of the compound. This is to be seen from the fact that complexes of amines with other metals (zinc, cadmium, silver and cobalt), though their catalase-like activity is far less than that of copper compounds, are subject to the general rules relating structure to activity. So far as one can judge from the limited data available, the sequence of arrangement of addenda which is responsible for an increase in activity in copper compounds is essentially the same for the other metals mentioned above.

Let us now turn to the oxidase-like activity of complexes. I intend to limit myself to a consideration of complexes which do not themselves contain a molecule of the substrate to be oxidized and which, therefore, do not lose the typical peculiarities of their structures in the course of the reaction. Porphyrins are complexes of such a type; however, they cannot be regarded simply as models, since they are, themselves, the active groups of enzymes.

We have succeeded in increasing the oxidase-like activity of the copper ion in respect of the oxidation of pyrogallol by oxygen, by the direct combination of the copper ion with ethanolamines, diamines and heterocyclic compounds of the pyridine series [10]. These compounds are probably among the simplest models of the active group of polyphenol oxidase. The reaction of oxidation of ascorbic acid is catalysed by complex compounds of the iron ion with pyrocatechin and antipyrin.

It is of the utmost interest that the addenda themselves, i.e. various amines, are good catalysts in the oxidation of pyrogallol [18]. However, when they are combined with a copper ion the activity is increased considerably so that the activity of the complex is far greater than the sum of the activities of the ion and the addendum.

In order to decide to what extent the complex compounds discussed above merit the name of models of active groups we must make a thorough analysis of the mechanism of their action and of the thermodynamic peculiarities characteristic of catalysis of this sort. As concerns the reaction mechanism, we must choose between an explanation based on the radical-chain theory and a treatment according to the theory of intermediate products. The rapid progress made by the radical-chain theory justifies the attempt to apply the same concepts to the mechanism of the action of enzymes [11].

However, it has now become clear, especially since the work of Chance, that an important part in the mechanism of action of many enzymes, catalase in particular, is played by an intermediate, enzyme-substrate product.* It is well known that the kinetic side of the theory of intermediate products was worked out in detail long ago (e.g. in the works of Michaelis) and agrees well with

---

* A. Goudot [17] believes that the ion of the metal may combine with electrons of the hydrogen peroxide molecule.

experimental data. At the same time, the catalytic activity of simple ions of the transition metals, both in their catalase-like and oxidase-like aspects, are, without the slightest doubt, associated with the setting up of chains of reactions in which free radicals take part. Thus, the question of the way in which complex compounds act as catalysts, i.e. whether they form intermediate products, or whether they only initiate a chain process, is obviously of fundamental importance in regard to the problem of the parallelism between the action of active groups and that of the models.

In many cases the catalytic action of comparatively simple anions, e.g. those of chromic, tungstic and molybdic acids, brings about the formation of intermediate products (see review of the work of E. I. Shpital'skiĭ, N. I. Kobozev and G. A. Bogdanov [12]). Detailed analysis of the catalytic action of catalase-like catalysts has shown that they form intermediate compounds with two molecules of peroxide [13, 14]. It is in this compound that the process of recombination occurs, leading to the formation of a molecule of oxygen.

On this basis we postulated that the catalytic activity of complex compounds of copper like those with ammonia was brought about by the entry of two molecules of hydrogen peroxide into the sphere of co-ordination of the ion. In doing so the molecules of the hydroxide must have driven two molecules of water out of this sphere. This hypothesis received some confirmation from the fact that the rate of the reaction catalysed by the copper-ammonium complexes first increased in proportion to the increase of concentration of hydrogen peroxide; the increase then fell off and the order of the reaction becomes null in relation to peroxide [14].

It was also shown that the rate of destruction of hydrogen peroxide increases as the pH rises, reaches a very spread-out maximum and, at high pH (13–14), decreases somewhat.

This sort of dependence on the concentration of hydrogen peroxide and on pH is completely out of accord with the equation obtained on the basis of the radical-chain theory [15]. On the other hand the kinetic picture obtained falls satisfactorily within the framework of the theory of intermediate products.

A well known way of indicating free radicals is provided by the study of the influence of methyl methacrylate (and, according to our evidence, also benzene) on the rate of decomposition of H_2O_2 [12].

Into a solution of hydrogen peroxide containing the catalyst, we introduced a small quantity of methyl methacrylate, with the idea that, owing to competition between the hydrogen peroxide and the methyl methacrylate for free radicals, the rate of the reaction would fall off if the process was brought about by the development of a chain. In fact, the catalytic activity of ions of copper and iron was very strongly depressed by the presence of methyl methacrylate. This was also to be expected as, in this case, the setting up of chains with the participation of OH and HO_2 radicals itself determines the whole course of the decomposition of peroxide. The presence of methyl methacrylate or benzene has no effect on the catalytic activity of complex compounds of copper.

From this we may conclude that the catalytic activity of complex compounds is different, in principle, from that of simple ions and also, like the activity of enzymes, it is based on the formation of intermediate products.

Let us now turn to a consideration of the thermodynamic peculiarities of catalysis by complexes.

In our laboratory A. P. Sychev, R. D. Korpusova, V. V. Yushina and I undertook the measurement of the energy of activation of various reactions catalysed by model compounds. We found that, in the case of the catalase reaction, the energy of activation in the presence of the catalyst was almost the same as the energy of activation of the thermal decomposition of hydrogen peroxide (cf. Table 3).

TABLE 3

Energy of activation of the reaction of decomposition of hydrogen peroxide catalysed by complex compounds of copper

Addendum	Energy of activation (cal./mole)
Methylamine . . .	17,000
Monoethanolamine . .	17,000
Diethanolamine . . .	17,000
*iso*Propanolamine . . .	18,400
Pyridine	17,500
Thermal decomposition . .	From 16,000 to 18,000

It follows that, in this case, the acceleration of the reaction is of purely entropic origin. L. S. Kitsenko and I obtained a similar result in a study of the catalytic activity of the manganese ion in the oxidation of indigo carmine by hydrogen peroxide.

Models of oxidases present a more complicated picture. R. D. Korpusova and I have studied the oxidation of pyrogallol by oxygen catalysed by copper complexes and found that the complex compounds had an effect on the entropy factor and on the energy of activation of the oxidative reaction [18]. The well-known formula of the theory of the transitional state:

$$\ln K = \ln e \cdot \frac{kT}{h} + \frac{\Delta S}{R} - \frac{E}{RT}$$

enables us to derive an expression for the rate of change of entropy in the catalysed and uncatalysed reaction in the form:

$$\frac{\Delta S^x - \Delta S_0^x}{R} = \ln \frac{K}{K_0} + (E - E_0)\frac{1}{RT}$$

ΔS^x = the entropy of activation for the catalysed reaction
ΔS_0^x = „   „   „   „   „   „   „ uncatalysed „

According to the nature of the addendum the difference $\Delta S - \Delta S_0$ may vary not only in magnitude but in sign, i.e. the catalyst may give rise to a transitional complex with either a greater or a lesser entropy than the complex of reaction without a catalyst.

Thus, for the catalytic oxidation of pyrogallol we obtained the following values for this difference, depending on the nature of the addendum (Table 4).

TABLE 4

Difference in entropy between the catalysed and uncatalysed reaction at 20°C

Addendum	$\Delta S^x - \Delta S^x_0$ (cal/mole/°C)
Monoethanolamine .	+2·60
Ethylenediamine . .	+3·36
*iso*Propanolamine .	+6·57
Pyridine . . .	−9·15
α-Picoline . . .	−5·98
β-Picoline . . .	−2·14

In those cases in which acceleration of the reaction is associated with an increase in the entropy of activation we must take it that the reaction is brought about by the formation of a 'loose' transitional complex. The existence of such 'loosening' of the structure at the moment of transformation is evident from the association, upon which I have already remarked, between instability and activity of the complex catalyst. Under favourable conditions (when there is a sufficient concentration of the addendum in the solution) the structure of the complex ion is re-established.

In biological systems there is probably a more precise method for the rapid restoration of that part of the active group in which loosening of the structure was required in order to attain a high degree of catalytic activity.

The formation of a complex compound often brings about a sudden increase in the pre-exponential multiplier. This is clearly the simplest way of increasing the activity of the ion. If one wishes to lower the energy of activation one must alter the nature of the addendum, i.e. follow the course which Langenbeck took.

Attempts to activate complex compounds by adsorption have been comparatively ineffective. We have tried to adsorb haemin and the iron ion on activated charcoals derived from various sources and found that the degree of dispersion of the particles of the carbon corresponded with the increase in activity both for simple and complex ions, but the degree of activation was greater for the simple iron ion than for the porphyrin complex. Thus, in general, complex formation hinders any increase in activity which may be brought about by adsorption. This result, of course, must be considered alongside the great specificity of the activizing effect of the protein components of biocatalysts. In this connection great interest attaches to those cases in which model structures can also be activated by adsorption on organic substances of high molecular weight [16].

In our laboratory V. V. Yushina [19] has studied models of dehydrogenases which consisted of a dyestuff whoch could be transformed into a leuco form, thus serving as a model of the active group of dehydrogenase and a carrier of a carbohydrate- or protein-like character. In particular, it was established that methylene blue and thionine could catalyse the oxidation of pyrogallol, metol and an aqueous solution of hydrogen sulphide by oxygen. The activity of the dyestuff was markedly increased by its adsorption on pastes of starch, dextrin, albumin and cellulose. The association of the dyestuff with the substances of high molecular weight even gave rise to a certain specificity in respect of the substrate. Thus, adsorption of thionine on starch or dextrin gives a catalyst which has an increased activity in respect of the oxidation of metol (Fig. 4). Methylene blue on starch is effective in the oxidation of pyrogallol.

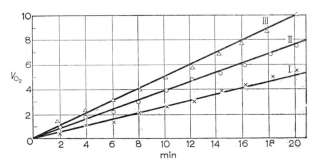

Fig. 4. The taking up of oxygen by solutions of metol at pH 7·2 and 27°C.

I = metol (10 mg/ml.)
II = metol + thionine
III = metol + thionine + starch (0·03%)
Volume of solution = 45 ml.   Concentration of thionine = 0·0012%.

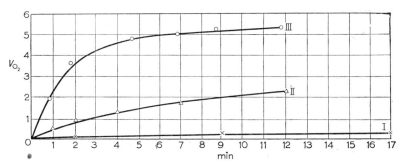

Fig. 5. The taking up of oxygen from the air by an aqueous solution of hydrogen sulphide. Concentration of H₂S = 0·05 M. Temp. = 15·5 °C. In the presence of:

I.   0·2 g cellulose
II. 5 mg indigo carmine
III. 0·2 g cellulose + 5 mg indigo carmine.

Indigo carmine adsorbed on cellulose is a very active catalyst in the oxidation of an aqueous solution of hydrogen sulphide by air [20] (Fig. 5). The rate of the reaction is determined by the rate of formation of the leuco form, which is

18

quickly oxidized by the oxygen of the air. The final product, sulphur, forms a sol, which, obviously, also plays a part in the kinetics of this reaction. When this reaction is carried out in alcoholic solution its rate is very markedly decreased because, in this case, the sulphur which is produced forms a true solution and causes a shifting of the equilibrium towards the formation of the leuco form.*

To summarize the characteristic features of the models we have discussed, we may tentatively state that complex compounds of copper containing four atoms of nitrogen in the co-ordination sphere are models of the active group of catalase. Some specific structures of the addenda leading to the formation of rings including the ion-complex link show a high activity (compounds with biuret or trimethylenediamine).

Compounds of a similar type containing iron or copper may serve as models of oxidases. The mechanism of action of models of catalases is obviously based on the formation of intermediate products. In the course of this the high values for the energy of activation taken with a high rate of reaction indicates a high entropy of activation. This means that there is a transitional state in the course of the reaction in which the structure of the catalyst is considerably loosened.

Dyestuffs which can assume the leuco- form reversibly, when adsorbed on carriers of high molecular weight, can act as models of dehydrogenases and, in this case, activation by adsorption is achieved far more easily than in the case of complexes containing metals.

REFERENCES

1. G. BREDIG, *Phys. Z.*, **2**, 7, 1900.
2. O. WARBURG, *Biochem. Z.*, **119**, 134, 1921; **145**, 461, 1924.
3. W. LANGENBECK, *Die organischen Katalysatoren und ihre Beziehungen zu den Fermenten*, Springer, Berlin, 1935.
4. W. LAUTSCH, W. BROSER, W. BIEDERMANN & H. GNICHTEL, *Angew. Chem.*, **66**, 5, 123, 1954.
5. L. A. NIKOLAEV, *Zh. fiz. Khim*, **25**, 712, 1951; *J. Chim. phys.*, **51**, 752, 1954.
6. A. MARTELL & M. CALVIN, *Chemistry of the Metal Chelate Compounds*, Prentice-Hill, 1952.
7. R. COURTNEY, R. GUSTAFSON, S. WESTERBACK, H. HYYTIAINEN, S. CHABEREK & A. MARTELL, *J. Amer. chem. Soc.*, **79**, 3030, 1957.
8. N. I. KOBOSEV (KOBOZEV), *Acta phys.-chim. U.R.S.S.*, **21**, 7, 1946; *Zh. fiz. Khim.*, **19**, 142, 1945.
9. W. HOLLAND, *Arch. Biochem. Biophys.*, **45**, 459, 1953.
10. R. D. KORPUSOVA & L. A. NIKOLAEV, *Zh. fiz. Khim.*, **30**, 2831, 1956; R. D. KORPUSOVA, *Nauchnye Dokl. Vyssheĭ Shkoly*, No. 1, 1958.
11. I. WEISS, *Advanc. Catalys.*, **4**, 343, 1952.
12. J. H. BAXENDALE, *Advanc. Catalys.*, **4**, 59, 1952.
13. N. I. KOBOZEV, *Zh. fiz. Khim.*, **15**, 882, 1941.
14. L. A. NIKOLAEV, *Vestn. Moskov. gosudarstvennuogo Universiteta*, **2**, 105, 1946.
15. A. KISS & E. LEDERER, *Rec. Trav. chim. Pays-Bas*, **46**, 453, 1927.
16. G. BREDIG & F. GERSTNER, *Biochem. Z.*, **250**, 414, 1932.
17. A. GOUDOT, *C. R. Acad. Sci.*, Paris, **244**, 1949, 1955; *Zh. fiz. Khim.* **31**, 1401, 1957.
18. R. D. KORPUSOVA & L. A. NIKOLAEV, *Nauchnye Doklady Vyssheĭ Shkoly* No. 2, 1958.
19. V. V. YUSHINA, *Zh. fiz. Khim.*, **31** (I), 2357, 1957.
20. L. A. NIKOLAEV, *Zh. fiz. Khim.*, **31** (I), 923, 1957.

* Catalysts of this type are somewhat reminiscent of the 'Faserkatalysatoren' of Bredig.

Experimental Demonstration of the Occurrence of Metabolic Processes in Simple Proteins

M. G. KRITSMAN & A. S. KONIKOVA

Institute of Therapeutics, Academy of Medical Sciences of the U.S.S.R., Moscow
Institute of Surgery, Academy of Medical Sciences of the U.S.S.R., Moscow

ONE OF the important questions at this stage in the study of the problem of the origin of life is the question of what were the actual evolutionary forms of the earliest period of the existence of living matter, i.e. at what level of complexity did chemical processes become biological.

From evidence available to science it is an incontestable fact that this transition could not have occurred before the appearance of a complicated chemical substance such as a protein. Until now, however, there has been acrimonious discussion as to whether the appearance of proteins was enough for the transition from chemistry to biology to take place or whether an even greater complexity of material was necessary for this purpose.

In our attempts to find out the truth about this question, the answer to which would lead directly to the discovery of the actual way in which life arose and developed, a leading part is played by the study of processes of formation and decomposition, i.e. the metabolism of proteins in biological systems of varying degrees of complexity, because it is by means of such processes that such systems can reproduce themselves and forms of life develop.

The application of the method of isotopic tracers has opened up great possibilities in this field of study.

The transfer of labelled, free, structural entities from the medium into protein molecules has been widely used as a generally acceptable indication of the formation of proteins. By using this method it has been established that there are differences in the rate and means of formation of proteins in the intact organism, in living sections of various tissues, in isolated cells and their component parts and even in homogenates and lysates of cells.

It has thus been found that the process of formation of proteins is essentially similar in isolated biological systems and in the intact organism.

The important fact revealed by these investigations was that the ability to synthesize proteins was retained when the cellular and intracellular structure was disrupted in various ways which led to different degrees of disintegration and different degrees of complexity of structure of the fragments, which may even have neither a definite biological nor a definite chemical nature.

275

TABLE I.

The chemical bonds formed during the incorporation of amino acids into the proteins of biological systems of varying degrees of complexity.

CO—NH = Bond between N and C.   S—S = Disulphide bond.   ~ = Labile bond.

Structural units of protein	Liver slices	Cells of bone marrow	Homogenates of liver	Microsomes	Nucleoprotein of liver	Isolated proteins			
						Blood serum	Myosin	Insulin	Liver enzyme
Alanine .	CO—NH	—	~ (30%) CO—NH (70%)	—	CO—NH	—	—	—	—
Glycine .	CO—NH	CO—NH	~ (30%) CO—NH (70%)	—	—	CO—NH (90%)	CO—NH (30%)	—	CO—NH
Glutamic acid .	CO—NH	—	—	~ (90%)	—	—	—	—	—
Histidine .	—	CO—NH	—	—	—	—	—	—	—
Leucine .	—	CO—NH	—	CO—NH	—	—	—	—	—
Lysine .	—	CO—NH	—	—	—	—	—	CO—NH	ε-CO—NH
Methionine .	CO—NH	—	CO—NH	—	—	S—S (30%) CO—NH (70%)	~ (30%) CO—NH (70%)	—	—
Tyrosine .	—	—	—	—	—	CO—NH (70%)	~ (40%) CO—NH (60%)	—	—
Cysteine .	S—S	—	S—S	—	—	S—S (95%)	S—S	—	—
Phenylalanine .	—	—	—	CO—NH	CO—NH	—	—	CO—NH	—
Glutathione .	—	—	—	—	—	S—S (95%)	—	—	—
Glycylglycine .	—	—	—	—	—	—	—	—	CO—NH
Tryptophylglycine .	—	—	—	—	—	—	—	—	CO—NH

Because a prolonged investigation, performed in many stages, of forms of life from the complicated to the simple could not lead to the definition of the actual limiting level, below which the process of protein anabolism did not occur, it may be thought that the correct way to approach the elucidation of this problem would be to investigate it from the opposite direction, beginning with the simple and going on to the complicated.

We therefore tried to discover whether there occurred in simple proteins such chemical processes as could develop into biological phenomena, i.e. could lead to self-reproduction, the alteration of protein molecules and further development.

From this point of view we had to investigate the possibility that processes of formation and decomposition might occur in simple proteins, as well as the extent to which the variability of the composition of proteins is governed by alterations in the surrounding medium.

We have shown in published work [1] that, as regards various labelled amino acids and the peptide glutathione, 15 different proteins have the power to incorporate the structural units of proteins into themselves at a rate which is of the same order as that for complicated biological systems.

This phenomenon has also been observed by other workers, the total number of proteins investigated being as great as 22 and the number of labelled structural units more than 10.

By means of a series of experiments it was shown that when free amino acids and peptides are incorporated into proteins, there are formed peptide, disulphide and other bonds characteristic of the protein molecule between the components of the protein and the structural units being incorporated (Table 1).

Furthermore it has been shown by partial hydrolysis that the strength of the bonds is substantially the same when tyrosine [1] or glycine are incorporated in myosin whether the incorporation occurs *in vivo* or *in vitro* (see Fig. 1).

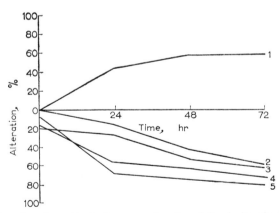

FIG. 1. Alterations in residual nitrogen and radioactivity during the hydrolysis of myosin labelled *in vitro* and *in vivo*.

1. Residual nitrogen
2. Radioactivity of protein labelled *in vitro*—acid hydrolysis
3.   ,,   ,,   ,,   ,, *in vivo* — ,,   ,,
4.   ,,   ,,   ,,   ,, *in vitro*—alkaline hydrolysis
5.   ,,   ,,   ,,   ,, *in vivo* — ,,   ,,

By using myosin in which different amino acids were labelled it was found that, as well as the process of incorporation of amino acids, which has just been mentioned, there was also elimination of amino acids.

The formation and breakdown of the protein of crystalline carboxypeptidase has been observed by Wood & Roberts [2]; a similar phenomenon has also been observed in experiments on trypsin.

This is evidence for the reversibility of the process of transfer of free amino acids into the structure of simple proteins.

This, together with the facts discussed earlier, give us reason to consider that the metabolism of protein, i.e. its formation and breakdown, can take place without the participation of biological structures and is a manifestation of the chemical properties of simple proteins, and that these processes are in many ways similar to the process of protein metabolism which takes place in complicated biological systems.

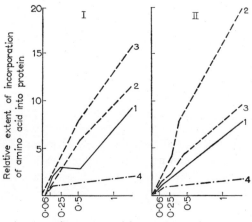

FIG 2. Relation between the amount of free amino acids taken up by an isolated protein and their concentration in the surrounding medium. Concentration of free amino acids in mg/ml.

I Serum protein. II Myosin.

1. Glycine. 2. Methionine. 3. Tyrosine. 4. Cysteine.

We took, as our unit of the amount of amino acid incorporated in a protein, the amount incorporated when the free amino acid was present to the extent of 0·06 mg/ml. in the medium.

Having found that free structural units of protein can be transferred from the surrounding medium and incorporated into the structure of isolated proteins, we considered it necessary to find out whether this process of protein metabolism provides a continual possibility of variability in the composition of protein molecules or whether it merely leads to the re-introduction of components of the same sort, as occurs in the exchange reaction between barium carbonate and the CO_2 of the air.

To clear up this point we undertook investigations which showed that the incorporation of structural units from the surrounding medium into proteins is, both quantitatively and qualititatively, a variable process, being directly dependent on the composition of the surrounding medium.

Thus, we demonstrated the effect on the process, of alteration of the concentration of amino acids in the surrounding medium (Fig. 2), and also a competitive relationship between some of the structural units of protein taking part in the process [3]. Furthermore adenosine triphosphate (ATP) had a variable influence on the process of incorporation of different amino acids by isolated proteins [4].

Thus, as may be seen from the evidence presented, according to the concentration and composition of the free structural units in the surrounding medium and to whether ATP is present or not, alterations may occur in the quantitative relations between the amino acid residues entering into a protein; this, in its turn, will lead to a corresponding alteration in the composition of simple proteins in the course of their formation and decomposition.

Besides the factors already discussed, which affect the reversible process of formation of simple proteins, we also observed the effect of nucleic acids on it, which, according to our preliminary studies on myosin, causes a shift in the relationship between the processes of incorporation and elimination of the structural units of a protein, leading to an increase in the total amount of protein (Table 2).

TABLE 2

The effect of the composition of the surrounding medium on the increase in the amount of protein during incubation of myosin

No. of expt.	Material in test soln.				Amount of protein (mg/test)	Increase in protein (%/hr)
	Myosin	ATP	Hydrolysate	Nucleic acid		
1	+	−	−	−	3·0	..
	+	−	−	+	3·0	o
	+	−	+	−	3·25	+ 8
	+	−	+	+	3·2	+ 7
	+	+	+	+	3·31	+10·3
2	+	−	−	−	3·0	..
	+	+	−	−	3·0	o
	+	+	+	−	3·32	+11
	+	−	+	+	3·40	+13
	+	+	+	+	3·60	+20
3	+	−	−	−	3·0	..
	+	−	−	+	3·0	o
	+	−	+	+	3·20	+ 7
	+	+	+	+	3·20	+ 7
4	+	−	−	−	3·7	..
	+	+	+	−	3·7	o
	+	−	+	+	4·2	+13

In our view, the material brought forward gives reason for regarding the reversible process, whereby free structural units are transferred from the surrounding medium into simple isolated proteins, as a process of protein metabolism which, under certain conditions, might give rise to the spontaneous reproduction, variability and increase in complication of a protein; that is to say, to that metabolism which is the foundation of biological phenomena.

REFERENCES

1. A. S. KONIKOVA & M. G. KRITSMAN, Sborn. dokl. Mezhdunarodnom Soveshchaniĭ 'Vozniknovenie zhizni na Zemle', 1957, p. 182.
2. T. WOOD & E. R. ROBERTS, Biochem. biophys. Acta, 15, 217, 1954.
3. O. P. SAMARINA, M. G. KRITSMAN & A. S. KONIKOVA, Biokhimiya, 21, 20, 1956.
4. M. G. KRITSMAN, B. S. SUKHAREVA, O. P. SAMARINA & A. S. KONIKOVA, Biokhimiya, 22, 449, 1957.

The Problem of the Origin of the Proteins

F. CEDRANGOLO

Department of Biological Chemistry, University of Naples, Italy

THE PROBLEM of the origin of life is, in our opinion, essentially the problem of the formation and of the appearance for the first time on our planet of the giant protein molecule. Once we respond satisfactorily to this problem, I believe that all the other related problems can be easily and surely solved.

The proteins must be considered, in fact, like the basal substance of the living material. Their molecules are of largest types of molecule (macromolecule) formed by a union of about one hundred simple molecules, that the plants and also the animals (these last, nevertheless, in very limited measure) are able to build, starting from a very simple substance, the plants starting from CO_2 and NH_3. Also, to day it is possible to produce natural amino acids in the laboratory. Right now about twenty amino acids are known and depending on the number, the order, and the proportion with which the amino acids are linked in the protein molecule, follows the great variation of the animal and vegetable proteins. Using Kossel's [1] very picturesque comparison of the twenty-one letters of the alphabets, united in various number, order, and proportion, they are able to explain an infinite number of thoughts.

The striking variety of living form, the individuality of every organism, is, essentially, the individuality of the proteins of which these organisms are composed [2]. Any protein is always the permutation and combination of about twenty amino acids which, instead, are always the same.

Synge [3] has calculated that for one typical protein with a molecular weight of 34,000 containing 288 residues with only twelve different amino acids, it is possible to obtain 10^{300} isomers! If only one molecule of each of these isomers existed on Earth, the mass total of the Earth would be 10^{280} grams! Fortunately the mass total of Earth is only 10^{27} grams, therefore the existence of all these possible isomers is impossible.

The problem of the origin of life in the first place is the problem of the origin and the appearance of the amino acids on the Earth, and in the second place the problem of the mechanism with which the amino acids are combined to build the protein macromolecule.

For this reason the hypothesis of Oparin [4] has produced an exciting glamour; in this hypothesis it is stated that the amino acids made their appearance on the

281

Earth when the atmosphere was constituted by methane, ammonia, water, and hydrogen. This hypothesis was accepted and followed successively by famous scientists like Urey and Bernal and was recently (1953) submitted to rigid experimental control by Stanley L. Miller [5]* in the Chemical Laboratory of the University of Chicago in the United States of America. Miller has constructed a special apparatus in which for a longest period of time (one week) was produced an electric discharge in an atmosphere constituted precisely by aqueous vapour, hydrogen, methane, and ammonia. The water circulates continuously in changing states from the liquid state in the boiling flask to the gaseous state in correspondence to the electrodes and then again for condensation in the liquid state in the flask. It was observed that, from the first day, the water was light yellow in colour and then turned decidedly to dark red at the end of a week. It was evident that the colour depended upon some organic compounds formed during the experiments: these compounds anyway were submitted to a very precise chemical analysis and were identified as amino acids. Among the recognized amino acids are glycine, α- and β-alanine, with large probability also aspartic acid and α-aminobutyric acid. From this model experiment, it is reasonable therefore to conclude [7, 8] that also on Earth at a certain period (exactly when its atmosphere was constituted by hydrogen, water, ammonia, and methane and not by oxygen, nitrogen, water, and carbon dioxide as presently) there was the possibility of the appearance of amino acids. Considering the probable existence in this primitive atmosphere also of hydrocarbons different from and more complex than methane, and considering also that surely the natural electric discharge must have had a greater energy than that employed in the Miller apparatus, anyone can think that in that time very numerous amino acids formed and also that this formation must have occurred in large quantities.

From the appearance of the amino acids on Earth until their organization in the molecules of one protid the way does not seem, at least from the theoretical point of view, too long, even if it is not now possible to give a satisfactory and conclusive solution to this problem. However, it is necessary to think that the process through which many hundreds of amino acids are combined to build a protein molecule is an endoergonic process and that the energy necessary must have been furnished either as electric energy or as another type (thermic, radiant energy produced in the dissimilation of organic compounds). We do not know yet how the long protein chains grow as we do not know how the same long chain of nucleic acids grow [9]. It is possible that the amino acids must have been phosphorylated by adenosine triphosphate before being included in the proteins. We have good reason to believe that the giant molecules of nucleic acids play a

---

* We believe that the experiment of Miller is in need of rapid confirmation considering its importance and also, from another point of view, because according to Roka [6] 'ob dieser Versuch allerdings schlüssig ist, wird angezweifelt'. According to Roka (*op. cit.*) 'nach mündlicher Mitteilung von K. Felix soll H. C. Urey, in dessen Institut das Experiment ausgeführt wurde, anzweifeln, ob Verunreinigungen mit Bakterien ausgeschlossen waren'. If the experiment is not reproducible, the appearance of amino acids on Earth and their formation from the components of the primitive atmosphere would be again subject of new discussion and new hypothesis, which would be valid only if supported by positive results of new experiments.

role in protein synthesis [9, 10] and certainly it is also possible, according to Haldane, that the nucleic acid needs for its growth a chain of protein patterns. At last it is also possible, according to Haldane, that the chains of the great molecules have grown without any help of catalytic substance, but more slowly and with less regular structure compared to what we observe to-day in the living organism.

From what has been said above it is logical to conclude that a probability exists that, at a certain period of time, on our planet the first protein molecule appeared through the help of natural and casual factors. This is, in fact, also the opinion of a great French biophysicist, Lecomte du Noüy; although it is not possible to agree with what the same scientist maintains later about the slight probability of this event. Lecomte du Noüy writes in fact [11]:

' ... Les molécules élémentaires des organismes vivants sont toutes caractérisées par une asymétrie trés importante. Or l'asymétrie peut s'exprimer par un nombre compris entre 0,5 et 1. Le nombre 1 correspondant à la dissymetrie maxima et le nombre 0,5 à la distribution la plus symétrique, la plus probable. Ces calculs ont été effectués par Charles Eugène Guye, pour une molécule de degré dissymetrique 0,9 dans le cas où le deminombre d'atomes constituants est égal à 1000, en supposant pour simplifier considérablement le problème, que les atomes appartiennent à 2 espèces seulement. Il y aurait donc 2000 atomes en tout. Le poids atomique de ces atomes étant supposé (nouvelle simplification) égal à 10, le poids moléculaire est de 20.000, chiffre inférieur à celui des protéines les plus simples (34.500) ... La probabilité d'apparition d'une configuration de degré dissymétrique 0,9 serait $2,02 \times 10^{-321}$. Pour qu'une telle probabilité se produisit il faudrait envisager un volume de substance qui dépasse toute imagination: celui d'une sphère dont le rayon serait si grand que la lumière mettrait 10^{82} années à le parcourir, c'est-à-dire incomparablement plus grand que tout l'univers y compris les galaxies les plus éloignées (plus de un sextillion de sextillion de sextillion plus grand). La probabilité de voir se former, sous l'action de l'agitation thermique, une seule molécule de dissymétrie élevée reste practiquement nulle ... Admettons que, par suite d'une chance inouie, quoique parfaitement admissible dans le cadre du calcul des probabilities, une molécule se soit trouvé formée. Une molécule isolée n'aurait servi de rien. Il nous faut, de toute nécessité, concevoir la production de plusieurs milliards de milliards de molécules ... Nous avons vu que la probabilité d'apparition d'une seule molécule dissymétrique était si faible qu'elle n'avait de chances de se produire que dans un espace de temps dépassant immensément l'age du soleil et l'age de l'univers. Admettre que ce phénomène—se soit produit milliards de fois dans un temps extrèmement court revient donc à nier complètement la possibilité d'application du calcul des probabilités a ce problème ... '

Until here Lecomte du Noüy. But contrary to this conclusion we object:

(1) that, because the spontaneous or casual formation of the amino acids was demonstrated possible, the problem of the origin of a protein molecule there is no longer the problem of how this molecule is formed by the atoms which composed it, but instead the more simple problem of its synthesis starting from the amino acids which form it. The probability of such an event is surely not to

be considered lightly, considering that we are dealing with a phenomenon of a simple aggregation or molecular polymerization (polymerization through condensation) reaction, or rather a series of reactions, in which evidently it is playing a relationship of direct proportionality between the quantity of the substances reacting (amino acids) and the quantity of substances formed in the reaction (proteins), following the well-known law of mass action. At this point it must be noted that the quantity of amino acids which presumably have been formed during the primitive condition of Earth must have been not too small, considering that in the Miller apparatus the yield of amino acids has been of the order of some milligrammes!

(2) that, once admitted the casual appearance of some special molecular configuration, for example of the type of virus or gene substance, one is not obliged to think that it is necessary to wait again a chance so that these molecules have been produced many time successively; because these particular configurations could have shown, since the first moment, that property which is particular to the virus and to the genic substance, that is the property of autoduplication*: namely, the property to synthesize a new molecule completely identical to the pattern. The idea and the considerations referred to above, however, suggest the hypothesis that at one determined stage of the Earth, a multiplicity and a variety of protein macromolecules, or better nucleoproteins, endowed with the power of autoduplication, have appeared. These molecules would have lived, so we say, in close association with themselves and with other organic substances in fluid masses and in microscopic drops, inside of some particular system that Oparin [4], using Bungenberg de Jong's teminology, called 'coacervate'. These macromolecules would not have been very different from the macromolecules of the actual virus and genic substances†. These macromolecules, because they

---

* Peculiar character of living beings is reproducibility. This character must not be considered today only from the cellular point of view, that is to say, that one cell has the possibility to reproduce another cell, but also from the molecular point of view, that is that the model macromolecules are able to synthesize new macromolecules perfectly identical to the model. It is a process that today has been defined as a process of auto-reproduction, or of autosynthesis or of duplication. This process underlines every protein or nucleic acid synthesis and has a fundamental importance also for the science of genetics to know the mechanism of the transmission of the hereditary character in the descendant and for pathology to know how the virus grows. This process looks very much like the process of continuous formation of new strata on the superficial layer of crystal. Also for the process of autosynthesis of the great organic molecules we must imagine that the element of the daughter layer assumes on the surface of the pattern the same spatial orientation of the pattern, that is to say, from the back to the front against the pattern [12]. Today in consideration of what has been said above [9–10], we can also admit that the model can be structurally different from the substance which is synthesized, for example, when it is supposed that a determined ribonucleic acid can be used as a model for the synthesis of a determined protein. Nevertheless between the model and the synthesized product there must always be a determined relationship in length and space; this, at least generally speaking, makes the second similar to the first.

† In reality, as is known, the molecules of viruses and genic substances are not simple proteins, but nucleoproteins. However, in this paper it was believed sufficient to consider, often for simplification, these molecules as simple proteins, especially because the difficulties that can be imagined for the synthesis and the biosynthesis of the protein group are surely not inferior to those that can be imagined for the synthesis and biosynthesis of nucleic acids.

are capable of autoduplication in the presence of substance with low molecular weight and of proper energetic conditions inside of the same 'coacervate', would have been the first living beings, structurally elementary and submicroscopic. The critical successive event of major importance would have been: 'La constitution d'une membrane semiperméable autour de plusieurs polymères autoreproducteurs de natures différentes' [9].

This representation of the primitive state of life*, nevertheless, knocks against the doubt faced by many authors [13] that substances of the type of virus can really represent the primordial kind of life which appeared on the Earth, because the viruses until to-day have never been seen multiplying themselves outside of cells of animal or vegetable organisms or outside of bacteria [13].

Against this objection, nevertheless, is the hypothesis [14] that the macromolecule of the kind of virus and genic substances in the primitive environmental condition would have had the possibility of autoreproduction in presence of single molecules (amino acids, peptides of simple construction, glycine, phosphoric acid, glyceraldehyde and compounds with 1 or 2 carbon atoms— etc. [6]). Then successively, because these primitive environmental conditions have changed, the macromolecules would have found only the possibility to have a parasitic life, and would have utilized fragments already well made offered by metabolism of the host. These macromolecules essentially would have utilized the energy produced in the processes of disintegration which are continually in progress in all the cells. In connection with this it seems opportune to recall that the research with isotopes [10] has demonstrated, referring to the bacteriophage, that inside the bacterium cells there does not exist any macromolecular precursor which is converted catalytically by infection into new molecular viruses. Rather a dynamic metabolic state develops in which the particles of virus are continuously formed from a mass of intermediates with low molecular weight, formed themselves in the process of synthesis and degradation of the host material.

In conclusion: if we wish to leave the camp of hypothesis and to bring the problem of the origin of life and of the first living beings, just as we have suggested above, on to positive ground and in the field of experimental reproduction, the biochemists must be able:

(1) to build *in vitro*, starting from the amino acid constituents, a living protein molecule. That is to say, a molecule, which properly linked with another one (molecule of nucleic acid†), gives a holocompound endowed with the power of autoduplication (cf. experiments of splitting and reconstruction *in vitro* of the tobacco mosaic virus [15, 16]. But we should be able to obtain in the laboratory the protidic molecule, using not the very refined technique of synthesis, with which organic chemistry to-day is endowed and will be more endowed to-

---

* The admission of this primitive stage of life would be in agreement with the famous happy expression of Bernal [6] 'Das Leben ist älter als die Lebewesen'.

† In reality it should also be possible to synthesize in the laboratory this molecule starting from fragments with low molecular weight.

morrow*, but using very simple technique, under the action of one or two factors similar or possibly identical to those which presumably have been able to act in the primitive atmosphere and lithosphere.

In conclusion we must transfer to the synthesis of one protid starting from the amino acids an experimental model similar to that used by Miller for the synthesis of amino acids starting from products which notoriously belong to the field of inorganic chemistry [7, 8];

(2) to demonstrate that the viruses are able to grow also outside of preconstituted living beings, which means in artificial organic medium in absence of cells. At this point we recall that Olitsky [19] has claimed to have obtained the reproduction of the virus of mosaic of tobacco and of tomatoes in one acellular extract obtained from the leaves and roots of tomato plants. Successively Mulvania [20] has demonstrated that it was an erroneous interpretation of the results, which were the same if the experiments were performed using distilled water instead of extracts. In reality, it seems to me that until now, not enough importance was given to the fact that the organization of thousands of amino acids and other simple components in one macromolecule is an endoergonic process [8, 14]. The cultivation of virus on artificial acellular medium (in which reactions with energy production do not take place) evidently cannot give positive results.

I refer at this time to a biochemical example: the synthesis of cocarboxylase from aneurin and phosphates does not happen in the usual acellular extract, but takes place only if we add to this extract a substance or a system able to furnish enough energy. So I [21, 22] since 1942 was able to construct an acellular model, which is able to synthesize the cocarboxylase from aneurin and phosphates. This model was composed of 2 systems: (a) system aneurin + phosphates + phosphatase. (b) D-amino acid + D-amino acid oxidase. The energy split off from system b (energy liberated from the deamination of the unnatural amino acid) was utilized from system a for the synthesis of the cocarboxylase. We believe it is opportune to report here the technique and the experimental data obtained in this research [21, 22].

D-AMINO ACID OXIDASE

Rat kidney (only cortical section) cut in little pieces and washed is crushed in an ice-chilled mortar with quartz sand. 20 ml of water are added for each g of

---

* The actual studies of the molecular structure of proteins suggest the existence of subunits which are always the same and are often repeated in the molecule. For example, it is admitted that in insulin exists a subunit with molecular weight of 6000 which is repeated 8 times in the molecule (6000 × 8 = 48,000—molecular weight of insulin). So far it is evident that the problem of the structure of one protid becomes a more simple problem and also the synthesis in the laboratory of one protid from amino acids which are forming it, seems to be a realizable aim in the near future. A recent editorial article in the *Nature, Lond.*, in connection with the important studies of Sanger on insulin, shows indeed '. . . the possibility that insulin itself may ultimately be completely synthesized in the laboratory' [17]. From another point of view, considering the practically infinite variety of proteins theoretically possible [1, 2], it is to be expected also that we can obtain very soon the synthesis of proteins which do not exist in nature. The study of the properties and of the biological actions of these artificial products will be stimulating [18].

substance and all is extracted for 10–20 min. It is centrifuged and filtered. In the extract are also phosphatase and pyrophosphatase.

PREPARATION OF THE REACTION MIXTURES

For each experiment 4 tests are performed. I: Extract 2 ml + phosphate 0·0375 M (pH 8·4) (0·5 ml) + 0·04 M arsenite (0·2 ml) + vitamin B_1 (200 μg). II: the same as the first, but vitamin B_1 is omitted (control). III: extract (2 ml) + phosphate (0·5 ml) + arsenite (0·2 ml) + vitamin B_1 (200 μg) + 1·0 M DL-alanine (0·1 ml). IV: the same as the third, but vitamin B_1 is omitted. The total quantity of the mixtures is 3·2 ml; presence of oxygen. After 2 hours of incubation all the tests are boiled for 2–3 min. (immediately before boiling, the vitamin B_1 is added), cooled, diluted and refrigerated.

PREPARATION OF SAMPLES FOR ASSAY

Ethiozymase (0.2 g) diluted in phosphate (pH 6·2) (1 ml) + phosphate (pH 6·2) (1 ml) + 0·2 ml of a solution containing $MgCl_2$ (1 mg) and $MnCl_2$ (100 μg) + 2·5 ml of centrifuged fluid are put in a Warburg flask; in the side arm is put sodium pyruvate (0·5 ml, 10 mg).

The synthesis of the cocarboxylase is expressed in mm^3 of extra CO_2, obtained from the difference between the CO_2 of the test incubated with vitamin B_1 and the test without B_1 (control — test). The two experiments reported in Table 1 are examples of many other experiments which always gave the same results.

TABLE 1

Acellular System which is able to synthesize Cocarboxylase from Vitamin B_1 and inorganic Phosphate

Exp. No.		mm^3 O_2 absorbed in 2 hours by the reaction mixtures	mm^3 CO_2 produced in 2 hours by the assay samples	Co-carboxylase synthesis (mm^3 of extra CO_2)
1	Rat kidney extract + As_2O_3 + B_1 added (control)	—	—	—
	+ B_1 incubated	25	246	
	+ DL-alanine + B_1 added (control)	28	250	4
	+ DL-alanine + B_1 incubated	136	243	—
		142	274	31
2	+ B_1 added (control)	6	264	—
	+ B_1 incubated	0	264	0
	+ DL-alanine + B_1 added (control)	60	266	—
	+ DL-alanine + B_1 incubated	66	284	18

A similar model must be used, from my point of view, in the tentative reproduction of virus on artificial medium.

Working experimentally in both these two directions, I think and hope that biochemists can arrive very soon to the threshold of a very fundamental discovery in the orbit of the fascinating and dramatic problem of the origin of life.

We have therefore a decisive goal in sight!

REFERENCES

1. A. KOSSEL, *Johns Hopk. Hosp. Bull.*, **23**, 65, 1912.
2. H. KREBS, *Brit. med. Bull.*, **9**, 97, 1953.
3. R. SYNGE, *Chem. Rev.*, **32**, 135, 1943.
4. A. OPARIN, *L'origine della vita sulla Terra.* Einaudi, 1956.
5. S. MILLER, *Science*, **117**, 528, 1953.
6. L. ROKA, in *Vergleichend Biochemische Fragen.* Springer, Berlin, 1956.
7. F. CEDRANGOLO, *Nuova Antol.*, **90**, 517, 1955.
8. F. CEDRANGOLO, *Biochimica appl.*, **3**, 1, 1956.
9. J. BERNAL, J. HALDANE, N. PIRIE & J. PRINGLE, *Une discussion sur l'origine de la vie.* Pubbl. de l'Union Rationaliste, Paris, 1955.
10. F. W. PUTNAM, *Annu. Rev. Biochem.*, **25**, 164, 1956.
11. LECOMTE DU NOÜY, *L'homme devant la Science.* Flammarion, Paris, 1939.
12. F. CEDRANGOLO, *L'Adattamento come problema di Enzimologia.* Meeting of Embr. and Genet. (Naples 13—18: VI: 1948). *Pubbl. Staz. Zool., Naples,* 1949. Supplement to volume **21**, p. 28.
13. P. RONDONI, *Nuova Antol.*, **91**, 451, 1956.
14. F. CEDRANGOLO, *Nuova Antol.*, **91**, 601, 1956.
15. H. FRAENKEL-CONRAT & R. WILLIAMS, *Science*, **122**, 1080, 1955.
16. Y. LIPPINCOTT & B. COMMONER, *Biochim. biophys. Acta*, **19**, 198, 1956.
17. ANON., *Nature, Lond.*, **176**, 1001, 1955.
18. F. CEDRANGOLO, *Chimica Biologica.* Morano Ed., Naples, 1956.
19. P. K. OLITSKY, *Science*, **60**, 592, 1924.
20. MULVANIA, *Science*, **62**, 37, 1925.
21. F. CEDRANGOLO & VILLANO, *Bol. Soc. ital. Biol. sper.*, **17**, 558, 1942.
22. F. CEDRANGOLO, BALBI & VILLANO, *Arch. Sci. Biol., Bologna,* **29**, 281, 1943.

S. E. BRESLER (U.S.S.R.):

Comment on the Papers of Pauling and Synge

I shall deal with what appears to me to be an extremely important aspect of the problem of proteins, namely the relation between structure and function. It is known that each protein fulfils a definite functional task (or number of tasks) in the organism. Enzymic activity is a typical example of a very important function. Evidence collected during recent years shows that the enzymic activity does not reside in the macromolecule of protein as a whole, but in a part of it known as the reactive centre. This was demonstrated by experiments in which it was shown that fragments of the molecule of comparatively low molecular weight, produced by proteolysis, possessed quite a considerable degree of enzymic activity. I have carried out similar experiments (in conjunction with Glikina and Frenkel) on aldolase and chymotrypsin. We carried out the separation of the active fragments from the protein by means of an ultracentrifuge in a special preparative cell. This allowed us to assign an upper limit to the molecular weight of the active particles. It was found to be of the order of 2000–3000 (i.e. to contain, on the average, 20–30 amino acid residues). A similar result was obtained at the same time by Gertrude Pearlman using pepsin. She used dialysis to separate the active particles from the protein. Finally, a little later on, Linderstrøm-Lang and Anfinsen and their colleagues came to the same conclusion about ribonuclease. This all shows that the enzymic function of the protein is inherent in relatively small regions of the macromolecule. The structure of the active centre is certainly strictly determinate. It often happens that the other parts of the molecule can undergo profound chemical changes (in particular decomposition) without any radical disturbance of the functional properties. These facts correspond with important observations in other fields. Fraenkel-Conrat has shown that, in virus infections, ribonucleic acid particles, having a molecular weight of the order of 200,000–300,000, are infective. These particles contain within themselves the whole of the information required for synthesizing the specific viral protein. As the mean molecular weight of the links in the polynucleotide chain is of the order of 400, the infective particles of ribonucleic acid must contain about 500 links. It is clear that several links of the nucleotide chain must correspond to one amino acid link in the polypeptide chain. This follows from the fact that the order of succession of about 20 different amino acids is recorded by means of 4 different nucleotides (cf. the correspondence between the ordinary alphabet and the alphabet of the Morse code). We do not yet know the nature of the code and so we cannot say exactly how many nucleotide groups are needed to specify one amino acid group. From logical considerations we may assume that the number is 2–3. A polynucleotide chain of 500 links would therefore contain information about the structure of a polypeptide chain of 150–200 links, i.e. a protein having a molecular weight of the order of only 15,000–22,000. Again, we see that what is needed for the manifestation of functional activity need not be the whole protein (the protein part of the tobacco mosaic virus has a molecular weight of about 2,000,000) but only some relatively small fragments of it. It is natural to suppose that the structure of the molecule is strictly determinate only within the limits of these functionally active fragments. In the other parts of the macromolecule of the protein one might expect that there would only be a certain statistical mean arrangement exhibiting certain common architectural features which confer stability on the protein, such as a large number of hydrogen bonds, a considerable number of hydrated groups etc. There is nothing surprising in such a view of the case. We must not forget that the proteins of contemporary living things which we have studied are the products of a long process of evolution. As the evolutionary changes of organisms proceeded, some proteins might retain their functions while others changed theirs, i.e. there has been a continual evolution of protein molecules. It is, therefore, natural that the structure of the macromolecules of proteins should retain the impression of many chance alterations which have taken place during the process of evolution. This is probably the explanation of what seem, at first glance, to be queer, general, statistical regularities, in the distribution of different amino acids in various proteins without any functional resemblance, which have been found by Tristram. This accounts for the similarity (in amino acid composition) of completely dissimilar proteins which was pointed out by Synge. If this concept is correct it will oblige us to take a different attitude to the whole problem of the chemical structure of proteins. For example, deciphering of the complete structural formula of a protein or the amino acid sequence of the whole macromolecule will lose its point. Only the functionally reactive centres are constructed in a definite way corresponding to their functions. The other parts of the molecule may not have any constant structure, being the vestigial relics of their earlier history.

A. G. Pasynskiĭ (U.S.S.R.):

Catalytic Protein Structures with reference to the Papers of Hoffmann-Ostenhof and Šorm

We are now in a position to put forward, tentatively, the idea that there are several stages in the formation of catalytic protein structures. At first relatively short polypeptide chains must have been formed from amino acids; it has, in fact been shown by recent work that even small polypeptide chains (of 25–30 residues or less) may have a catalytic activity. Oriented adsorption of such peptides, or simpler ones on kaolin (as suggested by Bernal) or silica gel etc. might be the next stage of significance for the formation of abiogenic or protobiogenic catalytic structures. However, this sort of adsorption on a carrier could not give the delicate and precise structure of the active centres which could be given by the folding of a long polypeptide chain, not to speak of the biological necessity of having the catalytic centres attached to polypeptide chains rather than to particles of clay etc. The formation of catalytic centres within the long polypeptide chains could, therefore, have attained an evolutionary predominance over adsorbed catalytic structures. This process could have culminated in the formation of catalytic protein molecules with their strictly determinate chemical structure. It must be mentioned that, as well as having a determinate structure of its active centre, the protein molecule can make extremely delicate modifications in the activity of the catalytic centre by changes in its composition, charge, configuration etc. The part played by the rest of the protein molecule must not, therefore, be considered, as suggested by Prof. Bresler, as being vestigial or atavistic, it is absolutely necessary. It is, however, certain that the active centre can only constitute a small part of the protein molecule and that, accordingly, there was no need for the complete protein molecule to be synthesized for the production of the first examples of enzymic activity based on peptide structures. Besides the evidence put forward by Bresler one may point to the recent work of Rogers & Kalnitsky (Biochim. biophys. Acta, 23, 525, 1957) on the active centre of ribonuclease. At the conference on proteins held in Prague in 1956, I gave a paper showing that if we compare the relative frequency of occurrence of different dipeptides, as calculated statistically from the amino acid composition, with the extent to which they actually occur in an amino acid chain, where it has been deciphered, as in insulin (Sanger), silk fibroin (Ioffe) and ribonuclease (Hirs, Stein & Moore), then we find that in a non-catalytic protein (fibroin) the calculated and actual results are approximately the same, while, in the specific proteins (insulin and ribonuclease) the actual amounts of most of the dipeptides agree with the calculated results, though the content of some dipeptides differs from what would be expected on statistical grounds by a factor of 8–10. Thus, it may be that the structure of the active centre is really determined by a different factor from that governing the protein molecule as a whole. The interesting facts given in Šorm's paper also show a predominance of some types of dipeptide linkages. It would be interesting to evaluate on models the magnitude of the kinetic parameters (ΔF^* and ΔH^*) determining the relative rates of condensation of different pairs of amino acids. According to Koshland (*J. Amer. chem. Soc.*, **73**, 4103, 1951) these rates may differ by a factor of 10–100 even for amino acids, which are similar to one another. This may explain the fact that Šorm found different proportions of such similar dipeptides as serylarginine and arginylserine etc.

S. OERIU (Rumänien):

Zur Diskussion über die Arbeit 'Der Ursprung der Enzyme' von O. Hoffmann-Ostenhof

In der sehr lehrreichen Arbeit des Herrn Prof. Hoffmann-Ostenof—'Über den Ursprung der Enzyme' wird gesagt: 'Wohl ist es möglich durch verschieden physikalische oder chemische Einflüsse (Strahlen, Wärme, mutogene Substanzen) die Häufigkeit der Mutationen wesentlich zu erhöhen, doch sei es ausgeschlossen, durch aüssere Faktoren eine gerichtete Beeinflussung des genetischen Apparates zu erzielen.'

An dieser so lehrreichen Arbeit anliegend, erlaube ich mir auf besonders interessante experimentelle Arbeiten, die in der letzten Zeit in Frankreich mitgeteilt wurden, hinzuweisen.

Jacques Benoit und Mitarbeiter haben in April 1957 die Arbeit 'Somatische Mutation einiger Vertebraten' an der Akademie der Wissenschaften Frankreichs mit folgenden Resultaten mitgeteilt [1].

Es sind zu Versuchszwecken zwei Entearten (Pekin und Khaki), die einander sehr entfernt stehen, folgenden Untersuchungen unterzogen worden:

(*a*) aus den lebenden Zellen der Pekin-Enten wurde Desoxyribonukleinsäure herausgezogen;

(*b*) diese so gewonnene Desoxyribonukleinsäure wurde an den Khaki Enten im Alter von 8 Tagen verabreicht, und zwar 6 Monate lang (jeden 7-ten Tag eingespritzt; im ganzen 20 Einspritzungen).

Diese Behandlung führte zu einer Änderung der Heriditäts-Eigenschaften der Khaki-Enten.

In einer zweiten Arbeit, die im Juli 1957 mitgeteilt wurde [2], behaupten die Verfasser, daß aus den 109 gelegten Eiern 109 Enten herauskamen, die zu 70% der Pekin-Entenart ähnelten (Kopf, Federn, Grösse, Körpergewicht, allgemeines Verhalten).

Es ist aus diesen Arbeiten ersichtlich, daß die Änderungen der Heriditäts-Charaktere, die zuerst künstlich an den Enten erworben wurden, wohl auch weiterhin übertragen werden konnten.

LITERATUR

1. J. BENOIT, P. LEROY, C. VENDRELY & R. VENDRELY, *C.R. Acad. Sci., Paris.*, **244**, 2320, 1957.
2. J. BENOIT, P. LEROY, C. VENDRELY & R. VENDRELY, *C.R. Acad. Sci., Paris*, **245**, 748, 1957.

G. F. GAUSE (U.S.S.R.):

The problem of the optical activity of protoplasm is now attracting much attention by biologists and biochemists and is of particular interest in connection with the question of the origin of life. This great problem may be divided into several separate partial problems. *In the first place*: Why is protoplasm optically active and not racemic? Optical activity favours a great intensity of chemical processes and must, therefore, have been enhanced by natural selection. Cells have special mechanisms to hinder racemization and ensure the optical purity of the components of protoplasm, which appear to be a product of evolution. To adapt the terminology of A. N. Severtsov, one may say that, in comparison with racemic protoplasm, optically active protoplasm represents considerable progress or apomorphosis.

In the second place: Why does all the protoplasm we know on the Earth have the L-configuration, the D- stereoisomers of amino acids being absent from its structure? Why has D-protoplasm never been found on the Earth? Obviously this indicates a common origin for all the life we know, from a single source.

A further very interesting question is that of the connection between inverse forms of organisms and inverse molecules in their composition. In cases when such phenomena have been studied in detail, as in *Bacillus mycoides*, it has been shown that in both the rare right-spiral and the typical left-spiral bacteria the protoplasm has the L-configuration and the inversion of form is evidently associated with optical inversion of some component of the bacterial cell wall. Unfortunately, it is today as it was 17 years ago when I wrote my book *The Asymmetry of Protoplasm*; we have not succeeded in isolating optically rotatory compounds from the cell walls of inverse bacteria and, therefore, nobody has yet been able to give direct experimental proof of the association between inverse forms of organisms and inverse molecules entering into their composition. We may hope that recent advances in the study of the chemical composition of the cell walls of bacteria and, in particular, the isolation from them of individual amino acids and a study of their optical rotation will be applied to work with right-spiral and left-spiral forms and will lead to a final solution of the question of the connection between morphological inversion and molecular inversion.

E. M. MAKOVSKIĬ (Rumania):

I want to give you hearty greetings from the people of Rumania and from the Rumanian scientists who are looking forward with great interest to the results of this Symposium.

Rumania is active in the struggle for peace, so I can assure Prof. Pauling that the idea of organizing peaceful international symposia of politicians and diplomats meets with our deepest sympathy.

Turning to our discussion, I wish to say a few words about what Prof. Akabori has told us today.

I find his hypothesis about the possibility of the formation of protopolypeptide chains by the action of aldehydes and unsaturated hydrocarbons on polyglycine interesting because with some amplification it might lead to an explanation of the appearance on the Earth of the first polypeptides with a periodic structure.

Investigations carried out by Prof. I. Tanasescu and his school, beginning in 1928 in the town of Cluj, showed that the action of light on cyclic *o*-nitrobenzylidene acetals of polyols led to photochemical isomerization of some, but not all, of the photochemically active groups, even when they seemed to be similar in all respects. The periodicity thus reveals its nature by its activity in the sense that if one group reacts photochemically its neighbour will not react and it will only be the third group which will react.

This leads to the idea, which needs to be tested experimentally, that the methylene groups of polyglycine might also, under certain circumstances, manifest periodic differences of potentialities in respect of their reactions with different aldehydes. In this case one and the same polyglycine chain, in the presence of a mixture of different aldehydes, might, from the very beginning, form a polypeptide chain having a periodic distribution of amino acids.

From this point of view, periodically constructed polypeptides, though, of course, of comparatively simple structure, might be seen as prototypes of the present-day protamines in which such a structural periodicity has been well demonstrated.

The fact to which Prof. Felix referred, that contemporary protamines, in combination with nucleic acids, play an important part in heredity, emphasizes once more the significance of comparatively simple periodic polypeptide structures in connection with the problem of the origin of life. Prof. Akabori's hypothesis sheds new light on the possibility that such structures were produced right at the beginning of the evolution of organic substances on the Earth.

A. M. GOLDOVSKIĬ (U.S.S.R.):

The Significance of the Multivariance of Chemical Reactions in the Processes of Emergence and Development of Life on the Earth

We wish to draw attention to one of the properties of chemical reactions which undoubtedly had a decisive importance in the emergence and development of life. We have used the term 'multivariance' for this property [1]; it refers to the fact that, in each chemical reaction in which organic substances are involved, the meeting and interaction of the reacting molecules always leads to the reaction developing in a multiplicity of directions with the formation of numerous products. Any reaction of organic substances under the ordinary conditions of artificial organic synthesis will serve as an example [2]. However, even when reactions occur under gentler conditions, approaching those of synthesis within the organism, we meet with the same multivariance of chemical reactions and the formation of mixtures of products [2].

The multivariance of reactions must, of course, inevitably occur even when the reactions take place within an organism. This property of reactions is to be found, not only in non-enzymic reactions, but also in the fundamental enzymic reactions occurring within the organism, for it is entailed by the actual mechanism of the reaction. Every enzyme or collection of enzymes, like any other catalyst, determines the general direction, the general character of a particular biochemical process, but does not prevent the occurrence, within limits, of a multiplicity of different variants, which are inevitably entailed by the actual course of the chemical reactions and lead to the formation of mixtures of substances [3]. For example, in experiments on the enzymic synthesis of polysaccharides *in vitro* by the action of potato phosphorylase on glucose 1-phosphate, there are formed mixtures of polysaccharides with different molecular weights [4, 5, 6], which are entailed by the actual mechanism of the reaction of polymerization or polycondensation.

Returning to *in vivo* synthesis within organisms, we find here unmistakable signs of the multivariance of biochemical reactions. This is seen in the fact that, in every organism, each narrow group of substances consists of a whole series (mixture) of very similar substances, with a common structural plan characteristic of the particular narrow group of substances, but with differences in their structural details (in high polymers there are differences in molecular weight and in degree of polymerization)*. This multiplicity of substances is, as our work has shown [7], a completely regular occurrence and applies to all groups of substances in the organism (the law of multiplicity of the representatives of every group of substances in the organism). For example, many proteins, especially protein enzymes, which are considered to be individual substances, may be separated into fractions having very similar properties; the glyceride components of fats are, in every organism, composed of mixtures of many triglycerides; multiplicity is characteristic of phosphatides, carotenoids, tocopherols, sterols, antibiotics, etc. [7].

The quantitative relationship between similar substances within a narrow group in any particular organism is usually such that one substance predominates while others are present in lesser amounts, so that one may make a provisional quantitative distinction between the main and the subsidiary substances.

Similarly, within the limits of each complicated biochemical reaction, one may make a provisional quantitative distinction between the main and subsidiary (side) reactions on the basis of their intensity. Every biochemical process is made up of a 'bundle' of biochemical reactions which must lead to the production of a multiplicity of similar compounds. The more the course of the side reactions deviates from that of the main reaction, the greater will be the differences, in quantity and structure, between the by-products and the main product.

As we shall see, multivariance occurs in chemical reactions no matter under what conditions they take place, whether they be the severe conditions of organic chemical synthesis or the gentler conditions of biosynthesis. Thus multivariance must have occurred during the emergence of life as well as during all the later stages of its development.

The multivariance of chemical reactions may have been of great significance even during the primary formation of organic compounds and their further transformation. It appears,

---

* The multiplicity of substances in an organism depends on a number of factors but, obviously, the most important cause is, in fact, the multivariance of chemical reactions in the organism.

from the well-known experiments of S. Miller [8] and also from those of K. Bahadur [9] and T. E. Pavlovskaya & A. G. Pasynskiĭ [10], that a complicated mixture of various compounds was formed. There is every reason to suppose that even in the first living material to be formed—the very first primaeval organism [11]—the multivariance of even the simplest of chemical reactions led to the development of complicated chemical activity giving rise to a great variety of substances—to materials with a very complicated structure. The multivariance of chemical reactions gave rise to a chemically diversified raw material on the basis of which there emerged the biochemical apparatus of unicellular and, later, multicellular organisms.

The multivariance of chemical reactions was, obviously, of decisive importance in the course of the process of evolution when changes were taking place in the external medium.

Changes in external conditions could strengthen or weaken particular tendencies and even cause the main tendency to become confused with others in the 'bundle' of reactions. This is indicated by the fact that the quantitative relationship between the amounts of similar substances belonging to any one narrow group, formed within an organism, may vary markedly under the influence of external factors (for examples, see my own work [3]).

The formation of proteins, in particular protein enzymes, and hence also the self-reproduction of the fundamental vital structures of the cells, thus constitutes a 'bundle' of biochemical reactions. By affecting the relationship between different tendencies in the bundle of reactions, changes in external circumstances can lead to changes in the fundamental vital structures of cells. In this way changes in 'bundles' of biochemical processes formed the basis for the process of variability of organisms under the action of external conditions in the course of evolution [3].

The existence and change of 'bundles' of biochemical reactions is also of importance in ontogenesis. Thus, processes of resynthesis in the renewal of substances in the organism are also 'bundles' of reactions and, thus, must obviously lead to a certain change in the composition of substances if there has been any change in the external or internal medium of the cells. It may be that the biological significance of the renewal of substances lies in the fact that it provides a possibility for the organism to react to external influences by means of certain changes in the chemical composition of the cells, tissues and organs.

The multiplicity of the components of any individual enzymes, differing from one another, to some extent, as to the optimal conditions for their action, may assure the organism of the necessary intensity of enzymic reactions under variable conditions of existence, which is important for the adaptation of the organism to the surrounding medium [3, 12].

It is our opinion that the multivariance of chemical reactions, entailing the occurrence of 'bundles' of reactions and thus the formation of a multiplicity of substances must be taken seriously in any consideration of questions relating to the process of the origin and development of life.

REFERENCES

1. A. M. GOLDOVSKIĬ, *Sovetskaya Botanika*, **14**, 255, 1946.
2. A. M. GOLDOVSKIĬ, *Shornik Rabot Vsesoyuznogo nauchno-issledovatel'skogo Instituta Zhirov* (1941–45). Leningrad, p. 251, 1946.
3. A. M. GOLDOVSKIĬ, *Izv. Akad. Nauk S.S.S.R., Ser. biol.* **1**, 31, 1957.
4. W. N. HAWORTH, R. L. HEATH & S. PEAT, *J. chem. Soc.*, **55**, 1942.
5. D. L. MOULD & R. L. M. SYNGE, *Biochem. J.*, **58**, 571, 1954.
6. W. J. WHELAN & J. M. BAILEY, *Biochem. J.*, **58**, 560, 1954.
7. A. M. GOLDOVSKIĬ, *Usp. sovremennoĭ Biol.*, **14**, 140, 1941; *Zhur. priklad. Khim.* **19**, 279, 1946; *Izv. Akad. Nauk S.S.S.R., Ser. Biol.* **6**, 87, 1954; *Usp. Sovremennoĭ Biol.* **40**, 289, 1955.
8. S. MILLER, this Symposium.
9. K. BAHADUR, this Symposium.
10. T. E. PAVLOVSKAYA & A. G. PASYNSKIĬ, this Symposium.
11. A. I. OPARIN, *Vozniknovenie Zhizni na Zemle*, Moscow & Leningrad Izd. Akad. Nauk, S.S.S.R. 1941.
12. B. A. RUBIN, *Vestnik Moskovskogo Universiteta, Ser. Biol., Pochvov., Geol., Geogr.* **1**, 3, 1956.

Chairman: S. AKABORI

The Origin of Proteins, Nucleoproteins and Enzymes
(*continued*)

Nucleic Acids as Carriers of Biological Information

ERWIN CHARGAFF

Columbia University, New York, U.S.A.

IS THERE A HIERARCHY OF CELLULAR CONSTITUENTS?

OUR TIME is probably the first in which mythology has penetrated to the molecular level. I read, for instance, in a recent article by a very distinguished biologist:

' ... In the early phases of the molecular stage of evolution, only simple molecules were formed. .... Later more complex molecules, such as amino acids and perhaps simple peptides, were formed.

'In the more advanced phases of this period it is believed that there appeared a molecule with two entirely new properties: the ability systematically to direct the formation of copies of itself from an array of simpler building blocks, and the property of acquiring new chemical configurations without loss of ability to reproduce. These properties, self-duplication and mutation, are characteristic of all living systems and they may therefore be said to provide an objective basis for defining the living state.

'Evidence is accumulating that the nucleic acids of present-day organisms possess these two properties, and it is perhaps no longer useless to speculate that the first "living" molecule might have been a simple nucleic acid, perhaps protected by an associated simple protein. ... '

Thus, what started cosmically with beautiful and profound legends has come down to a so-called 'macromolecule'. If poetry has suffered, precision has not gained. For we may ask whether a model that merely provides for one cell constituent continually to make itself can teach us much about life and its origins. We may also ask whether the postulation of a hierarchy of cellular constituents, in which the nucleic acids are elevated to a patriarchal role in the creation of living matter, is justified. I believe there is not sufficient evidence for so singling out this particular class of substances.

We know that autarkic entities (cells and cell communities) require the presence of a very large number of different compounds, foremost among which are the ubiquitous plastic constituents, namely: (1) Nucleic acids (both of the deoxypentose and pentose types, DNA and PNA); (2) proteins; (3) lipids;

297

(4) polysaccharides. Parasitic systems (viruses, phages) apparently require the presence of nucleic acids (DNA or PNA) and protein. But such a generic statement probably is no more meaningful than if we were to say that all machines consist of iron, copper, nickel, etc. For neither the knowledge of quantity nor that of quality alone can satisfy our inquiry; and for an understanding of what is meant by organization an entirely new dimension will have to be added: a dimension of which barely the foundations are discernible at present. Moreover, to return to the example of the machine, it is not likely that we could learn much about the 'origin of the automobile' from an inspection of the parts of a present-day car; nor could such an examination help us to decide whether there did not once exist an automobile made of glass, though we may conclude that, at any rate under present conditions, it would hardly have survived as the fittest means of locomotion.

In any event, even if we commit the oversimplifying fallacy of postulating a virus-like structure as the first 'living' molecule, we are still left to deal with a nucleoprotein: a singular that conceals a multitude of possible structures. If scientific facts were subject to a vote, the majority opinion would probably place the nucleic acids at the top of the hierarchy and let the proteins follow; something like this: DNA $\rightarrow$ PNA $\rightarrow$ Protein. But in my opinion it would be more honest to confess that we know very little indeed about these things and to say that the road to the future should not be uselessly cluttered up with shoddy, and often entirely baseless, hypotheses. It may, however, not be uninstructive to say a few words about the chemical connotations of the concept of biological information.

ON BIOLOGICAL INFORMATION
CHEMICALLY CONVEYED

A biochemist, when asked to consider this problem, probably would first of all translate it into the concept of chemical specificity—with which I have dealt in more detail on several occasions [1, 2]—and think of a substance of an elevated molecular weight, built of a number of chemically different monomers and possessing chemical or physical features which are preserved without change within the species, but which serve to distinguish the particular substance from analogous ones produced by other species. Specific polysaccharides, specific proteins, specific nucleic acids are the type of compounds that will come to mind immediately; and the immunological specificity exhibited by many representatives of the first two groups perhaps is their most striking property. The recognition of the existence of specific nucleic acids required much more time; but their specificity, too, can now be taken to be an established fact on both chemical and biological grounds [1–4]. It is, indeed, only in the fourth group of principal cell constituents, namely, the lipids, that difficulties with respect to the occurrence of species specificity still are encountered. As I have pointed out recently [5], one way in which the cell may be able to render lipids specific is in their arrangement as prosthetic groups of lipoproteins. But there exist indications that nervous tissue contains complex mucolipids of high molecular weight which could very well exhibit species specificity [6].

A warning is, however, in order. We cannot yet answer the question: How identical is identity? In considering cell replication, we like to assume that the complex and specific cell constituents are reproduced so as to give entirely invariant structures, with the hundreds or even thousands of different amino acids or nucleotides always arranged in an unchanged sequence. Actually, very little is known; the extent of play that nature may allow itself cannot yet be gauged.

It is, in any event, safe to assume that the real specificity of a given cell resides in the nature of its plastic constituents rather than in that of its catalytic components, which latter probably are a symptom rather than a cause. But there is a giant step from the establishment of sequential specificity in proteins, nucleic acids, polysaccharides to the formulation of the manner in which the 'information' stored in them is not only preserved, but also transferred from one class of components to the other. The polysaccharides and lipids cannot at all be fitted into what little we know. As regards the nucleic acids and proteins, however, it would appear to me safer, instead of postulating a hierarchy, to envisage a triangular relationship, e.g., as follows:

$$
\begin{array}{c}
\overset{1}{\text{DNA}} \\
\diagup \quad \diagdown \\
\underset{2}{\text{PNA}}\!\!-\!\!-\!\!\underset{3}{\text{Protein}}
\end{array}
$$

No arrows have been placed in this diagram, for their direction may conceivably be different in different systems; so that, for instance, in a plant virus the relation is between 2 and 3, in bacteriophage duplication and in bacterial transformations between 1 and 3, in autarkic systems between 1, 2 and 3. It is, moreover, quite conceivable that the transfer of information often can proceed in either direction and that the prevailing impression that it invariably flows from the nucleic acids to the proteins is mistaken. We may not yet have learned how to isolate suitable protein preparations; I should not be surprised if it were found eventually that both halves of a plant virus, the PNA and the protein, may be 'infective'. It was, therefore, not without purpose that I used the plural above in speaking of 'life and its origins'.

One could, however, ask: Is the cell really nothing but a system of ingenious stamping presses, stencilling its way from life to death? Is life itself only an intricate chain of templates and catalysts and products? My answer to these and many similar questions would be No; for I believe that our science has become too mechanomorphic, that we talk in metaphors in order to conceal our ignorance, and that there are categories in biochemistry for which we lack even a proper notation, let alone an idea of their outlines and dimensions.

Regardless, however, of whether we accept the currently fashionable template hypothesis, we must assume that there exist agents or complexes of agents in the cell that preside over the selection and specific arrangement of the constituents of all cell-specific polymers: proteins, nucleic acids, blood-group substances, bacterial polysaccharide antigens, etc. These agents must be able both to preserve and to transfer whatever codes are stored in the constituent sequence and the specific physical shapes of these compounds. How these agents operate is not yet within our power to describe; but there exists some evidence that the nucleic acids, both DNA and PNA, are concerned in these operations. It lies within the scope of these remarks to inquire whether there are any outstanding features that are common to all nucleic acids, for this may be of value for our understanding of the chemical characteristics of such information systems. In dividing the rest of the discussion under the headings of invariability, diversity, and regularity, it will be apparent that the first two qualities probably are common to all specific cell constituents, whereas the third is a most unusual feature of the nucleic acids which apparently is not shared by the other plastic cell substances.

INVARIABILITY OF NUCLEIC ACIDS

This is a property that is, often by tenet rather than by experience, held to be common to all macromolecular cell components. How limited our knowledge is, I have already emphasized before; but it is, in general, assumed that a given protein or specific polysaccharide or nucleic acid is invariable in structure in a particular species. Although, as I shall mention below, there exists impressive evidence that the nucleic acids of a cell comprise an entire series of different individuals, the constancy, with respect to characteristic base composition, of *total* deoxypentose nucleic acids appears well established [2]; a constancy that seems to apply to preparations from all tissues of the same host [7] or from different variants of the same microbial species [8].

As concerns pentose nucleic acids a decision appeared more difficult for some time owing to the unsatisfactory nature of isolated PNA preparations. When methods were developed permitting the analysis of total PNA without previous isolation, essentially in the form of nucleoprotein, it could, however, be shown that the nucleotide composition of the total pentose nucleic acid of a given cell also is nearly constant [9, 10]. In more recent experiments on the pentose nucleic acids of *Azotobacter vinelandii* [11] and of *E. coli* (unpublished) this remarkable invariability of PNA could also be demonstrated, in the latter case even under a variety of conditions, for instance, the presence or absence of simultaneous protein synthesis and with and without the addition of an excess of a single nucleoside.

DIVERSITY OF NUCLEIC ACIDS

Long before detailed chemical analysis had become possible the existence of many different proteins and polysaccharides had been recognized, often through their antigenic or other biological properties, characteristic physical qualities or some outstanding chemical components. The specific enzymic properties of many proteins also were noted very early. Direct biological tests are not often applicable to nucleic acids. The activity of specific deoxypentose nucleic acids in bacterial transformations is well established. The demonstration of the exclusive role of nucleic acids in virus growth and enzyme induction is, in my opinion, as yet far from unequivocal. But on the whole there surely exists enough evidence to speak of a diversity of nucleic acids on biological grounds.

The chemical diversity of DNA, as shown by widely different proportions of the constituent nucleotides in different specimens, has, since the time of its first discussion [1, 12], been demonstrated in very many instances [2]. Of more recent date is the discovery that a total DNA preparation can be fractionated into a whole series of differently composed, but regularly graded, fractions [13]. The distribution of these fractions in a given cell must, however, be constant within narrow limits, as shown by the invariability of total DNA mentioned above.

The variation in the composition of different PNA preparations is marked, though perhaps not quite as striking as in DNA [10]. In addition, there is some evidence of the existence of different pentose nucleic acids in the same cell; e.g., the nuclear and the cytoplasmic PNA of rat liver differ in composition [14]. A reliable chemical fractionation of PNA has, however, not yet been achieved.

REGULARITY OF NUCLEIC ACIDS

As I have mentioned before, this is perhaps the most unusual property distinguishing the nucleic acids from other cell-specific high polymers. In saying this, I am not referring to the regular position of the phosphodiester bridges connecting the nucleosides in the nucleic acid chain: they are assumed to be generally 3' : 5'-bridges; for the regularity of the links holding the monomers together is common to most biological polymers. What is so peculiar is the remarkable balance between the several constituents noticed in all deoxypentose and in almost all pentose nucleic acids: a type of equipoise that I am not aware of ever having been encountered in other mixed polymers that do not contain simple repeating units.

There are several regularities of which three are characteristic of only DNA [1, 2]. They are: (1) the molar quantity of adenine equals that of thymine. (2) The molar quantity of guanine equals that of cytosine (+ methylcytosine). (3) The sum of the purine nucleotides equals that of the pyrimidine nucleotides. The fourth regularity, finally, applies to nearly all nucleic acids, DNA and PNA [10]; it is: (4) The molar sum of nucleotides carrying 6-amino groups (adenylic, cytidylic acids) equals that of nucleotides having 6-keto groups (guanylic, thymidylic or uridylic acids).

In considering these regularities one must take into account that the nucleic acids are devoid of any perceptible periodicity or of repeating sub-units larger than a mononucleotide. They are complicated high polymers of a largely arrhythmic nucleotide sequence which, however, does not appear to be fortuitous [15].

CONCLUDING REMARKS

It is inviting to assume that the special biological functions of the nucleic acids are reflected in those chemical features that distinguish them from other high-molecular cell components, namely, in the unusual regularities in nucleotide composition mentioned above. In which way these functions are exerted cannot yet be said; but I already have pointed out before that in my opinion the nucleoproteins rather than the separate moieties of the conjugated proteins will eventually be found to be the operative units. In this connection, reference may be made to a recent discussion from our laboratory [10] in which an attempt was made to relate the one general regularity of both DNA and PNA, namely, the presence of equal numbers of 6-amino and 6-keto nucleotides, to the one regularity common to all proteins, the regular occurrence of peptide linkages. A detailed inquiry into the mechanism of this conjunction of protein and nucleic acid, let alone the construction of a reasonable model or the attempt at unravelling the information code of the cell, is premature; for no truly homogeneous nucleoprotein has yet been discovered of which it could be said that the particular nucleic acid molecule contained in it, with its unique nucleotide sequence, has given rise to the particular protein, with its equally unique amino acid sequence, or *vice versa*. In other words, we are still lacking the Rosetta stone of biochemistry.

It is not profitable to speculate on the direction in which the ancestral roles of the nucleic acids could be approached. But it can be predicted that further investigations along the following lines will be of value: (*a*) virus nucleoproteins; (*b*) mechanism of enzyme induction; (*c*) mechanism of antibody production; (*d*) role of priming substances in the enzymic synthesis of high polymers.

REFERENCES

1. E. CHARGAFF, *Experientia*, **6**, 201, 1950.
2. E. CHARGAFF, in *The Nucleic Acids*. (Ed. by E. CHARGAFF & J. N. DAVIDSON), Academic Press, New York, Vol. I, p. 307, 1955.
3. B. R. D. HOTCHKISS, in *The Nucleic Acids*, **2**, 435, 1955.
4. J. BRACHET, in *The Nucleic Acids*, **2**, 475, 1955.
5. E. CHARGAFF, in *Essays in Biochemistry*. New York, 1956.
6. A. ROSENBERG & E. CHARGAFF, *Biochim. biophys. Acta*, **21**, 588, 1956.
7. E. CHARGAFF & R. LIPSHITZ, *J. Amer. chem. Soc.*, **75**, 3658, 1953.
8. E. CHARGAFF, Symposium sur le métabolisme microbien, *Int. Congr. Biochem.*, Paris, p. 41, 1952.
9. D. ELSON, T. GUSTAFSON & E. CHARGAFF, *J. biol. Chem.*, **209**, 285, 1954.
10. D. ELSON & E. CHARGAFF, *Biochim. biophys. Acta*, **17**, 367, 1955.
11. A. LOMBARD & E. CHARGAFF, *Biochim. biophys. Acta*, **20**, 585, 1956.
12. E. CHARGAFF, E. VISCHER, R. DONIGER, C. GREEN & F. MISANI. *J. biol. Chem.*, **177**, 405, 1949.
13. E. CHARGAFF, C. F. CRAMPTON & R. LIPSHITZ, *Nature, Lond.*, **172**, 289, 1953.
14. D. ELSON, L. W. TRENT & E. CHARGAFF, *Biochim. biophys. Acta*, **17**, 362, 1955.
15. H. S. SHAPIRO & E. CHARGAFF, *Biochim. biophys. Acta*, **23**, 451, 1957.

The Infective Nucleic Acid from Tobacco Mosaic Virus

H. FRAENKEL-CONRAT & B. SINGER

Virus Laboratory, University of California, Berkeley, California, U.S.A.

OF THE two constituents of tobacco mosaic virus (TMV), the nucleic acid has, in recent years, come to occupy that central role in our interest which was formerly played by the protein. This is due to the realization that the nucleic acid alone can perform all the crucial functions of the virus, namely it can initiate infection and transmit the required genetic information [1–5]. This conclusion was not easily arrived at, because of the comparatively low efficiency of the nucleic acid as an infectious agent, and its great sensitivity to various materials, including one so seemingly harmless as 0·1 M phosphate buffer (pH 7). These difficulties in detecting and estimating the infectivity of the nucleic acid can be overcome by reconstituting new virus from it and added protein. The number of lesions given by a certain amount of nucleic acid is in that manner increased 10- to many 100-fold, and the sensitivity of the nucleic acid to salts, ribonuclease, metals etc. is abolished. It was in this manner that the infectivity of the nucleic acid was first detected [6].

The useful protecting activity of the protein represents an expression of its primary biological function. It continues to be of great interest to us what kind of bonds and affinities are involved in the remarkable ability of this particular protein to build up the macromolecular housing for the viral nucleic acid. But apart from its architectural role, the protein is also of considerable interest, because it represents an expression in terms of amino-acid sequences of information carried and transmitted by nucleotide sequences. Thus this system may represent the Rosetta stone of biochemical genetics, and the unravelling of this amino acid sequence may give us the clue needed for the deciphering of the meaning of nucleic acid structure. For all these reasons, our laboratory is actively engaged in the analysis of the structure of the TMV protein.

However, to the Symposium devoted to the origin of life, the nature of the nucleic acid may be of greater concern. For whatever claims to life viruses may possess, these are properties of the nucleic acid. And while viruses probably represent highly adapted twentieth century agents, evolved, be it forward or backward, to assure optimal survival value, their nucleic acid may be considerably closer in nature and structure to some primordial polynucleotide molecules. Thus, if we wish to assume that the most fundamental processes of life have always relied on the same principle mechanisms, then what we learn about the relationship of structure and function in viral or other genetically active nucleic

303

acids should also contribute to our incipient understanding of the possible origins of life.

Unfortunately, I will have little definite progress to report, in our understanding of nucleic acid structure and function. One of the important questions is that of size, or molecular weight. In that regard, Gierer & Schramm [2] and Gierer [7] have taken the firm stand that, in their preparations, the entire and intact nucleic acid complement of a virus particle of about 2 million molecular weight is the only functional entity while smaller molecules occurring in all preparations represent inactive degradation products.

In contrast, preparations made in our laboratory by splitting the virus with detergents, rather than phenol, appear upon ultracentrifugation to be composed of molecules only about one-tenth as big. Recently we have somewhat clarified this situation, in finding that the sedimentability of TMV-ribonucleic acid (RNA) is to an astonishing extent a function of the ionic strength. Thus, many of our preparations, when sedimented in 0·02 M phosphate, i.e. under the conditions used by Schramm's group, appear as big as their preparations, with $S_{20, w}$ values of 20–25. In contrast, their type of preparations, when sedimented in 0·001 M or lower phosphate concentrations, appear as small as ours. The important question remains to be solved, whether both types of preparations are actually of relatively low molecular weight, and aggregate to the more rapidly sedimenting material under the influence of the salt, or whether both are of the higher molecular weight, but acquire a completely abnormal sedimentability in 0·001 M or lower salt media, owing to charge effects. My colleagues and I favour the former concept, but further experimental work is required to settle this question.

Another line of research which is actively being pursued in our laboratory should also shed light on this question. For, we have studied the infectivity and the sedimentability of nucleic acid prepared from virus which had been inactivated by sonic oscillations [5]. Such virus preparations are largely composed of rods of one-third or less the original length, and usually contain about as many unbroken rods as are required to account for the remaining infectivity. This can be varied, not too predictably, over the range of 0·01% or less to 20% of the original infectivity. The release of nucleic acid from such material proceeds more readily than from intact virus. Surprisingly, the sedimentability of the two nucleic acid preparations is not significantly different, and of similar dependence upon the ionic medium. And in infectivity the nucleic acid from 'sonicated' virus is usually about one order of magnitude higher than might be expected from the activity of the virus preparation serving as source material. The tentative conclusion from this work, which is still in active progress, is that active nucleic acid subunits, weighing only a fraction of the total nucleic acid of each particle, also do not extend over the entire length of the particle and thus have a fair chance of remaining unbroken when the rods are fractured by sonication.

Studies concerning the instability of TMV-RNA in salts have yielded interesting results, but as yet no definite explanatory hypothesis. It has previously been reported that the nucleic acid loses its infectivity upon incubation in 0·1 M salts. It has now been found that this loss of infectivity is paralleled by a loss of sedimentability (in the presence of salt). All salts tested cause this gradual degradation at o·1 M and with a lesser rate at o·02 M concentration. However, pyrophosphate produces an appreciably slower degradation than other salts, as indicated by both the loss in sedimentability and in infectivity. This is of particular interest, because pyrophosphate has previously been found to represent a particularly favourable buffer for the reconstitution of virus from protein and nucleic acid [5]. With this buffer and under optimal conditions, which includes good protein and nucleic acid preparations, activities as high as 30% to 50% of the theoretical, based on the weight of nucleic acid, have often been obtained. The present studies suggest that pyrophosphate is of such advantage because this salt, while favouring the aggregation of protein and nucleic acid no less than other salts, causes the secondary degradation of the nucleic acid to proceed at a much slower rate than do other salts. Thus the nucleic acid can be built into its protecting coat of protein with greater efficiency in the presence of this than of other salts.

The mechanism of the protecting effect of pyrophosphate on TMV-RNA is not yet clear. Very preliminary studies with ^{32}P-labelled pyrophosphate indicate a definite binding of this ion to the polynucleotide chain, greatly in excess of the binding of phosphate under similar conditions. Since nucleotide-diphosphates have been found to act similarly to pyrophosphate in some of the experiments mentioned above, it is tempting to speculate that there may be metabolic significance in the binding of the pyrophosphate group by a nucleic acid endowed with replication-stimulating activity.

An early tentative interpretation of the effect of pyrophosphate and other diphosphates was that these acted through their ability to chelate metals [5]. This led to a study of the effects of metals on the infectivity of TMV-RNA. And indeed, the infectivity is lost upon incubation with most metals, and particularly with copper and iron, of which only 10^{-5} M concentrations are required. This inactivation is definitely time- and temperature-dependent, and thus cannot be attributed solely to an ion-interchange. The addition of pyrophosphate or ethylenediaminetetraacetate largely prevents this inactivation. Metal-chelation may well represent an additional benefit of the use of poyrophsphate. But its primary mode of action seems to be due to direct interaction with the nucleic acid.

I would now like to mention briefly some lines of research of our laboratory, aiming at chemical modification of certain groups of the nucleic acid. Dr Staehelin has studied in some detail the interaction of the nucleic acid with formaldehyde, described by us a few years ago. And a parallel study is being performed with iodoacetate. Both reagents contain ^{14}C, which has enabled us to detect very small amounts, and arrive at the conclusion that both reagents substitute amino groups in the nucleic acid and cause inactivation when only a very small proportion of these groups (about one or two in a thousand) have been substituted. In these studies the availability of the various synthetic polynucleotides, of which Professor Ochoa kindly supplied us with samples, has been of greatest value. It seems probable that the chemical basis of the preparation of formaldehyde vaccines from viruses resides in this reactivity of the nucleic acid.

This has been a survey of recent work concerned with some physico-chemical

20

and chemical aspects of TMV-RNA. In regard to its biological role, no new unpublished findings can be reported. I will therefore only briefly review what has previously been ascertained. Since the nucleic acid alone can cause infection leading to the formation of progeny virus, it is obvious that it contains all the necessary information for both its own replication and that of the protein with which it is normally associated. When mixed viruses were prepared, containing protein from one and nucleic acid from another strain of TMV, the symptoms of the disease were indistinguishable from those provoked by the nucleic acid alone, and by the original strain supplying the nucleic acid. Comparative analyses of the composition of the corresponding progeny proteins has revealed no significant and consistent differences. Although this question is still under investigation, there is no question that the infection caused by nucleic acid of a certain strain produces progeny protein very similar to that originally associated with this nucleic acid, and quite different from the protein from a different strain with which the nucleic acid may have been coated with prior to application.

Having thus failed to produce mutants at will by the mixture of protein and nucleic acid from different strains, other possible means to attain this end have been investigated. The only indications of partial success have been observed when the nucleic acids from two strains were mixed and then, with addition of protein, transformed into reconstituted virus. Many of the virus lesions produced by this material behaved as if they were predominantly or completely due to one strain, others appeared mixed, but lost their mixed character upon further propagation. In two instances, however, new and stable mutants were isolated from such mixtures which differed in disease symptoms and/or amino acid composition from the two parent strains. Since a stable mutant has also been observed upon propagation of a single nucleic acid, the two mutants isolated from progeny obtained with mixed nucleic acids may be accidental and not due to a fusion of the genetic material. Apart from the possible production of mutants, these experiments should also throw light on another question which has concerned us at the beginning of this lecture, namely the size of the infectious particle. For if we get an appreciable number of mixed lesions, this would be an indication that nucleic acid preparations contain small, and yet active, nucleic acid subunits, while predominantly pure lesions would favour the alternate concept that only the intact nucleic acid cores were infectious. Unfortunately, here as elsewhere in life and in chemistry, purity is difficult to establish or to measure, and therefore the solution to this problem, as so many others which I have mentioned, has to await the outcome of further experiments.

REFERENCES

1. H. FRAENKEL-CONRAT, *J. Amer. chem. Soc.*, **78**, 882, 1956.
2. A. GIERER & G. SCHRAMM, *Z. Naturf.*, **11b**, 138, 1956.
3. H. FRAENKEL-CONRAT, B. SINGER & R. C. WILLIAMS, in *The Chemical Basis of Heredity*, Ed. by W. D. McElroy and B. Glass), McCollum Pratt Symp. Johns Hopkins Press, Baltimore, p. 501, 1957.
4. H. FRAENKEL-CONRAT, B. SINGER & R. C. WILLIAMS, *Biochim. biophys. Acta*, **25**, 87, 1957.
5. H. FRAENKEL-CONRAT, *Ann. N. Y. Acad. Sci.*, in press.
6. H. FRAENKEL-CONRAT & R. C. WILLIAMS, *Proc. nat. Acad. Sci.*, *Wash.*, **41**, 690, 1955.
7. A. GIERER, *Nature, Lond.*, **179**, 1299, 1957.

Die Bedeutung der Virusforschung für die Erkenntnis biologischer Vermehrungsvorgänge

G. SCHRAMM

Max-Planck Institut für Virusforschung, Tübingen, Germany

EIN WICHTIGER Weg, um dem Problem der Entstehung des Lebens näher zu kommen, besteht in der Analyse der chemischen Prozesse in den Lebewesen. In dem Maße, wie es gelingt, die Vielfalt der Lebenserscheinungen auf allgemeine Grundsätze zurückzuführen, wird die Angabe von Minimalbedingungen erleichtert, die für das Zustandekommen des Lebens notwendig waren.

Nach den Überlegungen von A. I. Oparin, Staudinger und G. V. Schulz [1] ist für das Leben die Bildung hochmolekularer Substanzen eine wichtige Voraussetzung, da nur mit großen Molekülen eine genügend hohe Spezifität erreicht werden kann und nur so ein Auseinanderdiffundieren der einzelnen Komponenten eines Lebewesens verhindert werden kann. Die Frage, die wir hier behandeln wollen, ist also die nach der Bildung makromolekularer Substanzen in der Natur. Die biochemische Forschung der letzten Jahre hat gezeigt, daß die Bildung der wichtigsten biologischen Makromoleküle, der Polysaccharide, der Nucleinsäuren und Proteine, überraschend ähnlich verläuft. Die energieliefernde Reaktion besteht in allen Fällen in der Bildung von Phosphorsäure oder eines Phosphorsäureesters, z.B. von Adenosinphosphat.

Diese Reaktion kann auch im Reagenzglas vorteilhaft zur Synthese hochmolekularer Substanzen ausgenützt werden. Zusammen mit meinen Mitarbeitern Restle [2], Brunn-Leube [3] und Wissmann [4] haben wir einige Reaktionen zur Herstellung definierter höherer Peptide untersucht. Der Aufbau einer Peptid-Bindung erfordert eine Energie von etwa 3–4 kcal/Mol. Eine befriedigende Ausbeute an höheren Peptiden läßt sich nur erreichen, wenn man von energiereichen Derivaten der Aminosäuren ausgeht. Wir untersuchten zunächst ein bereits von E. Fischer angegebenes Verfahren, das im Erhitzen der Methylester der Peptide besteht. Hierbei erfolgt unter Abspaltung von Methanol eine Polykondensation. Bei Dipeptiden erhält man vorzugsweise die ringförmigen Diketopiperazine, beim Erhitzen von Tri- und höheren Peptid-Methylestern erhält man langkettige Verbindungen.

Neuerdings wurde von Wissman und mir [4] festgestellt, daß man auch ausgehend von den freien Tripeptiden eine glatte Polykondensation erreicht, wenn man diese in Gegenwart von Polyphosphaten in einem wasserfreien Medium einige Stunden auf 100 °C erwärmt.

Diese zweite Reaktion weist gewisse Ähnlichkeiten mit der biologischen Entstehung der Makromoleküle auf. Wir haben einen energiereichen Katalysator, der zunächst eine energiereiche Zwischenverbindung mit dem Ausgangsmaterial bildet. Diese Zwischenverbindung reagiert dann unter Abspaltung von Phosphat zum hochmolekularen Endprodukt. Zur Analyse des Reaktionsprodukts wurde zunächst mit Dinitrofluorbenzol umgesetzt, die Dinitrophenyl-Peptide chromatographisch getrennt und nach einem von Schiedt & Restle [5] entwickelten Verfahren ihre Kettenlänge durch Infrarot-Messung bestimmt. Die Ausbeuten an den verschiedenen Peptiden, die bei der Polykondensation von Alanylglycylglycin in Gegenwart von Polyphosphat auftraten, sind aus Tabelle 1 ersichtlich. Bei zweistündigem Erhitzen führte die Kondensation bis

TABELLE 1

Kondensation von Alanylglycylglycin mit
Polyphosphat 2 Std. 100°

Bande Nr.	Kettenglieder-zahl	Ausbeute in %
1	3	44,5
2	6	32,5
3	9	15,4
4	12	2,6
5	15	2,1
6	18	2,8
7	21	0,9
8	24	0,1

zum 24-Peptid, bei längerer Kondensationsdauer wurden Ketten mit bis zu 40 Aminosäureresten erhalten. Dadurch ist gezeigt, daß unter Bedingungen, die geologisch für frühere Perioden auf der Erdoberfläche durchaus möglich erscheinen, höhere Peptide aus Aminosäuren entstehen können. Nach den Untersuchungen von Miller [6] kann man die Anwesenheit von Aminosäuren voraussetzen. Diese Reaktionen hätten allerdings nur ablaufen können, wenn energiereiche Phosphor-Verbindungen ständig von aussen zugeführt wurden. Hiervon unabhängig wurden erst Lebewesen, die die Möglichkeit besassen, die Lichtenergie zum Aufbau solcher energiereicher Phosphor-Verbindungen auszunützen.

In Hefe und vielen anderen Mikroorganismen findet man noch heute erhebliche Mengen an Metaphosphaten, die in neuerer Zeit besonders von Ingleman [7] untersucht wurden. Man könnte sich vorstellen, daß die Funktion der Metaphosphate im Laufe der Entwicklung von organischen Di- und Triphosphaten übernommen wurde.

Wenn wir somit auch über die energetische Seite der Biosynthese der Makromoleküle verhältnismässig gut unterrichtet sind, so bleibt doch die Frage, wie die Spezifität der Reaktion erreicht wird, noch offen. Auffallend ist die Einheitlichkeit der makromolekularen Naturstoffe hinsichtlich Grösse und Reihenfolge der Bausteine. Um Vorstellungen zu entwickeln, wie diese Spezifität erreicht werden könnte, wäre es notwendig, die grundsätzlichen biochemischen Vorgänge bei den heutigen Lebewesen genauer zu kennen. Ich will mich im Folgenden auf die Vorgänge bei der Biosynthese der Proteine beschränken. Die Genetik hat gezeigt, daß die Biosynthese aller spezifischen Proteine durch Gene gesteuert wird, so daß man umgekehrt auch sagen kann: die Funktion eines Gens ist die Produktion eines biokatalytisch wirksamen Proteins. Wie wir aus zahlreichen Experimenten wissen, ist die Desoxyribonucleinsäure (DNS) der entscheidende Bestandteil der Gene. Wie die in der DNS niedergelegte genetische Information auf die Struktur der Proteine übertragen wird, ist allerdings im Einzelnen noch ungeklärt. Sicher scheint nur zu sein, daß hierbei die Ribonucleinsäure (RNS) eine wichtige Rolle spielt. Die Synthese der meisten Proteine ist an die Anwesenheit von RNS gebunden und die Geschwindigkeit der Protein-Bildung ist dem RNS-Gehalt proportional. Innerhalb der verschiedenen Zellfraktionen sind die Partikel mit dem höchsten Gehalt an RNS, nämlich die Mikrosomen, auch diejenigen, bei denen der Einbau der Aminosäuren in die Proteine am schnellsten verläuft [8]. Wenn wir also annehmen, daß die Protein-synthese durch die RNS gesteuert wird, so müssen wir auch schliessen, daß die RNS-Bildung ihrerseits wieder durch die DNS kontrolliert wird. Wir kommen auf diese Weise zu einem hierarchischen System in der Zelle, dessen Spitze von den Phosphor-haltigen Nucleinsäuren gebildet wird:

DNS → RNS → Enzymproteine → niedermolekularer Stoffwechsel

Einer der erfolgversprechendsten Wege, dieses stark vereinfachte Schema zu prüfen und auszubauen, ist die Erforschung der Virusvermehrung, da die Bildung eines Virusteilchens übersichtlicher ist als die Vermehrung eines vollständigen Organismus. Aus der Fülle des Materials möchte ich mich hier auf die Biosynthese des Tabakmosaikvirus (TMV) beschränken. Das TMV ist ein Nucleoproteid, das etwa 6% RNS enthält. Durch teilweisen Abbau des stäbchenförmigen Moleküls konnte gezeigt werden, daß die RNS einen einzelnen Strang im Innern des TMV bildet [9, 10]. Da dem TMV ein Molgewicht von etwa 40 Millionen zukommt, beträgt das Teilchengewicht der gesamten RNS 2,4 Millionen. Die TMV-Teilchen, die einen Teil ihres Proteins verloren hatten, erwiesen sich noch als infektiös. Für diesen Abbau benützten wir ein alkalisches Milieu vom pH 10,3. Das hierbei abgelöste Protein bezeichnen wir als A-Protein. Takahashi und andere Autoren [11] konnten zeigen, daß in infizierten Tabakpflanzen ein abnormales Protein, das sogenannte X-Protein, vorkommt, das in seinen Eigenschaften mit dem A-Protein übereinstimmt.

Weitere Versuche zeigten, daß die Infektiosität der RNS erhalten bleibt, wenn man das A-Protein vollständig abtrennt. Für diese Abtrennung benützten Gierer & Schramm [12] die Extraktion mit Phenol. Durch eine Reihe von Kontrollversuchen konnte gezeigt werden, daß die Infektiosität nicht auf einer Beimengung von intakten Virusteilchen oder auf der Anwesenheit von A-Protein beruht. Etwa gleichzeitig wurde von Fraenkel-Conrat [13] gefunden, daß auch mit Dodecylsulfat die Darstellung einer biologisch aktiven RNS aus TMV möglich ist. Die experimentellen Daten, die die Ergebnisse von Gierer & Schramm in vollem Umfang bestätigen, wurden kürzlich veröffentlicht [14].

Auf grund von Sedimentations- und Viskositätsmessungen kommt der Haupt-
komponente der infektiösen RNS ein Molgewicht von etwa 2,3 Millionen zu
[15]. Kleinere Beimengungen von abgebautem Material mit niedrigerem Molgewicht erwiesen sich als nicht infektiös. Dies wurde durch Abbauversuche mit
Ribonuclease bestätigt. Die quantitative Auswertung dieser Versuche ergab,
daß wahrscheinlich ein einziger Bruch des Nucleinsäurestrangs genügt, um die
Infektiosität zu zerstören. Nach diesen Ergebnissen scheint nur die intakte RNS
in der Lage zu sein, die Biosynthese des Virusproteins in der Zelle zu induzieren.
Aufgrund von Sedimentationsversuchen, die in destilliertem Wasser vorgenommen wurden, kommen Fraenkel-Conrat *et al.* [14] zu dem Schluss, daß auch
Teilchen mit niederem Molgewicht infektiös sein können. Diese Folgerung ist
jedoch nicht zwingend, da aus der Sedimentationskonstanten allein keine
Aussagen über das Molgewicht gemacht werden können. In destilliertem Wasser
erfolgt bei der RNS, wie bei anderen Polyelektrolyten, eine Streckung des
Moleküls, bei der die Sedimentationskonstante ohne Änderung des Molgewichts
erniedrigt wird, während die Viskosität ansteigt.

Die weitere Aufgabe besteht nun darin, zu untersuchen, wie die Bildung des
Virusproteins in der Zelle erfolgt. Versuche von Wildman *et al.* [16] und einige,
die wir mit Engler [17] durchführten, zeigen, daß bei Infektion mit der freien
RNS die Latenzphase wesentlich kürzer ist, als wenn man Protein-haltiges
Virus zur Infektion benützt. Die erste Phase der Infektion besteht also in einem
Abstreifen der Proteinhülle. Die weiteren Phasen sind noch ungewiss. Insbesondere ist noch nicht klar, in welchem Teil der Zelle, dem Nucleus oder dem
Cytoplasma, die Virussynthese vor sich geht. Neuere Versuche von Jeener *et al.*
[18] machen es sehr wahrscheinlich, daß das A-Protein eine Vorstufe des Virus
darstellt. Die Synthese des Virus wird also vermutlich auf ähnlichem Wege
erfolgen wie die Reconstitution, die von Fraenkel-Conrat [19, 20] beschrieben
wurde.

Die Aggregation des Nucleinsäure-freien A-Proteins zu stäbchenförmigen
Partikeln wurde zuerst 1947 beschrieben [21] und seitdem in allen Einzelheiten
sowohl mit physikalisch-chemischen Methoden [22] als auch röntgenographisch
[23] untersucht. Die kleinste Untereinheit des TMV ist ein Peptid mit einem
Molgewicht von etwa 16.500. Sechs dieser Peptideinheiten vereinigen sich in
Lösung zu dem A-Protein mit einem Molgewicht von etwa 100.000 (pH 10).
Bei Erniedrigung des pH tritt das A-Protein über mehrere Zwischenstufen zu
einem Stäbchen zusammen, das nach seinem äusseren Durchmesser und seiner
Form dem ursprünglichen TMV sehr ähnlich ist. Besonders charakteristisch ist
eine Zwischenstufe, die aus einem Proteinscheibchen mit einer Dicke von etwa
70 Å und einem zentralen Loch besteht. Mehrere derartige Scheiben legen sich
dann zu einem Stäbchen aufeinander. Die Röntgenuntersuchungen von Franklin
[24, 25] zeigen, daß die Peptideinheiten im TMV spiralig angeordnet sind. Vom
theoretischen Standpunkt ist es wichtig, darauf hinzuweisen, daß die Form des
hierbei entstehenden Hohlzylinders durch die Form der Peptidunterunterheiten
definiert ist und keine zusätzlichen Katalysatoren für die spezifische Anordnung
benötigt werden. Durch Vergleich der Röntgendiagramme des reaggregierten
A-Proteins mit dem Nucleinsäure-haltigen Virusstäbchen konnte auch die Lage

der RNS im Innern des Virus genauer festgelegt werden. Die Nucleinsäure bildet eine Spirale, die den Windungen der Proteinspirale folgt. Die Phosphor-Atome befinden sich in Abstand von 40 Å von der zentralen Achse. Im Innern des Virus ist ein Kanal, dessen Radius 20 Å beträgt. Diese aus Röntgendaten entwickelte Struktur konnte durch elektronenmikroskopische Untersuchungen, vor allem von Huxley [26, 27] bestätigt werden.

Sieht man die röntgenographischen Daten als gesichert an, so ergibt sich aus der Menge der im TMV enthaltenen Nucleotide, daß die RNS nur aus einer einzigen Nucleotidkette bestehen kann. Die Struktur ist also wesentlich verschieden von der Doppelspirale der DNS. Dieses Einstrang-Modell wird auch durch die Ergebnisse von Gierer [15] gestützt. Die Besonderheiten der Virus-nucleinsäure bestehen also darin, daß sie im Zellmilien ein Protein erzeugt, das sich leicht mit der Nucleinsäure vereinigen kann und der Nucleinsäure ausserhalb der Zelle einen Schutz gegen enzymatische und sonstige Einwirkungen bietet. Das Protein ist weiterhin so beschaffen, daß es ein leichtes Eindringen der Nucleinsäure in eine Wirtszelle ermöglicht und nach dem Eindringen leicht wieder abgespalten wird. Hierin unterscheidet sich also die Virusnucleinsäure von anderen RNS-Molekülen, die meist ein Protein produzieren, das losgelöst, von der RNS eigene Funktionen erfüllt.

Im Ganzen genommen sind unsere Kenntnisse über die Biosynthese des TMV noch lückenhaft. Keinesfalls scheint es zulässig, ein Virus als Vorstufe der Lebewesen zu betrachten, denn die Voraussetzung für die Vermehrung der Viren ist die Existenz lebender Zellen mit ihrem äusserst komplizierten Enzymapparat. Die Bedeutung der Virusforschung für das Problem der Entstehung des Lebens scheint mir vielmehr darin zu liegen, daß sie uns Einblick in die biochemischen Grundlagen der Vermehrung liefert. Wenn es uns gelingen sollte, die hierbei maßgeblichen Prinzipien zu erkennen, wird es vielleicht möglich sein, bessere Hypothesen über die Vorstufen des Lebens zu entwickeln und vor allem die Grundfrage nach der Spezifizität der Biosynthesen makromolekularer Naturstoffe zu beantworten.

LITERATURVERZEICHNIS

1. G. V. SCHULZ, *Naturwissenschaften*, **37**, 196, 223, 1950.
2. G. SCHRAMM & H. RESTLE, *Makromol. Chem.*, **13**, 103, 1954.
3. I. v. BRUNN-LEUBE & G. SCHRAMM, *Chem. Ber.*, **89**, 2045, 1956.
4. H. WISSMANN, Dissertation, Tübingen, 1957; G. SCHRAMM & H. WISSMANN, *Chem. Ber.*, **91**, 1073, 1958.
5. U. SCHIEDT & H. RESTLE, *Z. Naturf.*, **9b**, 182, 1954.
6. S. L. MILLER, *Science*, **117**, 528, 1953.
7. Zusammenfassung bei B. INGELMAN, in *Enzymes* (herausgegeben von J. B. SUMNER & K. MYRBÄCK). Academic Press, New York, Vol. 1, 1950.
8. Zusammenfassung bei J. BRACHET, in *Nucleic Acids* (herausgegeben von E. CHARGAFF & J. N. DAVIDSON). Academic Press, New York, Vol. 2, 1955.
9. G. SCHRAMM, G. SCHUMACHER & W. ZILLIG, *Z. Naturf.*, **10b**, 481 1955.
10. R. G. HART, *Proc. nat. Acad. Sci., Wash.*, **41**, 261, 1955.
11. Ausführliche Literaturzusammenstellung bei G. SCHRAMM, *Annu. Rev. Biochem.*, **27**, 101, 1958.
12. A. GIERER & G. SCHRAMM, *Z. Naturf.*, **11b**, 138, 1956; *Nature, Lond.*, **177**, 702, 1956.
13. H. FRAENKEL-CONRAT, *J. Amer. chem. Soc.*, **78**, 882, 1956.

14. H. Fraenkel-Conrat, B. Singer & R. C. Williams, *Biochim. biophys. Acta,* **25,** 87, 1957.
15. A. Gierer, *Nature, Lond.,* **179,** 1297, 1957.
16. A. Siegel, W. Ginoza & S. G. Wildman, *Virology,* **3,** 554, 1957.
17. G. Schramm & R. Engler, *Nature, Lond.,* **181,** 216, 1958.
18. C. v. Rysselberge & R. Jeener, *Biochim. biophys. Acta,* **23,** 18, 1957.
19. H. Fraenkel-Conrat & R. C. Williams, *Proc. nat. Acad. Sci., Wash.,* **41,** 690, 1955.
20. H. Fraenkel-Conrat & B. Singer, *Biochim. biophys. Acta,* **24,** 540, 1957.
21. G. Schramm, *Z. Naturf.,* **2b,** 249, 1947.
22. G. Schramm & W. Zillig, *Z. Naturf.,* **10b,** 493, 1955.
23. R. E. Franklin, *Biochim. biophys. Acta,* **18,** 313, 1955.
24. R. E. Franklin, *Nature, Lond.,* **177,** 928, 1956.
25. A. Klug & R. E. Franklin, *Biochim. biophys. Acta,* **23,** 199, 1957.
26. H. E. Huxley, First European Regional Conference on Electron Microscopy, Abstract, 1957. Academic Press, New York.
27. H. Fernandez-Moran & G. Schramm, *Z. Naturf.,* **13b,** 68, 1958.

On the Nature of Viruses, Genes and Life*

WENDELL M. STANLEY

Director of the Virus Laboratory, University of California, Berkeley, California, U.S.A.

RECENT scientific discoveries, especially in the virus field, are throwing new light on the basic nature of viruses, genes and even life itself. These discoveries are providing evidence for relationships between these three subjects which indicate that one may be dependent upon another to an extent not fully appreciated heretofore, and hence the time is appropriate for a declaration of the nature of the dependence that may be involved. Too often one works and thinks within too narrow a range and hence fails to recognize the significance of certain facts for other areas. Sometimes the important new ideas and subsequent fundamental discoveries come from the borderline areas between two well-established fields of investigation. I trust, therefore, that this discussion will result in the synthesis of new ideas regarding viruses, genes and life and that these ideas in turn will result in the doing of new experiments which may provide the basis for fundamental discoveries in these fields which are so important to every one of us.

Now I suppose there is no doubt but that, of the three topics, life is the one that most people would consider to be of the greatest importance. One would think that the nature of life would be easy to define since we are all experiencing it. However, just as life means different things to different people, we find that in reality it is extremely difficult to define just what we mean by life or by a living agent in its most simple form. There is no difficulty in recognizing an agent as living or non-living so long as we contemplate structures such as man, cats and dogs, or even small organisms such as the bacteria, or, at the other extreme, structures such as a piece of iron or glass, an atom of hydrogen or even a molecule of water, sugar or of our blood pigment, haemoglobin. The former are examples of animate or living agents whereas the latter are examples of inanimate or non-living things. But what is the true nature of the difference between a man and a piece of iron, or between a bacterial organism and a molecule of haemoglobin? The ability to grow or reproduce and to change or mutate have long been regarded as special properties characteristic of living agents. Certainly mankind and bacteria have the ability to assimilate and metabolize food, respond to external stimuli and to reproduce their kind—properties not shared by bits of iron or by molecules of haemoglobin. Now if viruses had not been discovered, all would have been well. The organisms of the biologist would have ranged from the largest of animals, whales and elephants and the like, all the way down to

* Adapted from a lecture given before the American Philosophical Society in Philadelphia, Pa., on April 25, 1957.

the smallest of the bacteria which are about 200 mμ, or a few millionths of an inch in diameter. There would have been a definite break with respect to size, since the largest molecules known to the chemist were less than 20 mμ in size.

Life and living agents would have been represented solely by those structures which possessed the ability to reproduce themselves and to change or mutate and all of these were about 200 mμ or larger in size, thus more than ten times larger than the largest known molecule. This would have provided a comfortable area of separation or discontinuity between living and non-living things and would have provided ample justification for considering life as something set distinctly apart and perhaps unapproachable and unexplainable by science.

Then around 1900 came the discovery of the viruses—first the plant virus of tobacco mosaic, then foot-and-mouth disease virus of cattle and then the first virus affecting man, namely, yellow fever virus. These infectious, disease producing agents are characterized by their small size, by their ability to grow or reproduce within specific living cells and by their ability to change or mutate during reproduction. Their inability to grow or reproduce on artificial or non-living media did not cause too much concern and their reproductive and mutative powers were enough to convince most people that viruses were merely still smaller ordinary living organisms. However, around 1930 the sizes of different viruses were determined with some precision, and it was found that some viruses were indeed quite small, actually smaller than certain protein molecules. Then in 1935 I had the good fortune to isolate the virus first discovered by Ivanovskiĭ, namely, tobacco mosaic, which is a middle-sized virus, in the form of a crystallizable material which was found to be a nucleoprotein, that is, a substance composed of nucleic acid and protein. This nucleoprotein molecule was found to be 15 mμ in cross-section and 300 mμ in length and to possess the unusually high molecular weight of about fifty millions. It was, therefore, larger than any molecule previously described, yet it was found to possess all of the usual properties associated with larger protein molecules. The same material could be obtained from different kinds of mosaic-diseased plants such as tomato, phlox and spinach plants, whereas plants diseased with different strains of tobacco mosaic virus yielded slightly different nucleoproteins. Many tests indicated that the new high-molecular-weight nucleoprotein was actually tobacco mosaic virus and it was concluded that this virus could, in fact, be a nucleoprotein molecule. Here, therefore, was a molecule that possessed the ability to reproduce itself and to mutate; hence the distinction between living and non-living things which had existed up to that time seemed to be tottering and soon a full-scale intellectual revolution was in progress.

To-day the revolution is past and we know that the gap between 20 and 200 mμ has been filled in completely by the viruses—so much so that there is actually an overlapping with respect to size at both ends. Some larger viruses are larger than certain well-accepted living organisms whereas some small viruses are actually smaller than certain protein molecules. We have, therefore, a continuity with respect to size as we go from the electrons, mesons, atoms and molecules of the physicist and the chemist, to the organisms of the biologist and on, if you please, to the stars and galaxies. Nowhere is it possible to draw a line in this continuity of structures and say that all above this size are living and all below are non-living. There appears to be a gradual transition with respect to size and complexity of structure as one goes from things that are normally considered to be alive to things that are generally considered to be non-living. One is reminded of the quotation attributed to Aristotle over 2000 years ago to the effect that Nature makes so gradual a transition from the animate to the inanimate that the boundary line between the two is doubtful and perhaps non-existent. Much scientific knowledge has been accumulated since Aristotle's time but the essence of his statement is as true to-day as it was when he made it. But does this mean there is really no difference between the animate and the inanimate? I do not believe that it does. However, we must be willing to define what we mean by life and then we must be willing to accept as living any structure possessing properties fulfilling such a definition.

The essence of life is the ability to reproduce. This is accomplished by the utilization of energy to create order out of disorder, to bring together into a specific predetermined pattern from semi-order or even from chaos all of the component parts of that pattern with the perpetuation of that pattern with time. This is life. Now there is another very basic property which seems to be characteristic of living things and that is the ability to mutate, to change or to respond to a stimulus. I do not believe this property is absolutely necessary for life, but it certainly lends grandeur to life, for not only is it responsible for the whole evolutionary process and thus for the myriads of kinds of life we have on earth but, most importantly for mankind, it permits one to dare to aspire. It is presumably responsible for man, his conscience and his faith. It is obvious that I believe that mutation merits much, much study.

The discovery of viruses has permitted us to contemplate the nature of life with a new understanding. It has enabled us to appreciate in a new light the inherent potentialities of chemical structure, whether that of a single molecule or that produced by the interaction of two or more molecules. Viruses were discovered by virtue of their ability to replicate and in the last analysis this ability to reproduce remains to-day as the only definitive way in which they can be recognized. We may purify and isolate preparations from virus-diseased tissues but it is only when a reasonably pure material is obtained and units of this are found to possess the ability to reproduce themselves that we are privileged to refer to the material as virus. Since the isolation of tobacco mosaic virus in the form of a crystallizable nucleoprotein 15 by 300 mμ in size, many other viruses have been obtained in pure form and characterized in part by their chemical and physical properties. My colleagues in the Virus Laboratory at the University of California in Berkeley, Arthur Knight, Robley Williams and Howard Schachman, have made major contributions to the biochemical, electron-microscopical and biophysical knowledge of viruses. Until two years ago all viruses studied had been found to be at least as complex as a nucleoprotein. However, some appear to have lipid, carbohydrate and in some cases a limiting membrane in addition to nucleic acid and protein. Whereas some viruses, like tobacco mosaic, are crystallizable nucleoproteins which have the usual molecular properties, other viruses, such as vaccinia, have a degree of morphological differentiation which can hardly be called molecular in nature and which is rather more organismal or cell-like in nature. Some of the bacterial viruses have a very complex morphology, with a head and tail somewhat similar to the sperm of higher organisms.

For a long time many investigators thought that the plant viruses differed basically from viruses affecting animals and man. This idea stemmed mainly from the fact that for twenty years all of the crystallizable viruses were plant viruses. This idea had to be relinquished two years ago when my colleagues, Carlton Schwerdt and Frederick Schaffer, obtained poliomyelitis virus, which is a typical animal or human virus, in crystalline form. This was the first virus affecting animals or man to be obtained in crystalline form, and it is interesting to note that crystalline poliovirus was obtained just twenty years after the isolation of tobacco mosaic virus in crystalline form. One other animal or human virus has just been crystallized and this is crystalline Coxsackie virus obtained by Dr. Mattern of the National Institutes of Health.

Hundreds of viruses are known and more are being discovered every month, yet only a dozen or so have been obtained in purified form. In view of the possibility that these may represent the more stable and more readily purified viruses, one cannot be certain that a true picture of the chemical and physical properties of viruses as a whole has been obtained as yet. However, I believe that we have sufficient sampling to be significant for the purposes of the present discussion, for we already know that viruses may range from small crystallizable animal, human or plant viruses, which are nucleoprotein molecules, through intermediate structures consisting of nucleoprotein, lipid and carbohydrate, to large structures possessing a morphology and composition similar to that of accepted cellular organisms. All of these diverse structures are bound together by one all-important property, that of being able to reproduce their own characteristic structure when placed within certain living cells. They are all, in short, by definition, alive.

Now I am only too fully aware of objections that some may have to considering a crystallizable nucleoprotein molecule as a living agent. Some may feel that life is a mystery which is and must remain beyond the comprehension of the human mind. With these I must disagree. Some may believe that a living molecule is contrary to religion. Here again I must disagree for I see no conflict whatsoever between science and religion and I see no wrong in accepting a molecule as a living structure. To many scientists the diverse expressions of chemical structure represent miracles, and our expanding knowledge of the wonders of nature provides ample opportunities to express our faith and only serves to make us full of humility. Some may prefer to regard a virus molecule in a crystal in a test tube as a potentially living structure and to restrict the term 'living' to a virus during the time that it is actually reproducing. I would have no serious objection to this, for I am reminded of the facts that certain tapeworms a foot or so in length can live and reproduce only in certain hosts and that even man himself can be regarded as requiring rather special conditions for life, yet no one objects to accepting man and tapeworms as examples of life. I am also reminded that we are taught that the essence of a thing is not what it is, but what it does and the doing of something involves time, hence there may be good reason always to consider the virus with time. Regardless of certain mental restrictions that may differ from person to person, I think there is no escape from the acceptance ultimately of viruses, including the crystallizable viral nucleoprotein molecules, as living agents. This must be done because of their ability to reproduce or to bring about their own replication. Certainly the essence of life is the ability to reproduce, to create a specific order out of disorder by the repetitive formation with time of a specific predetermined pattern and this the viral nucleoprotein molecules can do.

Of course, it would have been dull indeed if the first-formed living agent had been restricted to exact duplicates of itself. The logical reasoning provided in schemes such as those outlined by Oparin, Calvin and others by means of which relatively complex organic substances could have arisen from inorganic matter provides justification for assuming that a chemical structure, perhaps something like nucleic acid, which possessed the ability to replicate, did come into being once upon a time. It needed to have happened only once and thereafter without the great phenomenon of mutation it merely would have kept going until it had filled the world with replicates of this precise structure or until it had exhausted the starting materials. However, Nature has provided a built-in error so that the replication process is not perfect and about one in every million or so replicates is slightly different. This change, which has been of tremendous fundamental importance, we now recognize as mutation and as these errors or differences were accumulated by replicating structures it became necessary to make formal recognition of them. These differences or markers we now call genes. We do not recognize genes directly but only by differences. Needless to say, some physical structure had to be responsible for the accumulation, preservation, and potential exhibition of these differences and this assembly of genes we call a chromosome. The incorporation of one or more assemblies of genes into a structure possessing a limiting membrane, which we now call a cell, then made possible gene interchanges between these cellular assemblies. This genetic interchange by the fusion of two cells, a sexual process, also represents a phenomenon of the greatest fundamental importance for this permitted genetic recombination, a factor that has served to speed up the evolutionary process immeasurably. Therefore, life as we know it to-day is dependent not only upon reproduction but also upon mutation and genetic recombination.

Now let us consider for a moment the relationships between genes and viruses since we see that both are related to life. Muller's estimate of the maximum size of a gene would place it just below tobacco mosaic virus, near the middle of the viruses. Both genes and viruses seem to be nucleoproteins and both reproduce only within specific living cells. Both possess the ability to mutate. Although viruses generally reproduce many times within a given cell, some situations are known in which they appear to reproduce only once with each cell division. Genes usually reproduce once with each cell division but here also the rate can be changed, as, for example, in the case of polyploidy resulting from treatment with colchicine. Actually the similarities between genes and viruses are so remarkable that viruses very early were referred to as 'naked genes' or 'genes on the loose'. Three great discoveries, one which began in 1928, another which has resulted from Bordet's early work on lysogeny and the other which occurred in 1952 and has to do with transduction, have provided experimental evidence for an exceedingly intimate relationship between viruses and genes. In 1928 Griffith found that he could transform one specific S type of pneumococcus into another specific S type by injecting mice with non-virulent R forms together with large amounts of heat-killed S pneumococci of a type other than that of the organisms from which the R cells were derived. Living virulent S organisms of the same type as the heat-killed S forms were then recovered from the animals. Later Dawson and Sia as well as Alloway found that the addition of an extract of one type of capsulated pneumococcus to a culture of a non-capsulated rough form would convert the latter into the same type of capsulated pneumococcus which provided the extract. It was obvious that something was being transferred and in 1938 I discussed the possibility that this 'something' might be a virus. In 1944 Avery and his colleagues at the Rockefeller Institute proved that this something was a transforming principle consisting of deoxyribo-nucleic acid (DNA). Muller in 1947 discussed the possibility that the DNA might correspond to still viable parts of bacterial chromosomes loose in solution which, after entering the capsuleless bacteria, undergo a kind of crossing over with the chromosomes of the host, but this suggestion was not widely accepted. That the phenomenon was not an isolated one was demonstrated in 1953 by Leidy and Alexander, who obtained similar results with an influenza-bacteria system. The close relationship to genetics was further emphasized by work of Hotchkiss and by Ephrussi-Taylor who, as well as Leidy and Alexander, showed that drug resistance and other genetic factors could be so transferred. This work provided evidence that genetic factors or genes, if one prefers such a designation, can be represented by DNA and can be obtained in chemically pure solution.

The persistence of a bacterial virus in an apparently concealed form or pro-phage in lysogenic strains of bacteria, extensively investigated by Lwoff, provides further evidence in this direction. Lysogenic bacteria perpetuate in what may be considered a hereditary manner the property of being able to produce a bacterial virus. The term prophage is used to describe the form in which the potentiality to produce a bacterial virus is perpetuated in lysogenic bacteria. Prophage is non-pathogenic and non-infectious in the usual sense, but, since it is multiplied at least once with each cell division, it may be regarded as infectious in the sense that genes or chromosomes are infectious. In other words, the pro-phage might be considered as a temporary part of the genetic apparatus of the cell, the genetic element that differentiates a lysogenic from a sensitive cell, and at the same time as the non-infectious form of a bacterial virus. There are times, therefore, when a virus may not exhibit its normally infectious nature but have its potentially unlimited reproductive capacity under genetic control, so that it replicates only once with each cell division. There are times when a specific genetic element of a cell can be freed of the normal controlling mechanism of the cell and go forth in viable form in solution or associated with a virus, enter a different cell, replace a homologous chromosomal segment and resume its original specific function in the new cell. It is obvious that the latter phenomenon could readily be considered an infectious process, and that viruses can act as genes and genes as viruses under certain circumstances.

This information as well as our knowledge of viruses was soon fortified by the very important discovery by Zinder & Lederberg in 1952 of transduction in *Salmonella* by means of a bacterial virus. It was found that genetic factors could be carried from one type of *Salmonella* cells to another type by means of a bacterial virus. In this type of transformation the genetic fragment is not free but is carried within the structure of the bacterial virus. It is, for example, not affected by the enzyme deoxyribonuclease, and in this respect is unlike the DNA pneumococcus-transforming principle. However, it is not necessary for the virus actually to possess virus activity, for killing of the virus by ultraviolet light does not prevent the transduction of other traits. The closeness of the relationship between the virus and the genes of the host is emphasized by the fact that the transducing ability of any bacterial virus is determined strictly by the character of the cells on which the virus was most recently grown. Virus grown on Serotype E_2 *Salmonella* cells will, when added to Serotype E_1 cells, convert a fraction of these cells into Serotype E_2 cells. It is of interest to note that the virus in filtrates of toxin-forming bacterial strains will convert non-toxin-forming cells into toxin-forming cells. In transduction, a fragment of a chromosome which might be regarded as a gene or a collection of a few of even many genes can be transferred from one kind of donor cell to another kind of receiver cell and be incorporated into the genetic apparatus of the receiver cell. In the pneumococcus or influenza bacterium this can be caused by a DNA preparation which can be separated and isolated as such and in *Salmonella* this gene or gene collection rides within the bacterial virus, presumably with the viral DNA, which is added to the cell to be transduced. Here one hardly knows what to call a virus and what to call a gene for it is obvious that at times the two merge completely.

I hope that by this time it is obvious that viruses, genes and life are tied together by a series of relationships, that viruses can act as genes and genes as viruses under certain circumstances, and that viruses are structures at the twilight zone of life partaking both of living and of molecular properties. Let us now see if there is a common thread of understanding permeating all of these relationships. We know that viruses have been thought to be at least as complex as a nucleoprotein, but we also know that the transforming agent of the pneumococcus has been found to be a deoxyribonucleic acid and there is presumptive evidence that the genetic stuff of the bacterial viruses is also deoxyribonucleic acid. However, until recently no gene or chromosome or any of the ordinary viruses had been isolated as such in the form of nucleic acid, hence the 'stuff of life', as well as the viruses, has been considered to be nucleoprotein in nature with considerable doubt as to whether the protein or the nucleic acid or the combination of the two was really the biologically active structure.

A recent very important discovery made in our laboratory by Dr. Fraenkel-Conrat has changed the situation considerably and now makes it seem certain that nucleic acid is the all-important structure. It was reported by Fraenkel-Conrat and also shortly thereafter by Gierer & Schramm in Germany that special treatment of tobacco mosaic virus yielded a nucleic acid preparation possessing virus activity. It would now appear necessary to recognize that a nucleic acid structure of around 1,000,000 molecular weight can possess codes within its 3000 or so nucleotides not only all of the information that is necessary to bring about in the host cell the production of more of this same nucleic acid, but also apparently the *de novo* synthesis of its own characteristic and highly specific protein with which it eventually coats itself. This work provides wonderful evidence for a direct relationship between specific nucleic acid and specific protein synthesis and makes it possible to consider virus and gene action, including their relationships to the nature of life, in terms, not of nucleoprotein structure, but in terms of nucleic acid structure. We see, most importantly, that viruses, genes and life are all directly dependent upon the structure of nucleic acid.

It may be calculated that a thousand-unit polynucleotide linear chain consisting of a coded repeat of only four different components, adenine, guanine, cytosine and uracil in the same ratio as exists in tobacco mosaic virus nucleic acid could form about 10^{590} different arrangements. This number is so large that it is incomprehensible. Even a one-hundred-unit polynucleotide chain of this composition could exist in about 10^{57} different arrangements and this number is vastly larger than the total of all living things on earth and in the oceans. We have, therefore, in this structure consisting of the four chemicals, adenine, guanine, cytosine and uracil (thymine in the case of deoxyribonucleic acid) repeated many times over in unique fashion the code for every bit of life on earth and in the sea.

I believe that the elucidation of the structure of nucleic acid in all of its aspects is the most important scientific problem we face to-day. It is vastly more important than any of the problems associated with the structure of the atom, for in nucleic acid structure we are dealing with life itself and with a unique approach for bettering the lot of mankind on earth. It is possible that the solution of this scientific problem could lead eventually to the solution of major political and economic problems. Never before has it been possible to realize so fully our utter dependence upon the structure of nucleic acid. Eventually chemists should be able to synthesize a small polynucleotide specifically arranged, hence one may now dare to think of synthesizing in the laboratory a structure possessing genetic continuity and of all of the tremendous implications of such an accomplishment.

SELECTED REFERENCES

O. T. AVERY, C. M. MACLEOD & M. McCARTY, Studies on the chemical nature of the substance inducing transformation of pneumococcal types. Induction of transformation by a desoxyribonucleic acid fraction isolated from pneumococcus type III. *J. exp. Med.*, **79**, 137, 1944.

J. BORDET, The theories of the bacteriophage. *Proc. Roy. Soc.*, B, **107**, 398, 1931.

MELVIN CALVIN, Chemical evolution and the origin of life. *Amer. Scientist*, **44**, 248, 1956.

The Nature of Virus Multiplication (Eds. Sir PAUL FILDES and W. E. VAN HEYNINGEN). Cambridge University Press, 1953.

H. FRAENKEL-CONRAT & ROBLEY C. WILLIAMS, Reconstitution of active tobacco mosaic virus from its inactive protein and nucleic acid components. *Proc. nat. Acad. Sci., Wash.*, **41**, 690, 1955.

H. FRAENKEL-CONRAT, The role of the nucleic acid in the reconstitution of active tobacco mosaic virus. *J. Amer. chem. Soc.*, **78**, 882, 1956.

ALFRED GIERER & GERHARD SCHRAMM, Die Infektiosität der Nucleinsäure aus Tabak-mosaikvirus. *Z. Naturforsch.*, 11b, 138, 1956.

F. GRIFFITH, The significance of pneumococcal types. *J. Hyg.*, 27, 113, 1928.

JOSHUA LEDERBERG, Genetic transduction. *Amer. Scientist*, 44, 264, 1956.

A. I. OPARIN, *The Origin of Life* (Trans. by S. MORGULIS). Macmillan, New York, 1938.

THOMAS M. RIVERS, The infinitely small in biology. *Science*, 93, 143, 1941.

F. L. SCHAFFER & C. E. SCHWERDT, Crystallization of purified MEF-1 poliomyelitis virus particles. *Proc. nat. Acad. Sci., Wash.*, 41, 1020, 1955.

W. M. STANLEY, Isolation of a crystalline protein possessing the properties of tobacco-mosaic virus. *Science*, 81, 644, 1935.

W. M. STANLEY, The architecture of viruses. *Physiol. Rev.*, 19, 524, 1939.

W. M. STANLEY, Some chemical, medical and philosophical aspects of viruses. *Science*, 93, 145, 1941.

W. M. STANLEY, The isolation and properties of crystalline tobacco mosaic virus, *Les Prix Nobel en* 1947. P. A. Nordstedt & Söner, Stockholm, 1949.

N. D. ZINDER & J. LEDERBERG, Genetic exchange in *Salmonella*. *J. Bact.*, 64, 679, 1952.

ELSA M. ZITCER, JØRGEN FOGH & THELMA H. DUNNEBACKE, Human amnion cells for large-scale production of polio virus. *Science*, 122, 30, 1955.

On the Species Specificity of the Nucleic Acids of Bacteria

A. N. BELOZERSKIĬ

A. N. Bakh Institute of Biochemistry, U.S.S.R. Academy of Sciences,
and Faculty of Biology and Soil Science, Moscow State University

IN RECENT years our concepts of the specificity of the nucleic acids have undergone considerable changes. Whereas before there were no reasons for considering nucleic acids as highly specific substances, somewhat resembling proteins in this respect, now the situation is radically different. The need for this reappraisal was brought out most strikingly by the remarkable investigations of Professor Chargaff's laboratory. These investigations made it abundantly clear that deoxyribonucleic acid (DNA) from different biological sources differs in purine and pyrimidine contents. The work of this laboratory, coupled with certain other data, was also highly important because it provided a substantial stimulus to study the structure of nucleic acids, since it became obvious that the theory of the tetranucleotide structure of nucleic acids, formulated earlier in its final form by Levene, did not ally with the new experimental findings.

Furthermore, the new data on the structural chemistry of the nucleic acids revealed a non-uniform nucleotide distribution both in ribonucleic acid (RNA) and in DNA, which furnished grounds for assuming a possible and even far-reaching isomerism in this group of compounds.

Nevertheless, if the results of work on the specificity and heterogeneity of the nucleic acids are brought together, we may speak of the following possible types of specificity of the nucleic acids: (1) species specificity, (2) age specificity, (3) organ and tissue specificity, (4) organoid specificity, and finally, (5) molecular specificity, in which case, for example, the same cell organoid can contain a series of different molecules of nucleic acids [1].

For a final solution of the problem of the reality of these types of nucleic acid specificity it is necessary to accumulate far more experimental information. Whereas with respect to DNA the question of species specificity—and perhaps molecular specificity—can be considered in some degree answered, with respect to RNA there are few data and even these are often contradictory, this being due to the fact that RNA appears to be highly labile and its isolation from cells or tissues subjects it to a greater or lesser degree of degradation. At any rate in the first stage of investigations in this field it is particularly important to establish species specificity for both DNA and RNA. This is all the more important in view of the genetic role attributed to DNA, while RNA is believed by a number of investigators to be one of the decisive factors responsible for the specific distribution of the amino acids in the peptide chain that is formed.

For the past two years DNA and RNA specificity in various bacteria has been studied at our laboratory by A. S. Spirin and G. N. Zaĭtseva. This group of organisms seemed to us especially suitable for solving the problem of the species specificity of DNA and RNA. Besides this, the works of many investigators on different organisms with respect to nucleic acid composition and their specificity was concerned in most cases either only with RNA or only with DNA, and there are practically no systematic investigations of the composition of both nucleic acids on a number of biological objects. Bacteria are highly convenient material for this purpose.

The only satisfactory method of determining qualitative changes or differences of nucleic acids at present is the method of determining the quantitative ratios of their nitrogen bases. In our investigation we therefore carried out a comparative study of nucleic acid composition in the cultures under investigation by the most widely accepted methods of quantitative paper chromatography in combination with ultraviolet spectrophotometry [2, 3, 4]. It should be borne in mind that in most cases nucleic acid composition was studied by various investigators in preparations of these nucleic acids isolated from organisms. The faulty character of this approach with respect to RNA was shown, specifically, by Chargaff's laboratory, which started the systematic study of RNA composition *in toto*, i.e., without isolation [5, 6]. The same fact was established in our laboratory by Zaĭtseva in studying the RNA composition of *Azotobacter* [7]. With respect to DNA composition the literature is still dominated by data obtained through the study of DNA preparations. We proceeded on the assumption that such methods are not sufficiently reliable, owing to the possibly incomplete isolation of the substances, losses suffered in the course of obtaining the preparations, and, in some cases, its degradation, which may result in composition changes. Therefore, we endeavoured to study the composition of both RNA and DNA directly in the material under investigation, without first obtaining them as preparations.

The data for Azotobacter were obtained in our laboratory by G. N. Zaĭtseva; the data for all the other cultures, by A. S. Spirin.

Before undertaking the study of DNA and RNA composition in various systematic groups of bacteria, we turned our attention to age alteration of DNA and RNA composition. This was all the more important because if the composition of these nucleic acids altered in the course of development, it would have been necessary to carry out a systematic study on cultures in exactly one and the same phase of development.

Table 1 shows DNA composition for *Escherichia coli* I and *Azotobacter agile* D-22 depending on the age of the culture; Table 2 gives RNA composition for the same cultures.

It follows from the data presented in Tables 1 and 2 that the composition of DNA and RNA undergoes no appreciable change in the course of the development of the cultures studied. These findings, together with other data available in the literature [5, 8, 9, 10], give us reason to assume the absence of an age specificity of the nucleic acids for a wide range of organisms, at any rate as far as their composition specificity is concerned.

TABLE I

DNA composition of Escherichia coli and Azotobacter agile D-22 in relation to age of culture*

Culture	Age of culture in hours	Molar percentages of bases in DNA				Pur / Pyr	G + T / A + C	G + C / A + T
		G	A	C	T			
Escherichia coli I .	10	26·1	23·8	26·1	24·0	0·99	1·01	1·09
	20	25·9	23·9	26·3	23·9	0·99	0·99	1·09
	30	26·2	24·1	26·2	23·5	1·01	0·99	1·10
Azotobacter agile D-22	0	26·9	23·0	26·4	23·6	1·00	1·02	1·15
	6	27·6	22·5	25·9	24·0	1·00	1·06	1·15
	12	27·8	21·9	26·1	24·1	0·99	1·07	1·17
	16	28·0	22·5	25·6	23·8	1·02	1·07	1·16
	18	28·3	21·4	27·2	23·1	0·99	1·05	1·24
	24	26·6	22·0	26·1	24·2	0·99	1·07	1·16
	36	27·0	23·1	26·3	23·6	1·00	1·03	1·14
	48	26·7	21·9	27·1	24·1	0·95	1·03	1·19

* The following abbreviations have been adopted in Tables 1, 3 and 5: Pur—purine bases, Pyr—pyrimidine bases, G—guanine, A—adenine, C—cytosine, and T—thymine.

TABLE 2

RNA composition of Escherichia coli and Azotobacter agile D-22 in relation to age of culture*

Culture	Age of culture in hours	Molar percentages of nucleotides in RNA				Pur / Pyr	G + U / A + C	G + C / A + U
		G	A	C	U			
Escherichia coli I .	10	30·6	26·0	24·2	19·2	1·30	0·99	1·21
	20	30·8	26·0	24·1	19·1	1·31	1·00	1·22
	30	30·4	26·1	24·2	19·3	1·30	0·99	1·20
Azotobacter agile D-22	0	30·8	24·4	26·2	18·6	1·24	0·97	1·32
	6	31·3	24·3	26·5	17·9	1·25	0·97	1·37
	12	30·7	24·6	25·8	18·9	1·24	0·98	1·30
	16	30·8	23·7	26·3	19·2	1·20	0·99	1·33
	18	31·5	24·4	24·6	19·5	1·26	1·03	1·28
	24	30·8	24·4	25·7	19·1	1·24	0·99	1·30
	36	31·0	23·9	27·7	17·4	1·22	0·96	1·42
	48	31·0	24·1	26·7	18·3	1·22	0·97	1·36

* The following abbreviations have been adopted in Tables 2, 4 and 6: Pur—purine nucleotides, Pyr—pyrimidine nucleotides, G—guanylic acid, A—adenylic acid, C—cytidylic acid, and U—uridylic acid.

These results are also at variance with the concept of intracellular hetero-geneity of RNA, at least in regard to composition. It is well known that the RNA content undergoes marked quantitative changes in the process of onto-genesis. Specifically, in the case of bacteria in the stationary developmental phase the amount of RNA ranges from $\frac{2}{3}$ to $\frac{1}{3}$ of the amount in the logarithmic phase of growth. In our case, for example, the 10-hour *Escherichia coli* culture contained 9·6% RNA, whereas the 30-hour culture contained only 5·3% (in dry weight of bacterial mass). Total RNA composition can be constant in the event of such pronounced changes of its quantitative content if all the RNA molecules in the cell have roughly the same nucleotide composition, i.e., if there is no intracellular heterogeneity of the RNA molecules with regard to their composition. Another assumption is that the cell contains a number of RNA fractions of different composition, but in the age and associated metabolic changes there takes place an identical, uniform decrease or increase of the number of RNA molecules in each of these fractions. This supposition appears less probable, because functionally different fractions should behave differently.

In Table 3 we see the comparative data for DNA composition, and in Table 4, for RNA composition, in bacteria belonging to different systematic groups.

TABLE 3

DNA composition of different bacteria

Culture	Molar percentages of bases in DNA				$\dfrac{\text{Pur}}{\text{Pyr}}$	$\dfrac{\text{G}+\text{T}}{\text{A}+\text{C}}$	$\dfrac{\text{G}+\text{C}}{\text{A}+\text{T}}$
	G	A	C	T			
Clostridium perfringens .	15·8	34·1	15·1	35·0	1·00	1·03	0·45
Staphylococcus pyogenes aureus	17·3	32·3	17·4	33·0	0·98	1·01	0·53
Pasteurella tularensis . .	17·6	32·4	17·1	32·9	1·00	1·02	0·53
Proteus vulgaris . .	19·8	30·1	20·7	29·4	1·00	0·97	0·68
Escherichia coli . . .	26·0	23·9	26·2	23·9	1·00	1·00	1·09
Proteus morganii . .	26·3	23·7	26·7	23·3	1·00	0·98	1·13
Shigella dysenteriae . .	26·7	23·5	26·7	23·1	1·01	0·99	1·15
Salmonella typhosa . .	26·7	23·5	26·4	23·4	1·01	1·00	1·14
Salmonella typhimurium .	27·1	22·9	27·0	23·0	1·00	1·00	1·18
Erwinia carotovora . .	27·1	23·3	26·9	22·7	1·02	0·99	1·17
Corynebacterium diphtheriae .	27·2	22·5	27·3	23·0	0·99	1·01	1·20
Azotobacter agile . .	28·3	21·4	26·5	23·8	0·99	1·08	1·21
Azotobacter vinelandii .	27·4	22·1	28·9	21·7	0·98	0·97	1·28
Azotobacter chroococcum .	28·7	20·5	28·5	22·2	0·97	1·04	1·34
Aerobacter aerogenes .	28·8	21·3	28·0	21·9	1·00	1·03	1·31
Brucella abortus . . .	29·0	21·0	28·9	21·1	1·00	1·00	1·37
Alcaligenes faecalis . .	33·9	16·5	32·8	16·8	0·98	1·03	2·00
Pseudomonas aeruginosa .	33·0	16·8	34·0	16·2	0·99	0·97	2·03
Mycobacterium tuberculosis BCG	34·2	16·5	33·3	16·0	1·03	1·01	2·08
Sarcina lutea . . .	36·4	13·6	35·6	14·4	1·00	1·03	2·57
Actinomyces globisporus streptomycini	36·1	13·4	37·1	13·4	0·98	0·98	2·73

From the data in Table 3 it follows that DNA possesses a species specificity, i.e., each species is characterized by a particular DNA of specific nucleotide composition. The nucleotide composition of the DNA of bacteria varies very greatly, and among these organisms one may encounter representatives of a pronounced 'AT' type (e.g., *Clostridium perfringens*) and representatives of a distinct 'GC' type (e.g., *Actinomyces globisporus streptomycini*), as well as all the intermediate stages between these two types.

If we take closely-related representatives of the intestinal group, such as *Escherichia coli*, *Salmonella typhosa*, and *Salmonella typhimurium*, we find that their nucleotide composition exhibits closeness. However, the small variations observed in the values of the ratio $(G + C)/(A + T)$ are quite real, since they represent the mean value of a large number of determinations. This question was carefully studied by us. The more remote species such as *Alcaligenes faecalis*, *Proteus vulgaris* and *Pseudomonas aeruginosa* display increasing differences in nucleotide composition both among themselves and in relation to the afore-mentioned bacteria of the intestinal group. It appears highly probable that in closely related species there are differences in nucleotide composition only among some DNA molecules (assuming the correctness of the assumption about the heterogeneity of DNA in the same object) in view of which the total DNA

TABLE 4

RNA composition of different bacteria

Culture	Molar percentages of nucleotides in RNA				$\dfrac{\text{Pur}}{\text{Pyr}}$	$\dfrac{G + C}{A + U}$	$\dfrac{G + U}{A + C}$
	G	A	C	U			
Clostridium perfringens .	29·5	28·1	22·0	20·4	1·36	1·06	1·00
Staphylococcus pyogenes aureus	28·7	26·9	22·4	22·0	1·25	1·05	1·03
Pasteurella tularensis . .	29·8	27·3	21·0	21·9	1·33	1·03	1·07
Proteus vulgaris . . .	31·0	26·3	24·0	18·7	1·34	1·22	0·99
Escherichia coli . . .	30·7	26·0	24·1	19·2	1·31	1·21	1·00
Proteus morganii . .	31·1	26·0	23·7	19·2	1·31	1·21	1·01
Shigella dysenteriae . .	30·4	25·9	24·4	19·9	1·29	1·21	0·99
Salmonella typhosa . .	30·8	26·1	24·0	19·1	1·32	1·21	1·00
Salmonella typhimurium .	31·0	26·1	23·8	19·1	1·33	1·21	1·00
Erwinia carotovora . .	29·5	26·5	23·7	20·3	1·27	1·14	0·99
Corynebacterium diphtheriae .	31·6	23·1	23·8	21·5	1·21	1·24	1·13
Azotobacter agile . .	31·0	24·2	26·0	18·7	1·23	1·33	0·99
Azotobacter vinelandii . .	30·3	23·9	25·5	20·2	1·19	1·27	1·02
Azotobacter chroococcum .	30·4	24·7	24·7	20·1	1·18	1·23	1·02
Aerobacter aerogenes . .	30·3	26·0	24·1	19·6	1·29	1·19	1·00
Brucella abortus . . .	30·2	25·4	24·9	19·5	1·26	1·23	0·99
Alcaligenes faecalis . .	30·9	25·7	24·1	19·3	1·31	1·22	1·01
Pseudomonas aeruginosa .	31·6	25·1	23·8	19·5	1·31	1·24	1·05
Mycobacterium tuberculosis BCG	33·0	22·6	26·1	18·3	1·25	1·45	1·05
Sarcina lutea . . .	32·7	23·2	24·2	19·9	1·27	1·32	1·11
Actinomyces globisporus streptomycini	31·1	23·8	25·2	19·9	1·22	1·29	1·04

composition varies but insignificantly. On the other hand, we must not rule out the possibility that the DNA molecules in closely related species with identical nucleotide composition (e.g., *S. typhosa* and *Shigella dysenteriae*) differ in nucleotide sequence to a certain extent.

It must be mentioned that our findings and conclusion concerning species specificity of DNA are in accord with the data in the recently published paper of Ki Yong Lee, Wahl & Barbu [10], which contains a large amount of experimental research results concerning DNA specificity in bacteria.

The data of the above-mentioned writers, together with our own data, lead one to think that the nucleotide composition of DNA—on the one hand, owing to its high specificity, and on the other, owing to a certain closeness of related species—can probably be used as one of the systematic indications, at any rate in bacteria. The following example could be mentioned: Bergey, in his handbook, refers *Proteus morganii* to the *Proteus* group, together with *Proteus vulgaris*. In nucleotide composition, however, the DNA of *Proteus morganii* has nothing in common with the DNA of *Proteus vulgaris*, and, on the contrary, is very similar to the intestinal bacteria of the *Salmonella–Shigella* group. It may therefore be that the microbiologists who doubt the correctness of referring *Proteus morganii* to the *Proteus* group are right.

As for RNA, the data in Table 4 demonstrate that all the bacterial RNA's belong to the same 'GC' type. Moreover, all of them are extremely close in nucleotide composition [4, 11]. When the nucleotide composition of the DNA of bacteria varies very markedly, the nucleotide composition of their RNA, on the contrary, is similar even in the remotest species and the variations observed are insignificant. From this it follows that the nucleotide composition of RNA displays no marked conformity with the nucleotide composition of DNA and does not change considerably depending on the nature of an organism.

Hence, whereas in relation to DNA we can speak of a rather marked specificity even in studying its total composition, in the case of RNA it could be said only of remote species, and even then to a lesser degree. Still, the identity of RNA composition of the related species in no way excludes the possibility of its specificity, since this specificity may be exhibited in nucleotide sequence in different RNA while the total composition remains the same. Nevertheless, the similarity of nucleotide composition in different RNA speaks in favour of a relatively lower specificity of this nucleic acid as compared with DNA.

However, the existence of a certain positive correlation between DNA and RNA composition may be held thereby for highly probable [4]. This correlation is expressed in a certain tendency toward the increase of the ratio $(G + C)/(A + U)$ in RNA on passing from the species with the smaller value of the ratio $(G + C)/(A + T)$ in their DNA to those with the greater value of this ratio [4]. It should be remarked that in our case positive correlation between RNA and DNA composition is exemplified by twenty-one species of bacteria and that further investigations are certainly necessary to prove that this correlation is not fortuitous. Nevertheless, on the basis of the presented data we may suppose that a certain portion of cellular RNA (and, apparently, only a small portion of it, this fact being proved by the minute value of the regression $(G + C)/(A + U)$

RNA by $(G + C)/(A + T)$ DNA) may fully correlate by its composition with that of DNA. On the other hand, one may think that the main mass of cellular RNA does show no correlation with DNA, its composition being similar in very different species.

The pronounced specificity of DNA as compared with RNA is well illustrated by the data obtained in our laboratory by A. S. Spirin in studying the DNA of certain bacteria of the intestinal group in the process of their experimental variability [2]. The following cultures were chosen for this investigation: (1) the original culture of *Escherichia coli* 'CM'; experiments were conducted with this culture in direction of artificially altering its properties by growing it together with *Bacterium enteriditis* Breslau killed by heat; (2) *Bact. enteriditis* Breslau, No. 70, whose killed bodies were used as a specific substrate to alter the properties of *E. coli* 'CM'; (3) alkali-producing form 11–IV–4 obtained from *E. coli* 'CM' by growing it together with Breslau Bacteria No. 70 killed by heat, and (4) paratyphoid-like strain, 12–IV–4 obtained by growing the alkali producer 11–IV–4 with Breslau Bacteria, N. 70 killed by heat [12, 13].

Tables 5 and 6 show the results of the study of the nucleotide composition of DNA and RNA in the above-listed bacteria.

TABLE 5

DNA composition of investigated cultures

Culture	Molar percentage of bases in DNA				$\dfrac{\text{Pur}}{\text{Pyr}}$	$\dfrac{G + C}{A + T}$
	G	A	C	T		
Escherichia coli 'CM' . .	26·0	23·8	26·4	23·8	0·99	1·10
Alkali-producing form II–IV–4 .	33·3	16·5	33·7	16·5	0·99	2·03
Paratyphoid 12–IV–4 . . .	27·3	23·1	28·1	21·5	1·01	1·24
Breslau bacteria No. 70 . .	27·1	23·9	26·8	23·1	1·00	1·17

TABLE 6

RNA composition of investigated cultures

Culture	Molar percentage of nucleotides in RNA				$\dfrac{\text{Pur}}{\text{Pyr}}$	$\dfrac{G + U}{A + C}$	$\dfrac{G + C}{A + U}$
	G	A	C	U			
Escherichia coli 'CM' . .	30·6	26·0	24·1	19·3	1·30	1·00	1·21
Alkali-producing form II–IV–4	30·6	25·5	24·2	19·7	1·28	1·01	1·21
Paratyphoid 12–IV–4 . .	30·9	25·9	23·6	19·6	1·31	1·02	1·20
Breslau bacteria No. 70 .	31·0	26·1	23·8	19·1	1·33	1·00	1·21

When we compare RNA composition in initial and experimentally produced forms of bacteria (see Tables 5 and 6), we are struck, first and foremost, by the fact that DNA exhibits marked qualitative differences and alterations, whereas the RNA composition remains constant. The DNA composition and its changes are in good correlation with the alteration in the whole sum of hereditary properties. Thus, the alkali-producing form standing out in its biological [12, 13], chemical [14] and antigenic [13, 14] characteristics, as compared with both the original culture *E. coli* and the 'leader' culture of Breslau bacteria stands out just as prominently in DNA composition. The paratyphoid which arises from this alkali-producing form upon further influence and which is a culture similar to Breslau bacteria [13, 14] resembles these Breslau bacteria in DNA composition. In the light of these data it is difficult not to link up the specificity of cell DNA with the entire specificity of the nature of the organism. The correlation of changes in the specificity of DNA composition with changes in the antigenic specificity of the investigated cultures [13, 14] leads us to think that DNA is connected with specific protein synthesis, with the biological mechanism determining the specificity of proteins. Curiously, it is RNA, which many investigators now hold responsible for the specificity of protein synthesis, that does not alter its composition in the event of such profound change in the specificity of cell proteins. This leads us to the question of whether the entire specific role in protein synthesis can be ascribed to RNA alone. Furthermore, can the view that there is a direct genetic connection with the DNA in a cell be accepted without reservations? It is difficult to assume that, with the DNA composition so different, it will in some measure determine the synthesis of so identically composed RNA, just as it is difficult to assume the possibility of a direct transition of DNA into RNA, and *vice versa*. In this connection we would express doubt about possible direct interconversions between these two nucleic acids in processes of development, a viewpoint which became widespread after the investigations of Brachet in the thirties. Indeed, it is difficult to suppose that the interconversion of these nucleic acids could be effected in defiance of the disparity of their nucleotide composition.

Nevertheless, on the basis of the fact of positive correlation between the composition of RNA and DNA it is not excluded that some small portion of RNA (perhaps the functional analogue of nuclear RNA) depends upon DNA, being determined by its structure, or may be directly transformed into it and *vice versa*. But still, with respect to the main mass of RNA in the cell, we regard any possibility of its direct transformations into DNA and *vice versa* as hardly possible.

It is more probable to assume that should these nucleic acids be interdependent in the process of development, this is a mere parallelism of phenomena, perhaps interconnected, but based on different biosynthetic pathways.

In conclusion, a few considerations concerning the evolution of nucleic acids. There is no shadow of doubt about the fact that the nucleic acids played a significant part in the evolution of the organic world. However, it is doubtful that both RNA and DNA appeared simultaneously at the early stages of the development of life. The author of the present communication is inclined to think that the appearance of the ribonucleotides, followed by RNA, was primary. The DNA appeared much later, parallel with more complicated functions and an ever-increasing differentiation of protoplasm. The following considerations may be put forward in support of RNA priority: (1) RNA is found in all morphological elements of protoplasm without exception, whereas DNA is localized in the cell nucleus exclusively. (2) Growth and reproduction become possible only when the RNA level reaches a certain value characteristic of that type of cells. A vivid example of this is afforded by bacteria in whose cells, during the lag-phase period, there take place substantial alterations preparatory to subsequent reproduction and growth processes. Chemical analysis, specifically the analysis carried out in our laboratory by G. N. Zaĭtseva [15], reveals that one of the most typical changes in this period is the intense biosynthesis of RNA. It is only when the RNA reaches a certain fixed level that the bacterial cell enters the logarithmic phase of growth. (3) The RNA appears to be deprived of genetic functions. This is confirmed sufficiently weightily by the latest investigations of the laboratories of Schramm and Fraenkel-Conrat, who have proved RNA responsible for the reproduction of corresponding viruses. (4) Ribonucleotides participate in the most diverse phases of metabolism. Moreover, as this has been established in recent years by Leloir and others, all four nucleotides in RNA are associated with metabolism. Hence, through its nucleotides, RNA is closely associated with diverse aspects of metabolism.

DNA is much more highly specialized than RNA, this being witnessed by narrow localization in the cell, higher specificity than that of RNA, a higher degree of polymerization, and, finally, the fact that we still do not know of its nucleotides being as omnipotent in metabolic processes as RNA nucleotides. The very fact of greater specialization and differentiation appears to lend support to the belief that DNA had originated later than RNA.

It seems to us that our experimental findings concerning the nucleotide composition of DNA and RNA in diverse bacteria may also be interpreted as proof of this notion. Indeed, in this group of organisms, parallel with a relatively constant RNA composition, there took place substantial changes in DNA composition, proceeding simultaneously with the differentiation and specialization of individual groups of bacteria.

One thus gets the impression that RNA, which is associated with the most general manifestations of vital activity, arose at an earlier stage in the development of life, whereas the appearance of DNA is associated with the formation of narrower and phylogenetically later properties of organisms.

It is to be hoped that new data will be obtained in the near future, shedding light on the intimate mechanisms through which the nucleic acids play their part in the basic processes of life. The earnest of this is the acute interest felt in this problem and the large scale of research in this group of compounds.

REFERENCES

1. A. N. BELOZERSKIĬ & A. S. SPIRIN, *Usp. sovr. Biol.*, **41**, 144, 1956.
2. A. S. SPIRIN & A. N. BELOZERSKIĬ, *Biokhimiya*, **21**, 768, 1956.
3. A. S. SPIRIN, A. N. BELOZERSKIĬ & A. PRETEL-MARTINEZ, *Dokl. Akad. Nauk S.S.S.R.*, **111**, 1297, 1956.

4. A. S. Spirin, A. N. Belozerskiĭ, N. V. Shugayeva & B. F. Vanyushin, *Biokhimiya*, **22**, 744, 1957.
5. D. Elson, T. Gustafson & E. Chargaff, *J. biol. Chem.*, **209**, 285, 1954.
6. D. Elson & E. Chargaff, *Biochim. biophys. Acta*, **17**, 367, 1955.
7. G. N. Zaĭtseva & A. N. Belozerskiĭ, *Mikrobiologiya*, **26**, 1957.
8. K. K. Reddi, *Biochim. biophys. Acta*, **15**, 585, 1954.
9. S. K. Dutta, A. S. Jones & M. Stacey, *J. gen. Microbiol.*, **14**, 160, 1956.
10. Ki Yong Lee, R. Wahl & E. Barbu, *Ann. Inst. Pasteur*, **91**, 212, 1956.
11. A. S. Spirin & A. N. Belozerskiĭ, *Dokl. Akad. Nauk S.S.S.R.*, **113**, 650, 1957.
12. D. G. Kudlai, *Variability of the Bacteria of the Intestinal Group*. Medgiz, Moscow, 1954.
13. V. D. Tymakov, D. G. Kudlaĭ, A. G. Skavronskaya, A. S. Spirin & A. N. Belozerskiĭ, *Zh. Mikrob.*, **8**, 20, 1955.
14. A. N. Belozerskiĭ, A. S. Spirin, D. G. Kudlaĭ & A. G. Skavronskaya, *Biokhimiya*, **20**, 686, 1955.
15. A. Belozerskiĭ, G. N. Zaĭtseva, L. P. Gavrilova & L. Mineeva, *Mikrobiologiya*, **26**, 409, 1957.

Die Spezifizität
der Desoxyribonukleinsäure

A. WACKER

Organisch-Chemisches Institut der Technischen Universität, Berlin,
Berlin-Charlottenburg, Germany

WIE WIR erstmalig mit Hilfe von [^{82}Br]5-Bromuracil zeigten, wird dieses halogenierte Pyrimidin an Stelle von Thymin in die Desoxyribonukleinsäure (DNS) von *Streptococcus faecalis* R, *Enterococcus stei* und *Escherichia coli* 1883 Co eingebaut [1]. In Ergänzung dieser Arbeit [2] studierten wir mit radioaktiv markiertem 5-Bromuracil, und zwar mit [^{82}Br]- und [2-^{14}C]-5-Bromuracil, die 5-Bromuracil-Aufnahme bei weiteren Mikroorganismen und fanden, daß fast alle untersuchten Mikroben unter den gewählten Züchtungsbedingungen in wechselndem Maße 5-Bromuracil aufnahmen, ohne dabei in ihrem Wachstum gehemmt zu werden. Es sind dies: *Leuconostoc citrovorum* 8081, *Lactobacillus arabinosus* 17–5, *Lb. plantarum* 10 S, *E. coli* 113–3, *Micrococcus pyogenes* var. *aureus* 511, *Salmonella enteritidis*, *Salmonella paratyphi* B 8006, *Pseudomonas aeruginosa*, *Klebsiella pneumoniae*, *Staphylococcus pyogenes* 18, *Staphylococcus pyogenes* 4, *Salmonella schottmülleri*, *Bacillus prodigiosus*, *Streptococcus pyogenes*, *Aerobacter aerogenes* und *Bacillus firmus*. Kein 5-Bromuracil nahmen dagegen ein Pneumococcen-Stamm, *Corynebacterium*, *Bacillus subtilis* und *Saccharomyces carlsbergensis* auf. Bemerkenswert ist, daß der Pneumococcen-Stamm kein 5-Bromuracil in seine DNS einbaut. Gerade mit Pneumococcen lassen sich Transformationsversuche gut reproduzieren [3] und es wäre von Interesse gewesen, mit einer Bromuracil-haltigen DNS solche Versuche durchzuführen.

Es gibt aber auch Bakterienstämme, die in ihrem Wachstum durch 5-Bromuracil gehemmt werden, und zwar *Lb. leichmannii* und *Lb. acidophilus* R 26, beides Stämme, die entweder Vitamin B$_{12}$ oder Desoxyriboside zum Wachstum benötigen.

Durch Versuche mit radioaktivem 5-Bromuracil konnten wir ferner zeigen, daß auch ruhende Zellen, die in physiologischer Kochsalzlösung suspendiert waren, 5-Bromuracil aufnehmen [1]. Ist gleichzeitig Thymin vorhanden, so wird weniger 5-Bromuracil von den Zellen gebunden. Thymin kann auch in ruhenden Zellen, die bereits 5-Bromuracil aufgenommen haben, 5-Bromuracil wieder verdrängen.

Durch Züchtung größerer Mengen Bakterien gelang es, 5-Bromuracildesoxyribosid in kristalliner Form aus 5-Bromuracil-haltiger DNS, zu erhalten [4]. Bei *Lb. leichmannii* und auch *Lb. acidophilus* R 26 kann 5-Bromuracildesoxyribosid bei langer Bebrütungsdauer (38 Stunden) die natürlichen Desoxyriboside als Wuchsstoffe ersetzen; jedoch nur in Anwesenheit von Folsäure [5]. In dieser Eigenschaft unterscheidet sich 5-Bromuracildesoxyribosid von

Thymindesoxyribosid, das bei beiden Stämmen auch die Folsäure ersetzen kann.

Es erhebt sich nun die Frage, wieviel des Thymins der DNS durch 5-Bromuracil ersetzt werden kann. Bei *Enterococcus stei*, dem Stamm, der vergleichsweise die größte Menge 5-Bromuracil aufnimmt, werden etwa 70% des Thymins durch 5-Bromuracil ersetzt; auch bei einem Überangebot von 5-Bromuracil wird diese Menge nicht überschritten [2]. Entsprechend verhalten sich auch die übrigen Bakterien.

Diese Befunde könnte man nun wie folgt erklären! Es gibt entweder zwei Arten von DNS, eine, in die kein 5-Bromuracil eingebaut werden kann (genetische) und eine andere, in der das Thymin durch 5-Bromuracil ersetzbar ist (nicht genetische), oder innerhalb der DNS gibt est bestimmte Thyminstellen, die nicht von 5-Bromuracil besetzt werden können.

Bei *Lb. leichmannii* kann man Vitamin B_{12} als Wuchsstoff durch die Desoxyriboside der Purine und Pyrimidine ersetzen. Hierbei erhebt sich die Frage, ob in dem letzteren Falle für den Aufbau der DNS nur die in dem Desoxyribosid enthaltende Menge Desoxyribose dem Bakterium zur Verfügung steht. Es wurde deshalb der DNS-Gehalt [6] von *Lb. leichmannii*, gewachsen mit und ohne Vitamin B_{12}, geprüft. Dabei ergab sich nun ein bedeutender Unterschied [7]. Die mit Vitamin B_{12} gewachsenen Zellen enthalten ungefähr die vierfache Menge DNS (3,2 mg DNS/100 mg getrocknete Zellen) gegenüber den mit Desoxyribosiden gewachsenen (0,8 mg DNS/100 mg getrocknete Zellen). Die Bestimmung der RNS in den Zellen mit und ohne Vitamin B_{12} gewachsen, zeigte diesen auffallenden Unterschied nicht; innerhalb der Fehlergrenze enthalten alle Bakterien die gleiche Menge RNS.

Zusammenfassend ergibt sich aus all diesen Befunden, daß die DNS einer Bakterienzelle qualitativ und quantitativ großen Änderungen unterworfen werden kann, ohne daß sich hierdurch die Eigenschaften eines Bakteriums ändern.

LITERATURVERZEICHNIS

1. F. Weygand, A. Wacker & H. Dellweg, *Z. Naturf.*, **7b**, 19, 1952.
2. A. Wacker, A. Trebst, D. Jacherts & F. Weygand, *Z. Naturf.*, **9b**, 616, 1954.
3. Vergl. z. B. R. D. Hotchkiss, in *The Nucleic Acids* (Herausgegeben von E. Chargaff & J. N. Davidson). Academic Press, New York, vol. 2, S. 444 ff., 1955.
4. F. Weygand, A. Wacker & K. M. Patil, *Ber. dtsch. chem. Ges.*, **89**, 475, 1956.
5. A. Wacker, A. Trebst & F. Weygand, *Z. Naturf.*, **11b**, 7, 1956.
6. J. M. Webb & H. B. Levy, *J. biol. Chem.*, **213**, 107, 1955.
7. A. Wacker, D. Pfahl & I. Schröder, *Z. Naturf.*, **12b**, 1957.

Die Entstehung des dynamischen Zustandes

E. BRODA

I. Chemisches Institut, Universität Wien, Oesterreich

DAS WESEN DES DYNAMISCHEN ZUSTANDS

IN DER vorliegenden Untersuchung soll von der heute allgemein anerkannten Vorstellung ausgegangen werden, daß die Urformen des Lebens unter anaeroben Bedingungen durch einen Prozeß der allmählichen Selektion aus einer Mischung mehr oder weniger komplizierter organischer Stoffe entstanden sind, die im Ozean gelöst waren [1]. Für die Bildung der Urformen, die als prävitale [2] oder subvitale [3] Einheiten oder als Eobionten [4] bezeichnet werden können, standen sehr lange Zeiträume zur Verfügung. Die Eobionten unterschieden sich von den organischen Molekülen, aus denen sie hervorgingen, durch eine gewisse Fähigkeit zur Reproduktion. Andererseits müssen sie sich, wie im Folgenden diskutiert werden soll, von den späteren Lebewesen in charakteristischer Weise durch das Fehlen eines geregelten dynamischen Zustandes unterschieden haben.

R. Höber schrieb im Jahre 1926 im Anschluß an ältere Überlegungen von C. Bernard und E. Dubois-Reymond: 'In den Organismen haben wir nun chemische Systeme vor uns, die schon vor langer Zeit als bewegliche, als dynamische Gleichgewichte bezeichnet worden sind. Heute schwebt das Problem des dynamischen Gleichgewichts nicht mehr völlig in der Luft, sondern es läßt sich als der Schlußstein und die Krönung eines hohen und kühnen Gebäudes betrachten.' [5] Ganz besonders die Arbeiten mit Isotopen, die seit der Entdeckung des schweren Wasserstoffs und der künstlichen Radioaktivität geleistet wurden, haben in zunehmendem Maß die Bedeutung des 'dynamischen Zustandes der Körperbestandteile' aufgezeigt. Der dynamische Zustand äußert sich durch einen ständigen Ersatz von Körperbestandteilen durch neue, chemisch gleichartige Bestandteile [7, 8].

So haben G. Hevesy und andere Autoren—besonders an den Beispielen des Kalziums und des Phosphors des Skeletts—nachgewiesen, daß große Teile der Mineralsubstanz von Organismen auch denn einer ständigen Erneuerung unterliegen, wenn der Organismus und seine Organe sich im Stoffwechselgleichgewicht —also im stationären Zustand—befinden. Die Erneuerung wurde auch als 'biologische Rekristallisation' bezeichnet [9].

Gelöste Stoffe, darunter Kationen und Anionen, können gleichfalls insofern im dynamischen Zustand stehen, als sie im Stoffwechselgleichgewicht ständig durch die Membranen fließen, die für sie permeabel sind. Dies gilt auch dann, wenn im stationären Zustand zu beiden Seiten der Membran verschiedene Konzentrationen (genauer: thermodynamische Aktivitäten) der Ionen herrschen [10]. Beispielsweise strömen die (markierten) Natrium-Ionen im stationären Zustand, in dem die Ionenkonzentration innen viel größer ist als außen, rasch in beiden Richtungen durch die Froschhaut [11].

Die Aufrechterhaltung des Konzentrationsgefälles beruht also keineswegs darauf, daß die Haut für die Ionen von vornherein impermeabel wäre oder in einem Stadium des Prozesses impermeabel würde. Das Konzentrationsgefälle muß vielmehr entgegen der Ausgleichstendenz infolge der spontan wirkenden Diffusion durch eine 'Ionenpumpe' aufrechterhalten werden. Zum Betrieb einer solchen Ionenpumpe wird natürlich freie Energie verbraucht.

Schließlich hat Schoenheimer durch seine berühmten Untersuchungen an markierten Fettsäuren und Aminosäuren gezeigt, daß auch organische Verbindungen sich im lebenden Organismus im ständigen Fluß befinden [7]. Transport von solchen Verbindungen findet auch im stationären Zustand von Ort zu Ort statt. Z.B. werden Fettmoleküle oder deren Bestandteile innerhalb des Körpers von Wirbeltieren zwischen den Depots hin- und herverschoben.

Neben diesem dynamischen Ortswechsel beobachtet man einen ständigen, ebenfalls auch im stationären Zustand des Organismus weiter wirkenden chemischen Abbau und Aufbau organischer Verbindungen [7, 12, 13]. Man kann daher z.B. den Eiweißkörpern bestimmte Halbwertszeiten der Erneuerung zuschreiben. So wurde gefunden, daß die Halbwertszeiten von Serum-Eiweißstoffen dem reziproken Gewicht der Säugetierart korreliert sind [14]. Besonders schön hat sich die Erneuerung und ihre Abhängigkeit vom Gewicht der Tierart an den—der γ-Globulinfraktion angehörigen—Antikörpern von aktiv immunisierten Tieren verfolgen lassen [15, 16].

Schließlich sind noch die Nukleinsäuren zu nennen. Hier steht jedenfalls fest, daß die Ribonukleinsäuren aller Zellen, und zwar sowohl in den Zellkernen als auch im Cytoplasma, sich in einem dynamischen Zustand befinden [17, 18].

Bei den organischen Verbindungen besteht nicht nur die Möglichkeit der totalen Erneuerung der Moleküle, sondern es können auch—immer im stationären Zustand—Stücke des Moleküls herausgebrochen und durch chemisch gleichartige Stücke ersetzt werden. Diese Erscheinungsform des dynamischen Zustandes wurde von Gale am Eiweiß von Staphylokokken studiert [19].*

CHEMISCHER UND BIOLOGISCHER AUSTAUSCH

Inwiefern ist nun der Austausch, durch den sich der dynamische Zustand ausdrückt, eine spezifische Eigenschaft der belebten Substanz? Es scheint, daß eine wirklich scharfe Abgrenzung des hier zur Diskussion stehenden 'biologischen Austausches' vom rein 'chemischen Austausch' kaum gelingen wird. Ein wohlbekannter Fall eines rein chemischen Austausches ist jener zwischen dem Wasserstoff von Wasser und labilem Wasserstoff von Säuren oder Alkoholen. Aber auch Wasserstoffatome, die sonst als stabil gebunden betrachtet werden,

---

* Anmerkung bei der Korrektur. Siehe jedoch E. F. Gale, C. J. Shepherd & J. P. Folkes, *Nature, Lond.*, **182**, 592, 1958.

können—rein chemisch—katalytisch ausgetauscht werden; so kann der Wasserstoff von Wasser in Gegenwart von Platin durch freien Wassterstoff erneuert werden [20].

Als Katalysator für den Austausch von Wasserstoff zwischen molekularen Wasserstoff und Wasser kann auch ein Enzym dienen, z.B. Hydrogenase von Coli-Bakterien [21]. Auch als Ester gebundene Phosphatgruppen, z.B. in Glukosc-1-Phosphat, tauschen (gegen freies Phosphat-Ion) aus, wenn geeignete Katalysatoren (Phosphorylase aus *Pseudomonas saccharophila*) anwesend sind [13, 22].

Soll man Austauschvorgänge noch als 'chemisch' oder schon als 'biologisch' betrachten, weil—und nur weil—der Katalysator biogen ist? Obwohl die Enzyme allen anderen bisher bekannten Katalysatoren überlegen sind, so besteht doch kein prinzipielles Hindernis gegen die Existenz 'abiogener' Katalysatoren, die den Enzymen an Wirkung und Spezifität gleichkommen oder sie sogar übertreffen. Erste Versuche zur Synthese hochwirksamer spezifischer Katalysatoren für organische Reaktionen wurden schon vor längerer Zeit unternommen [23].

Mit dieser Schwierigkeit der Unterscheidung von chemischem und biologischem Austausch war insofern zu rechnen, als ja überhaupt keine scharfe Trennung zwischen den chemischen Reaktionen der belebten und der unbelebten Substanz möglich ist. 'Keine dieser Reaktionen (nämlich der Oxydation, Hydrolyse, Phosphorolyse, Transaminierung etc. E.B.) hat etwas für das Leben Spezifisches. Spezifisch für die lebenden Körper ist in erster Linie, daß diese einzelnen Reaktionen in ihnen in bestimmter Weise zeitlich organisiert und zu einem einheitlichen, ganzheitlichen System zusammengefaßt sind' [24]. Auch konnte ja bisher keine Definition aufgestellt werden, mit deren Hilfe in jedem Einzelfall zwischen belebter und unbelebter Substanz scharf und starr unterschieden werden kann [25]. Im Ganzen besteht aber natürlich kein Zweifel, daß die rasch und spezifisch verlaufenden Austauschvorgänge, die durch die Enzyme der lebenden Substanz katalysiert werden, für diese charakteristisch sind.

DIE VERBREITUNG DES DYNAMISCHEN ZUSTANDS

Ausnahmen vom dynamischen Zustand sind freilich bekannt. Unter den Eiweißkörpern wird das in großer Menge auftretende Kollagen nur langsam erneuert [26]. Am Globin [27] sowie an den Eiweißstoffen der Milch [28] und des Vogeleis [29] konnte kein dynamischer Abbau und Aufbau festgestellt werden. Schließlich unterliegen die Antikörper des passiv immunisierten Kaninchens gleichfalls keiner Erneuerung [16].

In größerer Allgemeinheit ist der dynamische Zustand der Eiweißkörper von einer Reihe von Autoren angezweifelt worden [30, 31]. Auf Grund von Experimenten an Bakterien, wo kein dynamischer Zustand festgestellt wurde, hat man den Gedanken ausgesprochen, daß der dynamische Zustand in Bezug auf das Eiweiß von vielzelligen tierischen Organismen dadurch vorgetäuscht sei, daß immer wieder Zellen untergehen und erneuert werden [32].

In Bezug auf die Desoxy-Ribonukleinsäure, deren dynamischer Zustand ebenfalls umstritten ist, schreiben Mirsky und seine Kollegen: 'Das Beweis-material zeigt, daß weder die DNS noch das Protein von Zellen, die sich nicht teilen, inert sind. Im Gegenteil ergibt sich ein Bild, wonach die Komponenten der Chromosomen in ständigem Gleichgewicht mit ihrer Umgebung sind ... Dieses Bild eines dynamischen Chromosoms, das das Ergebnis von Studien mit markierten Atomen an Säugetiergeweben ist, steht in schroffem Gegensatz zu den Verhältnissen in Bakterien ... Hier gibt es keinen Umsatz (von DNS) ... Die Experimente weisen darauf hin, daß ein fundamentaler Unterschied im Stoffwechsel bestehen mag zwischen der Bakterienzelle, die raschem Wachstum und Vermehrung ohne Umsatz angepaßt ist, und jenen Zellen der Säugetiere, wo der Umsatz ein Ausdruck der Fähigkeit der Zellen ist, durch ihre Zusammensetzung Änderungen im Milieu Rechnung zu tragen' [18].

Die kritische Prüfung des vorliegenden Gesamtmaterials dürfte zum Ergebnis führen, daß der dynamische Zustand der quantitativen Charakterisierung bedarf. Eine qualitative Beantwortung der Frage nach dem dynamischen Zustand eines bestimmten Körperbestandteils mit einem absoluten 'ja' oder 'nein' scheint im Allgemeinen wenig sinnvoll. Man wird die Bestandteile besser quantitativ durch die Halbwertszeiten der Erneuerung kennzeichnen. Diese können grundsätzlich—nach Überwindung der oft großen experimentellen Schwierigkeiten—letzten Endes immer durch die Isotopenmethode gemessen werden. Dabei mögen sich allerdings in manchen Fällen so lange Halbwertszeiten ergeben, daß die Erneuerung sogar qualitativ nur mehr mit Schwierigkeiten nachzuweisen ist.

Jedenfalls stellt der dynamische Zustand eine weit verbreitete Eigenschaft des Gewebes der höheren Tiere dar. Obwohl darüber weniger experimentelles Material vorliegt, besteht kein Grund zum Zweifel, daß auch höhere Pflanzen sich grundsätzlich ähnlich verhalten. Wenn auch in Bezug auf Einzeller gewisse Vorbehalte gemacht werden mußten, so dürften sich doch wenigstens manche ihrer Bestandteile in einem dynamischen Zustand befinden. Ihm muß daher ein allgemeiner positiver biologischer Wert zugeschrieben werden; er muß das Überleben und die Fortpflanzung der Organismen im Sinne der Abstammungslehre Darwins gefördert haben. Worin besteht nun dieser Wert?

DER METASTABILE ZUSTAND DER LEBEWESEN

Zur Beantwortung der Grundfrage nach dem biologischen Wert des dynamischen Zustandes kann man davon ausgehen, daß die belebte Substanz thermodynamisch metastabil ist. Ihr stationärer Zustand (Stoffwechselgleichgewicht) ist kein Gleichgewichtszustand im thermodynamischen Sinn, sondern ist durch einen gegenüber diesem Gleichgewichtszustand erhöhten Wert des Gehalts an freier Energie gekennzeichnet. Dementsprechend liegt die Entropie der belebten Materie weit unterhalb des Maximums. Beispielsweise enthält der Wirbeltierkörper neben oxydierbaren Stoffen an Hämoglobin gebundenen Sauerstoff. Auch manche chemische Reaktionen nicht oxydativer Natur, die eine Abnahme der freien Energie ergeben würden, z.B. die Hydrolyse von Polysacchariden und Peptiden oder die Glykolyse, sind innerhalb des lebenden Organismus nicht bis zu Ende abgelaufen. Offenbar muß der metastabile Zustand in allen Teilen der Lebewesen aufrechterhalten werden, wenn das Leben weiter bestehen soll.

22

Zur Bewahrung des metastabilen Zustandes stehen der Natur im Prinzip zwei Möglichkeiten zur Verfügung. Der metastabile Zustand kann entweder in einfacher Weise statisch oder aber in komplizierter Weise dynamisch vor der Zerstörung durch spontan ablaufende entropievermehrende Prozesse geschützt werden. Beispielsweise können Konzentrationsdifferenzen zwischen zwei benachbarten, von Flüssigkeit erfüllten und durch eine Membran getrennten Räumen statisch aufrecht erhalten werden, wenn die Membran für den gelösten Stoff undurchlässig ist. Auf diese Weise wird erklärt, daß Serumproteine nicht in Muskelzellen eindringen. Dagegen werden die Konzentrationsdifferenzen der Alkali-Ionen zwischen den Muskelzellen und der umspülenden extrazellulären Flüssigkeit, wie erwähnt, dynamisch durch 'aktiven Transport' aufrechterhalten.

In analoger Weise können organische Körperbestandteile statisch erhalten bleiben, wie dies weitgehend für die erwähnten Fälle des Kollagens und des Milcheiweiß zutrifft. Dann bleiben ein und dieselben Moleküle über längere Zeiträume intakt. Oder aber die Körperbestandteile werden dynamisch aufrechterhalten, wie dies an den verschiedenen Serumproteinen beobachtet wurde, d.h. der Abbau wird durch gleich schnellen Aufbau wettgemacht. Die dynamischen Prozesse kommen zum Stillstand, wenn die Belieferung des Systems mit freier Energie, die in geeigneten Nährstoffen enthalten ist, unterbrochen wird.

Ob in einem bestimmten Teilsystem des Organismus der notwendige metastabile Zustand statisch oder dynamisch erhalten wird, hängt von den Geschwindigkeiten der Reaktionen ab, durch die unter den Bedingungen, die in dem Teilsystem herrschen, der Zustand beseitigt werden kann. Dabei sind physikalische Prozesse, wie die freie Diffusion, der Durchtritt durch Membranen und die Konvektion, sowie chemische Prozesse zu berücksichtigen.

Unter den chemischen Faktoren ist in diesem Zusammenhang die Aktivierungsenergie der wichtigste [33]. Die Beständigkeit gewisser Eiweißstoffe, z.B. des Kollagens, gegen Hydrolyse der Peptidbindungen ist durch die Höhe der Energie verursacht, die unter den im Organismus herrschenden Bedingungen für die kinetische Aktivierung dieser Bindungen notwendig ist. Andererseits weist die Geschwindigkeit der Erneuerung der im dynamischen Zustand befindlichen Serumproteine—die z.T. in der Leber, z.T. in anderen Organen erfolgt—darauf hin, daß der bestimmende Prozeß (Öffnung und Schließung der Peptidbindungen) unter den gegebenen Bedingungen keine allzugroße Aktivierungsenergie erfordert. Da Peptidbindungen ganz allgemein für sich allein mit Wasser nur äußerst langsam reagieren, wie ja auch das Beispiel des Kollagens zeigt, muß der Abbau und Aufbau der Serumproteine in Anwesenheit von Katalysatoren erfolgen. Im konkreten Falle kommen als Katalysatoren Enzyme in Frage [34].

(Auch der Transport der Ionen durch die Zellwände erfolgt ohne Zweifel unter Mithilfe von Enzymen. Es ist nicht unmöglich, daß Enzyme auch an der biologischen Rekristallisation unlöslicher mineralischer Salze, z.B. des Knochens, beteiligt sind. Jedenfalls ist über die enzymatische Katalyse bei physikalischen Prozessen weniger als bei chemischen Prozessen bekannt.)

Unter sonst gleichen Umständen ist der Zustand eines Bestandteils eines lebenden Systems offenbar umso dynamischer, je stärker die Aktivierungsenergie durch die zur Wirkung kommenden Enzyme herabgesetzt wird und je größer die wirksame Konzentration dieser Enzyme ist.

Vom Standpunkt der biologischen Anpassung kann es nicht überraschen, daß z.B. das mechanischen Zwecken dienende Kollagen, das zum 'Export' bestimmtes Nährmittel Kasein und insbesondere die die genetische Kontinuität vermittelnde DNS in geringerem Maß einer Erneuerung unterworfen werden, als die Serum- oder Leberproteine oder die RNS, die im Stoffwechsel Schüsselpositionen einnehmen.

DIE 'ERFINDUNG' DER ENZYME

Nun seien diese Überlegungen auf die Entstehung und Entwicklung des Lebens angewendet. Man kann verschiedene Hypothesen über die Eobionten aufstellen. Man kann annehmen, daß sie nach Adsorption organischer Stoffe an bestimmten Mineralen gebildet wurden [35] oder die Form von Koazervaten hatten [1]. Was immer aber ihre chemische Natur und ihr Aggregatzustand war —jedenfalls waren die Eobionten metastabil, befanden sich also im inneren thermodynamischen Ungleichgewicht.

Die Geschwindigkeiten der chemischen Abbauprozesse im Ur-Ozean müssen genügend klein gewesen sein, daß die Eobionten während ihrer mittleren Lebensdauer Zeit fanden, im Durchschnitt mindestens einen neuen Eobionten zu reproduzieren; sonst wären sie ausgestorben. Katalysatoren, die den metastabilen Zustand bedrohten und den Abbau förderten, waren unvermeidlich vorhanden. Doch waren die damals existierenden anorganischen und einfachen organischen Stoffe katalytisch nicht besonders wirksam. Jedenfalls waren Eobionten von solcher Struktur im Vorteil, für deren Zersetzung es keine stark wirksamen Katalysatoren gab.

In einem späteren Stadium freilich begannen die Eobionten selbst Enzyme zu erzeugen [36]. Manche Enzyme katalysierten Reaktionen, die praktisch bis zum Ende ablaufen. So beseitigt die Katalase das giftige Stoffwechselprodukt Wasserstoffperoxyd. Andere Enzyme erleichtern den Abbau von Nährstoffen (geeigneten in Lösung befindlichen organischen Substanzen) mit anschließender Verwandlung ihrer Atome in Bestandteile der Eobionten. Die mit vorteilhaften Enzymen ausgerüsteten Eobionten siegten im Kampf ums Dasein.

Die Enzyme, die den Aufbau von Zellsubstanz vermittelten, katalysierten unvermeidlich auch die gegenläufige Reaktion. Es wurde also die Aktivierungsenergie sowohl für die Hin- als auch für die Rückreaktion herabgesetzt. Die Bildung solcher Enzyme brachte demnach, wenn sie auch einerseits von großem Vorteil war, andererseits die Gefahr einer Aufhebung des metastabilen Zustandes, d.h. einer Selbstzersetzung des Eobionten mit sich.

Beispielsweise war die 'Erfindung' von Enzymen zum Aufbau von Eiweißstoffen aus geeigneten—an freier Energie reichen—Ausgangsstoffen durch die Eobionten ein großer Schritt vorwärts. Aber die gleichen Enzyme beschleunigten gleichzeitig den Eiweißabbau, wobei das thermodynamische Gleichgewicht weit in Richtung des Abbaus liegt.

Ähnlich brachte die Entwicklung von Membranen, die mit katalytischen 'Fährbooten' ausgerüstet waren, einen wesentlichen evolutionären Vorteil. Durch diese Membranen konnten nun Ionen, die benötigt wurden, stark, rasch und spezifisch in das Innere von Zellen transportiert werden. Jedoch wurden die gleichen Ionen durch die gleichen Katalysatoren auch rasch in umgekehrter Richtung durch die Zellwand befördert.

Wenn also der immense Nutzen der Enzyme entwickelt, aber der Organismus vor Schaden bewahrt werden sollte, mußten Mechanismen zur Unschädlichmachung der 'verkehrten' Enzymwirkungen gebildet werden. *Die metastabilen Zustände mußten, da sie infolge der Anwesenheit der Enzyme nicht mehr statisch beständig waren, von nun an dynamisch aufrechterhalten werden.* Um den stationären Zustand nicht mit dem thermodynamischen Gleichgewichtszustand zusammenfallen zu lassen, mußten besondere, dauernd wirkende Mechanismen entwickelt werden, die Arbeit leisteten und zum Antrieb freie Energie verbrauchten. *Die freie Energie, die der Organismus—in Form von Nahrung—seither suchen muß, ist der Preis für die Benützung der Enzyme.*

Zur Deckung des Bedarfs an freier Energie für die Aufrechterhaltung des dynamischen Zustandes ergab sich die Notwendigkeit eines Stoffwechsels mit der Umgebung selbst im stationären Zustand—also auch dann, wenn die Eobionten keine äußere Arbeit leisteten. Die freie Energie wurde durch Verwertung von Nährstoffen im Rahmen eines 'Grundumsatzes' bestritten. Die zur Aufrechterhaltung metastabiler dynamischer Zustände notwendigen Arbeitsleistungen können unter Umständen zahlenmäßig abgeschätzt werden [2, 6]. Aber der Grundumsatz ist nicht einmal das einzige Opfer, das der Organismus bringen muß, wenn er sich der Vorteile des dynamischen Zustandes bedienen will. Er muß ja auch die komplizierten Mechanismen aufbauen und instand halten, die die Erhaltung metastabiler Zustände auf dynamischer Grundlage gewährleisten.

Jene historische Epoche, in der die Ausrüstung mit Enzymen, der dynamische Zustand und der regelmäßige Stoffwechsel auf breiter Grundlage begannen, darf zweckmäßig als die Periode des Übergangs vom Eobionten zum Lebewesen betrachtet werden. Natürlich war die Ausbildung der feinen, für den dynamischen Zustand erforderlichen Mechanismen ein stufenweise verlaufender, langwieriger Prozeß, der wahrscheinlich in der ganzen Entwicklung der Tier- und Pflanzenwelt nicht zu einem Abschluß gekommen ist. Die Vervollständigung der Ausrüstung mit Enzymen hat die Lebewesen in zunehmendem Maß zu Äquifinalität und Homöostasis befähigt; die katalytisch gesteuerten Reaktionsmechanismen ermöglichen dem Organismus, auch bei Abweichungen von den normalen Entwicklungs- und Lebensbedingungen normale Zusammensetzung, Struktur und Gestalt beizubehalten, oder doch zu diesen zurückzukehren.

Man hat die Lebewesen als 'offene Systeme' im thermodynamischen Sinn behandelt [37, 38]. Dabei wird als Synonym des Begriffs 'stationärer Zustand' auch der Begriff des 'Fließgleich gewichts' gebraucht [6]. In einer Arbeit wurde der Versuch gemacht, die phylogenetische Entwicklung von diesem Standpunkt aus zu beleuchten, und das Ergebnis erhalten, daß der Stoffwechsel und die Entropieerzeugung je Masseneinheit Minima zustreben [40]. Diese Gesetzmäßigkeit kann aber offenbar in dem Bereich des Übergangs von der statischen zur dynamischen Aufrechterhaltung des metastabilen Zustandes nicht gelten.

Mit dieser grundsätzlich gehaltenen Betrachtung wird natürlich über den Weg, auf dem der metastabile Zustand dynamisch aufrechterhalten wird, nichts ausgesagt. Eine Analyse der möglichen Mechanismen müßte zeigen, bis zu welchem Grad 'mikroskopische Reversibilität' eingehalten werden kann oder aber zyklische Prozesse auftreten müssen. Zyklische Prozesse werden ja tatsächlich gerade in Bezug auf den dynamischen Zustand des Eiweißes diskutiert. Mit größerer Sicherheit und mit vielen Einzelheiten sind die zyklischen Prozesse bei Kohlehydraten bekannt [39].

BEMERKUNGEN ÜBER VIREN

Eine andere Frage bedarf noch der Analyse; War die Entwicklung eines Mechanismus unmöglich, der die Vorteile der statischen und der dynamischen Aufrechterhaltung des metastabilen Zustandes vereinigt hätte? Man könnte sich vorstellen, daß der dynamische Zustand nur für die Wiederherstellung eines durch Beanspruchung verloren gegangenen stationären Normalzustandes in Funktion tritt, daß aber der dynamische Zustand unterbrochen wird, sobald die stationären Bedingungen wieder erreicht sind. Dann müßte also im Normalzustand keine Arbeit geleistet werden.

Z.B. könnten Membranen undurchlässig bleiben, solange zu beiden Seiten die physiologischen Normalkonzentrationen herrschen, so daß in diesem Ruhezustand aktiver Transport überflüssig wird. In Wirklichkeit treten aber, wie die Beobachtung zeigt, rasche Änderungen der Durchlässigkeit von Membranen nur in besonderen Fällen, z.B. bei der Übermittlung von Nervenimpulsen, auf. Auch der Abbau und Aufbau der Körperbestandteile dauert, wie dargelegt, im Normalzustand fort.

Vielleicht besteht die Ursache darin, daß die Regulierung der Funktionen des Organismus durch die Unterbrechung des dynamischen Zustandes zu sehr erschwert würde [2]. Analog wird ja bei warmblütigen Tieren die Normaltemperatur auch im Schlafe, also bei eingeschränkter Lebenstätigkeit, aufrechterhalten, obwohl dies auf den ersten Blick als Verschwendung von freier Energie erscheinen könnte. Nur bei der Degeneration von Lebewesen oder ihren Bestandteilen zu Viren tritt ein zeitweiser Verlust des dynamischen Zustands ein (siehe unten).

Rittenberg [8] hat sich über dieses Problem in folgender Weise ausgesprochen:

> 'The steady state system while energetically wasteful offers certain advantages. It is of course possible to imagine a living cell in which the structural components were fixed and the synthetic mechanisms were called on only to repair the metabolic mill. Such systems are well known in the non living world. They are for the most part dynamically unstable. The response of such systems is not proportional to a perturbation; a small disturbance results in a new equilibrium state; a larger one leads to a catastrophic response. Obviously neither result is desirable for the living cell. Systems in a steady state however, respond slowly to perturbations; the

resulting variation is proportional to the disturbance. An organism which maintains its form and structure by balancing opposing reactions is less likely to be fatally damaged than is an organism which responded to disturbances by turning on and off its chemical reactions.'

Eine Sonderstellung im Bereich der Lebenserscheinungen nehmen die in einfachen Fällen aus reinem Nukleoprotein bestehendren Viren ein. Diese werden von vielen Autoren gar nicht unter die Lebewesen eingereiht, obwohl sie lebender Substanz entstammen und sich in dieser vermehren. Der Parallelismus zwischen den Viren und den vermuteten Genen ist oft bemerkt worden.

Innerhalb des lebenden Wirts nehmen Viren am dynamischen Zustand teil. Z.B. tauscht das best untersuchte aller Pflanzenviren, das Tabakmosaikvirus (TMV)—selbst wenn es schon lange im Wirt (Tabakblatt) anwesend war und Sättigungskonzentration erreicht hatte—noch immer Radiokohlenstoff mit dem Wirt aus [41, 42]. Man muß annehmen, daß das TMV im Wirt auch enzymatisch wirksam ist, denn sonst könnte es ja die eigene Vermehrung nicht katalysieren.

Dagegen sind enzymatische Wirkungen von Viren ausserhalb der Wirte nur ausnahmsweise bekannt geworden [43]. Z.B. wurde am TMV bisher keine solche Wirkung mit Sicherheit festgestellt. Es ist nun bezeichnend, daß das TMV sich ausserhalb des Wirtes auch nicht im dynamischen Zustand befindet. Austausch isotoper Atome findet nicht einmal dann statt, wenn die chemische Zusammensetzung des Mediums der des Wirts (Tabakblatt) sehr ähnlich ist, wenn nämlich das Medium aus gemahlenem Tabakblatt besteht [44, 45].

Die heute existierenden Viren können keine Eobionten sein, da sie obligate Parasiten sind und nur innerhalb der Lebewesen autokatalytisch wirken. Doch meint Haldane, daß die Eobionten gewisse Ähnlichkeit mit den heutigen Viren aufgewiesen haben können [3]. Dieser Gedanke kann nun dahin ergänzt werden, daß die Viren bei ihrer Degeneration aus Mikroorganismen oder Zellbestandteilen und beim Verlust der extrazellulär wirkenden Enzyme offenbar auch die Fähigkeit zum extrazellulären dynamischen Zustand wieder verloren haben.

Viren in reinem Zustand, z.B. kristallisierte Pflanzenviren, sind also im Gegensatz zu ihren Ahnen nicht mehr deshalb beständig, weil sie den metastabilen Zustand durch Stoffwechselprozesse aufrechterhalten. Vielmehr ist nach Verlust der Enzyme die der spontanen Zersetzung im Wege stehende Aktivierungsenergie hinreichend hoch, um die Integrität der Viren auf dem Weg von Wirt zu Wirt zu gewährleisten. Viren im reinen Zustand sind also ebenso wie ehemals die Eobionten 'statisch metastabil'. (Freilich mußten die Eobionten im Gegensatz zu den Viren nicht gegen freien Sauerstoff widerstandsfähig sein, da es diesen zu ihrer Zeit nicht gab.) Indem die Viren außerhalb det Wirtszellen den dynamischen Zustand unterbrechen, lösen sie in gewissem Sinn das oben aufgeworfene Problem, wie im stationären Zustand der Verbrauch freier Energie überflüssig gemacht werden kann.

LITERATURVERZEICHNIS

1. Siehe A. I. OPARIN, *Die Entstehung des Lebens auf der Erde.* Berlin, 1957.
2. G. V. SCHULZ, *Naturwissenschaften,* **37,** 196, 223, 1950; *Z. Elektrochem.* **55,** 569, 1951.
3. J. B. S. HALDANE, in *New Biol.,* **16,** 1954.

4. N. W. Pirie, *Discovery*, **14**, 238, 1953; in *New Biol.*, **16**, 1954.
5. Zitiert nach [6].
6. L. Bertalanffy, *Biophysik des Fließgleichgewichts*. Braunschweig, 1953.
7. R. Schoenheimer, *The Dynamic State of Body Constituents*. Cambridge, Mass., 1949.
8. D. Rittenberg, *Harvey Lect.*, **44**, 200, 1948–49.
9. G. Hevesy, *Radioactive Indicators*. New York, 1949; *Naturw. Rdsch.*, **9**, 212, 1956.
10. A. V. Hill, *Trans. Faraday Soc.*, **26**, 667, 1930.
11. H. H. Ussing, *Advances in Enzymol.*, **13**, 21, 1952; *Genfer Atomenergiekonferenz* 1955, Bericht 908.
12. Siehe H. Tarver, in *The Proteins*, (Herausgegeben von H. Neurath & K. Bailey), New York, 1953.
13. Siehe E. Broda, *Radioaktive Isotope in der Biochemie*. Wien, 1958.
14. A. Niklas, W. Maurer & H. Krause, *Biochem. Z.*, **325**, 464, 1954.
15. F. J. Dixon, D. W. Talmage, P. H. Maurer & M. P. Deichmiller, *J. exp. Med.*, **96**, 313, 1952.
16. J. H. Humphrey & A. S. McFarlane, *Biochem. J.*, **57**, 186, 195, 1954.
17. Siehe E. Chargaff & J. N. Davidson (Hsg.), *The Nucleic Acids*. New York, 1955.
18. Siehe V. G. Allfrey, A. E. Mirsky & H. Stern, *Advanc. Enzymol.*, **16**, 411, 1955.
19. E. F. Gale, in *Amino Acid Metabolism* (Hsg. W. D. McElroy & H. B. Glass). Baltimore, 1955.
20. J. Horiuti & M. Polanyi, *Nature, Lond.*, **132**, 819, 1933; *Proc. Manchester phil. Soc.*, **78**, 47, 1934.
21. A. Farkas, L. Farkas & J. Yudkin, *Proc. roy. Soc.*, B **115**, 373, 1934.
22. M. Doudoroff, H. A. Barker & W. Z. Hassid, *J. biol. Chem.*, **168**, 725, 1947.
23. Siehe W. Langenbeck, *Advanc. Enzymol.*, **14**, 163, 1953.
24. A. I. Oparin, *Vestn. Akad. Nauk S.S.S.R.*, Heft 12, 39, 1953; *Sowjetwissenschaft-Naturwissenschaftliche Beiträge*, Berlin, 299, 1954.
25. N. W. Pirie, *The Meaninglessness of the Terms Life and Living*, in *Perspectives in Biochemistry*. Cambridge, 1939.
26. A. Neuberger, J. C. Perrone & H. G. Slack, *Biochem. J.*, **53**, 47, 1953.
27. W. F. Bale, C. L. Yuile, L. De la Vergne, L. L. Miller & G. H. Whipple, *J. exp. Med.*, **90**, 315, 1949.
28. J. M. Barry, *Biochem. J.*, **63**, 669, 1956.
29. W. N. Orechowitsch (Orekhovich), *Genfer Atomenergiekonferenz* 1955, Bericht 686.
30. H. Tarver & L. M. Morse, *J. biol. Chem.*, **173**, 53, 1948.
31. R. C. Thompson & J. E. Ballou, *J. biol. Chem.*, **223**, 795, 1956.
32. D. S. Hogness, M. Cohn & J. Monod, *Biochim. biophys. Acta*, **16**, 99, 1955.
33. Siehe C. Hinshelwood, *The Kinetics of Chemical Change*. Oxford, 1940.
34. Siehe O. Hoffmann-Ostenhof, *Enzymologie*. Wien, 1955.
35. J. D. Bernal, *The Physical Basis of Life*. London, 1951; in *New Biol.*, **16**, 1954.
36. Siehe O. Hoffmann-Ostenhof, *Der Ursprung der Enzyme*. Dieses Symposium.
37. S. R. de Groot, *Thermodynamics of Irreversible Processes*. Amsterdam, 1951.
38. I. Prigogine, *Introduction to the Thermodynamics of Irreversible Processes*. Springfield, Ill., 1955.
39. Siehe H. A. Krebs & H. L. Kornberg, *Energy Transformations in Living Matter*. Berlin, 1957.
40. I. Prigogine & J. M. Wiame, *Experientia*, **2**, 451, 1946.
41. H. Schönfellinger & E. Broda, *Mh. Chem.*, **83**, 837, 1952; **85**, 33, 1954.
42. R. Jeener, *Arch. int. Physiol.*, **60**, 546, 1952.
43. Siehe D. J. Bauer, *Metabolic Aspects of Virus Multiplication*. In *The Nature of Virus Multiplication*. Cambridge, 1953.
44. E. Broda, G. Wüstinger & H. Schönfellinger, *Naturwissenschaften*, **43**, 305, 1956.
45. M. L. Stephenson, K. V. Thimann & P. C. Zamecnik, *Arch. Biochem. Biophys.*, **65**, 194, 1956.

Synthèse Enzymatique des Ribopolynucléotides

MARIANNE GRUNBERG-MANAGO

*Institut de Biologie physico-chimique (Service de Biochimie),
13 rue Pierre Curie, Paris, 5, France*

ABRÉVIATIONS

5′-diphosphates (pyrophosphates d'adénosine, inosine, guanosine, uridine et cytidine): ADP, IDP, GDP, UDP, CDP.
5′-monophosphates des mêmes nucléosides: AMP, IMP, GMP, UMP et CMP.
3′-monophosphates correspondants: 3′-AMP, etc.
5′-triphosphates des mêmes nucléosides: ATP, ITP, GTP, UTP et CTP.
tri(hydroxyméthyl)aminométhane: TRIS.
acide éthylènediamine tétraacétique: EDTA.
orthophosphate: Pm.

TOUTE MATIÈRE vivante est caractérisée par le haut degré de spécificité de ses polymères: protéines et acides nucléiques. Aussi, dans la recherche sur l'origine de la vie, un des problèmes fondamentaux est celui des mécanismes intervenant pour combiner les éléments de monomères pour former les protéines et les acides nucléiques. On peut espérer que la connaissance des relations réciproques de la synthèse des proteines et des acides nucléiques nous amenera à comprendre comment les éléments de monomères peuvent être combinés suivant une séquence spécifique.

L'hypothèse selon laquelle les acides nucléiques, et tout particulièrement les acides ribonucléiques, interviennent dans la synthèse des protéines a été considérablement renforcée par les travaux de ces dernières années [1–4]. Tout récemment une découverte particulièrement importante a démontré le rôle fondamental de l'acide ribonucléique dans la synthèse des protéines. Fraenkel-Conrat & Williams [5], Gierer & Schramm [6] ont réussi à extraire un acide ribonucléique du virus de la mosaique de tabac qui est à lui seul infectieux. Cet acide ribonucléique, chez une cellule hôte, non seulement se reproduit lui-même, mais induit la synthèse d'une protéine spécifique, caractéristique de chaque souche de virus. L'acide ribonucléique est ainsi le déterminant génétique de la particule virulente. La connaissance de la structure de cet acide nucléique devient d'un intérêt immédiat. Il est permis d'espérer que l'on pourra dans un jour proche synthetiser *in vitro* un ribopolynucléotide capable chez une cellule hôte de se reproduire et d'engendrer une protéine spécifique. Un progrès considérable sera ainsi réalisé. Néanmoins il est probable que ce sont des enzymes protéiques qui synthétisent l'acide nucléique, la protéine pouvant même participer non enzymatiquement à cette synthèse, comme on le verra dans cet exposé. Il est donc difficile de séparer les deux synthèses : acides nucléiques et protéines, l'une de l'autre. On peut certes dans certaines conditions (variation du pH, de la concentration en sels du milieu, mélange de certains polymères [7–9]) obtenir une polymérisation spontanée de ribopolynucléotides, mais celle-ci se fait toujours à partir d'unités de polymère déjà existantes. Aussi est-il difficile de décider laquelle des deux synthèses : protéines ou acides nucléiques a précédé l'autre au cours de l'évolution.

Nos connaissances sur le mécanisme de synthèse des chaînes polynucléotidiques des acides ribo- et désoxyribonucléiques restaient très obscures jusqu'à ces dernières années. Une des raisons en était que la plupart des données provenaient d'expériences effectuées *in vivo*. Tout dernièrement deux enzymes ont été isolés des bactéries, l'un par Ochoa et moi-même [10] catalysant la synthèse des ribopolynucléotides à partir des nucléosides 5′-diphosphates, et l'autre par Kornberg [11] et ses collaborateurs catalysant la synthèse des désoxypolynucléotides à partir des desoxy-5′-triphosphates. Je me limiterai dans cet exposé à une mise au point du mécanisme de synthèse des ribopolynucléotides, m'étendant surtout sur nos résultats récents. Ceux-ci font ressortir l'importance de la configuration des ribopolynucléotides pour leur rôle biologique et concernent l'isolement à partir de la levure d'un nouveau système enzymatique catalysant une synthèse de polynucléotides, mais différent de l'enzyme bactérien.

L'enzyme bactérien isolé pour la première fois à partir d'*Azotobacter vinelandii* [10] catalyse la synthèse des polynucléotides à partir des nucléosides 5′-diphosphates avec une libération de phosphore. La réaction est reversible et il se produit un clivage phosphorolytique des ribopolynucléotides avec formation de nucléosides 5′-diphosphates. La réaction est donc analogue à la synthèse réversible des polysaccharides par la 'phosphorylase'; pour cette raison le nouvel enzyme a été appelé 'polynucléotide phosphorylase'. Il catalyse cette réaction :

$$n(\text{XRP–P}) \rightleftharpoons (\text{XRP})_n + n\text{Pm}$$

où R représente le ribose, P–P le pyrophosphate, Pm l'orthophosphate et X une ou plusieurs des bases suivantes : adenine, hypoxanthine, guanine, uracile ou cytosine. La Table 1 montre la stoechiométrie de la réaction en présence d'IDP, dans les deux directions. Dans l'expérience 1, la polynucléotide phosphorylase purifiée est incubée avec l'IDP, les quantités de P libéré, de polynucléotide formé et d'IDP disparu déterminé comme P libéré par un enzyme spécifique IDPase [12] sont environ les mêmes. Dans l'expérience 2 une partie aliquote du surnageant après destruction de l'IDP est incubée de nouveau avec la polynucléotide phosphorylase. Les quantités de P, de polynucléotides disparus et d'IDP formés sont stoechiométriques. Dans l'expérience 3 une solution dialysée du polymère I est incubée avec la polynucléotide phosphorylase en présence de Pm. Ici encore les quantités de polynucléotides, de Pm disparu et d'IDP formé sont équivalentes. La réaction requièrt le Mg.

TABLE I

Stoechiometrie et reversibilité de la reaction catalysée par la polynucléotide phosphorylase

Exper.	Incub. (min.)	μ moles		
		IDP	P_m	Poly-nucléotide
I	0	9,76	1,06	—
	90	4,30	7,10	5,39
	Δ	−5,46	+6,04	+5,39
2	0	0	14,2	3,44
	60	2,3	12,0	1,30
	Δ	+2,3	−2,2	−2,14
3	0	0,69	8,10	8,12
	90	1,96	6,74	6,75
	Δ	+1,27	−1,36	−1,37

1. Réaction de synthèse. 2. Réaction de phosphorolyse après élimination de l'excès d'IDP en 1. 3. Réaction de phosphorolyse avec un polynucléotide isolé.

La polynucléotide phosphorylase, en présence de Mg, incorpore le phosphate radioactif dans le groupement terminal des nucléosides 5′-diphosphates ce qui est dû au moins en partie à la reversibilité de la réaction. Le polynucléotide composé uniquement d'unités de nucléoside 5′-monophosphate n'est donc jamais marqué en présence de phosphate radioactif.

L'incorporation de phosphate ou l'échange a été utilisé comme test pour l'isolement et la purification de l'enzyme.

Des préparations environ 75% pures en enzyme ont pu être obtenues tout récemment au laboratoire de Dr Ochoa [13].

Des polymères simples contenant l'AMP, l'IMP, le CMP ou l'UMP comme seule unité de base ont été préparés en incubant l'enzyme avec les nucléosides diphosphates correspondants [10]. On les désignera respectivement par polyA, I, C, U. Si on évite la chaleur et l'acidité au cours de l'isolement des polymères, leur poids moléculaire moyen peut être élevé. Les valeurs de 570 000 et 800 000 ont été obtenues respectivement pour les polymères A et I par la méthode de diffusion de la lumière.

Des polymères mixtes, c'est à dire des polymères contenant deux ou plusieurs unités de bases différentes, ont été préparés en incubant des mélanges de nucléosides diphosphates avec la polynucléotide phosphorylase. Plusieurs de ces polymères ont été préparés à partir de mélanges d'adénosine et d'uridine diphosphates en proportions variées: polymères A–U [14]. Je reviendrai sur ce point au cours de mon exposé. A partir d'un mélange de nucléosides 5′-diphosphates d'adénosine, guanosine, uridine et cytidine l'enzyme catalyse la synthèse de polynucléotides contenant les 4 nucléotides présents dans l'acide ribonucléique naturel [10]. Deux polymères A–G–U–C ont été ainsi obtenus, l'un en partant de mélanges d'ADP, GDP, UDP et CDP en proportion 1 : 0,5 : 1 : 1 respectivement [10] et l'autre en partant de mélanges contenant les 4 diphosphates en proportion équimolaire [15].

On n'a pu préparer que des traces de polymère contenant l'acide guanylique (poly G). Le Dr Ochoa [15] non plus n'a pu obtenir que des traces de polynucléotides contenant l'AMP et le GMP (polymère A–G) ou bien le GMP et l'UMP (polymère G–U). Il se produit une légère libération de phosphate dans ces trois cas, mais il ne se forme que des traces de composé non dialysable. Nous ne connaissons pas encore la raison, pour laquelle on ne peut pas obtenir de polymères contenant la guanine comme seule unité de base, ou même de polymères à deux bases si la guanine est l'une d'elles. Pourtant, lorsque les 4 nucléosides diphosphates sont présents, l'acide guanylique est incorporé dans le polymère, en proportion même plus élevée que les autres nucléosides monophosphates. Littauer & Kornberg [16] ont observé cette particularité de l'acide guanylique, avec la polynucléotide phosphorylase extraite d'une autre bactérie *E. coli*.

La dégradation chimique et enzymatique des polynucléotides biosynthétiques prouve qu'ils sont formés d'unités de mononucléotides-5' unies les unes aux autres par des liens 3'-phosphoriboses comme dans les acides nucléiques [10]. La chaîne est terminée par un groupe phosphate lié au carbone 5' du nucléoside [17]; il en est de même pour l'acide ribonucléique d'*Azotobacter* [18]. Les produits obtenus par hydrolyse des polymères biosynthétiques avec l'alcali ou les phosphodiestérases spécifiques, celle du venin de serpent, de la rate ou de la ribonucléase pancréatique sont en accord avec ce que l'on connaît sur l'action de ces agents sur l'acide ribonucléique. En particulier après digestion très poussée par la ribonucléase, on retrouve dans le cas du polymère A–G–U–C ou d l'acide ribonucléique la même quantité de 'core' non dialysable [10].

Il a été prouvé que des liens (5', 3') phosphoriboses existent dans les polymères mixtes entre les mononucléotides de bases différentes [10].

Les données actuelles sur la structure, le poids moléculaire, le diagramme des rayons X et le comportement envers les différents enzymes, indiquent que les polymères biosynthétiques sont très proches de l'acide ribonucléique.

Les spectres de diffraction de rayons X sur les fibres obtenues à partir des polymères, A, U, A–U et A–G–U–C ont été étudiés par A. Rich [9] comparativement à ceux des fibres de l'acide ribonucléique. Il semble, qu'il faille la présence des 2 bases purine et pyrimidine, pour obtenir un spectre semblable à celui de l'acide ribonucléique naturel. Les poids moléculaires des polymères biosynthétiques varient entre 30 000 et 1 000 000. Ces valeurs sont de l'ordre de grandeur des poids moléculaires de différents acides ribonucléiques. De plus R. C. Warner [19] a obtenu pour le polymère A–G–U–C la même constante de sédimentation que celle de l'acide ribonucléique isolé des cellules d'*Azotobacter*.

La découverte de Hart & Smith [20] que les polymères biosynthétiques A–G–U–C, comme les acides ribonucléiques, réagissent avec la protéine du virus de la mosaique de tabac, en donnant des batonnets ressemblant au virus mais dépourvus de pouvoir infectant, est encore une indication de l'analogie de la structure macromoléculaire des polynucléotides biosynthétiques et des acides ribonucléiques. Pour qu'il y ait recombinaison entre l'acide ribonucléique et la protéine, il faut vraisemblablement que leurs structures soient complémentaires.

Il a été montré par Okamoto [21] et par Bernheimer [22] que la formation de la streptolysine S par *Streptococcus hemolyticus*, est stimulée par la fraction qui dans les divers acides ribonucléiques, résiste à la ribonucléase. Récemment Egami [23] a trouvé qu'une telle fraction du polymère A–G–U–C a une activité 3 fois plus grande que celle provenant de l'acide ribonucléique de levure.

Il ressort donc de ces études, que le polymère A–G–U–C, c'est-à-dire le polymère contenant les quatre résidus: adénylique, guanylique, uridylique et cytidylique, semble indifférentiable de l'acide ribonucléique naturel. A l'heure actuelle on ne saurait encore décider, si la réaction catalysée par la polynucléotide phosphorylase représente un mécanisme biologique pour la synthèse de l'acide ribonucléique, mais cette possibilité ne paraît pas invraisemblable, du moins chez les bactéries où l'enzyme est largement répandu. Il a été purifié à partir de *Alcaligenes faecalis* [24], *Escherichia coli* [16] et *Micrococcus lysodeikticus* [25], il a été mis en évidence chez *Staphylococcus aureus*, *Clostridium kluyverii* and *Streptococcus haemolyticus* [24].

De ce fait, le problème primordial à résoudre concerne la spécificité de la polynucléotide phosphorylase. Il semble bien en effet, que chaque acide nucléique est caractérisé par sa composition en nucléotides, ainsi que par leur séquence dont on admet généralement qu'elle détermine leur spécificité. Quels sont les facteurs influençant la composition des polymères biosynthétisés? Nous avons entrepris [14] une étude systématique de l'influence de la concentration des nucléotides sur la constitution des polymères. Nous avons préparé divers polymères A–U à partir de mélanges d'adénosine et d'uridine diphosphates en proportions variées. Chaque nucléoside était employé en quantité inférieure à celle nécessaire pour saturer l'enzyme, comme c'est probablement le cas dans la cellule. La Table 2 montre que la composition en nucléotides des polymères dépend étroitement des concentrations relatives initiales des nucléotides diphosphates à partir desquels ils sont synthétisés. La proportion de l'acide adénylique par rapport à l'acide uridylique est pratiquement la même que celle des nucléosides diphosphates, dans le cas des polymères A–U synthétisés à partir de mélanges équimoléculaires d'adénosine et d'uridine diphosphates ou de mélange contenant l'ADP/UDP en proportion 3/1.

Il faut remarquer qu'elle s'écarte légèrement lorsque le mélange contient 3 fois plus d'uridine que d'adénosine diphosphate. Cette différence est systématique, le polymère contient 4 et non pas 3 fois plus d'acide uridylique pour une raison que nous ne comprenons pas très bien. Mais même dans ce cas, la proportion des acides uridylique et adénylique dans le polynucléotide est voisine des concentrations relatives des nucléosides diphosphates utilisés pour leur synthèse. Nous avons ainsi à notre disposition un moyen de synthétiser des polynucléotides de composition voulue, il suffit de maintenir une proportion donnée de nucléosides diphosphates. On peut également tirer la conclusion importante, que si la polynucléotide phosphorylase est l'enzyme responsable de la synthèse *in vivo* de l'acide ribonucléique, la composition de celui-ci dépendrait étroitement des concentrations des nucléosides au lieu de synthèse.

TABLE 2

Influence de la concentration des nucléosides diphosphates sur la composition des polynucleotides biosynthétises à partir de ces nucléosides

Les polynucléotides étaient préparés suivant la technique habituelle [10]. Le mélange d'incubation contient par ml.: 100 μmoles TRIS pH 8,1, 10 μmoles $MgCl_2$, 1,8 unités de polynucléotide phosphorylase d'A.S = 14,8. Incubation de 23 à 36 h à 30°.

A la fin de l'incubation le liquide est refroidi à 0° et précipité par 2 vol. d'éthanol (à 96°) à froid. Le mélange est laissé 1 h. à 0° et centrifugé 10 minutes à 15 000 g. Le précipité est dissous dans l'eau distillée et précipité par l'éthanol comme la première fois. Ce dernier précipité dissous dans l'eau est dialysé 48 h avec agitation contre l'eau distillée à + 4° environ. La composition en nucléotides des polymères est déterminée de la manière suivante: le polynucléotide est hydrolysé 48 h à 37° dans la potasse 0,04 N, puis chromatographié suivant la technique de Krebs & Hems [26]. Les taches nucléotidiques sont éluées avec 5 ml. 0,01 N-HCl 48 h à la température de la pièce et les blancs (papier seul) défalqués.

	μMoles nucléosides par ml. dans le mélange d'incubation			μMoles de nucléosides élués après hydrolyse alcaline de A–U		
Exp.	ADP	UDP	ADP/UDP	AMP	UMP	AMP/UMP
1	21,2	64	$\frac{1}{3}$	0,334	1,55	$\frac{1}{4,7}$
				0,32	1,54	
2	21	65	$\frac{1}{3,1}$	0,315	1,36	$\frac{1}{4,3}$
				0,225	0,96	
3	41	43	$\frac{1}{1,05}$	0,370	0,38	$\frac{1}{1}$
				0,350	0,33	
4	61	22	$\frac{2,8}{1}$	1	0,32	$\frac{3,2}{1}$
				0,89	0,27	

La correction a été faite pour les impuretés présentes dans les échantillons de nucléotides diphosphates utilisés. L'ADP contenait 2% d'ATP et d'AMP, l'UDP contenait 5% d'UMP.

Le polymère A–G–U–C préparé par Smellie & Ochoa [27] à partir d'un mélange contenant les 4 diphosphates en proportion équimoléculaire, a une composition similaire à celle de l'acide ribonucléique d'*Azotobacter vinelandii*.

Il faut remarquer qu'ici aussi, alors que le polymère a été préparé à partir d'un mélange équimoléculaire de nucléosides diphosphates, la proportion des nucléotides dans le polymère biosynthétique n'est pas exactement équimoléculaire, mais proche de celle de l'acide ribonucléique d'*Azotobacter* et des bactéries en général. En effet, la composition en nucléotides des acides ribonucléiques ne varie pas d'une manière significative d'une espèce bactérienne à l'autre, comme c'est le cas de l'acide désoxyribonucléique (Belozersky) [28]. On doit donc supposer que dans la plupart des bactéries les nucléosides diphosphates sont en proportion équimoléculaire au lieu de synthèse de l'acide ribonucléique.

Mais si on peut comprendre que la polynucléotide phosphorylase peut synthétiser des acides ribonucléiques de composition différente, il reste à élucider les facteurs déterminant la séquence en nucléotides. La comparaison de la séquence des nucléotides dans le polymère A–G–U–C et dans l'acide ribonucléique d'*Azotobacter* sera très intéressante. Une étude systématique de la séquence dans les polymères mixtes pourra peut-être déterminer si elle est dûe ou non au hasard et contribuer à éclaircir la question. Mais il semble *a priori* difficile d'envisager une spécificité de l'enzyme sans faire intervenir un amorceur spécifique.

Si la polynucléotide phosphorylase est l'enzyme responsable de la synthèse de l'acide ribonucléique *in vivo*, un autre problème capital en plus de la spécificité de l'enzyme reste à résoudre. En effet, bien que nous n'ayons pas encore de données précises sur la constante d'équilibre on sait [10] que dans nos conditions expérimentales dans le sens de la synthèse du polynucléotide, la réaction se stabilise pour un rapport de concentrations P/mononucléotides restant, variant entre 1,5 et 2. La synthèse des polynucléotides est favorisée jusqu'à un certain point, comme on doit s'y attendre, car le lien P-P des nucléosides diphosphates est converti en un lien diesterphosphorique. Mais la réaction étant facilement reversible, il n'y aurait donc pas une très grande différence d'énergie entre la liaison phosphate des polynucléotides et celle des nucléosides diphosphates; ainsi la liaison phosphate de l'acide nucléique pourrait être placée dans la classe des liaisons de haute énergie. Cela signifierait qu'en principe l'acide ribonucléique serait facilement phosphorolysé en présence d'un excès de phosphate minéral. Or la cellule vivante contient de grandes quantités de phosphate minéral qui devraient être suffisantes pour inhiber la synthèse de l'acide ribonucléique, les quantités physiologiques des nucléotides diphosphates dans la cellule devant être en outre inférieures à celles nécessaires pour la vitesse maximum de synthèse.

Mais nous nous sommes aperçus que si les polymères simples sont phosphorolysés très facilement comme il était prévu, les polymères mixtes et l'acide ribonucléique le sont beaucoup plus lentement [10]. La Figure 1 montre la vitesse de phosphorolyse des différents polymères mixtes A–U, des polymères simples et d'un acide ribonucléique de levure [14].

Nous voyons que les polymères mixtes A–U sont phosphorolysés 3 fois plus lentement environ que les polymères simples; quant à lacide ribonucléique de levure il est comme le polymère AGUC attaqué très lentement. Les acides ribonucléiques d'*Azotobacter vinelandii*, de *E. coli*, de *Staphylococcus aureus* et du foie de boeuf sont tous phosphorolysés avec formation de 4 nucléosides diphosphates, mais environ à la même vitesse que l'acide ribonucléique de levure, c'est-à-dire très lentement.

Il y a pourtant un acide ribonucléique qui est phosphorolysé plus rapidement (sa vitesse de phosphorolyse est environ la même que celle des polymères simples), c'est l'acide ribonucléique du virus de la mosaique de tabac [29, 30]. Nous avons pensé tout d'abord que ces résultats pouvaient s'expliquer par le degré de

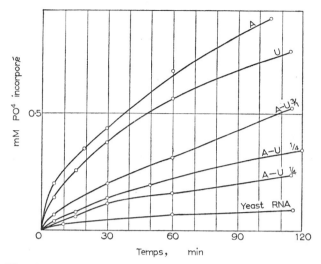

FIG. 1. Phosphorolyse des polynucléotides contenant des proportions variées d'acide adenylique et uridylique.

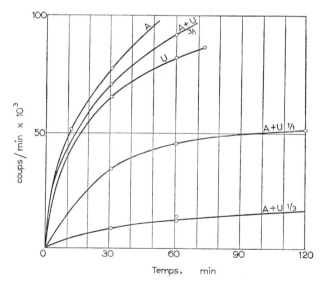

FIG. 2. Phosphorolyse des différents mélanges d'acides polyadenyliques et uridyliques.

Note—Figs. 1 & 2. Phosphorolyse des différents polynucléotides: 1 ml de mélange d'incubation contient 50 μmoles TRIS, pH 7,45; 7 μmoles MgCl$_2$; 8 μmoles tampon PO$_4$ (pH 7,4) contenant ^{32}P 265 à 540 × 10^3 cpm dans différentes expériences et la polynucléotide phosphorylase d'*Azotobacter* 0,062 mg à 0,124 mg. SA = 14,8 polynucléotide = 1,2 μmoles.

polymérisation des échantillons d'acide ribonucléique; en effet le 'core' de l'acide ribonucléique n'est pas phosphorolysé [10] et Singer [31] a montré que les polymères dégradés sont phosphorolysés à une vitesse plus faible que les polynucléotides polymérisés et à condition qu'ils ne soient pas terminés par un radical 3'PO₄. Mais il ne semble pas que ce soit la bonne explication. En effet un acide ribonucléique de levure bien polymérisé, qui nous a été envoyé par les Drs Pirie et Pierpoint, est phosphorolysé aussi très lentement.

Or nous savons maintenant, grâce aux travaux de Warner [8] et de Rich [9] que 2 polymères complémentaires, contenant chacun une seule unité de mononucléotide comme les polymères A et U par exemple, peuvent réagir en solution aqueuse pour former des complexes stables. Warner a montré le premier que quand on mélange ces 2 polymères, il se produit une chute de la densité optique à la longueur d'onde de leur maximum d'absorption dans l'U.V. Il se produit également une augmentation de viscosité. La formation du complexe est de plus indiquée par les observations suivantes: à l'électrophorèse, le mélange des 2 polymères simples A et U présente un seul pic avec une mobilité intermédiaire à celle des 2 polymères, et à l'ultracentrifugation, on n'obtient qu'un seul composé avec une constante de sédimentation plus élevée que celle des polymères A et U pris séparément.

Rich et Davies ont montré que les fibres obtenues à partir des solutions de mélange de polymères A et U fournissent des diagrammes de rayons X bien orientés, similaires à ceux obtenus avec l'acide désoxyribonucléique (DNA). Ces résultats s'expliquent d'après eux de la manière suivante: le polymère A et le polymère U ayant séparément une configuration irrégulière forment *in vitro* une double spirale qui ressemble en beaucoup de points à celle proposée pour le DNA. D'après leurs résultats ils concluent, que les résidus adénine et uracile peuvent être liés par des liens hydrogène, comme il a été postulé pour les résidus thymine et adénine dans le DNA. Le groupe hydroxyle additionnel de l'acide ribonucléique (RNA) n'empêche donc pas l'ossature du RNA d'avoir la même configuration que celle du DNA. Ces résultats très importants pourraient impliquer que le mécanisme de reproduction du RNA serait le même que celui du DNA. Tout récemment, Rich et collègues [32] ont montré que la quantité de complexes formés entre les acides polyadényliques et polyuridyliques dépend des concentrations relatives de ces deux acides. En présence de Mg et d'un excès d'acide polyuridylique, il peut se former un complexe à triple hélice entre les polymères U et A.

Si la vitesse de phosphorolyse des polynucléotides est déterminée par leur capacité de former des complexes, on devrait observer de grandes différences dans les vitesses de phosphorolyse des mélanges en proportions variées de polymères A et U. Les résultats [14] (Figure 2) montrent que c'est effectivement ce qui se produit. Alors que la vitesse initiale de phosphorolyse des polymères A et U est environ la même, celle des mélanges de ces deux polymères dépend de la proportion des deux polyacides. Le mélange des polymères A et U en proportion 3 : 1 est phosphorolysé presque aussi rapidement que le polymère A, celui des polyacides A et U = 1 : 1 est attaqué avec une vitesse environ trois fois plus faible que le polymère A, tandis que celui qui contient trois plus d'acide

PLATE IV

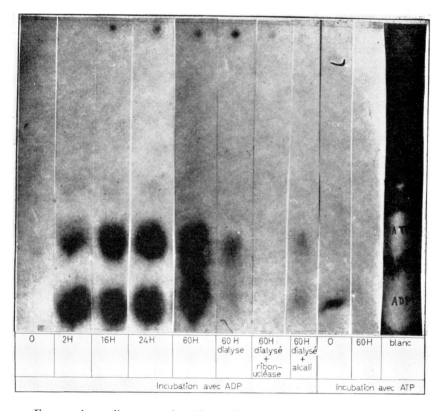

0	2H	16H	24H	60H	60 H dialyse	60H dialysé + ribon- ucléase	60H dialysé + alcali	0	60H	blanc
				Incubation avec ADP					Incubation avec ATP	

FIG. 3. Autoradiogramme du mêlange d'incubation. Dans 5 ml volume final: tampon TRIS, pH 7,45; 250 μmoles; $MgCl_2$, 100 μmoles; ADP ou ATP, 39,2 μmoles; Pm 5,8 μmoles avec 3200 $\times$ 10^3 coups/minute. Enzyme de levure—0,208 mg de protéine (AS = 10,2). Incubation à 30° en agitant.

La réaction est arrêtée par chauffage 1 min à 100°. Des prises de 0,1 sont pré-levées pour la chromatographie descendante suivant la technique de Krebs & Hems avec élimination préalable du phosphore minéral. Après 60 h d'incubation une partie du liquide est dialysée 48 h contre l'eau distillée, 0,1 ml du dialysat est prélevé pour la chromatographie. 0,1 ml est hydrolysé avec KOH (0,4 N conc. fin.) 48 h 37°. 0,1 ml est hydrolysé avec 1,7 unité de ribonucléase des feuille [préparation purifiée de Holden & Pirie [34] + tampon citrate (pH 5,5) 5 μ M]. L'autoradio-gramme montre l'apparition en fonction du temps d'un composé radioactif restant au point de départ. Les autres composés radioactifs sont l'ATP et l'ADP. L'incu-bation étant prolongée, les traces de myokinases sont suffisantes pour marquer l'ATP. L'ADP et l'ATP sont éliminés par dialyse tandisque le composé du point de départ reste. Il disparait après hydrolyse par l'alcali ou la ribonucléase, il y a trop peu de substance pour voir apparaitre dans cet autoradiogramme les produits d'hydrolyse du polynucléotide. Si le mélange d'incubation contient l'ATP au lieu d'ADP, il ne se forme pas de composés radioactifs. Le blanc correspond à une photo dans l'U.V. de la partie du chromatogramme contenant les nucléotides de référence.

MARIANNE GRUNBERG-MANAGO

PLATE V

FIG. 4. Photographie au contraste de phase (× 400) d'une fibre insoluble dans l'eau synthétisée par la préparation enzymatique de levure.

MARIANNE GRUNBERG-MANAGO

PLATE VI

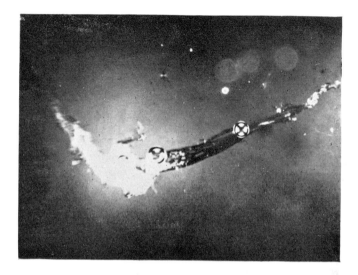

FIG. 5.

FIG. 6.

FIGS 5 et 6.   Les deux aspects au microscope polarisant d'une même fibre
synthétisée par la préparation enzymatique de levure.

MARIANNE GRUNBERG-MANAGO

PLATE VII

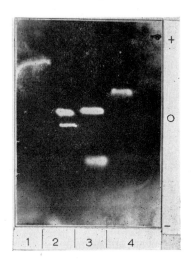

FIG. 7.   Électrophorèse sur papier.

Papier Whatman No. 3;
Tampon 0·2 M acétate (pH 3,75)—200 v/cm—Durée 1 h 45 min.
1, polymère de levure;
2, poly A + AMP3′ (le polymère reste au point o);
3, AMP5′ + adénine (l'adénine migre à la cathode);
4, ATP.

uridylique que d'acide adénylique n'est presque pas attaqué (10 fois plus lentement que le polymère A). C'est justement les conditions dans lesquelles il se forme, d'après Rich, le complexe à triple hélice: ce complexe ne pourrait être phosphorolysé. Au contraire, lorsque le mélange contient un excès de polymère A, le complexe est en faible quantité et la vitesse de phosphorolyse de ce mélange n'est pas éloignée de celle des polymères simples.

Pour éclaircir davantage le mécanisme intime de la réaction, nous avons élué et dosé [14] les diphosphates apparus au fur et à mesure de la phosphorolyse. Je ne voudrais pas insister davantage la dessus. Les résultats sont en accord avec l'hypothèse exposée. Par exemple dans le cas du mélange des polymères A : U = 1 : 3, la phosphorolyse ne libère que de l'UDP, à mettre la phrase suivante ce qui suggére que c'est l'excès de poly U qui ne fait pas partie du complexe qui est attaqué.

Les polymères mixtes et les acides ribonucléiques qui sont faiblement attaqués doivent donc former des complexes à liens hydrogène, comme les deux polymères A et U, ce qui les préserve d'être phosphorolysés. Les deux acides ribonucléiques des virus doivent avoir une séquence de nucléotides telle, que la formation de complexe est plus faible et ils peuvent facilement être phosphorolysés [1].

La phosphorolyse des ribopolynucléotides ne dépend donc pas seulement des concentrations relatives des substrats en présence, déterminant l'équilibre de la réaction, mais encore de la structure des polymères et particulièrement des complexes formés entre les différents nucléotides au moyen de liens hydrogène. Ces résultats font ressortir l'importance de la configuration de l'acide ribonucléique pour son rôle biologique. Cette configuration ne dépendra pas seulement de la séquence des nucléotides, mais aussi des conditions extérieures, température, pH, concentrations en sels du milieu. Par exemple, le polymère A seul peut avoir 2 configurations suivant le pH et la concentration en sel du milieu (Fresco & Doty [7]). Jusqu'ici on avait trés peu de renseignements sur la structure macromoléculaire de l'RNA en contraste à celle du DNA. Il est en effet difficile d'obtenir des échantillons de RNA orientés donnant de bons diagrammes de rayons X. Espérons que la polynucléotide phosphorylase, capable de catalyser la synthèse de nombreux polymères naturels ou non, contenant un, deux ou plusieurs nucléotides, nous aidera à éclaircir cette structure. Elle nous sera utile également pour donner des renseignements sur les propriétès chimiques et biologiques des acides nucléiques.

Jusqu'à maintenant, le seul mécanisme de synthèse connu des ribopolynucléotides était celui de la polynucléotide phosphorylase qui n'a été isolée qu'à partir des bactéries. Nous avons recherché si un autre microorganisme comme la levure possédait un enzyme identique ou similaire. Nous avons isolé, Monsieur Wisniewski et moi [33], à partir d'extrait de levure, un système enzymatique capable de synthétiser des polynucléotides à partir des nucléosides diphosphates. Nos recherches ne sont pas encore très avancées, mais on peut affirmer dès à présent que le mécanisme de synthèse et la constitution du polynucléotide formé sont différents de ceux trouvés avec l'enzyme bactérien.

Les extraits solubles d'une levure 'petite colonie' 59RA catalysent un échange

23

rapide entre le ^{32}P minéral et le phosphate terminal de l'adénosine diphosphate, le premier phosphate n'étant jamais marqué. Se basant sur ce test, cet enzyme a été purifié et son activité a été ainsi augmentée de 20 fois. Elle est alors du même ordre de grandeur que celle des preparations de polynucléotide phosphorylase employées dans les expériences exposées plus haut.

L'enzyme purifié de la plupart de phosphatases et d'une grande partie de la myokinase est inactif sur les nucléosides 5'-monophosphates ou triphosphates comme l'AMP, ATP, CTP, UTP, GTP. Il incorpore l'orthophosphate ^{32}P dans le groupement terminal de tous les nucléosides diphosphates essayés (GDP, UDP, CDP, IDP, ADP).

L'incorporation de phosphate n'exige apparemment aucun cofacteur. Cette réaction, à l'inverse de celle catalysée par l'enzyme bactérien, est même inhibée de 50 à 70% par le Mg. Dans ces conditions, absence de métaux, l'enzyme, même ajouté en grande quantité, ne libère de phosphate à partir d'aucun des nucléotides essayés mono-, di-ou triphosphates, bien qu'il incorpore très rapidement celui-ci dans l'ADP. Ceci rend improbable la possibilité que l'incorporation de phosphate soit dûe à la réversibilité de la réaction catalysée par la polynucléotide phosphorylase.

Lorsqu'on ajoute le Mg en assez grande quantité (2×10^{-2}M) il se produit une libération de phosphate à partir de l'ADP (20% environ de la quantité de P incorporé). L'enzyme est également actif sur les autres diphosphates mais la libération de phosphate reste toujours faible. Il n'y a aucune libération de PO$_4$ à partir de l'ATP ou de l'AMP$_3$' il s'en produit une très légère à partir de l'AMP$_5$' toujours 2 à 3 fois plus faible qu'à partir de l'ADP.

Nous ne pouvons à l'heure actuelle décider si les 2 activités, incorporation de P dans l'ADP et libération de P, sont dûes au même enzyme. Mais il semble peu probable que la libération de phosphate soit due à une phosphatase ordinaire, car on ne connait pas à l'heure actuelle de phosphatase inactive sur l'ATP et hydrolysant l'ADP spécifiquement.

Après incubation prolongée de l'enzyme purifié en présence d'ADP et de ^{32}P$_m$ on s'aperçoit qu'il y a formation d'un composé absorbant dans l'U.V. qui reste au point de départ du chromatogramme. Il ne diffuse pas pendant la dialyse contre l'eau distillée ou les sels dilués, ce qui montre qu'il s'agit d'un polynucléotide. Ce polynucléotide est radioactif à la différence du polymère synthétisé dans les mêmes conditions par l'enzyme bactérien (Figure 3). Il est hydrolysé par l'alcali et la ribonucléase des feuilles.

Aucun polymère ne se forme en l'absence de Mg ou si l'ADP est remplacé par le dérivé mono- ou triphosphorylé.

La formation du polymère exigeant le Mg et l'échange étant au contraire inhibé par celui-ci, la réaction doit procéder par deux étapes au moins.

Comme l'enzyme de levure n'incorpore lui aussi le phosphate que dans le groupement terminal de l'ADP, il est évident que la partie adénosine 5'-PO$_4$ de l'ADP n'est pas marquée en présence de ^{32}P. Le polynucléotide synthétisé par l'enzyme de levure étant radioactif ne peut être composé seulement d'unités d'acide adénylique comme c'est le cas pour le polymère synthétisé par l'enzyme bactérien, mais doit contenir des extra phosphates.

Le polynucléotide au fur et à mesure de sa formation précipite dans le mélange d'incubation lié à une protéine provenant de la préparation enzymatique. La plus grande partie du polynucléotide se présente sous cette forme insoluble. Dans cette réaction la préparation enzymatique fournit donc en même temps la protéine comme réactif et l'enzyme, ce qui explique probablement la faible quantité de produit synthétisé. Nous ne savons pas à l'heure actuelle si le polymère s'unit à la protéine de l'enzyme ou à une protéine contaminant la préparation enzymatique.

Dans beaucoup de cas il a été possible d'isoler la 'nucléoprotéine' formée sous forme de fibres insolubles dans l'eau et biréfringentes [35] (Figures 4, 5, 6). Le polynucléotide est isolé de la nucléoprotéine en dénaturant les protéines par un détergent, la majeure partie des protéines devient insoluble et en général la préparation de polynucléotides ne contient plus de protéines détectables.

Le polynucléotide synthétisé par l'enzyme de levure peut être différencié de celui synthétisé par l'enzyme bactérien, non seulement par les données isotopiques mais en se basant sur les faits suivants [35].

(1) Le spectre d'absorption du polymère A (synthétisé par l'enzyme d'*Azotobacter*) présente un maximum à 257 mμ à pH 7, à pH 4 celui-ci se déplace à 252 mμ, ce qui correspond à un changement de structure du polymère. Le polynucléotide de levure à un maximum à 259–260 mμ, à pH 7 et celui-ci ne change pas à pH 4. Le spectre de ce dernier est d'ailleurs plus étalé que celui du polymère A.

(2) Le polymère de levure ne réagit pas avec le polymère U synthétisé par l'enzyme d'*Azotobacter*.

(3) Alors que le polymère A ainsi que les dérivés de l'adénosine réagissent avec la formaldéhyde en donnant un changement de spectre, le polymère de levure ne réagit pas ou réagit très peu avec la formaldéhyde, c'est variable suivant les préparations. Cela suggère que certains groupements aminés ne sont pas libres.

(4) Le polymère de levure a une mobilité différente de celle du polymère A à pH 7 et à pH 3,75.

La Figure 7 montre le résultat d'une électrophorèse à pH 3,75. A ce pH le polymère A reste au point de départ, les charges de sa molécule étant neutralisées. L'AMP$_5'$, l'AMP$_3'$, l'ADP, l'ATP, se meuvent vers l'anode avec des vitesses croissantes.

Le polymère de levure a une mobilité plus grande que l'ATP. Il contient donc plus de charges négatives que le polymère A, ce qui est en accord avec le résultat précédent à savoir que le polymère de levure contient plus de phosphate que le polymère A.

Les produits d'hydrolyse du polymère de levure par l'alcali, l'acide et la ribonucléase des feuilles ne correspondent ni à l'AMP$_3'$, AMP$_5'$ ou adénine. La structure de ces produits est à l'étude.

Nous n'avons donc à l'heure actuelle qu'une connaissance très fragmentaire du mécanisme enzymatique et de la structure du polynucléotide formé par le ou les enzymes de levure. On peut toutefois affirmer qu'aussi bien le mécanisme enzymatique que la structure du polymère formé diffèrent de ceux trouvés avec la polynucléotide phosphorylase. Deux faits sont particulièrement intéressants:

(1) Le polynucléotide formé se présente lié à une protéine; on aurait ainsi un matériel propice pour l'étude des interactions protéines ribopolynucléotides.

(2) Le polynucléotide n'est pas composé simplement d'unités de nucléosides monophosphates, mais contient des groupements phosphates en plus.

A ce propos, je rappelerai qu'il pourrait exister un acide nucléique phosphate; certains travaux récents [36–39] semblent appuyer cette hypothèse proposée par Brachet [40]. Cet acide nucléique servirait d'agent phosphorylant, et dans la synthèse des protéines déterminerait la spécificité des protéines, en alignant les aminoacides sur la chaîne polynucléotidique.

De plus en plus d'ailleurs, il ressort des travaux récents [41] que l'acide nucléique pourrait se présenter sous deux formes, dont l'une serait active dans la synthèse des protéines.

C'est, il me semble, l'étude de ces formes actives de ribopolynucléotides qui contribuera à résoudre l'un des grand mystères de la vie: la spécificité de la matière vivante.

Je suis heureuse de remercier les Docteurs Pirie et Pierpoint pour m'avoir offert les préparations d'acide ribonucléique de levure et de ribonucléase des feuilles.
Je remercie Monsieur de Mende du Centre d'Electrophorèse du C.N.R.S. d'avoir bien voulu se charger des électrophorèses et Messieurs les professeurs Monnier et Lenormand pour l'aide qu'ils nous ont apporté dans l'étude microscopique.
Je tiens à remercier Monsieur Dan Broida de la maison Sigma qui m'a généreusement offert certains nucléotides diphosphates; sans son aide ce travail n'aurait pas été possible.

LITERATURE

1. J. BRACHET, Nucleic Acids, vol. 2, p. 476. Academic Press, New York, 1955.
2. E. F. GALE & J. P. FOLKES, Nature, Lond., 172, 1223, 1954.
3. S. SPIEGELMAN, Proc. 3rd int. Congr. Biochem. Academic Press, New York, p. 185, 1956.
4. A. B. PARDEE, Proc. nat. Acad. Sci., Wash., 40, 263, 1954.
5. H. FRAENKEL-CONRAT & R. C. WILLIAMS, Proc. nat. Acad. Sci., Wash., 41, 690, 1955.
6. A. GIERER & G. SCHRAMM, Z. Naturf., 116, 138, 1956.
7. J. R. FRESCO & P. DOTY, J. Amer. chem. Soc., sous presse.
8. R. C. WARNER, Fed. Proc., 15, 379, 1956.
9. A. RICH, Chemical Basis of Heredity, p. 557 (Ed. by W. D. McELROY & B. GLASS). Johns Hopkins Press, Baltimore, 1957.
10. M. GRUNBERG-MANAGO & S. OCHOA, J. Amer. chem. Soc., 77, 3165, 1955; M. GRUNBERG-MANAGO, P. J. ORTIZ & S. OCHOA, Science, 122, 907, 1955; M. GRUN-BERG-MANAGO, P. J. ORTIZ & S. OCHOA, Biochem. biophys. Acta, 20, 269, 1956.
11. A. KORNBERG, I. R. LEHMAN, M. J. BESSMAN & E. S. SIMMS, Biochim. biophys. Acta, 21, 197, 1956.
12. G. W. E. PLAUT, J. biol. Chem., 217, 235, 1955.
13. S. OCHOA, Communication personelle.
14. M. GRUNBERG-MANAGO, Résultats non publiés.
15. S. OCHOA & S. MII, Résultats non publiés.
16. U. Z. LITTAUER & A. KORNBERG, J. biol. Chem., 226, 1077, 1957.
17. S. OCHOA, Fed. Proc., 15, 832, 1956.
18. P. J. ORTIZ, Résultats non publiés.
19. R. C. WARNER, Résultats non publiés.
20. R. G. HART & J. O. SMITH, Nature, Lond., 178, 739, 1956.
21. H. OKAMOTO, Japan J. med. Sci. (IV, Pharmacol.), 12, 167, 1939.
22. A. W. BERNHEIMER, J. exp. Med., 90, 373, 1949.
23. F. EGAMI, Communication personelle.

24. D. O. BRUMMOND, M. STAEHELIN & S. OCHOA, *J. biol. Chem.*, **225**, 835, 1957.
25. R. F. BEERS, *Fed. Proc.*, **15**, 13, 1956; *Nature, Lond.*, **177**, 790, 1956.
26. H. A. KREBS & R. HEMS, *Biochim. biophys. Acta*, **12**, 172, 1953.
27. R. M. S. SMELLIE & S. OCHOA, Résultats non publiés.
28. A. N. BELOZERSKIĬ, *Dokl. Akad. Nauk S.S.S.R.*, **113**, 650, 1957; This Symposium.
29. S. OCHOA, *Arch. Biochem. Biophys.*, sous presse.
30. L. A. HEPPEL & J. D. SMITH, Résultats non publiés.
31. M. F. SINGER, *Fed. Proc.*, **16**, 250, 1957.
32. G. FELSENFELD, D. R. DAVIES & A. RICH, *J. Amer. chem. Soc.*, **79**, 2023, 1957.
33. M. GRUNBERG-MANAGO & J. WISNIEWSKI, *C.R. Acad. Sci.*, *Paris*, **245**, 750, 1957.
34. M. HOLDEN & N. W. PIRIE, *Biochem. J.*, **60**, 39, 1955.
35. M. GRUNBERG-MANAGO & J. R. FRESCO, Résultats non publiés.
36. R. CHAYEN, S. CHAYEN & E. R. ROBERTS, *Biochim. biophys. Acta*, **16**, 117, 1955.
37. A. N. BELOZERSKIĬ, Communications et rapports. 3 *Int. Congr. Biochem.*, *Bruxelles*, 1955.
38. S. E. BRESLER & E. I. NIDZYAN, *Dokl. Akad. Nauk S.S.S.R.*, **75**, 79, 1950.
39. A. L. DOUNCE & E. R. M. KAY, *Proc. Soc. exp. Biol.*, *N.Y.*, **83**, 321, 1953.
40. J. BRACHET, *Chemical Embryology.* Int. Publ. Inc., New York, p. 242, 1952.
41. H. CHANTRENNE, *Arch. Biochem. Biophys.*, **65**, 414, 1956.

A Note on the Evolution of Nucleic Acids

A. E. MIRSKY

Rockefeller Institute, New York, U.S.A.

LARGE MOLECULES such as those of proteins and nucleic acids are of importance for the organization of vital processes and for their highly specific characteristics. Knowledge concerning the synthesis of these molecules in the cell is now developing rapidly. How these molecules first came into being ages ago is, however, still altogether obscure. The problem would probably be more manageable if we can conceive of the origin of large molecules as occurring in stages rather than as happening all at once by some rare chance.

In this note I would like to present a group of observations which may possibly cast some light on the evolution of nucleic acids. Recent experiments have shown that small polynucleotides containing only some three or four nucleotides or larger polynucleotides of simple composition can perform one of the important functions that in the cell is normally accomplished by a complex nucleic acid containing a hundred or more nucleotides. The substitution within the nucleus of small or simple polynucleotides for the large complex ones normally present is possible experimentally if the structural background of the nucleus is maintained. A significant point about the function of nucleic acid to which I am referring is that it is relatively non-specific; it concerns the synthesis of adenosine triphosphate (ATP) rather than the transmission of hereditary specificity.

I must now describe the biochemical system in which it has been found that polynucleotides serve as 'cofactors' for ATP synthesis. Nuclei isolated from calf thymus are able under certain conditions to synthesize protein [1]. When these nuclei are treated with deoxyribonuclease most of their deoxyribonucleic acid (DNA) is removed and at the same time their ability to synthesize protein is greatly reduced. It is possible to 'restore' much of the DNA that has been removed and when this happens incorporation of amino acids commences again. At first the DNA restored to the nucleus was of course a carefully prepared sample of calf-thymus DNA. Then it was found that DNA prepared from other tissues of the calf or indeed from other organisms (from sea-urchin sperm, for example) would do as well as the homologous DNA in promoting amino acid uptake by the nuclei. Furthermore, the DNA molecule need not be intact, for alkali-denatured DNA and the split products obtained by DNAase digestion are just as effective as the original DNA preparation. Even ribonucleic acids will substitute for the DNA of the thymus in restoring amino acid incorporation into nuclear proteins. Finally, the lack of a specificity requirement is most conclusively shown by experiments in which [¹⁴C]alanine and [¹⁴C]leucine uptakes were restored in DNAase-treated nuclei by polyadenylic acid. (We are greatly indebted to Dr Severo Ochoa for his generosity in supplying this interesting material.)

Although the spectrum of suitable DNA substitutes is quite broad, it does not include a number of other related, and perhaps equally likely, compounds. For example, amino acid uptake cannot be restored by the free purine and pyrimidine bases or by mixtures of nucleosides. And, although ribonucleic acid will substitute for DNA, an alkaline digest of ribonucleic acid (RNA) will not. By the same token, a mixture of the nucleoside 2'- and 3'- phosphates has no effect on amino acid incorporation. Mixtures of the ribonucleoside 5'-phosphates, adenosine monophosphate, adenosine diphosphate and a number of dinucleotides were also tested and found inactive. (We are grateful to Dr R. B. Merrifield, of the Rockefeller Institute, for the gift of these dinucleotides.) Among the dinucleotides tested was adenylic-adenylic dinucleotide, chromatographically purified after rapid acid hydrolysis of yeast RNA; this failed to promote alanine uptake in DNAase-treated nuclei. This observation takes on added significance when it is compared with the previous finding that polyadenylic acid is a very effective agent in restoring alanine and leucine uptakes. Thus the polynucleotide is effective where the corresponding dinucleotide is not, and the molecular size of the polynucleotide emerges as one of the factors which determine its capacity to promote amino acid incorporation. A clue to the range of effective molecular size can be found in experiments which show that the diffusible split-products obtained from DNA (by DNAase digestion) can substitute for the DNA itself. This suggests that tri- and tetra-nucleotides may be effective in this system.

Let us now turn to another, but related, set of observations [2]. The nucleus possesses the same series of mononucleotides as is found in the cytoplasm. These nucleotides can be phosphorylated to the triphosphate from within the nucleus. Phosphorylation is aerobic and is inhibited by cyanide, dinitrophenol, azide and antimycin. Unlike phosphorylation in mitochondria the nuclear process is not affected by carbon monoxide, calcium ions, Janus green, methylene blue or dicoumarol. Incorporation of amino acids in the nucleus is closely linked to ATP synthesis; without ATP no protein synthesis occurs. It should be noted that only ATP already within the nucleus is effective; added ATP has no effect on the nucleus.

Recent experiments relate the DNA of the nucleus directly to the synthesis of adenosine triphosphate [3]. This is shown by two experiments: (1) nuclei pretreated with desoxyribonuclease lose their capacity to synthesize ATP; (2) the capacity of DNAase-treated nuclei to synthesize ATP is readily restored when they receive a DNA supplement. These experiments show that one function of DNA in the chromosome is to act as a 'cofactor' for ATP formation. Further experiments show that ATP synthesis in DNAase-treated nuclei can be restored by polynucleotides other than DNA; indeed some polynucleotides are in this respect more efficient than DNA. The ability of polynucleotides to mediate the synthesis of ATP would localize the ATP at the site of protein synthesis, where it is needed for amino acid activation.

The fact that small, relatively simple polynucleotides can function in ATP synthesis is of interest from the evolutionary point of view. It may be that this was the original role of the polynucleotide structure and that the evolution of the cell brought with it a parallel molecular evolution in which these non-specific polysaccharide molecules were gradually modified to take on a new complexity and assume a new function: a role in the transmission of hereditary specificity.

REFERENCES

1. V. G. ALLFREY, S. OSAWA & A. E. MIRSKY, *J. gen. Physiol.*, **40**, 451, 1957.
2. S. OSAWA, V. G. ALLFREY & A. E. MIRSKY, *J. gen. Physiol.*, **40**, 491, 1957.
3. V. G. ALLFREY & A. E. MIRSKY, *Proc. nat. Acad. Sci.*, *Wash.*, **43**, 589, 1957.

Les Acides Nucléiques et l'Origine des Protéines

J. BRACHET

Faculté des Sciences, Université de Bruxelles, Belgique

INTRODUCTION

TOUTE DISCUSSION des mécanismes biochimiques qui ont conduit à l'apparition de la vie sur la Terre se heurte à trois difficultés fondamentales: (1) notre ignorance des conditions physiques et chimiques qui prévalaient sur notre globe au moment où la vie s'y est fait jour; (2) la difficulté de définir la vie avec précision; (3) nous ne savons pas si les mécanismes biochimiques qui entrent en jeu dans les synthèses effectuées par les êtres vivants d'aujourd'hui fonctionnaient déjà au moment où la vie a apparu sur la Terre. Il faut espérer que le présent Symposium apportera des lumières nouvelles sur le premier des points qui viennent d'être soulevés: la parole, dans ce domaine, est aux géophysiciens et non aux biologistes. La seconde question, c'est-à-dire la définition de la vie et de l'être vivant, ne sera que brièvement discutée ici; quant au troisième point, force nous sera d'examiner surtout les mécanismes actuels des synthèses protéiques, puisque nous ne pouvons qu'émettre des hypothèses au sujet de l'origine des protéines chez les premiers êtres vivants.

DIFFICULTÉ DE DÉFINIR LA VIE

On a fait remarquer, à maintes reprises, que la découverte des virus végétaux cristallisables a rendu délicate la définition de l'être vivant: ces virus peuvent être considérés comme des 'molécules vivantes', qui constitueraient le chaînon manquant entre la matière et l'être vivant. Il ne nous appartient pas de discuter ce point de vue, qui sera certainement examiné avec beaucoup plus de compétence par d'autres participants au Symposium.

Mais nous tenons à faire remarquer que des difficultés comparables se présentent lorsqu'on se pose la question de la vie à propos de fragments d'organismes unicellulaires ou de cellules. La question—si souvent posée à la fin de conférences—de savoir si un noyau isolé ou un chromosome sont vivants est toujours irritante, parce qu'on ne peut lui fournir de réponse nette. L'impression qui découle de nos propres recherches, c'est que la notion de vie a plutôt une valeur quantitative que celle d'un concept qualitatif: il n'y a pas de 'loi du tout ou rien' qui sépare l'être vivant de la matière.

Si on compare, par exemple, un fragment anucléé d'amibe à une tige, également anucléée, de l'algue unicellulaire *Acetabularia*, on recueille l'impression

361

que la seconde est 'plus vivante' que le premier: après ablation du noyau, la tige d'*Acetabularia* reste capable de croître, de synthétiser des protéines et de l'acide ribonucléique (ARN) [1], et même de régénérer [2]; le chapeau formé par le fragment anucléé possède tous les caractères génétiques de l'espèce dont il provient. Au contraire, un fragment anucléé d'amibe n'est capable que d'un anabolisme extrêmement limité, très inférieur à celui qu'on trouve chez l'amibe normale: il ne peut plus ni se nourrir, ni se mouvoir; son volume ne cesse de diminuer, son métabolisme s'altère de telle manière que le cytoplasme devient incapable d'utiliser ses réserves de glycogène et de graisses; la teneur en protéines de l'amibe énucléée diminue rapidement [3]. Néanmoins, toute activité anabolique n'a pas entièrement disparu dans le fragment anucléé d'amibe, puisqu'il demeure capable d'incorporer des acides aminés dans ses protéines: la vitesse d'incorporation est toutefois diminuée par rapport aux fragments nucléés [4–5].

Si nous revenons aux fragments anucléés d'*Acetabularia*, nous constatons que leur activité anabolique se ralentit au bout d'une quinzaine de jours: ils sont donc 'moins vivants' que les algues entières; mais ils leur sont surtout inférieurs parce qu'ils ont perdu l'un des attributs fondamentaux de l'être vivant, la capacité de se reproduire. Seule l'introduction d'un noyau dans ces fragments anucléés leur permettrait de retrouver toutes leurs potentialités.

Il n'en reste pas moins vrai que l'enlèvement du noyau ne tue pas immédiatement l'organisme: le fragment anucléé d'amibe survit 2 semaines, celui d'*Acetabularia* plusieurs mois. Nous savons que ces fragments sont vivants—malgré l'absence du noyau—parce que, tôt ou tard, nous les verrons dégénérer, se fragmenter et mourir. Un fragment anucléé d'organisme unicellulaire est donc parfaitement vivant; mais ses activités biologiques sont diminuées par rapport à l'organisme intact.

On pourrait raisonner de même à propos du noyau cellulaire: les expériences de transplantations nucléaires de Comandon & de Fonbrune [6] chez l'amibe, celles de Briggs & King [7] chez les oeufs de Batraciens, ont montré qu'un contact bref avec le milieu extérieur suffit pour tuer 'le noyau': en réalité, il s'agit plutôt d'une inactivation du noyau telle qu'il devient incapable de se multiplier lorsqu'on le greffe dans du cytoplasme anucléé. Un jour viendra peut-être où un milieu artificiel, qui permettrait de conserver les noyaux 'vivants' pendant longtemps, sera mis au point. Mais il est douteux que des noyaux placés dans un tel milieu se divisent jamais: en effet, la mitose implique l'intervention de structures cytoplasmiques hautement spécialisées (centrosomes, fuseau) qu'un milieu artificiel ne peut fournir. En fait, l'expérience que nous venons d'imaginer se produit dans la nature; l'endosperme liquide des noix de coco contient des noyaux libres, qui peuvent se fragmenter par amitose; mais ils ne se divisent jamais par mitose vraie [8]. Ces noyaux libres sont certainement vivants; mais, à nouveau, leurs potentialités biologiques sont diminuées par rapport à la normale.

On ne peut répondre nettement, nous l'avons déjà dit, à la question de savoir si les noyaux isolés à partir d'un homogénat de foie ou de thymus sont encore 'vivants'. Il est très improbable qu'ils puissent encore se diviser, si on les réintroduisait dans une cellule anucléée de foie ou de thymus. Néanmoins, ces noyaux demeurent capables de processus anaboliques: dans le cas du thymus, ils incorporent vigoureusement les acides aminés dans leurs protéines, si on les place dans des conditions expérimentales favorables [9].

Cette discussion pourrait être reprise à propos des mitochondries ou des microsomes: ces derniers, selon des expériences de J. Le Clerc [10], semblent capables de se reproduire lorsqu'on les dépose sur la membrane chorioallantoïdienne d'un embryon de poulet. S'il en est réellement ainsi, il serait justifié de les considérer comme aussi 'vivants' que les virus.

Après ces remarques préliminaires, qui visaient à montrer que la notion de 'vivant' n'est pas beaucoup plus précise pour les fragments de cellules ou d'organismes unicellulaires que pour les virus, nous pouvons entrer dans le vif du sujet.

ACIDES NUCLÉIQUES ET SYNTHÈSE DES PROTÉINES

Nous ne pouvons songer à présenter ici les nombreux arguments qu'on peut avancer en faveur d'une intervention des acides nucléiques—de l'ARN en particulier—dans la synthèse des protéines; ces arguments ont été exposés en détails par l'auteur dans une revue récente [11].

Nous nous limiterons donc à un bref résumé des principaux faits sur lesquels l'hypothèse d'une intervention directe de l'ARN dans la synthèse protéique est basée. Cette hypothèse découle des observations cytochimiques de Caspersson [12] et de Brachet [13] montrant qu'il existe une corrélation étroite entre la teneur en ARN d'un organe et son aptitude à synthétiser des protéines. De nombreuses études cytochimiques et des dosages biochimiques ont confirmé depuis ces conclusions initiales. Signalons, à ce propos, une étude autoradiographique récente de Ficq & Brachet [14], montrant qu'il existe un lien constant entre la basophilie (c'est-à-dire la teneur en ARN) d'une cellule et sa capacité d'incorporer un acide aminé marqué dans ses protéines.

L'étude de nombreux micro-organismes a confirmé, de façon répétée, l'importance du rôle joué par l'ARN lors de la synthèse des protéines, celle d'enzymes adaptatifs en particulier: dans le cas de mutants exigeant de la thymine [15], dans celui de bactéries irradiées aux U.V. [16] la synthèse induite d'enzymes est liée à celle de l'ARN; par contre, cette synthèse induite n'exige pas une synthèse concomitante d'acide désoxyribonucléique (ADN). Ces expériences, ainsi que celles de Pardee [17] et de Spiegelman [18], conduisent à la conclusion que la production continuée de nouvelles molécules d'ARN est nécessaire pour obtenir la synthèse induite d'enzymes.

Une toute autre raison de penser que l'ARN est l'un des facteurs essentiels de la synthèse protéique résulte d'études portant sur l'incorporation des acides aminés dans les protéines des divers constituants cellulaires: dans les expériences de courte durée, ce sont les microsomes (et particulièrement les petits granules qu'ils renferment) qui montrent la plus grande activité [19–21]. Or ce sont précisément ces particules qui sont les plus riches en ARN dans la cellule;

l'addition de ribonucléase, qui détruit l'ARN, inhibe fortement la réaction d'incorporation dans les microsomes [22–23].

Des arguments beaucoup plus directs encore en faveur de l'idée que les acides nucléiques jouent un rôle dans la synthèse des protéines ont été recueillis récemment par Gale & Folkes [24] travaillant sur des staphylocoques brisés par les ultrasons; ils ont établi que l'enlèvement des acides nucléiques arrête la synthèse protéique. L'addition d'ARN ou d'ADN aux bactéries ainsi traitées leur permet de récupérer leurs capacités de synthèse protéique. Dans un cas comparable, celui des protoplastes de *Bacillus megatherium*, Landman & Spiegelman [25] ont montré que la ribonucléase (mais non la désoxyribonucléase) inhibe fortement la synthèse induite de la β-galactosidase: l'intégrité de l'ARN serait donc plus importante pour la synthèse des protéines que celle de l'ADN.

Enfin, des recherches effectuées principalement dans notre propre laboratoire ont montré que cette conclusion demeure valable pour des cellules intactes: la ribonucléase inhibe puissamment la synthèse des protéines, l'incorporation des acides aminés dans les protéines, la croissance et la division cellulaire dans de nombreuses cellules vivantes: racines d'oignon [26], amibes [27], tumeurs d'ascites [28], cultures de tissus [29]. Souvent l'addition d'ARN aux cellules traitées *in vivo* par la ribonucléase permet une reprise appréciable des synthèses protéiques et des activités biologiques. La ribonucléase empêche également la multiplication de certains virus contenant de l'ARN, notamment ceux de la grippe [30], et de la mosaïque du tabac [31].

Nous ne pouvons songer à résumer ici les nombreux travaux qui démontrent, de façon éclatante, l'importance fondamentale de l'ARN pour la reproduction du virus de la mosaïque du tabac [32]. Ces recherches ont atteint récemment leur point culminant: en effet, Fraenkel-Conrat & Williams [33] sont parvenus à séparer les composants protéique et ribonucléique du virus et à reconstituer des particules virulentes en mélangeant les deux fractions. Dans une étape ultérieure, Gierer & Schramm [34] ont montré que l'ARN du virus, à condition de l'isoler par une méthode suffisamment douce, est, à lui seul, infectieux: si on le dépose sur une feuille d'une plante sensible, il ne se reproduit pas seulement lui-même, il induit aussi la synthèse de la portion protéique du virus. Ces expériences suggèrent tout naturellement l'idée que c'est l'ARN qui constitue le déterminant génétique du virus: cette hypothèse a été brillamment démontrée par Fraenkel-Conrat [35], qui a séparé et recombiné les constituants protéique et ribonucléique de deux virus appartenant à des souches génétiquement différentes. Il a fabriqué ainsi des 'hybrides' expérimentaux entre les deux souches de virus et il a constaté que les lésions obtenues sont caractéristiques de la souche à laquelle l'ARN a été pris. La descendance de ces particules virulentes 'hybrides' contient à la fois l'ARN et la protéine du virus dont l'ARN provenait. Ces remarquables expériences démontrent, de façon convaincante, que l'ARN est réellement le déterminant génétique de la particule virulente; c'est sous l'influence organisatrice de cet ARN que s'opère la synthèse de la protéine spécifique, qui est caractéristique de chaque souche du virus.

Il convient d'ajouter quelques mots au sujet des mécanismes biochimiques de la synthèse protéique; nous serons bref, parce que la question vient d'être traitée recemment en détails par Borsook [36]. On admet généralement que la synthèse des protéines nécessite, outre l'ARN et les acides aminés, de l'acide adénosinetriphosphorique (ATP) et un enzyme soluble. Selon Littlefield *et al.* [21] l'acide guanosinediphosphorique (ou son dérivé triphosphorique) serait également nécessaire. Des travaux récents de Hoagland [37] et de De Moss & Novelli [38] ont considérablement clarifié nos idées en ce qui concerne le rôle de l'ATP et celui de la fraction enzymatique soluble: leur fonction est d'activer le groupe carboxylique des acides aminés, afin d'augmenter leur réactivité. Dans le cas de la leucine, par exemple, la forme activée serait un composé leucyl-acide adénosine-monophosphorique (AMP) [38].

Les acides aminés activés (qui se trouveraient donc sous cette forme acide aminé-AMP) doivent ensuite se combiner entre eux pour former des chaînes polypeptidiques; il importe, puisque le produit de la synthèse sera une protéine spécifique, que l'agencement des acides aminés se fasse selon une ordonnance bien précise. C'est ici qu'interviendrait l'ARN, qui jouerait le rôle d'un modèle (template des auteurs anglo-saxons): c'est sous l'influence de ce modèle spécifique que les acides aminés se placeraient dans un ordre correct. Tout ce que nous savons actuellement sur la structure de l'ARN et sur son rôle dans la synthèse des protéines, qu'il s'agisse de virus végétaux ou de cellules, plaide fortement en faveur de l'idée que le modèle n'est autre que l'ARN.

Le rôle de l'ADN dans la synthèse des protéines est beaucoup moins clair: le fait qu'une synthèse nette de protéines se produit dans une tige anucléée d'*Acetabularia* démontre clairement que cet acide nucléique, qui est localisé dans la chromatine, ne peut jouer de rôle direct dans la formation des protéines cytoplasmiques [1]. Nous avons déjà signalé aussi que la destruction d'une forte proportion de l'ADN n'empêche pas la synthèse induite d'un enzyme dans les protoplastes de *B. megatherium* [25]. Toutefois, l'addition d'ADN exerce un effet favorable sur les synthèses protéiques dans les staphylocoques désintégrés de Gale & Folkes [24]; en outre, l'intégrité de l'ADN est nécessaire pour que des noyaux de thymus isolés incorporent des acides aminés [9]. Il est donc vraisemblable que l'ADN joue, comme l'ARN, un rôle de modèle lors de la synthèse des protéines; mais ce rôle pourrait se limiter à la synthèse des protéines qui lui sont immédiatement associées, dans la chromatine ou les chromosomes. L'ADN n'interviendrait donc pas (ou n'interviendrait que de manière indirecte) dans la synthèse des protéines cytoplasmiques. Un mécanisme indirect se comprend si, comme l'a supposé Caspersson [12], l'ADN contrôlait la synthèse de l'ARN nucléolaire. Ce dernier serait le précurseur de l'ARN cytoplasmique, dont nous avons vu toute l'importance pour la synthèse des protéines. A l'heure actuelle, il n'existe pas d'arguments décisifs en faveur de l'idée que la synthèse de l'ARN du noyau serait contrôlée directement par l'ADN; la situation demeure donc obscure en ce qui concerne ce point. Quant à l'origine nucléaire de l'ARN cytoplasmique, elle demeure controversée: des expériences de transplantations nucléaires chez les amibes plaident fortement en faveur d'un tel mécanisme [39]. Mais, par contre, une synthèse nette d'ARN demeure possible, chez *Acetabularia*, après l'ablation du noyau [1]. Il faut en conclure que deux mécanismes distincts co-existent sans doute dans la cellule: transfert d'une partie de l'ARN du noyau vers le cytoplasme, et synthèse nette d'ARN dans le cytoplasme.

HYPOTHÈSES SUR L'ORIGINE DES PROTÉINES

Rien ne nous permet d'affirmer, répétons-le, que les mécanismes biochimiques qui président aujourd'hui à la synthèse des protéines sont ceux qui ont conduit à la formation de protéines à l'origine de la vie. Mais nous ne pouvons essayer de raisonner à ce sujet qu'en supposant qu'il existe une certaine similitude entre les deux processus.

On peut donc imaginer que la présence simultanée d'ARN et d'acides aminés activés ait été une condition nécessaire pour l'apparition des premières protéines. Si l'acide aminé activé était, comme on le croit pour les synthèses protéiques d'aujourd'hui, un composé contenant de l'AMP, il est concevable que l'enzyme soluble de Hoagland n'ait pas été encore nécessaire lors de l'origine des premières protéines: l'AMP est, en effet, l'un des constituants de l'ARN et on peut imaginer que, à un moment donné de l'histoire de la Terre, ce nucléotide (sans lequel on ne peut concevoir une forme de vie comparable à celle que nous connaissons) ait pu se combiner spontanément avec des acides aminés libres. Une telle hypothèse a son importance au point de vue de la logique du raisonnement: l'enzyme de Hoagland est, en effet, une protéine et il serait difficile d'expliquer son intervention au cas où nous supposerions que l'ARN a précédé les protéines dans l'évolution biochimique.

Si une pareille hypothèse paraît séduisante à première vue, en raison des expériences récentes de Gierer & Schramm [34] montrant que l'ARN qui a été isolé du virus de la mosaïque du tabac est capable, à lui seul, de synthétiser la portion protéique de ce virus, il faut bien admettre qu'elle devient fragile à la réflexion: si nous ignorons encore comment se fait la synthèse de l'ARN chez les organismes supérieurs, il n'est pas douteux que c'est un enzyme de nature protéique qui réalise cette synthèse, à partir des nucléosidediphosphates, chez les bactéries [40]. On pourrait, certes, supposer que des ARN se soient formés spontanément, par une sorte de polymérisation non-enzymatique, au moment où la vie a fait son apparition sur la Terre. Mais la même thèse pourrait être soutenue pour les protéines, évidemment. Un argument, de faible poids d'ailleurs, en faveur du caractère 'primitif' des acides nucléiques réside dans leur moindre complexité et leur résistance plus grande à la chaleur, quand on les compare aux protéines; peut-être le fait que la ribonucléase est un enzyme particulièrement thermostable et de composition simple signifie-t-il que le métabolisme de l'ARN est plus ancien que beaucoup d'autres dans l'évolution biochimique des êtres vivants.

Mais ces indices, il faut l'avouer, demeurent bien fragiles et on ne peut donc répondre nettement à la question: 'Qui a commencé, de l'ARN ou des protéines ?'. C'est, naturellement, la vieille question de l'origine de l'oeuf et de la poule qui se représente; cette dernière question semble d'ailleurs plus aisée à résoudre que la première, tout au moins pour un embryologiste qui ne peut concevoir que l'oeuf n'ait précédé la poule.

Espérons que le Symposium qui va se tenir jettera des lumières nouvelles sur les questions qui viennent d'être soulevées: la collaboration de chimistes, de physiciens et de théoriciens permettra peut-être de préciser si la synthèse, par polymérisation spontanée, d'un acide nucléique est plus probable que celle d'une protéine.

BIBLIOGRAPHIE

1. J. BRACHET, H. CHANTRENNE & F. VANDERHAEGHE, *Biochim. biophys. Acta*, **18**, 544, 1955.
2. J. HÄMMERLING, *Int. Rev. Cytol.*, **2**, 475, 1953.
3. J. BRACHET, *Biochim. biophys. Acta*, **18**, 247, 1955.
4. D. MAZIA & D. M. PRESCOTT, *Biochim. biophys. Acta*, **17**, 23, 1955.
5. A. FICQ, *Arch. int. Physiol.*, **64**, 129, 1956.
6. J. COMANDON & P. DE FONBRUNE, *C.R. Soc. Biol.*, *Paris*, **130**, 740, 1939.
7. R. BRIGGS & J. KING, *J. exp. Zool.*, **122**, 485, 1953.
8. V. M. CUTTER, Jr., S. W. WILSON & B. FREEMAN, *Amer. J. Bot.*, **12**, 109, 1955.
9. V. G. ALLFREY, A. E. MIRSKY & S. OSAWA, *Nature, Lond.*, **176**, 1042, 1955.
10. J. LE CLERC, *Experientia*, **10**, 251, 1954.
11. J. BRACHET, *Nucleic Acids.* Academic Press, New York, vol. 2, p. 476, 1955.
12. T. CASPERSSON, *Naturwissenschaften*, **28**, 33, 1941.
13. J. BRACHET, *Arch. Biol.*, *Paris*, **53**, 207, 1942.
14. A. FICQ & J. BRACHET, *Exp. Cell Res.*, **11**, 135, 1956.
15. S. S. COHEN & H. D. BARNER, *J. Bact.*, **69**, 59, 1955.
16. H. A. HALVORSON & I. JACKSON, *J. gen. Microbiol.*, **14**, 26, 1956.
17. A. B. PARDEE, *Proc. nat. Acad. Sci.*, *Wash.*, **40**, 263, 1954.
18. S. SPIEGELMAN, *Proc. 3rd int. Congr. Biochem.* Academic Press, New York, p. 185, 1956.
19. T. HULTIN, *Exp. Cell Res.*, **1**, 376, 599, 1950.
20. H. BORSOOK, *Physiol. Rev.*, **30**, 206, 1950.
21. J. W. LITTLEFIELD, E. B. KELLER, J. GROSS & P. C. ZAMECNIK, *J. biol. Chem.*, **217**, 111, 1955.
22. V. G. ALLFREY, M. M. DALY & A. E. MIRSKY, *J. gen. Physiol.*, **37**, 157, 1953.
23. P. C. ZAMECNIK & E. B. KELLER, *J. biol. Chem.*, **209**, 337, 1954.
24. E. F. GALE & J. P. FOLKES, *Nature, Lond.*, **172**, 1223, 1954.
25. O. E. LANDMAN & S. SPIEGELMAN, *Proc. nat. Acad. Sci.*, *Wash.*, **41**, 698, 1955.
26. J. BRACHET, *Nature, Lond.*, **174**, 876, 1954.
27. J. BRACHET, *Nature, Lond.*, **175**, 851, 1955.
28. L. LEDOUX & S. H. REVELL, *Biochim. biophys. Acta*, **18**, 416, 1955.
29. M. CHÈVREMONT & S. CHÈVREMONT-COMHAIRE, *Nature, Lond.*, **176**, 1075, 1955.
30. J. LE CLERC, *Nature, Lond.*, **177**, 578, 1956.
31. C. CASTERMAN & R. JEENER, *Biochim. biophys. Acta*, **16**, 433, 1955.
32. R. JEENER, *Advanc. Enzymol.*, **17**, 477, 1956.
33. H. FRAENKEL-CONRAT & R. C. WILLIAMS, *Proc. nat. Acad. Sci.*, *Wash.*, **41**, 690, 1955.
34. A. GIERER & G. SCHRAMM, *Z. Naturf.*, **11**b, 138, 1956.
35. H. FRAENKEL-CONRAT, *J. Amer. chem. Soc.*, **78**, 882, 1956.
36. H. BORSOOK, *J. cell. comp. Physiol.*, **47**, suppl. 1, 35, 1956.
37. M. B. HOAGLAND, *Biochim. biophys. Acta*, **16**, 288, 1955.
38. J. A. DE MOSS & G. D. NOVELLI, *Biochim. biophys. Acta*, **22**, 49, 1956.
39. L. GOLDSTEIN & W. PLAUT, *Proc. nat. Acad. Sci.*, *Wash.*, **41**, 874, 1955.
40. M. GRUNBERG-MANAGO, P. J. ORTIZ & S. OCHOA, *Biochim. biophys. Acta*, **20**, 269, 1956.

A. I. Oparin (U.S.S.R.):

It seems to me that our Symposium, so far, has shown that the problem of the essential nature of life is inseparable from that of its emergence, that the essential nature of life can only be understood in the light of its origin. As you have seen, however, it is a very vexed question at what level of complexity of evolving matter life arose, whether it was at the unimolecular or multimolecular level.

Is life only inherent in the individual molecule of protein, nucleic acid or nucleoprotein, and is the rest of the protoplasm merely a lifeless medium? Or is life inherent in a multimolecular system in which proteins and nucleic acids have an extremely important role, though it is that of a part, not that of the whole, just like the role of an organ fulfilling a corresponding function in the whole organism.

We may feel some regret that this gathering has not only not led to a merging of these two points of view, but has not even led to their approaching one another. However, it is clear that this required a great deal more work and would hardly have been possible at our first meeting.

Today I should like to formulate, in a couple of words, my own viewpoint which I have expounded and substantiated in my book. I assumed that what had arisen primarily, by abiogenic means, was not the functionally extremely efficiently constructed nucleic acids or proteins which we can now isolate from organisms, but only polynucleotides or polypeptides of a relatively disorderly structure, from which were formed the original systems. It was only on the basis of the evolution of these systems that there developed the functionally efficient forms of structure of molecules, not *vice versa*.

In the opposite case one would have to conceive of evolution as it was imagined by Empedocles, who held that first there developed arms, legs, eyes and ears and that later, owing to their combination, the organism developed.

I. Málek (Czechoslovakia):

Allow me to make a few small observations or, more accurately, to ask a question of the biologists, biochemists and chemists: A vast number of different reactions are characteristic of living matter. These reactions are related to one another and to all parts of the living material and chemical compounds, and also relate living material to the external world. Thus, in living materials there are no isolated chemical compounds but, on the contrary, there exists a dynamic association which is in constant motion. When we study this dynamic system from the biochemical point of view, we have to divide it into separate compounds or functional chains. We approach the study of the origin of this complicated system in more or less the same way. We discuss the mode of origin of the separate compounds of high molecular weight which characterize living materials—proteins, nucleic acids, lipids and polysaccharides. In doing so we assume that they arose more or less independently and that it was only when they had attained some degree of polymerization that they could combine together and interact with one another. It has occurred to me to question whether this is correct or whether it would not be better to suppose that the relationships between the different compounds and their functions, which characterize living material, arose, at least in part, at a lower stage in the development of matter and that the polymerization occurred, not on the level of individual compounds, but on the level of an aggregate of their precursors. There is, for example, the question of which came first, nucleic acids or proteins. Might one not suppose that they arose at the same time in mutual interdependence? This idea is in accord with Hoffmann-Ostenhof's hypothesis concerning the origin of the enzymic activity of proteins. This idea is, perhaps, contradicted by the well-known fact that proteins, in the chemically isolated state, combine very easily with nucleic acids. It is, therefore, not hard to imagine that, in the distant past, they began to combine as they were formed. Similar considerations can also be applied to the functional bonds between other compounds. All the same, the question remains— How did there arise in the past that capacity for combining which we know so well today? It seems to me that if we were to assume the possibility which I have just put forward, it would be far easier to picture the high reactivity of coacervates. Of course, it might not be possible to answer the question: Which came first, nucleic acids or proteins? or a number of questions of the same sort. However, this is the hypothesis or, better, the question. I still think that yet one more should be added to the questions put forward by Prof. Bernal, namely: At what stage in the development of living matter did there arise that tremendous wealth of functional, chemical and other linkages in the separate units of living systems; was it before or after their polymerization? It seems to me that such an idea would be of great importance for the further study of the origin of living material. It would help us in our search for the earlier stages in the development, not only of individual compounds, but of the functional associations, the abundance of which is characteristic of living material.

E. N. Pavlovskiĭ (U.S.S.R.):

The 15th International Congress of Zoology will be held in London in 1958. It will celebrate the centenary of the publication of that work of genius by Charles Darwin, *The Origin of Species*.

In his introductory remarks to our present symposium Oparin emphasized that evolutionary studies, as they are generally understood, began with the acceptance of the concept of the spontaneous generation of organisms. However, neither species of animals nor species of plants can be engendered as such. The process of evolution of organisms was preceded by a period of formation of organic material which had the power of metabolism in its most primitive form. Darwin did not touch on this aspect of evolution. This was no fault of Darwin's. The state of natural-historical science in his time did not allow him to formulate this question in such a way that it could be treated in real terms. The concept of the spontaneous generation of organisms must not be taken literally. It was understood to mean the spontaneous generation of some primitive creatures. Their further evolution led to the appearance of animals and plants.

The state of natural-historical science at present has enabled us to formulate a vast, new problem, that of the origin and development of the living material from which the primitive organisms were formed.

This is the aspect of the matter which is being discussed at our present Symposium. The problem of the formation of living material is, by its nature, the precursor of any consideration of the evolution of life in the forms in which it actually exists on the Earth. This connection is extremely important and should be reflected on the organizational level. As president of the organizing committee preparing for the participation of the Soviet delegation of zoologists to the 15th International Congress of Zoology, I should like to raise the question of whether the fundamental facts discussed by our present Symposium have been reported to the zoological congress which is celebrating the centenary of the publication of Charles Darwin's work, *The Origin of Species*. In this way a link would be made between investigation of the origin of life and that of the phylogenetic evolution of species of plants and animals.

But this is not all. In the process of formation of living material and the performance of its cardinal function of metabolism, there also came into being, of course, its various physiological functions. This was associated with the morphological individualization of the earliest organisms and with their subsequent evolution. Within physiology evolutionary physiology has developed, as well as comparative physiology; in morphology and com-

24

parative anatomy there has been a tendency towards the functional morphology and bio-chemistry of developing organisms.

As a next stage in the development of the study of the origin of life it would be valuable to set up an organization co-ordinating the specialities mentioned; until now each has been studied separately. It has already been shown that there is a close connection between cosmogony, astronomy, geology and synthetic, analytical and biological chemistry, a fact which has been clearly expressed in the Reports of our Symposium, but this group of studies must be extended to include some of the biological sciences which do not yet form part of it.

It would be valuable to use the 15th Zoological Congress to effect this association. I have requested the organizing committee of this Symposium that enough copies of the English texts of the Reports to the Symposium might be made available for them to be distributed to the delegations of the various countries at the Zoological Congress in honour of Darwin.

Finally, I should like to say a few words about an aspect of the problem of the origin of life which has not yet been directly touched on in this Symposium; it does, however, force itself upon one. Is there life anywhere else in the Universe? We naturally judge life by the way it manifests itself on the Earth. Life is the mode of existence of protein bodies. These, however, can only exist under narrowly limited conditions of the external, abio-logical medium. These latter are determined by the whole preceding history of the formation of our solar system. Supposing the temperature conditions were raised to 20–30°C above the present optimum, then life, as we know it today, would be impossible.

I would remind you of that excellent book by Alfred Russel Wallace—*Man's Place in the Universe* (1903). It was translated into the Russian language during the first World War. In discussing all the conditions necessary for life as it now exists, Wallace links them with the formation of the Earth as a planet in our solar system. He arrives at the perfectly well-founded conclusion that life could only have arisen outside the Earth if there had been an exact repetition of all the spatial, temporal and qualitative conditions of the evolution of the Earth in the solar system. It is hard to imagine that these could really have been reproduced 'letter for letter' anywhere in the Universe, for all the abundance of its stellar systems.

A few comments should, however, be added to this perfectly justifiable conclusion. In speaking of life somewhere outside the Earth, one thinks of those forms of life which exist on the Earth. There is, however, nothing improbable in the idea that, in some planets in the Universe, organic material may have arisen. If we substitute the concept of 'being' for that of life, there is nothing improbable in the idea of the possibility of the 'being' of such organic material even outside the Earth. On this hypothesis it would be pointless to try to assign to it those qualities which we know as the characteristic features of life on the Earth, still less those of the 'Martians' described by the lively imaginations of writers.

N. W. PIRIE (Gt. Britain):

I do not think that a discussion of the intimate details of the habits of tobacco mosaic virus (TMV) has any strict bearing on the origins of life. Furthermore I do not think that it is useful to speak of nucleic acids conveying the information needed for specifying a protein. They do not start protein synthesis in an empty structureless system but they may move into a host cell that was already making proteins and alter the specifications to which they are made. The differences may be trivial ones that concern only one or two amino-acids or one fold.

However, because the question of TMV has been raised, I would like to ask a question that may clarify a point about the infective preparations that can be made from it and that contain nucleic acid. Dr Schramm is perfectly correct in saying that the molecular weight of a long thin particle cannot be measured with an ultracentrifuge. But the length of a TMV particle can be measured with an electron microscope. If therefore all the particles of TMV in Dr Fraenkel-Conrat's TMV preparations were much shorter than is normal for TMV but gave a nucleic acid preparation of normal infectivity, then it is clear that there has either been reaggregation or else TMV fragments shorter than the normal can be infective. Could the earlier speakers tell us just how the infectivities of the different types of preparations compared?

A. A. SMORODINTSEV (U.S.S.R.):

Since the classical work of Prof. Stanley and his school on the biochemical composition and structure of viruses, published during the past 20 years, it has become indisputable that, in its simplest form, life can exist as crystalline molecules of nucleoproteins while retaining the essential characteristics of living material.

In 1956, however, Fraenkel-Conrat and Schramm extended the limits of what could be regarded as life, to include even simpler chemical structures than crystalline molecular nucleoproteins, namely nucleic acids.

There is as yet, of course, no basis for generalizing from these important discoveries to organisms other than viruses, bearing in mind that viruses probably followed a specialized evolutionary path associated with their circumscribed adaptation to a parasitic existence within the cells of bacteria, animals and plants. It is well known that parasitism evokes a far-reaching simplification of morphological and biochemical organization such as we do not see among free-living organisms anywhere on the Earth.

Although the biochemical, morphological and biological aspects of the earliest stages of viral multiplication are still rather obscure, there can be doubt that they will be elucidated by experiment. This would, in any case, seem to be a simpler task than the discovery of the secret of the origin of life on the Earth.

To avoid any unclearness in the fundamental concepts of viruses and life one must first justify the assumption that viruses are living exogenous parasites in cells which are susceptible to them. This applies equally to viral nucleic acids when they enter the cell by natural means or after their isolation in a biochemical laboratory. This important point in Stanley's paper deserves to be fully recognized.

However, Stanley's second point concerning the identity between viruses and genes— i.e. the normal hereditary factors of the susceptible cells, requires reconsideration, as it definitely contradicts the exogenous nature of viruses. This idea is supported by the argument that genes are capable of multiplication and mutation and can also be introduced into a cell from outside, e.g. the process of transformation or transduction from one group of cells to another. These processes, however, always involve the introduction into the cell of amounts of constitutional protein or nucleic acids which are quite adequate for the species concerned. This process cannot be regarded as infection and is only comparable with virus infection because, in both cases there is something introduced from outside and the reproduction of similar new material.

In virus infections, unlike the phenomena of transformation or transduction of nucleic acids, a foreign and, usually, harmful exogenous factor enters the cell, having nothing in common with any of the proteins or nucleic acids of the affected cell. The analogy between virus infection and transformation or transduction is thus merely superficial or formal in character and does not reflect the fundamental biological differences in the nature of the phenomena.

On the other hand the analogy between viruses and genes may give the illusion of the existence of viral processes when they are not present (transformation and transduction) while the parasitic process of reproduction of a virus will be removed from the category of exogenous infections to be considered as an endogenous process in which there is 'production' of virus by the cell instead of autonomous multiplication of similar particles.

From the biochemical point of view there may be no difference between the introduction of its own proper nucleic acid into a cell and the introduction of viral nucleic acid into it.

From the microbiological or medical points of view, however, they are two completely different phenomena. In the first case the cell receives an adequate hereditary factor and, under its influence, changes some of its characteristics, acquiring the ability to reproduce the new nucleic acid.

In the second case a completely foreign parasitic element enters the cell, leading, not to construction, but to the actual or potential destruction of the life of the cell. Although certain superficial analogies may be found between viruses and genes, nevertheless, the biological concept of these two categories of life is completely different.

H. L. Fraenkel-Conrat (U.S.A.):

I have been asked a question and I should like to answer it.

I have been asked about the ionic strength of the pyrophosphate which has a protective action on nucleic acid, and attention has been directed to the fact that high ionic strengths (greater than molar) may lead to the precipitation of nucleic acid. I quite agree with this. We use molar salts for the precipitation of nucleic acids while 0·1 M is the concentration which protects nucleic acid from the dissociation induced by other salts.

Now for Mr. Pirie's remarks.

Owing to the shortness of time I must have expressed myself unclearly. From the virus which had been destroyed by ultrasonic vibrations we obtained a nucleic acid, the molecules of which, during sedimentation in the presence of salt, resembled nucleic acid from the rods of virus which had not been destroyed. The activity of these acids, however, was greater than one would have expected from the activity of the preparation from which they were obtained, but it was less than that of the nucleic acid of the original virus. For example, if the activity of the virus destroyed by ultrasonic vibrations was 1% of that of the original virus, then the activity of its nucleic acid was about 0·1% of that of the original virus.

One short observation on the question of the transfer of information. It is clear that the specific information for the production of the whole nucleoprotein resides in a specific entity, namely the nucleic acid, and different strains of nucleic acid will produce different nucleoproteins. I believe that even if we can argue as to whether viruses are alive or not, still we cannot dispute the fact that viruses contain nucleic acid in which is inherent a considerable amount of specific information.

W. M. Stanley (U.S.A.):

As a biologist I can understand Dr. Smorodintsev's difficulties. But as a biochemist I cannot be answerable for the similarity between viruses and genes. The analogy between them, which I described, is simply a fact. Transduction is an experimental fact. I suggest that, as scientists, we should develop our ideas on the basis of such facts. I am in complete agreement with Prof. Smorodintsev as to the exogenous nature of viruses, that is to say, with the idea that viruses come from outside and are not already present within cells. But I am afraid we are faced with such conditions that it is hard to prove experimentally whether the virus developed within the cell or entered it from outside.

I an rather surprised with Prof. Smorodintsev for maintaining that viruses always bring about the destruction of the cell. He knows as well as I do that some viruses persist for years in a host without destroying cells and that there are latent viruses, e.g. a potato virus, which seems almost like a normal component of the cell of the potato plant. At the same time I agree with him in defining a virus as a pathogenic agent.

L. A. Zil'ber (U.S.S.R.):

I should like to make a few comments on the papers we have heard today.

The facts which demonstrate the possibility of resynthesis of the tobacco mosaic virus and the infectivity of isolated nucleic acid are of tremendous interest. The existence of such 'infectivity' allows one to draw many far-reaching conclusions of extreme importance both in regard to the problem of protein synthesis and to that of the pathology of infection.

The absence of intact virus in the preparations of nucleic acid prepared from tobacco mosaic virus is vouched for by the very sober evidence brought forward in today's papers by Fraenkel-Conrat and others. But is this evidence enough to allow us to maintain categorically that protein is completely absent from the 'infective' preparations of nucleic acid? It seemed to me that it would be useful to study this question by using the method of anaphylaxis which enables one to demonstrate the very slightest contamination by protein such as cannot be determine chemically. If these preparations had no power to sensitize guinea pigs to protein, this would be an important criterion of their purity. Immunologists, in general, cannot understand why biochemists so seldom and so inconfidently use immunological methods in their experiments. I should like to draw your attention to the fact that immunological methods enable one to distinguish, not only between the different compositions of various substances (not necessarily proteins), but also between their structures. For a long time nobody could differentiate chemically or immunologically between normal and immune globulins. Recently Adler has shown that they may be differentiated by the method of indirect haemagglutination. In our laboratory a clear differentiation has been achieved by using the method of anaphylaxis and desensitization. As immune globulins now provide one of the most satisfactory models for the study of protein synthesis, the great attraction of immunological methods for bringing about biochemical separations is that they are certainly effective. I should like to remark that the hypothesis of the matrix, which provides a good explanation for the formation of antibodies, is hard to apply to the phenomena discovered by Fraenkel-Conrat and Schramm. When one nucleic acid is introduced into a healthy plant there is, of course, no ready-made matrix in the plant for the synthesis of viral protein. It follows that in this case, as was shown convincingly in Fraenkel-Conrat's remarkable experiments on the hybridization of viruses, the nucleic acid acts as a genetic determinant, controlling the formation of a similar matrix, if only such a matrix is generally formed in this case.

A process which is, to some extent, analogous is seen in the transformation of pneumococci. An alteration in the specificity of the polysaccharide antigen is brought about in them by deoxyribonucleic acid which, of course, has no matrix for the reproduction of a polysaccharide antigen.

The question of the mechanism of action of a genetic determinant, such as nucleic acid, obviously is of the greatest importance at present. It would therefore undoubtedly be interesting to carry out a detailed immunological study of a disease induced by a single nucleic acid. Immunological studies could, at least, reveal the time and quantity of the formation of the virus, even before the signs of the disease became manifest. They could thus yield some information as to the process of formation of virus particles, both infective and non-infective.

Essential information as to the specific structure of the protein synthesized under the control of the nucleic acid might also be obtained by immunological methods.

V. RYZHKOV (U.S.S.R.):

I should like to touch upon some logical questions, the consideration of which is especially important when we are faced with such difficult problems as those with which we are now dealing.

First there is the question of the definition of life. I should like to recall the statement of Engels that a definition is of little scientific value. The content of an idea must be revealed in its entirety, but this has already ceased to be a definition. I think that the place of viruses in nature can be understood, not on the basis of a formal short definition, but only by a study of all the connections in which viruses exist in nature. The fact that viruses are capable of multiplication might indicate their living nature to a lesser extent than the fact that viruses circulate in nature as actual living creatures, for the isolated organoids of cells are also capable of multiplication.

I should like to call attention to the fact that we still do not know much about viruses in a state of biological activity. We have in our hands preparations of virus particles which have been fully studied, but we now know that virus particles represent the spore stage of viruses. One can as little judge the life of viruses from their spore stages as one can judge the life of bacteria from their spores or the life of a wheat plant from a well-dried grain of wheat.

I should like to raise a protest against reference to virus particles as molecules. In scale they are on a molecular level, but their structure is biologically adapted to function and is not known among non-living molecules. I have in mind, primarily, the dense envelope of protein which protects the viral spore or virus particle.

We have here been given well-founded evidence for the fact that viruses, being highly specialized parasites, can hardly enable us to understand the earliest forms of life. From this point of view a greater interest attaches to the saprophytic ultramicrobes which were first isolated by Laidlaw from drain water and have now been fairly well studied. One may wonder why they have not attracted the attention of specialists in the origin of life.

What has been said does not detract from the significance of viruses in connection with the study of the specific synthesis of proteins and other compounds of high molecular weight. Twenty years ago, when I began my study of the physiology of viruses, I definitely had the idea that work in this direction was of importance, not merely for the understanding of viruses, but also for the understanding of specific biosynthesis. I take great satisfaction in the fact that this point of view is now generally accepted.

A. N. BELOZERSKIĬ (U.S.S.R.):

May I say a few words in connection with Prof. Schramm's paper ? Prof. Schramm puts forward the suggestion that polyphosphates, which are widely distributed in present-day bacteria, played a part in the development of living things. The idea of the possible significance of polyphosphates in the development of life was also thrown out by Prof. Bernal in the lectures which he gave recently in Moscow University. Roka also postulates the participation of polyphosphates in the original formation of desoxyribonucleic acid.

It seems to me that everyone who is directly interested and concerned with the problem of the origin and development of life on the Earth should pay attention to this group of phosphorus-containing compounds which may really have played an essential part in the establishment and further development of life.

What circumstances lead to this suggestion ?

In the first place, polyphosphates are only found in lower organisms, such as bacteria, fungi and algae. The work of a considerable number of laboratories, including our own, has shown that polyphosphates play an essential part in the vital activities of these micro-organisms. They are directly associated with the phenomena of growth and multiplication, or, to speak more concretely, they appear to be energy donors for such important bio-syntheses as those of proteins and nucleic acids, while in the latter case they may also serve as sources of phosphorus.

According to Yoshida's findings polyphosphates should be regarded as high-energy compounds.

Only such polyphosphates as are associated with organic substrates are physiologically active. Many investigators consider that physiologically active polyphosphates are bound to proteins but, according to our evidence, they are bound to ribonucleic acid. In any case, in one way or another, the utilization of these compounds of phosphorus by micro-organisms takes place on the basis of organic compounds.

In view of all this we may suppose that, at the time when living material became established, inorganic polyphosphates already existed in nature, and that energy was stored in this form. However, activation of the phosphates may have been necessary for the directed use of this energy in organic syntheses, and this may have been brought about by means of compounds of inorganic polyphosphates with some suitable pre-existing organic compounds.

Such an association may have led to the development of the prototype of later energy-yielding systems which were perfected by selection in the course of further development.

It is obviously not a matter of chance that, throughout the organic world, we find energy-yielding systems in the form of derivatives of phosphoric acid or, more accurately, derivatives of polyphosphates.

It is not impossible that a similar means for the storage of energy in the organic world was, at some time, brought in from inorganic nature, in the form of mineral polyphosphates.

G. Schramm (Federal German Republic):

To begin with, I want to thank Dr. Belozerskiĭ for his remarks. I am very glad that our ideas about metaphosphates are not altogether mistaken. I should like to speak about the application of serological methods to the study of viruses. We have used the methods extensively in looking for the absence of proteins from preparations of nucleic acids. By means of the complement-fixing reaction it is possible to detect a very small amount of viral protein; the preparations of nucleic acids which we obtained by the phenol method contained less than 0·02% of viral protein. The detection of smaller amounts of protein in larger amounts of nucleic acid would be hard by chemical means. Infectious ribonucleic acid was also prepared from several animal viruses such as poliomyelitis virus (Colter, Bird, Moyer, Brown) and meningo encephalitis virus (Colter, Bird, Brown) and eastern equine encephalitis virus (Wecker, Schäfer).

As I understood, Dr. Fraenkel-Conrat studied the decrease in infectivity of the virus and of the nucleic acid obtained from the virus after unltrasonic treatment. I do not doubt the correctness of his results. They may be explained by the separation of part of the protein from the virus particles under the influence of ultrasonic vibrations. The infectivity of the protein-containing material would then become less, while the nucleic acid, if it had not already been damaged, might remain infective. I think that one should use the method worked out by Williams to calculate the number of short particles and then establish a relationship between infectivity and the number of short particles. Dr. Fraenkel-Conrat emphasized that these experiments were only just beginning and we must await further facts.

V. S. Tongur (U.S.S.R.):

The formation and properties of nucleoproteins, especially deoxyribonucleoproteins (DNP), have been far too little studied. Moreover, it is not clear what is the quantitative relationship between protein and deoxyribonucleic acid (DNA) in the formation of DNP. How are the properties of DNP changed when there are changes in the amount of protein in it? and so on. Together with L. S. Diskina and D. M. Spitkovskiĭ at the Institute of Experimental Biology, I have made an attempt to study some of these problems. We wanted to find the point of inversion, i.e. the point at which a molecule of DNP is converted into a molecule of DNA by measuring the viscosity of DNP which was being gradually deproteinized. (The DNP was prepared from the liver and pancreas of oxen.) The results showed that, over a fairly wide range of protein-content in DNP (from 70–75% down to about 25%) achieved by repeated deproteinization, the viscosity, and, therefore, also the form of its molecules, remained unchanged, i.e. the tertiary structure of DNP has a reasonably good configurational stability. However, if the protein content of the DNP is further lowered (to 15–25%), there is a sharp rise in the viscosity, which increases to about twice its former value. When this happens, according to our hypothesis, there is a transition from the tertiary structure of DNP to the tertiary structure of DNA. If the experiment is carried out in the reverse direction, that is to say by combining DNA with various proteins, then inversion takes place when the ratio of DNA to protein is about the same and the DNP and the complexes of DNA which are formed have a viscosity considerably lower than the original viscosity of the DNA. The actual viscosity of the DNP depends on the nature of the protein which enters into the artificial complex. This would appear to indicate that, on combination with DNA, each protein forms the tertiary structure of DNP, having a different specific packing according to the nature of the protein component. Thus, the tertiary structure of DNP appears, according to our view, when protein is present in the complex to the extent of about 15–25% and the molecule which contains components in this proportion to one another may be called the true molecule of nucleoprotein.

It is not without interest to note that the so-called 'residual protein' of DNP constitutes about 15–20% of the weight of the DNP. This encourages the idea, though, to be sure, it is still only a speculation, that the tertiary structure of DNP is maintained by the essential, residual protein which is disposed around the DNA in the fully extended form in the β-configuration and in complete steric correspondence with the DNA.

We went on to formulate an equation for the greatest amounts of various proteins which can enter into a complex with DNA and which have different molecular weights and different numbers of basic groups. This equation shows that, for DNA of a given molecular weight, the molar ratio between the amounts of DNA and protein entering into the complex depends strictly on the molecular weight of the protein. The amount of bound protein is inversely proportional to its molecular weight. The ratio of the weights of protein and DNA entering into the complex remains constant for different proteins. Thus, for example, DNA from both liver and pancreas (having a molecular weight of the order of 5×10^6), can bind up to 1000 molecules of serum albumin or up to 3000 molecules of α-chymotrypsin. This indicates that, in the formation of DNP, a great part is played, not only by salt and other linkages, but also by the ratio of the sizes of the reacting molecules.

As our calculations show, the maximum number of protein molecules which can be linked with DNA experimentally cannot be arranged around the latter either in the native or in the fully extended form. Calculations on the asymmetry of molecules of DNP contradict the supposition that the molecules of protein are arranged perpendicularly to the axis of the molecules of DNA and our experiments on the viscosity and relaxation of DNP exclude the possibility that, in such a case, multiple layers of protein may be formed on the molecule of DNA. On the other hand, the continual diminution of the magnitude of the relaxation of DNP as the amount of protein in it is increased suggests the gradual blocking of the 'centres' in the molecule of DNP which are responsible for its highly elastic properties. Thus, experiment shows that when 900–1000 molecules of serum albumin are combined with each molecule of DNA the relaxation of the artificial complex is 0, while the viscosity with this amount of protein does not differ from that in DNP containing only 300–400 molecules of protein per molecule of DNA. This forces us to assume that the greater number of the protein molecules are directly attached to the DNA even if only by part of their surfaces.

Study of the relaxational properties of nucleoproteins in relation to the amount of protein present in them has shown that these properties appear when there is about 60% of protein in the DNP. It must be supposed that, in this case, owing to interweaving of submolecular structures, there arises the possibility of the formation of what we might call structures of the fourth order. This does not exclude the possibility of relaxation of individual molecules of DNP.

Thus, we arrive at the conclusion that DNP shows two points of inversion, the first when the protein content is 15–25%, which corresponds with the appearance of the true molecule of DNP with its specific tertiary structure and elasticity; the second when the protein content is 60%, which corresponds (within fairly wide limits of concentration) to the quaternary structure of DNP, with its characteristic structural-mechanical properties.

In conclusion, it must be noted that, when the DNA is carrying less than the maximal load of protein, a part of its surface remains free and can, therefore, take part in specific biochemical reactions, i.e. a nucleoprotein can 'work' as a protein, as DNA and as a nucleoprotein.

S. E. Bresler (U.S.S.R.):

The astonishing advances in biochemistry over the past five years enable us to make an experimental approach to the problem of the chemical mechanism of protein synthesis. It is now generally accepted that the synthesis of protein takes place on a template of ribonucleic acid (RNA). The latest results of Fraenkel-Conrat and Schramm make this conclusion almost inescapable. On the other hand it is extremely probable that the energy required for this synthesis is obtained in the form of the chemical energy of macroergic groups, for example the pyrophosphate groups of adenosine triphosphate (ATP). In the experiments of Straub, Khesin, Anfinsen and others ATP itself serves as the donor of energy for the synthesis. Finally, very recently indeed, Hoagland, Zamecnik and their colleagues have identified chemically labile intermediate compounds, namely anhydrides of amino acids with adenylic acid. They are formed from the amino acids and ATP under the influence of a specific enzyme and mineral pyrophosphate is split off at the time of their formation.

We suggest that these anhydrides are typical specimens of these labile starting compounds with high levels of free energy from which protein is synthesized. In this connection I should like to deal shortly with some experiments which have been carried out in our laboratory and are still in progress.

In our first experiments in 1950 (with Nidzyan) it was shown that when isolating ribonucleic acid from yeast or from animal tissues one can transfer to it the external phosphate groups of ATP using a small quantity of a homogenate of liver as a transferring enzyme. These experiments have been repeated and confirmed by Brachet and also by Dounce & Kay.

The latter workers have shown that, for this transphosphorylation, one can use purified myokinase, the well known enzyme which brings about the disproportionation of nucleotide polyphosphates. Using this enzyme they were able to prepare phosphorylated RNA in considerable quantities. In our work (with Rubina) a similar phosphorylation of RNA (from yeast and pancreas) was obtained, the excess of phosphate amounting to as much as 70%. This excess of phosphate could be hydrolysed by acid like the phosphate of ATP. Our present views of the structure of RNA, put forward by Todd and his school, indicate that the phosphoric acid in RNA is combined with the $5'$ position of the ribose, just as it is in ATP, and the structure of each link in the polymer is just like the structure of adenylic acid. The completeness of the analogy between the behaviour of nucleotide phosphates of low molecular weight and that of their polymeric analogues should therefore occasion no surprise.

The next step was to demonstrate the macroergic character of the excess phosphate in phosphorylated RNA. This was done in two typical cases. The acceptor used at first was fructose 6-phosphate which, with phosphorylated RNA and the ordinary enzyme phosphofructokinase, is converted into fructose diphosphate. This reaction had the advantage that it permitted very specific enzymic methods of control to be applied. The product of the reaction (more correctly its trichloroacetic acid filtrate) was treated with aldolase which converted it into triose phosphates, substances which can easily be estimated quantitatively. The reaction of transfer of phosphate groups from phosphorylated RNA to fructose 6-phosphate went very well, just as well as with ATP itself.

The other substances which we used as an acceptor for phosphate was creatine. By the use of the enzyme creatine-phosphotransferase from muscle phosphate was transferred from RNA to creatine, which demonstrated conclusively the macroergic nature of phosphorylated RNA.

It should also be remembered that phosphate-rich preparations of RNA, containing an excess of phosphate as compared with the ordinary formula, have been obtained by a number of authors (Brachet, Belozerskiĭ) from yeast and other cells and tissues in a state of active growth. This also would seem to be an argument in favour of the idea that phosphorylated RNA is not an artifact but is an important endogenous substance of cells.

All this enables us to put forward the hypothesis that, under the influence of such enzymic systems as were used by Hoagland in his experiments, amino acid residues should combine with phosphorylated RNA, forming anhydrides with the phosphate groups and, at the same time, splitting off mineral phosphate. It seems to us very probable that such a reaction occurs and it provides a means for the combination of amino acids with a template in the form of a labile compound with a high level of free energy. The later hydrolysis of such anhydrides could be accompanied by their condensation into polypeptide chains. Thermodynamically such a process is quite possible. It is shown to be chemically possible by non-enzymic model experiments carried out by many authors actually using phosphoric acid derivatives of amino acids (e.g. by the experiments of Katchalski).

At present we are trying to prove that amino acids really are bound in the form of anhydrides to the polymeric chain of RNA. If this were firmly proved many new possibilities would be opened up, in particular the possibility of systematic experimental progress towards deciphering the peculiar code in which the structure of a protein is recorded in the chain of a nucleic acid. As Chargaff put it, we have no Rosetta stone for deciphering this code. However, unlike the archaeologists, we can do experiments, asking questions of Nature. Today, owing to the discoveries of Ochoa and Grunberg-Manago, we can synthesize polynucleotides of simple structure. With their help it will be possible to direct a systematic effort towards the elucidation of the 'chemical memory' of RNA, based on experiment and not on general statistical considerations like those on which Gamow tried, without much success, to base his work.

A. S. Konikova (U.S.S.R.):

To make any progress with the problem of the origin of life, it is necessary to have some definition of the essential properties of this form of existence of matter, i.e. life.

It has been suggested here by Mr. Pirie, I think, that the definition of the concept of life is arbitrary and conditioned by our aesthetic feelings. However, this conditioning is, in its turn, determined by the facts of the real world which are known to us and by the strict laws of logic. The arbitrariness and conditionality of our conceptions of life are, therefore, only apparent. The impression of arbitrariness depends less on aesthetic feelings and more on the fact that, with the help of the rules of logic, each investigator correlates the existing experimental data and interprets them. The more correctly this work is carried out the closer to objective reality our concepts will be. I suggest that the evidence of this Symposium will allow such an approach to reality to be made.

All the facts indicate that, if we do not have recourse to the existence of supernatural forces, then, before the appearance of living things, nothing existed in nature apart from physics and chemistry.

Prof. Horowitz's communication is therefore profoundly correct in that part in which he maintains that life originates at the level of chemical molecules. It is, however, very hard to agree with his second proposition, that the substances of the surrounding medium were more complicated than the living molecules which were present in it. It is hard to agree with this mainly because, among the objects of non-living nature, there is nothing so complicated as a living thing, if we take complication to mean the extensiveness of the possibility of the manifestation of properties by the particular compound.

As life began on the chemical level it follows that it was also on the level of molecular chemical reactions which assured the minimal difference between chemistry and biology. There is no direct transition from these relatively simple transformations to the organism because to solve the problem of the origin of life it is necessary to explain which chemical substances accomplished the reactions which brought about the minimal transformation which led to the origin of living from non-living material.

From what we now know of the problem of life three substances must be considered from this point of view, namely nucleoprotein, protein and nucleic acid.

The claim of nucleic acid to be considered has arisen quite recently, after the work in which it was demonstrated that the tobacco mosaic virus is formed when tobacco leaves are infected with nucleic acid, and also since it has been shown the process of synthesis of nucleic acid can take place even when protein synthesis is prevented.

It must, however, be remembered that all these phenomena were observed in complicated biological systems and, so long as it has not been established experimentally that self-reproduction of the component particles of isolated nucleic acid itself can occur, there is no reason to consider it as being the earliest form of life.

As Engels supposed, protein is of great importance in this connection and later investigations indicate that so is nucleoprotein, because both these substances have been shown experimentally to have the power of independent metabolism in an artificial medium, giving rise to material like and unlike themselves, which could initiate development.

Further investigations will show whether the formation of a complex of protein and nucleic acids is necessary to ensure the transition from chemistry to biology.

According to the evidence of our work this is not necessary; but the properties of proteins point in the same direction. The size of the protein molecule, the heterogeneity of its component parts and bonds and the reactivity of proteins are such that their exchange reactions with the substances of the medium are enough, in themselves, to provide for the appearance of the earliest properties of life.

Analysis of the data already available gives reason for considering that a concentration of attention on the laws of metabolism of the simplest forms of life, bordering on chemistry, will open up perspectives for an understanding of the processes of their elaboration and development and also of the transformation of these simplest forms of life into the reversibly inhibited state, as obviously occurs in the case of an isolated virus.

M. Grunberg-Manago (France):

Je voudrais dire juste quelques mots au sujet de la remarque de M. Bresler. Il est très possible effectivement que l' 'extra' P du polynucleotide synthétisé par l'enzyme de levure sert de lien entre la protéine et l'acide nucleique. Nous avons en effet constaté la formation d'un acide hydroxamique durant la synthése de la 'Nucleoprotéine'. Nous ne pouvons à l'heure actuelle être sûr cet acide hydroxamique soit relié à la synthése du polynucléotide mais c'est fort possible.

K. G. Ioffe (U.S.S.R.):

My contribution concerns the connection between the sequence of amino acids in the polypeptide chains of proteins and that of purine and pyrimidine bases in ribonucleic acid (RNA). It seems to me that there must certainly be such a connection, especially since the work of Fraenkel-Conrat and Schramm. It is clear that a definite sequence of bases in a RNA corresponds with its appropriate sequence of amino acids in a particular protein.

But where can one get such pure individual RNA and protein which can confidently be compared with one another?

Although the structure of a few proteins (insulin, the adrenocorticotropic hormone, melanophore-stimulating hormone and glucagon) has been established, they are not suitable for this purpose. Their amino acid composition is too complicated and their polypeptide chains too anomalously various for them to be suitable for comparing with the corresponding RNA. Furthermore, there is yet another difficulty in the impossibility of isolating from a cell, which synthesizes many proteins, the very RNA corresponding with a particular protein.

From what has been said above the following conditions emerge:

1. The cell should elaborate one protein in a strikingly large quantity compared with the sum of all the other proteins of the cell.
2. The protein should be easy to isolate and its structure should already be known.
3. The polypeptide chain of the protein should be monotonous with continual repetition of the same amino acids or sequences of amino acids.

If the first condition is fulfilled and the cell really elaborates, for the most part, only one protein, then the quantity of the corresponding RNA in the cell will also be markedly greater than that of other RNA, and the order of the bases in it will also be monotonous with frequent repetition of the same bases or groups of bases.

The success of a comparison between the two sequences would then be assured.

But where can we find such cells containing parallel inscriptions in two languages, in that of RNA and that of protein?

Probably such Rosetta stones exist in Nature and are not rare. I shall give you one example now.

It concerns the fibroin of silk. Its structure has been elucidated to the extent of 50–60% and the part which is known may be expressed: $(X. Gly. Ala. Gly. Ala. Gly.)_n$ or $(Ala. Gly. Ala. Gly. X. Gly.)_n$ where Ala = alanine, Gly = glycine and X = other amino acids. I have put forward the following structure for the tyrosine-containing part of fibroin:

Ser. Gly. Ala. Gly. Ala. Gly. Ser. Gly. Ala. Gly. Ala. Gly. Tyr. Gly. Ala. Gly. Ala. Gly. Val. Gly. Ala. Gly. Ala. Gly or

Ser. Gly. Ala. Gly. Ala. Gly. Tyr. Gly. Ala. Gly. Ala. Gly. Val. Gly. Ala. Gly. Ala. Gly. Ser. Gly. Ala. Gly. Ala. Gly

where Ser = serine, Tyr = tyrosine and Val = valine [1].

This structure has been confirmed to some extent by Lucas et al. [2].

As the peptide Ala. Gly. Ala. Gly. accounts for exactly 2/3 of the amino acid residues of the tyrosine-containing part of fibroin, so also it is repeated almost as often in the whole molecule of fibroin in that this sequence is also repeated many times in the length of the peptide chain.

Therefore, one must expect that in the RNA which synthesizes the fibroin there will also be frequent repetitions of the same bases along the length of the molecule.

The fibroin-manufacturing part of the silk gland of the silkworm *Bombyx mori* is sharply demarcated from the rest. From the walls of the gland one can obtain cells of one sort, free from other cells. The posterior part of the gland produced enormous amounts of pure fibroin without sericin. Therefore the form of RNA which synthesizes fibroin should predominate markedly over all other forms. The RNA corresponding to fibroin should contain many individual bases arranged in such a way as to correspond with the repetitive peptide Ala. Gly. Ala. Gly of the protein.

Such a frequency encountered sequences of bases in the RNA could be associated with the peptide Ala. Gly. Ala. Gly of the protein.

Thus there is a Rosetta stone. It would be possible to decipher the RNA symbols for two amino acids, alanine and glycine, and also that for the tetrapeptide Ala. Gly. Ala. Gly.

REFERENCES

1. K. G. IOFFE, *Biokhimiya*, **19**, (4), 1954.
2. F. LUCAS, J. T. B. SHAW & S. G. SMITH, *Biochem. J.*, **66**, 468, 1957.

N. I. NUZHDIN (U.S.S.R.):

1. *The Qualitative Specificity of Living Material*

The first question with which I want to deal is that of the qualitative specificity of living material. It seems to me that in solving the problem of the origin of life on the Earth, one must first answer the question: What is this life which distinguishes living from non-living material? Otherwise it is hard to look for a solution if there is no clear idea of what one is solving. There is no paradox here, for in the collection of published communications there is no definition of the concept of life or the concept of living material. In many of the papers this question is touched upon but is relegated to the category of 'proscribed questions', to which it is difficult or impossible to find an answer.

Furthermore, the necessity for such an answer is dictated by the ever-growing tendency to ignore the qualitative specificity of living material which distinguishes it from non-living material. This tendency has come into biology from physics. Having made such a tremendous jump forwards during the past decades, in the understanding of the structure of matter and in the search for means of directing intranuclear processes, many physicists consider the possibility of a more complete explanation of biological phenomena solely in terms of their understanding of the laws of physics and chemistry. This tendency, which began with Schroedinger's pronouncement, has, unfortunately become more and more extensive. In the meanwhile it is forgotten that Schroedinger himself, having taken up the position that there is a purely physical explanation of life, was unable to maintain it and was forced to appeal to 'divine quantum mechanics'.

Unfortunately, many biologists accept this tendency uncritically and, following the physicists, ignore the qualitative peculiarities of living material and expect to find the solution exclusively in terms of the processes of physics and chemistry. This tendency can also be perceived in a number of the communications presented at our conference. For example, I cannot agree in the slightest with Prof. Brachet, who maintains that 'the definition of the idea of life has a quantitative value rather than being a qualitative concept.' (p. 361).

There can surely be no need to substantiate the incorrectness of this formulation. If living material did not possess qualitative properties which do not characterize non-living ones, then, probably there would be no necessity to call a conference on the problem of the origin of life for there would be no living material as a peculiar specific form of the motion of matter.

I have dealt with this important problem because although it is put correctly in A. I. Oparin's monograph *The Origin of Life on the Earth* it has not received sufficient attention in the communications put before this conference.

2. *The Origin of Life and the Problem of the Material Carriers of Heredity*

The second problem with which I shall deal is that of the material basis of heredity. In his well-known article defending previously held hypotheses, Muller, in 1950, stated that the problem of the origin of life could only be solved on the basis of the concept of the gene. Without embarking on a criticism of this conception as a whole, I would remark that the attempt to associate a hypothesis about the primary living structure with one about the material carriers of heredity is not new. In the book already mentioned, Academician Oparin rightly pointed out that the concepts of 'idioplasm', 'biogenes', 'plastomes' and so on, of earlier authors included not only the idea of a unit of heredity, but also that of the elementary unit of life, the 'living molecule'.

Surely one cannot doubt the obvious suggestion that the original organic material, which manifested the earliest elementary characteristics of living material, also had the ability to hand on hereditary characteristics. Such an inalienable feature of living material as the reproduction of material like itself, which is a prerequisite for the maintenance of living material, and also the ability to change as conditions change, must have originated along with the origin of life.

It must be emphasized that it is only the genetic theory of Michurin which regards heredity as an inalienable property of living material. This theory denies the existence of any special carriers of heredity, whether they are supposed to be in the nucleus or the cytoplasm. The proponents of so-called 'classical genetics' have a different idea of heredity, believing it to be connected with special carriers, i.e. genes. I am not going to deal, here, with the fundamental changes, which have taken place during the last 20 years, in the chromosomal theory of heredity. At present, while dismissing the gene as a corpuscle of a chromosome, geneticists put forward the molecule of deoxyribonucleic acid (DNA) as the unit of heredity, ascribing genetic properties to it.

This idea has also been emphasized in a number of contributions to our present meeting. In particular, Prof. Belozerskii not only ascribes a genetic role to DNA, but, in developing the idea of the evolution of nucleic acids, he sees it as taking place from ribonucleotides to ribonucleic acid (RNA) and then on to the appearance of DNA. According to Prof. Belozerskii this is what determines the genetic peculiarities of RNA and DNA. The former is associated with the more general aspects of the vital activity of the organism, while the latter is associated with the narrower and phylogenetically more recent properties of the organism. It must not be forgotten that this is no new idea, although it is given a new formulation. In the twenties of the present century Prof. Filipchenko took the view that the cytoplasm passes on the characteristics of higher systematic categories while he ascribed to the nucleus the role of carrying the species and racial characteristics of the organism. This hypothesis has not been accepted by geneticists and has been justly criticized.

I am glad to point out that, both in Academician Oparin's monograph and in many of the papers, many suggestions have been made concerning the question on which I am touching. It will undoubtedly play a great part, not only in the study of the origin of life, but also in genetics. From what has been said it clearly follows that, however important the part played by nucleic acid in biological processes, its molecule was not the original basis of life. It is not a 'living molecule' but one of the parts of a living structure which can only fulfil its biological function against the general background of metabolic processes taking place within the cell. The synthesis of the protein molecule depends on nucleic acid just as much as the synthesis of the latter depends on the protein molecule. This is quite understandable. Living material is a complex of compounds which determine the regular course of the processes which constitute life. One cannot isolate an individual component without interfering with the living material, still less can one understand life on the basis of such an isolated component, however thoroughly its functions may have been studied. The same applies to the phenomenon of heredity as well and, in general, to any property of living material.

The Origin of Structure and Metabolism

The Scale of Structural Units in Biopoesis

J. D. BERNAL

Birkbeck College, University of London

IN ALL discussions referring to the evolution of material systems, be they galaxies, organisms or societies, two aspects have to be kept in mind simultaneously at every stage in the discussion—the *dynamic* and the *static*—the *processes* and the *structures*. Living organisms are built from atoms and at the same time they react and change according to the laws of atomic combination. Systems of extraordinary complexity and variety are built up, maintained and modified but all repose on the same elements, that is on certain simple properties common to all actual or possible life. These provide the given data into which all schemes of biopoesis must be fitted. At the first stage of emergence from the inorganic world this corresponds to the considerations of the physical and chemical properties of the simple molecules of water, carbon dioxide and ammonia, discussed by Henderson in his *Fitness of the Environment*; later they include the colloidal properties of globular and fibrous polymers of the proteins, nucleic acids and of bimolecular lipid sheets, exemplified in terrestrial life by structures such as those of the proteins. We have learned of these properties largely through their occurrence in organic structures but once the structures are provided the properties have nothing specifically vital about them, as has been shown by their occurrence in synthetic plastics and fibres. My object here is to show that much of the apparent complexity and arbitrariness of living systems is due to just such physical conditioning and that the true biopoetic problems represent the residue after these have been allowed for.

One argument which has been used from the highest antiquity against any spontaneous evolution of life has been the apparent impossibility of such an arrangement coming together by chance. It was already urged against the early Greek atomists, of which we catch a seventeenth-century echo in John Hall's *Epicurean Ode*:

> 'Since that this thing we call the world
> By chance on Atomes is begot,
> Which though in dayly motions hurld,
> Yet weary not,
> How doth it prove
> Thou art so fair and I in Love?'

Some have taken up the same theme less poetically in modern times and have claimed to demonstrate by mathematical arguments that even such a small part of organized nature as a molecule of ribonucleic acid would, if it had to come together by chance from a congeries of atoms, take almost infinitely more time than the presumed age of the universe. I know Professor Haldane [1] has argued that a very unlikely thing is not an impossible thing and that the chance origin of life cannot be altogether neglected, but most of those bringing forward such arguments use them in a purely negative sense. If life could not have come together by pure chance, they argue, then its presence is either an illusion or that life was created and guided at every step by an intelligent agent or at least by a teleological seeking for perfection. I do not want here to enter into these arguments, which are more philosophical than scientific, but I do want to make the point that the problem has been wrongly posed. There is no question, to anyone who has examined the evidence, of the need to explain the origin of life as consisting of one decisive step, because it plainly did not originate as such. Even

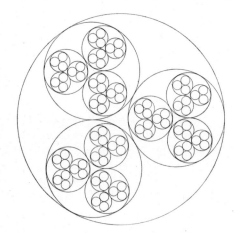

FIG. 1. Formal scheme of five orders of a sequence of inscribed circles. Each unit contains three of the order beneath it.

if we cannot as yet precisely determine the stages of biopoesis, their general character is already apparent, as I have attempted to sketch in my other contribution. Over and above any hypothesis of stages in time, we have before us in biochemistry and ultra-cytology concrete evidence of a series of grades of structure of increasing complexity. The structures that we observe or study are not arranged in a continuous order but a discontinuous one.

Each type of structure seems to be composed of units of fairly definite sizes which come together to form another unit on the next level (Fig. 1). Take for example a vertebrate striated-muscle cell or fibre, itself a member with thousands of others of a macroscopic muscle (Fig. 2). Leaving aside the cell membrane, nucleus, mitochondria and other organelles, the functional element is the striated muscle fibril. This is composed of some hundred elements, the myomeres, each with its transverse M and Z membranes still of unknown composition and function. Each myomere contains a parallel arrangement of some thousand distinct myosin fibrils, interleaved with actomyosin fibrils. Both fibrils contain some hundred polypeptide chains [2, 3]. The chains are made of specific sequences of amino acids which in turn are made of between ten and thirty atoms. Here

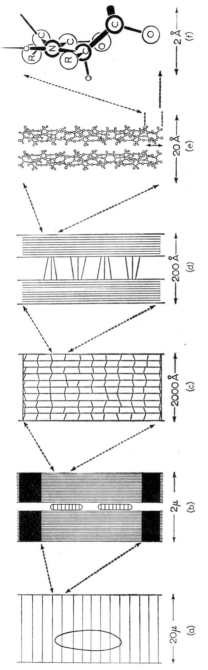

FIG. 2. Six successive orders of a magnification of a muscle cell.

(*a*)—part of a cell of striated muscle as seen in the light microscope: magnification $\times 10^3$; (*b*)—muscle fibril showing one striation Z band and mitochondria as seen in the electron microscope: magnification $\times 10^4$; (*c*)—part of a muscle fibril showing myofibrils and connecting crosspieces as seen in the electron microscope: magnification $\times 10^5$; (*d*)—myofibrils showing protein molecular chains, inferred from electron microscope and X-ray analysis: magnification $\times 10^6$; (*e*)—chains of myosin—Pauling helix model—as inferred by X-rays: magnification 10^7; (*f*)—part of a polypeptide chain showing two amino acid residues as inferred by X-ray and chemical analysis: magnification 10^8.

therefore are six objectively separate levels of organization, each one including all those beneath it.

This example brings out the main thesis of this paper, namely that: *The probability of formation of a highly complex structure from its elements is increased, or the number of possible ways of doing it diminished, if the structure in question can be broken down into a finite series of successively inclusive sub-structures.* I believe this theorem is capable of formal proof if it can be properly formulated, but I leave this task to the logicians. Here I am concerned primarily to demonstrate that such sub-structures can be formed from atoms related by the known laws of physics and chemistry. Further, I want to show that each kind of substructural unit corresponds to a definite and limited range of absolute sizes and shapes and that at each level the laws of association of the units are qualitatively different. None of this, in principle, depends on biological analysis; it would hold for all combinations consisting mainly of the four elements hydrogen, carbon, nitrogen and oxygen. As, however, only a few of these structures have been produced synthetically, examples, particularly of the most complicated forms, will be sought in the field of biological structures.

The size range, the shapes and the methods of mutual attachment of the units of every level depend on factors which are partly physical—that is in respect to the nature of the mutual potentials or attractive or repulsive forces between the particles—and partly geometrical, determined by their relative sizes and shapes. It will be convenient to deal with this geometrical or formal element first, as it is common to all sizes and natures of mutual potentials. Indeed formal analogies to microbiological structures can even be found from human technical experience which in fact provides them with their vocabulary such as piling, twisting, twining and pleating. A logical starting point is the quasi-spherical particle, for others of different shape can always be constructed from such particles. All that need be postulated of them is a more or less fixed radius and the capacity of joining to one or more similar particles. The number that it can join on to may be called its co-ordination number, analogous to the valency of atoms. The lower limit of the co-ordination number is not necessarily fixed; that is a particle can be linked to fewer than it can accommodate but the upper number is limited by close-packing considerations to 12–14.

In the simpler cases we are concerned with the linking of similar particles or at least, as in proteins and nucleic acids, of particles with similar linkage systems though with different side groups. More complicated relations involving more than one type of co-ordination can occur with heterogeneous particles and some of these may be very important, such as those of the nucleoproteins, the lipoproteins and the mucoproteins, but the structure of these plainly depends on that of their homogeneous components, which must be treated first.

The co-ordination number of a particle with similar particles is not merely an intrinsic property but also depends on external conditions and may be very sensitive to them in cases where the difference in the free energy of association of different kinds is small.

How this can occur can be illustrated in the following ideal case. In Fig. 3 (*a* and *c*) are shown two forms of the mutual potential surfaces of a pair of particles with respect to a third particle in its vicinity. In (a) in the region of the potential minimum there is a shallow trough along the axis of the particle pair, in (c) it lies along the equator. The addition of a third particle to the system will be collinear in the case of (a) and triangular in that of (c) (Fig. 3 b and d). It is easy to see that this will lead, with further additions, to the formation of a fibre in the first case and a close-packed crystal in the other without there being much to choose between them in their mutual energies of association. This is borned out in practice by the very common occurrence of the so-called reversible fibrous-globular (f-g) transition in many proteins of which that of insulin has been most studied [4]. The fibrous association may be, so to speak, vulcanized by primary valence formation as in the case of the physiologically important fibrinogen-fibrin transformation, so as to make reversibility difficult.

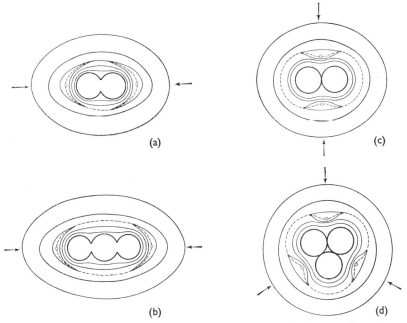

FIG. 3. Determination of type of co-ordination of particles in two dimensions by shape of mutual equipotential curves.

(a) and (b)—with troughs of potential along axis leading to linear co-ordination; (c) and (d)—with troughs of potential at right angles to axis leading to close-packed agglomerations. ○ —potential minima; → —direction of attachment of further particles.

A co-ordination number of one can only lead to a particle pair, but such pairs seem to be common among the proteins, notably in insulin where the chemical unit of 5500 molecular weight is nearly always found in solution as 11,000 or some higher multiple, 33,000 or 44,000. It also arises when a single metal atom is co-ordinated with protein molecules, as in the case of the mercury-albumin complexes. Here steric co-ordinations limit the association to two, which will be the general rule where the co-ordinating agent is small compared to the co-ordinated [30].

A co-ordination number of *two* leads to an unbranched linear association. If the two co-ordinating are nearly at 180° the result is a nearly straight line polymer of indefinite length; if the angle is smaller it is a ring or close helix. Angles of 90° or less will produce fourfold or triple aggregations without much waste space, as for instance in the 33,000 mol. wt unit in zinc insulin. The helix will be the most probable form for larger angles owing to the stabilizing effect of secondary interactions between successive coils. This seems to be the explanation for the arrangement of the protein shell in the rod-like viruses such as tobacco mosaic virus, though we cannot be sure yet whether in this case there is one closely packed helix or an aggregation of several slightly coiled helices.

The simplest form of *three* co-ordinated pattern is that of a hexagonal plane net. This, however, unless stabilized, is likely to curl into a cylinder or spiral roll. At any rate no indisputable example of it has been analysed though it may account for the protein part of cellular or intracellular membranes. Another product of three co-ordination is the closed basket of cubic, often of isoctahedral, symmetry (532) which has been revealed as the shell of the globular viruses—

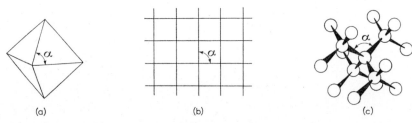

(a)   (b)   (c)

FIG. 4.   Types of aggregate formed by 4 co-ordination when angle α between vectors joining neighbours is:

(*a*)—less than 90° leading to closed octahedron; (*b*)—equal to 90° leading to an indefinite plane square net; (*c*)—greater than 90° leading to a three-dimensional extended (diamond) structure.

tomato bushy stunt and turnip yellow [5, 6]. Higher co-ordinations lead to clump-like aggregates or to indefinitely extending crystals. The former occur if the points of attachments are concentrated on one side of the particles. For instance, four attachments in the form of a pyramid would lead to a closed group of six in the form of an octahedron, while four in the form of a tetrahedron would lead to an indefinite arrangement of the type of a diamond crystal (Fig. 4).

If we consider the further aggregations, not of quasi-spherical particles, but of the kinds of structures which, as shown above, can be derived from them, there are further possibilities of complexity. In essence, however, these reduce to two: the packing of elongated particles, which may include twining; and the piling of platy ones, which may include rolling up. The simplest arrangement of straight or quasi-straight elongated particles is hexagonal packing (Fig. 5, *a* and *b*). This will result in two kinds of structures according as to whether the elongated particles can be arranged with all their ends in parallel shells, nearly normal to their general direction, or not. In the latter case, which is the only one for particles of unequal length, a long aggregate with characteristic grain will be formed which, if the transverse direction is limited, will have the structure of a roving or thread according to the degree of twist.

The case of long particles of equal length occurs predominantly in organized nature for derivatives of long-carbon-chain compounds, fatty acids, phospholipids, lipoproteins. These seem to be the basis of the double layers found in almost all cells from which, by a spiral rolling up, are formed the myelin sheaths of nerves. With them are associated sterols and other more complex elongated molecules of approximately the same length, 20 Å–25 Å, as the predominant C_{16}–C_{20} straight-chain hydrocarbons.

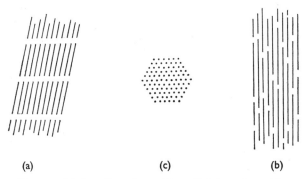

(a) (c) (b)

FIG. 5. Modes of regular packing of elongated particles.

(a)—when these are of equal length leading to multiple sheet structure; (b)—when these are of unequal length leading to tactoid or fibre structure; (c)—illustrates the hexagonal net packing common to (a) and (b).

The packing of helical particles offers more complexities. Close-coiled helices approximate to cylinders and pack accordingly in hexagonal close packing. If, however, the helices are of the same sense their coils may interlock as appears to be the case for tobacco mosaic virus [7] (Fig. 6). This process may go further still in more loosely coiled helices. Where the pitch is equal to twice or more of the diameter of the helical particle, more than one helix may share a common axis, leading to the two- or three-fold twined helices such as are found in deoxyribosenucleic acid (DNA) and in collagen. Such compound helices may themselves be straight or may have an axis forming another helix of different pitch (coiled coil). This may lead in turn to further coiling and so to cable-like structures of almost indefinite complexity (Fig. 6).

These considerations are all of an extremely general kind, involving hardly more than the geometrical consequences of the arrangements of impenetrable solids whose shape can in turn be evolved from the aggregation of spherical particles. Such a phenomenon as crystallization, in the sense of indefinite regular aggregations, can be exemplified by structures on a variety of scales from atoms, viruses, and bacteria [8] up to matches and cannon balls. To correspond with an actual scale of structures other more physical conditions have to be invoked and filled in to the more abstract geometrical ones already described. If we confine ourselves to structures stable in water and ionic solutions, and this is

sufficient to cover all terrestrial life, we can set out a sequence of five interparticulate forces or mutual interaction energies. In this sequence each of these
corresponds to a longer range of action and a weaker interaction energy than
those preceding it and, what is perhaps most important, the steps though broad
are separated by wider gaps.

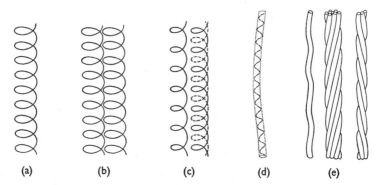

(a)   (b)   (c)   (d)   (e)

FIG. 6.   Types of diagrammatic aggregation of helical molecules.

(*a*)—simple helix; (*b*)—interleaved helices on adjacent axes; (*c*)—interleaved helices
sharing common axes (double helix); (*d*)—coiled coil helix (after Pauling);
(*e*)—combination of coiled coil helices to form twined cables.

Only homopolar forces, the hydrogen bond and ionic forces are reasonably
well understood and will not be further discussed here (see Table 1). The
mechanism of the remaining two, which I have called *cryohydric* and *long-range*
forces, are still unexplained theoretically or are the subject of current controversy.
There is, however, little doubt about the reality of these forces and of their range
of action because these are revealed by determinate structures which so far can
only be explained by postulating them. They are in my own view distinct. The
cryohydric forces imply an ordered but not necessarily ice-like grouping of water
molecules such as, for instance, occurs in the rare-gas hydrates. They are operative up to the range at which such structures can be maintained, itself a function
of the temperature, at room temperature something of the order of 20 Å. They
are also a function of the size of the particles they bind together, being greater
the larger and flatter these are. In the case of montmorillonite clay, where these
conditions are optimal, the range is at least up to 40 Å [9].

The long-range forces on the other hand operate through a medium indistinguishable from water or ionic solution, incapable of showing rigidity. Whether
they are due to simple Van der Waals forces, demonstrated to exist between
extended solids [10, 11], or, as Kirkwood has suggested [12], due to virtual
ionization, they seem to operate wherever there are particles of over 100 Å in
diameter containing ionizable groups. In terms of energy there seems to be a
minimum which leads to a condition of equilibrium at a definite distance, provided that the thermal energy is not greater than that of the interaction minima.
The position of the minimum is not notably sensitive to temperature but as old
experiments on tobacco mosaic virus [13] have shown, it is much affected by pH.

The existence under certain circumstances of this equilibrium results in the division of the solution containing them into two parts whenever the overall concentration of particles is less than that which would ensure the equilibrium distance. In the more concentrated regions this critical concentration is maintained: in the rest there is in general a far more dilute solution.

TABLE I

Types of interparticulate forces

Name	Mechanism	Order of magnitude of interaction energy (kcal/mole)	Range of action (Å)	Kinds of unit between which such forces act	Examples
Homopolar	Electron sharing	500	1–2 in organic compounds	Electron-deficient atoms	All organic compounds Long-chain polymers
Hydrogen bond	Action of incompletely screened hydrogen atom attached to one atom or other polarizable atoms	15	2·4–3·2 usually 2·7	OH- and NH-groups in relation to OH and CO	Water. Acids. Sugars. Urea. Purines (Nucleic acids). Proteins
Ionic	Coulomb attraction between ions or charged atoms of different sign	20	2–3	Basic NH_2 or NH_3^+ groups and acid COO^- groups. Halogens, etc.	Soaps. Basic hydrochlorides. Zwitterions. Glycine
Cryohydric	Linking of ions or charged atoms of different signs through layers of water molecules in fixed positions (ice-like)	5	3–20	Medium-sized molecules 10 Å or more in diameter containing OH groups in presence of limited amounts of H_2O	Bentonite clays. Protein crystals
Long range	Imperfectly known but may depend on mutually induced ionization of amphoteric molecules	<1	20–3000	Very large amphoteric particles 100 Å or more in diameter in water or ionic solutions	Bentonite gels. Iridescent hydroxide gels. Tactoids (tobacco mosaic virus). Coacervates (Tipula virus)

The long-range forces are undirected, but the shapes of mutual equipotential surfaces around flat or elongated particles ensure a tendency towards parallelism. This leads, in the case of identical particles such as viruses, to a liquid-crystal condition for equilibrium sols of such particles with one- or two-dimensional long-range order. For spherical particles only short-range order is maintained usually leading to a quasi-liquid arrangement of the particles.

In this last case we find the typical spherical coacervate droplets; in the two first, the parallelism ensures an anisotropic surface tension resulting in spindle-shaped drops or tactoids [13], or, when the particles are extremely elongated, to swollen fibres with a regular hexagonal arrangement as in muscle [2].

It will be seen from this brief consideration of the nature of interparticulate forces that not only do they form a sequence of decreasing strength with increasing distance, but also that they operate between particles of increasing scale. It is as if each kind of particle had to be assembled by forces of a lower order until it reached the size at which the higher-order forces operate. It will be noticed that the largest order of magnitude referred to, the full range of the so-called long-range forces, is 1000 Å or one-tenth of a micron, still less than the wavelength of visible light, so that there is still a large step between their range of action and the structures observable in the light microscope. Nevertheless, structures formed by means of them are responsible for the macroscopic appearances and mechanical properties of units of sub-cellular and cellular levels. Most of these ultimately depend on the tensile strength of membranes or fibres and the question is therefore resolvable into that of the weakest forces holding the particles of such fibres together. Owing, however, to the considerable elasticity of configurational or rubber-like character of most of these structures, stresses are so evenly distributed that considerable tensions and pressures can be sustained. By combining the knowledge, still very qualitative, of the interparticle forces with that of the geometrical conditions it is possible to provide some approximately rational classification of the different stages of aggregation occurring in biological structures (Table 2).

The first stage, that of aggregation of single atoms, is covered by the theories of organic chemistry. It ends with the formation of small molecular groups with open or cyclic chains, most of which are found again in higher associations and so may be referred to as monomers. It is noticeable that, apart from the lipids, there are few if any directly atomic polymers found in organisms. It would almost appear that the monomer formation and polymerization processes were intrinsically separate, or at any rate corresponded to different periods in the biopoetic process.

The second stage, the formation of polymers, is still in the field of organic chemistry though in a more recent part of it and its kinetic mechanism has still to be elucidated. For our purpose here it would seem that relatively few types of link are involved which may be put in some order of lability, beginning with the polymetaphosphate link, the sugar-phosphate link occurring in nucleic acids, the peptide link occurring in protein, the polysaccharide link, occurring in starches and celluloses, and the carbon-carbon link, occurring in lipids and rubber. These may also be, as I have indicated in my first paper (p. 38), the order of occurrence in biopoesis, though I would favour, for reasons given there, placing the peptide link before the sugar phosphate.

The nucleic acids and the proteins differ from the other natural polymers in that they are intrinsically heteropolymeric; they are made of a number of different monomers arranged for each type of protein or nucleic acid in a characteristic order. The order of amino acids and of nucleotides in related nucleic acids and proteins may be connected (this will certainly be discussed at the Symposium) but here we are concerned with the specific questions of order

TABLE 2

Stages of aggregation occurring in biological structures

Name of particle	Nature of last stage binding	Order of magnitude of molecular weight	Order of magnitude of particle dimensions	Examples
Simple molecule (monomer)	Homopolar bonds	50–200	10 Å³	Amino acids. Purines. Porphyrins. Sugars. Lipids
Chain polymer (Homo or hetero)	The same	1000–100,000	$5 \times 10 \times 1000$ Å	Silk fibroin, β-type. Denatured proteins. Cellulose. Rubber
Coiled polymers	Hydrogen bonds or S—S links	The same	$10 \times 10 \times 500$ Å	Coiled fibrous protein, α-type. Deoxyribosenucleic acid
Folded or coiled-coil polymers Globular particles	The same	10,000–100,000	(50 Å)³	Smaller globular proteins. Ribonuclease
Homogeneous agglo-merated particles Twined fibres	Ionic or cryo-hydric forces	50,000–1,000,000	(100 Å)³ $20 \times 20 \times 1000$ Å³	Larger globular proteins. Haemoglobin. Seed glo-bulins. Haemocyanin. Fibrous insulin. Collagen
Heterogeneous agglo-merated particles or fibre aggregates	The same	10,000,000	(200 Å)³ $100 \times 100 \times 5000$ Å	Nucleoproteins. Lipoproteins. Mucoproteins, etc. Smaller viruses

only in so far as they affect the configuration of the polymer. One aspect of the polymerization process, however, is relevant to this—its termination—which determines the size of the resulting polymer. In the case of polyamino acids we find in nature to-day a whole range of length from oligopeptides, with from 5 to 20 units like gramicidin S (10), oxytocin (9), adrenocorticotropin (50), through the smaller proteins like insulin (60) to ribonuclease (128). Whether the number is ever much larger, except in the fibrous proteins like myosin and keratin, is not clear. It seems, however, that the molecules of the larger globular proteins are not constructed of one but several peptide chains.

With the nucleic acids we know less of the existence of oligomers beyond the dimers, but this may be simply because they cannot as yet be crystallized. Most of those isolated by centrifugation are certainly very high polymers. Even here, however, there seems to be some natural limit [14, 15]. The size of polymers is of physico-chemical importance because it determines the nature of the forces, not only between similar particles of polymer as described above, but also between one particle and smaller molecules, offering, for instance, possibilities of oriented adsorption.

Nearly all linear polymers, and certainly those found in organisms, are not rigid structures and can exist in a number of *configurations* depending on such external circumstances as the temperature, pH and other properties of the medium in which they are placed. This is also a function of the shape and chemical activity of the monomers, particularly of the parts not immediately involved in the main polymer chains, namely the residues or side chains. Where these are neutral and small, as in the methyl residues of polyisoprene rubber, different chain arrangements have all approximately the same energy and the configuration is random. Where, on the other hand, the residues themselves contain, as in the proteins, polar groups such as NH_4^+ or COO^- or, as in the nucleic acids, the large aromatoid molecules of the pyrimidines and purines, stable, low-energy configurations are preferred and these for steric reasons tend to take on a helical form. Hence come the hydrogen-bonded Huggins-Pauling helices of the protein or the double Watson-Crick helices of the deoxyribose-nucleic acids, stabilized by the piling of their purine and pyrimidine residues.

The major factor responsible for the configuration of the proteins is the possibility for hydrogen-bond formation. It would appear that in all such con-figurations every or nearly every available bond-forming hydrogen atom, that is all in —OH, —NH or —NH$_2$ groups, normally form hydrogen bonds to suitable acceptors such as —O—OH or H_2O. This naturally holds as much for side chains as for main-chain groups. Configurations which do not permit the maximum number of bonds will be of high energy and be unlikely to occur. To judge from the degree of order observed in protein crystals, entropy effects do not seem to be important. However, there will in general be a number of configurations of approximately the same maximal hydrogen-bond number and consequently of approximately the same energy, and therefore the actual configuration may depend on other factors—steric effects in the chain itself, relations to other chains or with molecules in the medium. As hydrogen bonds can be formed quite as easily between adjacent or distant portions of the same chain or its side groups or between different chains, the possibility of alternative quasi-stable structures is enormous.

The simple α-helix form, internally hydrogen-bonded, though probably the most stable for polypeptides with medium or large side chains is not so for small-side-chain polypeptides, which favour the crosslinked β-form of silk. Nor is it that adopted by most of the natural crystalline or globular proteins. In the normal pH range and in the absence of strong hydrogen-bond-breaking substances such as urea, that is, in the undenatured state, such proteins have molecules approxi-mating more to the spherical than to the thread-like shape. This may be simply a consequence of the large effective surface of the pattern. A quasi-spherical form implies a more complex folding or coiled coiling of the polypeptide chain than occurs in simple spirals. What precisely is this configuration has yet to be determined in any single case. This is the great object of protein crystal analysis but it must be admitted that so far this has led only to negative results: that is, we know that some of the simpler arrangements of parallel-packed spirals cannot account for the observed intensities of X-ray diffraction from globular protein crystals. We cannot really claim, though here success may be very close, that even the principle of packing of the chains in globular protein is yet understood. All that can be said is that there appears, from the study of the distribution of the shorter interatomic vectors in the analysis of their crystals, that more than one basic arrangement is possible. The configuration in ribonuclease [16, 17] differs from that in haemoglobin and related compounds [18, 19].

However, recent work by Kendrew [31] on the structure of whale myoglobin, using multiple heavy-atom substitution to fix the complex phases of X-ray reflections, indicates an irregularly bent tangle, presumably of polypeptide helices surrounding the haem group.

The biological significance of the folding of protein chains to form globular molecules is not altogether clear. It would appear from studies on enzymic activity [20] that this is equally effective in the extended form produced in strong urea solutions. Further, from the amount of space available, about 10–20 Å, presumably, for enzyme protein molecules in the interstices of mitochondria, they can only be in the form of single or double extended peptide chains. Nevertheless, in solution in tissue fluids and possibly also in intracellular fluid, they are present as compact thicker molecules. Also, protein crystals, presumably formed of globular molecules, are occasionally found in cells while the outer shells of viruses and possibly of microsomes as well are also formed of them. We may provisionally, therefore, think of the globular form as one state, possibly only the equilibrium or resting state, of the protein molecules. The biological importance of the larger globular molecules may indeed be rather physico-chemical and colloidal. They would secure by their shape the maximum of easy diffusion and by their size a relative freedom from thermal disturbance. This would give them an importance in maintaining osmotic pressure and as a transport mechanism for amino acids.

Evidence is accumulating that the larger globular protein molecules of mol. wt above 14,000 and even less, as in the case of insulin, are formed of secondary agglomerations of identical or quasi-identical subunits of the minimal simple peptide of between 30 and 100 monomers. This can be proved only by reversible disaggregation, as in the case of haemoglobin with four units which can be split first into two and then into four subunits of the myoglobin type. The way this disaggregation is affected, by the use of extreme pH or strong ionic conditions, suggests that the links between the units are ionic and a similar explanation would account for the triple association of zinc insulin. With even bigger molecules such as haemocyanin, with a molecular weight of second or even third order, agglomeration of an even more labile character seems to occur and here the subunits are large enough to be seen in the electron microscope.

Another type of agglomeration of protein molecules seems to occur in crystallization, where the studies of Perutz [21] and his school have shown that linking through water molecules plays a predominant role. The amount of water can be very variable, but it would seem as if protein molecules are separated normally only by one or two layers of water molecules and that in the more hydrated cases the large lacunae between the molecules are filled with ordered water molecules as in ice or cryohydrates. Crystallization is not, however, a common biological phenomenon and aggregates of this sort are probably of very minor importance in biopoesis.

The forms of aggregation of nucleic acid do not at the moment seem to be as complex as those of proteins, but this may be simply on account of our smaller knowledge of them. The necessity of packing the purine pyrimidine groups in a quasi-parallel arrangement leads to a very open helix [22]. Indeed it is too wide for a double helix [23], but this seems to be stabilized in the case of DNA by the complementary purine-pyrimidine double hydrogen-bond linkage, as also is the poly-ribose-adenine, poly-ribose-uridine complex synthesized by Rich [24]. The width and rigidity of the DNA helix would indicate a molecule some 1000 Å or more long and forming a parallel hexagonal arrangement [25] and this has also been shown *in vivo* in sperm heads [26–28]. However, this cannot always be the case, for in the DNA-containing bacteriophages the width of the head is not more than 200 Å, so that some kind of folding or alternative packing must be possible.

The most complex as well as the most interesting structures based on polymer association are the heterogeneous complexes of which the most studied have been the nucleoproteins, though to understand biological structures much will also have to be learned of the lipoproteins and mucoproteins. At the moment it would appear that there are two different kinds of nucleoprotein: one, occurring in sperm, where DNA is linked with small basic protamine molecules; and the other in viruses containing ribosenucleic acid molecules embedded in a protein shell consisting of large-molecule proteins [25, 28]. In the first case the nucleic acid molecule seems to determine the structure, in the latter case the protein for an almost identical shell can be assembled without nucleic acid. In both cases, however, there can be no doubt that the synthesis of the protein is connected primarily with the nucleic acid, for, in the virus at least, the kind of protein produced in the cell of the infected plant is entirely determined by the kind of nucleic acid introduced.

It is between particles of the order of magnitude of viruses and microsomes (100–300 Å) that the long-range forces discussed above can most effectively operate. However, it is difficult to follow out their operation *in vivo* on account of the number of other particles of approximately the same dimensions usually found in cells, and because of the presence of extensive lipid membranes. Theoretically, however, we would expect such forces to be responsible for the slow movements of internal parts of cells in, for instance, chromosome pairing and mitosis, though here there may also be the effect of the formation of fibres by the (g–f) transformation and their subsequent contraction in a way that I have speculated on elsewhere [29].

This sketch of the structure and mutual relations of the particles that are found in present-day biological structures is still tantalizingly vague in the more complex regions involving the largest particles. It should serve, however, to bring out the main thesis of this paper: that the existence of a whole series of such structures, each with characteristically different properties, goes a long way to help to explain how such an apparently almost infinitely complex organization such as the cell could have been produced step by step from simpler structures right back to the atomic layer, in such a way as I have described in my other paper or in any other based on the same geometrical and physical conditions. Although it would be a mistake to equate precisely the successively more complicated grades of organization described here with the hypothetical temporal stages of biopoesis, the two must have a rough parallelism. The formation of a structure of suitable complexity is a necessary, though not a sufficient, condition for certain physico-chemical functions. For example, the colloidal behaviour always found inside living systems, and probably absolutely necessary for them, must rest on coiled and folded polymers built inside the system itself. It is not my place here to try to trace out these relationships in detail; this will appear from many other contributions. It should be sufficient here to lay down an ordered description of the various types of building blocks and bonds available for biopoesis, as a guide to those who are concerned with other and more dynamic aspects of it.

REFERENCES

1. J. B. S. HALDANE, *New Biol.*, **16**, 12, 1954.
2. H. E. HUXLEY, *Biochim. biophys. Acta*, **12**, 387, 1953.
3. A. J. HODGE, *J. biophys. biochem. Cytol.*, **2**, 131, 1954.
4. D. F. WAUGH et al., *J. Amer. chem. Soc.*, **75**, 2591, 1953.
5. D. L. D. CASPAR, *Nature, Lond.*, **177**, 475, 1956.
6. A. KLUG & R. E. FRANKLIN, *Biochim. biophys. Acta*, **23**, 199, 1957.
7. R. E. FRANKLIN, *Biochim. biophys. Acta*, **19**, 403, 1956.
8. R. J. GOLDACRE, *Nature, Lond.*, **174**, 732, 1954.
9. K. NORRISH, *Discuss. Faraday Soc.*, **18**, 120, 1954.
10. J. TH. G. OVERBEEK & M. J. SPARNAAY, *Discuss. Faraday Soc.*, **18**, 12, 1954.
11. B. V. DERYAGIN et al., *Discuss. Faraday Soc.*, **18**, 24, 1954.
12. J. G. KIRKWOOD, *Proc. nat. Acad. Sci., Wash.*, **38**, 863, 1952.
13. J. D. BERNAL & I. FANKUCHEN, *J. gen. Physiol.*, **25**, 111, 1941.
14. W. FRISCH-NIGGEMEYER, *Nature, Lond.*, **178**, 307, 1956.
15. P. Y. CHENG, *Nature, Lond.*, **179**, 426, 1957.
16. C. H. CARLISLE et al., *Proc. Roy. Soc.*, B, **141**, 85, 1953.
17. F. H. C. CRICK, *Acta cryst., Camb.*, **9**, 908, 1956.
18. Sir L. BRAGG & M. PERUTZ, *Proc. Roy. Soc.*, A, **225**, 315, 1954.
19. J. C. KENDREW, *Proc. Roy. Soc.*, A, **237**, 255, II; **238**, 305, III, 1956.
20. C. B. ANFINSEN et al. (including LINDERSTRØM-LANG), *Biochim. biophys. Acta*, **17**, 141, 1955.
21. Sir L. BRAGG & M. PERUTZ, *Proc. Roy. Soc.*, A, **213**, 425, 1952.
22. S. FURBERG, *Acta chem. scand.*, **6**, 634, 1952.
23. J. D. WATSON & F. H. C. CRICK, *Nature, Lond.*, **171**, 964, 1953.
24. A. RICH, *J. Amer. chem. Soc.*, **78**, 3548, 1956.
25. R. E. FRANKLIN, *Nature, Lond.*, **177**, 930, 1956.
26. F. RINNE, *Nature, Lond.*, **126**, 279, 1930.
27. M. H. WILKINS & J. T. RANDALL, *Biochim. biophys. Acta*, **10**, 192, 1953.
28. M. FEUGHELMAN et al. (including M. H. F. WILKINS), *Nature, Lond.*, **175**, 834, 1955.
29. J. D. BERNAL, *The Cell and Protoplasm* (Ed. by F. R. MOULTON). American Association for the Advancement of Science, Washington, 1940.
30. J. D. BERNAL, *Discuss. Faraday Soc.*, **25**, 7, 1958.
31. J. C. KENDREW, *Proc. Roy. Soc.*, A, **246**, 369, 1958.

The Part Played by Structural Elements in the Biochemical Function of Cells

N. M. SISAKYAN

A.N. Bakh Institute of Biochemistry of the Academy of Sciences of the U.S.S.R., Moscow

AN IMPORTANT feature of the development of contemporary biochemistry is the way in which it penetrates deeper and deeper in its knowledge of the processes which take place within the cell. There has now accumulated a large amount of literature devoted to various aspects of the biochemistry of the organoids of cells [1–12].

Low temperatures, differential centrifugation, isotopes, chromatography, spectroscopy and electron microscopy, which are widely used in biochemical experiments, have provided the prerequisites for the study of the chemical mechanism of microstructures and for the understanding, on that basis, of the significance of the various intracellular structures in the biochemical function of the cell. In this respect we are living in a period when the objects forming the subjects of biochemical investigation become smaller and smaller. As a result of extensive investigations carried out in various laboratories over the last 10 to 15 years, there has arisen a general picture of the localization of biochemical properties within cells. It would seem that the structural formations of the cell differ in important respects from one another, both in their chemical composition and in their enzymic activity, and that some enzymic systems and compounds are preferentially concentrated in particular structural elements of the cell. These studies have provided the prerequisites for the development of the 'biochemical topography' of cells and for an understanding, based on this, of the interdependence of structures and functions.

From the point of view of contemporary biochemistry, structural organization in the origin of the first forms of life on the Earth is of specially great importance. According to the ideas of A. I. Oparin [13] the formation of coacervates signalized the appearance of a qualitatively new and significantly more dynamic system of reactions.

The orderliness and harmony of biochemical processes, which is characteristic of the living cell, is achieved owing to the heterogeneity of protoplasm, which made its appearance at the very beginning of the existence of life and has continued to change in the direction of greater complexity and differentiation throughout the course of the evolution of living forms.

Thus the heterogeneity of protoplasm would appear to have been a necessary condition for the localization of biochemical properties in the cell. As a result of heterogeneity in the presence of selectivity of the ingredients of protoplasm there occurred a correlation of biochemical functions with particular structures. In this sense one may speak of the absolute meaning of the correlation of biochemical functions with structures, for wherever there is life in any of its forms, there one may find heterogeneity and, in one form or another, a spatial arrangement of biochemical processes and functions leading to the separation of individual processes in close contact with others.

The investigations of recent years have revealed some general laws of the spatial arrangement of biochemical functions in the living cell. However, these rules are different for different forms of living things; in other words, the actual correlation of biochemical processes and functions is not always of the same type. There is no single plan of arrangement of functions applicable to all living things just as there is no uniform structural formation of all living things.

In the course of evolution there was a continual alteration and development of the protoplasmic structures towards greater differentiation and specialization. This alteration took place in the whole unit of form and function.

The development of biochemical function took place at the same time as the structural organization became more complicated. The increase in the complexity of the structural organization, or the appearance of new structural elements, took place on the basis of laws of chemical reaction which had already been established. However, at a particular stage, the structural organization, in the course of its stabilization, itself created the necessary conditions for the appearance of a new dynamism and direction in the chemical mechanism of the earliest forms of life. The evidence of the biochemical evolution of both animals and plants is in favour of this idea.

A similar hypothesis allows the possibility that the correlation of a biochemical function with a particular structural organization arose during the process of evolution and is adaptive in nature. Unfortunately we have not enough factual evidence, but there are isolated facts which indicate the possibility that the chemical mechanism of reactions of a uniform type might have become more complicated during the phylogenetic development of the organism. For example, the acyl-coenzyme A system is known to function in both bacteria and animals. The way in which this system is used is, however, different in the two groups. Bacteria split acyl-coenzyme A by means of phosphate, with the formation of acyl phosphate and coenzyme A. In animal tissues mineral phosphate is combined with the coenzyme part of the complex of acyl-coenzyme A. The acyl group is later set free in the form of the acid.

Investigation of the biochemical properties of the intracellular organoids of various phylogenetic groups of organisms is of great importance for revealing the genesis of intracellular structures.

At present an increase in the depth of our knowledge of the biochemical functions of living cells is only possible by adopting a different approach to each particular structural formation of cells. It has now become evident that some of the ideas which were put forward on the basis of an overall evaluation of the biochemical activity of the organism and of the cell as a whole require to be made more precise. We are fully justified in speaking of the biochemical diversity of quality of the structures of cells in the sense that each structure has a particular

26

biochemical function which also depends on the physiological state of the organism and is subject to regular change in the process of development. This fact is of theoretical importance in that the biochemical property of any particular structures should not be considered in isolation from the physiological characteristics of the whole organism and the actual conditions of its existence.

The method of differential centrifugation has given us the possibility of identifying various structures, each of which is characterized by its size, its chemical composition and its specific biological activity. Among these structures are the nucleus, the plastids (which are peculiar to plant cells), the mitochondria and the microsomes. There is also the residual centrifugate or dissolved fraction, which contains various components derived from the structural elements during the process of their separation. In the cells of the liver, which are often used for the differential separation of structures, the difference in the diameters of the particles is as follows:

nucleus 50–100 μ, mitochondria 1 μ, microsomes 0·15 μ.

This paper does not give a review of the whole of the extensive literature on the biochemistry of intracellular structures. We wish to limit the field of the communication to a few features of the uniformity and diversity which are to be noticed in both the chemical composition and biochemical function of particular structural elements of plant and animal cells. The paper does not try to give an answer to all the questions which might arise out of such a review. We only wished to present certain problems for assessment as this might lead to the undertaking of new investigations in the direction indicated.

CHANGES IN THE BIOCHEMICAL FUNCTIONS OF INTRACELLULAR STRUCTURES DEPENDING ON THE PECULIARITIES OF THE ORGANISM AND THE CONDITIONS OF ITS DEVELOPMENT

Even if we have utterly inadequate information about the phylogenetic changes in the biochemical properties of structures of a single type, some facts of interest have been obtained in regard to the ontogenetic changeability of their biochemical properties. As may be seen from Fig. 1, the activity of the invertase of the plastids of the sugar beet undergoes considerable change in the process of the development of the individual organism. The maximal enzymic activity in the chloroplasts of the sugar beet is to be seen in the period of intensive accumulation of sugar, while the greatest activity of the plastids of the root of this plant occurs at the end of vegetative growth and the beginning of the period of storage. These facts suggest that the biochemical function of any intracellular structure is not laid down beforehand; it is not an unchanging property but, on the contrary, it is subject to regular alteration depending on the internal state of the organism and on the external conditions which surround it. This circumstance is of great importance in connection with the study of the nature of the intracellular localization of biochemical functions. In the light of new facts, as has been said above, the concept of the localization of biochemical functions must only be taken in a relative sense. It is scarcely possible to regard as scientific the attempts of some workers to consider the enzymic functions of the structural elements of cells without taking into account the external conditions and the physiological state of the organism. Unfortunately such failure to take account of the changeability associated with stages of growth and physiological states is commonly met with in investigations of the structural elements of animal cells.

The localization of biochemical functions depends, not only on the type of the structures, but also on the nature of the organism itself. This proposition may be illustrated most strikingly by the example of the synthesis of proteins, a biochemical function which is universal in all forms of life.

It has been established that, in isolated systems, the individual structural elements of the animal cell have unequal powers of incorporating radioactively labelled substances into their proteins. In the works of Keller, Siekevitz,

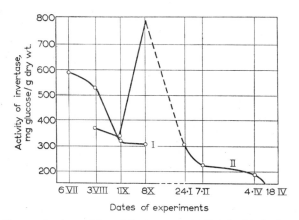

FIG. I. Changes in the activity of the invertase in the plastids in the process of development of the organism.

I—Chloroplasts.   II—Leucoplasts.

Zamecnik [14–16] and others, it has been shown that when labelled amino acids are introduced *in vivo* the greatest incorporation of label is found in the proteins of the microsome fraction obtained from a homogenate by differential centrifugation, while, when the individual isolated fractions (nuclei, mitochondria and microsomes) are incubated with labelled amino acids, this is not observed. Incorporation is only observed when the individual fractions are incubated together. In the experiments of Siekevitz [15] it was shown that maximal incorporation is brought about by a combination of the microsomal and mitochondrial fractions under conditions which allow oxidative phosphorylation to take place. In such experiments the mitochondrial fraction may be successfully replaced by a non-protein factor obtained from mitochondria after their preliminary incubation under conditions suitable for oxidative phosphorylation. In the experiments of Zamecnik and his colleagues [16] it was shown that, when the individual cellular fractions are incubated with labelled amino acids under anaerobic conditions, maximal incorporation of label is found when the microsomal fraction is combined with the supernatant.

In all these experiments the incorporation of labelled amino acids in the proteins of the isolated structures served as a criterion of the formation of peptide bonds.

In the work of other authors [17] attempts have been made to study the synthesis of protein by another method—by determining the increase of activity of a particular enzyme (the amylase of the pancreas). According to Khesin's data, the synthesis of protein is brought about in large, light granules by the agency of factors produced by the mitochondria.

Recent investigations [18, 19] have shown that, under special circumstances, radioactive labels are incorporated *in vitro* into the protein of the cellular nucleus, the increase in radioactivity being associated, not with exchange of the amino acids of the protein for amino acids of the surrounding medium, but with synthesis of protein *de novo*.

As concerns the structure of plant cells, it has been shown in Webster's laboratory [20, 21] that the synthesis of peptide bonds of peptides of low molecular weight takes place in the mitochondria of plant cells and so does the incorporation of labelled amino acids into the protein of these structures.

Webster [21] later demonstrated the incorporation of labelled amino acids into the protein of other structural elements in the cells of etiolated plants. Webster's experiments provide evidence for the participation of the mitochondria, microsomes and nuclei in the protein synthesis of the cell, incorporation occurring most effectively in particles precipitated from the homogenate of etiolated plants during centrifugation in the region of 10,000–40,000 g. The following fraction, composed of smaller particles, brings about the incorporation of labels at a considerably slower rate. Just as in the experiments of Siekevitz [15] and Keller [14] the incorporation is most effective when the mitochondria and microsomes are incubated together. It would seem that these findings allow us to accept the existence of general features of the localization of protein synthesis in animal and plant cells. It must, however, be emphasized that Webster's findings refer only to the structural elements of etiolated plants. This being so we cannot yet be sure that this type of localization of protein synthesis within the cell is the same in all vegetable organisms.

In this connection the study of protein synthesis in the cells of chlorophyll-containing plants is of special interest. The chloroplasts, which are the essential agents of photosynthesis in the plant cell, attract particular attention.

The possibility of the synthesis of peptide bonds by plastids has been studied in our laboratory [2]. It was found that when the plants are etiolated a marked depletion of the enzymes of the plastids takes place while, when they are exposed to light, a very sharp increase in the enzymic activity of the plastids is observed. The transition from leucoplasts to chloroplasts, which occurs on exposure to light, is thus accompanied by an increase in the enzymic power of these structures [22–27]. Since then indirect evidence has also been obtained in other experiments [28, 29] of the participation of chloroplasts in protein synthesis and of its connection with photosynthesis.

In 1955 we found [30] in our laboratory that, in isolated chloroplasts of the young plant, there are at least two different enzymic systems taking part in the synthesis of the peptide bond. One system brings about the synthesis of peptide bonds by the transpeptidase reaction, while the other catalyses the formation of peptide bonds directly from free amino acids. It has been shown by other workers [31], in experiments *in vivo*, that methionine containing labelled sulphur is incorporated most quickly into the protein of the fraction which is composed of chloroplasts and mitochondria with a predominance of chloroplasts. In experiments with isolated structures from the cells of green plants we [32] found another regularly occurring phenomenon.

It seemed that the rate of incorporation of [^{14}C]glycine into the mitochondria of plant cells was about 10 times greater than that of its incorporation into chloroplasts. Thus if, as Webster's data indicate [21], the incorporation of [^{14}C]glycine into mitochondria taken from the shoots of broad beans amounts to 0·03 μmole of [^{14}C]glycine/g. protein/hr, then the amount in the chloroplasts will be 0·002–0·005 μmole. We found a similar picture in our investigation of various fractions of a homogenate of tobacco leaves.

TABLE I

The incorporation of [^{14}C]glycine into protein and alterations in their amount in various fractions of a homogenate of tobacco leaves

Fraction of tobacco leaves	Rate of centrifugation (g)	Time of centrifugation (min.)	Chlorophyll content (mg/100 mg dry wt.)	Decrease or increase of protein nitrogen at the expense of added amino acids (% of total nitrogen)	Incorporation of [^{14}C]-glycine into the protein of the fraction (counts/min/mg. protein/hr)
I	150	1	0·02	−32·0	80
II	1000	12	0·40	+ 0·7	90
III	3000	45	1·46	+ 3·2	140
IV	40,000	15	0·12	− 7·8	2680
V	supernatant	—	0·08	−22·5	39

As the Table shows, the labelled glycine is incorporated into the protein of all the fractions of a homogenate of tobacco leaves. The greatest incorporation is found in the fraction which comes down at 40,000 g. This fraction has a comparatively low chlorophyll content and evidently consists of mitochondria contaminated by fragments of the granules of the chloroplasts and also, of course, of microsomes. In the fraction with a high chlorophyll content, which is thrown down at 3000 g the power to incorporate labelled glycine is weaker. Furthermore, this fraction, which has the highest chlorophyll content, is the only one in which there appears to be any significant power to increase the protein nitrogen at the expense of added amino acids.

These data suggest that the transformation of proteins, which may be assessed to some extent by the rate of incorporation of labelled glycine, occurs most intensively in the mitochondrial fraction. However, accumulation of protein does not occur in these fractions. This is clearly to be explained by the occurrence of intensive proteolytic processes at the same time as the incorporation of the labelled compound. Although the metabolic rate of the chloroplast fraction is low, as may be seen from the lower rate of incorporation of labelled glycine, a very considerable increase in protein occurs there.

Thus, the available facts and observations lead to the idea that the function of protein synthesis is not associated with a strictly determinate structural organization but is brought about by various types of structures (nuclei, mitochondria, microsomes) with a different degree of intensity and with peculiarities determined by the organoidal specificity of the proteins.

The brilliant work of Gale and his colleagues [33, 34] has shown, quite recently, that protein can be synthesized by disrupted bacterial cells. All this, taken together, indicates the relative nature of the association of a biochemical function with a particular structural organization and means that one must be very careful how one uses the concept of the 'localization' of biochemical function.

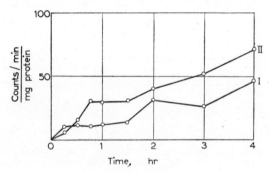

FIG. 2. Relation of the incorporation of [14C]glycine into the chloroplasts to
time of incubation.

I—Without the addition of amino acids.
II—With a mixture of 15 amino acids.

Comparison of the data derived from a comparative study of the synthesis of the peptide bond in the protoplasmic structures of the animal and plant cell reveals points of difference as well as points of resemblance. Differences are present, not only in the localization of protein synthesis, but also in the chemical mechanism of the actual process of the synthesis of protein in different structures. The differences are to be seen in the kinetics of the process and also in the energic conditions, the optimum pH and the susceptibility to inhibiting substances.

Thus, in homogenates of animal cells the incorporation of a labelled amino acid into protein is directly proportional to the time of incubation of the homogenate with the labelled amino acid [35], while in the incorporation of labelled glycine into the protein of the chloroplasts a linear relationship between the intensity of incorporation and time is not found.

In Fig. 2 it may be seen that, during the first 35–40 minutes, the incorporation of the labelled compound proceeds very fast. The process of incorporation is then seen to become slower or stop during the next 45–60 minutes, after which it begins to get faster again though it does not become so fast as it was at first. The optimum pH (8·5) for the incorporation of labelled glycine into the protein of the chloroplasts is different from that (7·0) for structures derived from animal sources. Furthermore, the process of incorporation of amino acids into the protein of the structures of animal and plant cells is affected in a different way by the inhibitory factor which we discovered in a supernatant of a homogenate of leaves. It may be hoped that a further comparative study of the biochemical properties of the protoplasmic structures of animal and plant cells will enable us to explain the peculiarities which characterize the qualitatively new laws of metabolism of the green plant. The differences in the catalytic and functional properties of structures of different origins is closely associated with features of the chemical nature of the protoplasmic structures. Table 2 shows some of the differences in the chemical nature of the protoplasmic structures.

TABLE 2

Chemical composition of the cell units

(% of dry weight)

	Proteins	Lipids	Nucleic acids	Reference
Animal cells				
nuclei . . .	47–72	10–46	26–44	[36, 37]
mitochondria . .	65–70	25–30	0·5	[38]
microsomes .	32–61	36–51	2·6–17	[39, 40, 17]
Plant cells				
plastids . . .	41–55	18–37	0·3–3·5	[41, 42, 43, 44, 45, 46, 47, 48]
mitochondria . .	38–45	25–38·7	0·6–0·65	} [49]
microsomes .	22–40	48–56	0·8–1·0	

Thus, judging from the figures given in Table 2, there are definite differences in the chemical composition of the fundamental types of structural formation of the plant and animal cells. Such differences, however, are not only found between structures of the same type, of animal and plant origin, but also in one and the same structure, depending on the physiological state of the organism and the type of metabolism. Thus, as may be seen from Table 3, the nucleic acid content changes considerably with changes in the physiological state of the plant. The arrangement of the nucleic acid of the chloroplast by layers, which is characteristic of the stage of bud formation and of the ripening of the seeds, is radically changed during the flowering period of the plant.

The differences in the chemical composition of the chloroplasts are determined, not merely by the physiological state of the organism, but also by the type of its metabolism. Thus, according to Osipova's findings (see Table 4) [50–52], the contents of proteins, lipids, starch and chlorophyll in the chloroplasts of the leaves of the broad bean, the sunflower and the potato are signi-

TABLE 3

Changes in the ribonucleic acid content of the chloroplasts of tobacco and sunflower, according to the leaf layer and stage of development of the plant

Stage of development and date of taking specimen	Leaf layer	Ribonucleic acid content in % of air-dried weight of the plastid	
		By phosphorus	By purines
Chloroplasts of tobacco			
Budding 27 July 1954 .	Upper	1·76	1·85
	Middle	1·23	1·35
	Lower	1·04	1·12
Flowering 29 July 1954 .	Upper	0·89	0·97
	Middle	1·18	1·33
	Lower	1·24	1·30
Ripening of seed 24 Aug. 1954 . . .	Upper	1·45	1·60
	Middle	1·11	1·39
	Lower	1·08	1·18
Chloroplasts of sunflower			
Budding 19 July 1954 .	Upper	2·47	2·70
	Middle	1·93	1·85
	Lower	1·65	1·80
Flowering 5 Aug. 1954 .	Upper	1·25	1·42
	Middle	1·35	1·50
	Lower	1·39	1·57
Ripening of seeds 6 Sept. 1954 . . .	Upper	1·49	1·45
	Middle	1·22	1·34
	Lower	1·15	1·30

TABLE 4

Chemical composition of the chloroplasts in % of dry weight

(after Osipova [52])

Object studied and stage of development	Chlorophyll	Protein	Starch	Lipids
Broad bean				
Before flowering . .	2·4	43·6	10·0	28·3
Ripening of seeds . .	2·9	48·1	6·5	26·1
Sunflower				
Before flowering . .	4·0	32·2	11·1	21·5
Ripening of seeds . .	4·6	40·0	4·5	26·1
Potato				
Before flowering . .	3·0	27·7	4·8	49·6
Ripening of tubers . .	3·7	35·4	4·0	33·5

ficantly different. This difference is not only to be found before flowering but remains present during the period of ripening of the seeds and maturation of the tubers.

THE COMMON FEATURES OF THE QUANTITATIVE AMINO ACID COMPOSITION OF THE PROTEINS OF DIFFERENT STRUCTURES

As well as these differences in chemical composition and catalytic activity we may observe many common features in structures of different origins. This is based on the amino acid composition of the proteins. The qualitative amino acid composition of the proteins of the structures of the photosynthesizing organs is just the same for all classes of plants. This applies to the proteins of the leaves of monocotyledonous and dicotyledonous plants and to the proteins of algae of all classes. We have not found any information as to the amino acid composition of photosynthesizing bacteria.

Among the amino acids of which the proteins of the photosynthesizing organs are composed, 17–18 have been identified (some by chromatographic methods), which are common to the proteins of various organisms. These are: aspartic and glutamic acids, serine, threonine, glycine, alanine, valine, leucine, isoleucine, phenylalanine, tyrosine, proline, tryptophan, methionine, cystine, arginine, histidine and lysine [53–56].

In the overall composition of the proteins of the plastids which we isolated, and in an individual protein-containing compound (a lipoprotein) obtained from the leucoplasts and chloroplasts of the sugar-beet, the same 18 amino acids were found as in the proteins of leaves or algae [57–61].

It would be interesting to compare the amino acid compositions of different plant chromoproteins. As yet, however, only the most stable complexes of protein with pigment have been isolated, namely the phycobilins—phycoerythrin from red algae (*Porphyra tenera* and *Callithamnion rybosum*) and phycocyanin from blue-green algae (in particular from some species of *Oscillatoria*) [62–65].

The nature of the bond between the chlorophyll and the protein has not been established. The chlorophyll–protein complex is unstable and the problem of its isolation has not yet been solved. Some authors have cast doubt on the nature of the crystalline chlorophyll–protein compound which has recently been isolated by Takashima [66–68] from various classes of plants. Thus Krasnovskiĭ & Brin [69] believe that these crystals are chlorophyll crystals and the protein and other substances are contaminants mixed with them.

The amino acid composition of phycocyanin has been determined chromatographically by Wassink & Ragetli [63]. As well as thirteen common amino acids they found three unknown compounds as indicated by position on the chromatogram. These findings were confirmed by Fujiwara [65] on the basis of the appearance of extra peaks during the quantitative determination of amino acids by the methods of Moore & Stein [85].

However, the question of whether there are uncommon amino acids, which are not found in higher plants, in the proteins of blue-green algae, cannot be answered conclusively without a full identification of the compounds which have been found. The conditions under which the protein was hydrolysed arouse a suspicion that the spots which were found on the chromatogram may have been the spots of peptides which resisted hydrolysis [63].

When studying the chromatographic amino acid composition of phycoerythrin from *Callithamnion rybosum* we only found 17 amino acids common to the proteins of higher plants [70]. Tryptophan was not found. Small quantities of α- and γ-aminobutyric acids were formed, we suppose, from threonine and glutamic acid respectively during hydrolysis. Our findings were confirmed by Fujiwara for phycoerythrin from *Porphyra tenera* [65]. Analysis of the curves presented by Fujiwara shows that, in his experiments too, there were traces of α- and γ-aminobutyric acids.

Unlike the qualitative amino acid composition of the proteins of the photosynthesizing organs, their quantitative amino acid composition is not similar in different classes of plants, as may be seen from Table 5.

TABLE 5

Amino acid composition of the proteins of photosynthesizing organs

(N of amino acids as % of N of protein)

Amino acids	Red, blue-green and other algae [56]	Green algae [56]	Monocotyledons (grasses) [54]	Dicotyledons (legumes) [54]	Cytoplasmic proteins (barley) [55]	Chloroplasts (spinach) [53]	Phyco-erythrin [65]	Phyco-cyanin [65]
Aspartic acid .	5·1–6·9	6·4	4·9–5·4	4·7–5·4	6·4	5·8	6·9	6·5
Glutamic acid	4·6–7·8	7·8	6·6–7·8	6·4–6·7	8·2	6·5	2·6	2·1
Serine .	2·4–4·2	3·3	—	—	3·5	—	5·7	5·6
Threonine .	2·9–5·7	2·9	3·0	4·0	4·0	—	2·2	2·6
Glycine .	5·5–6·2	6·2	0·4	—	6·7	—	3·3	4·2
Alanine .	6·0–8·4	7·7	4·4–5·1	—	7·9	—	12·8	8·8
Valine .	5·5–7·5	5·5	3·3–4·2	4·5	4·9	—	4·5	3·9
Leucine .	6·1–7·4	6·1⎫	7·1–8·8	⎧7·3	5·9	—	4·0	5·6
Isoleucine .	3·5–4·1	3·5⎭		⎩3·6	4·2	—	2·5	3·0
Phenylalanine	2·8–3·4	2·8	2·5–2·6	2·4	3·0	—	0·9	1·5
Tyrosine .	1·6–3·0	2·8	2·3–2·5	2·3–2·6	2·3	2·6	1·2	2·4
Proline .	5·0–6·2	5·8	3·1	—	4·1	—	3·1	2·0
Tryptophan .	1·0–2·1	2·1	1·8–2·1	1·6–1·9	2·0	1·7	—	—
Methionine .	1·2–1·4	1·4	1·4–1·6	1·2–1·4	1·4	1·3	1·3	1·1
Cystine .	0·2	0·2	1·3–1·5	1·1–1·3	0·9	1·2	1·3	1·4
Arginine .	9·2–15·9	15·8	13·7–14·3	13·0–14·0	15·0	13·9	12·7	13·6
Histidine .	2·5–3·7	3·3	3·6–3·7	3·8–4·0	4·1	3·3	1·2	0·3
Lysine .	6·6–10·2	10·2	6·3–6·6	6·4–6·5	7·1	4·7	5·8	5·7
Amide N .	6·1–8·0	6·1	4·7–5·3	5·1–5·3	4·8	—	(9·3)	(9·9)
Humins .	—	—	—	—	3·0	—	—	—
Total N .	89·7–98·9	99·9	74·4	—	98·2	—	81·3	85·5

This is understandable when we remember that the quantitative amino acid composition of the protein of even a single organism varies with differences in the physiological state, as has been shown in a large number of recent investigations [50–52, 60, 61, 86].

Table 5 shows the amino acid composition of the proteins of different classes of plant organism—blue-green and red algae, and diatoms as well as green algae and others, the leaves of both monocotyledonous and dicotyledonous higher plants. For comparison we have also given figures for cytoplasmic proteins, the total protein of the chloroplasts and also the individual chromoprotein complexes, phycoerythrin and phycocyanin. As may be seen from the figures given, the amino acid content of the proteins varies, sometimes quite considerably. The proteins of photosynthesizing organs also show some common features such as a relatively high content of basic amino acids (Table 5 and [62, 86]).

This all suggests that the qualitative biochemical variability of protoplasmic structures derived from different sources is, most probably, associated with the more intimate structural peculiarities of the proteins which determine their specificity. The discovery of these extremely fine differences in the proteins will only be possible after the establishment of the amino acid sequence and other structural features of the protein molecules.

STRUCTURE AND BIOCHEMICAL FUNCTIONS

In understanding the biochemical functions of cells, great importance is attached to the study of the structural organization and the manifestation of enzymic activity [71–75].

Experimental evidence shows that the functional and, in particular, the enzymic activity depend, not only on structural organization, but also on the conditions of the medium under the influence of which the formation of the structures takes place. This concept may be illustrated by facts derived from the study of the activity of enzymes of the cyclophorase system in the structural elements of plant cells.

Recent investigations have established, beyond doubt, the existence, in the structural formations of plant cells, of a cyclophorase system of enzymes, which brings about the transformation of di- and tri-carboxylic acids [76–80]. Cyclophorase activity was found in structures isolated from both etiolated and green plants. However, the question of its localization in any particular structures cannot be considered to be conclusively settled. Some workers take the view that cyclophorase activity is concentrated solely in structures of a mitochondrial type. Others believe that cyclophorase activity is concentrated in the chloroplasts. Naturally the identification of the structural carriers of particular biochemical functions is a task of the utmost importance for the elucidation of their part in cellular metabolism.

We have established [81] that cyclophorase activity in green plants grown under indoor illumination (Fig. 3, curves I) is concentrated mainly in the fraction of particles which come down within the range of 3000–8500 g. The absorption of O_2 in this fraction of particles at the expense of the oxidation of succinic acid amounted to 145 μl. O_2/mg N after 1 hour, and was associated with the absorption of inorganic phosphorus. The slight activity (22 μl. O_2/mg N) found in the first fraction (3000 × *g*) indicates that the structures possessing the cyclophorase activity begin to come down at rather lower rates of centrifugation than 3000 *g*. Activity is absent from the fraction containing the smallest particles, which comes down in the range 8500–16,500 *g*. Microscopic checking showed that the fractions which had been studied were composed of structures of two types, complete and partly disrupted chloroplasts and particles of a perfectly circular shape many times smaller than whole chloroplasts. The first fraction which comes down at 3000 × *g* consists mainly of chloroplasts and fragments of chloroplasts with a small admixture in the form of finer structures. The reverse quantitative relationship obtains in the second and more active fraction which comes down at 8500 × *g*. This fraction contains mainly fine structures with a small admixture of chloroplasts and pieces of chloroplasts. The third fraction contains a small quantity, which is probably to be regarded as due to contamination, of the structures which come down in the second fraction. There are no other visible structures in this fraction.

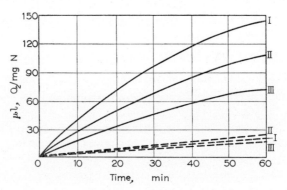

FIG. 3. Cyclophorase activity in fractions of intracellular structures from the shoots of peas. I—Green plants grown under indoor illumination; II—Etiolated plants; III—Green plants grown at low temperatures.

Dotted curves represent fractions brought down at 3000 *g*; *solid curves* those brought down at 8000 *g*.

From these facts it is quite clear that the different character of the cyclophorase activity in the different fractions is associated with a non-uniform distribution of structures.

It has further been established (cf. curves II in Fig. 3) that the character of the distribution of cyclophorase activity is just the same in etiolated and green plants. It seems that structures isolated from plants which have been grown in summer under conditions of natural illumination at temperatures of 20–25°C either do not have any cyclophorase activity or have it only to a very slight extent. Thus, cyclophorase activity depends, not only on structural organization, but also on the intensity of illumination and the temperature conditions under which the structures were formed. At comparatively high temperatures (20–25°C) activity of the cycle is only to be found under conditions of inadequate illumination, e.g. in completely etiolated plants and in plants grown indoors. The ratio of chlorophyll to total nitrogen in structures isolated from green plants grown under indoor illumination is 0·3–0·35. In plants which receive enough energy in the form of light, cyclophorase activity only manifests itself at low temperatures, e.g. when the plant is grown under natural conditions in the autumn, when the temperature is 2–12°C. Curves III, in Fig. 3, represent the distribution of cyclophorase activity in the different fractions in plants grown under natural illumination in the autumn. It does not differ from the results of the experiments with partly and completely etiolated plants. In this case also, the second fraction has the greatest activity; it is negligible in the first fraction and completely absent from the third.

In connection with the discovery of photosynthetic phosphorylation [82, 83] which, along with the process of oxidative phosphorylation, is the mainstay of the energy metabolism of the cell, the facts which we have put forward suggest the idea that the enzymic system for oxidizing acids of the di- and tri-carboxylic acid cycle is brought into the process of metabolism under strictly determinate conditions. When this happens the function of the system is obviously, in many ways, dependent, not only on the character of the structures, but also on the temperature conditions, the intensity of illumination and, as we shall show, the qualitative composition of the light.

In this connection the appearance and inclusion of the cyclophorase system in the metabolism of the plant organism may be regarded as a characteristic adaptive reaction of the organism, which enables it to maintain the necessary level of energy under conditions when the normal ways in which the plant acquires energy are interfered with.

Recently there has been accumulating an ever larger number of experimental facts indicating the association of structure and function. Damage to the structural organization affects, to a greater or lesser extent, the biochemical activity. The data obtained by Oparin, Gel'man and Zhukova [84] provide fresh evidence in this direction. These authors have shown that interference with the structural integrity of the bacterial protoplast leads to both a slowing of the processes of respiration and the incorporation of radioactive labels into the protein of the protoplast.

Owing to new biochemical evidence the concept of lyo- and desmo-enzymes also needs to be made more precise.

Generally known facts testify to the fact that the activity of two large groups of enzymes, at least, is closely associated with a definite structural organization. The activity of the enzymes of the cytochrome system and of the enzymes which catalyse the oxidation of the acids of the di- and tri-carboxylic acid cycle is only manifested in the presence of particular structural elements of the cell.

The action of enzymes of the glycolytic system may be produced in solution and therefore the part played by intracellular structures in the production of the catalytic activity of this enzymic system has not been conclusively elucidated. For some enzymes it has been definitely shown that in the bound state they lose their catalytic activity. It is interesting to remark, in this connection, that the firmness of the bond between the enzyme and the proteins of the intracellular structures changes according to the physiological state of the organism. For example, we have obtained data for the invertase of the plastids of the sugar beet (Table 6).

TABLE 6

Changes in the firmness of the bond between invertase and the protein complex of the plastids

Character of the bond	Amount of invertase (by activity)	
	September	December
Free	14·28	33·58
Loosely bound . .	32·25	43·54
Firmly bound . .	53·35	32·88

Thus, with reference to the form of the bonding of enzymic systems with structural elements of cells we may distinguish at least four main categories: a group of enzymes which is active only when associated with structures; enzymes which are present in the absence of structures; enzymes which lose their activity when their association with structures is interfered with; and enzymes which lose their catalytic activity in the bound state.

CONCLUSIONS

On the basis of the numerous experiments which have been done during recent years with cellular fractions from rats' livers, there emerges a rough picture of the localization of biochemical processes within the cell.

In the *nuclear fraction* of the animal cell we find the enzymes responsible for nucleotide metabolism—adenosine 5-phosphatase, adenosine deaminase, DPN-nucleosidase, nucleoside phosphorylase and others. Furthermore, the nucleus is the site of synthesis of the basic nucleotide and uridine coenzymes (DPN and UTP), which take part in glycolytic processes, which would appear to occur in the soluble cellular fraction. It is quite likely that the enzymes of glycolytic metabolism are also localized within the nuclei of the cells but are washed out of them during the process of isolation. Enzymes of the glycolytic system have been found in nuclei which have been isolated in a non-aqueous medium.

The *mitochondria* form the special metabolic centre of the cell. In them are localized the fundamental processes associated with oxidative energy metabolism, namely the tricarboxylic acid cycle, the cytochrome system, the system of oxidative phosphorylation, the oxidation of fatty acids. In addition the mitochondria take part in the metabolism of amino acids and lipids. Several syntheses (e.g. that of urea) either begin or culminate in them. The activity of many of the enzymes of the mitochondria, especially those which are closely associated with their structure, depends on the conditions of the surrounding medium. Great changes are brought about in the activity by alterations in the osmotic pressure, concentration of electrolytes and other factors which affect the structure of the mitochondria.

The mitochondria of plant cells can also carry out oxidative phosphorylation. In the plant cell, however, many of the functions which are characteristic of the mitochondria of the animal cell are carried out by the plastids.

The *plastids* are similar to the mitochondria in their enzymic properties. Oxidative enzymes, dehydrases, hydrolases, and esterases have been found in them. In the general complexity of the plastids, about twenty enzymic systems have been found, which take part in the various metabolic processes of the cell.

In the plastids, in particular the chloroplasts, there occurs the formation of peptide bonds and of phospholipids, the synthesis and oxidation of fatty acids, and photosynthetic phosphorylation.

An important part in the synthesis of proteins in the animal cell is ascribed to the *microsomes,* which are the smallest of the intracellular structures. Their participation in the synthesis of protein has been demonstrated by many experiments on the incorporation of labelled amino acids *in vivo* and *in vitro*. In such *in vitro* experiments it has been shown that this requires the participation of energy-giving processes which are brought about either in the mitochondria under conditions of oxidative phosphorylation or in the dissolved fraction under conditions of anaerobic glycolysis.

In the plant cell the synthesis of the peptide bond occurs in both the mitochondria and the chloroplasts.

Thus, the general activity and integration of the chemical processes of the cell are secured by the interaction of polyenzymic systems of all the intracellular structures and the soluble fraction. The role of the structural elements seems to consist in the preferential localization on them of individual links in the total chain of the single process of biological metabolism. The development and manifestation of a biochemical function in any particular given structure of the cell is co-ordinated with the chemical nature and enzymic activity of the other structures and intracellular components.

REFERENCES

1. J. T. EDSALL, *Enzymes and Enzyme Systems: Their State in Nature.* Harvard University Press, 1951.
2. N. M. SISAKYAN, *Fermentativnaya aktivnost' protoplazmennykh struktur,* Izd. Akad. Nauk S.S.S.R., Moscow, 1951.
3. S. OCHOA, D. GREEN et al., *Symposium sur le cycle tricarboxylique.* Sèdes, Paris, 1952.
4. N. M. SISAKYAN, *II Congrès int. Biochim.,* Paris, 1952.
5. N. M. SISAKYAN, *Usp. sovrem. Biol.,* **36**, 322, 1953.
6. N. M. SISAKYAN, *Vop. Bot.,* **1**, 195, 1954.
7. D. GREEN, *Biol. Rev.,* **29**, 330, 1954.
8. O. LINDBERG & L. ERNSTER, *Chemistry and Physiology of Mitochondria and Microsomes.* Springer Verlag, Wien, 1954.
9. W. C. SCHNEIDER, *Conférences et Rapports, III Congr. int. Biochim.,* 1956.
10. N. M. SISAKYAN, *Izv. Akad. Nauk S.S.S.R.,* Ser. biol. **5**, 6, 1956.
11. N. M. SISAKYAN, *Proc. III Congrès int. Biochim.,* Brussels, 1956.
12. N. M. SISAKYAN, *Biochemie der Kulturpflanzen,* Berlin, 1956.
13. A. I. OPARIN, *The Origin of Life on the Earth.* Oliver & Boyd, Edinburgh, 1957.
14. E. B. KELLER, *Fed. Proc.,* **10**, 206, 1951.
15. P. SIEKEVITZ, *J. biol. Chem.,* **195**, 549, 1952.
16. O. C. ZAMECNIK & E. B. KELLER, *J. biol. Chem.,* **209**, 337, 1954.
17. R. B. KHESIN, *Rol' strukturnykh komponentov tsitoplazmy kletok pecheni i podzheludochnoĭ zhelezy v protsessakh sinteza belka,* Dissertation, 1953.

18. V. G. ALLFREY, A. E. MIRSKY & SYOZO OSAWA, *Nature, Lond.*, **176**, 1042, 1955.
19. I. B. ZBARSKIĬ & K. A. PEREVOSHCHIKOVA, *Dokl. Akad. Nauk S.S.S.R.*, 1956.
20. G. S. WEBSTER, *Plant Physiol.*, **29**, 202, 1954.
21. G. S. WEBSTER, *Plant Physiol.*, **30**, 351, 1955.
22. N. M. SISAKYAN & A. M. KOBYAKOVA, *Dokl. Akad. Nauk S.S.S.R.*, **61**, 1065, 1948.
23. N. M. SISAKYAN & A. M. KOBYAKOVA, *Biokhimiya*, **13**, 88, 1949.
24. N. M. SISAKYAN & A. M. KOBYAKOVA, *Biokhimiya*, **14**, 86, 1950.
25. N. M. SISAKYAN, A. M. ZOLKOVER & V. I. BIRYUSOVA, *Dokl. Akad. Nauk S.S.S.R.*, **60**, 1213, 1948.
26. N. M. SISAKYAN, V. I. BIRYUSOVA & A. M. KOBYAKOVA, *Biokhimiya*, **15**, 449, 1951.
27. N. M. SISAKYAN, *Usp. biol. Khim.*, **1**, 372, 1950.
28. G. A. ANDREEVA & E. G. PLYSHEVSKAYA, *Dokl. Akad. Nauk S.S.S.R.*, 1952.
29. M. DEKEN-GRENSON, *Biochem. biophys. Acta*, **2**, 203, 1954.
30. N. M. SISAKYAN & I. I. FILIPPOVICH, *Dokl. Akad. Nauk S.S.S.R.*, **103**, 579, 1955.
31. B. P. PLESHKOV & S. H. IVANKO, *Biokhimiya*, **21**, 496, 1956.
32. N. M. SISAKYAN & I. I. FILIPPOVICH, *Biokhimiya*, **22**, 375, 1957.
33. E. F. GALE, *Conférences et Rapports, III Congr. int. Biochim.*, p. 345, 1956.
34. E. F. GALE & J. P. FOLKES, *Nature, Lond.*, **173**, 1223, 1954.
35. T. WINNICK, F. FREDBERG & D. GREENBERG, *J. biol. Chem.*, **175**, 117, 1948.
36. I. B. ZBARSKIĬ, *Usp. sovrem. Biol.*, **1**, 1950.
37. S. I. URYSON, *Biokhimiya*, **21**, 262, 1956.
38. H. CHANTRENNE, *Biochim. biophys. Acta*, **1**, 437, 1947.
39. R. JEENER, *Biochim. biophys. Acta*, **2**, 633, 1948.
40. G. J. ADA, *Biochem. J.*, **45**, 422, 1949.
41. W. MENKE, *Z. Bot.*, **32**, 273, 1937.
42. W. MENKE & E. JACOB, *Hoppe-Seyl. Z.*, **257**, 43, 1938.
43. A. S. NEISH, *Biochem. J.*, **33**, 380, 1939.
44. A. S. VECHER, *Khimicheskaya priroda plastid i metody ikh issledovaniya*, Doctoral Dissertation, Moscow, 1950.
45. N. M. SISAKYAN, S. S. MELIK-SARKISYAN & E. N. BEZINGER, *Biokhimiya*, **17**, 626, 1952.
46. N. M. SISAKYAN & M. S. CHERNYAK, *Dokl. Akad. Nauk S.S.S.R.*, **87**, 469, 1952.
47. N. M. SISAKYAN & M. S. ODINTSOVA, *Dokl. Akad. Nauk S.S.S.R.*, **97**, 119, 1954.
48. N. M. SISAKYAN & B. P. SMIRNOV, *Biokhimiya*, **21**, 273, 1956.
49. E. M. MARTIN & R. K. MORTON, *Biochem. J.*, **64**, 221, 1956.
50. O. P. OSIPOVA & I. V. TIMOFEEVA, *Dokl. Akad. Nauk S.S.S.R.*, **67**, 105, 1949.
51. O. P. OSIPOVA, *Izv. Akad. Nauk S.S.S.R., Ser. biol.*, **1**, 96, 1953.
52. O. P. OSIPOVA, *Fiziologiya Rasteniĭ*, **3**, 125, 1956.
53. A. C. CHIBNALL, *Protein Metabolism in the Plant*, New Haven, 1939.
54. J. W. H. LUGG, *Advanc. Protein Chem.*, **5**, 229, 1949.
55. E. W. YEMM & B. F. FOLKES, *Biochem. J.*, **55**, 700, 1953.
56. L. FOWDEN, *Ann. Bot. N.S.*, **18**, 257, 1954.
57. N. M. SISAKYAN, E. N. BEZINGER & E. G. KUVAEVA, *Dokl. Akad. Nauk S.S.S.R.*, **74**, 987, 1950.
58. N. M. SISAKYAN & E. N. BEZINGER, *Biokhimiya*, **16**, 358, 1951.
59. N. M. SISAKYAN, E. N. BEZINGER & E. B. KUVAEVA, *Dokl. Akad. Nauk S.S.S.R.*, **87**, 113, 1952.
60. N. M. SISAKYAN, E. N. BEZINGER & N. A. GOMILEVSKAYA, *Dokl. Akad. Nauk S.S.S.R.* **91**, 907, 1953.
61. N. M. SISAKYAN, E. N. BEZINGER, N. A. GOMILEVSKAYA & N. P. DUKYANOVA, *Biokhimiya*, **20**, 368, 1955.
62. A. A. KRASNOVSKIĬ, V. B. EVSTIGNEEV, G. P. BRIN & V. A. GAVRILOVA, *Dokl. Akad. Nauk S.S.S.R.*, **82**, 947, 1952.
63. E. C. WASSINK & H. W. J. RAGETLI, *Proc. Acad. Sci. Amst.*, **4**, 462, 1952.
64. G. E. FOGG & M. WOLF, *Autotrophic Microorganisms IV Symposium*, Cambridge, 1954.
65. T. FUJIWARA, *J. Biochem. (Tokyo)*, **42**, 411, 1955; **43**, 195, 1956.
66. S. TAKASHIMA, *Nature, Lond.*, **169**, 182, 1952.
67. R. LUMRY, J. D. SPIKES & H. EYRING quoted in *Annu. Rev. Plant Physiol.*, **5**, 271, 1954.
68. J. D. SPIKES, R. LUMRY & FUJII, *Proc. Utah Acad. Sci.*, **31**, 106, 1954.
69. A. A. KRASNOVSKIĬ & G. P. BRIN, *Dokl. Akad. Nauk S.S.S.R.*, **95**, 611, 1954.

70. N. M. Sisakyan, E. N. Bezinger & F. P. Kivkutsan, *Dokl. Akad. Nauk S.S.S.R.*, **98**, 111, 1954.

71. H. Metzner, *Naturwissenschaften*, **39**, 64, 1952; *Biol. Zbl.*, **71**, 257, 1953.

72. N. M. Sisakyan & K. G. Chamova, *Dokl. Akad. Nauk S.S.S.R.*, **67**, 337, 1949.

73. N. M. Sisakyan & I. I. Filippovich, *Dokl. Akad. Nauk S.S.S.R.*, **76**, 517, 1949.

74. N. M. Sisakyan & E. B. Kovagva, *Dokl. Akad. Nauk S.S.S.R.*, **62**, 121, 1948.

75. N. M. Sisakyan, *Primenenie* C^{14} *i* P^{32} *v issledovanii sinteticheskikh funktsiĭ izolirovannykh plastid. Sessiya Akad. Nauk S.S.S.R. Po mirnomu ispolzovaniyu atomnoĭ energii. Zasedaniya otdeleniya biologicheskikh nauk.* Izd. Akad. Nauk S.S.S.R., Moscow, 1955.

76. A. Millerd, J. Bonner, B. Axelrod & R. S. Bandurcki, *Proc. nat. Acad. Sci., Wash.*, **37**, 855, 1951.

77. J. Bonner & A. M. Millerd, *Arch. Biochem. Biophys.*, **42**, 135, 1953.

78. N. M. Sisakyan & I. M. Mosolova, *Biokhimiya*, **19**, 485, 1954.

79. T. Ohmura, *Arch. Biochem. Biophys.*, **57**, 187, 1955; *Nature, Lond.*, **176**, 467, 1955.

80. R. M. Smillie, *Austr. J. biol. Sci.*, **8**, 186, 1955; **9**, 339, 1956.

81. N. M. Sisakyan, R. M. Bekina & I. M. Mosolova, *Dokl. Akad. Nauk S.S.S.R.*, **112**, 781, 1957.

82. D. I. Arnon, *Nature, Lond.*, **162**, 341, 1948; *Plant Physiol.*, **24**, 1, 1949; *Nature, Lond.*, **167**, 1008, 1951.

83. D. I. Arnon, M. B. Allen & F. R. Whatley, *Nature, Lond.*, **174**, 394, 1954.

84. A. I. Oparin, N. S. Gel'man & I. G. Zhukova, *Dokl. Akad. Nauk S.S.S.R.*, **105**, 1036, 1955.

85. S. Moore & W. Stern, *J. biol. Chem.*, **211**, 893, 1954.

86. M. Metzner, *Planta*, **45**, 493, 1955.

Problèmes d'Évolution dans la Thermodynamique des Phénomènes Irréversibles

I. PRIGOGINE

Faculté des Sciences de l'Université de Bruxelles, Belgique

1. LES PROBLÈMES de la vie occupent une place toute particulière parmi les problèmes évolutifs de la science. Il est, en effet, trivial de rappeler que les êtres vivants sont caractérisés par une haute organisation maintenue grâce à des échanges constants avec le monde extérieur. De plus la reproduction confère à la vie un caractère cyclique remarquable.

Il est intéressant de considérer ces problèmes du point de vue de la thermodynamique des phénomènes irréversibles qui a pu analyser les lois générales de l'évolution en physique avec plus de précision que la thermodynamique classique. Ce sera le but de cet exposé [1, 2, 3]. Il ne faut évidemment pas, lorsqu'on procède à une telle analyse, s'attendre à trouver des réponses spécifiques à des problèmes précis comme par exemple celui du mécanisme de l'évolution biologique. On ne peut, du moins pour le moment, que les situer dans une perspective plus vaste et de cette manière mieux dégager quelques caractéristiques générales.

2. Un grand nombre d'auteurs ont depuis longtemps discuté l'application de la thermodynamique à la biologie. Il faut toutefois souligner que la physique classique n'était pas bien adaptée à ce problème et cela à cause de son caractère *global*. La thermodynamique classique nous a appris que l'entropie d'un système isolé croît lorsqu'il s'y produit des phénomènes irréversibles. En fait il y a peu de doute que si nous considérons notre système planétaire comme un système isolé, l'ensemble des phénomènes irréversibles y fait croître l'entropie. Mais ce que nous voulons c'est considérer non l'entièreté de ce système mais le *sous-système* que constitue la biosphère.

Pour cela nous devons d'abord formuler le second principe de manière *locale* applicable à toute région macroscopique du système global. Considérons une telle région macroscopique. Son entropie S variera par suite d'une création d'entropie par les phénomènes irréversibles qui s'y produisent et aussi par suite d'un apport d'entropie (par suite d'échanges de matière et d'énergie) avec le monde extérieur. Désignons par $d_i S$ la création d'entropie pendant le temps dt et par $d_e S$ l'apport d'entropie. Nous pourrons alors écrire [2, 3]

$$dS = d_i S + d_e S \qquad (2.1)$$

418

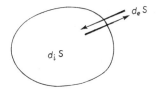

FIG. 2.1.

La formulation locale du second principe consiste à exiger que la production d'entropie dans tout système soit positive ou nulle

$$d_i S \geq 0 \qquad (2.2)$$

quels que soient par ailleurs les échanges avec le monde extérieur.

La production d'entropie par unité de temps $d_i S/dt$ est la grandeur centrale utilisée en thermodynamique des phénomènes irréversibles. Elle mesure le 'contenu d'irréversibilité' pendant le laps de temps dt. L'entropie produite peut définir une échelle de temps locale mesurée non en déplacementes réversibles comme en mécanique classique mais en contenu d'irréversibilité. Nous avons montré ailleurs comment on peut, en principe, construire une telle échelle et nous ne nous y arrêterons pas ici [2].

Mais nous voulons insister sur le fait que la production d'entropie est la grandeur centrale de toute théorie macroscopique de l'irréversibilité, permettant de poser le problème de l'irreversibilité sous une forme quantitative indépendante des mécanismes moléculaires.

Dans les problèmes biologiques la production d'entropie est due essentiellement aux réactions chimiques (et photochimiques); elle est alors de la forme

$$\frac{d_i S}{dt} = \Sigma A_\rho \, V_\rho \geq 0 \qquad (2.3)$$

où V_ρ est la vitesse de la réaction ρ et A l'affinité (au sens de DeDonder) liée à cette réaction*.

La production d'entropie est ainsi une forme *bilinéaire* des vitesses des réactions chimiques et des 'causes', les affinités, qui les produisent. A l'équilibre on a évidemment

$$A_\rho = 0 \quad \text{et} \quad V_\rho = 0 \qquad (2.4)$$

et

$$\frac{d_i S}{dt} = 0 \qquad (2.4)$$

La valeur de la production d'entropie caractérise ainsi la distance à l'équilibre thermodynamique. Une grande valeur de la production d'entropie signifie que le système évolue loin de l'équilibre thermodynamique. Notons aussi que

---

* Pour simplifier nous écrirons A_ρ à la place de la notation usuelle A_ρ/T (cf. [2, 3]).

d_iS/dt est une grandeur semithermodynamique (par les affinités) semicinétique (par les vitesses).

Comment se manifeste physiquement la production d'entropie ? Si le système était isolé la production d'entropie augmenterait simplement l'entropie elle-même du système c'est-à-dire le désordre moléculaire du système. Mais il n'en est plus de même dans le cas général car l'apport (au sens algébrique) d'entropie permet de rejeter cette production d'entropie vers le monde extérieur. Rien n'empêche donc qu'un système à haute production d'entropie maintienne de manière prolongée un état à basse entropie grâce à un flux d'entropie approprié. Ainsi supposons que le système considéré soit dans un état stationnaire. Nous aurons alors $dS = 0$ et (2.1)–(2.2) nous donnent

$$d_eS = - \, d_iS \leq 0 \qquad\qquad (2.5)$$

Ce flux entropique doit être négatif à l'état stationnaire pour compenser la production d'entropie. Le système reçoit moins d'entropie qu'il ne rejette. On peut encore dire qu'il reçoit des 'aliments' hautement organisés (donc à faible entropie) qu'il restitue au monde extérieur partiellement désorganisés.

3. Les problèmes évolutifs qui nous intéressent sont ceux du sous-système 'biosphère' considéré au paragraphe précédent. Pendant que le système isolé qui l'englobe tend vers son état à entropie maximum ce sous-système évolue-t-il vers un état stationnaire remarquable et dans l'affirmative vers lequel ?

Pour qu'on puisse parler d'un état asymptotique stationnaire de non équi-libre au sein d'un milieu en évolution il faut que l'on puisse classer les temps de relaxation caractéristiques du système en deux groupes : l'un formé par des temps de relaxation très longs et l'autre des temps très courts. En d'autres termes *il faut une double échelle de temps.*

Illustrons cela par des exemples. Prenons deux thermostats à températures différentes et connectons—les par un capillaire, le tout formant un système isolé. Ce petit capillaire atteindra rapidement son état de régime, c.-à-d. son état stationnaire pour les températures des thermostats données. Cela correspond à l'échelle de temps court. D'un autre côté les températures des thermostats évoluent lentement jusqu'à ce que l'entièreté du système prenne une tempéra-ture uniforme. Cette seconde évolution correspond à l'échelle longue.

Un second exemple se rattachant à la thermodiffusion. Dans un récipient dont deux côtés sont maintenus à des températures différentes un gaz (par exemple l'hydrogène) s'enrichira du côté chaud l'autre (par exemple l'azote) du côté froid. Il s'établit un état stationnaire de non-équilibre qui se maintiendra aussi longtemps que la différence des températures. Si nous incluons ce système dans un système isolé si grand soit-il, l'équilibre thermique finira par se réaliser et la thermodiffusion s'arrêtera. Nous avons d'ailleurs ici un exemple simple où l'hétérogénéité (la séparation par thermodiffusion) ne se maintient qu'aussi longtemps que le système fait partie d'un 'univers' hors de l'équilibre.

On peut penser qu'aussi longtemps que l'on considère les êtres vivants dans leur individualité la condition des deux échelles de temps est bien réalisée. L'être vivant se développe dans un univers très loin de l'équilibre thermodynamique et dont les conditions changent peu sur l'space du temps de vie d'un individu*.

4. Plaçons-nous dans les conditions où la notion de double échelle de temps discutée dans le §3 est valable. Nous nous intéresserons seulement à l'évolution du sous-système vers son état asymptotique sur des temps pendant lesquels le système global dans lequel il est inclus ne présente pas de modifications appréciables. La description mathématique de cette situation est l'introduction de conditions aux limites pour le sous-système qui sont indépendantes du temps†.

Dans de telles conditions, P. Glansdorff et l'auteur ont démontré un théorème général [4] qui contient comme cas particulier les résultats obtenus antérieurement par l'auteur [2, 3].

Posons

$$P = \frac{d_i S}{dt} \tag{4.1}$$

et

$$dP = d_A P + d_v P \tag{4.2}$$

avec (cf. 2.3)

$$d_A P = \Sigma v_\rho \, dA_\rho \qquad d_v P = \Sigma A_\rho \, dv_\rho \tag{4.3}$$

Le sens de ces formules est simple: P désigne la production d'entropie par unité de temps. Cette grandeur varie elle-même en général avec le temps et nous décomposons sa variation en 2 termes dont l'un provient de la variation des affinités et l'autre de celle des vitesses de réaction.

Le théorème général est alors

$$d_A P \leq 0 \tag{4.4}$$

c'est-à-dire les affinités varient toujours de manière à abaisser la valeur de la production d'entropie. Bien entendu à l'état stationnaire $d_A P = 0$ car les affinités y sont indépendantes du temps. Ce théorème exprime une sorte de principe de 'modération' de Lechatelier-Braun. Pour le voir, prenons le cas d'une seule variable indépendante et supposons que le système évolue suffisamment près de l'équilibre pour que l'on puisse écrire (cf. §5) la relation de proportionalité entre V et A

$$V = LA \tag{4.5}$$

Nous aurons alors, en vertu de (4.4)

$$LA \, dA \leq 0 \tag{4.6}$$

D'un autre côté L est positif car à cause de (4.5) la production d'entropie est ici

$$\frac{d_i S}{dt} = LA^2 \geq 0, \text{ d'où } L > 0 \tag{4.7}$$

---

* Du point de vue mécanique la distinction des 2 échelles de temps correspond à la distinction de 2 types de termes dans l'hamiltonin (classique ou quantique).

† C'est là toutefois une approximation car le système tout entier évolue lentement vers l'équilibre. Il est probable que dans une description mécanique satisfaisante il faille remplacer ces conditions par des conditions *lentement variables avec le temps.*

Nous voyons donc que

$$A \, \mathrm{d}A \leq 0 \qquad (4.8)$$

L'accroissement de l'affinité est de signe contraire à sa valeur; c'est bien là une formulation classique des théorèmes de modération [5].

Dans le cas général (c.-à-d. lorsque (4.5) n'est pas valable le sens physique de l'inégalité (4.4) n'est pas aussi facile à formuler) nous voyons toutefois clairement que la direction d'évolution n'est pas liée à la valeur de l'entropie. La valeur de l'entropie peut aussi bien augmenter que diminuer suivant les cas dans l'évolution du système vers son état stationnaire asymptotique (un exemple de diminution est le cas de la thermodiffusion cité dans le §2). C'est au contraire la variation de la production d'entropie qui est le facteur essentiel.

Notons que $\mathrm{d}_A P$ n'est en général pas la différentielle d'une fonction telle que

$$\mathrm{d}_A P = - \, \mathrm{d} \, \phi \qquad (4.9)$$

Il existe comme nous le prouvons au §5 des cas importants où la fonction ϕ existe mais ce n'est pas le cas général [6]. Le théorème (4.4) exprime donc une propriété *différentielle* (et non intégrale ou globale) de la production d'entropie. Cette situation rappelle quelque peu le cas de la mécanique classique où une formulation intégrale (principe d'Hamilton) n'est pas toujours possible tandis qu'une formulation différentielle (principes de Gauss et Hertz) existe toujours.

Toutefois on peut définir une fonction

$$M = - \frac{\mathrm{d}_v P}{\mathrm{d}t} = - \Sigma v_\rho \frac{\mathrm{d}A_\rho}{\mathrm{d}t} \geq 0 \qquad (4.10)$$

qui sera nulle à *l'état stationnaire* et positive partout ailleurs. Elle généralise donc les propriétés de la production d'entropie qui est nulle à l'état *d'équilibre* et positive partout ailleurs.

Les dérivées $\mathrm{d}A_\rho / \mathrm{d}t$ s'expriment bilinéairement à l'aide des vitesses réactionnelles v_ρ. L'expression (4.10) s'écrit donc encore comme une forme quadratique des vitesses

$$M = \Sigma m_{ij} \, v_i \, v_j \geq 0 \qquad (4.11)$$

Nous pouvons dire de manière quelque peu imagée que l'état stationnaire se caractérise par un 'rendement optimum' en termes de la grandeur *cinétique* M tandis que l'équilibre d'un système isolé n'est déterminé que par le poids statistique des différentes configurations moléculaires possibles.

5. Passons à l'application spécifique de l'inégalité générale (4.4). Considérons un système de coordonnées $A_1, A_2 \ldots A_r$. L'état stationnaire y sera représenté par le point S. Au contraire O représente l'état d'équilibre thermodynamique. Il est important de distinguer (Fig. 5.1) le cas où S est dans le voisinage de O de celui où il est loin de O*.

* Les distances dans l'espace $A_1 \ldots A_r$ doivent se mesurer en unités R. Le point S sera donc au voisinage de O si $(A_1) \ldots (A_r)$ sont $\ll R$.

Dans ce paragraphe nous considérerons le cas du voisinage de l'équilibre qui est le mieux connu. Nous pouvons alors développer les vitesses en fonction des affinités et nous limiter aux termes du premier ordre

$$V_\rho = \Sigma L_{\rho\rho'} A_{\rho'} \tag{5.1}$$

De telles lois linéaires sont bien connues dans les phénomènes de transport (lois d'Ohm, Fourier, Fick ...) Elles sont aussi valables dans le cas chimique si les réactions se déroulent au voisinage de l'équilibre. Une propriété fondamentale des coefficients $L_{\rho\rho'}$ est la réciprocité formulée de manière générale par Onsager [7] et dont des cas particuliers étaient connus depuis longtemps.*

$$L_{\rho\rho'} = L_{\rho'\rho} \tag{5.2}$$

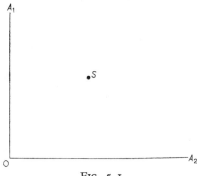

Fig. 5.1.

La conséquence de (5.2) est que (5.1) peut s'écrire aussi

$$v_\rho = -\frac{\partial\psi}{\partial A\rho} \quad \psi = -\frac{1}{2} \sum_{\rho\rho'} L_{\rho\rho'} A_{\rho'} A_\rho \tag{5.3}$$

Au voisinage de l'équilibre les vitesses réactionnelles dérivent d'un potentiel qui n'est autre en vertu de (2.3), de (5.1) et de (5.2) que la production d'entropie

$$\psi = -\frac{1}{2} \frac{d_i S}{dt} \tag{5.4}$$

Examinons à l'aide de la Figure 5.1 comment le système se rapproche de l'équilibre. L'existence du potentiel ψ signifie que l'évolution se fait suivant des normales à ψ constant et que des *rotations* dans l'espace des affinités sont impossibles.

* Dans le cas chimique qui nous intéresse il n'est pas nécessaire de tenir compte de complications qui peuvent se présenter dans les phénomènes de transport, telles que forces de Coriolis.

Nous aurons ainsi la disposition indiquée schématiquement sur la Figure 5.2.

Il n'y a pas d'oscillation dans l'approche vers l'état stationnaire. En particulier ceci est vrai pour l'approche vers l'état d'équilibre. Dans ces conditions le théorème général (4.4) prend une forme explicite remarquable. Nous aurons en effet ici

$$\mathrm{d}_A P = \Sigma v_\rho \, \mathrm{d}A_\rho = - \, \mathrm{d}\psi \leq \mathrm{o} \tag{5.5}$$

$\mathrm{d}_A P$ est donc une différentielle totale et à l'état stationnaire est maximum ou la production d'entropie (cf. 5.4) minimum*.

La fonction caractérisant l'état stationnaire a donc dans ce cas un sens physique particulièrement simple et intuitif: c'est, peut-on dire, *l'irréversibilité elle-même* qui devient dans l'état stationnaire aussi petite que possible [2].

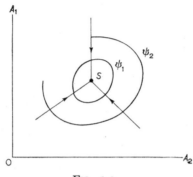

FIG. 5.2.

Insistons encore une fois à propos de cet exemple sur la différence entre le minimum de la production d'entropie et le maximum (ou le minimum) de l'entropie elle-même. Le minimum de la production d'entropie n'implique rien sur l'entropie elle-même. L'organisation mesurée par l'entropie peut être élevée ou basse, ce qui compte c'est l'efficacité thermodynamique du système et on peut dire que le minimum de la production d'entropie consiste en quelque manière en un principe '*métabolique*'. Toutefois on peut penser qu'en général une grande efficacité métabolique ne peut être acquise que par une organisation plus élévée à l'échelle biochimique.

6. Passons au cas où l'état stationnaire est loin de l'équilibre. Ici encore tout comme en (5.1) nous pouvons développer les vitesses en série mais cette fois autour de l'état stationnaire. Désignons par δA_ρ la différence entre A_ρ et sa valeur à l'état stationnaire. Nous aurons alors au voisinage de l'état stationnaire†

$$v_\rho = \Sigma L_{\rho\rho'} \delta A_{\rho'}$$

* Une autre méthode pour arriver rapidement à ce résultat est d'observer qu'ici $\mathrm{d}_A P = \mathrm{d}_v P = \frac{1}{2} \, \mathrm{d}P$. Dans ces conditions (4.4) est équivalent à $\mathrm{d}P \leq \mathrm{o}$.

† Dans (5.1) les $L_{\rho\rho'}$ doivent être évalués à l'état d'équilibre et dans (6.1) à l'état stationnaire.

Mais nous n'avons plus en général aucune relation qui remplacerait les relations de réciprocité (5.2). Il en résulte qu'il n'existe plus en général de potentiel dont dériveraient les vitesses (pour l'étude de quelques exemples, cf. [6]). Des rotations autour de l'état stationnaire sont maintenant possibles et l'approche vers cet état aura la forme spirale schématisée sur la Figure 6.1.

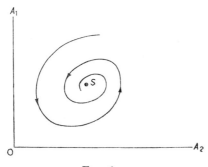

FIG. 6.1.

Nous voyons que lorsque l'état stationnaire est loin de l'équilibre des oscillations deviennent possibles dans l'évolution vers cet état. Un cas particulier qui a pu être analysé de manière complète par R. Balescu et l'auteur [8] est celui où les formules (6.1) ne contiennent qu'une partie antisymétrique.

$$L_{\rho\rho'} = -L_{\rho'\rho} \qquad (6.2)$$

Dans ce cas le système ne peut plus atteindre l'état stationnaire (s'il ne s'y trouvait pas initialement) mais décrit des courbes fermées autour de cet état (cf. Fig. 6.2)

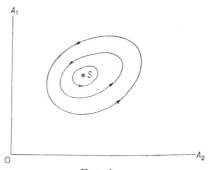

FIG. 6.2.

Ce comportement cyclique est moins exceptionnel qu'il ne semble à première vue. Un très intéressant exemple a été étudié par Volterra [9] dans sa 'Théorie mathématique de la lutte pour la vie'. Volterra étudie la coexistence de différentes espèces animales (par exemple des poissons) dans un milieu biologique invariable. Le cas le plus simple est celui de deux espèces A et B telles que B mange

A tandis que A est herbivore. Si on introduit les 'équations cinétiques' d'évolution (A, B concentrations des espèces A et B)

$$\frac{dA}{dt} = \epsilon_1 A - A B \tag{6.3}$$

$$\frac{dB}{dt} = AB - \epsilon_2 B$$

dont le sens physique est évident, les lignes d'évolution sont des courbes fermées autour de l'état stationnaire

$$\epsilon_1 A - AB = 0 \quad AB - \epsilon_2 B = 0 \tag{6.4}$$

Notons que dans cet exemple la condition de la double échelle de temps discutée au § 3 est bien réalisée: l'échelle courte est celle de l'évolution de la coexistence des deux espèces biologiques, l'échelle longue l'évolution du milieu ambiant (supposé constant).

Un exemple physicochimique qui nous a été signalé par le Professeur Christiansen est un système de trois enzymes:

Ils transforment le milieu par ex. suivant les réactions

$$
\begin{aligned}
A + X &\to B + Y \\
B + Y &\to C + Z \\
C + Z &\to A + X' \\
\hline
X &\to X'
\end{aligned}
\tag{6.5}
$$

Le sous-système formé par les trois enzymes effectue une transformation cyclique (aussi longtemps que les concentrations du milieu 'ambiant' X, Y, Z, X' sont maintenues constantes).

Il est intéressant de voir ce que devient le théorème général (4.4) dans ce cas. Pour fixer les idées nous supposons qu'il n'y a que deux réactions. Alors (6.1) et (6.2) se réduisent à

$$V_1 = L_{12}\delta A_2 \quad V_2 = - L_{12}\delta A_1 \tag{6.6}$$

et dès lors

$$d_A P = V_1 dA_1 + V_2 dA_2 = L_{12}\,(\delta A_2\,dA_1 - \delta A_1\,dA_2) \leq 0 \tag{6.7}$$

utilisons des coordonnées polaires θ, ρ dans l'espace $A_1 A_2$ autour de l'état stationnaire. Alors (6.7) prend la forme

$$\frac{d_A P}{dt} = L_{12} \rho^2 \frac{d\theta}{dt} \leq 0 \tag{6.8}$$

Cette inégalité prend ainsi un sens très simple: Pour un signe donné de L_{12} *un seul sens de rotation* autour de l'état stationnaire est possible. Nous voyons donc que dans le cas où le système ne peut atteindre un état stationnaire la thermodynamique impose le sens de la rotation. Le caractère cyclique d'un sous-système n'est nullement incompatible avec la thermodynamique mais à ce caractère cyclique est associé un sens de rotation privilégié.

7. Achevons ce travail par quelques remarques générales. L'évolution chimique d'un système vivant ou non est probablement déterminée par les équations différentielles qui caractérisent sa cinétique. L'objet de la thermodynamique des phénomènes irréversibles est de discuter autant que possible des propriétés générales de ces équations sans faire d'hypothèses particulières sur leur structure.

Etant donné la variété des équations possibles et leur caractère non linéaire on ne peut s'attendre à des résultats toujours nombreux mais les résultats existants permettent déjà de poser et de discuter quelques problèmes essentiels.

Vie et probabilité: La discussion présentée dans ce travail et dans nos travaux antérieurs montre que la formation de structures complexes dans des sous-systèmes moyennant des conditions particulières (double échelle de temps, par exemple) rentre parfaitement dans le cadre des processus évolutifs possibles du point de vue thermodynamique.

Vie et métabolisme: Le facteur essentiel dans cette évolution vers des structures plus complexes serait du point de vue thermodynamique l'évolution vers une grande efficacité thermodynamique chiffrée au voisinage de l'équilibre par la production d'entropie.

RÉFÉRENCES

1. I. Prigogine & J. M. Viame, *Experientia*, **2**, 451, 1946.
2. I. Prigogine, *Étude thermodynamique des phénomènes irréversibles*. Liège, Desoer, 1947.
3. I. Prigogine, *Introduction to Thermodynamics of Irreversible Processes*. Thomas Publishers, Chicago, 1955.
4. P. Glansdorff & I. Prigogine, *Physica*, 's Grav., **20**, 773, 1954.
5. I. Prigogine & R. Defay, *Thermodynamique chimique*. Liège, Desoer, 1950; Traduction anglaise par E. Everett. Longmans Green & Co., London, 1954.
6. I. Prigogine & R. Balescu, *Bull. Acad. Belg. Cl. Sci.*, **41**, 917, 1955.
7. L. Onsager, *Phys. Rev.*, **37**, 405, 1931; **38**, 2265, 1931.
8. I. Prigogine & R. Balescu, *Bull. Acad. Belg. Cl. Sci.*, **42**, 256, 1956.
9. V. Volterra, *Théorie mathématique de la lutte pour la vie*. Gauthier-Villars, Paris, 1931.

Biochemical Processes in the Simplest Structures

A. I. OPARIN

A. N. Bakh Institute of Biochemistry, U.S.S.R. Academy of Sciences, Moscow

IN OUR view the type of organization peculiar to life could originate only as a result of the evolution of a multimolecular organic system, separated from its environment by a distinct boundary, but constantly interacting with this environment in the manner of 'open' systems. Since, as evidenced by a number of features, present-day protoplasm possesses a coacervate structure, the mentioned systems, which represent the starting point for the evolution leading to the origin of life, could have been coacervate drops. But in contrast to the coacervates artificially obtained by laboratory methods these drops had to possess a certain pattern of reactions interlinked in time as characteristic for open systems. Moreover, in the course of their evolution the initial systems must gradually have become more complex and elaborate both in space (in regard to their structure), and in time (i.e., in relation to the reaction pattern).

In a general form these concepts have been discussed in my book *The Origin of Life on the Earth* (3rd ed., Oliver & Boyd, Edinburgh, 1957). In the present paper only single experimental data are presented obtained within recent time in my laboratory.

Since initial systems of this type were bound to be destroyed at early stages of the development of life owing to natural selection, and could not have persisted up to the present time under natural conditions, we can put the suggested processes of evolution to the test either by gradually increasing the complexity of artificially obtained systems, or by destroying to a certain extent natural protoplasmic structures and making a study of the fragments thus obtained. It is in these two directions that our experiments have been carried out. Of course they can only be regarded as preliminary ones.

To attain the former aim, we chose, in collaboration with T. Evreïnova, T. A. Shubert, M. N. Nestyuk and G. Larionova artificially prepared coacervate drops.

To make their organization approach more closely the organization of protoplasm it was necessary, in the first place, to induce in these drops chemical transformations disturbing their static type of stability. This can most readily be achieved by incorporation, into the coacervate drops, of enzymes which catalyse transformations of substances forming part of these drops. Such incorporation, in principle, is quite possible, but it can only be realized if certain rules are observed.

PLATE VIII

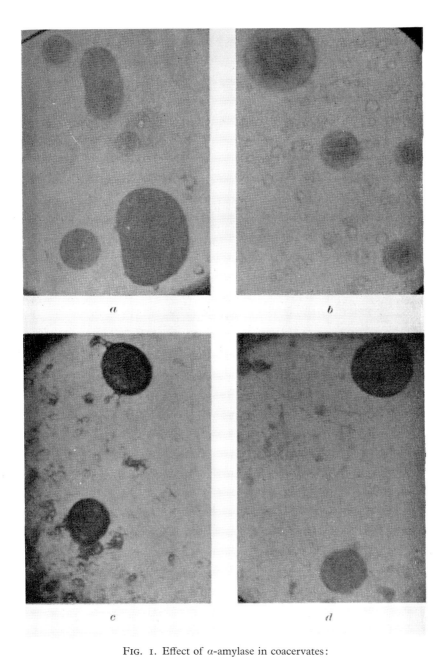

Fig. 1. Effect of α-amylase in coacervates:

(a)—starch-containing coacervates; (b)—starch has been broken down to amylo-dextrins; (c)—starch has been broken down to erythrodextrins; (d)—starch has been broken down to achroodextrins.

A. I. OPARIN

In such experiments it must, for one, be kept in mind that coacervates formed from certain components can exist only within relatively narrow limits of pH, while the activity of the enzyme to be included into the system requires, in its turn, a definite optimal range of actual acidity. Therefore the success of the work can be assured only if the coacervate selected for observing enzymic activity can exist in the pH range optimal for the activity of the enzyme in point.

Let us consider some actual experimental examples of the inclusion of enzymes into coacervate drops. The condition common to all these experiments is that the coacervates should be prepared from diluted solutions (0·01–0·1%), at a definite temperature. Thirty minutes after incorporation of the enzyme and substrate into the coacervate droplets, the latter are separated from the solution by centrifugation (1500–3000 rev./min), and in the sediment and supernatant thus obtained determinations are made of the products of action of the enzyme embodied in the coacervate drops.

To study the effect of α-amylase [1] a coacervate was obtained which consisted of soluble starch, gelatin and of protamine sulphate prepared according to Kossel's [2] method from the spawn of Amur salmon. Coacervation was effected in the following way: 0·4 ml of a 0·5% solution of protamine sulphate, 1·2 ml of 0·67% gelatin solution and 0·1 ml α-amylase solution, containing 0·2 mg enzyme, were added to 0·4 ml. of 0·1% soluble starch. The mixture was brought to pH 7·0 with the temperature at 50°. At fixed intervals samples were taken, stained with iodine and photographed with an ultraviolet microscope and chromoscope on colour film.

Figure 1a shows coacervates containing starch; Fig. 1b coacervates in which the starch was broken down to amylodextrins; Fig. 1c to erythrodextrins; and in Fig. 1d it is seen that the degradation of starch reached a stage approaching achroodextrin.

Further analysis showed that under the given conditions the activity of the enzyme in the coacervate was lower than in the aqueous solution of the constituents from which the coacervate was obtained. Evidently, in the coacervate drops possessing considerable viscosity due to their high content of protamine and gelatin, the rate of movement of the substances diminishes, while the adsorption capacity of the drops is increased. The experiment shows how marked an influence even a structure so primitive in the biological sense as are coacervate drops may have on the course of individual enzymic reactions.

A study of the degradation of starch to sugar in coacervate drops was made with the use of β-amylase [3]. To obtain coacervate drops, 2 ml of 0·67% aqueous solutions of gelatin and gum arabic, taken in the ratio 5 : 3, were mixed with 0·5 ml of a 1% solution of phosphorylated or soluble starch and 0·5 ml of 0·05% amylase solution. The mixture was brought to pH 4·82–4·85 with the temperature at 40–42° and kept 15 minutes at this temperature. Preliminary sampling showed that the amount of starch of the coacervate drops was equal to 13·1% of the total starch present in the whole coacervate (drops and liquid phase).

Calculation for unit volume shows that the concentration of starch in the coacervate drops was 4·5 times higher than in the equilibrium fluid. The β-

amylase was determined in the drops with the indicated starch content. The results are given in Table 1.

TABLE I

The effect of β-amylase on starch in coacervate drops

Substrate preparation	Sample	0·01 N-KMnO₄ (ml)			
		Coacervate drops		Equilibrium fluid	
		(Sediment)		(Supernatant)	
		1	2	1	2
Soluble starch . .	Experimental	0·65	0·75	3·45	3·70
	Control	0·19	0·20	0·20	0·20
Phosphorylated starch	Experimental	1·10	1·24	7·46	7·42
	Control	0·62	0·57	0·33	0·33

The figures in the table show that the concentration of reducing sugars, computed for unit volume, was four times greater in the coacervates than in the equilibrium fluid. Consequently, formation of the reaction products is concentrated in the coacervates due to the fact that they contain the enzyme. In this case also we can regard the coacervates as systems in which the morphological structure substantially influences the nature of the process.

In order to test the alternative possibility that the increased concentration of reaction products in the coacervate drops was due to absorbed sugar from the surrounding solution, control experiments were made with the addition of maltose to coacervate containing inactivated amylase; in this case all the added maltose was recovered in the equilibrium fluid, and not in the coacervate sediment. Evidently, we are justified in regarding the presence of maltose in the coacervate drops under the adopted experimental conditions as a result of the action of β-amylase in the coacervate drops on starch embodied in these drops.

A good illustration of the incorporation of enzymes into coacervates are our experiments on the coacervation of bacterial lysates. A solution (lysate) of *Micrococcus lysodeikticus* cells with high catalase activity was obtained from N. Gel'man. The experiments were carried out in the following way: 0·2 ml of 0·01 M phosphate buffer with a fixed pH, 0·1 ml of bacterial lysate diluted 1 : 100, (the method of preparing the lysate is given in the following section) followed by 0·25 ml of 0·67% aqueous solution of gum arabic were added to 0·5 ml of 1·5% aqueous solution of protamine sulphate obtained from the spawn of sevruga sturgeon by Kossel's method. The complete mixture with pH 6·0 was maintained in a water bath for 3 minutes at temperature of + 41–43°C. The formation of coacervate drops was controlled with the microscope in all experiments. Then 0·2 ml of 0·64% H_2O_2 solution was added to the mixture. Incubation with hydrogen peroxide lasted from 2 to 5 minutes. After this the enzyme was inactivated by 0·4 ml of 10% (w/v) H_2SO_4. The activity of the enzyme was expressed in terms of ml. 0·01 N-KMnO₄ consumed for titration of the remaining hydrogen peroxide. Simultaneous control determinations were made on samples with inactivated enzyme. The catalase of the lysate was inactivated in the autoclave at 1 atm. for 30 minutes.

In this way we determined the total catalase activity of the whole coacervate, consisting of coacervate drops and the surrounding equilibrium fluid.

To decide the question as to how the enzyme was distributed between the coacervate drops and the equilibrium fluid, we prepared two coacervates, 'A' and 'B'. Coacervate 'A' contained the active enzyme, while coacervate 'B' contained inactivated enzyme. Both coacervates were kept without H_2O_2 for three minutes at a temperature of + 41–43 °C and then centrifuged in the cold. The supernatant of coacervate 'B' was added to the sediment of coacervate 'A', while the sediment of coacervate 'B' was added to the equilibrium fluid (supernatant) of coacervate 'A'.

Thus, the first system corresponded to the coacervate drops of the coacervate containing the active enzyme, and the second system to the equilibrium fluid of that same coacervate.

These mixtures were placed in a thermostat at 41–43 °C for three minutes; then hydrogen peroxide was added to them and the activity of the enzyme was determined in the manner described above.

The results of the experiments are shown in Table 2.

TABLE 2

Determination of the activity of catalase in coacervates

	0·01 N-KMnO₄ (ml.)		
	Time of incubation with H_2O_2		
System	2 min.	3 min.	5 min.
Coacervate A (coac. drops + equil. fluid)	2·23–2·55	1·50	0·73
Coacervate B (enzyme inactivated) .	7·23–7·30	7·0	7·25
Coacervate drops A + equil. liquid B .	2·10–2·20	1·70	0·70
Equil. liquid A + coacervate drops B .	7·05–7·05	7·23	7·00

The figures given above show that the catalase activity of the bacterial lysate is concentrated entirely in the coacervate drops, while there is practically no enzyme in the equilibrium fluid.

The second method of investigation suggested by us was applied in studies carried out in collaboration with N. Gel'man and I. Zhukova. Methods recently developed for the isolation of separate structural elements of the cell have made possible the study of the connection between the structure of the cell and the processes taking place within it. In our experiments we made use of the fact that by treatment of the cells of *Micrococcus lysodeikticus* with lysozyme in the presence of different concentrations of sucrose, fragments of bacterial cells—protoplasts—can be obtained with a greater or lesser degree of destruction of the cell structure. In the experiments we used cultures of *Micrococcus lysodeikticus* No. 2665, Fleming strain, grown for 24 hours on meat peptone agar. The lysozyme was obtained by the method of Alderton, Ward & Fevold [4]. The mixture in which the lysis was conducted consisted of 3·53 mg NaCl, 12·84 mg succinic acid neutralized with 0·1% NaOH solution to pH 6·5, 0·05 mg MgSO₄, 0·4 mg of lysozyme, and sucrose solution, the concentration of which varied according to the conditions of the experiment. The protoplasts were obtained at the following molar concentrations of sucrose: 0·84; 0·74; 0·64; 0·54; 0·44; 0·34 and 0·24. The total volume of the reaction mixture was 2 ml. The weight of bacterial mass for the experiments on incorporation of labelled amino acids was 54 mg; for experiments on the biosynthesis of protein and for the determination of phosphate fractions it amounted to 150 mg per sample. Lysis lasted for 30 minutes at a temperature of 37°. Photographs taken in phase contrast and with dark-field illumination testify that the protoplasts obtained after lysis were completely homogenous structures, sharply distinct from intact cells, and contained no admixture of the latter (Fig. 2). The micrographs of the protoplasts illustrate the process of the gradual breakdown of the cell with varying concentrations of sucrose present in the medium during lysis (Fig. 3). Lysis of bacteria in different concentrations of sucrose led to the passage of intracellular substance into the surrounding solution; this can be estimated by measuring the absorption at 260 mμ. The breakdown of the structure greatly influences the course of various processes. We were interested primarily in the integrated multistage processes of respiration and protein synthesis in which particularly marked co-ordinating effects of cell structure could be expected. We succeeded [5] in finding the threshold of preservation of the 'structure' below which the mentioned processes are sharply inhibited. This threshold proved to be different for respiration and for the incorporation of labelled amino acids. As shown by the following graph lowering of the sucrose concentration in the medium to less than 0·64 M results in a decrease of the uptake of oxygen by the protoplasts associated with alteration of the respiratory quotient (0·85–0·50). The latter phenomenon provides evidence that there occurs not only a decrease in intensity of the process but also a failure of the co-ordination of its links (Fig. 4).

Experiments on the incorporation of labelled amino acids were carried on with [¹⁴C]glycine, added at a level of 150,000 counts/min/ml of reaction mixture. After incubation the reaction was stopped with trichloroacetic acid. The precipitate was then washed in the centrifuge (25 times), dried and assayed for radioactivity. From the radiometric data given in Fig. 4, it can be seen that within the limits of 0·84 to 0·44 M-sucrose concentration the rates of incorporation are approximately equal (1200–1000 counts/min/10 mg of dry weight of the protoplasts). On lowering the sucrose concentration below the level indicated, the incorporation was abruptly inhibited. In the absence of sucrose there is practically no incorporation, in accordance with the findings of other authors. The incorporation of glycine in the protoplasts is completely suppressed by biomycin (200 μg/ml of reaction mixture); considerable inhibition (of the order of 90–95%) is caused by 2 : 4-dinitrophenol, potassium cyanide, sodium azide, or sodium fluoride. It may be concluded from these data that the incorporation

PLATE IX

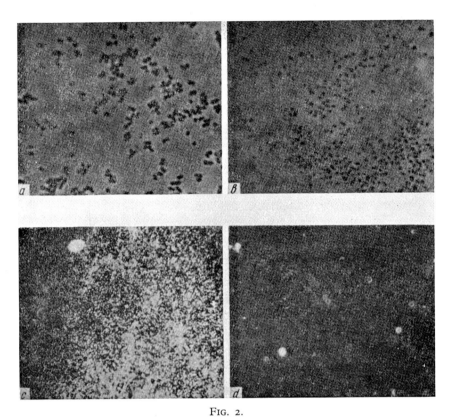

FIG. 2.

(*a*)—intact cells (phase-contrast 90 × 7); (*b*)—same after lysis in 0·64 M-sucrose;
(*c*)—intact cells (dark field 8 × 7); (*d*)—same after lysis in 0·44 M-sucrose.

A. I. OPARIN

PLATE X

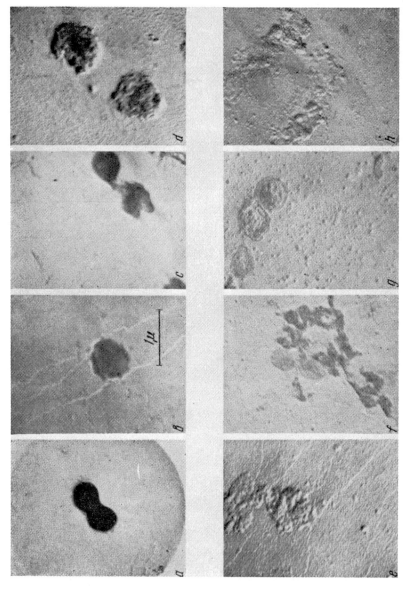

Fig. 3. Structure of *M. lysodeikticus* protoplasts at various sucrose concentrations:

(*a*)—intact cells; (*b*)—0·84 M; (*c*)—0·74 M; (*d*)—0·64 M; (*e*)—0·54 M; (*f*)—0·44 M; (*g*)—0·34 M; (*h*)—0·24 M. The scale indicated in (*b*) refers to all the figures.

A. I. OPARIN

of amino acids into the protein of the protoplasts under study is indeed one of the possible stages of the synthesis of protein, as suggested by Gale [6] and Borsook [7]. Energy is required for this reaction, as indicated by its suppression with 2 : 4-dinitrophenol and sodium azide. However, the amount of energy needed is probably not great since incorporation still continues at those levels of destruction of the cell at which the protoplasts exhibit a low intensity of the respiratory process.

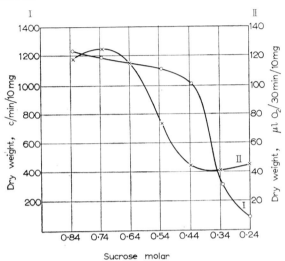

FIG. 4.   Respiration of protoplasts (II) of *M. lysodeikticus* and incorporation of labelled glycine (I).

With the aim of ascertaining the sources of energy for the process of incorporation we determined some fractions of soluble phosphorus compounds in the filtrates obtained upon precipitation of the protoplasts with trichloroacetic acid. The mineral P (orthophosphate) and the '7-minute P' (after hydrolysis for 7 minutes with N-HCl) were determined. The phosphorus was estimated by

TABLE 3

Assimilation of mineral phosphate during 120 minutes by protoplasts obtained at different sucrose concentrations

Results expressed as μg P in the total volume of the reaction mixture (1 ml)

Molarity of sucrose	Mineral P		7-minute P	
	Initial	After 120 min.	Initial	After 120 min.
0·84	135	123	167	140
0·64	140	127	169	140
0·44	140	131	165	153
0·24	149	132	176	145
Intact cells	132	88	160	130

the Lowry-Lopez method. 100 μg of orthophosphate per 150 mg of bacterial mixture were added to the reaction mixture. The total volume of the samples was 1 ml (Table 3).

The figures in the table show that mineral phosphorus from the experimental mixture is assimilated both by the intact cells and by the protoplasts obtained after lysis at different sucrose concentrations. According to the data given by Kane & Umbreit [8], and recently by Rose & Ochoa [9] the disappearing phosphate is recovered in the fraction of easily hydrolysed organic phosphorus compounds. According to our data the phosphorus of the mentioned fraction not only does not increase but even decreases, which may indicate an accumulation of organic phosphorus compounds of the type of polynucleotides. Such observations were made earlier by A. N. Belozerskiĭ for actinomycetes [10].

It should be noted that the nature of the process and its intensity are practically unaltered in protoplasts obtained at different concentrations of sucrose, as opposed to the processes of respiration and of incorporation of labelled amino acids. The process is, evidently, already impaired in the protoplasts from 0·84 M-sucrose solution, as compared with the intact cells; thus it is very sensitive and readily subject to 'uncoupling'.

The findings concerning the transformation of the fractions of phosphates in different preparations of protoplasts confirm our assumption that the incorporation of labelled amino acids requires but very small amounts of energy, as produced even in such disrupted systems as the protoplasts obtained under conditions of lysis in the presence of 0·44 M-sucrose. Obviously it is not the lack of energy which is the cause of suppression of the process of incorporation in protoplasts prepared under conditions of lysis at sucrose concentrations lower than 0·44 M. Here we are dealing with some kind of serious damage to the cell structure which completely inhibits the incorporation of labelled amino acid into the protoplasts.

Preliminary experiments were further carried out on the biosynthesis of protein in protoplasts prepared as described. To perform such experiments was of interest both with a view to investigating the process of protein biosyntheses as such, and for the purpose of elucidating the role of cell structure in this process. A number of studies, particularly those published recently, have been devoted to investigation of the process of protein biosynthesis in bacterial extracts, or cellular fragments. As an example of this we can cite the well-known experiments of Gale with fragments of the cell of *Staphylococcus aureus* and the work of the French scientists Nisman, Hirsch, Marmur & Cousin [11]. In most of the studies on protein biosynthesis in different objects the process was measured by the increase in activity of some enzyme, selected by the investigator. Yet we believe that the increase in enzymic activity which takes place during incubation of cells, disrupted by one method or another, with amino acids and some other substances (particularly ATP) cannot in itself be considered as an entirely reliable indication of the synthesis of protein.

The fact is that the enzymes, as shown by the author's earlier studies as well as those recently performed in his laboratory, can exist in the cell in a bound, inactive state, and can be liberated by the action of various factors. For example, the invertase of the yeast *Saccharomyces globosus* which is incapable of fermenting sucrose, is revealed upon treating the cells with ultrasonic waves, or after prolonged autolysis, these agents disrupting the complex of the enzyme with other high-molecular substances of the cell [12].

With these considerations in mind we undertook to measure the biosynthesis of proteins by determining the increase of protein nitrogen. In similar experiments, made with liver granules Khesin observed [13] a 10–20% increase in protein nitrogen. In our experiments 0·1 ml of a solution of 19 amino acids, containing 40 mg each amino acid/ml. was added to 2 ml. of the bacterial lysate representing a suspension of protoplasts in buffer solution with the selected concentration of sucrose. The experiments in which we determined the increase of protein nitrogen in the presence of the complete set of amino acids were conducted at pH 8·7, i.e., in conditions ensuring solubility of all amino acids in the reaction mixture. After incubation and precipitation with five volumes of trichloroacetic acid (10%) the samples were centrifuged and the precipitates were quantitatively transferred to combustion flasks.

The data obtained are of a preliminary nature; they show that the maximum increase of protein nitrogen in the protoplasts can be observed when the latter are obtained by lysis in 0·84 M-sucrose solution. In these experiments bacteria lysed in the absence of sucrose and incubated with amino acids in the same conditions served as the control (Table 4).

TABLE 4

Protein nitrogen content of protoplasts after incubation with complete set of amino acids

Molarity of sucrose	Per cent increase of protein nitrogen		
	Experiment		
	No. 1	No. 2	No. 3
0·84	10	11	12
0·64	—	6	12
0·44	—	5	8
0·24	—	0·00	0·00

These figures show that the increase in protein nitrogen, which to a certain extent proves the biosynthesis of the protein, directly depends on the state of the structure of the protoplasts, to which this process is related in a similar manner as has been found for the incorporation of labelled amino acids. It should be emphasized however that these data are of a preliminary kind, since it is essential to investigate the effects on this process of drugs inhibiting respiration and biosynthesis, for example, dinitrophenol, potassium cyanide, sodium azide and others. Besides, another difficult problem still remains to be solved: the correlation which exists between the action of proteolytic enzymes and the concentration of the products of disintegration in the medium, for we must keep in mind that the systems under investigation have active proteases, while the concentrations of added amino acids are quite high.

In the conditions of our experiments only the concentration of sucrose was varied, which altered the multimolecular structural elements, but had no effect on the number and structure of molecules constituting them.

The data reported above indicate that integrity of the multimolecular structure is a necessary condition for the complete synthesis of protein, as measured by the increase of protein nitrogen. It is, moreover, noteworthy that preservation of a constant amount of nucleic acids in the system is not yet a sufficient factor for the normal course of protein biosynthesis.

REFERENCES

1. A. I. OPARIN, T. EVREINOVA, T. A. SHUBERT & M. N. NESTYUK, *Dokl. Akad. Nauk S.S.S.R.*, **104**, 581, 1955.
2. H. KOSSEL, *Hoppe-Seyl. Z.*, **22**, 177, 1896.
3. T. EVREINOVA, T. SHUBERT & M. NESTYUK, *Dokl. Akad. Nauk S.S.S.R.*, **105**, 137, 1955.
4. W. ALDERTON, H. WARD & J. FEVOLD, *J. biol. Chem.*, **157**, 43, 1945.
5. A. I. OPARIN, N. GEL'MAN & I. ZHUKOVA, *Dokl. Akad. Nauk S.S.S.R.*, **105**, 1036, 1955.
6. E. F. GALE, *Rapports et Conférences de 3-ème Congr. de Biochimie.* Liège, 1956.
7. H. BORSOOK, *Rapports et Conférences de 3-ème Congr. de Biochimie.* Liège, 1956.
8. D. O'KANE & W. UMBREIT, *J. biol. Chem.*, **142**, 25, 1942.
9. J. ROSE & S. OCHOA, *J. biol. Chem.*, **220**, 307, 1956.
10. A. N. BELOZERSKIĬ, in press.
11. B. NISMAN, M. HIRSCH, J. MARMUR & D. COUSIN, *C.R. Acad. Sci.*, Paris, **241**, 1349, 1955.
12. A. I. OPARIN, N. GEL'MAN & I. ZHUKOVA, *Dokl. Akad. Nauk S.S.S.R.*, **97**, 293, 1954.
13. R. B. KHESIN & S. K. PETRASHKAĬTE, *Biokhimiya*, **20**, 597, 1955.

The Origin of Life and the Formation and Organizing Functions of Natural Membranes

P. MITCHELL

Department of Zoology, University of Edinburgh, Scotland

THE SPEAKERS in this Symposium are concerned with the description of different aspects of the processes by which living organisms, as we know them to-day, came to acquire the qualitatively different properties that distinguish them from the inanimate things of their environment. I shall attempt to consider the mechanism whereby the contact between the organism and its environment is regulated, particularly in relation to the functions of the membranes that form the boundary between the organism and its environment. It will be appreciated that I cannot therefore consider the organism without its environment, and that from a formal point of view the two may be regarded as equivalent phases between which dynamic contact is maintained by the membranes that separate and link them. This circumstance serves at the outset to emphasize the fact that living organisms are distinguished, not by their momentary appearance, but by their behaviour and by their relationship to their environment.

I assume that we are attempting to show that a living organism, described by Haldane [1] as a 'self-perpetuating pattern of chemical reactions'—may evolve from inanimate things by the operation of general physical laws, even if requiring events of rare occurrence at certain stages. Our task is presumably to describe the least improbable course of events, which may be tantamount to describing a spontaneous process or a natural law. The consideration of general principles that might govern the origin and evolution of living organisms is made doubly difficult because we know very little either about the chemicals available at the time when the evolutionary process of living organisms may be said to have begun, nor do we possess much information about the mechanisms of stabilization, growth, and reproduction of living organisms as they exist to-day—the latter fact often being overlooked in discussions about the meaning of the word life.

I shall attempt to describe certain generalities about the properties of the things of which present-day organisms are made that may help towards the definition of our problem. This approach is essentially a logical extension of that adopted by Schrödinger [2] and of Haldane [3], and makes use of the concepts of molecular architecture mainly developed by Linus Pauling that recently led

Watson & Crick [4] to formulate a hypothesis of the structure of deoxyribonucleic acid and to suggest a principle for its duplication [5].

There are two main classes into which things fall according to the cause of the persistence of their form. The things in the larger of the two classes, which we may conveniently call statids (comprising solids and fluids), owe their form to the physical and chemical bonds between their constituent atoms; while the smaller class, which we conveniently call fluctids, are formed by a specifically directed flux of certain materials of the environment through the space that they occupy. The shape of a statid is dependent upon the equilibrium between the randomly directed thermal energy of the atoms and the potential energy of the physical and chemical bonds between them. The shape of the fluctid, on the other hand, is determined by transformations between the potential energy of the component atoms and their *spatially directed* kinetic energy. The fluctids include the steady-state and open systems that have been considered in many of the recent treatments of the definition of living organisms. The importance of the spatial distribution of the substances in such systems has not, however, generally been considered; but Reiner & Spiegelman [6] pointed out that the entropy increase due to diffusion may partially compensate for the entropy decrease accompanying the synthesis reactions in living cells, and more recently Turing [7] reported that, by taking diffusion into account, it could be shown mathematically that stable things could be produced in an initially homogeneous medium by two interacting substances which were generated and destroyed according to simple laws. Turing's model is a perfect fluctid, for its form is not influenced by the type of forces governing the form of statids. This is not, however, the case with most open systems such, for example, as a gas flame, for in this case the form is partly determined by the shape of the burner from which the flame issues. It might, perhaps, be useful to refer to such a system as a fluctoid. The comparison has often been made between flames and living organisms: they owe their similarity to the fact that both are formed by a combination of statid and fluctid elements.

Bertalanffy [8] has pointed out that while an individual living organism may be compared to 'a hierarchical order of open system which maintains itself in the exchange of components by virtue of its system conditions', the historical character of living organisms does not have its counterpart in the model open systems. This is because Bertalanffy's open systems are effectively perfect fluctids and possess no (statid) chemical memory. A consideration of different kinds of solids shows how certain structures are particularly suited for replication and may be capable of stabilizing the individual organism and of causing the historical continuity of the evolutionary process.

Solids may be divided into classes according to the degree and type of periodicity of their component atoms or molecules. Schrödinger [2] considered the distinction between periodic and what he called aperiodic solids in biological materials in the following general terms: 'A small molecule might be called "the germ of a solid."' Starting from such a small solid germ, there seem to be two different ways of building up larger and larger associations. One is the comparatively dull way of repeating the same structure in three dimensions again and again. That is the way followed in a growing crystal. Once the periodicity is established there is no definite limit to the size of the aggregate. The other way is that of building up a more and more extended aggregate without the dull device of repetition. That is the case of the more and more complicated organic molecule in which every atom, and every group of atoms, plays an individual role, not entirely equivalent to that of many others (as is the case in a periodic structure). We might quite properly call that an aperiodic crystal or solid and express our hypothesis by saying: 'We believe a gene—or perhaps the whole chromosome fibre—to be an aperiodic crystal'. Generalizations which follow from a knowledge of the structure of proteins, deoxyribonucleic acid, and synthetic polymers allow us to add to Schrödinger's two classes of solids an intermediate group of semiperiodic solids. These may be described as being formed upon a backbone, sheet, or lattice, of regular periodic structure, attached to which at regular intervals there are groups of atoms that may be different in different parts of the structure. These solids have a most important property which is lacking in the aperiodic group: they may be formed by a simple repetitive process of polymerization of monomeric constituents which would give rise to a random arrangement of the aperiodic part of the structure unless this arrangement were determined by some added spatial constraint. In the semiperiodic solids formed upon a three-dimensional periodic lattice, there is no obvious molecular mechanism for the application of the constraint required to arrange the aperiodic part, but for the laminar and linear cases the constraint can be due to the juxtaposition of another semiperiodic structure, tending to lower the free energy of the particular aperiodic arrangement by residual bonding with it. Such is the essential molecular basis of all template hypotheses, even though they may invoke the mediation of the surfaces of enzymes to couple the process of polymerization to the placing of the monomers upon the semiperiodic template [9]. The two semiperiodic polymers concerned would be related to each other in the sense that either might cause the orderly polymerization of the other—with only occasional mistakes in arrangement (mutations), the frequency of which would partly depend upon the tightness of coupling between the polymerization process and the placing of monomers on the complementary semiperiodic solid. The periodic parts of the two solids might be the same or different, and in either case a synthesis of the appropriate polymer would be expected to be driven forward by the supply of the appropriate proportions of its monomers. A deficit of one of the monomers would be expected to lead to slowing of polymerization and to accumulation of the other monomers—a condition which could exert a regulatory effect on the flow of the monomers. As pointed out earlier, the replication in this way of semiperiodic solids would be expected to be restricted to the linear and laminar groups. Of these, however, the linear group would display the more versatile properties, particularly if free rotation were possible around the bonds of the backbones; for this would allow the long-chain solid greater freedom of alignment with another semiperiodic chain, and it might also close-pack upon itself, possibly in a number of alternative stable configurations.

Watson & Crick [5] suggested that the replication of the paired complementary polynucleotide chains in the double helix of deoxyribonucleic acid may occur by the polymerization of the appropriate nucleotides on to either member of the helix, the copying process being due to hydrogen bonding and close packing of the nucleotides into the complementary polynucleotide chain. They also suggested that this process may be the basis of genetic replication. If, as proponents of template hypotheses have suggested or implied [10, 11], the order of polymerization of amino acids to form structural and catalytically active protein may be determined by the base pairs in the deoxyribonucleic acid chain, we would seem to have the requirements for a system capable of exhibiting both the open-system characteristics described by Bertalanffy [8] and the chemical memory necessary to give the properties of stability to the individual and continuity to the lineage. According to Dixon [12], 'For life to exist, we must have a certain minimum number of enzymes linked together in a system which can both bring about energy-yielding reactions and also transfer and use this energy for other purposes'. I suggest that the minimum requirement for an organism capable of stepwise evolution therefore consists essentially of a group of paired semi-periodic solids which determine the order of polymerization in another group of unpaired semiperiodic solids of different backbone structure which, by their catalytic and carrier activities, make available the required concentrations of the monomeric precursors of the genetic and catalytic polymers. Seeing that the choice of molecular shapes and types of bonding is quite restricted I suggest that the occurrence of proteins and nucleic acids as the main types of semi-periodic solids found in all living organisms that have been examined may be governed by the fact that other types of materially and energetically inexpensive semiperiodic substances do not display the complementariness required to give efficient replication. The polypeptide and the polyribosephosphate or polydeoxyribosephosphate backbones are relatively simple and are composed of substances that may well have been amongst the first organic materials available.

The minimum requirement for an organism capable of stepwise evolution described above includes the system that makes available the required concentrations of the monomeric precursors of the genetic and catalytic polymers. In this context, Haldane's assertion [3] that 'The critical event which may best be called the origin of life was the enclosure of several different self-reproducing polymers within a semipermeable membrane' is very relevant, for we have not yet considered the spatial requirements of the above system. As Haldane has implied, the genetic and catalytic machinery could not function unless the small-molecular-weight substances which act as substrates and precursors were retained within a membrane. It is not sufficient, however, to shut the chemical machinery off from environmental pressures which supply the raw materials and the environment by an inert membrane, for this would isolate the organism from the environmental pressures which supply the raw materials and the free energy required for the processes of synthesis. Moreover, the materials of the membrane must be synthesized or accumulated from the environment, and must be organized in a stable arrangement between the environment and the inner aqueous medium of the organism. There are two questions that we must consider: first, the mechanism of formation and stabilization of natural membranes, and second, how such membranes may couple the organism with certain environmental components while isolating it from others.

Pringle [13] has discussed the different hypotheses that have been advanced to explain the appearance of heterogeneity which must have been a precondition for the independent development of living organisms. Of these, only the approach adopted by Oparin [14] seems to be consistent with the general concepts of molecular architecture developed in the paper. Oparin pointed out that ' . . . as soon as organic substance became spatially concentrated into coacervate droplets or bits of semi-liquid colloidal gels; as soon as these droplets became separated from the surrounding medium by a more or less definite border, they at once acquired a certain degree of individuality'. The work on coacervate systems, largely carried out by Bungenberg de Jong and his collaborators [15], shows that the separation of coacervates is due to an association between substances (usually of large molecular weight) which carry opposite ionic charges. This association is not as regular or as close packed as in a crystal, but it occurs spontaneously because the approximation of dipoles or of charges of opposite sign (and in some cases also the packing together of hydrophobic groups) results in a lowering of the free energy of the system. As Oparin pointed out, the coacervates may separate as droplets in equilibrium with very low bulk concentrations of their components. The point which is of particular interest to us here is that coacervates containing lipids are covered by membranes which are probably composed of two monolayers, and that droplets of medium within a coacervate drop may also be covered and prevented from coalescing by similar lipid membranes [15]. These spontaneously formed membranes resemble the lipid plasma-membranes which cover the protoplasm of all the present-day organisms that have been studied [16, 17], and it is therefore reasonable to suggest that both the natural and the coacervate membranes may owe their formation and stability to the same simple laws of approximation of charges and separate close packing of hydrophobic and hydrophilic parts.

Five years ago, at a symposium on active transport and secretion, I pointed out [18] that 'the view expressed nicely by Rosenberg [19] that by virtue of specific permeability properties, the natural membranes act as connecting links between particular components of the phases which they separate has its counterpart in the view of the enzymes as couplers of reactions which can proceed only on or in the enzyme molecules. Rosenberg's treatment shows, in fact, that the energetics of the reactions in two phases connected by a membrane can be described in the same terms as 'homogeneous' enzyme-linked reactions; the important implication being that the efficiency (or reversibility) of transport reactions is determined by the specificity of membrane permeability, exactly as the efficiency of coupled enzyme reactions is determined by the enzyme-substrate and enzyme-carrier specificities. In complex biochemical systems such as those carrying out oxidative phosphorylation [20], the osmotic and enzymic specificities appear to be equally important and may be practically synonymous'. Recent work [21–23] has provided additional support for the view that osmotic and enzymic coupling may be regarded as analogous mechanisms which depend upon the properties of specific proteins in present-day living organisms. Further, it has been shown that certain osmotic-linkage (active-transport) systems of bacteria may be induced by their substrates in an analogous manner to inducible enzyme systems, and that such systems can be genetically determined since mutants occur which lack them [24]. Although the osmotic and chemical coupling mechanisms may be regarded as formally equivalent, the osmotic linkage systems occupy a dominant position because it is the properties of these systems that control the exchange of substances between the environment and the catalytic and genetic systems of the organism. While a genetic alteration that results in a change of the catalytic and carrier complement of the organism may cause alterations in the efficiency or rate of utilization or synthesis of certain components, which may lead to changes in the concentrations of these components in the organism and indirectly cause changes in the exchange of material with the environment, a genetic alteration which gives rise to a change of osmotic coupling through the membrane may cause a direct change in the relationship between the organism and its environment by excluding a substance which might interfere with the catalytic or genetic solids or reactions (and would therefore exert a toxic effect) or by allowing or promoting the entry of a potential substrate. The open systems of enzymes and substrates may be controlled by feed-back mechanisms such as those described by Hinshelwood [25]. In these systems, the direction of the reactions and the state of the system are determined by catalyses channelled by shape relationships between catalysts and substrates which make contact in a single phase. The feedback which can occur by the coupling of the internal catalytic and genetic systems with the osmotic linkage systems regulating membrane permeability and transport, will give rise to types of stabilization or adjustment similar to those considered by Hinshelwood, and they would be expected to play a dominant and essential role in the regulation of the relationship between the organism and its environment.

Living organisms are, in effect, complex catalysts which are regenerated by the pressures of certain environmental components. But, the complication of the system required to stabilize both the individual and the lineage would seem to be such that, as Haldane [3] has recently suggested, the occurrence of the first living organisms in the sense of this context must have been very improbable; or, in other words, it must have taken a long time in an environment rich in the appropriate organic and inorganic substances.

I would like to acknowledge the receipt of a personal grant from the Scottish Hospital Endowments Research Trust.

REFERENCES

1. J. B. S. HALDANE, *Rationalist Annual*, 1929, Published in 1933 as *Science and Human Life*, N.Y.
2. E. SCHRÖDINGER, *What is Life?* Cambridge University Press, 1944.
3. J. B. S. HALDANE, *New Biol.*, **16**, 12, 1954.
4. J. D. WATSON & F. H. CRICK, *Nature, Lond.*, **171**, 737, 1953.
5. J. D. WATSON & F. H. CRICK, *Nature, Lond.*, **171**, 964, 1953.
6. J. M. REINER & S. SPIEGELMAN, *J. phys. Chem.*, **49**, 81, 1945.
7. A. M. TURING, *Phil. Trans.*, **237**B, 37, 1952.
8. L. V. BERTALANFFY, *Problems of Life.* London, 1952.
9. A. L. DOUNCE, *Enzymologia*, **15**, 251, 1952.

10. F. HAUROWITZ, *Chemistry and Biology of Proteins.* Academic Press, New York, 1950.
11. P. C. CALDWELL & C. N. HINSHELWOOD, *J. chem. Soc.*, p. 3156, 1950.
12. M. DIXON, *Multi-enzyme Systems.* Cambridge University Press, 1949.
13. J. W. S. PRINGLE, *Symp. Soc. exp. Biol.*, **7**, 1, 1953.
14. A. I. OPARIN, *The Origin of Life.* N.Y., 1938.
15. H. G. BUNGENBERG DE JONG, *Colloid Science* (Ed. by H. R. KRUYT). New York, vol. 2, 1949.
16. H. DAVSON & J. F. DANIELLI, *The Permeability of Natural Membranes.* Cambridge University Press, 1943.
17. A. FREY-WYSSLING, *Submicroscopic Morphology of Protoplasm and its Derivatives.* New York, 1948.
18. P. MITCHELL, *Symp. Soc. exp. biol.*, **8**, 254, 1954.
19. T. ROSENBERG, *Acta chem. scand.*, **2**, 14, 1948.
20. E. C. SLATER & K. W. CLELAND, *Biochem. J.*, **53**, 557, 1953.
21. H. H. USSING, *Ion Transport Across Membranes* (Ed. by H. CLARKE & D. NACHMANSON). Academic Press, New York, p. 3, 1954.
22. P. MITCHELL & J. MOYLE, *Symp. Soc. gen. Microbiol.*, **6**, 150, 1956.
23. J. MONOD, in *Enzymes: Units of Biological Structure and Function* (Ed. by O. H. GAEBLER). Academic Press, New York, p. 7, 1956.
24. H. V. RICKENBERG, G. N. COHEN, G. BUTTIN & J. MONOD. In Press.
25. C. HINSHELWOOD, *Symp. Soc. exp. Biol.*, **7**, 31, 1953.

Enzymic Reactions in Stationary Open Systems

A. G. PASYNSKIĬ

A. N. Bakh Institute of Biochemistry of the Academy of Sciences of the U.S.S.R., Moscow

THE CONSTANT exchange of matter and energy with the surrounding medium is characteristic of life in all its forms. In this respect all living organisms are so-called 'open systems'. As A. I. Oparin has discussed in detail [1], from the evolutionary point of view the emergence of the simplest forms of life in the form of biological open systems must have been preceded by the formation of non-living, chemical, open systems in which the spatial-temporal organization, co-ordinating the chemical reactions within the framework of a definite structure, had not yet led to the self-reproduction and self-maintainance of the system. Investigations of the thermodynamics [2, 3] and kinetics [4] of irreversible stationary chemical processes in open systems have, in recent years, brought about a considerable development in physics and chemistry; obviously the general properties of catalysed chemical reactions (especially enzymic ones) in open systems must be of practical interest to biochemists as well [5].

The study of enzymic reactions has hitherto been mainly limited to reactions in enclosed systems in which the concentration of reacting substances and the rate of the reaction changed continually with time until the process finished. On the other hand, enzymic reactions in any cell in the living body take place under conditions of constant diffusion of metabolites in the cell and transport of the products of the reaction into the surrounding medium, i.e. under the conditions of an open system. In contrast to reactions in an enclosed system, a stationary state may be established in an open system (it differs in principle in many ways from the thermodynamic equilibrium in an enclosed system [5]). Owing to the continual exchange with the medium this may be maintained dynamically for as long as one likes. In the present work, which was done in collaboration with V. P. Blokhina, the stationary state of an enzymic reaction was studied, using as an example the simplest reaction of enzymic oxidation of ascorbic acid A–D in the presence of peroxidase.

Let us suppose that substance A is continually coming in from the medium with a coefficient of transfer (diffusion or permeability) of K_0 at a concentration S, and that the product of the reaction, D, is continually leaving the system with a coefficient of transfer of K_z at a concentration Z. In this case we obtain an open system

$$S \xrightarrow{\;K_0\;} A \underset{K'}{\overset{K}{\rightleftarrows}} D \xrightarrow{\;K_z\;} Z$$

where the boundaries of the system are indicated by the dotted lines, S and Z refer to the external medium and K and K' are the velocity constants of the forward and backward chemical reactions $A \rightleftharpoons D$. If the processes of transfer take place according to Fick's law and the chemical reaction follows an equation of the first order, then if the stationary concentration of substance A is dynamically maintained constant at a, then, by the method of Burton and Denbigh [6, 7] we obtain the equation

$$a = \frac{K_0(K'+K_z)S+K'K_zZ}{K_0K_z+K_0K'+KK_z} \tag{1}$$

In the conditions of the experiments which I am about to describe the transfer of substance D took place in pure running water ($Z = 0$), furthermore, for an irreversible reaction such as the oxidation of ascorbic acid by hydrogen peroxide, $K' = 0$. In this case equation (1) is greatly simplified and becomes:

$$a = \frac{1}{1 + \dfrac{K}{K_0}} S \tag{2}$$

From equation (2) one may see that the value of a depends on the concentration of the source S, the constant of transfer K_0 and the velocity constant of the chemical reaction K. A change in any one of these parameters of the open system, or in the external conditions (temperature, pressure etc.) will cause the concentration of ascorbic acid to find a new stationary state.

From the general theory of open systems [5] there emerge the following characteristic properties of the stationary state which are of interest in connection with our present work: In an open system catalysts (enzymes) affect not only the rate of the reaction, but also the stationary concentration of the reacting substances. If the conditions of the stationary state in an open system are changed, compensatory processes develop which tend to conserve the properties of the system; this is an extension of Le Chatelier's principle (the dynamic stabilization of the stationary state). The transition from one stationary state to another in an open system does not follow a uniform curve but passes through extreme states (usually through maximal or minimal states).

In the literature, these properties have been investigated on hydrodynamic models with running water [6] and in the reaction of persulphuric acid with glucose [7]. As we have already mentioned, the present investigations were for the first time carried out on an enzymic reaction (the oxidation of ascorbic acid).

EXPERIMENTAL SECTION

The ascorbic acid was crystalline. The hydrogen peroxide was chemically pure (28%). The peroxidase was isolated from horse radish, the preparation having an activity of about 35% on the purpurogallin scale. The concentration of ascorbic acid in the mixture was 0·6%, and that of hydrogen peroxide 0·1%, i.e. the molar concentration of ascorbic acid was rather higher (by 15%). 1–3 mg of the enzyme preparation (dissolved in 1 ml of water) was added to 25 ml of a mixture of equal volumes of 1·2% ascorbic acid and 0·2% hydrogen peroxide. During the course of the reaction samples of 0·1 ml of the solution were removed every 10 min and their ascorbic acid content was determined by titration with 0·001 M-KIO₃ in the presence of KI, the completion of the reaction being indicated by the starch–iodine reaction. The titrations were reproducible to within 0·02 ml, i.e. 0·2–0·3% of the amount being measured. The removal of the samples did not disturb the progress of the reaction as they constituted only 0·4% of the volume of the solution, which did not have any significant effect on the course of the curve.

When the experiment was carried out under static conditions (in a glass at 20° C, pH 3·0) the ascorbic acid content in a mixture of equal volumes of 1·5% ascorbic acid and 0·2% hydrogen peroxide fell according to a uniform curve for many hours (Fig. 1) which was somewhat steeper when the enzyme was added.

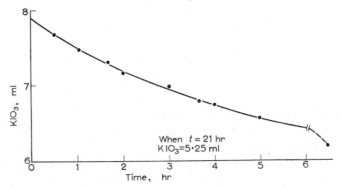

FIG. 1. Kinetics of oxidation of ascorbic acid under static conditions.

The curve corresponds closely with that for the equation for a reaction of the second order with a velocity constant $K = 2·2 \times 10^{-4}$ l/mole-sec. Owing to the irreversibility of the reaction A→D the equilibrium state was not reached in the experiment.

The experiments under stationary conditions were carried out in the apparatus shown in Fig. 2. The reacting mixture was placed in the cylinder A with a cellophan membrane stretched over the bottom. Three sizes of apparatus were used, the diameters of the membranes being I, 1·6; II, 2·4; III, 3·7 cm. Cylinder A was placed in vessel B through which there was a constant flow of thermostatically controlled distilled water (in most cases at 20° C), bathing the outside of membrane C and flowing out over the edge of the vessel into a receiver. Both the reacting solutions were continuously admitted to cylinder A from vessels D and D′ through narrow capillary tubes ($r = 0·1$ mm) the ends of which were submerged in the solution. The concentration of hydrogen peroxide in the solution being admitted was the same as that in the original solution, while that of ascorbic acid was somewhat higher (in cylinders I and II $S = 1·5\%$ or 0·0852 M, in cylinder III $S = 2·5\%$ or 0·142 M). The flow of the reacting

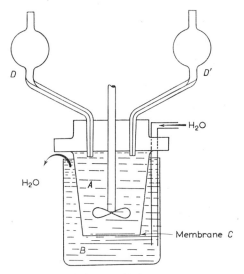

FIG. 2. Diagram of the apparatus.

substances from vessels D and D' was about 2–2·5 ml/hr and the volume of these vessels was 10 ml, the level of the liquid in these vessels being maintained constant. Thus, during the course of the experiment (1·5–2 hr) the flow proceeded at an almost constant rate. Practically, flowing conditions were assured by the fact that the components of the reaction were continually entering the constant volume of the solution in cylinder A at a rate commensurable with that of diffusion, while the products of the reaction, together with part of the starting material, left the cylinder through membrane C.

In each experiment the reaction in cylinder A was first studied without the enzyme, then, after a stationary concentration of ascorbic acid had been established for 50–60 min, AB, (cf. Fig. 3), the enzyme preparation was added and its effect on the establishment of a new stationary state was studied. The addition of 1 ml of water at point B, instead of the enzyme in control experiments, had no appreciable influence on the stationary concentration of ascorbic acid. The addition of 1 ml of enzyme solution (1–3 mg of enzyme) at point B naturally

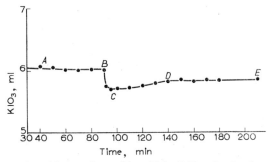

FIG. 3. Enzymic oxidation of ascorbic acid (0·6%) under flowing conditions.

accelerated the reaction and the titre of ascorbic acid fell to point C, but later there was a corresponding diminution in diffusional loss through the membrane owing to which a new stationary state, DE, was established for the system with the enzyme, just as constant over a period as the original state AB, but at a lower level. It is interesting that the state DE was established at a level far nearer to AB than that of the minimum C. Thus, the transition from one stationary state to another does not follow a smooth curve ABDE, but passes through a minimum BCD. Similar results have been obtained using concentrations of ascorbic acid (in the mixture) of 0·3 and 1·1% with corresponding changes in the concentrations of the inflowing liquids (0·7 and 2·5%) and in the level of the stationary concentration (Fig. 4).

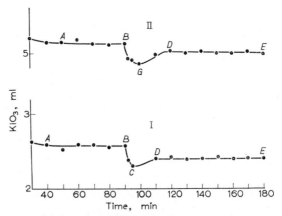

FIG. 4. Enzymic oxidation of ascorbic acid under flowing conditions at different concentrations.

If the enzymes were added in two portions each of 0·5 mg in 1 ml of water with an interval of 120 min between the additions (Fig. 5), then, after the establishment of the original stationary state AB (without the enzyme) and the introduction of the first portion of enzyme, a transition through a minimum, BCD, was observed, followed by the establishment of a stationary state, DE, which was maintained for 90 min. When the second portion of the enzyme was introduced at point E, the curve was once more seen to pass through a minimum

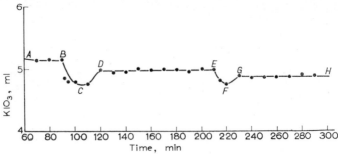

FIG. 5. Enzymic oxidation of ascorbic acid under flowing conditions when the enzyme is added in two portions.

EFG in its transition to a new stationary state GH. Thus at each new acceleration of the chemical reaction the system passed over to a new stationary state;
in each case it passed through an intermediate extreme position.

The stationary state of the reaction does not only depend on the rate of the
reaction (changing with the addition of an enzyme, cf. Figs. 3–5), or on the
original concentration (cf. Fig. 4), but also on the diffusion parameters of the
system.

In the apparatus described above (Fig. 2) we used different membranes with
diameters of 1·6, 2·4 and 3·7 cm; this corresponds with a change in the area over
which diffusion was taking place in the ratio of 1 : 2·2 : 5·3. In each of these
vessels experiments were carried out using a different concentration of enzyme
which changed the kinetic parameters of the system in a different way. In this
case the curves were similar to those in Figs 3–6, but for each vessel it was
found that, at a particular value of K, curves of this first type (Fig. 6, I) changed

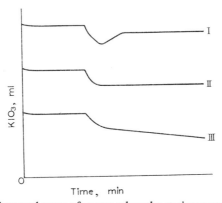

FIG. 6. Fundamental types of curves when the stationary state is changed.

into curves of the second type (Fig. 6, II) in which the new stationary state
remains at the lowest level and the concentration does not rise again from the
minimum. We shall return to this question later, in our discussion of Table 1.

Finally, in a number of experiments we studied the effect of altering the rate
of the reaction by heating or cooling the system (these experiments were done
in vessel II). Heating was not carried above 40°C so that inactivation of the
enzyme could be held to be excluded (inactivation of the enzyme by heat was
not observed below 80°C). The first part of the experiment—the establishment
of the stationary state without the enzyme and the transition to a new stationary
state after the addition of the enzyme—was carried out in just the same way
as the preceding experiments. The solution was then heated quickly to 40°C
and the temperature was maintained by the passage of running water, heated to
42°C which bathed the outside of the membrane for 60 min. As may be seen
from Fig. 7 (curve I) the system had not yet attained a stationary state by the
end of that time (third type of curve, Fig. 6, III). However, when heated to
30°C the system still attained the stationary state although in this case the
minimum was shallow (Fig. 7, curve II). On the other hand, when the system

29

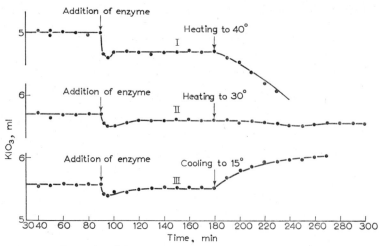

FIG. 7. Enzymic oxidation of ascorbic acid under flowing conditions at different temperatures.

was cooled to 15°C and the reaction became slower, a reverse began to take place in the course of the process (Fig. 7, curve III). In this case also, the stationary state of the system was not reached after two hours. Similar results were obtained from experiments in which the heating and cooling of the system was carried out in the absence of the enzyme. Thus, in experiments in cylinder II, the stationary state of the system was shown to be limited by changes in temperature over a range of only a few degrees.

DISCUSSION OF RESULTS

The enzymic oxidation of ascorbic acid under flowing conditions is one of the simplest examples of an open enzymic system. It differs from the systems in enclosed vessels which are usually studied, by the existence of a constant connection with a surrounding medium, both in respect of receiving reacting substances from the environment and in respect of casting out the products of the reaction into it. From the evidence which has been adduced it is clear that, even in its simplest form, such a system has new, distinctive properties which are absent from an enclosed system—in the first place there is the development of a state which remains stationary over an unlimited period of time. This is based on the continual renewal of the composition of the system and a dynamic balance of the processes of inflow and outflow. From equation (2) it may be seen that the establishment of this state depends on a particular relationship between the kinetic and diffusional parameters of the system and the initial concentration of the components. If any one of these parameters is changed, the system passes from one stationary state to another. In fact, it may be seen from the curves in Figs. 3–7 that an open system has considerable adaptability in respect of alterations in the rate of reaction (brought about, in our experiments, by changes in the amount of enzyme, heating or cooling the system, repeated addition of enzyme and combination of the effects of enzyme and temperature), to alteration in the concentration of the components and to alteration in the diffusion of components out of the system (brought about, in our experiments, by changing the area of the membrane). In this connection it is noteworthy that, in the establishment of a new stationary state, there was first an initial comparatively sharp alteration, after which the concentration returned to a level far closer to the original level, which indicates that open systems have the power of dynamic stabilization of the stationary state (in the spirit of an extension of Le Chatelier's principle) [5–7].

It is interesting to note that this latter power is only retained when the changes in open systems are kept within definite limits. If the chemical reaction is accelerated too greatly (by the addition of different amounts of enzyme) or if the diffusion is increased too much, or if the temperature is raised by more than $10°C$ or lowered by more than $5°C$, the ability of the system to compensate for the change falls off and the transition to stationary states follows curve II in Fig. 6, and, at last, there is a general impairment of the possibility of establishing the stationary state (Fig. 6, curve III).

From equation (2) one may determine the quantitative limits of changes in the kinetic parameters of the system compatible with its maintainance of the stabilized stationary states (of the type of Fig. 6, curve I).

In equation (2), as we have already stated, S is the molarity of the inflowing ascorbic acid solution and a is the molarity of the ascorbic acid solution in the stationary state, calculated from the curves in Figs. 3–5 and 7 (sections AB and DE); from the ratio S/a in equation (2) one can calculate the relative change K/K_0 before and after introduction of the enzyme. It must be pointed out that the values for K and K_0 in the apparatus shown in Fig. 2 differ from those in equation (2) in that K_0 denotes the accession of ascorbic acid by inflow and not by diffusion, while K denotes the total loss of ascorbic acid resulting from a chemical reaction of the second order in cylinder A and from diffusion through membrane C; but, in view of the fact that the factors of transfer (K_0 and K_z) are not influenced by the introduction of the enzyme, the relative change K/K_0 calculated from equation (2) remains solely dependent on the change in the kinetic parameter K resulting from the introduction of the enzyme. Furthermore, the ratio of the stationary levels a/a_0, before and after the introduction of the enzyme, was calculated. The results of the calculations from experiments carried out in cylinders I, II, and III are given in Table 1. The columns of this table denote : first, the diameter of the membrane of the cylinder; second, the number of the enzyme preparation and the amount used in mg (the original preparation with an activity of 35% on the purpurogallin scale is referred to as I while the same preparation, after having been kept and having a lower activity, is referred to as II); third, the value of S; fourth, the value of $(S/a)_0$ for the initial stationary state in the absence of the enzyme; fifth, the value of Δ, the relative change in value of K/K_0 for the initial stationary state and the point of the minimum after the introduction of the enzyme; sixth, the value of a/a_0; seventh the character of the stability of the stationary state of the system under the given experimental conditions (according to whether the curves resemble curve I or curve II in Fig. 6).

TABLE I

No. of prep.	Diameter of membrane, (cm)	Enzyme	S	$(S/a)_0$	Δ	a/a_0	Type of curve (Fig. 6)
I	1·6	I, 1	0·0852	3·05	1·04	0·978	I
		I, 3	0·0852	2·94	1·16	0·905	II
		I, 10	0·0852	2·88	1·26	0·858	II
II	2·4	II, 5	0·0852	2·93	1·06	0·984	I
		II, 10	0·0852	2·88	1·075	0·970	I
		II, 25	0·0852	2·92	1·10	0·950	II
III	3·7	II, 15	0·142	4·30	1·09	0·947	I
		II, 60	0·142	4·40	1·12	0·925	I
		II, 120	0·142	4·62	1·22	0·850	II

From Table I it may be seen that the system which we studied could stabilize itself by altering the stationary state when the kinetic parameter Δ was changed by 7–12% and correspondingly when the stationary state is changed by 2–7%. If the kinetic parameter Δ is altered by 16–26% the change in the stationary state no longer follows a curve of the same type as curve I in Fig 6 but follows one like curve II in Fig. 6, with a loss of ability of the system to compensate by a change in the stationary state. It must be noted that the limiting values of these changes are not the same in the various cylinders and under all experimental conditions. Thus, if the diameter of the membrane was 3·7 cm and $S = 0·142$ the change over to a curve like curve II in Fig. 6 occurred at values of Δ between 1·12 and 1·22, while, when the diameter of the membrane was 2·4 cm and $S = 0·0852$ it occurred at values of Δ between 1·075 and 1·10. Similarly, in regard to the size of changes in the stationary level, the limiting figure lies at 0·925 in cylinder III, at 0·970 in cylinder II, and apparently at about 0·978 in cylinder I (and $\Delta = 1·04$). Thus, the 'threshold of endurance' of an open enzymic system depends on the intensity of the processes of diffusion and chemical transformation in the system.

Thus, even in the simplest enzymic reactions in open systems which have been studied, there appear a number of properties which are different from those of the same reaction when it occurs in enclosed systems. Among these properties are: (1) The possibility of maintaining, in the system, concentrations of the reacting substances which do not vary with time (stationary), while, in an enclosed system, these concentrations are bound to fall; (2) the possibility of the catalysts (enzymes) affecting, not only the rate of the reaction, but also the apparent equilibrium of the system, i.e. the stationary concentrations of the reacting substances; (3) the ability of the system to undergo reparative processes (homoeostasis) when the external conditions change (Figs. 3–7); (4) the power of dynamic stabilization of the stationary state, which is, in essence, an extension of Le Chatelier's principle. It only holds good within definite limits of alteration of the external conditions; (5) it must be noted that continual exchange of substances with the external medium is necessary for the very existence of an open system.

It is easy to see that all these new laws apply to any living organism, because they are common to all open systems. Thus, in the course of evolution, catalysed, chemical, open systems may be regarded as a necessary stage in the prebiological period of development, preparing in advance, as it were, some of the properties of the living organism, although these chemical open systems still did not have the full ability to reproduce themselves.

At this Symposium we have heard a number of papers describing the gradual increase in complexity of substances during the history of the Earth, starting with the simplest organic substances and going on to proteins, nucleic acids and nucleoproteins. Three sessions of the Symposium have been devoted to this. Unfortunately the other side of the problem, namely the formation and development of the open systems, within the framework of which complicated macromolecules were assembled and functioned, has received far less ventilation in the Symposium. None the less, in our view, life could not have developed on the basis of isolated macromolecules of whatever degree of complexity. Only the emergence of organized exchange of substances within an open system constructed on the basis of complicated macromolecules of protein, nucleoprotein and other complexes could have led to the reproduction of such a system and thus to the origin of life [5]. This stage is decisive for the problem of the origin of life in that, from that time, the evolution of metabolism in forms of life which were growing more complicated had already begun.

In what circumstances did there occur the formation of open systems of integrated chemical reactions with the elaboration of the macromolecules and molecular structures entering into their composition? Two circumstances must be noted here. In the first place, the elaboration of macromolecules facilitated coacervation and the spatial demarcation from the surrounding medium which is a prerequisite for the existence of open systems. Secondly, we notice a close connection between structures and processes in an open system. Of course, a change in structure or, even more, the introduction of new, complicated macromolecules, could produce a sharp alteration in the processes of exchange, i.e. the whole distribution of the kinetic parameters in the system. It has now been established that the structures of nucleoproteins and, in particular, of the deoxyribonucleic acids of chromosomes, viruses, etc., is of great importance in the handing on of hereditary traits, though all these structures can function only in particular living organisms, i.e. within a framework determined by pre-existing open systems. In normal processes of inheritance, the reproduction of these structures, although its mechanism is not yet clear, takes place simultaneously with the reproduction of the system as a whole. When it remains in existence for a long time such a system cannot be anything other than an open system. From this point of view, study of the properties of catalysed open systems, along with a study of the complicated, specific, molecular structures associated with them, is absolutely necessary for the elucidation of the conditions under which the elementary manifestations of life arose, and for the creation of models of them.

REFERENCES

1. A. I. OPARIN, *The Origin of Life on the Earth*. Oliver & Boyd, Edinburgh, 1957.
2. J. PRIGOGINE, *An Introduction to the Thermodynamics of Irreversible Processes*. New York, 1955.
3. K. G. DENBIGH, *The Thermodynamics of the Steady State*. London & New York, 1951.
4. A. DEAN & C. N. HINSHELWOOD, chapter in *Progress in Biophysics*, vol. 5, p. 1. Pergamon Press, London, 1955.
5. A. G. PASYNSKIĬ, *Usp. sovrem. Biol.* 43, No. 3, 1957.
6. A. BURTON, *J. cell. comp. Physiol.*, 14, 327, 1939.
7. K. G. DENBIGH, M. HICKS & F. PAGE, *Trans. Faraday Soc.*, 44, 479, 1948.

Biosynthesis of Enzymes and their Origin

F. B. STRAUB

Institute of Chemistry, University Medical School, Budapest, Hungary

ONE WAY of contributing to the development of ideas about the origin of life is to search contemporary biochemistry for data revealing the essential difference between living and non-living. Current research has placed the interrelated problems of the formation of proteins and nucleic acids into the foreground of such speculations. It is the formation of enzymes which occupies our thoughts in our laboratory. I should like to present briefly some experimental results and use them to speculate on the evolution of enzymes during the process of the evolution of the living from non-living.

To dive *in medias res*, we have studied the formation of amylase in cell-free systems, homogenates and soluble fractions from pancreas [1–6]. We have established that, measured by enzymic assay, the amylase content of such preparations increases, if adenosine triphosphate (ATP), appropriate salts and two amino acids (e.g. histidine and threonine in case of the dog pancreas) are added. Such formation of amylase in cell-free systems is inhibited by very low concentrations of chloramphenicol, *p*-fluorophenylalanine and diaminoacridines and is also abolished upon incubation with ribonuclease. It could be safely concluded that amylase is formed in the cell-free system through a synthetic reaction.

A deeper understanding of these phenomena was reached when we were able to measure the rate of incorporation of radioactive amino acids into the amylase protein molecule.

We have devised a simple micro-scale isolation method for amylase, which enabled us to isolate the enzyme in a practically pure state and in rather high yield. Using this method we have studied the incorporation of added radioactive amino acids into the amylase, both in tissue slices and in cell-free systems. Whereas there is a very extensive incorporation in tissue slices, absolutely no incorporation was found in a homogenate or in a soluble system. Yet, the increase of amylase activity is comparable in all cases. All data available at present indicate that amylase is formed in the pancreas in at least two distinct steps. One is the formation of an enzymically inactive precursor protein and the other the transformation of the precursor into amylase. Whereas both occur in tissue slices, only the second is preserved in the cell-free systems.

Short of isolating a precursor and demonstrating its transformation into the final product, the best experimental proof of a precursor is the observation of a time lag in the incorporation of radioactive amino acids into the final product. Peters [7], Green & Anker [8], Junqueira *et al.* [9], have tried to apply this method for the study of the formation of serum albumin in liver slices and of the proteins of the pancreatic secretion respectively. However, a time curve of incorporation, showing a lag period, can only be accepted if transport processes and bound forms of the protein can be excluded. On this ground, all the above experiments were rightly criticized. We have therefore studied the time course of the incorporation of radioactive amino acids into the amylase of pancreas slices *in vitro*, taking care to isolate not only the free, but also all of the bound enzyme.

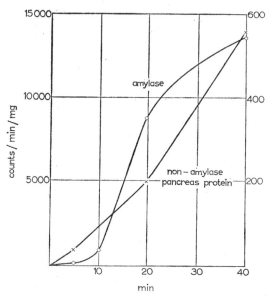

FIG. I.   Time course of incorporation of [^{14}COOH]glycine into pancreas components.

Fig. I shows the result of such an experiment. It is clear that the labelling shows a definite lag period of about 10 minutes. In further experiments we have studied the rate of labelling of the amylase bound to several tissue components. After incubating the slices of pancreas, we have homogenized them and isolated the nuclear fraction, the fraction of heavier and lighter granules, moreover the fraction which is rich in zymogen granules, and finally the soluble fraction. From all these fractions the amylase was isolated and separately examined for the label it contains. Without going into details I want to mention only that the labelling of the amylase found in the heavier granules showed the same lag period. The labelling of the amylase in all other fractions was nearly linear. In short-time experiments the labelling of the amylase in the lighter granules (microsomes) was the highest, yet its time course was also linear (Table I).

It seems therefore that the synthesis of amylase protein begins in the microsomes, where a precursor is formed from amino acids. This is transferred into the heavier granules, where it is synthetically transformed into the active enzyme.

I do not want to go into details of our work on the second phase of these events. The soluble system affords good opportunities for the study of the factors involved. We have succeeded in showing the presence of several components, all of them necessary for the transformation of the precursor protein into amylase. ATP is absolutely needed, two amino acids (threonine and histidine in case of dog pancreas), ribonucleic acid and a protein fraction which can be replaced by a purified enzyme preparation, which catalyses the acyl activation of threonine and histidine.

TABLE I

Purity and specific activity of amylase isolated from different subcellular fractions of pigeon pancreas

Subcellular fractions	No. of exp.	Time of incubation (min.)	Purity of amylase	Specific activity (counts/min./ mg protein)
Zymogen granules	1	30	0·87	1,020
	2	30	0·86	705
	3	15	0·73	595
		30	—	—
	4	10	0·73	745
		30	0·80	3,840
Mitochondria .	1	30	0·87	1,020
	2	30	1·03	7,450
	3	15	0·80	1,720
		30	1·08	10,600
	4	10	1·15	1,000
		30	1·00	11,000
Microsomes .	1	30	0·57	3,900
	2	30	0·64	8,820
	3	15	0·39	1,960
		30	0·34	7,100
	4	10	0·16	1,200
		30	0·24	5,800
Soluble fraction .	1	30	1·00	438
	2	30	0·92	1,210
	3	15	0·91	1,310
		30	0·77	4,700
	4	10	1·00	1,025
		30	1·04	5,850

Slices were incubated in Krebs' bicarbonate solution in the presence of an amino acid mixture, 0·6% glucose and [^{14}COOH]glycine and homogenized and fractionated after experiment in isotonic sucrose.

Summing up we may say that the enzyme amylase is formed through an intermediary stage, and the synthetic transformation of the precursor into the active enzyme is bound to the presence of ribonucleic acid (RNA). If the existence of precursor proteins may be found in the course of the formation of other enzymes also, it is conceivable that one and the same precursor might serve for the production of different specific proteins. The chemistry of corticotropin and the melanophore-stimulating hormone has revealed that the same unit consisting of 13 amino acids occurs in both of them.

It is tempting to apply the same hypothesis to the formation of inducible enzymes. In our laboratory Dr Kramer made the very important observation, that an inducible strain of *Bacillus cereus* will start synthesizing penicillinase if it is treated under appropriate conditions with an extract containing a specific RNA prepared from a strain which has the property of forming penicillinase [10, 11, 12]. I do not want to go into the details of this work, which has already been published, but it must be clear that this phenomenon has nothing to do with the known transformations which were obtained with DNA preparations. Our case is in essence an induction of the synthesis of an enzyme without inductor but with a specific RNA.

Naturally only such strains of *B. cereus* may be used with success, which are inducible, i.e. genetically determined as being able to produce the enzyme. In my opinion the genetic determination, of being inducible or not, may be explained by the presence or absence of a protein precursor which can be transformed into penicillinase.

Earlier work on the formation of β-galactosidase seems to have eliminated this hypothesis but the experimental proof is not convincing. What has been proved is only that the hypothetical precursor does not exist in a measurable concentration. But this is no objection if we suppose that the same precursor, which upon induction gives rise to the induced enzyme protein is converted in uninduced cells into some other specific protein, i.e. into the PZ protein in the case of *Escherichia coli*.

I am aware that our views are not in accord with current trends in the field of protein biosynthesis. Nevertheless, only further work can decide how far the assumption of intermediary stages in protein synthesis can help in clarifying the complicated biochemical and genetical problems involved. Looking now at the problem of the origin of life I should like to present a few remarks on the problem of the origin of the enzymes.

Every year brings out a startling crop of new enzymic activities detected in simple organisms, so that it is quite impossible to imagine that such a living system could have arisen from the non-living. We have to assume that the primary forms have been heterotrophic to a very much greater extent than is known to us to-day. This I believe is not against common sense. Organic compounds are very unstable at the present day, when existing living forms avidly destroy and use up any organic material with which they come into contact. However, before the appearance of life, those organic compounds, which had been accidentally synthesized by inorganic catalysts, must have accumulated all the time.

They may have accidentally been concentrated at some spots and thus might have realized the conditions necessary for the reduplication of the simplest living substance.

The point I want to make is, that the most primitive living system need not have had a broad spectrum of enzymes, it would perhaps have been enough to have a most primitive structure which coupled a breakdown process with a synthetic one producing a limited number of peptide chains. In this case it is supposed that the environment contained all the organic substances necessary for this primitive living thing in the appropriate concentrations. It is only later evolution, which led to the formation of the specific enzymes, necessary for organisms which can live on simpler materials, transforming simpler compounds to the necessary ones.

It appears at first sight a weak point to suppose the induction of enzymes, able to supply materials that are missing from the environment, i.e. induction through the absence of a substrate. This is however not so fantastic if we think of the reversibility of enzyme reactions: the presence of the necessary organic compounds at the beginning elicits the inductive formation of enzymes which decompose them into smaller compounds. When the original compounds were not present any more, only their decomposition products, the reverse function of the enzyme was able to sustain life under the changed conditions.

If we suppose that an organism produces a limited number of precursor proteins or precursor polypeptide chains, and each of these may give rise upon induction to several enzymes, and if we suppose that the presence of a variety of enzymes to catalyse metabolic reactions was not a prerequisite of the primitive living system, we can visualize metabolism, which is the basic definitive property of the living of to-day, as being acquired later in the course of development than reduplication of living matter.

REFERENCES

1. Á. ULLMAN & F. B. STRAUB, *Acta physiol. hung.*, **6**, 377, 1954.
2. Á. ULLMAN & F. B. STRAUB, *Acta physiol. hung.*, **8**, 278, 1955.
3. Á. ULLMAN & F. B. STRAUB, *Acta physiol. hung.*, **10**, 137, 1956.
4. Á. ULLMAN & F. B. STRAUB, *Acta physiol. hung.*, **11**, 11, 1957.
5. Á. ULLMAN & F. B. STRAUB, *Acta physiol. hung.*, **11**, 31, 1957.
6. T. GARZÓ, K. PERL, M. T.-SZABÓ, Á. ULLMAN & F. B. STRAUB, *Acta physiol. hung.*, **11**, 23, 1957.
7. T. PETERS, *J. biol. Chem.*, **200**, 461, 1953.
8. H. GREEN & H. S. ANKER, *J. gen. Physiol.*, **38**, 283, 1955.
9. L. C. U. JUNQUEIRA, C. G. HIRSCH & H. A. ROTHSCHILD, *Biochem. J.*, **61**, 275, 1955.
10. M. KRAMER & F. B. STRAUB, *Acta physiol. hung.*, **11**, 133, 1957.
11. M. KRAMER & F. B. STRAUB, *Acta physiol. hung.*, **11**, 139, 1957.
12. M. KRAMER & F. B. STRAUB, *Biochim. biophys. Acta*, **21**, 401, 1956.

Cell Structure and Protein Synthesis

R. KHESIN

Institute of Biophysics, Academy of Sciences of the U.S.S.R., Moscow

IN CONSIDERING the problem of the origin of life, the most important question is that of origination and reproduction (synthesis) of protein, for the process of protein formation is, in fact, the basic process in vital activity of organisms at all stages of their evolutionary development. As far as we know, at the contemporary stage of evolution synthesis of proteins in natural conditions takes place only within cells. Indeed, organisms which are at the pre-cellular stage of development, such as viruses and phages, are capable of reproducing their own protein component only in the host's cells. Relatively recently, in 1946, Northrop stressed the significance of the fact that three fundamental reactions of living matter, synthesis of proteins, photosynthesis and fixation of nitrogen, all require energy and all are hitherto inseparable from the activity of living, intact cells. Thus, the question arises, whether the whole cell structure in its integrity is required for effecting synthesis of proteins, and what is the role of the various cell components in different phases of this process.

The first data on this question were obtained by Winnick *et al.*, beginning from 1948, when it was shown that labelled amino acids are, in certain conditions, incorporated into the proteins when incubated with preparations obtained from destroyed cells. However, the incorporation of amino acids apparently can take place in experiments *in vitro* as a result of processes by no means identical with synthesis of proteins. Therefore we cannot estimate protein synthesis merely relying on the evidence of incorporation of amino acids *in vitro*.

In 1952 we made an attempt to solve the problem of protein synthesis after destruction of cells; for this purpose we studied the synthesis of an enzyme amylase, during incubation of homogenates and isolated cytoplasmic granules from pigeon's pancreas. In these experiments the tissue was ground and the homogenates, freed from the remaining intact cells and from a considerable part of the nuclei, were centrifuged in order to separate cytoplasmic granules. It was found that during aerobic incubation of a suspension of these granules in a medium containing salts, glucose, adenosine triphosphate (ATP), cytochrome *c*, and a respiratory substrate, in the presence of a set of amino acids, there takes place synthesis of amylase. It should be mentioned that amylase formation required the simultaneous presence in the medium of all those amino acids which form part of the enzyme protein. In the absence of even one of the amino acids, amylase is not synthesized. It should be noted that in these experiments only a small quantity of the enzyme was formed, amounting to a few per cent of its initial content.

The total fraction of cytoplasmic granules was divided by differential centrifuging into mitochondria, microsomes and intermediate granules, termed 'light large granules', which are different from mitochondria or microsomes. Upon separate incubation of each of these three fractions of granules, no synthesis of amylase occurred. It was further found that amylase can be synthesized from amino acids by the 'light large granules' if they are supplemented with mitochondria or with a medium in which mitochondria were preliminarily incubated. The medium is activated and capable of stimulating amylase synthesis in the 'light large granules' only if the mitochondria were incubated in aerobic conditions in the presence of ATP and of a respiratory substrate. Hence, mitochondria form some substances which in addition to amino acids are required by other granules for protein synthesis. These substances ('mitochondrial factor'), are, possibly, identical to the 'Siekevitz factor' required for incorporation of labelled alanine into the proteins during incubation of microsomes. The 'mitochondrial factor' may be formed in the absence of added amino acids. But since mitochondria always contain some quantity of free amino acids, the possibility that amino acids form part of the 'factor' cannot be excluded.

As regards these experiments the objection was brought forward that there might have occurred in the course of incubation of the granules, an activation of some precursor rather than a synthesis of amylase. Therefore experiments were undertaken to determine the total amount of protein before and after incubation of granules in different conditions. It was shown that incubation of 'light large granules' in the presence of amino acids and of the medium preincubated with mitochondria results in an increase of the total protein content of the system. The overall synthesis of total protein, like the formation of individual proteins, requires the simultaneous presence of a full set of amino acids. If the medium is lacking even one of the essential or non-essential amino acids, the rate of synthesis of total protein is greatly lowered. Apparently no synthesis of proteins, with changed amino acid composition, occurs when individual amino acids are absent. These data and those of the experiments on amylase formation show that upon incubation of granules there occurs synthesis of the specific proteins characteristic of the granules of the utilized tissue.

'Light large granules' were obtained not only from the pigeon pancreas, but also from regenerating rat liver. The liver granules synthesize proteins in the same conditions as the pancreatic granules. In these experiments the total amount of protein formed during 30 minutes' incubation occasionally reached 10% of the initial quantity of protein in the granules.

Thus, synthesis of many proteins proceeds in cytoplasmic granules of a definite type, different from the mitochondria and microsomes. The 'light large granules' exhibit a high content of ribonucleic acid; its concentration can reach 260 μg/mg of dry protein, i.e. not less than in the microsomes which were hitherto considered as the cytoplasmic units containing the largest quantity of ribonucleic acid. A study of the incorporation of labelled amino acids injected into the living organism has shown that our conclusion concerning the role of 'light large granules' in protein synthesis, which was based on experiments *in vitro*, also applies to the processes which take place in the intact cells of a living organism.

The conclusion was drawn from the above-mentioned facts that proteins can be synthesized in certain conditions even after destruction of the cell. Integrity of cell structure is not absolutely necessary for protein synthesis, which can also take place in isolated structural components of cells.

Later, in 1953–54, this conclusion was supported by the beautiful experiments of Gale & Folkes with partially destroyed staphylococci, by the studies of Straub on amylase and penicillinase, the investigations of Sisakyan and of other scientists. Now it is established beyond doubt that proteins may be formed not only in intact cells but also in particular types of isolated cytoplasmic granules. The question therefore arises concerning the character and mechanism of participation in this process of other structural components of the cell.

Let us first consider the role played by the mitochondria. As already mentioned, mitochondria form some substances which are required by other granules for the synthesis of proteins. The nature of these substances has not yet been elucidated. The active 'mitochondrial factor' is formed only in the course of aerobic incubation of mitochondria; but in the presence of 'mitochondrial factor' the cytoplasmic granules can synthesize proteins even in anaerobic conditions.

It has been found that the active factor is associated with a fraction obtained from the incubation medium of mitochondria, which contains a large amount of ribonucleic acid (up to 50% of dry weight of the active fraction). It is known that mitochondria contain the major part of the oxidative enzymes of the cell and particularly the cytochrome oxidase system. Hence, it appears that respiration and protein synthesis are topographically separated in the cells; respiration is carried out mainly by mitochondria, while protein synthesis is effected by other granules.

It is also known that mitochondria together with hyaloplasm synthesize many amino acids which are subsequently used for protein formation. Finally, mitochondria are the site of oxidative phosphorylation, which results in the synthesis of the universal energy source, ATP. ATP is required for elaboration of the 'mitochondrial factor', and we may assume that synthesis of proteins is associated with utilization of the energy enclosed in the 'factor'. As a result of glycolysis, ATP is also formed in hyaloplasm.

A comparison of biochemical evidence with cytological data, obtained with the aid of electron microscope by other authors, indicates that the 'light large granules' are derived from the ergastoplasm. Therefore, the latter can be considered as the main site of protein synthesis in the cell. The other structural parts of the cell in the first place, mitochondria and hyaloplasm, are involved in making available the conditions required by ergastoplasmic structures for protein synthesis. This in our opinion is the principal role played by these elements of the cell where proteins are not directly synthesized, or are synthesized on a small scale.

Up till now we have left aside the role played by the cell nucleus; as a matter of fact, the important significance of this component is beyond any doubt.

It is well known that formation in a cell of a variety of active enzymes—proteins —depends on the properties of nuclear constituents. Indeed, it has been shown that definite mutational changes of single genes in lower and higher plants and animals, including man, are associated with changes of enzymic pattern, consisting in inactivation, disappearance, or, on the contrary, activation of individual enzymes. It should be emphasized that the state of the enzymes which catalyse various intermediate steps in the metabolism of different substances (amino acids, vitamins, pigments, coenzymes etc.) depends on the stage of genes.

Numerous studies have shown that transfer of the nuclear substance, deoxyribonucleic acid, from one form of micro-organisms to another can result in appearance in the recipient of the capacity to form new enzymes which were not inherent in the recipient namely before, of enzymes characteristic of those organisms from which the deoxyribonucleic acid was taken. Consequently, it is the specific deoxyribonucleic acid, a characteristic nuclear substance, that can induce synthesis of definite enzymes.

It thus seems certain that the nature of enzymic properties of the cytoplasm depends to a large extent on the nature of the cell nucleus. However, this is not contradictory to the fact that the bulk of proteins are synthesized in the cytoplasm rather than in the nucleus. Brachet *et al.* have shown that a considerable quantity of proteins is formed in enucleated cell fragments of some unicellular organisms. We may assume that once the cytoplasmic elements were formed, they are capable of functioning relatively independently of the nucleus. This is confirmed by a number of data, among which we may cite the following fact, revealed in the course of our studies on the phenomenon of 'maternal effect' in *Drosophila*.

It is known that some lethal mutations cause in the homozygous state death not only of the whole organism but also of individual cells, which can be revealed with the aid of so-called somatic crossing-over. Such lethal mutations were named 'cell lethals'. However, it was found that embryos developing in the eggs of a normal mother, but homozygous 'cell lethals', develop normally during a long period of time. This shows that life and growth of the embryonic cells depend on the cytoplasm formed in the body of the maternal organism before fertilization. After the cytoplasm has been formed in the presence of normal nuclei, it functions relatively independently of the nucleus, and the abnormal structure of the nuclear substance of the embryo itself is revealed only very gradually, at late stages of embryonic development.

These facts and many others show that the character of cytoplasm elements is, to some degree, dependent on the nucleus. Apparently, the nucleus influences in the first place the enzymic properties of the cytoplasm. In this connection it should be remembered that some coenzymes, the pyridine nucleotides, are synthesized in the nuclei.

The nature of the influence of the nucleus on cytoplasmic functions has not yet been made clear. It has been suggested that deoxyribonucleic acid participates in the formation of specific ribonucleic acid in the nucleus; the ribonucleic acid then enters the cytoplasm and controls the specificity of proteins synthesized in it. However, the synthesis of cytoplasmic ribonucleic acid in the nuclei has not yet been finally proved.

It seems probable that the nucleus is the site of synthesis of some of the enzymes forming part of cytoplasmic structures. But it is known that certain enzymes found in cytoplasm (e.g. catalase, according to Brachet) can also be formed after the nuclei are removed. At the present very few data are available concerning protein synthesis in the nuclei. Allfrey & Mirsky were the first to show that during incubation of isolated thymus nuclei in certain conditions there occurs incorporation of amino acids into proteins but these data are not conclusive, for the incorporation of amino acids does not prove the *de novo* synthesis of protein molecules.

Our preliminary experiments have shown that, during incubation of isolated nuclei, proteins are synthesized from amino acids approximately in the same conditions in which proteins are formed during incubation of cytoplasmic granules. The nature of the proteins synthesized by nuclei is still unknown.

Summing up all stated above we can state that protein synthesis is effected in the cell in certain cytoplasmic structures of the ergastoplasm and, perhaps, in the nuclei, but conditions for the synthesis are created by different cell components. Moreover, the very character of the structures involved in the synthesis of proteins depends on other parts of the cell, especially on the cell nucleus.

It is well known that all living structures capable of synthesizing proteins contain, in addition to protein, nucleic acid of some type. In this respect the 'light large granules' of the cytoplasm are not an exception. As mentioned above, they contain ribonucleic acid. Beside this they contain a considerable quantity of lipids. In general these structures represent comparatively highly-organized formations, possessing, for example, a membrane and correspondingly endowed with osmotic activity. They contain some enzymes, such as cathepsin, ribonuclease, phosphatase and others. In this connection the question arises as to the nature of the chemical components of cytoplasmic granules which are directly required for protein synthesis. This question involves another one: is protein synthesis possible after destruction not only of the cells, but also of the intracellular granules?

In order to answer these questions, experiments were undertaken in which the 'light large granules' of the regenerating rat liver were destroyed by treatment with acetone or ethanol. The preparations obtained from the granules after removal of lipids consisted practically of two components—protein and ribonucleic acid. It was found that during incubation of such preparations in the presence of amino acids and the medium produced by mitochondria there takes place a formation of protein, the amount of which, within 30 minutes of incubation, is increased by 5–10%. Thus, the destruction of granules does not deprive them of the capacity to synthesize proteins. Synthesis of some quantity of protein, at least, may be effected in systems consisting of protein and nucleic acid, provided that amino acids and certain cofactors are made available.

Our preparations cannot be defined as individual nucleoproteins, but the experimental results suggest the possibility of protein synthesis in isolated nucleoproteins.

The data obtained show that protein synthesis requires a system devoid of morphological structure, and only possessing chemical structures which consist of protein and nucleic acid. It seems that in adequate conditions nucleoproteins may form not only proteins, but also nucleic acid, i.e. be capable of self-repro-duction. However, it is necessary to bear in mind that the adequate conditions for protein synthesis in these systems depend upon the interaction of practically all the cell components, including, first of all, nuclei, mitochondria and hyalo-plasm. Namely this, apparently, explains the fact that viruses, which also consist of a protein and nucleic acid, can be reproduced only in living cells where they are provided with the adequate conditions.

We can conclude with the statement: protein synthesis is catalysed directly by a chemical system representing a complex of protein and nucleic acid; this system can be devoid of morphological organization form. The cell structure at the present stage of evolution of life is necessary only for creating conditions that make possible the synthesis of protein by nucleoproteins, i.e. first and fore-most, for providing the latter with the necessary energy and materials for the synthetic processes.

Some Relationships Between Coacervates and Enzymes

E. MACOVSCHI

*Institute of Biochemistry, Academy of Sciences of the Rumanian People's Republic,
Bucharest*

THE FIRST investigations of the relationship between coacervates and enzymes were begun recently by A. I. Oparin and his colleagues [1–5]. These investigations were aimed at elucidating the relationships between coacervates and enzymes which were either incorporated in artificial coacervates or are present in natural structures similar to coacervates. Investigations of other relationships such as the influence of coacervate droplets on enzymic processes taking place in the surrounding liquid, the action of enzymes on coacervates as such and the introduction of enzymes present on artificial and natural structures, which are afterwards introduced into coacervates, have been started in our laboratory.

We began our study of the influence of dispersed droplets on enzymic reactions taking place in the surrounding liquid, with hydrophobic emulsions.

By the use of emulsions of benzene, toluene and *cyclo*hexane in aqueous solutions of catalase [6–9] and polyphenol oxidase [10] with the appropriate substrates, and also with an emulsion of lecithin in an aqueous solution of succinic dehydrogenase [11] it has been shown that the presence of the emulsified phase can affect the enzymic reactions in question, for example, by suppressing them. It was found that the nature of the lipid–water interface which is formed during emulsification plays an important part in the processes of absorption and inactivation of the enzymes. Thus, the addition of a relatively insignificant quantity (2%) of higher fatty acids or higher alcohols to the emulsified phase decreases the inhibitory power of the emulsified phase, while, in the presence of cholesterol, the enzymic reaction proceeds in almost the same way as it does in the absence of the emulsified phase.

This marked change in the properties of the lipid-water interface under the influence of higher fatty acids and alcohols and cholesterol was confirmed by altering the permeability of these 'liquid membranes' [12, 13] by means of the droplet method which we have worked out [14, 15].

Coming to coacervates, and bearing in mind their hydrophilic character, it might be expected, *a priori*, that they would show more complicated relationships with enzymes than hydrophobic emulsions.

Investigations of the action of urease on urea in the presence of a protamine-gum arabic coacervate [16] showed that, in both cases, the dispersed coacervate drops slowed the course of the enzymic reaction.

In spite of the apparent similarity with what has been established in the case of emulsions, the mechanism of the effect of coacervate droplets on the reactions in question is completely different. While hydrophobic emulsions of hydrocarbons adsorb and partially inactivate enzymes, coacervate droplets draw the enzymes into themselves from the surrounding aqueous medium, lowering their concentration and, therefore, decreasing their activity. This means that, as D. N. Nasonov [17] would have expressed it, we are here dealing with sorptional processes in which an important part is played, not only by the permeability of the material of the coacervate, but also by the insertion of 'liquid envelopes' in relation to the enzyme if structures of this sort become differentiated on the surface of the coacervate drops, or simply 'liquid surfaces' separating the coacervate drops from the surrounding medium. Naturally, the introduction of lipid complexes into protein coacervates, studied by G. A. Deborin [18] can create new possibilities for changing the properties of the coacervates, causing their properties to be more like those of hydrophobic emulsions.

The gradual sorption of enzymes by coacervate droplets from the surrounding medium is analogous to the well known sorption of dyes and other substances [19, 20]. We are convinced that study of this process, and also of the possible passing out of enzymes from coacervates, of which A. I. Oparin has reminded us to-day, could give new data for increasing the exactitude of our knowledge of the distribution of enzymes between living material and the vacuoles adjacent to it and other liquids, the interaction between the coacervate surfaces of living material and the enzymic reactions which occur in these same liquids, the intracellular and intercellular migration of enzymes, the excretion of enzymes by organisms, by their transmission to the soil through the roots of plants, etc.

The sorption of enzymes by coacervate drops is also interesting from the point of view of the origin of life. It indicates that the appearance of the first enzymes in coacervate formations could have occurred, not only by their being formed within the coacervates as described by A. I. Oparin [21] (the endogenous method), but also on account of the entrance into the coacervate drops of various enzymically active proteins, if any could have made their appearance in the waters of the Earth independently of the process of coacervation (exogenous method).

Another field of interest to us is the action of enzymes in the surrounding medium on coacervates as such. With this in view we have, so far, studied the formation and behaviour of a coacervate of gelatin and gum arabic in the presence of pepsin, trypsin and papain and some digestive juices [22].

It was found that, in the presence of these enzymes, the intensity of coacervation falls so far that, in some cases, e.g. when papain is used, coacervate droplets cannot separate out. The addition of the enzymes mentioned to a ready-made coacervate also has a destructive effect and often leads to the rapid disappearance of the coacervate drops.

And yet this action of proteolytic enzymes on a coacervate of gelatin and gum arabic is not enzymic in character. It occurs even when the pH of the medium is of such a value that the enzymic activity is inhibited and it is not accompanied by proteolysis in so far as the formation of free amino acids is not observed and it occurs too fast compared to the rates of the reactions brought about by the enzymes in question under ordinary conditions. In all probability the enzymes, in these cases, affect the coacervates by virtue of being proteins rather than by virtue of being enzymes. What might be called their 'coacervatolytic activity' increases with an increase in their concentration in the solution; in pepsin and trypsin the activity is decreased by denaturation while in papain it is completely destroyed; furthermore, some native proteins which have no proteolytic activity, such as haemoglobin, egg albumin and others [23] behave just like the enzymes referred to in relation to a coacervate of gelatin and gum arabic.

Experiments have shown that human gastric juice and duodenal juice give almost the same results as solutions of the corresponding proteolytic enzymes. These experiments showed that the salts of the biliary acids can, to some extent, stabilize the drops of a coacervate of gelatin and gum arabic. However, not all protein-containing coacervates behave like coacervates of gelatin and gum arabic in relation to proteolytic enzymes; for example, some coacervates obtained from blood serum show quite different properties, so that one can study proteolysis on drops of them.

It is obvious that the synthesis of proteins, which must have occurred in the remote past at a particular level of development of native coacervates, could have been of decisive significance for the further evolution of coacervate drops. The appearance of proteins with 'coacervatolytic' properties would have led to the rapid destruction of coacervate drops and it was only the synthesis, within the coacervate drops, of proteins which did not destroy these drops which could have had a positive significance for the evolutionary transition from coacervates to the organic formations which constituted the germs of life.

A few words remain to be said about the introduction into coacervates of artificial and natural formations (structures) containing enzymes.

The possibility of incorporating, into coacervate drops, solid and liquid particles such as fine particles of Indian ink, indigo, collargol, emulsified droplets, erythrocytes, bacteria, pollen grains, spores and even such unicellular organisms as *Euglena*, was demonstrated by H. G. Bungenberg de Jong even in his earliest papers [19]. This subject has also been touched on by other authors such as A. S. Troshin [20].

Our work in this field has only just begun. By bringing about the formation of coacervates in aqueous suspensions of adsorbent materials on which enzymes are adsorbed; in suspensions of plastids, nuclei and other intracellular formations; in emulsions of coacervates which have already had enzymes introduced into them and so forth, one may bring about the inclusion of these particles in coacervate drops or the mass of the coacervate, and one may study the behaviour of the enzymes under these peculiar conditions which approximate to those found in living organisms.

The ease with which all sorts of suspensions and emulsions can be introduced into coacervate drops is also of interest in connection with the theory of the origin of life.

It may be supposed that, at the period when coacervates were formed, the waters of the ocean must have been, not merely a solution of various compounds, but also a medium in which were emulsified and suspended particles of diverse organic substances which are insoluble in water. Furthermore, there must have been suspended in the primaeval waters many mineral substances similar to the detritus suspended in the water of the present day. Thus, the primary formation of coacervates could have taken place, not only in a macrohomogeneous solution, but also in macroheterogeneous medium, i.e. under conditions which would make possible the incorporation in the coacervate drops of solid and liquid particles of various sorts. In this case, however, the incorporated particles could either preclude the further evolution of the coacervates or hasten the formation of the internal structures to which A. I. Oparin attaches such great importance in the process of the genesis of life.

The evidence presented in this paper about the relationship between coacervates and enzymes is too meagre and is only of a preliminary nature. Some of the considerations discussed in connection with the problem of the origin of life are of the same nature. They lead, however, to the conclusion that work in this field may provide interesting results, not only for scientific, but also for practical purposes.

REFERENCES

1. A. I. OPARIN, *The Origin of Life on the Earth*, p. 321. Oliver & Boyd, Edinburgh, 1957.
2. A. I. OPARIN, *Dokl. Akad. Nauk S.S.S.R.*, **104**, 581, 1955.
3. T. N. EVREINOVA, T. A. SHUBERT & M. N. NESTYUK, *Dokl. Akad. Nauk S.S.S.R.*, **105**, 137, 1955.
4. A. I. OPARIN, p. 428.
5. A. I. OPARIN, N. S. GEL'MAN & I. G. ZHUKOVA, *Dokl. Akad. Nauk S.S.S.R.*, **105**, 1036, 1955.
6. E. M. MACOVSCHI & V. GHEORGHE, *Comunicările Academiei R.P.R.* [*Comun. Acad. R.P.R.*], **1**, 477, 1951.
7. E. MACOVSCHI & V. GHEORGHE, *Buletin Stiintific al Sectici de Stiinte biologice a Academici R.P.R.* [*Bul. Stiint. Sect. Stiint. biol. Acad. R.P.R.*], **4**, 473, 1952.
8. E. MACOVSCHI, *Comun. Acad. R.P.R.*, **2**, 29, 1952.
9. V. GHEORGHE, *Comun. Acad. R.P.R.*, **2**, 35, 1952.
10. E. MACOVSCHI, & C. PRETORIAN, *Comun. Acad. R.P.R.*, **1**, 1063, 1951.
11. S. VASU, *Commun. Acad. R.P.R.*, **5**, 529, 1955.
12. E. MACOVSCHI & C. IORDACHE, *Comun. Acad. R.P.R.*, **1**, 409, 1951.
13. C. IORDACHE, *Studii si Cercetări de chimie ale Academiei R.P.R.*, **1**, 51, 1953.
14. E. MACOVSCHI, *Bul. Stiint. Sect. Stiint biol. Acad. R.P.R.*, **3**, 229, 1951.
15. E. MACOVSCHI, *Comun. Acad. R.P.R.*, **2**, 137, 1952.
16. E. MACOVSCHI, S. VASU & M. CÂRSTEANU, *Revue de Chimie (Roumania)* **2**, 279, 1957.
17. D. N. NASONOV, *Membrannaya kontseptsiya v uchenii o pronitsaemosti.* In Sbornik: *Problema pronitsaemosti. Trudy konferentsii Moskovskogo obshchestva fiziologov, biokhimikov i farmakologov*, 13–17.v.36. Medgiz, Moscow & Leningrad, 1939.
18. G. A. DEBORIN, p. 470.
19. H. G. BUNGENBERG DE JONG, *Protoplasma*, **15**, 110, 156, 160, 1932.
20. A. S. TROSHIN, *Problema kletochnoĭ pronitsaemosti*, Izd. Akad. Nauk S.S.S.R., pp. 52, 72. Moscow & Leningrad, 1956.
21. A. I. OPARIN, *The Origin of Life on the Earth*, p. 301. Oliver & Boyd, Edinburgh, 1957.
22. E. MACOVSCHI, L. ARNET & B. ROZENZWEIG, *Revue de Chimie (Roumania)* **2**, 287, 1957.
23. L. ARNET, *Studii si cercetari de Biochimie (Roumania)*, **1**, 363, 1958.

Protein Complexes as Biochemically Active Systems

G. A. DEBORIN

A. N. Bakh Institute of Biochemistry, U.S.S.R. Academy of Sciences, Moscow

SCIENCE TO-DAY is in possession of certain information about the possible paths of evolution of matter from inorganic compounds resulting in the appearance of organic substances, amino acids, polypeptides, etc. The least-studied stage in the development of matter towards the appearance of life seems to be the transition from relatively simple protein-like substances to biochemical systems of ever increasing complexity and then to complex protein systems displaying metabolism [1].

The data accumulated by biochemistry indicate that, owing to their high reactivity, proteins do not, as a rule, occur in contemporary living organisms in the free state, but are to be found in them in various complex formations with one another and with other substances. This appears to be one of the causes of what is known as the microheterogeneity of proteins. It is also characteristic that most enzymes are compounds of proteins with non-protein substances, which are largely responsible for the specificity and activity of enzymes.

These facts suggest that the first phase in the appearance of multimolecular protein systems might have been the formation of complexes of varying degrees of complexity, the components of which might have been primordial proteins and various groups of non-protein substances that, compounded with a corresponding protein, become capable of diverse transformations. The formation of such complexes may have been one of the stages in the appearance of conjugated proteins, including enzymes. In the process of their subsequent evolution these compounds acquired the specific functions in which they fundamentally differ from their constituents.

In connection with these concepts it appears highly interesting to elucidate the mechanism of formation and biochemical peculiarities of protein complexes, since the data obtained in this way would enable us to gain an insight into certain chemical processes underlying biological phenomena.

The information available concerning the interaction of proteins with other proteins [2] nucleic acids [3], polysaccharides [4], lipids [5], detergents [6], ions [7] etc., indicates that, depending on the chemical nature of the reactants, the character of the bonds arising between them may differ. Evidence is on hand pointing to the fact that the links between the components of such complexes may be based either on electrostatic interactions, or hydrogen bonds, or van der Waals' forces, or, finally, on covalent chemical bonds. It is natural to expect that the functions of both the protein and the non-protein components of the complex will depend on the type of bond, on the chemical groups affected by them and their influence on protein macrostructure. What appears particularly important is the alteration of the catalytic functions of the proteins in the process of complex formation, which, judging from all the available information, may play a certain controlling role in the creation of the multitude of enzymic processes which take place in a living organism. The discovery of such alterations would provide a basis for a deeper understanding of the mechanism of enzymic activity of the living cell and would help to establish certain notions concerning the possible paths of evolution of the primary proteins.

Owing to the importance of nucleic acids and lipids in the organism, investigators naturally gave their attention first to studying the influence of these types of compounds on the activity of certain proteolytic and hydrolytic enzymes. Slavik & Smetana [8] demonstrated that yeast ribonucleic acid (RNA) and adenine in physiological concentrations inhibit the action of proteinases below their isoelectric point. Chepinoga & Pavlovskiĭ [9] established the reversible inhibition of the enzymic activity of aldolase and enolase on their combining with nucleic acids, especially with highly polymerized deoxyribonucleic acid. It was discovered by Šorm & Grubešova [10] that pancreatic proteases are inactivated by pancreatic RNA. It is noteworthy that the inhibition of the protease activity of chymotrypsin does not involve alteration of its ability to participate in polypeptide synthesis. Robert & Polonovsky [11] found that the destruction of lipoprotein complexes enhances the activity of milk xanthine oxidase, while Spiegelman [12] revealed that treatment of the protoplasts of *Bacillus megaterium* by trypsin and lipase totally suppresses the synthesis of enzymes in these protoplasts. There are a number of indications that protein substrates, when associated with nucleic acids, lipids or polysaccharides, are more stable to attack by a number of enzymes [13]. The study of the action of pharmacologic agents in the organism revealed that interaction with proteins reduces the physiological activity of a number of drugs. Thus, blood plasma lowers the activity of penicillin [14]; interaction with serum albumin reduces the antibacterial activity of oleic acid with regard to *Mycobacterium tuberculosis* [15] and the haemolytic activity of the fatty acids with respect to erythrocytes [16], and so on. The limited data at our disposal at present thus definitely confirm the view that when proteins form complexes with other substances, this can appreciably alter the activity of both components.

Another trend in the study of lipoproteins aims at elucidating their rôle in the formation of coacervates, the surface layers of cellular organoids, protoplasmic membranes and other structural elements of living matter. Bungenberg de Yong [17] demonstrated, in a series of papers, that the first stage in protein and lipid coacervation is the formation of complexes between them, with surface phenomena at the interphase playing a substantial part. There is an extensive literature [18–20] to confirm that protein and lipoprotein surface layers play an important part in the formation of cellular structures, determining not only the permeability of these structures, but also, largely, the metabolic processes in the protoplasm. It is natural to assume therefore, that great importance in establishing the rôle of morphological structures in biochemical processes in the cell attaches, among other problems, to the study of the whole series of problems relating to the interaction of proteins and lipids.

Model experiments were staged by the author of the present paper to study the interaction of certain proteins with hydrophobic substances of a lipid nature; their interaction, by virtue of the specific features in the chemical structure of the constituents, is due chiefly to van der Waals' forces, and does not cause substantial changes in the energy characteristics of the protein molecule. In earlier papers [21] it was pointed out that egg albumin, when mixed with crystalline ergosterol at 37–40 °C, forms a complex containing one sterol molecule for every two protein molecules. Further investigations revealed that the protein-sterol complex is stable within a definite pH range (4–5) close to the isoelectric point of the protein. To ascertain what factors influence the formation and stability of protein–sterol complexes, we investigated the action of various denaturing agents. It was shown [22] that the addition of guanidine or urea to the initial protein solution inhibits its ability to form a complex with sterol, while their addition to the already formed complex does not lead to its decomposition in these same conditions, provided the optimal range of pH for complex formation is retained. It was also found [23] that the addition of 0·25% of cysteine to the solution stabilizes the complex to ultra-violet irradiation, which in the absence of cysteine decomposes the complex. From these experiments we drew the conclusion that the ability of the protein to form complexes with sterol depends on the preservation of its native structure, and that the complexes of egg albumin with ergosterol are more stable with respect to denaturing influences than the initial protein is.

In subsequent papers [24–25] we established, in conformity with the facts known concerning natural lipoproteins, that the lability of artificial protein–lipid complexes is not only determined by the state of the protein molecule, but also depends on the condition of the sterol molecule. More specifically, it was established that if a solution of the complex is kept in contact with air for several hours, it is split into its initial components. The decomposition of the complex in these conditions was found to be due to sterol oxidation, which can be catalysed by copper ions, just as in the case of natural lipoproteins. This pointed to a certain similarity between our artificial protein–lipid complexes and the lipoproteins isolated from organisms; the similarity is in composition and stability conditions, which helps to understand the factors controlling the transformations of these important compounds in the organism. It should be noted that we established formation of the above-mentioned protein–sterol complexes by means of two independent methods: by studying the isotherms of compressibility of the protein in a unimolecular layer on 5% ammonium sulphate solution and by the method of paper electrophoresis.

It was particularly interesting, in relation to the problem we are studying, to obtain complexes of lipid substances with enzyme proteins and to investigate the changes in enzyme activity resulting from complex formation. For this purpose we prepared complexes of trypsin with ergosterol according to the method described earlier. The formation of these complexes was determined on the basis of the isotherms of trypsin compressibility in a monolayer on 5% ammonium sulphate solution. Fig. 1 gives curves for the dependence of the surface pressure F on the product FA in a unimolecular layer for trypsin (curve I) and for the trypsin-ergosterol complex (curve II). These curves [26] indicate that the molecular weight of trypsin in the monolayer, as calculated according to the equation of ideal gases from the length of the section β between the intersections of the curves with the FA axis, equals 40,000 for trypsin and 80,000 for its complex with ergosterol. Thus just as in the case of egg albumin, trypsin, in forming a complex with ergosterol, produces associates detectable in the monolayer. Special experiments revealed that this complex is maintained during 48 hours at a pH of 7·5–8·1.

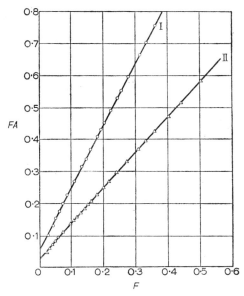

FIG. 1. The dependence of the surface pressure F on the product FA in a monomolecular layer for trypsin (I) and for the trypsin–ergosterol complex (II).

The proteolytic activity of trypsin was determined spectrophotometrically according to the Kunitz method [27] at 280 mμ and according to a modified Kunitz method at 400 mμ, as well as by determining the amino nitrogen in the incubated sample according to Van Slyke's method after precipitation by trichloroacetic acid.

Fig. 2 gives curves for the digestion of serum albumin by trypsin (curve I) and by the trypsin—ergosterol complex (curve II) as a function of the amount of enzyme. Here the extinction at 280 mμ is plotted against the enzyme-substrate ratio. It follows from these curves that the complex has a higher proteolytic activity than pure trypsin, especially at enzyme/substrate ratios within the range 1/200–1/50. Table 1 lists the results of another experiment. In this case the optical densities (ΔE_1 for trypsin and ΔE_2 for the complex) are obtained by subtracting the optical density after 90 minutes of proteolysis from the optical

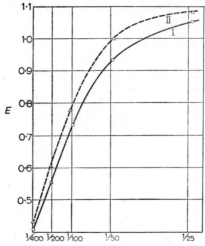

FIG. 2. The digestion of serum albumin by trypsin (I) and by the trypsin–ergosterol complex (II) as a function of the amount of enzyme (see text).

density at zero time. These data are in accord with the experimental results in Fig. 2. On the basis of these data we selected an enzyme/substrate ratio lying between 1/50–1/100 to study the kinetics of proteolysis of serum albumin by trypsin–ergosterol complex.

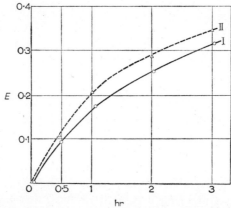

FIG. 3. The kinetic curves for serum albumin proteolysis by trypsin (I) and by its complex with ergosterol (II) obtained spectrophotometrically.

Fig. 3 gives the kinetic curves for serum albumin proteolysis by trypsin (curve I) and by its complex with ergosterol (curve II); the curves are obtained spectrophotometrically. Fig. 4 gives similar curves representing the rates of increase of amino N, as determined by the method of Van Slyke.

Here the volumetric readings in ml N_2 are plotted against the time in hours. From the data of Fig. 3 and Fig. 4 it follows that the formation of the complex appreciably increases the proteolytic activity of the enzyme and the degree of substrate hydrolysis. Similar data were obtained by us for the proteolysis by trypsin and by its complex with ergosterol of heat-denatured egg albumin and of casein.

Special experiments have been carried out in order to study the changes in proteolysis of serum albumin by another proteolytic enzyme, viz. pepsin, as dependent on whether pepsin is free or forms a complex with ergosterol. The

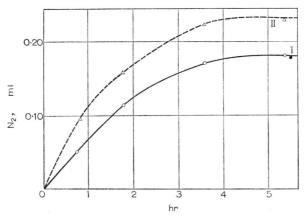

FIG. 4. The kinetic curves for serum albumin proteolysis by trypsin (I) and by its complex with ergosterol (II) determined by Van Slyke's method.

TABLE I

Activity of trypsin and trypsin-ergosterol complex as a function of enzyme amount

(Determined at 400 mμ—see text)

Enzyme/substrate ratio	ΔE_1 for trypsin	ΔE_2 for complex	$\Delta E_2 - \Delta E_1$
1/400	140	160	20
1/200	200	230	30
1/100	275	295	20
1/50	307	330	23
1/25	325	360	35

results of the experiments, in which the same procedure was used as in trypsin experiments (enzyme/substrate ratio 1/500 and 1/1000), showed that with the pepsin–ergosterol complex proteolysis proceeds at a much higher rate than with pepsin alone).

It is concluded, therefore, that the course of proteolysis is changed by the interaction of the enzyme protein with lipid substances. In our view [28], these results indicate that the formation and breakdown of protein–lipid complexes is one of the possible tools for controlling enzymic processes going on within the organism.

As pointed out above, there are a number of indications that the activity of
certain enzymes is altered in the presence of nucleic acids. The study of these
phenomena has in the main centred around the rôle of ribonucleic acid and has
been carried out, for the most part, at pH values below the isoelectric point of
the enzyme and the substrate. In these conditions, as is known, insoluble nucleoproteins are precipitated, this being the result of the formation of salt-like links
between the acid and basic groups of the reactants. We thought that it might be
preferable to study the effect of deoxyribonucleic acid (DNA) on the proteolytic
process under conditions in which the interaction of DNA with the enzyme does
not cause precipitation. Therefore we conducted our experiments at pH values
above the isoelectric point of trypsin and serum albumin, i.e., at the optimum
values for proteolysis (phosphate buffer, pH 8–8·4). The DNA used was obtained

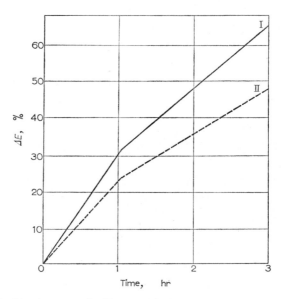

FIG. 5.   The kinetic curves for the proteolysis of serum albumin by trypsin (I)
and by trypsin with DNA (II).

from calf's thymus. The molecular weight of the DNA, determined viscosi-
metrically [29] was 0·8-1·5·10⁶. The kinetics of proteolysis were determined by
the modified spectrophotometric method of Kunitz at 400 mμ.

Fig. 5 gives the kinetic curves for the proteolysis of serum albumin by trypsin
(curve I) and trypsin with DNA (curve II). Here the difference between the
initial and subsequently measured value of extinction (the latter in percentages
of the initial value) is plotted against the time in hours. It is apparent that in the
presence of DNA the proteolytic process is retarded and the degree of hydrolysis
decreased.

To gain an insight into the mode of inhibition of proteolysis by DNA we
studied the effect of preliminary incubation of the enzyme or substrate with
DNA. The curves obtained are shown in Fig. 6. Curve I is for serum albumin

preincubated with NaCl for 45 minutes at 37 °C, after which the curve for proteolysis by trypsin (added after preincubation) was plotted. Curve II is for serum albumin preincubated with DNA, after which the course of proteolysis by trypsin was plotted.

Curve III is for trypsin preincubated with NaCl, after which substrate was added and the proteolysis curve plotted then. In the case of curve IV the trypsin was preincubated with DNA, after which proteolysis was plotted for serum albumin. For curves II and IV the amount of DNA was the same and the DNA/protein ratio was equal to 0·066; the enzyme/substrate ratio in these experiments was 1/70.

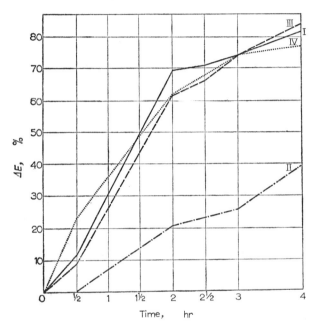

FIG. 6. The effect of preincubation of the enzyme or substrate with DNA on the proteolysis of serum albumin by trypsin (see text)

It follows from the experiment that marked inhibition of proteolysis occurred only if there was preliminary incubation of the substrate with DNA, whereas preliminary incubation of the enzyme with DNA had practically no effect on the kinetics of proteolysis. The conclusion to be drawn from these results is that DNA in the serum albumin–trypsin system affects not the enzyme, but the substrate, producing inhibition of the proteolytic process.

The author of the present paper also studied the influence of DNA on proteolysis at various DNA/substrate ratios. These findings are given in Fig. 7, where the curve for the proteolysis of serum albumin by trypsin in the absence of DNA served as a control. The DNA/substrate ratio for curves I, II and III is equal to 0·33, 0·66 and 0·99 respectively. It was also found that at a DNA/substrate ratio equal to 1/100 proteolysis is likewise retarded appreciably.

Inhibition of proteolysis in the presence of DNA was also observed when heat-denatured egg albumin or casein were used as substrates of tryptic hydrolysis.

The experimental results here reported show that enzymic processes *in vitro* can be affected by the presence in the reaction mixture of small quantities of substances such as lipids or nucleic acids, which are capable of interacting with the proteins taking part in the process. In the highly complex and multicomponent system of the living cell such effects are evidently much more pronounced, and they are made still more complicated by the influence of the numerous interfaces between cellular organoids.

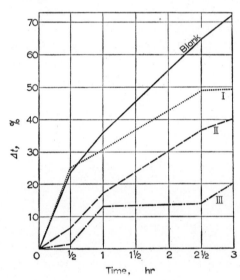

FIG. 7. The kinetic curves for the proteolysis of serum albumin by trypsin at various DNA/substrate ratios (see text).

The author is of the opinion that the formation of complexes by primordial proteins with one another and with other organic substances could have given rise to an enormous variety of compounds and chemical processes which, in the course of subsequent evolution, could have produced various conjugated proteins possessing specific biochemical functions, and could have engendered the whole set of enzymic processes essential to life.

The author wishes to acknowledge the participation of V. Z. Baranova, M. I. Bystrova and G. F. Ivashchenko in the experimental work.

REFERENCES

1. A. I. OPARIN, *The Origin of Life on Earth.* 3rd. ed. Izd. Akad. Nauk S.S.S.R., Moscow, 1957.
2. D. F. WAUGH, *Advanc. Protein Chem.*, **9**, 326, 1954.
3. O. P. CHEPINOGA, *Nucleic Acids and Their Biological Significance.* Izd. Akad. Nauk Ukr.S.S.R., Kiev, 1956.
4. E. CHARGAFF, M. ZIFF & D. H. MOORE, *J. biol. Chem.*, **139**, 383, 1941.

5. D. F. DERVICHIAN, *Discuss. Faraday Soc.*, **6**, 7, 1949.
6. F. PUTNAM, *Advances in Protein Chemistry*, **4**, 80, 1948.
7. J. KLOTZ, *The Proteins*, vol. I. New York, 1953.
8. K. SLAVIK & R. SMETANA, *Chem. Listy*, **47**, 253, 1953.
9. O. CHEPINOGA & I. PAVLOVSKIĬ *Zh. Biokhem.*, **28**, 308, 1956.
10. F. ŠORM & M. GRUBEŠOVA, *Sborn. chechoslov. khim. Rabot*, **20**, 531, 1955.
11. L. ROBERT & J. POLONOVSKY, *Discuss. Faraday Soc.*, **20**, 54, 1955.
12. S. SPIEGELMAN, in *Ionizing Radiations and Cell Metabolism* (Ed. by G. WOLSTENHOLME & C. COPNOR). Churchill, London, p. 185, 1956.
13. S. VON PRZYLECKI, *Enzymologia*, **8**, 153, 1937.
14. R. TOMPSETT, S. SCHULZ & W. MCDERMOTT, *J. Bact.*, **53**, 581, 1947.
15. B. DAVIS & R. DUBOS, *J. exp. Med.*, **86**, 215, 1947.
16. P. BOVER, G. BALLOU & J. LUCK, *J. biol. Chem.*, **167**, 407, 1947.
17. H. BUNGENBERG DE JONG, *Proc. Acad. Sci. Amst.*, **45**, 601, 1942; **55**, 317, 329, 338, 347, 360, 1952; **56**, 203, 1953; **57**, 1, 13, 192, 204, 285, 1954.
18. H. BOOIJ, *Discuss. Faraday Soc.*, **6**, 143, 1949.
19. E. PONDER, *Discuss. Faraday Soc.*, **6**, 152, 1949.
20. T. HAYASHI, *Amer. Nat.*, **87**, 209, 1953.
21. G. DEBORIN & L. GORBACHEVA, *Biokhimiya*, **18**, 618, 1953.
22. G. DEBORIN & L. GORBACHEVA, *Dokl. Akad. Nauk S.S.S.R.*, **95**, 317, 1954.
23. G. DEBORIN & O. SHIBANOVA, *Dokl. Akad. Nauk S.S.S.R.*, **105**, 526, 1955.
24. G. DEBORIN, M. BYSTROVA & G. IVASHCHENKO, *Izv. Akad. Nauk S.S.S.R., Ser. biol.*, **4**, 116, 1956.
25. G. DEBORIN, *Dokl. Akad. Nauk S.S.S.R.*, **108**, 680, 1956.
26. *Monomolecular Layers* (ed. SOBOTKA). Washington, 1954.
27. D. NORTHROP, M. KUNITZ & R. HERRIOTT, *Crystalline Enzymes*. New York, 1948.
28. A. OPARIN, N. GEL'MAN & G. DEBORIN, *Arch. Biochem. Biophys.*, **69**, 582, 1957.
29. D. SPITKOVSKIĬ, *Biofizika*, **1**, 319, 1956.

Session V   DISCUSSION

K. Mothes (Gatersleben, Germany):

Über die Verjüngung alternder Blätter

Ich bedanke mich sehr für die freundliche Aufforderung, zu Ihnen über einen Gegenstand meiner Arbeiten zu sprechen. Doch liegen diese nur am Rande unseres Symposiums.

Aber ich denke, wenn man erforschen will, wie das Leben entstanden ist, muß man wissen, was das Leben ist, muß man wissen, was notwendig ist, damit Leben sein kann.

Es ist hier davon gesprochen worden, wie die Teile einer Zelle zusammen spielen müßen, damit Leben ist. Und dasselbe gilt für die Teile eines ganzen höheren Organismus.

Viele unsere Kenntnisse über das Wesen des Lebens verdanken wir dem Studium der Störungen des Lebens. Die experimentelle Pathologie ist ein wichtiges Mittel der Lebensforschung. Hierher gehört auch das Studium des Alterns und des Sterbens und der Überwindung des Todes, der Wiederverjüngung. Wir haben uns in den letzten Jahren mit dem Altern und dem Verjüngen von Blättern beschäftigt.

Einige Pflanzen erscheinen unsterblich. Sie wachsen durch Jahrtausende immer fort. Andere haben nur ein sehr kurzes Leben. Hierzu gehören die 'Einjährigen' und im allgemeineren Sinne die hapaxanthen Gewächse, die Gewächse, die nur einmal blühen und fruchten und dann sterben.

Müssen diese Gewächse sterben? Neuere Untersuchungen haben gezeigt, daß die Pflanzen keineswegs sterben, weil sie physiologisch früh gealtert sind. Sie sterben auf Grund gewisser Korrelationen zwischen den verschiedenen Organen.

Die primäre Störung erfolgt unter dem Einfluß der Blütenbildung und bedeutet eine Hemmung der Tätigkeit der Wurzel.

Sie wächst nicht mehr. Die Wurzel des Tabaks bildet kein Nikotin mehr. Vor allem aber nimmt sie nicht mehr genügend Stickstoff aus dem Boden auf.

Die Pflanze benötigt aber Stickstoff zur Bildung der Proteine in den sich entwickelnden Früchten. So geben die Wurzeln und die untersten Blätter allmählich ihren Stickstoff an die oberen Teile der Pflanze ab. Die unteren vergilben und sterben.

Man kann diese Inaktivierung der Wurzel vermeiden, wenn man die Pflanzen am Blühen hindert. Am einfachsten geht das bei photoperiodisch empfindlichen Pflanzen. Im Schema 1 ist der Protein-N-Gehalt einer Wurzel einer Langtagpflanze (*Nicotiana sylvestris* oder *Hyoscyamus niger*) dargestellt. Im Langtag erreicht der Protein-Gehalt mit dem Blühen ein Maximum und fällt dann ab; im Kurztag, in dem die Pflanze nicht blüht, steigt der Protein-Gehalt stetig an.

Wurzeln sind sehr wahrscheinlich unbegrenzt wachsende Organe.

Aber auch die ganze Pflanze wächst im Kurztag offenbar sehr lange Zeit, veilleicht beliebig lange weiter. Sie bildet immer neue Blätter und verharrt im Rosettenstadium (Schema 2). Solche Pflanzen werden also mehrjährig.

Viel schwieriger liegen die Verhältnisse bei den Blättern. Sproß und Wurzel haben eine offene Organisation und können mit Hilfe ihrer Spitzenmeristeme immer weiter wachsen. Das Blatt hat wie das Tier eine geschlossene Organisation. Es scheint nach einer gewissen Zeit ausgewachsen zu sein. Muß es dann altern und sterben?

Wenn ein Blatt an einer blühenden Pflanze gelb wird, Eiweiß und Chlorophyll verliert, so ist das meist nicht die Folge eines physiologischen Alterns, sondern nur der Ausdruck der oben geschilderten Korrelationen. Besprüht man ein solches Blatt regelmäßig mit Lösungen von Harnstoff oder NH_4NO_3, so bleibt es grün, während die anderen Blätter allmählich vergilben und sterben.

Viel entscheidender ist aber folgender einfacher Versuch. Wenn man z.B. bei einer blühenden Tabakpflanze alle Blüten, Knospen, Blätter abschneidet bis auf ein einziges

480

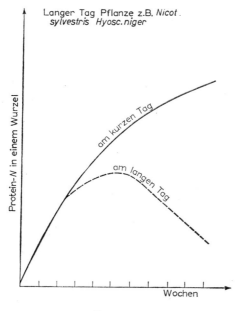

SCHEMA 1.

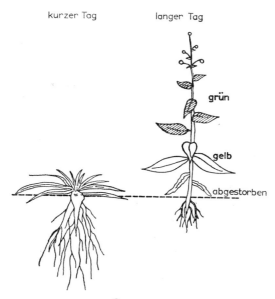

SCHEMA 2.

31

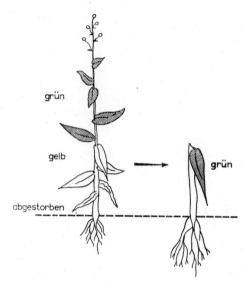

SCHEMA 3.

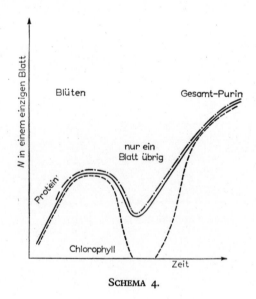

SCHEMA 4.

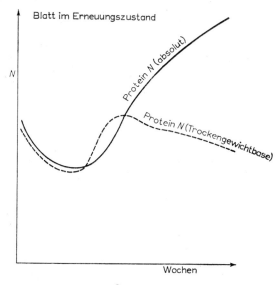

SCHEMA 5.

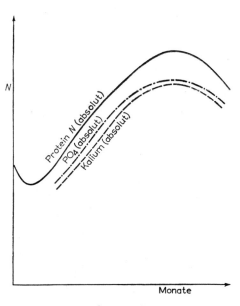

SCHEMA 6.

(Schema 3), so kann dieses in kurzer Zeit wieder ergrünen, es wächst sogar und kann das Mehrfache des ursprünglichen Gewichtes erreichen. Entscheidend ist, daß das Wurzelsystem funktioniert. Es liefert nicht allein Nährstoffe, sondern noch andere Stoffe, die für die Erhaltung der 'Jugend' eines Blattes von Bedeutung sind.

Schema 4 zeigt in grober Annäherung die chemischen Verhältnisse in einem Tabak-Blatt bis zur Zeit der Blüte, bis zum 'Altern' and im Laufe der Verjüngung durch Beseitigung aller konkurrierenden Organe. Es ist auffällig, daß die Fraktion 'Gesamt-Purin' in einem ziemlich konstanten Verhältnis zum Eiweiß steht. Auch das Chlorophyll korreliert mit dem Eiweiß. Jedoch kann es im alternden Blatt praktisch völlig verschwinden.

Man könnte aus diesem Schema entnehmen, daß ein Blatt ebenfalls durch geeignete Methoden der Verjüngung unsterblich werden könnte. Das scheint aber nicht der Fall zu sein. Schema 5 zeigt, daß wohl der absolute Protein-Gehalt zunächst stetig zunimmt, daß aber der relative Proteingehalt auch in der Phase der Wiederverjüngung bald abnimmt.

Weiter hat sich gezeigt, daß in dem 'verjüngten' Blatt wohl ein starkes Wachstum stattfindet. Aber dieses erfolgt allein durch Vergrößerung der Zellen und nicht durch Zellteilung! Es ist uns noch niemals gelungen, diese Hemmung der Zellteilung zu überwinden. Auch der von amerikanischen Forschern entdeckte Zellteilungsstoff Kinetin wirkt hier nicht.

Verlängert man das Leben eines Blattes auf solche Weise um viele Monate, dann zeigen sich allmählich Verfallserscheinungen. Sie äußern sich in der Abnahme des absoluten Eiweißgehaltes, des Kaliums, des Phosphates, des Chlorophylls (Schema 6).

Vielleicht würde man durch bessere Bedingungen der Ernährung und der Kultur ein längeres Leben erzielen können. Aber es scheint doch so, daß ein Blatt nicht unsterblich ist. In ihm gehen typische Veränderungen vor, die vielleicht Ursache oder Ausdruck des Alterns sind. So nimmt offenbar die Fähigkeit zur Methylierung ab, die oxydative Demethylierung nimmt zu, gewisse Enzyme des Oxydationssystems verlieren ihre Aktivität (z.B. Glykolsäuredehydrogenase). Auch ist von amerikanischen Forschern behauptet worden, daß ein altes Blatt gewisser 'essentieller' Aminosäuren bedarf, während ein junges noch völlig autotroph ist im Bereich der Eiweißsynthese.

Diese komplizierten Verhältnisse müssen gerade in bezug auf die Nukleinsäuren und die Wuchshormone noch eingehender studiert werden. (Diese Untersuchungen wurden gemeinsam mit Frl. Dr. Engelbrecht und Herrn Parthier durchgeführt.)

O. B. LEPESHINSKAYA (U.S.S.R.):

We fully share the view of A. I. Oparin that the origin of life was associated with the evolution of multimolecular organic systems in the form of coacervates.

We cannot, however, agree with A. I. Oparin's other proposition that forms of life similar to the original ones cannot exist under natural conditions at the present time.

There exists an enormous variety of very simple bacteria and viruses which, in the course of evolution, have elaborated adaptions by virtue of which, not only are they not annihilated by higher organisms, but sometimes even endanger their existence. Furthermore, we take the view that under natural conditions there is, even now, an extensive distribution of the precellular forms of the existence of matter, arising in the process of the individual development of the cells of contemporary living things in obedience to the biogenetic law of recapitulation. This is the lowest link in the cycle of development of contemporary living material. The contemporary precellular form of existence of living material should, in accordance with the biogenetic law, be similar to but not identical with the primary living material from which present-day organisms have evolved. In its time this hypothesis encouraged us to look for the means by which non-cellular forms of life can be transformed experimentally into formed cells. This has now been fully demonstrated for bacteria. It has, in fact, been shown that the so-called 'filterable' forms of bacteria transform themselves into cells. Much work has been done on this subject in many countries. G. P. Kalina's large monograph (1954) is devoted to it. The transformation of bacterial living material into microbial cells has also been confirmed by the interesting work of Klieneberger-Nobel, who has demonstrated the regeneration of the so-called L-form after filtration.

Thus the new cellular theory, which denies the immutability of the principle that 'cells only arise from cells', is completely confirmed by the evidence of contemporary microbiology.

As concerns the world of microbes, the controversy between the old and new cellular theories may be considered to have been concluded in favour of the latter. The position is different as regards the field of investigation of the ability of the cells of higher plants and animals to develop. In this field controversy is still going on.

According to our evidence, division is not the only mechanism of production of cells of higher living things. On the other hand, this evidence of ours has been criticized in a number of papers.

I maintain that our respected opponents, while sometimes correctly criticizing details in our earlier work, have not by any means confuted the fundamental data and the fundamental propositions of our theory in its application to the cells of higher living things. During the last few years alone the proponents of the new cellular theory have published more than 150 experimental studies confirming our evidence. The new cellular theory has given a new direction to biology which cannot be ignored.

In our conference the question of the origin of life has been considered, essentially on a biochemical level. In this connection I want to direct your attention to the biochemical investigation of living material carried out in the laboratory which I direct. These investigations confirm that metabolic processes can take place in material at a lower level of organization than the cell. This applies not only to mitochondria, but also to other protoplasmic formations. It also seems to us that biochemists should be interested in the work of Diskina, in which it has been shown that compounds of nucleic acid with crystalline trypsin form artificial nucleoproteins having many of the properties of natural nucleoproteins. This agrees with the concept of the part played by nucleic acids in the development of living material which we put forward long ago.

In conclusion, I want to emphasize that the principle of the new formation of cells from precellular forms of living material opens up wide perspectives for the study of the question of the origin of life. The theory of the development of living material enables us to make use of material closer to the original form of life than the cell. This material provides all transitional forms between the simplest precellular material and the protoplasm of the cell with all its morphological, chemical and biological complexity. I must say a few more words. Our conference is not yet finished but it is already clear that many people believe that the processes of life are not confined within the framework of cellular organization. This valuable exchange of ideas leads us closer to the conclusion that the material of life is protein which can develop and determine development. And then we remember again with thankfulness the words of Frederick Engels: 'Life is the mode of existence of albuminous bodies'.

M. V. Vol'kenshteĭn (U.S.S.R.):

The thermodynamics of irreversible reactions, to which Prof. Prigogine's very interesting paper was devoted, is undoubtedly of great importance for an understanding of the essential features of biological processes. In physics it seems perfectly natural and inevitable to begin the study of new phenomena with a phenomenological, thermodynamical analysis. Such an analysis always gives extremely incomplete, but nevertheless particularly reliable information. The conclusions reached by the application of 'irreversible thermodynamics' to biology are completely valid, although, naturally, they do not reach the essence of the subject.

Until recently 'irreversible thermodynamics' has been confined to a consideration of linear relationships, based on the correlations of Onsager. Linear relationships are only valid for processes which are taking place near to a state of equilibrium. Biological processes are clearly very far from a state of equilibrium. This caused Eyring to deny the applicability of irreversible thermodynamics to biology. Eyring prefers the alternative, kinetic approach.

Thermodynamics has, however, a greater general applicability than kinetics, in that it does not make use of a hypothetical model of the process. On the other hand, a linear approximation is, undoubtedly, useful even for an understanding of non-linear processes. Physics shows a number of examples of situations of this sort—for example, in the theory of the perturbations of anharmonically related systems. Finally, irreversible biochemical processes take place by stages, and for each stage the deviations of energy from equilibrium may not be large, although the process as a whole may be very far from being in equilibrium. I do not, therefore, feel that the criticism contained in Eyring's work really precludes the application of irreversible thermodynamics to biology. Naturally, if we follow this course, we must observe caution.

At the same time, there are great possibilities for the development of non-linear thermodynamics of irreversible processes. Prof. Prigogine's paper contains valuable new ideas in this field.

Recently it has been emphasized in the literature (in particular in the works of Prof. Prigogine) that an organism growing under normal conditions is in a stationary (though, naturally, not in a static) thermodynamic state. In the light of the new ideas put forward by Prof. Prigogine it is becoming obvious that this is only a rough approximation. Of course, in real biological processes both cycles and spiral approximations to and deviations from the stationary state are to be found. There is, for example, the cycle of sleeping and waking, or the cyclic changes in the numbers of populations of plants and animals caused by interspecies or, mainly, by intraspecies competition.

I should like to point out one interesting possibility of development of the theory. That outstanding Soviet physicist, the late Academician Mandel'shtam, developed a general theory of non-linear perturbations, the theory of the stability of perturbations. I think that the further development of the ideas put forward by Prof. Prigogine can be carried out along the lines of Mandel'shtam's theory on the basis of a mathematical analogy between the equations of non-linear irreversible thermodynamics and the theory of non-linear perturbations. This is a real physical problem which we hope to take up.

I have already spoken here about the possibility of a detailed determination of the specific peculiarities of macromolecules, as distinct from small molecules, which determine their biological roles. From the thermodynamic aspect too, there are corresponding peculiarities. Polymeric chains have an enormous number of mechanical degrees of freedom as well as chemical ones. Chemical reactions of macromolecules can be accompanied by mechanical processes of twisting or untwisting of the chain. This gives a serious possibility of concealing a deficit in free energy in biochemical processes. Finally, even processes which take place at a supramolecular level must be accompanied by chemical processes. Aggregation of macromolecules into bundles, their crystallization and mutual orientation as well as the opposite processes, must play a part, along with chemical reactions, in the cell. In this respect the cycle of spiralization of the chromosomes is a component part of the chemico-biological cycle.

In conclusion, I should like to affirm my conviction that 'irreversible thermodynamics' can be applied with advantage, not only to the life of the individual organism, but also to the process of evolution as a whole. From a mathematical point of view this process is a network of the probability chains of Markov. From the point of view of thermodynamics both the biosphere as a whole and its individual parts are open systems the development of which can be characterized by the rate of change of entropy.

Of course, 'irreversible' thermodynamics cannot explain the origin of life. Thermodynamic analysis is, however, absolutely necessary for the solution of this problem.

A. G. PASYNSKIĬ (U.S.S.R.):

The Application of Thermodynamics to Biology
(with reference to Prof. Prigogine's paper)

Studies of the theory of irreversible chemical processes are of great importance for biochemistry and, in this respect, the thermodynamic studies of Prof. Prigogine are of fundamental interest, especially his principle of the minimal rate of production of entropy in the stationary state. It seems to me, however, that the direct comparison of the rate of development of entropy and the intensity of metabolic processes made in Prof. Prigogine's work is scarcely proper, especially when this principle is being put forward as the driving force of the process of evolution (e.g. in the works of Prigogine and Viames). This concept does not agree with the factual evidence, for Netter has shown that the uptake of oxygen per unit mass by *Paramoecium* is similar to that of vertebrates; it is inacceptable even on theoretical grounds since the entropic characteristic is regular, but is, in principle, insufficient for the analysis of biochemical processes. Changes in the metabolism of living organisms are directed to improving their adaptation to the conditions of their existence and are not in any way determined by the level of production of entropy. It is probable that any level of production of entropy could be established by evolution, though it would, of course, be at the expense of the uptake of a sufficient quantity of energy from the medium.

The next question concerns the limits of applicability of linear relationships between the rates of reactions and changes in the expression $\Delta v = L\delta A\rho$, applied to the thermodynamics of irreversible processes. According to the evidence of Eyring and his colleagues these linear relationships (with an accuracy of about 10%), are limited to changes $\Delta F \sim 0.2$ kcal/mole. These are, certainly, very narrow limits, in biochemical processes, even when they occur by many stages $\Delta F \geqslant 1$–2 kcal/mole. The question then arises as to whether it is possible to extend the theory by making use of non-linear terms, and I should like to be clear about Prof. Prigogine's ideas on this possibility. In the third place I should like to consider the kinetic aspect of the direction of reactions in open systems. The basic principle here is the idea, formulated by Hinshelwood, that, within the network of connected chemical reactions in an open system, the direction of the chemical reactions is determined by the principle of maximal rate of the reactions. This formulation is not concerned with the molecular mechanism of the reactions and it may, therefore, be taken in conjunction with Prof. Prigogine's principle determining the thermodynamic criteria for the direction of processes in the system and their approximation to the stationary state. In essence, these principles also determine the evolution of chemical systems in the prebiological stage of development which has also been discussed by Prof. Calvin, though the factors which he adduced (the presence of sources of energy, autocatalysis, etc.) are partial phenomena of the Hinshelwood-Prigogine principle. It may also be pointed out that there is a close connection between the 'dynamic state', considered by Prof. Broda, and the theory of open systems. I should like to conclude with the hope that there will be a successful development of the theory of open systems which is of great biological importance, especially for the problem of the origin of life.

K. S. TRINCHER (U.S.S.R.):

The Principle of the Acceleration of the Increase of Entropy of a Closed System as the Physical Basis of Vital Processes

Let us consider a closed system undergoing energy exchange with the external medium and having, in the stationary state, a constant potential (chemical) energy in the form of macroergic substances. The closed system consists of a collection of open or living systems and the medium surrounding them. In an open system there occur irreversible processes consisting in the transformation of the chemical energy of the macroergic substances. In the course of the irreversible changes 'uncompensated heat' [1] is formed (eq. 1) and entropy arises:

$$T\mathrm{d}S_{\text{irrev.}} = \mathrm{d}q. \tag{1}$$

Let us suppose that the chemical reactions are the only reason for the irreversibility, the rate of increase of entropy will then be:

$$T_\sigma\left(\frac{\mathrm{d}S}{\mathrm{d}t}\right)_{\text{irrev.}} = \frac{\mathrm{d}\xi}{\mathrm{d}t} A, \tag{2}$$

where T_σ represents the temperature of the surrounding medium, $d\xi/dt$ the rate of the reaction and A the 'affinity' of the system. If T_σ is low $d\xi/dt$ will be practically equal to zero and the entropy of a 'frozen' system does not increase even though $A > 0$.

In actually existing systems there must be catalysts which enable the chemical reactions to occur at T_σ. Let us suppose that in the open systems there are catalysts under the influence of which

$$\left(\frac{d\xi}{dt}\right)_{cat._1} = \text{const.} = a.$$

Then, if we consider the 'affinity' A as being of constant magnitude, we obtain:

$$T_\sigma\left(\frac{dS}{dt}\right)_{\text{irrev. cat.}_1} = \left(\frac{d\xi}{dt}\right)_{cat._1} A = aA = C_1$$

and

$$T_\sigma\Delta S(t)_{\text{irrev. cat.}_1} = C_1\Delta t + C_2 \tag{3}$$

From equation (1) the magnitude $T_\sigma\Delta S(t)_{\text{irrev. cat.}_1}$ is equal to the whole amount of 'uncompensated heat'. Hence:

$$T_\sigma\Delta S(t)_{\text{irrev. cat.}_1} = \Delta q(t) = C_1\Delta t \tag{4}$$

As for the sum $C_1\Delta t + C_2$ this is equal to the total amount of potential energy $\Delta\Pi_{cat._1}$ which is dissipated during the course of the irreversible process:

$$\Delta\Pi_{cat._1} = T_\sigma\Delta S(t)_{\text{irrev. cat.}_1} + C_2 \tag{5}$$

Furthermore, equation (5) shows that the process must necessarily take place in one direction, from left to right, in that the term denoting the entropy is a function of time. $\Delta q(t)$ represents the flow of heat. According to Fourier's law

$$q \sim \text{grad } T.$$

The temperature of the open system, $T_{cat.}$, must therefore be higher than the temperature of the surrounding medium. Under stationary conditions the flow of heat outwards from the open system is [2]:

$$\Delta q(t) = B\bar{k}(T_{cat._1} - T_\sigma)\Delta t \tag{6}$$

where B is a form factor and $\bar{k}$ is the mean conductivity of the material concerned for the particular temperature difference. Before the beginning of the flow of heat the internal energy of the open system must have increased to a value of $\bar{C}_v(T_{cat.} - T_\sigma)$ where $\bar{C}_v$ is the mean thermal capacity of the open system. Hence

$$C_2 = \bar{C}_v(T_{cat.} - T_\sigma) \tag{7}$$

From equations (4), (5), (6) and (7) we obtain an equation for the motion of the whole system:

$$\Delta\Pi_{cat._1} = B\bar{k}(T_{cat.} - T_\sigma)\Delta t + \bar{C}_v(T_{cat.} - T_\sigma) \tag{8}$$

Let us suppose that there are, within the open system, catalysts (cat.$_2$) under the influence of which the rate of the chemical reactions is a function of time:

$$\left(\frac{d\xi}{dt}\right)_{cat._2} = a + \varphi(t) \tag{9}$$

If the state of the whole system is sharply displaced in relation to the thermodynamic equilibrium, then the rate of the chemical reaction will be exponential in nature [3]:

$$\varphi(t) = f(t)e^{kt} \tag{10}$$

where $f(t)$ is a function of time and k is a constant.

From (9), (10) and (2) we obtain

$$T_\sigma\left(\frac{dS}{dt}\right)_{\text{irrev. cat.}_2} = [a + f(t)e^{kt}]\,A$$

and

$$T_\sigma\Delta S(t)_{\text{irrev. cat.}_2} = A\int_0^{\Delta t} f(t)e^{kt}dt + B\bar{k}(T_{cat.} - T_\sigma)\Delta t \tag{11}$$

Equation (11) expresses the 'principle of the acceleration of the increase of total entropy' for a closed system.

The complete equation for the motion of the whole system in accordance with (5) and (7) is:

$$\Delta\Pi_{\text{cat.}_2} = A \int_0^{\Delta t} f(t)e^{kt}dt + B\bar{k}(T_{\text{cat.}} - T_\sigma)\Delta t + C_v(T_{\text{cat.}} - T_\sigma) \tag{12}$$

As may be seen from equation (12) the total amount of potential energy is transformed into three separate forms of energy namely: internal energy, heat and the magnitude

$$A \int_0^{\Delta t} f(t)e^{kt}dt.$$

This magnitude must be identical with the whole sum of the working processes carried out by the open systems. In accordance with the First Law of Thermodynamics this result may be expressed

$$A \int_0^{\Delta t} f(t)e^{kt}dt \equiv \sum_i^{n(t)} X_i x_i \tag{13}$$

where X_i is an intensity factor and x_i is a factor representing the capacity of the individual working process.

Let us consider one individual open system which expends a constant amount of potential energy $\Delta\Pi^x_{\text{cat.}_2}$ during a given time Δt starting from any given moment t,

$$\Delta\Pi^x_{\text{cat.}_2} = A \int_t^{t+\Delta t} f(t)e^{kt}dt + B\bar{k}(T_{\text{cat.}} - T_\sigma)\Delta t = \text{const.} \tag{14}$$

From (14) it follows that $e^{kt} = 1$ and that $f(t)$ must be a periodic function of time:

$$e^{kt} = 1 \quad \text{or} \quad k = 0 \tag{15a}$$

and

$$f(t) = f^{(t)}_{\text{per. }(\tau)} \tag{15b}$$

the time of a single period τ being considerably shorter than the time Δt ($\tau \ll \Delta t$).

Hence we obtain an equation for the motion of the whole system when there is only one open system present.

$$\Delta\Pi^x_{\text{cat.}_2} = A \int_t^{t+\Delta t} f^{(t)}_{\text{per. }(\tau)} dt + B\bar{k}(T_{\text{cat.}} - T_\sigma)\Delta t = \text{const.} \tag{16}$$

and, in the same way, that for the rate of increase of entropy:

$$T_\sigma \frac{\Delta S^x(t)_{\text{irrev. cat.}_2}}{\Delta t} = \frac{A \int_t^{t+\Delta t} f^{(t)}_{\text{per.}}{}_{(\tau)}dt}{\Delta t} + B\bar{k}(T_{\text{cat.}} - T_\sigma) \tag{17}$$

The interpretation of this equation is as follows.

The rate of increase of the total entropy of a system consisting of a single open system and its surrounding medium is equal to the rate of outflow of entropy from the open system associated with its working processes, plus the rate of development of entropy within the open system associated with the flow of heat.

The entropy-producing nature of the working processes carried out by an open system consists in their decreasing the entropy within the open system while, at the same time, increasing the entropy of the surrounding medium to the same extent. The double significance, in regard to entropy, of the working processes may be explained by the fact that the open system obtains the energy for its working processes in the form of highly organized macroergic substances and converts them, in the course of its working, into substances of lower energy which are eliminated.

Prigogine's theorem [4] concerning the minimal rate of development of entropy in the course of stationary irreversible processes specifies a simultaneous maximal conversion of potential energy into working processes. By virtue of its working processes an open system has the power of self-conservation, the ability to renew continually its structure which is continually being submitted to the disintegrating and destructive action of the heating processes of friction [5].

The complete equation for the motion of a whole system consisting of a collection of open systems and the medium surrounding them is of the following form.

$$\Delta\Pi_{cat._2} = A \int_0^{\Delta t} f_{per.\,(\tau)}^{(t)} e^{kt}dt + B\bar{k}(T_{cat.} - T_\sigma)\Delta t + \bar{C}_v(T_{cat.} - T_\sigma) \tag{18}$$

For the rate of development of entropy in the whole system we get:

$$T_\sigma \frac{\Delta S(t)_{irrev.\ cat._2}}{\Delta t} = \frac{A \int_t^{t+\Delta t} f_{per.\,(\tau)}^{(t)} e^{kt}\,dt}{\Delta t} + B\bar{k}(T_{cat.} - T_\sigma) \tag{19}$$

where

$$\frac{A \int_t^{t+\Delta t} f_{per.\,(\tau)}^{(t)} e^{kt}\,dt}{\Delta t} \equiv \frac{\sum\limits_i^{p(t)} X_i x_i}{\Delta t} \equiv \begin{array}{l}\text{rate of outflow of entropy}\\ \text{from all the open systems.}\end{array}$$

All open systems have the property of continually augmenting their working processes. The co-existence of this property, which increases the demands on the potential energy of the system by all the open systems, with the property of the constant demand for potential energy by a single open system, indicates that each individual open system must have the power of increasing itself.

We have thus reached the conclusion that the open system possesses three cardinal properties of living matter: (1) Self-conservation based on the antientropic character of the working processes; (2) Enlargement (function e^{kt}) and (3) a rhythmic nature of the working processes (function $f_{per.\,(\tau)}^{(t)}$) [6].

The specificity of the working processes which give rise to the outflow of entropy from the open system depends on the nature and rate of the chemical transformations. In an open system under stationary conditions where alternative paths are available for the chemical reactions, the final direction of the irreversible process is determined by the principle of the maximal rate for the chemical reaction [7]. We have already interpreted Prigogine's principle of the minimal rate of development of entropy in an open system as being the principle of the maximal conversion of potential energy into working processes. Prigogine's principle, in conjunction with the principle of the maximal rate for the chemical reaction, as applied to open systems, indicates the following property:

When there are several open systems, the system which will acquire the greatest share of the potential energy available will be that system in which the intensity of the working processes is greatest under the given stationary conditions of the surrounding medium. Thus the working processes carried out by an open system acquire the status of an evolutionary factor.

REFERENCES

1. DE DONDER & VAN RYSSELBERGHE, *Thermodynamic Theory of Affinity.* Stanford University, 1936.
2. R. C. L. BOSWORTH, *Heat Transfer Phenomena.* Pitman Press, London.
3. YA. N. FRENKEL', *Kineticheskaya teoriya zhidkosteĭ,* Izd. Akad. Nauk S.S.S.R., Moscow, 1945.
4. I. PRIGOGINE, *An Introduction to the Thermodynamics of Irreversible Processes.* New York, 1955.
5. J. BELEHRADEK, *Protoplasma,* 48(1), 55, 1957.
6. W. SEIFRIZ, *A Symposium on the Structure of Protoplasm,* Iowa State Univ. Press, 1942.
7. A. DEAN & C. N. HINSHELWOOD, chapter in *Progress in Biophysics,* vol. 5, pp. 1–40. Pergamon Press, London, 1955.

ZH. ÏORDANOV (Bulgaria):

Even before the second World War, but especially since it, Academician Oparin's theory has been widely known in Bulgaria. This is due to Academician Oparin's consistent, materialistic approach to the solution of the problem and to the convincing nature of the chemical and geological arguments.

I believe that it is the chemistry of coacervates which will lead us closer to a solution of the phenomenon of life. It is this which I see as the practical significance of Oparin's theory: the experimental reproduction of the phenomenon of life should be brought about by means of coacervates.

As a histologist and cytologist I am convinced that many of the appearances seen in cells and tissues and many morphological peculiarities are completely consistent with the coacervate theory. Take for example the yolk globules of egg-cells. Irrespective of whether they can develop into cells or not, everyone who has studied their origin, histochemical and physicochemical properties and their transformations under natural and experimental conditions has been able to convince himself that the key to an understanding of the essential nature of these formations, which are complex systems of proteins, lipids and even enzymes, could be found in a study of their behaviour in terms of coacervates. Like my teacher, Academician Khadzhiolov, I believe that, as well as studying the coacervate state of substances, we must consider another similar state of substances in the cell. Khadzhiolov, who has made important histological investigations of the lipids in tissues, showed, long ago, that the metabolism and activity in the organism of many substances, which are important from a biological point of view (fat-soluble vitamins, hormones, etc.), may be brought about by means of a transition from the fat-soluble to the water-soluble state. In the course of various functional manifestations of cells and when they are becoming adapted to the conditions of tissue culture, there appear within them morphologically peculiar lipid inclusions which may 'disappear' in the presence of other so-called hydrotropic substances, becoming water-soluble. This is an important process and is characteristic of the living system.

The present Symposium has shown that the problem of the origin of life on the Earth has passed beyond the stage of a purely theoretical treatment. It has important tasks ahead of it and their accomplishment will prepare, at some future time, for the production under laboratory conditions of the first artificial living system. As has been shown earlier, this will require the concerted efforts of scientists working in different fields—biochemists, biologists, cytologists, geologists and astronomers.

G. M. FRANK (U.S.S.R.):

In the light of considerations which have been put forward to-day I should like to call attention to what I consider to be a very important peculiarity, namely the motility of the structures of living things.

If disturbances of structure disorganize metabolic processes one may, logically, easily admit that a modification of structure is necessary for another form of the course of metabolic processes. To this extent it is permissible to speak of the structural regulation of chemical processes.

Even at an early stage of the development of living matter one may observe one of its most important properties, namely irritability. This is manifest in the simplest living system, where it is clearly shown by corresponding changes in metabolic processes and structural reorganization.

Therefore, when speaking of the interdependence of chemical mechanism and structure I should like to emphasize not merely the presence of determinate structural organization, but also the presence of a certain degree of motility of structures. This motility is most clearly to be seen in such a perfect structural chemical mechanism of motion as muscle. However, as may be shown by many examples, the ability to move is not a particularly specialized or limited function. One should regard it as the development of some general property.

In this connection I should like to put forward just one example. As we have succeeded in showing, the propagation of the excitation along the nerve fibre corresponds to a wave of structural processes, altering the mechanical and optical properties of the nerve fibre, and is accompanied by a thickening of the nerve by about a twenty-thousandth of its diameter. This minute thickening is propagated at the same rate as that of the wave of excitation during summation, each individual excitation impulse may even be demonstrated by means of the interference microscope. Any objects, no matter how simple, if they are observed with sufficient care, show structural reorganization, sometimes fast, sometimes slower, associated with changes in chemical mechanism. In speaking of the origin of self-maintaining chemical processes in biopoesis and the structures corresponding with them, one must, at some quite early stage in the development of proto-organisms, also take account of structural motility, not only as forming the basis for the growth and development of the organisms, but also as forming that of their functional adaptation to rapid changes in the external environment.

One must ask what part is played by this apparently more or less universal property of the motility of living structures. I should like, here, to make an analogy, while fully recognizing the danger of such a formulation of the question. Contemporary technology has led to an extensive working out of the theory of automatically self-regulating systems which build up complicated aggregates, making use, at each particular moment, of the most favourable available conditions, and changing themselves with changing circumstances. Regulation of this sort is fundamental to the so-called 'feed-back' principle, i.e. forward and backward interactions within a functioning system. Is there no interdependence between structures and the metabolic functions which they subserve, and, conversely, no dependence of metabolic processes on the structural organization of the living thing? Is there nothing similar to such a feed-back which gives rise to the remarkable regulating mechanism which is characteristic of living things?

S. W. Fox (U.S.A.):

Comment 1.—It is of interest to compare some of the knowledge in the field of proteolytic enzymes with the proposal of Dr Straub. It is unnecessary to mention the work of Northrop and co-workers. Desnuelle and others have recently shown that chymotrypsin and trypsin, usually thought of as being specifically different, each have *N*-isoleucylvalyl dipeptides in the structure. This seems to be quite consistent with Dr Straub's proposal. It should be added that in the U.S.A. Michael Laskowski, Jr, has found a small amount of chymotryptic activity in trypsin which he claims cannot be explained by contamination of trypsin by chymotrypsin.

Comment 2.—I believe that many of us have been overwhelmed for many years by the *potentialities* of protein isomerism. As we have learned to assess the *actual* diversity of protein molecules (see S. W. Fox, *Amer. Scient.*, 44,347, 1956) we find a highly limited diversity of protein molecules, analogously to Dr Bernal's description of physical structures.

This situation, to put it necessarily in qualitative form, poses the problem of how to explain the great diversity of organisms on a foundation of relatively narrow diversity of macromolecular types.

I believe the answer is to be found in the interactions of protein molecules, of which Dr Deborin spoke. Interactions of a limited variety of protein molecules among themselves, or with a probably even more limited variety of nucleic acid molecules, could provide an exponentially very much greater number of phenotypes.

F. Sokol (Czechoslovakia):

The Formation of Bonds between Proteins and Nucleic Acids

In connection with Prof. Deborin's paper and Prof. Tongur's contribution to the discussion I should like to make the following comment. It seems to me that, in artificial complexes of nucleic acids and proteins, the nature of the bond between the components is somewhat different from that in nucleoproteins, e.g. those of viruses. We have made observations on the formation of soluble complexes of deoxyribonucleic acid and serum albumin at pH 5·1–6·2 with media of various ionic strengths and with various relationships and concentrations of the components. It was found, in this way, that the molecular weight, size and shape of the complex formed was very strongly dependent on the conditions mentioned. Some of the properties of these complexes suggest that salt bonds are formed in them between the negative phosphate groups of the nucleate and the positive groups of the protein. It is, however, well known that natural nucleoproteins, such as those of viruses, are stable over a considerably greater range of pH and ionic strength of the medium. Thus, we may suppose that, in natural nucleoproteins, the protein component has a spatial configuration such that it permits the formation, not only of salt bonds, but also of hydrogen and covalent bonds. The question arises as to which are the groups of the protein and nucleic acid between which covalent bonds can be formed in such cases. Measurements of the ultraviolet absorption of tobacco mosaic virus and other naturally occurring nucleoproteins showed that the purines and pyrimidines of nucleic acids do not take part in the binding of protein. It is, therefore, most likely that the covalent bonds in naturally occurring nucleoproteins are formed between the amino groups of the protein and the phosphate groups of the nucleic acids. It seems to me that the solution of the problem of the nature of the bond between nucleic acid and protein is necessary for an understanding of the mechanism of the production of nucleoproteins and also of their biological activity and specificity.

T. N. Evreinova (U.S.S.R.):

Coacervates

More than 20 years ago Bungenberg de Jong worked out the theory of coacervation and demonstrated the extensive prevalence of the phenomenon in living nature. At present it is the accepted view that the structure of protoplasm is coacervate-like.

According to the hypothesis worked out by A. I. Oparin, coacervate drops could have been one of the forms in which life originated on the Earth [1]. Coacervates are formed in both hydrophilic and hydrophobic colloidal solutions. Coacervate drops may be obtained from inorganic compounds, from sodium silicate and alcoholic ammonia, from complex salts of cobalt and also from organic substances, polyvinyl derivatives, acetylcellulose in chloroform, carbohydrates, proteins, lipids, nucleic acids and so forth [2].

The present communication deals with: (1) The determination of the amount of nucleic acids and their derivatives in coacervate drops and also the question, (2) the formation of coacervate drops, not only from solutions but also from colloidal precipitates.

1. When looked at with the ultraviolet microscope (E. M. Brumberg) with a luminescent screen, coacervate droplets containing ribonucleic and deoxyribonucleic acids, and also purine and pyrimidine bases, appeared red. The appearance of these drops is shown in Fig. 1.

If the equilibrium liquid surrounding the drops also contains the above-mentioned compounds, e.g. nucleic acid, the background of the field of vision is also coloured.

Thus, without any complicated chemical determinations, a single observation serves to decide the question of the distribution of substances absorbing ultraviolet light between the coacervate drops and the equilibrium liquid. Photographs of coacervate drops containing nucleic acid taken by ultraviolet and visible light are given in Figs. 2 and 3.

The quantitative determination of nucleic acid in a single coacervate droplet has been carried out by means of the ultraviolet microscope and photospectral quartz stage of S. A. Gershgorin. The work was done in collaboration with N. V. Korolev. To measure the concentration of nucleic acid, spectral analyses were made of the radiations passing through coacervate drops, some of which contained nucleic acids while others did not, and also through solutions containing known concentrations of the sodium salt of the nucleic acid.

The spectrograms obtained on the photographic plates were submitted to photometry and the nucleic acid content was then calculated from a fairly simple formula [3].

Figs. 4 and 5 show spectrograms for coacervate drops containing nucleic acid (Fig. 4) and without neucleic acid (Fig. 5).

It has been shown that, for a spherical coacervate droplet having a diameter of 29 μ, the concentration of nucleic acid is 760 mg %. This concentration is 15 times greater than that for the coacervate system as a whole, including the equilibrium liquid. Thus the co-acervate droplets concentrate nucleic acids. The content of nucleic acid found in this particular droplet is of about the same order as that in the nuclei of the cells of mouse liver as determined by Kasperson & Brodskiï [3].

2. From the works of Kroit and Bungenberg de Jong and his pupils as well as from our own observations during the preparation of complex coacervates composed of proteins, carbohydrates, nucleic acids and enzymes, one might imagine that a coacervate occupies an intermediate position between a colloidal solution and a colloidal precipitate and could be obtained either from a solution or from a precipitate. Hitherto, however, attention has been mainly directed towards obtaining coacervates from solutions.

By means of interval micro-cinematography we have succeeded, in collaboration with A. M. Kudryavtsev, in taking a small film of the formation of coacervates from colloidal precipitates. Thanks to such a film we have been able to study the continuity of the process of development of coacervates from a formless, flocky precipitate into formed coacervate drops (cinema film shown). Figs. 6, 7, 8 and 9 are stills from the film.

The process of formation of coacervate droplets from the precipitate actually took 20 minutes at a temperature of $+40$–$45°C$ on the warm stage of the microscope.

On the basis of the material which has been demonstrated, it seems to me that one may put forward the hypothesis that the formation of precipitates might have been a stage in the individualization of substances in the form of coacervate drops. Organic substances were concentrated in these precipitates and served as good material for the formation from them of coacervate drops.

(Figs. 1 to 9 appear between pages 496/497)

REFERENCES

1. A. I. Oparin, *The Origin of Life on the Earth.* Oliver & Boyd, Edinburgh, 1957.
2. T. N. Evreinova, *Usp. sovremen. Biol.,* **37,** 177, 1954.
3. T. N. Evreinova, *Biofizika,* **1,** 167, 1956.

V. I. Vorobiev (U.S.S.R.):

The Formation of Fibrillar Protein Complexes as a Stage in the Evolution of Structures

One of the most important trends in the study of the evolution of structures is the production of model systems having more and more complicated properties. The sugges-tions made in this Symposium by Oparin, Deborin, Macovschii and Tongur show that this is a fruitful method.

I should like to emphasize that the fundamental components of biological structures, namely proteins and nucleic acids, are electrolytes of high molecular weight and that, therefore, they can combine very readily to form complicated complexes. Some years ago we began to study artificial complexes formed by the interaction of deosyribonucleic acid with globular proteins. The structures thus formed had very interesting properties which were absent from each of the components taken separately. They had a definite, morphological individuality and, most importantly, they were demarcated from the medium in which they were formed. Double refraction, mechanical rigidity, very great elasticity and the ability to swell up or be dehydrated were also characteristic of these model systems. These formations, which were similar to coacervates, behaved as a separate phase in relation to the solution around them. It was found that, in accordance with the findings of Oparin, the concentration of various substances in these structures and in the surrounding medium might differ. This might be the property of the fibrillar complexes which served as the factor permitting the development of complexes with many components, demarcated from their surrounding medium without the formation of a definite morphological limiting membrane.

It was especially interesting to us to observe that these artificial structural formations changed their shape when the composition of the surrounding medium was changed. Thus, they manifested mechano-chemical reactivity, i.e. they had such properties as might serve as a basis for the emergence of irritability, which is a universal property of protoplasm. It may be said that these systems already possessed irritability at a molecular level. I should like to point out that the attempt to discover the molecular basis for the reaction of cellular protoplasm to external stimulation has already produced the denaturation theory of excitation and damage put forward by Nasonov & Aleksandrov.

In conclusion, I should like to emphasize again that it seems to us that alteration in the configuration of fibrillar protein complexes, i.e. alteration of the mechanochemical reactivity of these polyelectrolyte systems, may be regarded as a primitive form of irritability, that is to say, as the molecular basis for the evolution of the mechanisms whereby protoplasm reacts to stimuli from its environment.

G. P. KALINA (U.S.S.R.):

At present viruses are widely used as a subject for the study of life in its, morphologically and biochemically, most primitive structures. The investigations of Fraenkel-Conrat and Schramm, demonstrating the infectivity of the nucleic acid of tobacco mosaic virus when freed from protein represent a scientific discovery of the greatest importance. I should like to call attention to a subject for study which has been unjustly neglected, both in this Symposium and in the latest edition of Acad. A. I. Oparin's book, which is very important and may well be more satisfactory for the study of the problem in which we are interested, namely the filterable forms of bacteria. The phenomenon of the formation, by bacteria, of filterable forms has already been known for 50 years and is now generally accepted. It may also be taken that the filterable forms are produced by the breakdown of bacterial cells, most probably after impairment of the integrity of the bacterial cell, being similar in nature to the protoplasts described by Weilbull, Stähelin, Oparin et al., McQuillen, Salton, Lederberg and others. Filterable forms, however, can readily be differentiated from protoplasts by virtue of their considerable stability in the external medium, the fact that they can be conserved in the absence of a 'stabilizer', and also by the relative ease with which they can regenerate into cellular forms. We have shown that filterable forms are to be found even in fresh cultures of bacteria which have not been exposed to the action of mechanical, physical, chemical or biological factors. Of all the properties of the filterable forms, the most noteworthy are their considerable stability in respect of physical and chemical action, which exceeds the stability of the cellular forms, and also their inability to multiply before they have turned into young cells. As Hauduroy has shown, filterable forms may retain the potential ability to regenerate for many years without any sign of metabolism. This anabiotic, 'lifeless' condition changes under favourable conditions, with the restoration of vital processes. When this occurs, the successive stages of regeneration of the bacterial culture from the filterable forms bears the unmistakable sign of ontogenic development, showing the essential stages of phylogenesis of the species in question. Hence, one may put forward the hypothesis that the earliest stage of this ontogenesis corresponds, to some degree, with the earliest stage of phylogenesis, i.e. with the primitive coacervate state which, according to Oparin, was the first manifestation of life on the terrestrial globe. This also receives indirect confirmation from the fact that the regeneration of bacterial cells from filterable forms can be hastened by increasing concentrations of salt solutions which, it would seem, facilitate the coacervation of the fine, filterable forms into the larger and more complicated molecules, which begin to carry out independent metabolism.

In view of what has been said, I must beg all who are interested in the problem of the origin of life to use filterable forms, as being the most satisfactory models for the solution of many of the partial questions associated with this problem.

M. I. Gol'din (U.S.S.R.):

In connection with the work of Fraenkel-Conrat and Schramm on the reconstruction of the tobacco mosaic virus and the elucidation of the part played by ribonucleic acid in the infectivity of the virus, I should like to call attention to the recent work of Wang & Commoner [1] in which they obtained the complementary results. According to their account, a mixture of deoxyribonucleic acids from a healthy tobacco plant and non-infective protein from tobacco infected with the tobacco mosaic virus in corresponding combinations turned into the active virus of tobacco mosaic.

As Prof. Stanley rightly said, it is necessary to come to an agreement as to what we include in the concept of life. The virus particle is often called the virus molecule, it is held to be alive and some virologists even call it an organism.

One may speak of the virus molecule as living but having many of the properties of non-living material (e.g. the phenomenon of crystallization and its unimolecular structure), but it is also permissible to regard a virus as something non-living which has many of the properties of a living thing.

The ability to mutate and general variability of tobacco mosaic and other viruses are evidence in favour of their living nature. However, one must note, in the first place, that the evidence for the variability of tobacco mosaic virus is based on an imperfect method of separating the pure virus from a single necrosis. In our work, published in 1956 [2], we have set forth a more satisfactory process based on the separation of viruses by taking samples from the lower side of the necrosis. Furthermore, there is evidence that one necrosis may be caused by two viruses. If this is so, the method of separation from a single necrosis cannot be used without specially critical assessments, so that this method does not give a complete guarantee of the isolation of a single virus.

I suggest that we must differentiate between variation and variability. We find ourselves confronted with a paradox. The living nature of the virus is vouched for by its variability, but this very variability is shown to exist by means of an argument which assumes, *a priori*, that viruses are living. I will make the example clearer. The variation of the tobacco mosaic virus in the test-tube experiments of Fraenkel-Conrat and others only differs from a chemical reaction by reason of the later introduction of the virus particles into a living cell, but what occurs there, and what or who is responsible for these changes— that is still a question.

In conclusion, I should like to touch on the work which I have done in collaboration with Brodskiĭ and Fedotina [3]. It is known that viral inclusions are very similar to the protein inclusions of healthy plants, and I should say that they are suspiciously similar. Using ultraspectromicroscopy, we have shown that the protein inclusions in the healthy tuber of the potato are nucleoproteins. The same is true of the intranuclear inclusions in cow-wheat (*Melampyrum nemorosum*).

Thus, nucleic acids (nucleoproteins) may not only be centres of activity in the living cell, but may also function as inert products of the same sort as excretory products.

I believe that the correct approach is not simply to regard viruses as living rudiments which may provide evidence for elucidating the nature of other complicated systems, but, on the contrary, to study these various systems and phenomena in the living cell and in their interactions with the virus, in order to understand the nature of viruses without pre-judging the question as to whether they are living or non-living.

REFERENCES

1. T. Wang & B. Commoner, *Proc. Nat. Acad. Sci., Wash.*, **42**, 831, 1956.
2. M. Gol'din, *Dokl. Akad. Nauk S.S.S.R.*, **108**, 151, 1956.
3. M. Gol'din, V. Brodskiĭ & V. Fedotina, *Zh. obshch. Biol.*, **17**, 393, 1956.

R. L. Berg (U.S.S.R.):

On Accelerating the Tempo of Evolution

I should like to comment on the part of Prof. Pauling's paper in which he discusses the rate of the elementary evolutionary process. This is an important question. It gives

PLATE XI

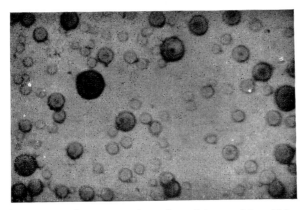

Fig. 1. Appearance of coacervate drops (containing nucleic acids) under the ultraviolet microscope with a luminescent screen. (× 180.)

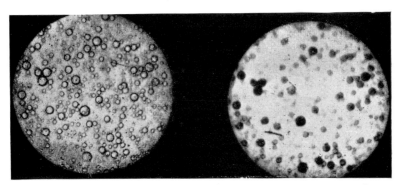

Fig. 2. Coacervate drops containing nucleic acids photographed by ultraviolet rays (250–280 mμ) 'A', and visible light 'B'. (× 80.)

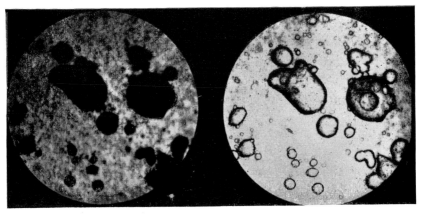

Fig. 3. Coacervate drops containing nucleic acids photographed by ultraviolet rays (250–280 mμ), 'A' and by visible light 'B'. (× 320.)

[DISCUSSION by T. N. EVREINOVA : *Coacervates*].

PLATE XII

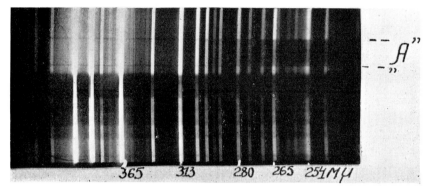

FIG. 4. Spectrum of coacervate drop with nucleic acid.
A = coacervate drop. (× 400.)

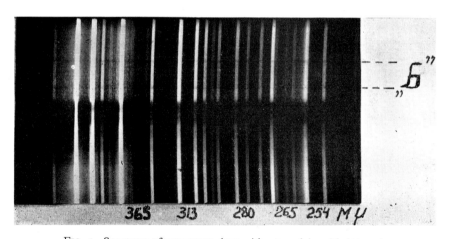

FIG. 5. Spectrum of coacervate drop without nucleic acid. (×400.)

[DISCUSSION by T. N. EVREINOVA: *Coacervates*].

PLATE XIII

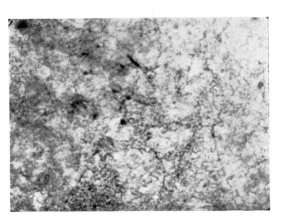

FIG. 6. Precipitate. (× 170.)

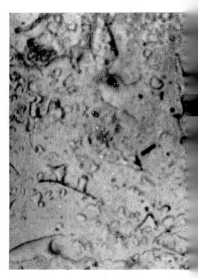

FIG. 7. Beginning of the formation of coacervate drops. (× 170.)

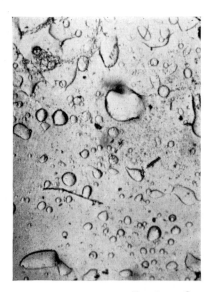

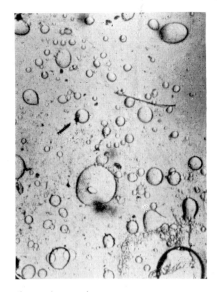

FIG. 8–9. Coacervate drops. (× 170.)

[DISCUSSION by T. N. EVREINOVA: *Coacervates*].

us an idea of the time during which evolution has been going on on our planet and, hence, also of the time of origin of life.

As well as the considerations brought forward by Pauling as a basis for his calculations, namely the significance of selection, the rate of replacement of generations and relative numbers of normal and mutated allelomorphs, we must include the pressure of the mutational process in the calculation. There is a type of mutation of which it may reasonably be assumed that there is a single appearance of each particular type. These are inversions and for their appearance they require the concurrence of two genetic events. Inversions are now widely used for the study of the courses of evolution of Diptera. They can be used for calculation of the rate of evolution.

So-called point mutations or genovariations arise repeatedly. The repeated occurrence of a mutation cuts down the ages which must have passed according to Pauling's calculations. These ages are still further curtailed if we reckon that this mutability is, itself, being attained by the action of selection. The work of a number of authors, in particular Timofeev-Risovskii, Demerec, Mempell, Tinyakov and many others, has shown that there are genotypic causes which determine the frequency of the appearance of mutations. But this means that selection in favour of a mutant implies selection in favour of mutability and, therefore, a distribution in the normal part of the population, which does not contain the mutation, of the genotypic causes which bring about increased mutability in the same direction as selection of the mutant. This view is supported by experimental evidence. By artificial selection it is possible to imitate the processes which occur in populations under natural conditions. Two methods are available, imitation of individual selection and imitation of the selection of groups. We have succeeded in bringing about an increase in mutability in *Drosophila* by both methods. In particular, together with Pomerantseva, we selected from natural populations mutant males, carrying sex-linked mutations and compared the frequency of the appearance of lethal, semilethal and visible mutations in their genotype and in that of normal males. The mutability of the mutants was higher than that of the normal individuals.

In another experiment the selection of mutable lines, i.e. the selection of groups, led to an increase in mutability. Thus, mutability is achieved by artificial selection and this lends probability to the suggestion that it is also achieved by natural selection and, if this is so, it supports the hypothesis of the acceleration of the tempo of evolution. The acceleration of the tempo of evolution must be taken into account in calculations of the length of time during which evolution has been taking place. What I have been speaking of in connection with the interdependence of mutability and selection is only one of the factors affecting the acceleration of evolution; however, this example demonstrates, not merely the acceleration of evolution, but also the acceleration of this acceleration.

V. S. Tongur (U.S.S.R.):

In considering the problem of the origin of structure and metabolism, the question immediately and inevitably arises as to whether metabolism appears along with the origin of structure in the chemical sense, i.e. is the structure of high-polymers, even such complex ones as proteins, nucleic acids and nucleoproteins, sufficient, or in some sort of cytological structure necessary for the origin of metabolism ? It would seem that this question cannot be answered at present. To judge from the papers and contributions to this Symposium, both points of view have their supporters. The evidence required for the solution of this problem, the general biological importance of which it is hard to reassess, should be provided by experiments on the disappearance of metabolism with the degradation of cytoplasmic structures. Together with A. M. Zubovskaya, I have carried out such experiments at the Institute of Experimental Biology.

The work was carried out on the granules isolated from homogenates of the livers of rats by differential centrifugation at 5000 g. These granules are, in fact, a mixture of large light granules and the mitochondria proper. In what follows, they will be provisionally referred to as mitochondria. The isolated granules were disrupted by lysis in distilled water and we studied their ability to synthesize protein in the presence of a

32

a collection of amino acids and of the medium in which mitochondria had been incubated (prepared by the method of Siekevitz and Khesin.) It must be mentioned here that, notwithstanding what Siekevitz has said, this medium contains an appreciable amount of protein precipitated by trichloroacetic acid. We estimated the synthesis of protein by the increase in protein nitrogen and by an increase in the number of peptide bonds as shown by the biuret method.

The results showed that the synthesis of protein in the disrupted mitochondria proceeds even more intensively than in intact ones and the increase may amount to 17–19% of the original protein. It must be supposed that this occurs on account of the greater accessibility of the active centres of synthesis to the added amino acids in the disrupted, as opposed to the intact, mitochondria. Furthermore, the possibility is not ruled out that there may be activation of some enzymes in the course of disruption of the mitochondria.

Thus it was shown that the structural integrity of the mitochondria is not essential if they are to retain their synthetic ability under conditions in which activizing energetic factors are present.

An examination of photographs of the disrupted mitochondria taken with the electron microscope shows that, as a result of lysis, the envelope of the mitochondrium was punctured and the fundamental part contained within it escaped. The granularity of the contents, however, remained unimpaired, while the envelope of the mitochondrium was scarcely affected. All this indicates that the synthetic ability of the mitochondrium is concentrated in one or other of its component parts. These parts, however, are considerably larger and more complicated formations than molecules of nucleoprotein, and only a further degradation of the granular structures will enable us to solve the problem posed at the beginning of this paper.

The observation of synthesis of protein in disrupted mitochondria raised the question of the way in which the energetic requirements of the synthesis are satisfied. Experiments with enzyme poisons were carried out with a view to solving this problem. It appeared that sodium fluoride does not in the least hinder synthesis either by complete or by disrupted mitochondria. This indicates that, under the conditions which we were using, glycolytic processes do not play a direct part in protein synthesis. The addition of dinitrophenol markedly inhibited the synthesis by intact and disrupted mitochondria, which is evidence for the participation of a process of oxidative phosphorylation in the biosynthesis of protein. At the same time, it is well known that the system of oxidative phosphorylation is destroyed during the disruption of the mitochondrium. One must therefore suppose that the medium from incubated mitochondria, which was added as an activator, in some way reconstructs the processes of oxidative phosphorylation in the disrupted granules, while the addition of dinitrophenol, by inhibiting oxidative phosphorylation, leads to a loss of the ability to synthesize protein.

Thus, although our investigations show that structural integrity of the mitochondria is not essential to their synthetic ability, nevertheless, this synthetic ability is only manifest on the addition of a medium in which intact mitochondria have been incubated.

That is, in fact, it raises the new question, how far is the integrity of the mitochondrium necessary, not for the actual process of protein synthesis, but for providing the energy required for it? According to our preliminary evidence, this integrity is, in fact, necessary for the elaboration of the active medium made by incubation.

In conclusion, it must be mentioned that our results, as well as the reports in the literature concerning the synthesis of protein in disrupted microsomes and other material would appear to contradict the evidence put forward in Acad. A. I. Oparin's paper. We believe that this contradiction is only apparent. It is simply evidence for the multiple organization of the chain of biochemical processes leading to the biosynthesis of protein.

B. S. DISKINA (U.S.S.R.):

Proteolytic Activity Associated with Deoxyribonucleic Acid-chymotrypsin

The formation of nucleoproteins is one of the stages of the evolutionary development of living material, and a study of their biological role is essential to an understanding of the biochemical and biophysical bases of life.

One method of investigation, which opens up new possibilities for the study of the structural relationships which enter into the composition of the components of nucleoprotein, is the study of artificial complexes obtained from native preparations of nucleic acid and protein. The study of these is of interest in connection with the findings, which have recently appeared in the literature, concerning the alteration in the biological activity of proteins when they are bound in a complex with nucleic acid and which probably depends on the specificity of the unfolding of the protein molecules on the molecule of nucleic acid. Thus, the work of Japanese scientists has shown an activation of the enzyme urease when it is combined with ribonucleic acid. A number of other authors (Klingenberg, Slavik & Smetana; Šorm) have demonstrated the inactivation of various proteases by ribonucleic acid. In the investigations which he has described G. A. Deborin has also demonstrated the inactivation of trypsin by deoxyribonucleic acid (DNA). We have tried to make a comparative study of some of the physicochemical and enzymic properties of artificial nucleoproteins made from DNA and α-chymotrypsin, depending on the amount of the latter present in the complex. We made the complexes from highly polymeric DNA (mol. wt. 3–3·5 × 10⁶), and crystalline α-chymotrypsin, used in a concentration corresponding with its existence in the monomeric form, in the mild conditions under which they were prepared in an insoluble state (pH 4·5) and could be separated in the pure state from the starting materials which had not entered into the reaction.

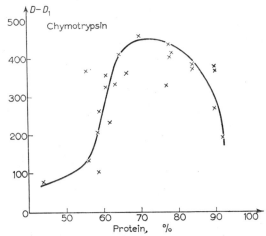

FIG. 1. Specific proteolytic activity of α-chymotrypsin bound to DNA depending on the proportion of the former in the complex.

The compounds obtained had a number of the properties of natural nucleoproteins; they formed fibrillar precipitates in physiological solutions of sodium chloride; they showed the decrease in viscosity characteristic of artificial and natural nucleoproteins, which is caused by a decrease in the asymmetry of the DNA molecule when it combines with protein; they had the characteristic capacity of nucleoproteins for high-elastic deformation.

When studying the conditions of formation of the complexes it was found that if the proportion of protein to DNA in the reaction mixture was increased, the amount of protein bound to each molecule of DNA was increased. Thus, by varying the starting proportions of protein and DNA, it was possible to obtain a series of complexes containing different proportions of protein and DNA and to study the dependence of some of their physicochemical and biological properties on this factor. This aspect of our investigations allowed us to establish interesting, regular associations between the structural–mechanical properties of the complexes (viscosity, relative relaxation) and the amount of protein in them; the results of this part of our study have been shortly described by V. S. Tongur in his communication.

Studies of the specific proteolytic activity of the chymotrypsin in complexes with different protein contents, varying over a wide range, from 45–92%, were carried out under the same conditions of enzymic concentration (calculated from the protein content of the complex) and relationship of the enzyme to the substrate.

The results obtained, shown in Fig. 1, show that when chymotrypsin is combined with DNA it is inactivated, but that the degree of inactivation of the proteolytic activity of the chymotrypsin in complexes of varying protein content is different.

The specific proteolytic activity of the enzyme was very low in complexes containing a minimal quantity of protein; as the amount of protein in the complex increased, the specific activity of the enzyme increased sharply, almost reaching the original level of activity of the chymotrypsin (when the protein content was about 68–70%); as the protein content of the complex was further increased the activity of the enzyme again decreased markedly.

The phenomenon may be explained in many ways; it is, however, beyond doubt that in these explanations the presence of structural alterations in protein when it combines with the DNA molecule plays a definite part, accompanied, perhaps, by partial blocking of the active centres and alterations in the arrangement of the reacting groups in the molecule of the enzyme. Thus, it is possible that the nature of the structural changes in the protein on the DNA is not uniform and the relative amounts of protein unfolded in various ways on the molecule of DNA determine the overall effect of the activity of the enzyme in complexes having different protein contents.

We are at present studying the mechanism of these phenomena.

The establishment of the fact of the dependence of the proteolytic activity of the enzyme in the complex on the amount of protein entering into combination with the DNA and on the structure of the protein in the molecule of nucleoprotein is clearly of decisive importance for an understanding of the metabolic processes which characterize the biological synthesis of protein.

J. D. BERNAL (Great Britain):

I should like to make a few small observations on Deborin's paper and on the contributions of two other speakers on the question of the association between proteins and other molecules in the cell, namely lipids and nucleic acids. This interaction is determined to some extent, by the shape of the molecules themselves and does not depend on special biological factors.

It has been shown that in lipoproteins there is a layer of lipid which also determines the structure. This is well seen in the case of plastids and the double membranes within cells. We have also shown that in the proteins of gluten which have this structure even in the grain, the lipid is so closely bound to the protein that it has not been possible to observe it. The other case occurs when the fundamental molecule is in the form of an extended polymer. Sometimes molecules of this or a similar type twist themselves round one another and this does not necessarily occur at a time of growth. As Mitchell has shown, two such molecules, when they twist up, may become entangled with one another *in vitro* automatically and, from the physical point of view, it may be shown that we are dealing with two types of nucleoprotein. In one case the fundamental partner is the nucleic acid as, for example, in the case of the nucleoprotein of sperm; in the other case the predominant partner is the protein, as in viruses.

Thus, most of the structures which we find in the cell are seen to be the result of the purely colloidal and crystallographic properties of matter.

I. PRIGOGINE (Belgium):

I should like to answer, very briefly, the interesting communication of Prof. Pasynskiĭ. I agree with most of his remarks but I should like to say that in our work with Wiame one must distinguish clearly between that which has been demonstrated conclusively and that which is more or less hypothetical. It has been shown that, near to the position of equilibrium, the rate of production of entropy by the system has a characteristic magnitude, characterizing the stationary state. Can one, as we suggest, identify the rate of production of entropy with the rate of the metabolic process? This is a question which, in my view, the biologists should solve and it is beyond my power. Now, about the nonlinear and linear nature of the equations of entropy. In the first place one must not set the kinetic and thermodynamic characteristics of the process in opposition to one another. In other words, the kinetic characteristics must satisfy the requirements of thermodynamics.

Chairman: K. FELIX

The Evolution of Metabolism

L'Extension de la Biosphère et l'Évolution Biochimique

MARCEL FLORKIN

Laboratoires de Biochimie de l'Université, Liège, Belgique

I. INTRODUCTION

CHAQUE ORGANISME est un chaînon d'une chaîne alimentaire dont le début varie selon les associations d'êtres vivants. Dans une mare, les bactéries et les autres microorganismes constituent le point de départ de la chaîne. Les Crustacés se nourrissent de microorganismes et sont eux-mêmes un aliment pour les Insectes aquatiques que mangent les Poissons. Les cadavres de ces derniers servent d'aliments aux bactéries. Les animaux qui se nourrissent de végétaux sont eux-mêmes la proie d'animaux carnivores, eux-mêmes consommés par d'autres carnivores. Ce tableau des chaînes alimentaires montre que les macromolécules des cellules d'un organisme peuvent servir de nourriture à d'autres, qui commencent par les hydrolyser grâce à l'arsenal d'hydrolases très généralement répandu dans la biosphère. Une portion de la biosphère alimente ainsi dans une autre portion les réactions génératrices de l'adénosine triphosphate (ATP) et de matériaux servant aux biosynthèses, et ces réactions présentent dans l'ensemble de la biosphère une remarquable unité.

Si la biosphère recourait uniquement à la méthode consistant à fournir la matière d'un de ses territoires pour l'alimentation d'un autre territoire, la vie irait s'éteignant progressivement et s'abolirait elle-même en un temps très court. En certains points de la biosphère s'opèrent des entrées de matière et des entrées d'énergie et, d'autre part, le sol et les eaux sont les tombeaux naturels des plantes et des animaux. Dans ces régions de la biosphère et de l'hydrosphère, la matière biosphérique retourne au monde inorganique, par l'action des microorganismes. Ces derniers eux-mêmes s'autolysent lorsque les conditions défavorables interrompent leur multiplication. Les cycles des entrées et des sorties s'insèrent dans le métabolisme de la biosphère, et sont les facteurs de la régulation de sa masse et de la distribution de cette dernière, à la surface du globe. Chaque secteur de la biosphère, composé par une communauté d'organismes occupant une niche écologique, est en unité fonctionnelle avec le milieu. Dans un milieu terrestre tel qu'un sol habité par des organismes, un écosystème peut subsister s'il est composé de producteurs, de décomposants et de transformateurs. Un tel écosystème peut être composé par exemple par des bactéries autotrophes (producteurs), des bactéries attaquant les cadavres de ces dernières (décomposants) et des bactéries (transformateurs) transformant les substances

503

inorganiques résultant de l'activité des décomposants en substances (nitrates, sulfates, etc.) utilisables par les producteurs.

La biosphère a sans doute, au cours de son histoire, traversé une période au cours de laquelle sa masse était relativement faible et sa nature uniformément monocellulaire, et c'est l'une des raisons qui confèrent un intérêt particulier aux travaux d'écologie microbienne. L'expansion de la biosphère s'est vraisemblablement accomplie par le développement d'organismes pluricellulaires et par l'accroissement du volume des autotrophes tels que les végétaux, accroisement lui-même limité par celui du volume des consommateurs: herbivores consommant les plantes vertes, carnivores primaires mangeant les herbivores, carnivores secondaires consommant les carnivores primaires, etc.

Au cours de son extension, la biosphère s'est donc différenciée et cette différenciation, traduite par la diversité biochimique des organismes, présente un ordre qui est la condition de l'intégration et de la régulation du métabolisme de la biosphère. L'un des aspects de l'ordre de la nature à travers la diversité biochimique des organismes est représenté par ce qu'on appelle encore l'évolution biochimique. Quelle que soit la signification qu'on donne aux arbres phylogénétiques de la classification naturelle dressés par les taxonomistes, on peut convenir que tout changement biochimique constaté le long d'un rameau de ces arbres peut-être tenu pour un fait d'évolution biochimique reposant sur la comparaison d'un aspect plus primitif et d'un aspect plus spécialisé. Par la collection des faits d'évolution biochimique ainsi conçus, on peut espérer arriver à comprendre la méthode selon laquelle la biosphère a pu s'étendre, reposant d'une part sur une prédominance des entrées sur les sorties (des biosynthèses sur les dégradations dans la biosphère *in toto*), et d'autre part sur la réalisation d'une diversité biochimique assurant la colonisation des divers biotopes tout en maintenant l'existence d'un métabolisme de la biosphère en relations d'échanges avec le monde inorganique.

II. EVOLUTION DES CONSTITUANTS BIOCHIMIQUES

Pour considérer les aspects de l'évolution des organismes sous l'angle de la biochimie, il importe de définir quelques concepts utiles.

Isologie

On appellera *isologues* les unités biochimiques, molécules ou macromolécules présentant des liens de parenté chimique. Les cytochromes, la peroxydase, la catalase, l'hémoglobine, la chlorocruorine sont isologues parce que ces structures chimiques sont des dérivés d'hèmes. L'isologie est maximum dans le cas des hémoglobines de deux chiens de la même portée, moindre si on considère l'hémoglobine du chien et celle du chacal, moindre encore si on considère l'hémoglobine d'un chien et celle d'un cheval. Dans tous ces cas, l'hème est identique, c'est le protohème, les degrés d'isologie étant dépendants de la nature de la globine. L'isologie est moindre encore dans le cas d'une hémoglobine et d'une catalase, les portions protéiques étant plus différent que dans le cas de deux hémoglobines. Un autre cas d'isologie moins marquée que celle de deux hémoglobines est fourni par l'hémoglobine et la chlorocruorine, dans lesquelles les hèmes sonts différents. Comme on le voit, il y a une grande variété de degrés d'isologie, toujours précisables en termes de chimie organique, l'isologie étant un concept purement chimique.

Analogie

On appellera analogues les unités biochimiques jouant le même rôle dans un système biochimique. La phosphocréatine et la phosphoarginine des systèmes glycolytiques musculaires, respectivement chez les Mammifères et chez les Crustacés, par exemple, sont analogues. Des unités biochimiques analogues peuvent aussi être isologues, comme c'est le cas par exemple pour une hémoglobine sanguine et une chlorocruorine sanguine : toutes deux sont des transporteurs d'oxygène. Mais elles peuvent ne pas l'être : une hémoglobine sanguine et une hémocyanine sont analogues, mais elles ne sont pas isologues.

Lorsque nous sommes informés au sujet de la position systématique relative d'une série d'espèces, et au sujet des relations d'isologie de l'un ou l'autre de leurs constituants biochimiques, il est possible de tirer des conclusions relatives à l'évolution biochimique de ces constituants. Prenons l'exemple du transporteur d'oxygène des Chlorhémiens, des Sabelliens et des Serpuliens, la chlorocruorine. Ce transporteur se trouve dans le sang de trois familles d'Annélides polychètes. Les Chlorhémiens sont des Spionides, catégorie systématique qui groupe, parmi les Annélides polychètes sédentaires, lesquelles descendent des Annélides polychètes errantes, les formes dont le lobe préoral n'est pas enfoncé dans le premier segment du métasome, se nourrissant de plancton flottant qu'ils attirent au moyen d'antennes postérieures en forme de longs palpes parcourus par une gouttière ciliée. Ils vivent dans le sable ou la vase et sécrètent un tube membraneux recouvert d'une fine couche de boue. Les Chlorhémiens sont des Spionides ayant perdu en grande partie les dissépiments et même la segmentation externe. Leur sang est vert, et leurs palpes sont rabattus vers l'avant. Aux Spionides se rattachent les Annélides cryptocéphales, à lobe préoral enfoncé dans le premier segment du tronc, mais à appendices creux comme ceux des Spionides. Sedentaires et tubicoles, les Cryptocéphales comportent deux subdivisions, les Sabellariides, qui, bien que sédentaires et microphages, ont conservé l'antenne impaire, et les Sabelliformes qui n'ont que les antennes paires et dont les palpes forment un panache en corolle multicolore. Les Sabelliformes se divisent en Sabellides, à tube muqueux, membraneux ou corné et en Serpulides, à tube calcaire.

Les sangs des Spionides autres que les Chlorhémiens sont colorés en rouge par l'hémoglobine. Quant aux Sabellariides, dont un des genres est *Sabellaria*, leur sang est chargé d'hémoglobine. Chez les Sabelliformes, encore appelés Serpuliformes, la chlorocruorine est le pigment sanguin caractéristique. Tous les Sabellides étudiés jusqu'ici la contiennent. Chez les Serpulides, le sang des espèces du genre *Serpula* contient à la fois chlorocruorine et hémoglobine et dans le genre *Spirorbis* une espèce, *S. borealis*, a un sang coloré par la chlorocruorine, une autre, *S. corrugatus*, a comme pigment sanguin l'hémoglobine et

une troisième, *S. militaris*, a un sang incolore. Fox [1] n'a pas trouvé de chlorocruorine dans les tissus ou le liquide coelomique des formes ayant de la chlorocruorine dans le sang et il n'est pas douteux que la synthèse de la chlorocruorine
est, chez les formes qui la possèdent, une variante de la synthèse d'hémoglobine
telle qu'elle s'opérait chez leurs ancêtres Annélides possédant le système de
cette synthèse. La chlorocruorine est d'ailleurs un isologue proche de l'hémoglobine des Annélides, dont elle a de nombreux caractères. L'hème de la
chlorocruorine, le chlorocruorohème, ne diffère de la protophorphyrine que
par un détail, l'oxydation du groupement vinyle 2. Quant à la portion protéique,
elle est très proche de celle des hémoglobines d'Annélides comme le montrent
les chiffres relatifs au point isoélectrique, au poids moléculaire et à la composition en acides aminés, réunis dans le Tableau 1 :

TABLEAU 1

	Point iso-électrique (pH)	Poids molé-culaire[5] × 17000	Teneur en acides aminés[6]			
			Cys-tine %	Argi-nine %	Histi-dine %	Ly-sine %
Hémoglobine de cheval .	6,78[1]	4	0,74	3,57	8,13	8,31
Hémoglobine de lombric .	5,28[2]	192	1,41	10,07	4,68	1,73
Hémoglobine d'arénicole .	4,76[3]	192	4,08	10,04	4,03	1,85
Chlorocruorine de *Spiro-graphis*	4,3[4]	192	1,64	9,64	2,38	3,64

[1] D. D. VAN SLYKE, A. B. HASTINGS, M. HEIDELBERGER & J. M. NEIL, *J. biol. Chem.*, **54**, 81, 1922.
[2] T. SVEDBERG, *J. biol. Chem.*, **103**, 311, 1933.
[3] K. O. PEDERSEN, *Kolloidzschr.*, **63**, 268, 1933.
[4] J. ROCHE, *C.R. Soc. Biol.*, Paris., **114**, 1190, 1933.
[5] T. SVEDBERG, *Proc. Roy. Soc.* [B], **127**, 1, 1939.
[6] J. ROCHE & G. JEAN, *Bull. Soc. Chim. biol.*, Paris, **16**, 769, 1934; J. ROCHE & M. MOURGUE, *Bull. Soc. Chim. biol.*, Paris, **23**, 1329, 1941.

Dans le cas de la chlorocruorine, nous avons une entité chimique isologue par
rapport à l'hémoglobine et présente dans des catégories systématiques dont la
morphologie comparée nous montre la relation phylogénique avec d'autres
catégories dont les membres ont un sang qui contient de l'hémoglobine. On peut
ici parler d'évolution d'une unité biochimique. Dans les cas de ce genre on a
non seulement isologie, mais isologie phylogénique, ou encore, pour reprendre
un terme autrefois proposé par Lankester, *homogénie*.

Parallélisme biochimique

Quand des constituants biochimiques isologues sont présents dans des
catégories systématiques qui n'ont pas de relations phylogéniques, on dira
qu'il y a parallélisme. L'apparition d'hémoglobine chez les Mollusques et chez
les Echinodermes est un exemple de parallélisme. En fait les parallélismes sont
des témoignages de l'unité de plan biochimique des organismes.

Convergence biochimique

Quand des constituants biochimiques sont analogues sans être isologues, comme c'est le cas pour l'hémoglobine et l'hémocyanine, on dira qu'il y a convergence biochimique.

Evolution hétéromorphique

L'isologie phylogénique que présentent les chlorocruorines et les hémoglobines d'Annélides fournit un exemple de ce qu'on peut appeler une évolution hétéromorphique, traduite par l'acquisition d'un constituant modifié, d'une isologie moins complète. Les hémoglobines à affinité forte pour l'oxygène apparaissent aussi comme plus primitive que les hémoglobines à affinité faible, et c'est là une évolution hétéromorphique de leur constituant protéique.

Chez les animaux supérieurs, la dissociation de l'hémoglobine varie avec son oxygénation. L'oxygénation de l'hémoglobine déplace son point isoélectrique: chez le cheval, par exemple, alors que le point isoélectrique de l'hémoglobine réduite correspond au pH 6,78, celui de l'oxyhémoglobine correspond au pH 6,65. Au pH isoélectrique, l'hémoglobine fixe des quantités équivalentes, assez faibles, d'acides et de bases, mais le pH régnant dans les hématies étant alcalin par rapport au point isoélectrique, l'hémoglobine s'y trouve à l'état de sel, en combinaison avec des bases.

Au pH du sang, l'hémoglobine se comporte comme un acide polyvalent disposant d'au moins cinq groupements acides par atome de fer.

L'oxyhémoglobine du cheval dont le point isoélectrique correspond au pH 6,65, contient, entre autres, une fonction acide (ou un groupe de fonctions) faiblement dissociée dont le pK $= 6,16$. Cette fonction, dans les hématies du sang oxygéné de cheval dont le pH est égal à 7,1, est en grande partie saturée par des bases. L'hémoglobine présente un caractère moins acide, puisque son point isoélectrique est au pH 6,8. Cette modification du point isoélectrique par suite de la variation d'oxygénation est due à une forte diminution de la dissociation des groupements acides voisins du groupement oxygénable. Leur pK passe de 6,16 à 7,80. Lorsqu'une telle transformation se produit dans un milieu dont le pH ne varie pratiquement pas, elle comporte la libération des bases fixées à cette fonction. Le fait que la réduction du sang relève la courbe d'absorption du CO_2, connu sous le nom d' 'effet Haldane', apparaît comme un caractère d'évolution de l'hémoglobine au niveau de son constituant protéique et par conséquent un fait d'évolution hétéromorphique. On ne le décèle pas, en effet, dans le sang de la raie, de la roussette *Mustelus canis* ou de l'Echiurien *Urechis caupo* qui contiennent des hémoglobines dont la dissociation ne varie pas avec l'oxygénation.

L'évolution hétéromorphique des protéines est évidemment, comme l'indiquent déjà les exemples ci-dessus, un aspect essentiel de l'évolution des organismes. Des travaux récents, permettant de saisir plus clairement les aspects hétéromorphiques de protéines plus ou moins isologues, ouvrent des perspectives nouvelles à ces études.

Les poids moléculaires des hémoglobines de Vertébrés se situent dans le voisinage de 65.000–68.000 g./mole. Ces molécules sont vraisemblablement formées de deux systèmes de trois chaînes peptidiques. La nature des séquences *N*-terminales d'une série d'hémoglobines est indiquée dans le Tableau 2. Elle montre une similitude en ce qui concerne une chaîne fondamentale commune, et une addition d'autres chaînes dans différents cas.

TABLEAU 2

(Ozawa & Satake [2])

Espèces	Séquences *N*-terminales		
Cheval, porc . . .	Val. Leu	Val. Gly	Val. Glu (Leu)
Chien	Val. Leu	Val. Gly	Val. Asp
Boeuf, Chèvre, Mouton .	Val. Leu	Met. Gly	
Cobaye	Val. Leu	Val. Ser	Val. Asp
Lapin, Serpent . .	Val. Leu	Val. Gly	
Poule	Val. Leu		

Il serait agréable de pouvoir suivre au niveau des tissus homologues, dans toutes les lignées phylétiques, les étapes de l'évolution biochimique de chacune des espèces de macromolécules qui constituent leurs cellules. Mais nos connaissances dans le domaine de la biochimie comparée sont loin de permettre de formuler une telle filiation. D'autre part, dans le domaine de la phylogénie, les lacunes laissées dans la filiation même des séries sont immenses et le monde actuel des êtres vivants présente sous ce rapport de telles solutions de continuité qu'elles conduisent certains auteurs à nier la notion même de l'évolution. Il est fréquent de constater la présence de constituants biochimiques dans un groupe

TABLEAU 3

(W. Bergmann [3])

Distribution de la portion insaponifiable des lipides des animaux

Phyla ou Classes	% de l'insaponifiable par rapport aux lipides totaux	Nombre d'exemples
Protozoa . . .	35	2
Porifera . . .	37	45
Coelenterata . .	35	16
Nemathelminthes .	25	1
Annelida . .	22	7
Crustacea . .	16	14
Myriapoda . .	21	1
Insecta . .	7	31
Mollusca (marins) .	13	18
Echinodermata .	19	10
Chordata . .	1,2	50

défini de la classification sans qu'on puisse soumettre à l'étude biochimique un groupe qui puisse lui être assigné avec certitude comme un prédécesseur immédiat dans la sériation phylétique. Les lignes générales de la phylogénie peuvent aussi servir à définir le caractère plus ou moins primitif ou spécialisé d'un constituant biochimique. W. Bergmann a par exemple souligné le fait, visible dans le Tableau 3, de l'existence d'une différence nette entre le matériel soluble dans les solvants des graisses, chez les Vertébrés et les Invertébrés; et le fait de la plus grande proportion de constituants insaponifiables chez ces derniers.

D'autre part, considérant la distribution des stérols chez les animaux, Bergmann note le fait que la plus grande diversité de stérols s'observe chez les groupes les plus primitifs et aboutit chez les plus spécialisés à l'utilisation presque exclusive du cholestérol (Tableau 4).

TABLEAU 4

(Bergmann [3, 4])

Distribution des stérols chez les animaux

Phyla et Classes	Principaux Stérols
Porifera . .	Cholestérol, cholestanol, clionastérol, poriferastérol, chalinastérol, néospongostérol, chondrillastérol, haliclonastérol, aptostanol et d'autres
Coelenterata .	Cholestérol, clionastérol, chalinastérol, palystérol et d'autres
Annelida . .	Cholestérol
Arthropoda . .	Cholestérol
Mollusca	
Pelecypoda .	Chalinastérol, brassicastérol, corbistérol, cholestérol et d'autres
Gastropoda .	Cholestérol
Cephalopoda .	Cholestérol
Echinodermata	
Asteroidea .	Stellastérols
Holothuroidea .	Stellastérols
Echinoidea .	Cholestérol
Protochordata .	Cholestérol
Chordata . .	Cholestérol

Parmi les stérols des groupes animaux les moins spécialisés, on trouve des corps en C_{28} ou C_{29}. Les stérols de cette nature diffèrent sous le rapport du degré et du type d'insaturation, sous le rapport de la nature du radical fixé en C-24, etc. [4]. D'autre part, il résulte d'une série d'études de Haslewood et collaborateurs [5], que chez des Poissons téléostéens ou élasmobranches, chez des Amphibiens, chez des Crocodiles et des Alligators, chez un Lézard, chez des Chéloniens et chez certains oiseaux, on trouve dans la bile des sels biliaires contenant des alcools et des acides en C_{27}, C_{28} (ou éventuellement en C_{29}) tandis que chez les Serpents et des Mammifères, on n'a pas trouvé de substances de cette catégorie. Par contre, la présence d'acides biliaires en C_{24} a été mise en evidence chez les Serpents, les Poissons téléostéens, les Mammifères et les Oiseaux, mais non chez les Elasmobranches, les Batraciens ou les Reptiles tels que les Crocodiliens et les Chéloniens.

D'une manière générale, les sels biliaires en C_{27}, C_{28} et éventuellement C_{29} accompagnent donc une position phylogénique plus primitive que celle, plus spécialisée, des organismes animaux ayant des sels biliaires de C_{24}.

Un autre aspect lié à la conception générale de la phylogénie est le fait, mis en évidence par Comfort, que le dépôt d'uroporphyrine dans les coquilles est répandu surtout parmi les Archaeogastropoda les moins spécialisés. Et on pourrait en citer beaucoup d'autres.

III. EVOLUTION DES SYSTÈMES BIOCHIMIQUES

Dans ce qui précède, nous avons considéré les constituants d'un organisme animal, c'est-à-dire l'aspect d'agrégats de macromolécules et de molécules organiques qu'il présente. Mais évidemment ce sont làd es résultantes de la mise en jeu de systèmes biosynthétiques et, dans la descendance avec modification que représente par exemple le remplacement d'une hémoglobine par une chlorocruorine, le changement est situé au niveau du système biosynthétique qui produit le transporteur d'oxygène. Il est donc situé au niveau d'un système enzymatique, c'est-à-dire d'un système de macromolécules dont la nature est contrôlée dans chaque cas par un gène, lui-même étant éventuellement l'objet d'une évolution hétéromorphique et d'une réduction de l'isologie de ses nucléoprotéines avec celles de ses ancêtres. Si nous admettons que le schéma de la photosynthèse est une variante métabolique du shunt des hexose-monophosphates, la photosynthèse dans son aspect de réduction du CO_2 sera tenue par un système plus spécialisé que le shunt des hexose-monophosphates. S'il est vrai d'ailleurs que la biosphère à ses débuts était dépourvue de CO_2, la photosynthèse n'a pu apparaître qu'après la libération de cette substance par les volcans et par le métabolisme primitif. S'il est vrai que la présence d'oxygène dans l'atmosphère terrestre a dépendu de la photosynthèse, la respiration est un aspect biochimique plus spécialisé que l'aspect constitué par la glycolyse et shunt des hexose-monophosphates. Mais cela est du domaine de la préhistoire biochimique et par conséquent forcément spéculatif. Dans la biosphère actuelle nous sommes devant ce qui reste des archives de la diversification du schéma général actuel de la biochimie cellulaire, laquelle a été evidemment précédée de système plus primitifs et aujourd'hui disparus. Les exemples qui suivent montrent divers aspects de l'évolution des systèmes biochimiques chez les animaux.

(a) *Spécialisation par modifications quantitatives ou topographiques*

La digestion extracellulaire comparée à la digestion intracellulaire implique une spécialisation dans le sens d'une biosynthèse relativement considérable d'enzymes rejetés dans la lumière du tube digestif et constamment renouvelés. La digestion intracellulaire constitue la forme primitive. Elle est la forme exclusive de la digestion chez le Spongiaires.

Comme Yonge l'a souligné, un exemple très démonstratif des relations entre le système de la digestion intracellulaire et celui de la digestion extracellulaire nous est fourni par les Mollusques: on trouve chez eux toutes les étapes entre une digestion presque exclusivement intracellulaire et une digestion extra-cellulaire totale, reposant sur la sécrétion de solutions de protéines enzymatiques dans la lumière du tube digestif. De manière générale, les Lamellibranches se nourrissent par des mécanismes ciliaires assurant la collection de fines parti-cules, principalement de phytoplancton. La seule phase extracellulaire de la digestion est chez eux une action amylasique, les autres actions enzymatiques étant intracellulaires. Parmi les Gastéropodes herbivores (les Pulmonés exceptés), on peut reconnaître, comme le fait Yonge, deux groupes : ceux qui possèdent un style cristallin et ceux qui n'en possèdent pas. Chez les premiers, comme par exemple les Streptoneures, les conditions sont très analogues à celles qu'on observe chez les Lamellibranches, et l'amylase est le seul enzyme extracellulaire, les diverticules digestifs étant des organes d'absorption et de digestion intra-cellulaire, mais nullement des organes sécrétants. Le second groupe de Gas-téropodes herbivores, ceux qui n'ont pas de style cristallin, comme c'est le cas chez les Tectibranches et les Nudibranches, montre une grande diversité et dans certains cas la présence d'une protéinase dans le suc présent dans la lumière du tube digestif. Quant aux Gastéropodes carnivores tels que *Murex*, on trouve toujours dans la lumière de leur tube digestif une protéinase active sécrétée par les diverticules digestifs. Au niveau de ces derniers il y a d'ailleurs aussi une digestion intracellulaire. Les glandes salivaires sécrètent d'autre part une amylase. Chez les Pulmonés, tels que l'escargot, les processus hydrolasiques sont presque totalement extracellulaires. Seule l'hydrolyse des protéines est intracellulaire.

Chez les Céphalopodes, la digestion est exclusivement extracellulaire et la digestion intracellulaire a disparu.

(b) *Spécialisation par acquisition de constituants nouveaux résultant d'une évolution hétéromorphique*

Un système enzymatique peut, au cours de l'évolution de la différenciation des cellules qui le contiennent, être l'objet d'une spécialisation d'ordre nouveau. Les Serpents, par exemple, ne mélangent pas leurs proies avec des sécrétions digestives au cours d'une opération de dilacération ou de mastication. Ils avalent leur proie après l'avoir injectée d'une sécrétion amorçant les phénomènes hydrolasiques. Dans les formes les moins spécialisées, comme c'est par exemple le cas pour les *Colubridae opisthoglyphae*, une simple dent à sécrétion apparaît à l'arrière de la machoire supérieure, servant à l'injection dans la proie d'une sécrétion dont la signification est uniquement digestive. Dans les formes plus spécialisées, cet organe, par suite de la réduction de la longueur du maxillaire dans la phylogénie, se rapproche de la région antérieure de la cavité buccale et devient un organe agressif et défensif, comme c'est le cas chez les *Colubridae protero-glyphae*, et plus encore chez les *Viperidae*.

L'origine digestive de la sécrétion ext encore attestée par la présence, dans les venins de Serpents, d'hydrolases telles que protéases, peptidases, phosphatases, estérases, et lécithinases. La spécialisation nouvelle se traduit par la présence d'hyaluronidase, qui assure la diffusion du venin, et par la présence de sub-stances hautement toxiques [6].

(c) *Spécialisation par perte de constituants*

Un système enzymatique peut se spécialiser, non seulement par l'acquisition d'enzymes nouveaux, mais aussi par la perte de certains de ceux qui le composent. Un exemple est fourni par le système enzymatique de l'uricolyse. La forme la plus complète de ce système, observée par exemple chez les Crustacés marins, est représentée dans la Fig. 1.

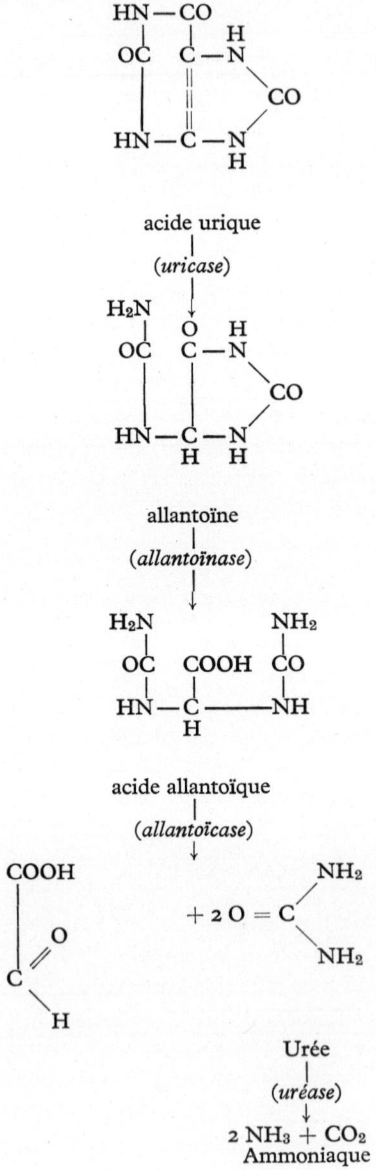

acide urique
|
(*uricase*)

allantoïne
|
(*allantoïnase*)

acide allantoïque
|
(*allantoïcase*)

Urée
|
(*uréase*)
↓
$2 NH_3 + CO_2$
Ammoniaque

FIG. 1. Le système enzymatique de l'uricolyse.

La plupart des Insectes ne poussent l'uricolyse que jusqu'au stade d'acide urique. La forme du système enzymatique de l'uricolyse des Insectes se caractérise par rapport à la forme plus primitive des Crustacés par la perte de l'uréase, de l'allantoïcase, de l'allantoïnase et de l'uricase. Le système enzymatique de l'uricolyse comporte l'uricase, l'allantoïnase et l'allantoïcase chez les Batraciens, tandis qu'il ne comporte que l'uricase chez les Mammifères, à l'exception des Primates qui ont perdu toute la série des enzymes, de même que les Reptiles terrestres et les Oiseaux.

(d) *Introduction d'un constituant biochimique ancien dans un système nouveau*

Une forme fréquente de l'évolution des systèmes enzymatiques et de leurs systèmes associés (substrats, enzymes, coenzymes, régulateurs hormonaux, etc.) est l'introduction d'un ou plusieurs de leurs constituants dans un système

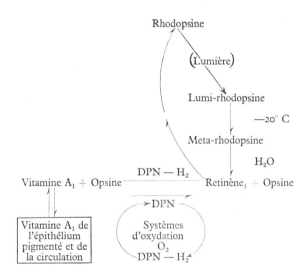

FIG. 2.   Le système de la rhodopsine [7].

nouveau, plus spécialisé. La rhodopsine, présente dans la rétine des poissons marins, des Reptiles, des Oiseaux, et des Mammifères, représente une spécialisation par rapport à la porphyropsine, plus primitive, des Vertébrés d'eau douce. La rhodopsine est un dérivé de la vitamine A_1, tandis que la porphyropsine est un dérivé de la vitimine A_2. La fonction visuelle des vitamines A est la seule qu'on puisse mettre en évidence chez les animaux autres que les Mammifères et les Oiseaux. Chez ces derniers, elle joue en outre le rôle d'une vitamine, indispensable à la fonction normale des cellules épithéliales. Dans ce dernier fait nous trouvons l'indice du développement d'un système biochimique nouveau dans lequel s'insère un composant biochimique précédemment déjà utilisé dans un autre système. Et le système biochimique de la photoréception au niveau des bâtonnets de la rétine des animaux qui possèdent un oeil différencié nous donne un autre exemple de cette forme d'évolution, en ce qui concerne un système enzymatique. Au niveau des bâtonnets de la rétine, chez un animal à rhodopsine, le rétinène$_1$ est le produit d'oxydation (déshydrogénation) de la vitamine A$_1$ et le rétinène$_1$, inversement, est le produit de la réduction de cette dernière. L'enzyme catalysant cette opération a été appelé d'abord rétinène-réductase. Nous savons aujourd'hui que c'est l'alcooldéshydrogénase comme Bliss l'a montré. Cet enzyme universellement répandu trouve ici son insertion dans un nouveau système extrêmement spécialisé (Fig. 2).

Les mécanismes de régulation hormonale présentent de nombreux aspects de ces insertions de constituants anciens dans des systèmes nouveaux. La sécrétion lactée, caractérisant une différenciation biochimique d'une catégorie de cellules des Mammifères, est déclenchée et contrôlée par la prolactine, produit de la spécialisation biochimique d'une autre catégorie de cellules, celles de l'adénohypophyse. Mais la prolactine est sécrétée par l'adénohypophyse des Poissons, des Amphibiens et des Reptiles. Son intervention au niveau de la sécrétion lactée des Mammifères s'insère donc dans un système biochimique nouveau.

Un autre exemple du même genre est fourni par l'action de la pitocine sur l'utérus des Mammifères. L'hormone existant chez tous les Vertébrés et exerçant chez tous un rôle dans le métabolisme de l'eau, son action sur l'utérus des Mammifères traduit son insertion dans un système plus spécialisé.

(e) *Spécialisation d'un système biochimique ancien par introduction d'un constituant d'un autre système ancien*

L'un des aspects importants de l'évolution biochimique des Vertébrés est l'acquisition, au niveau des cellules mésodermiques, de biosynthèses nouvelles de stéroïdes (évolution hétéromorphique) et des systèmes enzymatiques que comportent ces biosynthèses. L'un des aspects physiologiques de cette évolution est la régulation ionique résultant de l'action des hormones corticostéroïdes au niveau du tube urinaire. Ce système biochimique établi au niveau de la cellule du tube urinaire, une nouvelle évolution biochimique s'accomplit à son niveau, à partir des Amphibiens, par l'établissement de relations biochimiques avec un autre système déjà existant, celui de la régulation d'origine hypophysaire. L'adaptation à la vie terrestre, telle qu'elle apparaît à partir de certains Amphibiens, tels que le crapaud, dépend en effet d'une réabsorption d'eau commandée par l'intervention de principes hypophysaires au niveau du système biochimique du tube urinaire, dont les principes corticostéroïdes sont des constituants fondamentaux [8].

Les exemples qui précèdent, tirés de la biochimie comparée des animaux, n'épuisent certainement pas la liste des méthodes de l'évolution biochimique, c'est-à-dire de la différenciation biochimique de la biosphère, par lesquelles, au cours de son extension, se sont accomplies la régulation de son métabolisme et la colonisation des biotopes les plus divers.

BIBLIOGRAPHIE

1. H. M. Fox, *Proc. Roy. Soc.*, B., **136**, 378, 1949–50.
2. H. Ozawa & K. Satake, *J. Biochem.*, *Tokyo*, **42**, 641, 1955.
3. W. Bergmann, *Sears Found. J. Marine Res.*, **8**, 137, 1949.
4. W. Bergmann, Chapter in *Progress in the Chemistry of Fats and other Lipids*, vol. 1,
    p. 18.   Pergamon Press, London & New York, 1952.
5. G. A. D. Haslewood, *Physiol. Rev.*, **35**, 178, 1955.
6. E. Albert Zeller, *Advanc. Enzymol.*, **8**, 469, 1948.
7. G. Wald, *Science*, **113**, 287, 1951.
8. I. C. Jones, *The Adrenal Cortex*.   Cambridge University Press, 1957.

Über einige wahrscheinliche Wege der Evolution des Stoffwechsels bei den Mikroorganismen

V. N. SHAPOSHNIKOV

Institut für Mikrobiologie, Akademie der Wissenschaften der U.d.S.S.R., Moskau

DIE Mannigfaltigkeit der Stoffwechseltypen in der Welt der Mikroorganismen lässt sich, soweit es sich um die Verwendung von Kohlenstoffverbindungen im konstruktiven Stoffwechsel handelt, durch folgende Begriffe charakterisieren: photoautotrophe, chemoautotrophe, photoheteretrophe und (chemo)heterotrophe Lebensweise. Ausserdem lassen sich im Hinblick auf das verschiedene Verhalten gegenüber molekularem Sauerstoff unterscheiden: die mit der Photoassimilation verschiedener Formen von Kohlenstoff verbundene Anaerobiose, die von Licht unabhängige, mit chemischen Verwandlungen vorwiegend organischer Stoffe (Gärung) verbundene Anaerobiose, und schliesslich die Aerobiose, welche unter Beteiligung von molekularem Sauerstoff an den chemischen Verwandlungen organischer oder anorganischer Stoffe verläuft.

Alle diese Stoffwechseltypen, und die mit ihnen verknüpften sogenannten energetischen Verwandlungen der Stoffe, lassen sich bei vergleichender Analyse in genetische Reihen ordnen, die eine fortschreitende Evolution darstellen. Dies gelingt, wenn man sie als Prozesse betrachtet, die auf gekoppelten Reduktions- und Oxydationsreaktionen beruhen [1] zu denen noch eine Reihe anderer Reaktionen (Kondensation, Spaltung, Phosphorylierung usw.) als komplizierende Begleiterscheinungen hinzutreten.

Was die Verwandlungen von Kohlenstoffverbindungen im konstruktiven Stoffwechsel anbelangt, so glauben wir den primitivsten Stoffwechsel in der Photoassimilation des Kohlensäure-Kohlenstoffes* durch die Purpurschwefelbakterien und grünen Schwefelbakterien sehen zu dürfen, die unter den Bedingungen der Anaerobiose verläuft.

Die Photoassimilation des Kohlensäurekohlenstoffes durch die genannten Schwefelbakterien ist ein typischer Prozess der Reduktion von Kohlensäure, gekoppelt mit der Oxydation von Schwefelwasserstoff oder anderen oxydier-

---

* Diese Ausdruckweise scheint uns, besonders für die Photosynthese bei Bakterien, angemessener zu sein, als die herkömmliche: 'Assimilation des Kohlendioxyds da in wässeriger Lösung das Kohlendioxyd immer durch Kohlensäure vertreten ist: in Bakteriennährböden, einem meistens alkalischen Medium, ist die Kohlensäure in Karbonaten gegeben.

baren Stoffen. Dieser Prozess wird meistens durch das Schema van Niels [2] dargestellt.

$$CO_2 + 2H_2S = (CH_2O) + H_2O + 2S.$$

Später [3] schlug van Niel eine allgemeine Form desselben Schemas vor:

$$CO_2 + 2H_2A = (CH_2O) + H_2O + 2A$$

In diesem Schema sind durch 'H$_2$A' verschiedene oxydierbare Stoffe bezeichnet, die ursprünglich als Wasserstoff-Donatoren bei der Reduktion des Kohlenstoffes betrachtet wurden. Noch später [4] ist van Niel zu einer plausibeleren Auffassung gelangt, die die Photosynthese bei Bakterien und Pflanzen unter einheitlichem Gesichtspunkt zusammenfasst. Nach dieser Auffassung geschieht die Reduktion des Kohlendioxyds (bzw. der Kohlensäure) durch den Wasserstoff des Wassermoleküls, während die Oxydation des Schwefelwasserstoffs und anderer Stoffe durch Hydroxyl bewirkt wird. (Deshalb ist es zutreffender, die bei der Photosynthese der Bakterien oxydierte Stoffe nicht als Wasserstoff-Donatoren, sondern eher als Sauerstoff-Akzeptoren zu bezeichnen.)

Es muss aber gleich darauf hingewiesen werden, dass die obigen Formen für die Bakterien-Photosynthese mit wesentlichen Mängeln behaftet sind, welche bereits von van Niel selbst und anderen Forschern bekannt wurden, obwohl diese Formeln weitläufige Anwendung finden.

Der wesentlichste Manget ist die Bezeichnung der Produkte der Bakterien-Photosynthese durch (CH$_2$O), eine Bezeichnung, die aus der Physiologie der höheren Pflanzen übernommen ist. Dort hatte sie, wenn auch mit gewissem Vorbehalte, ihre Berechtigung, da als die Produkte der Photosynthese in den Zellen abgelagerten Kohlehydrate dasselbe Verhältnis von C, H und O aufweisen, wie der Formaldehyd—(CH$_2$O). Wir haben jedoch gar keinen Grund auch für die Purpurschwefelbakterien als Ergebnis der Photosynthese Kohlehydrate anzunehmen: als Ergebnis der Photosynthese müssen wir hier vielmehr die Gesamtheit der Stoffe des Bakterienkörpers betrachten. Das folgt daraus, dass die Purpurschwefelbakterien im Gegensatz zu den Pflanzen sich ausschliesslich *unter Einwirkung des Lichts* entwickeln, und dass noch niemand die Möglichkeit ihres Wachstums auf Kosten von in der Zelle abgelagerten Reservestoffen nachgewiesen hat. Eben darum machen alle Autoren (van Niel, Muller u. a.), die in ihren Beiträgen die Formel van Niels gebrauchen, den Vorbehalt, dass die Bezeichnung (CH$_2$O) inbezug auf das Verhältnis der Elemente weniger reduzierten Stoffen (Kohlehydraten) entspricht als die Gesamtsubstanz der Bakterien. Daraus folgt ebenfalls, dass der Koeffizient '2' für den Schwefelwasserstoff in den Formeln van Niels nicht dem wirklichen Verbrauch an Schwefelwasserstoff bei der Photosynthese der Bakterien entspricht.

Es ist durchaus begrifflich, dass die Summe der in ihrer Zusammensetzung recht mannigfaltigen Körpersubstanzen nicht durch eine einheitliche Formel bezeichnet werden kann. Wenn man also das Ergebnis der Photosynthese durch ein Symbol ausdrücken will, so muss man es eben symbolisch bezeichnen, etwa durch C_K^H, d.h. 'Verbrauch von Kohlenstoff (C) durch Reduktion (H) im 'konstruktiven Stoffwechsel' (K). Wenn es darauf kommt, das quantitative

Verhältnis von Kohlenstoff, Wasserstoff und Sauerstoff in den Körperstoffen der Bakterien zu kennzeichnen, so kann dieses Verhältnis auf Grund der Ergebnisse der Gesamtanalyse der Körpersubstanz der Bakterien, und speziell der Purpurschwefelbakterien (vgl. [3]), etwa wie folgt dargestellt werden:

$$C_nH_{n+x} + O_x \text{ oder auch } C_nH_n (H_2O)_x$$

Eine solche Bezeichnung ist freilich nicht vollkommen exakt, jedoch kommt sie dem wirklichen Verhältnis von diesen Elementen im Körper der Bakterien bedeutend näher.

DIE PHOTOSYNTHESE
BEI DEN PURPURSCHWEFELBAKTERIEN UND HÖHEREN PFLANZEN VOM STANDPUNKT DER FUNKTIONEN-EVOLUTION

Der Gedanke, in das Schema der Bakterienphotosynthese die Bezeichnung (CH_2O) einzuführen, die aus der Physiologie der pflanzlichen Photosynthese übernommen ist, geht wohl auf den durchaus begreiflichen Wunsch zurück, eine Verbindung zwischen diesen beiden Prozessen im Sinne der genetischen Evolution herzustellen. Der konsequenteste Ausdruck dieses Gedankens ist das bekannte Schema van Niels [4], in dem die Photosynthese der Bakterien mit der der grünen Pflanzen vereinigt ist:

Dieses Schema betont manche biochemisch ähnliche Züge beider Prozesse: die notwendige Photoreduktion des Kohlendioxyds (bzw. der Kohlensäure), das Auftreten von Fermenten (E′ und E″) als Zwischenakzeptoren von H und OH; es betont andererseits eine gewisse Verschiedenheit der Prozesse (die Notwendigkeit spezifischer Akzeptoren von Sauerstoff bei der Photosynthese der Bakterien). Das ist ein zweifelloser Vorzug dieses Schemas.

Für die Feststellung von Gesetzmässigkeiten der genetischen Evolution reicht das gesagte jedoch nicht aus. Es kommt dabei noch darauf an, die biologische Seite der vorhandenen Verschiedenheiten zu berücksichtigen und die möglichen Wege ihrer Entstehung zu umreissen.

Die Entwicklung von Purpurschwefelbakterienkulturen verläuft, ähnlich wie die Assimilation des Kohlensäure-Kohlenstoffes, nur unter Einwirkung des Lichts. Die mehrmals wiederholten Versuche, diese Bakterien unter den verschiedenen Bedingungen ohne Licht zu züchten, blieben stets erfolglos [5]. Das lässt augenscheinlich darauf schliessen, dass der Umfang der Photosynthese der Bakterien dem Umfang des Verbrauches von Assimilationsprodukten im konstrucktiven Stoffwechsel gleichkommt.

Im Reich der grünen Pflanzen ist es darum anders bestellt: die Entwicklung der Pflanze ist mit dem Lichte und damit auch mit der Photosynthese nicht unmittelbar verbunden; sie kann bis zu einem gewissen Grade in völliger Dunkelheit fortschreiten. Die Erklärung hierfür ist, dass unter normalen Bedingungen der Umfang der Photosynthese den Umfang des Verbrauchs der Assimilate übertrifft, so dass die letzteren zum Teil in der Form von Kohlehydraten u.a. als Vorrat abgelagert werden.

Die Wege der Evolution, die zu einer relativen Vergrösserung des Umfangs der Photoassimilation gegenüber dem Verbrauch der Assimilate führen, sind nicht klar; man könnte sie suchen:

(a) In der Vervollkommnung der photosynthesierenden Apparate*.

(b) Darin, dass die pflanzliche Photosynthese von der notwendigen Zufuhr exogener spezifischer Sauerstoff-Akzeptoren unabhängig geworden ist. Dies wurde ermöglicht durch die Entwicklung eines Mechanismus, bei dem die OH-Gruppen zu Peroxyden umgewandelt werden, worauf dann eine Zerlegung der letzteren und Ausscheidung von molekularem Sauerstoff folgt.

(c) Man könnte sie schliesslich in einer Beschränkung des photosynthetischen Prozesses auf die Bildung von Kohlehydraten suchen. Diese sind, wie bereits gezeigt wurde, für die Photosynthese der Pflanzen kennzeichnend und stellen bis zu einem gewissen Grad Erzeugnisse einer nicht ganz vollendeten Photosynthese dar.

Die relative Vergrösserung des Umfangs der Photoassimilation gegenüber dem unmittelbaren Bedarf des konstruktiven Stoffwechsels hat eine grosse biologische Bedeutung: enthält die Voraussetzung nicht für eine Trennung der Funktionen der Entwicklung und der Photosynthese ihrem Umfange nach, sondern auch für ihre räumliche Trennung, wie dies bei den höheren Pflanzen der Fall ist (das Blatt und der Wachstumskegel). Diese räumliche Trennung aber ist ihrerseits Vorbedingung für die Differenzierung und Spezialisierung bestimmter Organe und Gewebe der Pflanzen.

DIE CHEMOSYNTHESE

Betrachtet man im Sinne der hier vorgelegten Gedanken die chemosynthetische Assimilation des Kohlensäure-Kohlenstoffes als das Ergebnis gekoppelter Reduktions-Oxydationsreaktionen, die unter Verbrauch des Wasserstoffs des

---

* Es kann sich hier um eine Evolution des Aufbaus der Chloroplasten niederer Algen sowie der je nach der Beleuchtung ihre Lage in der Zelle ändernden Chlorophyllkörper der Pflanzen handeln, ferner um eine Veränderung der Pigmentsysteme im Zusammenhang mit der ungleichen Absorbtion der Lichtstrahlen in verschiedenen Bezirken des Spektrums, u. s. w.

Wassers verlaufen, so kann es nicht schwer fallen, gewisse Verwandtschafts-momente zwischen der Photosynthese und der Chemosynthese aufzustellen.

Dass eine solche Deutung der Chemosynthese möglich ist, zeigt vor allem die Analyse des Stoffwechsels bei dem zuerst von Beijerinck [6] beschriebenen Bakterium, das ursprünglich *Thiobacillus denitrificans* genannt wurde und später die Bezeichnung *Sulfomonas denitrificans* Jensen erhielt.

Bei diesen Bakterien erfolgt die Assimilation des Kohlensäure-Kohlenstoffes durch den Prozess der Sulfodenitrifizierung. Letzterer besteht in der Oxy-dierung von elementarem Schwefel (Schwefelblüte) unter anaeroben Bedin-gungen auf Kosten der Reduktion von Nitraten zu molekularem Stickstoff. Eine ähnliche Erscheinung ist auch für das wasserstoffoxydierende Bakterium *Bac. pycnoticus* Ruhl. bekannt, das in Anaerobiose Wasserstoff auf Kosten der Reduktion von Nitraten oxydieren kann [7].

Dasselbe wurde neulich für obligat anaerobe sulfatreduzierende Bakterien nachgewiesen [8], bei denen die Assimilation von CO_2 durch Oxydation von H_2 unter gleichzeitiger Reaktion von Sulfaten zu Schwefelwasserstoff erfolgt*.

Wenn somit die Assimilation von Kohlensäure-Kohlenstoff bei der Photo-synthese der Bakterien als Ergebnis von gekoppelten Reduktions-Oxydations-reaktionen aufgefasst werden kann, deren Umfang durch die Wasserstoffmenge bestimmt wird, die für die Umwandlung des Kohlenstoffes der Kohlensäure zu Kohlenstoff der Körpersubstanz der Bakterien notwendig ist, so verlangt die chemosynthetische Assimilation statt des 'Lichtes' eine zusätzliche Oxydation des Sauerstoff-Akzeptors, wobei der überschüssige, für die Reduktion der Kohlensäure nicht aufgebrachte Wasserstoff gebunden wird.

Daher lässt sich die photosynthetische Assimilation durch folgende Schema darstellen:

$$H_2CO_3 + n(H_2O) + nAH_2 + \boxed{\text{Licht}} \rightarrow C_K^{nH_2} + nA + xH_2O$$

Die Chemosynthese wird auf analoge Art durch ein komplizierteres Schema darzustellen sein:

$$H_2CO_3 + n(H_2O) + nAH_2 + \boxed{AH_2 + /O \cdot H_2/ + B} \rightarrow C_K^{nH_2} + nA + ABH_2yH_2O,$$

$$H_2CO_3 + (n^+)(H_2O) + (n^+)AH_2B \rightarrow C_K^{nH_2} + (n^+)A + BH_2 + yH_2O$$

B bezeichnet hier den Akzeptor des überschüssigen Wasserstoffs.

---

* Um die weitere Darlegung zu vereinfachen, seien hier zwei folgende Momente betont: (a) die Denitrifizierungsprozesse (vor allem die Sulfodenitrifizierungsprozesse) können schwerlich anders aufgefasst werden, als das Ergebnis eines Reduktions—Oxy-dationsprozesses mit Wasserionen; (b) bei den Denitrifizierungsprozessen kann als Akzep-tor für OH (Nitrate) molekularer Wasserstoff fungieren; in der letzten Zeit wurde das auch für Sulfonitrifizierungsprozesse nachgewiesen [9].

Somit hindert uns nichts daran, die Oxydation des Wasserstoffs durch wasserstoff-oxydierende Bakterien als Reduktion des Sauerstoffs zu betrachten.

$$2H_2 + 2(O \cdot H_2) + O_2 = 4H_2O$$

DIE 'HETEROTROPHE PHOTOASSIMILATION'

Um eine Brücke zu schlagen von der primitivsten (im Sinne des Stoffwechseltyps*) photoautotrophen Lebensweise der Purpurschwefelbakterien zur typisch heterotrophen, wollen wir hier kurz auf das Verhalten verschiedener photosynthesierender Bakterien gegenüber organischen Stoffen eingehen.

Dieser Frage wird seit der Veröffentlichung der ersten Arbeit van Niels [2] bis jetzt grosse Beachtung geschenkt. Das ist durchaus begreiflich, denn auf diesem Wege konnte man hoffen, zumindest eine annähernde Vorstellung zu bekommen über die Zwischenglieder der Verwandlung des Kohlensäure-Kohlenstoffes in den Kohlenstoff der gesamten Körpersubstanz der Bakterien.

Wie Elsden [10] richtig betont, beziehen sich die vorhandenen Angaben leider nur auf einzelne Vertreter der Familie *Athiorhodaceae*. Was jedoch die Purpurschwefelbakterien (*Thiorhodaceae*) anbelangt, so begnügt man sich bei der Charakterisierung ihres Verhaltens gegenüber organischen Stoffen gewöhnlich damit, dass letzteren die Rolle von Wasserstoff-Akzeptoren zuerkannt wird.

H. Molisch [11], der mehrere Vertreter der Familie *Athiorhodaceae* beschrieben hat, charakterisierte sie als erster als eigenartige 'photoheterotrophe' Organismen, die sich bei Licht unter Assimilation organischer Stoffe entwickeln. Eingehender erforscht wurde diese Gruppe durch van Niel [4]. Van Niel hat nachgewiesen, dass die Mehrzahl der Vertreter dieser Familie sich bei Licht unter anaeroben Bedingungen gut entwickeln, wobei sie verschiedene organische Säuren verbrauchen. (Darüber hinaus wurde festgestellt, dass sie den Zusatz von Vitaminen zum Nährboden verlangen). J. M. Siegel [12], der mit *Rhodopseud. gelatinosa* arbeitete, hat experimentell nachgewiesen, dass diese Bakterien, wenn sie sich bei Licht entwickeln, Kohlenstoff aus Aceton assimilieren. Er hat ermittelt, dass bei der Assimilation von Aceton-Kohlenstoffatomen zugleich 17 Kohlenstoffatome aus CO_2 verbraucht werden.

Siegel vertritt die Meinung, dass hierbei eine Kondensation des Aceton mit Kohlendioxyd stattfindet†, und gibt an, dass neben Aceton-Kohlenstoff auch der Kohlenstoff des Isopropylalkohols und der Acetessigsäure assimiliert werden kann.

Das Verhalten der Purpurbakterien gegenüber organischen Stoffen wurde eingehender beleuchtet in den von E. N. Kondratjewa in unserem Laboratorium durchgeführten Arbeiten [13] an *Rhodopseud. palustris*. Dieses Bakterium wird üblicherweise zu den *Athiorhodaceae* gezählt (vgl. [4], aber mit demselben Recht (siehe weiter unten) kann es auch zu den *Thiorhodaceae* gezählt werden, denn es entwickelt sich gut auf dem Mineralnährboden van Niels mit Schwefelwasserstoff, ohne Spuren von organischen Stoffen und ohne Vitamin-Zusatz.

Kondratjewa hat gezeigt, dass der von ihr erforschte Organismus sich gut auf einem Nährboden ohne Schwefelwasserstoff entwickelt, wobei Kohlenstoff

---

* Dies wird betont, um nicht den Eindruck aufkommen zu lassen, als halte der Verfasser die photosynthesierenden Bakterien für primäre, als erste auf der Erde erschienene Lebewesen. Der hier angewandte Ausdruck 'primitive' ist nur auf die hier besprochenen Stoffwecheselvorgänge, jedoch nicht auf die dieselben bewerkstelligenden Organismen bezogen (Der Verfasser).

† Diese Behauptung steht jedoch nicht im Einklang mit dem in der genannten Arbeit angeführten Verhältnis des Acetonverbrauchs und des Verbrauchs von Kohlendioxyd.

aus Essigsäure und anderen organischen Säuren bei Vorhandensein von Karbonaten im Nährboden assimiliert wird. Er entwickelt sich jedoch gut auch ohne CO_2, falls der Nährboden zwei organische Säuren enthält, z.B. Essigsäure und Fumarsäure, u.a.

Unserer Meinung nach kommt es vor allem darauf an, dass der Nährboden Stoffe enthalte, die sowohl für Sauerstoff als auch für Wasserstoff als Akzeptoren dienen können.

Wir haben bereits darauf hingewiesen, dass die Fähigkeit der photosynthesierenden Bakterien, konstruktiven Stoffwechsel der Kohlenstofforganischer Stoffe zu verwerten, nur für einzelne Vertreter der Familie *Athiorhodaceae* nachgewiesen wurde. Wenn dies auch für die typischen Purpurschwefelbakterien gezeigt werden könnte die bis jetzt als obligat autotrophe Organismen betrachtet werden in denen organische Stoffe lediglich als Sauerstoff—Akzeptoren dienen können—so bliebe der einzige Unterschied zwischen *Thiorhodaceae* und *Athiorhodaceae* darin bestehen, dass die letzteren die Fähigkeit zur autotrophen Assimilation mehr oder weniger vollständig eingebüsst haben.

Es scheint durchaus wahrscheinlich, dass photoautotrophe Organismen gewisse organische Stoffe verwerten können, denn es leuchtet ohne weiteres ein, dass die Überführung des Kohlenstoffes aus der Kohlensäure in die Körperstoffe der Bakterien eine Reihe immer komplizierterer Etappen durchläuft. Es fragt sich nur, was das für Etappen sind, und unter welchen Bedingungen sich weitere Verwandlungen vollziehen.

Deswegen wurden in unserem Laboratorium durch M. W. Nefelowa Experimente vorgenommen, die ermitteln sollten, ob die Assimilation mancher organischer Säuren für einen typischen Vertreter der Purpurschwefelbakterien— *Chromatium vinosum*—möglich ist.

Die Bakterien wurden in Nährlösungen nach van Niel gezüchtet die folgende Zusammensetzung hatten: NH_4Cl—1 g; K_2HPO_4—0,5 g; $MgSO_4$—0,2 g; NaCl—2 g; $NaHCO_3$—1 g; $Na_2S,9H_2O$—2 g; Wasser—1 l. Je nach der gestellten Aufgabe wurden in dieser Lösung die Karbonate oder Sulfide durch verschiedene organische Säuren, Alkohole usw. ersetzt.

Die Bedingungen der Versuche waren folgende: der pH—Wert der Nährlösung betrug zu Beginn des Versuches 7,5; die Züchtung erfolgte in bis an den Rand erfüllten Gefässen, mit eingeschliffenen Glasstopfen; zur Beimpfung diente 1% 7 Tage alte Kultur, welche auf Mineralnährlösung gezüchtet war und 2–4 $\times$ 10⁵ Bakterien in 1 ml. enthielt. Die Dauer der Züchtung betrug 10 Tage.

Die einleitenden Versuche haben in Uebereinstimmung mit van Niel, Müller u.a. ergeben, dass der Schwefelwasserstoff in Nährboden mit Erfolg durch verschiedene organische Verbindungen ersetzt werden kann—durch organische Säuren, Alkohole usw. Der Bakterienertrag war dabei auf Nährlösungen mit Essigsäure und Propionsäure, sowie mit Aethylalkohol, bedeutend grösser, als auf der ursprünglichen Mineralnährlösung (Fig. 1)*.

---

* Wenn in der Nährlösung der Schwefelwasserstoff durch organische Stoffe ersetzt wird, erwies es sich als nützlich, zur Herabsetzung des Redox-Potentials eine kleine Menge (0·01%) Na_2S einzuführen. Im Kontrollversuch, d. h. in Nährlösungen ohne organische Stoffe, ergab derselbe Na_2S—Zusatz nur eine sehr schwache Bakterienentwicklung, nicht über 2.10^6 Bakterien in 1 ml.

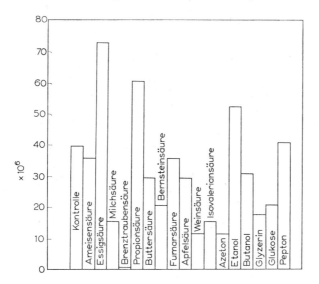

FIG. 1. Bakterienertrag (Zellen/ml) auf Nährlösungen nach van Niel, H₂S durch organische Säuren ersetzt. Kontrollversuch Nährlösung nach van Niel. Dauer der Kulture—10 Tage.

Weiter konnten aus den Nährlösungen die Karbonate (und CO₂) ausgeschlossen und durch bestimmte organische Säuren (jedoch nicht durch Alkohole) ersetzt werden. Eine besonders intensive Entwicklung war zu bezeichnen, wenn die Karbonate durch Salze der Essigsäure, der Fumarsäure und der Bernsteinsäure ersetzt wurden (Fig. 2).

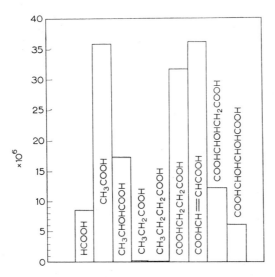

FIG. 2. Bakterienertrag (Zellen/ml) auf Nährlösungen nach van Niel, NaHCO₃ durch Salze organischer Säuren ersetzt. Dauer der Kultur—10 Tage.

Somit wurde bereits durch diese einleitenden Versuche gezeigt, dass der Kohlenstoff bestimmter organischer Säuren als Material für den Aufbau der Kohlenstoffgerüste der Bakterienkörpersubstanz dienen kann.

Bei den weiteren Versuchen wurden aus dem Nährboden sowohl der Schwefelwasserstoff (siehe jedoch die Fussnote über Na_2S) als auch die Karbonate ausgeschlossen und durch eine Kombination von zwei organischen Stoffen ersetzt. Der eine dieser Stoffe war Essigsäure, der andere—Ameisensäure, Brenztraubensäure, Propionsäure, Buttersäure oder Aethylalkohol.

In allen Fällen wurde ein hoher Bakterienertrag erzielt—54 bis 67 Millionen Bakterien in 1 ml. Nährlösung (Fig. 3).

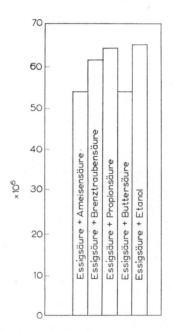

FIG. 3. Bakterienertrag (Zellen/ml) auf Nährlösungen nach van Niel ohne $NaHCO_3$ und Na_2S, die durch eine Kombination von zwei organischen Säuren ersetzt sind. Dauer der Kultivierung—10 Tage.

Diese Ergebnisse veranlassten uns, eine Reihe von Versuchen durchzuführen, bei denen die Nährlösungen verschiedene Kombinationen von organischen Säuren mit Schwefelwasserstoff und Karbonaten enthielten, wobei auch die Kohlenstoff-Bilanz berücksichtigt wurde.

Es ist mir nicht möglich, hier auf die Ergebnisse dieser Versuche im einzelnen einzugehen, sowie auf die Schlussfolgerungen die bezüglich des wahrscheinlichen Verlaufs der Kohlenstoff-Photoassimilation bei der Bakterien-Photosynthese schliessen lassen. (Diese Angaben werden in der Zeitschrift *Mikrobiologiya* veröffentlicht.) Die wichtigsten Ergebnisse sind im Fig. 4 dargestellt.

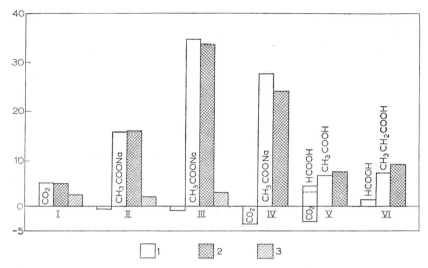

FIG. 4. Verbrauch (und Ausscheidung) von Kohlensäure-Kohlenstoff; Kohlenstoff in der Bakterienkörpersubstanz (Ertrag) und Verbrauch von H₂S in m-Molen. Dauer der Kultur—10 Tage.

I—HCO₃ + Na₂S;   II—CH₃COOH + Na₂S;   III—CH₃COOH + NaHCO₃ +Na₂S;   IV—CH₃COOH + NaHCO₃;   V—CH₃COOH + HCOOH;   VI— CH₃CH₂COOH | HCOOH.

1—Kohlenstoffverbindungen; 2—Kohlenstoff im Körper der Bakterien; 3—Verbrauch von Schwefelwasserstoff in m-Molen.

Es sei hier nur bemerkt, dass diese Versuche (die jetzt von uns in erweitertem Umfang fortgesetzt werden) beweisen, dass der Kohlenstoff der Essigsäure unter bestimmten Bedingungen bei der Photosynthese in die Körpersubstanz der Purpurschwefelbakterien übergehen kann. Die Versuche zeigen ferner die möglichen Wege der Verwandlung von Kohlensäure und mancher organischer Säuren in Bakterien-Körperstoffe.

Eine weitere Analyse des konstruktiven Stoffwechsels der heterotrophen Mikroorganismen vom Standpunkt der Evolution des Kohlenstoffwechsels ist zur Zeit leider nur schwer durchführbar, da es an einschlägigen experimentellen Angaben fehlt: die heutige Mikrobiologie verfügt nur über solche Angaben, über den Kohlenstoffwechsel, die verschiedene Typen des 'energetischen' Stoffwechsels kennzeichnen, welcher sich unter den Bedingungen der Anaerobiose vollzieht und vor allem mit Umwandlungen der Kohlehydrate zusammenhängt. Manche Angaben zur Characterisierung der Gärungsprozesse vom Standpunkt der Funktionen-Evolution enthalten die Beiträge von V. N. Shaposhnikov [14].

LITERATUR

1. A. KLUYVER, *Arch. Mikrobiol.*, **1**, 181, 1930.
2. C. B. VAN NIEL, *Arch. Mikrobiol.*, **3**, 1, 1931.
3. C. B. VAN NIEL, *Arch. Mikrobiol.*, **7**, 323, 1936.

4. C. B. VAN NIEL, *Bact. Rev.*, **8**, 1, 1944.
   C. B. VAN NIEL, *Amer. Scient.*, **37**, 171, 1949.
5. F. H. MÜLLER, *Arch. Mikrobiol.*, **4**, 131, 1933.
6. M. W. BEIJERINCK, *König. Acad. Wetensch. Amst.*, **22**, 899, 1920.
7. W. RUHLAND, *Jb. wiss. Bot.*, **69**, 321, 1924.
8. YU. SOROKIN, *Dokl. Akad. Nauk S.S.S.R.*, **60**, 895, 1953.
9. K. BAALSRUD & K. S. BAALSRUD, *Arch. Mikrobiol.*, **20**, 34, 1954.
10. S. R. ELSDEN, *Autotrophic Micro-organisms.* *Symp. Soc. gen. Microbiol.*, 203, 1954.
11. H. MOLISCH, *Die Purpurbacterien nach neuen Untersuchungen.* Jena, 1907.
12. J. M. SIEGEL, *J. Bact.*, **60**, 595, 1950.
13. E. N. KONDRAT'EVA, *Mikrobiologiya*, **25**, 393, 1956.
   E. N. KONDRAT'EVA, *Mikrobiologiya*, 1957, im Druck.
14. V. N. SHAPOSHNIKOV, *Izv. Akad. Nauk S.S.S.R. Ser. biol.*, **3**, 16.

The Pathways of Biological Assimilation and Dissimilation of Nitrogen and Some Aspects of Their Evolution

A. E. BRAUNSHTEĬN

Institute of Biological and Medical Chemistry, Academy of Medical Sciences of the U.S.S.R., Moscow

BIOCHEMICAL evolution is not my special field of research, and I do not intend to consider the whole problem of the evolution of nitrogen metabolism. My aim is to discuss a few selected questions concerning the formation of amino acids from ammonia and the paths of nitrogen dissimilation.

This seems justified insofar as amino acids are the first organic products of nitrogen assimilation and the main precursors of secondary nitrogenous metabolites, including vitamins, porphyrins, purines etc. On the other hand, ammonia is the immediate mother substance of organic nitrogen. Although many organisms can utilize nitrates, nitrites or molecular nitrogen, it would appear that these nitrogen sources of higher oxidation level must always undergo preliminary reduction to ammonia.

One of the most impressive general results of modern biochemical research is the recognition of far-reaching unity of chemical structures and processes in all contemporary forms of life. In all organisms, the proteins, nucleic acids, coenzymes and other important nitrogenous body constituents are made up from nearly identical building units, arranged into similar structural patterns. There is also relatively little difference in the paths of biosynthesis of the simpler subunits. In all organisms of our epoch, the synthesis of amino acids, vitamins, heterocyclic bases etc. proceeds through similar steps and is effected with the aid of closely related catalytic agents.

Such unity implies that the biosynthetic mechanisms operating in present-day organisms are of exceedingly ancient origin. Only the latest evolutionary changes of these intricate and highly perfected mechanisms can be evaluated on the basis of the data of comparative biochemistry. In attempting to arrive at some understanding of how these mechanisms could have arisen from simpler or, at any rate, qualitatively very different primordial modes of abiogenic and biological synthesis, we must heavily lean upon conjecture and indirect reasoning.

Two different ways of nitrogenous nutrition provide for the synthesis of proteins and other nitrogenous body constituents in contemporary organisms. On the one hand, the organisms can utilize amino acids, heterocyclic bases, etc., synthesized in other organisms and absorbed as food; this is the heterotrophic

527

type of nitrogenous nutrition. On the other hand, the same sub-units can be synthesized by the organisms themselves from nitrogen-free organic compounds and inorganic nitrogen, chiefly ammonia; that is what we call the aminoauto-trophic type of nutrition. All grades of transition are known from total amino-autotrophy (in green plants and many micro-organisms) to high degrees of nitrogen heterotrophy, e.g. in the animals, which fail to synthesize B-vitamins and a number of amino acids. Heterotrophy reaches extreme levels in lactic acid bacteria and in certain parasitic organisms exhibiting still more restricted capacities for the synthesis of amino acids, nitrogenous heterocycles etc. [1].

The widely differing abilities of various organisms to synthesize the amino acids chiefly reflect variations of their capacity to build the corresponding carbon skeletons.

Here again we meet with a wide range of intermediate levels between the absolute carboautotrophy of chemo- and photosynthesizing organisms, and the greatly narrowed synthetic potentialities of animals and those microbes which thrive on proteins or protein fragments. But even the extreme aminohetero-trophs are able, to a lesser or greater extent, to utilize ammonia and incorporate it into amino acids, including the essential ones, when supplied with adequate nitrogen-free precursors, e.g. in the form of α-keto acids.

The more closely the type of nutrition of an organism approximates to total carbon and nitrogen autotrophy, the more complete and elaborate must neces-sarily be the array of enzyme systems at its disposal for the synthesis of proteins and all other body constituents. This implies that chemo- or photosynthesizing autotrophs can only have arisen, through gradual evolution, from primordial heterotrophic forms of life which thrived on organic compounds of abiogenic origin [2]. The heterotrophy of the present-day organisms, which feed on the products of biosynthesis of carbo- and aminoautotrophs, is of secondary origin; its development involves adaptive regression and simplification of superfluous enzyme systems.

During the last decades great progress has been achieved in elucidating the principal stages of the biogenesis of all amino acids (and of important secondary nitrogenous metabolites), and the major steps of their catabolic degradation in various organisms [3–5]. This progress has been due, to a considerable extent, to ingenious studies involving the use of isotopically labelled compounds [6], and especially to the utilization of artificially induced mutations in micro-organisms, resulting in the blocking of single enzymic reactions [3, 5].

These investigations have revealed the striking uniformity of the pathways for biogenesis of amino acids and other nitrogen compounds in all organisms (to the extent they are able to synthesize these metabolites), and the close simi-larity of the enzymes and coenzymes involved in these syntheses in organisms belonging to widely differing types. Lysine is the only amino acid synthesized by two independent routes (in bacteria and in moulds, respectively) [5].

Contemporary organisms build the structural skeletons of the amino acids from intermediates of the biosynthesis of sugars and of their anaerobic or oxi-dative breakdown, i.e. from triose and pentose phosphates, phosphoglycerate, pyruvate and the acids involved in the respiratory tricarboxylic acid cycle.

It was formerly thought that most α-amino acids were formed from the corresponding α-keto acids, by way of reductive amination or transamination. Nowadays it is known that in the process of primary biogenesis the amino groups are frequently incorporated into the molecules at earlier stages of the synthesis, so that many amino acids are not being synthesized from their keto analogues, but rather from other amino acids by way of remodelling of, or further additions to, their side chains.

As shown in Fig. 1, glutamic acid is transformed, with retention of its original nitrogen, into proline, hydroxyproline, ornithine and arginine. Aspartic acid is converted to homoserine, methionine, threonine, glycine, and (in bacteria) to diaminopimelic acid and lysine; from threonine, via intermediate keto acids, is formed isoleucine. Serine and glycine are interconvertible and undergo transformation into cysteine, tryptophan, kynurenine and alanine. Phenylalanine is the precursor of tyrosine, dihydroxyphenylalanine and thyroxine, etc.

In Fig. 1 are also shown the principal intermediates of carbohydrate metabolism, giving rise to 'genetic sequences' of amino acids in the course of biosynthesis.

The biosynthetic paths of the amino acids and their secondary metabolic transformations include a variety of reactions effected by enzymes containing pyridoxal phosphate as the prosthetic group [7, 8, 3]. Pyridoxal enzymes catalyse decarboxylation and racemization of amino acids, the formation and removal of amino groups by transamination, and many reactions of condensation, replacement and cleavage by which the skeletons of amino acids are remodelled. In Fig. 1 transformations involving the action of pyridoxal enzymes are denoted by the symbol PP.

According to the theory of Braunshteïn & Shemyakin [9], the reactions catalysed by pyridoxal enzymes are made possible by the peculiar chemical properties of the Schiff bases, or azomethines, formed by the condensation of amino acids with the CO-group of pyridoxal. Owing to the pronounced electrophilic properties of the substituents on the α-carbon atom of such azomethines (and of the tautomeric azomethines formed by shift of the double bond) the electron density of the α-carbon atom is greatly lowered. This results in polarization and weakening (activation) of the bonds between the α-carbon atom and its substituents and, in the case of certain structural prerequisites (in suitably substituted amino acids), also of bonds at the β- and γ-carbon atoms (Fig. 2).

That is why azomethines of this kind can readily undergo reactions of cleavage or substitution (condensation) involving rupture of the weakened bonds, as indicated in Fig. 2. Generally spoken, the properties and transformations of such azomethines are similar to those of the analogous keto acids, rather than of the original amino acids.

Several of these transformations can occur non-enzymically when amino acids interact under relatively mild conditions with free pyridoxal, especially in the presence of certain metals (e.g., Cu, Fe, Al, Ni). The discovery and detailed investigation of these model reactions is due to Snell and his associates [10, 11]. In 1954, they published a general theory of pyridoxal catalysis [11], the essential features of which coincide with those of our theory (Braunshteïn & Shemyakin,

34

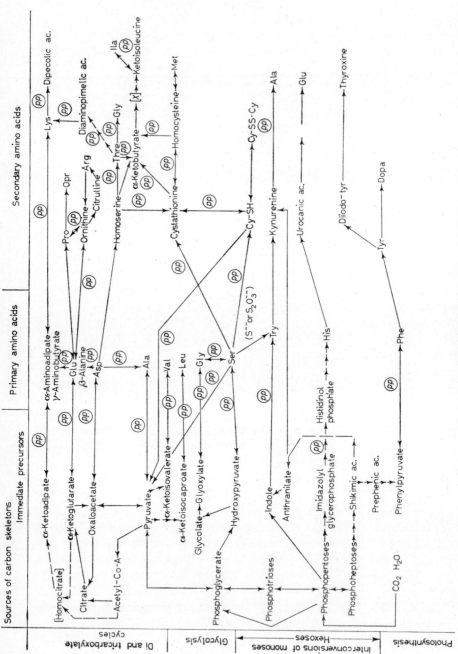

Fig. I. The main paths of biogenesis of the amino acids.

1952, 1953). However, Snell and his coworkers have stressed the role of chelation of the azomethines with some metal or other, considering this as the factor of major importance in intensifying the decrease of electron density of the α-carbon atom and in determining the prevalence of definite transformations of the azomethines. This is certainly correct with respect to the non-enzymic model reactions. But it is evident that, in most instances of reactions catalysed by pyridoxal enzymes, the same functions are exercized by the specific enzyme proteins, or apoenzymes [7, 8, 9], instead of chelating metals.

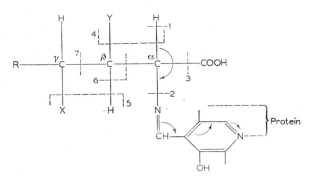

FIG. 2. Activation (weakening) of chemical bonds in amino acid molecules by pyridoxal enzymes

Ruptured bonds:	Reaction types:	Enzymes:
1. α-C—H	Dissociation of α-H	Aminopherases, racemases etc.
	Condensations of glycine	Serine synthease; δ-aminolevulinic acid synthease
2. α-C—N	Transamination; deamination	Aminopherases; Diamine oxidase
3. α-C—COOH	α-Decarboxylation	Amino acid α-decarboxylases
4. α-C—H and β-C—Y	Removal (or replacement) of α-H and β-substituent	Tryptophanase; serine- and threonine-dehydrases; β-thionases; alliinase; tryptophan synthease; cystathionine synthease
5. β-C—H and γ-C—X	Removal (or replacement) of β-H and γ-substituent	Homoserine deaminase; γ-thionases; threonine-synthease
6. α-C—β-C and β-C—H	Aldol decondensation of α-hydroxy amino acids	Serine- and threonine-aldolases
7. β-C—γ-C	Cleavage of γ-keto-α-amino acids	Kynureninase
	β-Decarboxylation	Aspartic-β-decarboxylase

With a view to the problem of abiogenic synthesis it is particularly important that, as shown by Snell's group, many transformations of amino acids in model systems, including condensations, can also be effected if pyridoxal is replaced by simpler aromatic aldehydes of similar electronic structure and even by a carbonyl compound as simple as glyoxylic acid—the oxidation product of glycine. It was shown, for instance [12], that glyoxylic acid readily catalyses, especially in the presence of aluminium or copper salts, the cleavage of hydroxy amino acids to aldehydes and glycine, and the back reactions of glycine with aldehydes to form, e.g., serine, threonine, phenylserine (reaction 1).

The glycine-glyoxylate azomethine rapidly condenses with an excess of glyoxylate (R·CHO; R = HOOC) to form hydroxyaspartic acid.

It may be expected that glyoxylic acid, like pyridoxal, will catalyse, under suitable conditions, substitution reactions at the β-C atom of serine, resulting in the formation of cysteine, cystathionine, tryptophan, tyrosine and other β-substituted α-aminopropionic acids. Similarly to serine its β-carboxy derivative, hydroxyaspartate, can eventually be degraded by glyoxylate to H_2O, ammonia and oxaloacetate. The intermediate azomethines would be expected to be highly reactive in condensation reactions analogous to steps in the enzymic biosynthesis of amino and keto acids with longer and branched side chains.

These considerations suggest one of the probable ways for abiogenic conversion of simple amino acids to amino acids with complicated side chains in the prebiological era.

Much earlier than vitamin B_6 or reactions of the citric acid cycle had made their appearance, such amino acids could have been synthesized by non-enzymic condensation reactions involving azomethine complexes of glycine or serine with glyoxylic acid and a chelating metal atom, e.g. aluminium. If this atom was fixed in the surface of clay or a similar solid, the resulting chemosorption could increase the efficiency and specificity of catalysis.

Of great importance is the recent discovery [30] that a pyridoxal enzyme is involved in the first step of porphyrin biogenesis, namely, in the synthesis of δ-aminolaevulinic acid by way of a Dakin–West type condensation between glycine and 'active succinate', presumably succinyl-coenzyme A (reaction 2). The following steps of porphyrin biosynthesis—the Knorr type condensation of 2 molecules of δ-aminolaevulinic acid to porphobilinogen (reaction 3) and the conversion of 4 molecules of porphobilinogen to uroporphyrin III (reaction 4) are reactions known to proceed spontaneously and rapidly even in dilute aqueous solutions under quite mild conditions. Uroporphyrinogen III or a similar reduced intermediate is considered as the common precursor of the metalloporphyrin biocatalysts—haems and chlorophyll.

It is plausible that under suitable conditions a soluble or chemosorbed metal chelate of glycine–glyoxylate azomethine could condense with a reactive succinyl compound of abiogenic origin, e.g. the mononitrile, the thio acid or an ester of succinic acid, to yield δ-aminolaevulinic acid (reaction 2a), similarly to the

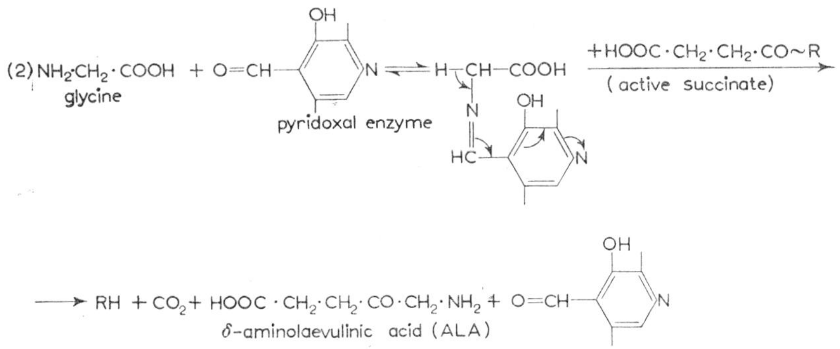

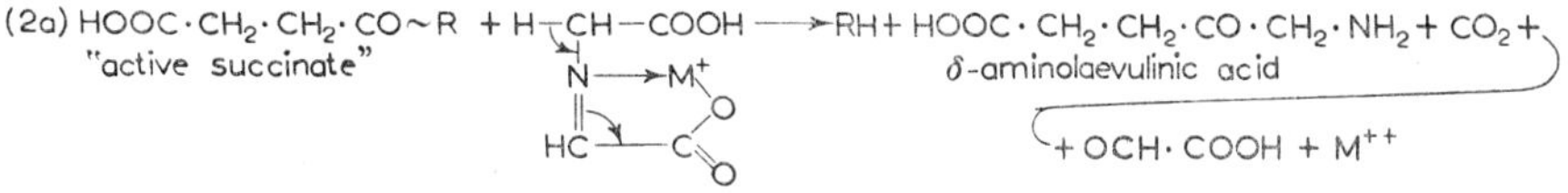

(2) NH2·CH2·COOH + O=CH
glycine
OH
N
pyridoxal enzyme
H—CH—COOH
N
HC
OH
N
+HOOC·CH2·CH2·CO~R
(active succinate)
RH + CO2 + HOOC·CH2·CH2·CO·CH2·NH2 + O=CH
δ-aminolaevulinic acid (ALA)
OH
N

(2a) HOOC·CH2·CH2·CO~R + H—CH—COOH
"active succinate"
N
M+
HC
C
O
O
RH+ HOOC·CH2·CH2·CO·CH2·NH2 + CO2 +
δ-aminolaevulinic acid
+ OCH·COOH + M++

II

(3)

COOH
CH2
CH2
CO
CH2
NH2
+
COOH
CH2
CH2
CO
CH2
NH2
-2H2O
COOH
CH2
COOH
CH2
CH2
CH2
NH
NH2

2 ALA

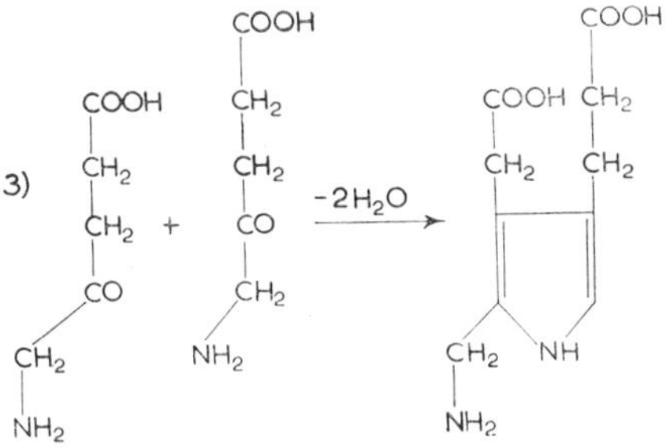

pyridoxal-dependent enzymic reaction. If such were the case, there would inevitably follow spontaneous formation of porphyrins.

This speculation suggests a solution of the perplexing and very important problem of early abiogenic formation of biocatalytic porphyrin pigments.

I would like to add one comment which may be of interest with respect to the problem of biopoesis. Spontaneous formation of the highly intricate structure of the porphyrin molecule from small organic molecules like glycine and succinate would, at the first glance, appear as an extremely improbable event. Yet this molecule has a considerably lower free energy and enthalpy than the sum of its precursors. This is due to the marked resonance stabilization of the porphyrin ring with its extensive system of conjugated double bonds. In fact, the formation of 'active succinate' is the only energy-requiring, 'uphill' step in the mentioned reaction chain of porphyrin biosynthesis, and even the activation energies are rather low for most of the following steps, since they can proceed

Porphobilinogen(PBg)

(4) 4 PBg $\xrightarrow{-4\,NH_3}$ Uroporphyrinogen III $\longrightarrow$

       ↓

    Coproporphyrinogen III

       ↓

     Protoporphyrin

     ↙   ↘

   Haem   Chlorophyll

Uroporphyrin III

spontaneously. This is an instructive example of the pitfalls of superficial and incompetent appreciation of the thermodynamic probability of the spontaneous formation of orderly structures.

*   *   *

Let us now consider the nature of the primary reactions leading to the assimilation of ammonia in biological amino acid synthesis.

The classical Embden–Knoop theory, assuming that the organisms synthesize α-amino acids from their α-keto analogues and ammonia by reductive amination, has undergone substantial revision [3, 4, 5, 13, 15].

The role of α-keto acids as the direct natural precursors of a number of amino acids (about ten, see Fig. 1) is confirmed by the recent studies on biosynthesis [5, 3]. However, there is a considerable body of evidence showing that in most organisms α-oxoglutaric acid is the only α-keto acid that can act as the immediate acceptor of the assimilated ammonia [14, 15]. The formation of glutamic acid by reductive amination of α-oxoglutarate is a reversible reaction catalysed by the specific glutamic dehydrogenase. This is the only widespread and highly active enzyme hitherto known to effect reductive amination.

Some plants and bacteria contain the enzyme, aspartase, which forms aspartic acid by the reversible addition of ammonia across the double bond of fumaric acid; in present-day organisms, with the possible exception of some types of bacteria, this reaction seems to be of minor importance in nitrogen assimilation.

During the last two decades, the pathways of assimilation of ammonia in animals, plants and micro-organisms (and of oxidized forms of nitrogen in certain types of organisms capable of utilizing them) have been thoroughly studied by many authors (see [3, 15, 16]). Different approaches have been used for this purpose, e.g. direct chemical analysis of the products of nitrogen assimilation in yeast cells or pea seedlings (Virtanen and associates), investigation of the metabolic fates of compounds labelled with ^{15}N (Schoenheimer, Vickery,

Burris and others), studies on amino acid synthesis in 'wild' and mutant strains of micro-organisms (Snell, Adelberg, Meister, Fincham, and others), and on the effects of specific inhibition of single enzymes on the synthesis of amino acids in animal tissues *in vitro* and *in vivo* (Braunshteïn and colleagues).

The concordant results of all these investigations have shown that glutamic acid is the first organic product of nitrogen assimilation in most organisms. All other amino acids are formed by transamination of various carbonyl compounds (usually α-keto acids) directly with glutamate or with amino acids having formerly obtained their amino groups from glutamic acid, and by secondary transformations of the structural skeletons of glutamate and of other primary amino acids.

Glutamic acid is also an intermediate link in many important processes leading to the dissimilation of amino acids or to their conversion into secondary nitrogenous metabolites [3, 15; *vide infra*].

The fundamental importance of indirect paths of assimilation and dissimilation of nitrogen, based on linkage of transamination reactions with specific enzymic transformations of the aminodicarboxylic acids, was suggested in 1937–39 in Braunshteïn's first communications on enzymic transamination [17]. This concept has later been developed and supported by experimental evidence in a series of papers from this laboratory [14, 15, 18, 19]. Attention was focussed, in the first place, on the mechanisms of indirect reductive amination of α-keto acids, or 'transreamination' (Braunshteïn), and of indirect oxidative deamination of natural amino acids, or 'transdeamination', through the linked action of glutamic dehydrogenase and aminopherases, according to scheme 3 (Fig. 3).

With regard to the synthesis of amino acids, especially in plants, similar hypotheses have been proposed by Euler (1938) and Virtanen (1939).

The idea of the general importance of such indirect transformations in nitrogen metabolism has for some time been viewed sceptically by many leading biochemists. The main objections rested on the erroneous opinion (P. Cohen and others) that only a few amino and keto acids could participate in transamination. This argument has been invalidated by the discovery, since 1950, of various widespread aminopherases which catalyse transamination reactions involving not only all natural α-amino acids, but also the transfer of β-, γ-, δ and ε-amino groups [3, 7, 8, 13].

To-day it is almost generally accepted that α-oxoglutarate is usually the practically unique substrate of direct reduction amination, whereas other amino acids are the products of transreamination and(or) remodelling of carbon skeletons. (In some bacterial species, e.g. in *Bacillus subtilis*, which possesses a DPN-dependent, reversibly-acting L-alanine dehydrogenase [31], alanine rather than glutamate is probably formed as the main primary product of reductive amination, from which the other amino acids derive their NH_2 groups.)

In mammals the tissues are devoid of significant L-amino acid oxidase activity. In these animals the dissimilation of natural amino acids also proceeds through the intermediary formation of glutamic acid, by way of transdeamination and of a second indirect path associated with urea formation (see p. 540).

The above statements are supported by a considerable body of experimental evidence, obtained by Braunshteïn and his coworkers and by many other investigators, working either with animal tissues or with bacteria and fungi (in higher plants the paths of amino acid synthesis and catabolism have not been thoroughly studied as yet). For a survey of these investigations see the review by Braunshteïn [15].

Some authors (F. Cedrangolo [20]; S. Kaplanskiĭ and coworkers [21]) suppose that in animal tissues L-alanine and L-aspartic acid are synthesized and deaminated directly, rather than *via* glutamic acid. V. Kretovich [22] holds the same opinion with regard to plants.

As a matter of fact, the importance of the mechanisms of transreamination and transdeamination can be demonstrated in the most convincing manner precisely for alanine and aspartic acid. It should be noted that these two amino acids, along with glutamic acid, are immediately related to the citric acid cycle; in surviving tissues they are transaminated, synthesized, and deaminated more actively than all other L-amino acids.

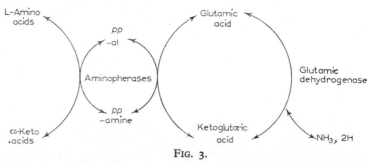

FIG. 3.

In perfect agreement with the mechanism of transreamination, the rate of formation of amino acids from ammonia and pyruvate or oxaloacetate is greatly lowered (whereas the amination of oxoglutarate is not impaired) in the tissues of rats (Braunshteïn & Azarkh [18]) or of birds (Efimochkina) when the aminopherase activity is suppressed, e.g. in vitamin B_6-deficient animals subjected to acute intoxication with *iso*nicotinylhydrazide (a carbonyl fixative blocking the CO-group of pyridoxal). Under these conditions, the depressed amination of pyruvate to alanine in liver homogenate can be restored by the addition, *in vitro*, of purified glutamic-alanine aminopherase (Table 1).

As expected in the case of transreamination, the amination of pyruvate or oxaloacetate (but not of oxoglutarate) is also depressed if formation of oxoglutarate in the surviving tissue is inhibited with the aid of fluoroacetate, fluorocitrate [19], or other specific inhibitors of the citric acid cycle, e.g. cocaine or *meso*tartrate [15].

In such experiments the synthesis of amino acids, e.g. from pyruvate, can be completely restored if the transreamination mechanism is restituted by supplementation of the system with glutamic acid or other oxoglutarate precursors situated below the inhibited link of the respiratory cycle (Table 2). It should be noted that even normally the rate of oxidation of pyruvate is the limiting factor of the overall rate of the transreamination process; the addition of small amounts of glutamate or oxoglutarate does, therefore, greatly stimulate the formation of NH_2–N and of alanine from pyruvate even in the absence of inhibitors.

TABLE 1

Effect of B_6-deficiency combined with isonicotinylhydrazide intoxication on transamination and on the synthesis of amino acids in rat liver homogenate
(Braunshteïn & Azarkh [18])

(Averages of values obtained in experiments with 4 control and 6 experimental animals)

Liver homogenates stabilized with Versene, adenosine triphosphate and Mg²⁺	Transamination between pyruvate and L-glutamate: Δ Pyruvate in 15 minutes (per cent)	Amino acid sythesis in 40 min., μmoles/g tissue						
		NH₃+pyruvate			NH₃+oxoglutarate			
		Δ NH₂—N	Δ Alanine	Δ Glutamate	Δ NH₂—N	Δ Alanine	Δ Glutamate	Δ Aspartate
From control rats . .	−45	133	90	25	173	27	101	23
Same, with added aminopherase	−46	163	94	10	—	—	—	—
From experimental rats .	−5	62	15	32	188	16	101	44
Same, with added aminopherase	−43	134	76	17	—	—	—	—

TABLE 2

Effect of fluorocitrate (FC) on the synthesis of amino acids from ammonia and pyruvate in stabilized rat liver homogenate
(Braunshteïn & Azarkh [19])

(Average values)

Samples containing 200 mg homogenized liver in a volume of 3 ml were incubated 1 hr without and with pyruvate (80 μmoles) and in the presence or absence of supplements of FC (10 μg), and glutamate (20 μmoles). The Δ values show the differences between the samples incubated with pyruvate and the controls, respectively, between the pyruvate samples without FC and in its presence.

FC	Glutamate	Δ due to pyruvate, μmoles/g				Δ due to FC (with pyruvate), μmoles/g (and per cent)			
		NH₂-N	Alanine	Glutamate	Aspartate	NH₂—N	Alanine	Glutamate	Aspartate
−	−	+149	+81	+24	+28	—	—	—	—
+	−	+40	+36	0	−26	−109 (−73%)	−45 (−56%)	−24	−54
−	+	+235	+92	+41	+23	—	—	—	—
+	+	+160	+147	−21	−15	−75 (−31%)	+55 (+62%)	−62	−38

For contemporary organisms the rôle of oxoglutaric acid as the principal or unique acceptor of ammonia in aminoautotrophic nitrogen assimilation is firmly established.

From the evolutionary viewpoint, however, the question arises whether this keto acid could have performed the same function in very ancient organisms, at the dawn of the autotrophic mode of nitrogenous nutrition.

Contemporary organisms synthesize oxoglutaric acid by way of the tri-carboxylic acid cycle. This is a very elaborate process which necessitates a highly organized system of many enzymes and coenzymes, embodying most of the B-vitamins.

Therefore, the tricarboxylic acid cycle must have arisen relatively late in the course of phylogeny. Most probably it has been preceded by simpler cycles of oxidative transformations of organic acids, e.g. by C_4-dicarboxylic acid cycles, such as those still important in the respiratory metabolism of some present-day micro-organisms.

The formation of fumarate in such cycles and its conversion to aspartic acid by aspartase is a process requiring a considerably simpler set of biocatalysts than the synthesis of ketoglutarate and glutamate *via* the citric acid cycle.

At present, this process plays only a subordinate part, in certain bacterial species and, possibly, in some plants. But it seems possible that the synthesis of aspartic acid by the aspartase reaction was the principal mechanism of primary nitrogen assimilation at the dawn of aminoautotrophism. One is tempted to suppose that, on these primitive levels of biological evolution before the citric acid cycle had developed, glutamic acid and the other amino acids of the C_5-family could have been synthesized from aspartic acid by way of secondary condensation reactions.

A suggestive analogy in support of the possibility of this different, more ancient mode of glutamate formation is the existence, in contemporary organisms, of two parallel pathways for the biogenesis of lysine:—from aspartic acid, *via* threonine and diaminopimelic acid in bacteria, and in the higher organized fungi—by was of α-oxo- and α-amino-adipic acids, arising probably through a special homocitric acid cycle superposed to the ordinary tricarboxylic cycle (cf. Fig. 1).

The existence in contemporary organisms of aminopherases effecting direct transfer of NH_2-groups from aspartate to α-keto acids is subject to doubt. However, amino acids could have been synthesized by transreamination *via* aspartic acid (instead of glutamic) in ancestral organisms, if they possessed aspartic aminopherases, which disappeared at later stages of evolution, or if the transfer of amino groups was preceded by the synthesis of asparagine. Highly active asparagine and glutamine aminopherases transferring the α-amino groups of these amides to diverse α-keto acids have been discovered in mammalian liver by A. Meister [13]. Similar enzymes were later found in various plants (Olenicheva, 1955) and in some bacteria (Domaradskiï, 1955) [15].

It is well known that asparagine and glutamine act as the most efficient single nitrogen sources for protein synthesis and growth in many micro-organisms and plant tissues. It is possible that transreamination with the intermediary formation of glutamine or asparagine may represent a widespread mechanism for the indirect synthesis of amino acids (especially those with complicated carbon skeletons); this possibility is in need of direct experimental verification.

The paths of nitrogenous catabolism in different organisms are much more variable than the relatively uniform mechanisms of nitrogen assimilation.

In green plants and in markedly aminoautotrophic micro-organisms (yeasts and some types of bacteria) the assimilation of nitrogen greatly outweighs its dissimilation. Under normal conditions these organisms do not form ammonia or other excretory nitrogenous metabolites. This is due, in part, to the active reutilization of nitrogen in biosynthetic processes, but chiefly to low activity of the enzymes of amino acid catabolism.

Other organisms, particularly the animals and saprophytic micro-organisms feeding on products of protein cleavage, handle the nitrogen of amino acids less economically, and ultimately convert it into ammonia or other excretory end-products.

The simplest and most common excretory form of nitrogen in micro-organisms and lower types of animals is ammonia, liberated from amino acids, amines, and other nitrogen compounds by the action of various deaminating enzymes.

There exist several mechanisms for the deamination of amino acids; among these the most important, especially in animals, are processes of oxidative de-amination, either direct, by the action of amino acid oxidases, or indirect, by way of transdeamination.

Our discussion will be chiefly confined to the dissimilation of nitrogen in animals. A number of different end-products of nitrogen metabolism are known to occur in the various classes and types of animals. In the course of evolution, the predominance of one form of nitrogen excretion or another in the several groups of animals has arisen mainly as a result of adaptation to changing environmental conditions of life and development. According to the well-known conceptions of J. Needham, E. Baldwin and others, the major factors affecting the evolution of the type of nitrogen catabolism in animals are: the conditions of water metabolism at different stages of their ontogeny, and in some cases the participation of nitrogenous metabolites in osmoregulation [23, 24]. Little is known, for the present, about the changes in enzyme systems which form the basis of the shifts in type of nitrogen catabolism.

It will be recalled that aquatic invertebrates and freshwater fishes excrete mainly ammonia (ammoniotelic type of nitrogen catabolism); in insects, many reptiles (snakes, lizards), and in birds the excretion of uric acid is predominant (uricotelic nitrogen catabolism); in amphibia, turtles, the mammals (including man) and in ganoid and selachian fishes the chief excretory product is urea (ureotelic type of nitrogen catabolism).

We can leave aside some special nitrogenous end-products occurring in particular groups of animals, e.g. trimethylamine oxide in the marine teleostians, guanine in spiders, etc.

It is a familiar fact that the tissues of mammals are almost devoid of L-amino acid oxidases, apart from L-glutamic dehydrogenase.

In these tissues the natural amino acids are deaminated either very slowly or not at all, with the exception of a few L-amino acids, like histidine, the hydroxy and mercapto amino acids, which are partly degraded by non-oxidative reactions with liberation of ammonia.

We have studied the paths of dissimilation of amino acids in animal tissues with the aid of procedures, mentioned above, for the suppression of trans-amination reactions (pyridoxine deficiency; isoniazid) or of oxoglutarate form-ation (fluoroacetate and other inhibitors of the citric acid cycle). In this way, it could be shown that the slight formation of ammonia from natural amino acids (beside those subject to non-oxidative deamination, as stated above) in the liver and kidney of rats proceeds only by way of transdeamination [15].

But the extent of this process is quite restricted, no more than 2–3% of the theoretical amount of ammonia being formed; the thermodynamic conditions of equilibrium in the reversible deamination of glutamic acid are such that accumulation of the products of transdeamination even in low concentrations will result in dominance of the opposite process, or transreamination.

E. F. Efimochkina has established that the rates of deamination of natural amino acids in liver and kidney of birds (chicks, turkey poults, pigeons) are considerably higher than in mammalian tissues, alanine, aspartic acid and, partly, phenylalanine and leucine being dissimilated *via* transdeamination. In addition to this indirect mechanism, however, the avian tissues contain special amino acid oxidases, absent in the mammals, which effect the direct deamination of basic L-amino acids (Boulanger & Osteux), of L-tryptophan and glycine (Efimochkina), and of some other L-amino acids.

Preliminary experiments (Efimochkina) indicate that deamination of alanine and aspartate proceeds by the indirect path in frog liver, which forms urea, and probably by straight oxidation in liver of freshwater fish belonging to the ammoniotelic type.

In mammals deamination (anaerobic cleavage of some L-amino acids, direct oxidation of L-glutamate and L-proline, and slow transdeamination of other L-isomers and glycine) is not the only path of dissimilation of amino acid nitrogen.

A large part of the catabolized protein nitrogen (about one half of this nitro-gen) is converted to urea in the mammalian liver *via* reactions of intermolecular transfer of amino groups, without the intermediary liberation of ammonia.

It is known, at present, that in the 'ornithine cycle' of ureogenesis one nitro-gen atom of the urea molecule is derived from ammonia (at the ornithine → citrul-line stage), whereas L-aspartic acid acts as the immediate source of the second nitrogen atom (in the citrulline → arginine step; Ratner & Pappas, 1947 [25]), as shown opposite.

In perfect agreement with this scheme, it has been demonstrated in our laboratory (I. V. Klyuge [26]) that most natural amino acids fail to be deamin-ated at physiological concentrations, in surviving rat liver tissue. Yet under appropriate conditions ensuring the rapid formation of arginine in the second phase of the ornithine cycle, the nitrogen of these amino acids (as well as ammonia N) is readily transferred to citrulline and converted to urea in liver

Intermediary steps and balance of the ornithine cycle of urea synthesis

N-Acetyl-glutamate

1. $NH_3 + CO_2 + ATP \xrightarrow{\hspace{3cm}} $ Carbamyl phosphate $+ ADP$;
2. Carbamyl phosphate $+$ Ornithine $\rightarrow$ Citrulline $+ H_3PO_4$;
3. Citrulline $+$ Aspartate $+ ATP \rightarrow$ Argininosuccinate $+ ADP + H_3PO_4$;
4. Argininosuccinate $\rightarrow$ Arginine $+$ Fumarate;
5. Arginine $+ H_2O \rightarrow$ Ornithine $+$ Urea;

Balance $(1 + 2 + 3 + 4 + 5)$

$$NH_3 + CO_2 + \underset{\underset{\underset{COOH}{|}}{\underset{CH_2}{|}}}{\overset{\overset{COOH}{|}}{CHNH_2}} + 2ATP \rightarrow \underset{\underset{NH_2}{\diagdown}}{\overset{\overset{NH_2}{\diagup}}{CO}} + \underset{\underset{\underset{COOH}{|}}{CH}}{\overset{\overset{COOH}{|}}{CH}} + 2ADP + 2H_3PO_4$$

homogenate. By making use of specific enzyme inhibitors for the suppression of various intermediary reactions, I. Klyuge was able to show that the nitrogen of L-amino acids and of glycine must first be transferred to L-aspartate by way of two-stage transamination (*via* glutamate), and the nitrogen of ammonia by transreamination, i.e. likewise *via* glutamate. This is followed by the reaction of aspartate with citrulline to yield arginine (*via* argininosuccinate) and further, urea.

Estimations of the disappearance of added substrates from the homogenate have shown [26] that in rat liver tissue the dissimilation of natural amino acids, e.g., glycine, L-lysine, and even L-alanine, proceeds at a sufficiently rapid rate only when the equilibria of the reversible transamination reactions are shifted unidirectionally by being coupled with the irreversible reaction between aspartate and citrulline, so that the amino nitrogen is trapped and channelled towards the formation of urea.

These studies have provided direct experimental evidence in support of our contention (Braunshteïn, [4, 27]), that in mammals about one half of the catabolic nitrogen is converted in the liver to urea by repeated transfer reactions, *via* the dicarboxylic amino acids, without preliminary deamination; at present, this view is rapidly gaining general acceptance.

As regards the ammonia which supplies the other moiety of urea nitrogen in the first step of the ornithine cycle, its major part must be of extrahepatic origin: it is evidently formed diffusely in various organs by the slow deamination (chiefly indirect) of amino acids, and is transferred to liver with the blood, mainly as the amide group of serum glutamine. Under physiological conditions this glutamine may constitute the principal source of both nitrogen atoms of urea.

From the evolutionary standpoint it is noteworthy that in the mammals, which have shifted from ammoniotelic to ureotelic nitrogen catabolism, the tissues are almost completely devoid of L-amino acid oxidases, while these enzymes are very active in micro-organisms and lower animals, which excrete ammonia.

Concomitantly, the conversion of ornithine *via* citrulline to arginine, i.e., the phylogenetically very ancient path of biosynthesis of an amino acid of major importance, has been transformed, by the addition of the arginase reaction, into a cycle leading to the production of the new nitrogenous end-product, urea. It is appropriate to point out that the second phase of this cycle is not merely the final step of nitrogen catabolism in the liver. In mammals this phase has acquired the significance of an obligatory condition, or prerequisite, for the dissimilation of nitrogen; in its absence, the transformations of amino acids in the liver are mainly confined to reversible shuttling of the amino nitrogen in transamination reactions.

This fact serves to explain a biochemical paradox of long standing, namely, the well-known incongruity between the ease and rapidity with which the natural amino acids are catabolized to urea in the living mammalian organism, and the considerable inertia usually displayed by the same amino acids in attempts to bring about their dissimilation with the aid of surviving tissues.

In this connection it is possibly significant that in some lower organisms excreting ammonia, citrulline may be transformed into arginine by reversible condensation with ammonia, rather than by the interaction with aspartic acid. This has been observed by Szorenyi and his co-workers [28] in the crayfish; it is possible that the same mechanism of arginine synthesis occurs in those types of bacteria in which this amino acid is split into citrulline and ammonia by arginine desiminase [3, 25].

Green plants and yeasts, which normally do not form ammonia and actively assimilate nitrogen, apparently synthesize arginine *via* argininosuccinic acid, like the mammals.

As shown by Efimochkina (*vide supra*), L-amino acids are deaminated at fairly high rates, directly in part and partly by way of transdeamination, in avian liver and kidneys. Active L-amino acid oxidases are also present in the tissues (and venom) of snakes. It would seem that there is some relation, as yet obscure, between the active deamination of amino acids in birds and snakes, and their uricotelic type of nitrogen catabolism.

Yet it is remarkable that the mechanism of synthesis of uric acid implies, at least in principle, that in uricotelic organisms one half of the protein nitrogen may undergo dissimilation by way of transfer reactions without intermediary deamination, similarly to what has been shown experimentally for the mammals (*vide supra*).

It is known, indeed (cf. [3]), that, of the four nitrogen atoms in the purine ring of uric acid, one atom (N-1) is derived from the amino group of aspartic acid and another (N-7) belongs to a molecule of glycine, into which the nitrogen of other amino acids is incorporated by transamination. And only the remaining two nitrogen atoms (N-3 and N-9), i.e. one half of the nitrogen of uric acid, originate from ammonia *via* the amide group of glutamine [29].

We do not yet know what the relations are between direct deamination and the indirect paths of oxidative dissimilation of the amino acids in cold-blooded vertebrates with ureotelic (amphibia, ganoid and selachian fishes) and ammoniotelic (freshwater teleosts, amphibian larvae) nitrogen metabolism, and also in insects (uricotelic metabolism). No data are available on the reactions leading from citrulline to arginine in most invertebrates, in fungi and in other lower organisms. Owing to the lack of information on these and related questions, it is not possible at present to formulate more definite statements concerning the connections between the evolution of mechanisms of amino acid dissimilation and the shift of types of nitrogen catabolism. Elucidation of these interesting relationships will have to await the results of further detailed investigations in the field of comparative biochemistry of the enzyme systems and intermediary reactions of nitrogen metabolism.

REFERENCES

1. N. D. IERUSALIMSKIĬ, *Nitrogen and Vitamin Nutrition of Microorganisms* (Russ.). Izd. Akad. Nauk S.S.S.R., 1949.
   J. R. PORTER, *Bacterial Chemistry and Physiology.* John Wiley, New York, 1946.
2. A. I. OPARIN, *The Origin of Life.* Izd. Akad. Nauk S.S.S.R., Moscow, 1957.
3. W. D. MCELROY & H. B. GLASS (eds.). *A Symposium on Amino Acid Metabolism.* Johns Hopkins Press, Baltimore, 1955.
4. A. E. BRAUNSHTEĬN, *Biochemistry of Amino Acid Metabolism* (Russ.). Moscow, 1949; *Ukr. Biokhim. Zh.,* **22**, 273, 1950.
5. B. D. DAVIES, *Advanc. Enzymol.,* **16**, 247, 1955.
6. G. EHRENSVÄRD, *Ann. Rev. Biochem.,* **24**, 275, 1955.
7. A. E. BRAUNSHTEĬN, *Usp. sovremennoĭ Biol.,* **35**, 27, 1953.
8. A. E. BRAUNSHTEĬN, *Ukr. Biokhim. Zh.,* **27**, 421, 1955.
9. A. E. BRAUNSHTEĬN, M. M. SHEMYAKIN, *Dokl. Akad. Nauk S.S.S.R.,* **85**, 1115, 1952; *Biokhimiya,* **18**, 393, 1953.
10. E. E. SNELL *et al., J. Amer. chem. Soc.,* **67**, 194, 1945; **74**, 979, 1952; **75**, 2786, 1953; **76**, 639, 4900, 1954; *J. biol. Chem.,* **198**, 353, 1952; **213**, 229, 1955.
11. D. METZLER, M. IKAWA & E. E. SNELL, *J. Amer. chem. Soc.,* **76**, 648, 1954.
12. D. METZLER, J. OLIVARD & E. E. SNELL, *J. Amer. chem. Soc.,* **76**, 644, 1954.
13. A. MEISTER, *Advanc. Enzymol.,* **16**, 185, 1955.
14. A. E. BRAUNSHTEĬN, *Advanc. Protein Chem.,* **3**, 1, 1947.
15. A. E. BRAUNSHTEĬN, *The Main Paths of Nitrogen Assimilation and Dissimilation in Animals.* 12th Annual A. Bakh Lecture, Izd. Akad. Nauk S.S.S.R., Moscow, 1956; *Advanc. Enzymol.,* **19**, 335, 1957.
16. W. D. MCELROY & H. B. GLASS (eds.). *A Symposium on the Metabolism of Inorganic Nitrogen Compounds.* Johns Hopkins Press, Baltimore, 1956.
17. A. E. BRAUNSHTEĬN & M. G. KRITZMANN, *Enzymologia,* **2**, 1929, 1937; A. E. BRAUNSHTEĬN, *Enzymologia,* **7**, 25, 1939.
18. A. E. BRAUNSHTEĬN & R. M. AZARKH, *Biokhimiya,* **22**, 430, 1957.
19. A. E. BRAUNSHTEĬN & R. M. AZARKH, *Arch. Biochem. Biophys.,* **69**, 634, 1957.
20. F. CEDRANGOLO, *Le Transaminazioni, Giornale biochim. Italo-Franco-Elvetiche*; Ed. Consil. Naz. di Ricercha, Roma, 1954.
21. S. YA. KAPLANSKIĬ & N. N. BEREZOVSKAYA, *Biokhimiya,* **21**, 119, 1956 (cf. *Biokhimiya,* **10**, 296, 401, 1945).
22. V. L. KRETOVICH, *Principles of Plant Biochemistry* (Russ.). 2nd ed., Moscow, 1956.
23. J. NEEDHAM, *Chemical Embryology.* Cambridge Univ. Press, 1931.
24. E. BALDWIN, *An Introduction to Comparative Biochemistry.* Cambridge Univ. Press, 1937.
25. S. RATNER, *Advances in Enzymology,* **15**, 319, 1954.
26. I. V. KLYUGE, *Biokhimiya,* **21**, 516, 1956.
27. A. E. BRAUNSHTEĬN, *Vestn. Akad. med. Nauk S.S.S.R.,* **5**, 19, 1948.
28. E. T. SZÖRENYI, *Ukr. Biokhim. Zh.,* **27**, 394, 1955.
    E. SZÖRENYI, P. ELODY & T. DEUTSCH, *Acta physiol. hung.,* **5**, 337, 1954.
29. J. M. BUCHANAN *et al., J. biol. Chem.,* **220**, 369, 379, 1956.
30. M. P. SCHULMAN & D. A. RICHERT, *J. biol. Chem.,* **226**, 181, 1957.
31. A. S. FAIRHURST *et al., Biochem. J.,* **51**, xi, 1952; J. M. WIAME, *Advanc. Enzymol.,* **18**, 241, 1957.

Le Rôle de l'Ammoniaque dans l'Assimilation Autotrophe de l'Azote

V. L. KRETOVICH

Institut de Biochimie A. N. Bakh de L'Academie des Sciences de l'U.R.S.S., Moscou

ON NE pourrait se faire une idée, fut-elle approximative, des mécanismes enzymatiques qui permettaient l'assimilation de l'azote par les organismes primitifs qu'à partir de l'étude des réactions biochimiques correspondantes qui sont à la base de l'assimilation de l'azote chez les organismes contemporains.

Il faut cependant prendre en considération que la forme la plus ancienne de la nutrition azotée fut probablement celle de l'assimilation des acides aminés formés par la voie abiogène à la suite des processus semblables à ceux qu'ont étudiés Miller et Bahadur. Cependant les quantités d'azote faisant partie des acides aminés d'origine abiogène n'étaient que fort insignifiantes et ne pouvaient assurer une existence normale aux organismes primitifs. C'est pour cette raison qu'au cours de l'évolution des mécanismes biochimiques se sont fait jour, ayant permis aux organismes primitifs de s'assimiler l'azote sous ses formes inorganiques et que se sont formés les organismes autotrophes par rapport à la nutrition azotée.

L'ammoniaque, les nitrates, les nitrites et l'azote gazeux peuvent servir de source de nutrition azotée aux organismes autotrophes par rapport à l'azote. L'ammoniaque, aussi bien que les nitrates et les nitrites qui se transforment finalement en ammoniaque sont des sources d'azote assurant la synthèse de tous les acides aminés et protéines chez les végétaux supérieurs, chez une grande partie des microorganismes hétérotrophes par rapport au carbone et chez le microorganismes tant nitrifiants que dénitrifiants. Seulement les organisme⁵ disposant d'une source correspondante de nutrition carbonée sous forme dˢ composés organiques peuvent assimiler l'azote gazeux. Les composés organiqese en question peuvent être assimilés de différentes façons par les organismes fixant l'azote. Ils peuvent être présent en tant que produits finis sous forme de sucre, de mannite, etc. comme cela a lieu chez les fixateurs de l'azote tels que *Azotobacter* et *Clostridium*. Dans d'autres cas la nutrition azotée du microorganisme s'effectue au moyen de la symbiose. Il en est ainsi pour l'assimilation symbiotique de l'azote gazeux chez les légumineuses, chez certaines plantes tropicales de la famille des *Rubiaceae* et chez l'Aune. Enfin un groupe important de microorganismes a la propriété d'effectuer une assimilation de l'azote gazeux qui est lié à la photosynthese, source de nutrition carbonée. Différentes Bactéries photosynthétisantes (*Rhodospirillum*, *Rhodopseudomonas*, etc.), les Algues bleues de la famille *Nostocaceae* et *Calothrix* font partie de ce dernier groupe.

544

L'examen de toutes les données expérimentales relatives au problème du chimisme de l'assimilation autotrophe de l'azote dont nous disposons actuellement permet d'affirmer que l'ammoniaque joue un rôle de premier ordre en tant que composé initial sous la forme duquel s'effectue l'incorporation de l'azote inorganique dans les composés organiques. La réaction de l'amination directe des composés organiques par l'ammoniaque joue un rôle déterminant dans le processus de la synthèse des acides aminés et des protéines chez tous les organismes autotrophes par rapport à l'azote.

Chez les organismes hétérotrophes par rapport à la nutrition carbonée, tels que les différentes Bactéries, les Moisissures, les Levures, aptés en même tempe à l'assimilation autotrophe de l'azote inorganique, ce sont les nitrates, les nitrites et l'ammoniaque qui peuvent servir de celui-ci. Ces mêmes corps constituent des sources d'azote inorganique pour les organismes photoautotrophes. Actuellement on peut considérer comme établi le fait que la transformation des nitrates se produit chez tous ces organismes selon le schéma suivant:

$$\text{nitrates} \rightarrow \text{nitrites} \rightarrow \text{hyponitrite} \rightarrow \text{hydroxylamine} \rightarrow \text{ammoniaque.}$$

De nombreux chercheurs ont étudié et identifié les systèmes enzymatiques catalysant les différentes étapes de ce schéma. Ainsi, plusieurs auteurs y compris Egami et collaborateurs ont extrait de certaines Bactéries des préparations pures des ferments jouant le rôle de catalyseurs lors de la réduction des nitrates, des nitrites et de l'hydroxylamine en ammoniaque [1]. Des préparations enzymatiques analogues ont été obtenues à partir des végétaux supérieurs. Ainsi le schéma ci-dessus de la réduction des nitrates conduisant en fin de compte à la formation de l'ammoniaque peut-il être considéré comme définitivement établi. Il va de soi qu'au cours de l'évolution, la nature et les conditions, systèmes enzymatiques, catalysants les différents chaînons de la réduction des nitrates subissaient, elles-aussi, des modifications et revêtaient les traits spécifiques propres à un tel où tel groupe d'organismes. Signalons, en particulier, que chez les organismes photoautotrophes un rôle important revient, à ce qu'il paraît, à la réduction photochimique des nitrates [2].

Il existe des faits confirmant que l'hydroxylamine qui se forme comme le produit intermédiaire de la réduction des nitrates peut servir à son tour, chez de nombreux microrganismes, de source de groupements aminés pour la synthèse des acides aminés. Virtanen et coll. poursuivent ces dernières années des études fort intéressantes dans ce sens [3]. Quant aux photoautotrophes, la question de la participation directe de l'hydroxylamine à la synthèse des acides aminés chez ceux-ci doit être étudiée ultérieurement. Cependant chez les organismes hétérotrophes par rapport au carbone et aussi chez les organismes photoautotrophes l'ammoniaque sert de même de substance initiale essentielle dans la synthèse des acides aminés et des protéines.

La tâche s'impose d'établir les mécanismes grâce auxquels s'effectue l'incorporation de l'ammoniaque dans un tel ou tel composé organique conduisant à la formation ultérieure des acides aminés. Dans ce cas, comme dans celui des microorganismes fixant l'azote gazeux, un rôle primordial revient à la réaction

35

de l'amination réductrice directe de l'acide α-cétoglutarique par l'ammoniaque. Euler et coll. [4] ont montré pour la première fois cette réaction pour les Levures et les tissus animaux. En ce qui concerne les végétaux supérieurs, seules des données indirectes ont été obtenues relatives à cette question; ces données ont été rassemblées dans le laboratoire de Euler [5].

Nous avons montré en collaboration avec Bundel et Gunar [6] qu'il s'effectue une synthèse intense d'acide glutamique dans les homogénats et les tissus vivants des plantules du pois lorsque l'on y incorpore de l'acide α-cétoglutarique et de l'ammoniaque. Nous avons aussi montré la réaction de l'amination enzymatique de l'acide α-cétoglutarique par l'ammoniaque à l'aide des préparations enzymatiques obtenues à partir de plantules de pois.

Ces résultats ont été obtenus à la suite d'expériences au cours desquelles l'acide glutamique était déterminé au moyen de la méthode chromatographique selon Krétovich & Bundel [7] sur une colonne en oxyde d'aluminium. Les données de Krétovich & Yakovleva [8] obtenues à l'aide de la méthode de la détermination des acides aminés au moyen de la chromatographie quantitative sur papier selon la méthode modifiée de Lissitzky & Laurent [9] ont confirmé les résultats en question. Ainsi, dans les homogénats des plantules de pois après une exposition d'une durée de trois heurs à un pH de 7,7 il se formait les quantités suivantes d'acide glutamique (Tableau 1).

TABLEAU 1

Acide glutamique en mg pour 1 g de substance sèche

N° de l'expèrience	Il a été additionné à l' homogénat			
	α-cétoglutarate NH₄ + cozymase + glucose	α-cétoglutarate NH₄	α-cétoglutarate K	Eau
1	29,76	22,32	—	12,30
2	—	22,91	15,94	9,75

Il est fort notoire que l'acide glutamique se forme aisément à partir d'ammoniaque et d'acide α-cétoglutarique dans les tissus végétaux vivants. Ainsi, dans une de nos expériences au cours desquelles l'on introduisait de l'acide α-cétoglutarique dans des épis de blé, avant la maturité au moyen de l'absorbtion des solutions correspondantes à travers la tige, les quantités suivantes d'acide glutamique ont été déterminés :

Solution introduite dans les épis	Quantité d'acide glutamique déterminé en µg/g de substance sèche
Eau	59
α-cétoglutarate de potasse .	48
α-cétoglutarate d'ammonium .	79

Le processus de l'amination de l'acide α-cétoglutarique par l'ammoniaque s'effectue de la manière la plus active à un pH de 7,7. On signalera que cette réaction se stimule par la cozymase. Il est un fait fort notoire que se fait jour lors de la comparaison des données relatives aux conditions de la biosynthèse enzymatique de l'acide glutamique chez les différents organismes. C'est que le pH optima pour la synthèse de l'acide glutamique par la voie de l'amination réductrice de l'acide α-cétoglutarique par l'ammoniaque est pratiquemment le même pour les organismes les plus variés: chez les animaux ce pH optima est de 7,45, chez les microorganismes de 7,5 et chez les végétaux supérieurs de 7,7. La préparation purifiée de l'enzyme, catalysant l'amination réductrice de l'acide α-cétoglutarique par l'ammoniaque a été obtenue et étudiée par Strecker [10].

L'assimilation de l'ammoniaque s'effectue non seulement sous la forme d'acide glutamique mais encore sous celle d'acide aspartique dont la formation est dûe soit à une réaction entre l'ammoniaque et l'acide fumarique sous l'action de l'aspartase, soit à l'amination réductrice de l'acide oxalacétique par l'ammoniaque. La présence d'aspartase chez les Bactéries a été mise en évidence par plusieurs chercheurs [11]. C'est dans les travaux de Ellfolk [12] que l'on trouve une étude détaillée de cet enzyme. Les expériences réalisées dans notre laboratoire ont montré que les végétaux supérieurs réalisent la même synthèse de l'acide aspartique à partir de l'acide fumarique et de l'ammoniaque.

Quant à la synthèse de l'acide aspartique au moyen de l'amination de l'acide oxalacétique, ce processus a été établi par nous pour les homogénats obtenus à partir de plantules de pois, pour les préparations enzyme et pour des plantules vivantes dans lesquelles ont été infiltrés de l'acide oxalacétique et de l'ammoniaque [13].

L'alanine joue elle aussi un rôle important (après l'acide glutamique et l'acide aspartique) en tant que produit de fixation de l'ammoniaque assimilé. Cela a été montré pour une série de microorganismes et ressort avec le plus d'évidence des résultats de Fairhurst, King & Sewell [14] obtenus avec des cellules lavées de *Bacillus subtilis*.

Les résultats de l'une de ces expériences sont reproduits dans le Tableau 2.

TABLEAU 2

Formation d'alanine par les cellules lavées de B. subtilis

Pyruvate de sodium	+	+	+	—
Sulfate d'ammonium . . .	+	+	—	+
Eau	—	—	+	+
Durée de l'incubation (en heures) .	3	0	3	3
Formation d'alanine au cours de l'expérience (en mg d'azote)	5,02	0,05	0,00	0,08

Il importe de signaler qu'au cours des expériences de Fairhurst, King & Sewell il se formait par la voie d'amination réductrice par l'ammoniaque de la valine à partir de l'acide α-céto*iso*valérianique, de la leucine à partir de l'acide α-céto*iso*caproique et de l'acide α-aminobutyrique à partir de l'acide α-cétobutyrique. Chez les Levures la formation d'alanine à partir d'acide pyruvique et d'ammonium a été mise en évidence par Fromageot & Minard [15]. En ce qui concerne les végétaux supérieurs mentionnons que la synthèse de l'alanine dans les homogénats, les extraits et les tissus vivants des plantules de pois a été montrée par Kretovich & Bundel [16]. Ces mêmes auteurs ont établi dans un travail ultérieur que la synthèse de l'alanine à partir du pyruvate d'ammonium s'effectue de même en présence d'une préparation enzymatique purifiée obtenue à partir de plantules de pois [17]. Aussi les données reproduites permettent d'affirmer que chez les microorganismes comme chez les végétaux supérieurs la synthèse de certains acides aminés s'effectue par la voie de l'amination réductrice des acides aminés cétoniques correspondants par l'ammoniaque. Les acides aminés ainsi formés participent ensuite à des réactions de transamination enzymatique et forment de nouveaux acides aminés.

Outre la réaction de l'amination réductrice dans le processus de l'assimilation de l'ammoniaque par les cellules, une importance primordiale appartient aux réactions de la synthèse de l'asparagine et de la glutamine à partir des acides aminés dicarboxyliques correspondants.

Déjà dans ses travaux classiques, D. N. Prianichnikov a montré que l'asparagine peut être synthétisée dans un organisme végétal non seulement par la voie de la dissimilation des protéines, mais aussi au cours du processus de l'assimilation des sels ammoniacaux introduits artificiellement dans la plante [18]. Il a été montré au cours d'une série d'expériences ultérieures que lors de l'introduction des sels d'ammoniaque dans les plantules de Lupin, de Potiron et de Maïs il se forme d'importantes quantités d'asparagine [19]. La synthèse de la glutamine, à partir de l'ammoniaque introduit artificiellement fut démontrée par Vickery, Pucher & Clark [20] dans des conditions d'ammendement abondant de la Betterave à sucre en sulfate d'ammonium. En même temps Greenhill & Chibnall [21] ont établi qu'une nutrition intense de certains végétaux en sels ammoniacaux conduit à l'excrétion de glutamine au cours de la guttation, processus accompagné de la cristallisation de celui-ci aux extrémités des feuilles.

Ainsi a été démontrée la justesse de la pensée de Prianichnikov selon laquelle l'asparagine et la glutamine sont des composés sous la forme desquelles s'effectue la liaison et l'enrayement de l'action de l'ammoniaque. En même temps ces expériences ont mis en évidence que l'asparagine et la glutamine peuvent se former toutes deux dans un organisme végétal par la voie de la synthèse à partir de l'ammoniaque introduit artificiellement.

Kretovich, Evstignéeva & Plychevskaja [22] ont étudié le problème de la vitesse de la fixation de l'ammoniaque dans les plantes sous forme de groupements aminés et amidés de l'asparagine et de la glutamine. Il s'agissait d'établir si cette vitesse est la même.

Lors de ces expériences une préparation de nitrate d'ammonium contenant $^{15}NH_4$ était utilisée en tant que source d'ammoniaque. On utilisait pour expériences $0,1N-^{15}NH_4NO_3$. La Betterave à sucre a servi d'objet d'étude de la synthèse de la glutamine, des plantules étiolées de Lupin et de Vesce pour celle de la synthèse de l'asparagine.

En 1954 et 1955 des préparations de glutamine, purifiées par voie de la récristallisation et identifiées selon la température de fusion ont été obtenues à partir de la Betterave ayant été soumise à un régime de nutrition en ammonium.

La détermination de la teneur des préparations obtenues en ^{15}N a abouti aux résultats ci-dessous (Tableau 3).

TABLEAU 3

Teneur en ^{15}N de l'azote de la glutamine et de l'azote du groupement amidé de celui-ci

Préparation	Température de fusion	Teneur en ^{15}N de la preparation initiale			Teneur en ^{15}N de l'azote global			Teneur en ^{15}N de l'azote du groupement amidé			Teneur en ^{15}N du groupement aminé		
		Degré de l'enrichissement en ^{15}N	% atomique	Excès % at.	Degré de l'enrichissement en ^{15}N	% atomique	Excès % at.	Degré de l'enrichissement en ^{15}N	% atomique	Excès % at.	Degré de l'enrichissement en ^{15}N	% atomique	Excès % at.
Glutamine préparation N° 1	182-183°C	25,0	9,50	9,12	8,83	3,31	2,98	11,75	4,40	4,02	5,91	2,22	1,84
Glutamine préparation N° 2	183-184°C	28,90	11,0	10,62	8,65	3,29	2,91	13,00	4,94	4,56	4,30	1,64	12,6

Les préparations d'asparagine obtenues à partir des plantules de Lupin et de Vesce ont été purifiées au moyen de recristallisation et soumises par la suite à des analyses pour determiner ^{15}N. Les résultats obtenus sont reproduits dans le Tableau 4.

Les donnés figurants dans les tableaux permettent d'affirmer que l'ammoniaque introduit dans le plante est facilement utilisé à la synthèse de l'asparagine et de la glutamine.

En même temps les donnés obtenus mettent en évidence que l'incorporation de l'ammoniaque dans la glutamine s'effectue d'une façon beaucoup plus active que son incorporation dans l'asparagine. En réalité, les préparations de glutamine et d'asparagine obtenues lors de l'utilisation des mêmes préparations de nitrate d'ammonium ayant une teneur de 9,5 at. % où 11,0 at. % en ^{15}N diffèrent nettement les unes des autres quant à leur teneur en ^{15}N. Dans les préparations de glutamine la teneur en isotope est presque de quatre fois supérieure à celle décelée dans l'asparagine.

Ces données s'accordent avec les indications que l'on retrouve dans la littérature, selon lesquelles la glutamine est un composé beaucoup plus mobile que l'asparagine, quant au métabolisme des végétaux [23, 24].

La comparaison de la teneur en ^{15}N du groupement amidé et du groupement aminé d'un même amide permet d'établir que la teneur en ^{15}N des groupements amidés est de loin supérieur à celle des groupements aminés. Les évaluations reproduites dans le Tableau 5 mettent ce fait en évidence.

TABLEAU 4

Teneur en ^{15}N de l'azote de l'asparagine et de l'azote du groupe amidé

Préparations	Température de fusion, °C	Teneur en ^{15}N de la préparation initiale NH₄NO₃			Teneur en ^{15}N de l'azote total			Teneur en ^{15}N de l'azote du groupe amidé			Teneur en ^{15}N de l'azote du groupe aminé		
		Degré de l'enrichissement en [15]N	% atomique	Excès % at.	Degré de l'enrichissement en [15]N	% atomique	Excès % at.	Degré de l'enrichissement en [15]N	% atomique	Excès % at.	Degré de l'enrichissement en [15]N	% atomique	Excès % at.
Asparagine de lupin: Nᵒ 1 .	226	5,00	1,90	1,52	1,38	0,52	0,14	1,63	0,62	0,24	1,13	0,42	0,04
Nᵒ 2 .	225	25,00	9,50	9,12	1,81	0,77	0,39	2,71	1,01	0,63	0,91	0,53	0,15
Nᵒ 3 .	220	25,00	9,50	9,12	3,71	1,40	1,02	4,93	1,88	1,50	2,44	0,92	0,54
Asparagine de vesce Nᵒ 4 .	226	28,90	11,00	10,62	2,78	0,94	0,56	4,15	1,58	1,20	1,41	0,54	0,16

TABLEAU 5

Distribution de ^{15}N dans les groupements amidés et aminés de l'asparagine et de la glutamine

(en pourcent par rapport à le teneur en ^{15}N dans l'amide en question)

Prèparation	[15]N dans le groupe amidé	[15]N dans le groupe aminé
Glutamine N:		
1 . .	66,6	33,4
2 . .	75,1	24,9
1 . .	59,0	41,0
Asparagine N:		
2 . .	74.6	25,4
3 . .	66,5	33,5
4 . .	74,9	25,1

Il est de toute évidence que, indépendamment de la teneur absolue en ^{15}N de l'amide en question, la distribution de ^{15}N entre le groupement amidé et le groupement aminé est à peu près la même pour l'asparagine et la glutamine.

La différence considérable de teneur en ^{15}N des groupements amidés et aminés de l'asparagine et de la glutamine témoigne du fait que le processus de l'incorporation de l'ammoniaque introduit dans le groupement aminé s'effectue d'une façon moins active que son incorporation dans le groupement amidé.

Il conviendrait de rappeler qu'au cours des expériences effectuées par Wilson et coll. á l'aide de l'isotope de l'azote ^{15}N sur *Clostridium pasteurianum* une incorporation fort intense de ^{15}N dans les groupements amidés de l'asparagine et de la glutamine fût de même observée.

Ainsi les groupements amidés de l'asparagine et de la glutamine sont-ils une forme des plus importantes de l'enrayement de l'action et de la mise en réserve de l'ammoniaque introduit dans la cellule.

Tout porte à croire que les groupements amidés de l'asparagine et de la glutamine faisant partie des protéines sont à même de lier de fort grandes quantités d'ammoniaque. Cela découle en premier lieu des données mettant en évidence que c'est à partir des groupements amidés faisant partie des protéines des amides que se produit une partie importante de l'ammoniaque qui se forme lors de l'hydrolyse des protéines. Ce problème, quant au végétaux supérieurs, est actuellement à l'étude dans notre laboratoire. L'étude s'effectue au moyen de l'azote marqué ^{15}N.

Les données rassemblées au cours de ces dernières années permettent d'affirmer que ce n'est pas seulement en tant qu'acides aminés se formant à la suite de l'amination des acides cétoniques et d'autres acides organiques correspondants, non seulement par la voie de la formation de l'asparagine et de la glutamine, mais encore au moyen de la formation de différents autres composés azotés que l'ammoniaque est lié et mis en réserve.

Les travaux de Ruhland et collaborateurs [25] ont montré que chez différents végétaux l'ammoniaque s'accumule sous forme de sels ammoniacaux des acides organiques—malique, fumarique, citrique etc. Ces végétaux ont été baptisé 'végétaux acides' ou 'ammoniaques'. D'autre part les travaux de Fosse [26], Brunel [27], Mothes et Engelbrecht [28] ont mis en évidence que chez nombre de plantes l'assimilation de l'ammoniaque peut s'effectuer aussi sous la forme d'allantoine, d'acide allantoique et de citrulline.

Dans les tissus de certains végétaux ces composés constituent la plus grande partie de la réserve d'azote solvant, se formant à partir des sels azotés introduits de l'extérieur et participant par la suite à la synthèse des protéines lors de la formation des jeunes tissus.

Enfin on ne pourrait ne pas mentionner la découverte de γ-metylèneglutamine [29] qui est un des composés azotés de nature non protéique, jouant un rôle analogue à celui de la glutamine dans d'autres organismes.

Si nous nous adressons au problème du chimisme de la fixation de l'azote gazeux, nous verrons que, ces derniers temps, de nombreux travaux, et en particulier ceux effectués à l'aide de l'azote marqué ^{15}N ont mis en évidence que l'idée que la fixation de l'azote conduisant à la formation de composés tels que l'oxyde azoteux (N_2O) ou l'acide hypoazoteux $(NOH)_2$ s'effectue par la voie de l'oxydation, se trouve de moins en moins confirmée. D'autre part des données expérimentales s'accumulent toujours davantage confirmant l'hypothèse de Kostytchev et de Winogradski selon laquelle le processus de la fixation de l'azote gazeux s'effectue grâce à une série de processus enzymatiques conduisant à la formation de l'ammoniaque [30].

Les résultats obtenus par Burris et collaborateurs [31] sont fort interessant sous ce rapport. Ces chercheurs ont étudié à l'aide de l'azote marqué ^{15}N la distribution de cet isotope dans les acides aminés des protéines globales isolés des cellules de différents microorganismes fixateurs de l'azote gazeux et ayant été pourvus d'azote gazeux ou de sel ammoniacal en guise de source d'azote. Des analyses ont montré que l'assimilation d'un ion d'ammonium et d'azote gazeux s'effectue de façon analogue; ce qui découle avec évidence des données, caractérisant la distribution de l'isotope dans les différents acides aminées du hydrolysat. Chez tous les organismes pour l'azote ammoniacal aussi bien que pour l'azote gazeux, les plus grandes quantités d'azote marqué étaient décélées dans l'acide glutamique. Ensuite venaient l'acide aspartique et l'alanine qui se forment vraisemblablement à la suite de l'amination des acides oxalacétique et pyruvique et aussi par la voie de la transamination de l'acide glutamique avec ces acides cétoniques. Une concentration considérable d'azote marqué fut de même déterminée dans la fraction de l'ammoniaque dont font partie l'ammoniaque libre ainsi que l'azote aminé se libérant lors de l'hydrolyse des résidus apartiques et glutamiques des protéines. Dans des expériences effectuées avec *Clostridium pasteurianum* une fort importante concentration d'azote marqué fut également décelée dans l'asparagine et dans la glutamine excrétées par les cellules dans le milieu. Ainsi les groupes amidés de l'asparagine et de la glutamine constituent chez les fixateurs de l'azote une forme importante de l'enrayement de l'action de l'excès d'ammoniaque; ils servent en même temps de source importante de l'azote nécessaire à la synthèse ultérieure de différents acides aminés et de protéines. En ce qui concerne l'ammoniaque, la 'dilution' rapide de ^{15}N incorporé sous forme d'ammonium témoigne du fait de la présence d'une 'réserve métabolique' d'ammoniaque dans les cellules, réserve indispensable au cours normal du processus du métabolisme azoté chez les microorganismes étudiés fixateurs de l'azote. Des résultats fort importants ont été obtenus lors de l'étude de la cinétique de l'assimilation de l'azote gazeux et ammoniaque chez *Azotobacter vinelandii* et chez d'autres organismes. Il a été montré que d'autant plus courte est la période de l'assimilation de l'ammonium où de l'azote gazeux d'autant plus haute est la concentration de ^{15}N dans l'acide glutamique. Ceci témoigne du fait que la formation de l'acide glutamique chez les fixateurs d'azote s'opère par la voie de l'amination réductrice directe de l'acide α-céto-glutarique par l'ammoniaque [32].

En même temps les expériences effectuées avec *Clostridium pasteurianum* et avec *Azotobacter* ont montré que ces organismes assimilent l'ammoniaque, pour ainsi dire, immédiatement, sans aucune adaptation préliminaire.

Ainsi une série de données expérimentales obtenues ces derniers temps à l'aide d'un isotope de l'azote permettent d'affirmer que l'ammoniaque ets réellement le produit final de la transformation de l'azote gazeux et aussi le produit initial sous la forme duquel l'azote réagit avec les composés organiques, en formant des acides aminés et par la suite, des protéines.

Or, la question suivante se pose: quels sont les produits intermédiaires qui se forment chez les fixateurs de l'azote lors de la réduction de l'azote en ammoniaque? Les données expérimentales obtenues et le coté enzymologique du problème ne sont étudiés que bien insuffisamment. L'hypothèse selon laquelle l'acide hypoazoteux est le produit intermédiare entre l'azote gazeux et l'ammoniaque n'a pas été confirmée par la voie expérimentale. Quant à l'hydroxylamine, les travaux de Virtanen effectuées sur les légumineuses indiquent son rôle éventuel dans le processus de la fixation de l'azote [33]. Virtanen avait montré antérieurement que les racines de légumineuses excrètent dans des conditions favorables de l'acide aspartique et que, pour cette raison, l'hydroxylamine réagit beaucoup plus rapidement avec l'acide oxalacétique qu'avec l'acide α-cétoglutarique. Virtanen a émis l'hypothèse que l'hydroxylamine réagit de préférence avec le premier de ces acides cétoniques et forme en premier lieu l'acide oximinosuccinique et ensuite l'acide aspartique. Plus tard Virtanen a décelé l'acide glutamique parmi les produits excrétés par les racines de légumineuses. Cependant l'interaction immédiate de l'hydroxylamine avec les acides cétoniques conduisant à la formation des oximes correspondants et, par la suite des acides aminés n'est pas, a ce qu'il semble, la voie principale de la transformation de l'hydroxylamine. Il est probable qu'il se produit une réduction ulterieure de celui-ci en ammoniaque qui réagit lui-même avec les acides cétoniques. Depuis que l'on a décelé dans les nodosités des légumineuses la leghémoglobine il est permis de croire, que la transformation de l'hydroxylamine s'effectue d'après Colter & Quastel [34], selon l'équation suivante:

$$NH_2OH + 2\,\text{leghémoglobines} + H_2O \longrightarrow 2\,\text{methémoglobines} + NH_3 + 2OH^-.$$

Il est hors de doute que les mécanismes enzymatiques contrôlant les différents chaînons du processus de la transformation de l'azote gazeux en ammoniaque peuvent différer essentiellement chez les différents fixateurs de l'azote. Cependant l'ammoniaque reste chez tous les organismes fixant l'azote le produit final de la transformation de l'azote gazeux et l'essentiel corps initial sous la forme duquel l'azote s'incorpore dans les composés organiques.

Pour conclure, soulignons que les données experimentales témoignent du rôle important de l'ammoniaque dans le métabolisme azoté, chez les organismes, chez lesquels, au cours de leur évolution, se sont formés des mécanismes divers de la fixation de l'ammoniaque et de la mise en réserve de l'azote sous forme de tel ou autre composé organique.

BIBLIOGRAPHIE

1. SH. TANIGUCHI & F. EGAMI, *J. Biochem. Japan*, **40**, 175, 1953.
2. D. M. MIKHLIN, *L' oxydation biologique.* Izd. Akad. Nauk S.S.S.R., Moscow, 1956.
3. A. VIRTANEN & H. SARYS, *Acta chem. scand.*, **10**, 483, 1956.
4. H. EULER, E. ADLER, G. GÜNTHER & N. DAS, *Hoppe-Seyl. Z.*, **254**, 61, 1938.
5. E. ADLER, N. DAS, H. EULER & H. HEYMAN, *C.R. Lab. Carlsberg*, **22**, 15, 1938.
6. V. L. KRETOVICH, A. A. BUNDEL & V. I. GUNAR, *Ukr. biochim. Zh.*, **27**, 342, 1955.
7. V. L. KRETOVICH & A. A. BUNDEL, *Dokl. Akad. Nauk S.S.S.R.*, **73**, 137, 1950.
8. V. L. KRETOVICH & V. I. YAKOVLEVA. *Dokl. Akad. Nauk S.S.S.R.*, **116**, 755, 1957.

9. S. LISSITZKY & G. LAURENT, *Bull. Soc. Chim. biol.*, Paris, **37**, 1177, 1955.
10. H. J. STRECKER, *Arch. Biochem. Biophys.*, **46**, 128, 1953.
11. J. H. QUASTEL & B. WOOLF, *Biochem. J.*, **20**, 545, 1926; A. I. VIRTANEN & J. TARNANEN, *Biochem. Z.*, **250**, 193, 1932.
12. N. ELLFOLK, *Acta chem. scand.*, **7**, 824, 1953; **7**, 1155, 1953; **8**, 151, 443, 1954.
13. V. L. KRETOVICH, A. A. BUNDEL & K. B. ASEEVA, *Dokl. Akad. Nauk S.S.S.R.*, **80**, 225, 1951.
14. A. S. FAIRHURST, H. K. KING & C. E. SEWELL, *J. gen. Microbiol.*, **15**, 106, 1956.
15. C. FROMAGEOT & G. MINARD, *Bull. Soc. Chim. biol.*, Paris, **18**, 1454, 1936.
16. V. L. KRETOVICH & A. A. BUNDEL, *Dokl. Akad. Nauk S.S.S.R.*, **59**, 1595, 1948.
17. V. L. KRETOVICH & A. A. BUNDEL, *Dokl. Akad. Nauk S.S.S.R.*, **74**, 107, 1950.
18. D. N. PRYANISHNIKOV, *Azot v Zhizni Rastenii i v Zemledelii SSSR*. Moscow and Leningrad. Izd. Akad. Nauk S.S.S.R., 1945.
19. V. L. KRETOVICH, Z. G. EVSTIGNEEVA & M. M. MAKARENKO, *Biokhimiya Zerna, Sbornik no.* **2**, 161, 1953, Izd. Akad. Nauk S.S.S.R., Moscow.
20. H. B. VICKERY, G. W. PUCHER & H. E. CLARK, *Plant Physiol.*, **11**, 413, 1936.
21. A. W. GREENHILL & A. C. CHIBNALL, *Biochem. J.*, **28**, 1422, 1934.
22. V. L. KRETOVICH, Z. G. EVSTIGNEEVA & E. G. PLYSHEVSKAYA, *Dokl. Akad. Nauk S.S.S.R.*, **109**, 1001, 1956.
23. K. MOTHES, *Planta*, **30**, 726, 1940.
24. E. W. YEMM, *New Phytol.*, **48**, 315, 1949.
25. W. RUHLAND & K. WETZEL, *Planta*, **1**, 558, 1926; **1**, 588, 1926; **3**, 765, 1927; **7**, 503, 1929.
26. R. FOSSE, *et al.*, *C.R. Acad. Sci.*, Paris, **196**, 883, 1933; R. FOSSE, *C.R. Acad. Sci.*, Paris, **208**, 865, 1939.
27. A. BRUNEL & G. CAPELLE, *Bull. Soc. Chim. biol.*, Paris, **129**, 427, 1947.
28. K. MOTHES & L. ENGELBRECHT, *Flora, Jena*, **132**, 586, 1952; **141**, 356, 1954. L. ENGELBRECHT, *Flora, Jena*, **141**, 501, 1954; **142**, 25, 1954.
29. J. DONE & L. FOWDEN, *Biochem. J.*, **51**, 451, 1952.
30. P. W. WILSON, *Advanc. Enzymol.*, **13**, 345, 1952.
31. I. ZELITCH, E. D. ROSENBLUM, R. N. BURRIS & P. W. WILSON, *J. Bact.*, **62**, 747, 1951; I. ZELITCH, P. W. WILSON & R. H. BURRIS, *Plant Physiol.*, **27**, 1, 1952.
32. P. W. WILSON, *Advanc. Enzymol.*, **13**, 366, 1952.
33. A. VIRTANEN, *Biol. Rev.*, **22**, 239, 1947; *Öst. Chem. Ztg*, **7-9**, 94, 1953; A. VIRTANEN, A. KEMPPI & E. SALMENOJA, *Acta chem. scand.*, **8**, 1729, 1954.
34. J. S. COLTER & J. H. QUASTEL, *Arch. Biochem.*, **27**, 368, 1950.

Meaning of Nitrate and Sulphate Reduction in the Process of Metabolic Evolution

M. ISHIMOTO AND F. EGAMI

Faculty of Science, Nagoya University Chikusa, Nagoya, Japan

THERE ARE a great variety of metabolic pathways in the present living organisms. This complexity is not due to the chemical nature of the substrates, but it was formed gradually in the long history of living organisms, in the course of evolution of the metabolic enzyme systems.

It has been known that the evolution of life on the Earth proceeded from anaerobes to aerobes and from heterotrophs to autotrophs [1], and some speculations were made on the meanings of nitrate and sulphate reduction in that process [2]. The authors have been studying the enzymic reduction of nitrate and sulphate at Nagoya and Tokyo Universities. Now we try to summarize the development in these fields and compare it with other metabolic processes and speculate about the evolutionary processes leading to the formation of respiratory systems.

Biological reductions of nitrate and sulphate which take place in organisms have several meanings for their life. Nitrate and sulphate are abundant on the Earth and the latter is the sole mineral source of sulphur available to organisms. Organisms must reduce and convert them into organic nitrogen and sulphur compounds, indispensable for the building up of their cells. On the other hand, by the metabolic evolution, ultimate hydrogen acceptor systems were simultaneously acquired, which may function as an energy-yielding mechanism instead of oxygen respiration.

Studies on the mechanisms of nitrate and sulphate reduction indicate that enzyme systems responsible for assimilation are quite different from those of energy supply. So we shall discuss them separately; firstly the energy-yielding systems and secondly the assimilative systems.

The free-energy change in reduction of nitrate is less than in that of oxygen, but fairly higher than in the reduction of organic compounds. The potential of sulphate reduction is much lower and comparable to that of the organic metabolites (Table 1).

These values decide the characteristic pattern of nitrate and sulphate reduction. The metabolic systems concerning both have double characters. They resemble respiratory systems since inorganic substances are involved as ultimate hydrogen acceptors like oxygen. On the other hand, from the view of the redox potential consideration, they, especially sulphate-reducing systems, resemble systems for fermentation, i.e. oxidation of organic substances by organic substances. These characteristics were also reflected in peculiarly linked donor systems.

TABLE I

Free-energy changes in various reductions

Oxidizer	Reaction	ΔF (calories)
Oxygen	$H_2 + \frac{1}{2} O_2 \rightarrow H_2O$	$- 56,690$
Nitrate	$H_2 + \frac{1}{4} NO_3^- + \frac{1}{2} H^+ \rightarrow \frac{1}{4} NH_4^+ + \frac{3}{4} H_2O$	$- 35,900$
Sulphate	$H_2 + \frac{1}{4} SO_4^{--} + \frac{1}{2} H^+ \rightarrow \frac{1}{4} H_2S(g) + H_2O$	$- 9,500$
Organic substances	$H_2 + \text{Fumarate} \rightarrow \text{Succinate}$	$- 20,470$
	$H_2 + \text{Pyruvate} \rightarrow \text{Lactate}$	$- 11,100$
	$H_2 + HCO_3^- \rightarrow HCOO^- + H_2O$	$+ 800$

In the presence of nitrate, *Escherichia coli* grows anaerobically on media containing succinate or lactate as a sole carbon source. However, without nitrate it does not grow in the same conditions [3]. In this case, nitrate substitutes for oxygen.

The products of fermentation by resting cells of *E. coli* are changed greatly by the addition of nitrate. According to Verhoeven [4], added nitrate caused decrease in the amount of ethanol, lactate and succinate and a remarkable increase of carbon dioxide (Table 2). These results clearly indicate stimulation by nitrate of more complete oxidation of substrates, and resemblance of the nitrate reduction to respiration.

TABLE 2

Products of nitrate reduction by glucose in E. coli. (*Percentage of* C *calculated on carbon content of glucose consumed in fermentation.*)

Product of reduction	$- NO_3$	$+ NO_3$
Carbon dioxide	7·3	26·6
Lactic acid	42·4	10·2
Succinic acid	20·6	8·6
Formic acid	0·4	0·4
Acetic acid	14·3	50·5
Ethanol	14·3	0·4

The sulphate reduction as an energy-yielding reaction is quite confined to special organisms, sulphate reducers *Desulfovibrio*. They are strict anaerobes and their growth depends on the oxidation of lactate with sulphate in many cases;

some of them are devoid of glycolysis system. Chief utilizable substrates for their growth are lactate, pyruvate, malate, formate, hydrogen etc. Utilization of succinate is rare [5] and the presence of the tricarboxylic acid cycle has not been known. These metabolic main features are decided by the low potential nature of sulphate reduction. *Desulfovibrio* does not grow without sulphate even in the presence of lactate or other organic substrates (except pyruvate) [6]. These data place the physiological characters of sulphate reduction just between respiration and fermentation.

The mechanism of nitrate reduction by bacteria has been studied for a long time. In 1937, Yamagata [7], a Japanese biologist, proposed a scheme for nitrate-reducing systems, according to which the reduction took place by the co-operative action of a reductase specific for nitrate, dehydrogenase systems offering hydrogen from substrate and intermediary hydrogen carriers. Egami, Sato, Taniguchi and their co-workers studied nitrate reduction by several types of bacteria, and stated that nitrate, nitrite and hydroxylamine were reduced in a halotolerant bacterium and that each step of the reduction was catalysed by nitrate reductase, nitrite reductase and hydroxylamine reductase respectively. They were extracted and separated from each other and their nature was studied [8]. The system is indicated schematically in scheme 1:

Scheme 1

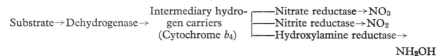

Besides flavins or synthetic dyes which serve as the hydrogen carriers in the cell-free systems, Egami & Sato found that cytochrome played a rôle as the carrier. Also in the cell suspension cytochrome is reduced by addition of substrates and oxidized anaerobically by nitrate as well as by oxygen. The results of inhibition experiments also show the participation of the cytochrome as the carrier in the reduction. This was the first proposal that cytochrome participated in anaerobic oxidoreduction [9].

Such behaviour of cytochrome suggests not only resemblance of the electron transport system of nitrate reduction to that of respiration, but also energy yielding by the oxidation with nitrate in anaerobiosis. When cells of *E. coli* oxidized formate with oxygen in the presence of phosphate labelled with ^{32}P, the radioactivity was observed in the washed cells after the reaction period. Similar results were obtained also in the course of anaerobic nitrate reduction [10] (Table 3).

Incorporation of ^{32}P indicates active transfer of phosphate and presumably the occurrence of oxidative phosphorylation. So, the possible formation of energy-rich phosphate bonds by electron transfer in the course of oxidation by nitrate as well as by oxygen can be considered.

Besides this type of nitrate reduction, so-called 'nitrate respiration', another type of non-assimilatory nitrate reduction is found in anaerobes, e.g. *Clostridium welchii*. In this case, the presence of cytochrome has been observed and the enzyme systems seem to be quite different [11].

TABLE 3

Incorporation of [^{32}P]phosphate coupled with nitrate reduction

Composition of the reaction media	Condition of reaction					
	Aerobic			Anaerobic		
	Experiment No.					
	1	2	3	4	5	6
Cell suspension (ml) . . .	2·0	2·0	2·0	2·0	2·0	2·0
^{32}P solution (ml)	0·4	0·4	0·4	0·4	0·4	0·4
M/5 sodium formate (ml) . .	1·4	0	1·4	1·4	0	0
M-KNO$_3$ (ml)	0	0	0·2	0	0·2	0
Water (ml)	0·2	1·6	0	0·2	1·4	1·6
Experimental results						
Oxygen uptake (μmoles) . .	58·3	0	—	—	—	—
Nitrite produced (μmoles) . .	—	—	167·2	0·7	2·1	0·3
Inorganic phosphate in the medium (μmoles)	24·5	24·8	25·2	24·8	25·3	25·4
Specific activity of the cells, counts/min./mg cell	189·5	109·5	143·8	107·0	109·8	94·2
Increase in P turnover % . .	73·1	—	52·7	11·4	16·6	—

Nitrate reduction to nitrite was observed in cotyledons of germinating bean seeds *Vigna sesquipedalis*, which are actually under anaerobic conditions. The nitrate-reducing enzyme system may resemble that of *Clostridium* judging from the lack of reactivity with cytochrome present in the same tissues [12].

Nitrate reduction of this type may cause the substrate oxidation and promote energy yielding in anaerobiosis (nitrate fermentation).

Recently, in the early course of development of the frog a predominant activity of nitrate reduction was found in the transient stage from glycolysis to respiration [13].

The common character of these systems of nitrate reduction for energy supply is the fact of the complete inhibition by oxygen, and in this respect differs from those for assimilation. In the germinating stage of bean seed, the conditions of the cotyledons are anaerobic and favour the dissimilatory reduction of nitrate to nitrite and on the other hand, in seedlings assimilatory nitrate reduction proceeds beyond nitrite in aerobiosis.

By analogy with nitrate-reducing systems, enzyme systems for sulphate reduction in *Desulfovibrio* are also considered to consist of reductase, dehydrogenase and intermediary hydrogen carrier. The kind of cytochrome present in this type of bacteria, in spite of its strictly anaerobic nature, is quite different. This cytochrome was discovered by Postgate [14] and by Ishimoto [15] independently. It has absorption maxima of α-band at 553 mμ and a very low redox potential ($E_0' = $ 200 mV). In living cells, it is reduced by hydrogen and formate and oxidized by sulphate, sulphite and thiosulphate, etc. Its rôle as the intermediary carrier can be suggested. Reductases for sulphite and thiosulphate, hydrogenase and formic and lactic dehydrogenase were extracted from the cells [16]. Ishimoto *et al.* showed that an intermediary electron carrier was necessary for the thiosulphate reduction with hydrogen [17] and that the purified cytochrome was utilizable as the carrier [18]. These experiments offer direct proof for the participation of the cytochrome in electron transfer in the anaerobic reaction of strict anaerobes.

The cytochrome acts also in hydrogen production. When the cytochrome is reduced enzymically with formate and formic dehydrogenase system or chemically with sodium dithionite, production of molecular hydrogen is observed in the presence of hydrogenase [19]. This cytochrome is autoxidizable and can be oxidized with colloidal sulphur, hydroxylamine and nitrite.

Experimental results indicating phosphate incorporation in the cells, during the reduction of sulphate with hydrogen, suggest the presence of a phosphorylation process, not on the level of substrate dehydrogenation, but on the level of electron transfer in the sulphate reduction [20].

There are many autotrophic strains among *Desulfovibrio* [21] and even some heterotrophic strains can grow under supply of hydrogen, sulphate, carbon dioxide, inorganic nitrogen source and small amounts of growth factors [22]. Phosphate incorporation was observed even in the heterotrophic strain employed in the above experiments.

Now, we try to propose a scheme for the evolution of respiratory systems by the comparison of different types of cytochrome. There are several groups of cytochromes which are different in their chemical nature and physiological function. The first group is that of *Desulfovibrio*, which has very low potential and strong reducing ability for many inorganic substances through corresponding reductases. The second is that of photoreductive and photosynthetic organisms including higher plants, algae and bacteria. A kind of them was found also in anaerobic photoreductive bacteria *Chlorobium* [23]; they have high redox potential and are generally conceived to be oxidized photochemically and reduced by suitable substrates to yield free energy. Some species of anaerobic photosynthetic bacteria with such cytochrome have the ability to oxidize various substances including fatty acids, which are not usually oxidized by nonphotosynthetic anaerobes [24]. The former may occupy the position between aerobes and anaerobes. The third group includes the cytochrome systems of aerobic respiration. They are miscellaneous in their nature. Frequently, several sorts of cytochromes co-operate in series, e.g. those of *a*, *b*, *c* type in mammalian muscle and yeast. The common function of the cytochrome systems is transfer of electrons in biological oxidoreduction and formation of energy-rich phosphate bonds accompanying it.

According to the above grouping, we can speculate on the course of evolution of cytochromes in the evolution of metabolism. Cytochrome had been playing a rôle as an electron carrier already in anaerobic primaeval organisms. It may be necessary for the phosphorylation in electron transfer, a new type of energy-yielding systems, different from substrate level phosphorylation. The ability of phosphorylation in the electron transfer should provide the energetical base of autotrophic life. In the primaeval reaction cytochrome participated in the reaction with hydrogen-hydrogenase and with reductase for sulphate, nitrate or other inorganic compounds.

In the second step cytochrome became connected with photo-oxidation, which induced high redox potential and prepared conditions for oxidation of various types of compounds.

In the third step, respiration started and developed with the appearance of oxygen in the atmosphere. The complexity of the respiratory system corresponds to its higher efficiency in energy yielding.

Enzyme systems of nitrate and sulphate reduction for assimilation differ greatly from those for energy yielding. Assimilatory reduction which is observed in higher plants, *Neurospora* and bacteria in some conditions, is carried out by molybdenum-containing flavoproteins. The reduction in seedlings of bean has already been mentioned.

Sulphate reduction for assimilation leading to organic sulphur compounds takes place widely in micro-organisms and plants, but only few data on the mechanism were offered. Recently Lipmann discovered the activation of sulphate by adenosine triphosphate in extracts of *Neurospora* [25], which might be a preparatory step for sulphate reduction. The path of sulphite reduction to cysteine in mammalian tissues is not through direct sulphite reduction to inorganic sulphide but through reduction of cysteine sulfinic acid, which is formed from pyruvate and sulphite through addition and transamination [26]. Intermediary formation of inorganic sulphide in the process of sulphate assimilation was denied by several authors in the field of biochemical genetics [27].

When and how did these differences arise in the path and enzyme systems between assimilatory and non-assimilatory reduction of nitrate and sulphate? Before the appearance of oxygen on the Earth, the most abundant inorganic forms of nitrogen and sulphur were possibly ammonia and sulphide. Accordingly, living organisms could utilize ammonia and sulphide for body building, and necessity of reduction for assimilation might arise only after the appearance of oxygen in the atmosphere and consequent decrease of ammonia disappearance and of sulphide by oxidation.

The first type of nitrate reduction might be one, like nitrate fermentation in *Clostridium* or cotyledons, and has effects on the oxidation of substrate and on the elevation of potential in the organisms. Along with the evolution of cytochrome, there appeared the coupling of nitrate reductase with the cytochrome system. Assimilatory reduction evolved from the first type of nitrate reduction independently from the systems of nitrate respiration.

Studies on enzymic mechanisms of nitrogen fixation have not given conclusive results and little information on its evolution has been obtained. But the facts, that biogenic nitrogen gas was not present in the atmosphere and that many anaerobes as well as aerobes perform nitrogen fixation, may indicate the precedence of that process before respiration. Denitrification, which is carried out by facultative anaerobes, can be considered to appear later.

We believe that studies on nitrate and sulphate reduction may offer valuable data for the evolution of energy-yielding systems as well as of intermediary nitrogen and sulphur metabolism.

REFERENCES

1. A. I. OPARIN, *Origin of Life*. New York, 1937.
2. D. I. SAPOZHNIKOV, *Mikrobiologiya*, **20**, 419, 1951.
3. J. H. QUASTEL, M. STEPHENSON & M. D. WHETHAM, *Biochem. J.*, **19**, 304, 1925.
4. W. VERHOEVEN, *Symposium on Inorganic Nitrogen Metabolism*, p. 61, 1956.
5, 6. J. POSTGATE, *Research, Tokyo*, **5**, 189, 1952.
7. S. YAMAGATA, *Acta phytochim., Lond.*, **11**, 145, 1939–1940.
8. S. TANIGUCHI, F. EGAMI & R. SATO, *Symposium on Inorganic Nitrogen Metabolism*, p. 87, 1956.
9. R. SATO & F. EGAMI, *Bull. chem. Soc. Japan*, **22**, 137, 1949.
   R. SATO & M. NIWA, *Bull. chem. Soc. Japan*, **25**, 202, 1952.
10. H. TAKAHASHI, S. TANIGUCHI & F. EGAMI, *J. Biochem., Tokyo*, **43**, 223, 1956.
11. J. KOYAMA, *J. Jap. biochem. Soc.*, **28**, Spec. No. p. 74, 1956.
12. F. EGAMI, K. OOMACHI, K. LIDA & S. TANIGUCHI, *Biokhimiya*, in press.
13. M. OHARA & T. SUYAMA, *Nature, Lond.*, **169**, 285, 1952.
    Y. KURATA, *Protein, Nucleic Acid and Enzyme (Japan)*, **1**, 33, 1956.
14. J. POSTGATE, *Biochem. J.*, **56**, XI, 1954.
15. M. ISHIMOTO, J. KOYAMA & Y. NAGAI, *Bull. chem. Soc. Japan*, **27**, 565, 1954; *J. Biochem., Tokyo*, **41**, 763, 1954.
16. M. ISHIMOTO, J. KOYAMA & Y. NAGAI, *J. Biochem., Tokyo*, **42**, 41, 1955.
17. M. ISHIMOTO & J. KOYAMA, *Symposia on Enzyme Chem.*, **10**, 77, 1954.
18. M. ISHIMOTO & J. KOYAMA, *Bull. chem. Soc. Japan*, **28**, 231, 1955.
19. M. ISHIMOTO, T. YAGI & M. SHIRAKI, *Symposia on Enzyme Chem.*, **11**, 184, 1956.
20. M. ISHIMOTO, T. YAGI & M. SHIRAKI. Unpublished.
21. K. R. BUTLIN, M. E. ADAMS & M. THOMAS, *J. gen. Microbiol.*, **3**, 46, 1949.
22. J. C. SENEZ, *Ann. Inst. Pasteur*, **84**, 595, 1953.
23. L. P. VERNON & M. D. KAMEN, *J. biol. Chem.*, **211**, 643, 1954.
24. S. R. ELSDEN, *Autotrophic Micro-organisms, Symp. Soc. gen. Microbiol. (London)*, No. 4, p. 202, 1954.
25. H. HILZ & F. LIPMANN, *Proc. nat. Acad. Sci., Wash.*, **41**, 880, 1955.
26. F. CHAPEVILLE & F. FROMAGEOT, *Biochim. biophys. Acta*, **14**, 415, 1954.
27. D. J. HOCKENHULL, *Biochim. biophys. Acta*, **3**, 326, 1949.

The Comparative Characters of the Oxidative Systems of Various Groups of Organisms in Relation to Their Evolution

B. A. RUBIN

*A. N. Bakh Institute of Biochemistry of the Academy of Sciences of the U.S.S.R.
and Moscow State University, Moscow*

THE EVIDENCE of contemporary biochemistry shows that many of the properties characteristic of living material are not strictly specific, in that each of them separately is also met with in inorganic nature.

It must not, however, be ignored that, as well as properties of this sort, there are also attributes which are only present in living organisms. Among these attributes we are justified in including the tendency to so-called 'adaptive change', the ability of living bodies to adapt themselves to the conditions of the environment in which the development of the organic form in question is taking place. One expression of this specific characteristic of living bodies is their ability to form adaptive enzymes which may be induced by various organic compounds.

At present material is being accumulated which indicates that physical and chemical factors such as temperature, light, partial pressure of oxygen etc. exert a similar influence on the plant organism. This may be illustrated by examples in connection with the enzymes which catalyse the so-called 'terminal stage' of respiration, namely the oxidation of hydrogen. Nowadays there is nobody who doubts the fact that the oxidative enzymic systems have undergone prolonged evolution.

In this connection it is interesting to compare the specific peculiarities of the systems of terminal oxidases in the various groups of organisms which inhabit our planet. Unfortunately there is but little evidence on this question. Furthermore, in generalizing about them, one must not ignore the incompleteness of contemporary methods of determining individual oxidases.

Nevertheless, comparison of the available evidence leads to the conclusion that the peculiarities of the structure of the complex of terminal oxidases is closely associated with the biological specificity of organisms and with the conditions under which their tissues carry out the process of respiration.

It is known that the conditions under which respiration occurs in green plants differ markedly from those in higher forms (warm-blooded) of animals. In the

562

first instance this refers to the temperature and the concentration of oxygen in the internal gaseous medium. In plants these factors are characteristically variable with sharp fluctuations, their temperature varies within practically the same limits as that of the surrounding atmosphere.

The content of O_2 and CO_2 in the internal gaseous medium of plant tissues is also extremely inconstant. For example, during the course of 24 hours the percentage of O_2 in the internal atmosphere of the blades of leaves varies, according to our findings, from 7·1 to 17·4, while that of CO_2 varies from 0·9 to 5·1. In organs having a parenchyma of many layers the content of oxygen, depending on the depth of the tissue at which it was measured, varies from 0·8 to 17·2% and that of CO_2 from 3·0 to 40%.

The exact opposite is true for warm-blooded animals in which there is, characteristically, not only a constant body temperature, but also a fairly good equalization of the gaseous composition of the tissues. According to Campbell the pressures of O_2 and CO_2 (in mm Hg) are [1]:

	Subcutaneous tissues		Peritoneal cavity	
	O_2	CO_2	O_2	CO_2
Rabbit . .	23	49	37	47
Rat . .	24	52	33	52
Guinea pig .	20	52	28	56
Cat . .	22	43	24	41

The situation is different in animals at a lower stage of evolutionary development. For example, in fish the body temperature fluctuates within the same limits as that of the waters in which they live, exceeding this temperature by only 0·3–1·0° C [2]. In cold-blooded animals fluctuations in temperature are also associated with changes in the composition of the gaseous medium. In the toad, for example, also according to Campbell, the oxygen pressure in the subcutaneous tissues at 3° C is 100 mm Hg while at 17° C it is 49 mm Hg. At the same time the pressure of CO_2 changes from 4 to 12 mm Hg [2]. It is obvious that the ability to carry out respiration in the face of such sharp variations in temperature and oxygen concentration must be determined, in different groups of animals, by specific peculiarities of the oxidative enzymic systems.

A consideration of these peculiarities forms the subject of this communication.

One of the most characteristic metabolic peculiarities, peculiar to green plants, is rhythmicity, which is brought about by regular changes in the action of enzymes. This refers to the seasonal and diurnal rhythms studied in detail in the works of B. A. Rubin, N. M. Sisakyan and others. This rhythmicity affects the most various aspects of metabolism, among them oxidative metabolism [3].

There is now no doubt that the terminal stage of respiration in higher plants can be brought about by the participation of the different oxidases which are normally all present in the tissues of any particular organism at once.

Apart from the Fe- and Cu- protein enzymes, one must also include in this group the flavine enzymes which, until recently, were regarded as enzymes which had no metals in them and which, therefore, were not susceptible to enzymic poisons (KCN, NaN_3).

In the very most recent years, however, it has been shown that in plants there is a special group of metalloflavine enzymes, some of which contain molybdenum (e.g. aldehyde or xanthine oxidase), or copper (butyryl-coenzyme A dehydrase). Catalytically active iron derivatives of flavines have also been found. Unlike the ordinary flavoprotein oxidases, all these enzymes are inhibited by cyanide [4].

As well as the oxidation of sugars by glycolysis, the direct, so-called apotomic, method of breakdown of carbohydrates must play an appreciable part in plants [5]. The physiological significance of the presence in the cell of several enzymes which catalyse one and the same chemical reaction is, it would seem, that the individual representatives of the complex vary in their character according to the environmental conditions.

For example, it has been established that the influence of the partial pressure of oxygen on the action of different plant oxidases is different. Cytochrome oxidase has the greatest affinity for oxygen; its activity reaches the maximum when the concentration of this gas is considerably less than that in the air. The complete opposite is true of the flavine enzymes, the activity of which increases markedly with an increase in the concentration of oxygen in the gaseous medium. The copper-containing proteins (polyphenol oxidase and ascorbic acid oxidase) occupy an intermediate position.

It is interesting to note, in this connection, that in compact tissues (having a parenchyma of many layers) cytochrome oxidase is considerably more active in the deeper layers which are distinguished by their very low oxygen contents.

There is a fairly definite distinction between the terminal oxidases of plants in their relations to temperature. For instance, a high temperature coefficient, often reaching 4–6, is characteristic of cytochrome oxidase. This is considerably higher than the value of Q_{10} for the flavoproteins of the same tissues in the same phase of development of the plant.

The significance of this peculiarity of the enzymes of the flavoprotein group may be discussed with reference to plants of the *Arum* family. The respiration of the spadix of these plants is completely resistant to the effects of cyanide and other enzymic poisons, the intensity of the process increasing in direct proportion to the concentration of oxygen (right up to 100%). All this shows that the respiration of the spadix is brought about at the expense of auto-oxidizable flavoproteins. It is interesting that the formation of the spadix usually takes place at the very beginning of spring, a period which is characterized by low air temperatures.

Polyphenol oxidase occupies a position similar to that of the flavine enzymes, also having a characteristically low Q_{10}.

Another piece of evidence of the heterogeneity of the system of oxidases is provided by the results of experiments in which it has been shown that a whole number of enzymes, which have, until recently, been regarded as individual compounds, are, in fact, systems having many components. Thus, in 1942, when Theorell [6] first isolated a crystalline preparation of peroxidase from the horse radish, he showed, from its electrophoretic and other properties, that it (peroxidase II) was substantially different from the non-crystalline fraction of the enzyme paraperoxidase (peroxidase I). By differential adsorption on alumina gel Kondo & Morita [7] isolated two peroxidases (a and b) from the sweet potato. Jermyn & Thomas [8], by electrophoresis on paper, separated the peroxidase of horse radish into first four and later five components. The ratios in which they occurred varied with the time of year. In the spring, for example, only three of the five components were found. One of these is constantly present in the juice of the horse radish and corresponds with Theorell's crystalline peroxidase. The other two both carried a negative charge at pH5 but differed in their substrates. For example, one of them is characterized by a positive peroxidase action on benzidine and none on guaiacol, while the other component, on the contrary, mainly oxidized guaiacol.

Nelson & Dawson [9] separated the polyphenol oxidase of the mushroom, *Psalliota campestris,* into two components, differing from one another in their abilities to oxidize catechol and cresol. These differences were associated with particular features of the protein molecules of each of the enzymes. In our

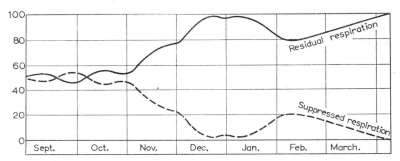

FIG. 1. The part played by different groups of oxidases in the respiration of the peel of a lemon at different periods in the life of the fruit (% of total respiration).

laboratory it has been shown that, in the tissues of citruses, an aldehyde oxidase, an amino acid oxidase and a glucose oxidase are all present.

Evidence has recently been obtained indicating that some cellular hydrolases are also made up of many components. Thus, Gilligan & Reece [10] have shown that the 'cellulase' of a number of bacteria may be separated chromatographically into several enzymes which may be distinguished by their abilities to break down carboxymethylcellulose, native and swollen cotton fibres etc.

A very important feature of the catalytic apparatus of the plant cells is their inconstancy, the variability of the ratios of the different components of the complex to one another.

This concerns what is known as the shift of the enzymic systems during the ontogenesis of the plant. It was described by Sisakyan & Rubin [11] in the leaves of apple trees, and by Mikhlin & Kolesnikov [12] in the shoots of barley and has since been confirmed by the work of many other investigators on the most varied material.

I will give two of the many available examples. According to our evidence, in citrus fruits, during the course of their development, one may observe a regular replacement of metal-containing oxidases by flavoprotein enzymes. This replacement is part of the process of ripening of the fruit (Fig. 1). Not uncommonly, substantial changes in enzymic systems may be observed after short intervals of time. According to Todd, in the period of active growth of the tubers of the potato, cytochrome oxidase occupies the central place in its respiration, while after harvesting the tubers this is occupied by tyrosinase. However, according to the findings of our laboratory, just before the potato tubers emerge from the resting stage there is a considerable activation of their flavoprotein oxidase and also of cytochrome oxidase with a weakening of the activity of the proteins.

Sisakyan [13] showed that cytochrome oxidase retains its activity in wheat shoots only until they have completed the stage of vernalization after which the enzyme cannot be found. The leaves of the plants, however, again show cytochrome oxidase activity when they are two months old. James [14] has established that the growing zone of the rootlets of barley during the first 4–5 days of

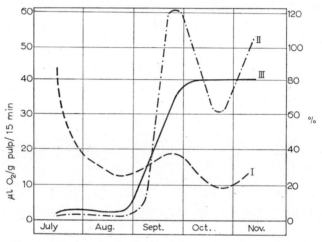

FIG. 2. The distribution of polyphenol oxidase in the cells of apples at different stages in their development. I—In the plastids, II—In the juice, III—In the juice, as % of total activity.

life, respires owing to the action of cytochrome oxidase which is then replaced by ascorbinase. According to Beevers & Gibbs [15] the route of direct oxidation of glucose, which is hardly ever used in the tissues of young fruit plants, accounts for about half the total respiration of the same object in a more mature state.

One may also observe substantial changes, associated with growth, in the enzymic systems which catalyse glycolytic processes in the tissues of higher plants. Thus, according to Ducet & Rosenberg [16], in the leaves of young plants under anaerobic conditions CO prevented the evolution of CO_2, while in fruit-bearing plants this factor had the opposite effect. Intracellular localization of enzymes may serve as a factor which further strengthens the heterogeneity of the biocatalytic systems of plants. In recent years this problem has attracted great attention [17, 18].

In the work of E. V. Artsikhovskaya in the A. N. Bakh Institute of Biochemistry of the Academy of Sciences of the U.S.S.R. it has been shown that in immature apples 95% of the polyphenol oxidase activity is due to the plastids and only 5% to the cytoplasm. At the time of complete ripeness of the fruit by far the greater part of the polyphenol oxidase is in the cytoplasm (80%), only about one-fifth of the whole enzyme content remaining in the plastids (Fig. 2). In potato tubers in August 97% of the polyphenol oxidase is in the plastids while in February they contain less than 30%. With M. Ladygina [19] I have observed a similar picture while studying the cytochrome oxidase of barley shoots. If, when the shoots were 8 days old, the proportion of cytochrome oxidase concentrated in the organoids was 92%, than at 18 days this value would fall to 63% and at 22 days to 56%. Accordingly, the cytoplasm of the young plants, which was almost free of enzyme became, in the course of 15 days, the repository of almost half of the whole cytochrome oxidase activity of the cell (Fig. 3).

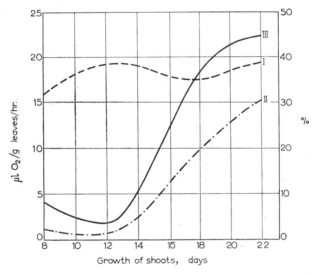

FIG. 3. Distribution of cytochrome oxidase in the leaves of barley at different stages of growth. I, II and III as in Fig. 2.

These findings are of interest in view of the fact that the localization of the enzyme affects its dependence on the action of external factors. Ladygina's experiments show, for example, that oxidation of cytochrome by a suspension reaches its maximum when the concentration of oxygen in the medium is as low as 5–10%, while the oxidation of cytochrome by a preparation of organoids continues to increase even when the partial pressure of oxygen is raised above 21% (Fig. 4).

The causes of all these substitutions in the activity of the oxidative enzymes have still not been thoroughly studied. There is reason to believe that they have an adaptive significance.

The replacement, which has already been mentioned, of Fe- and Cu-proteins by enzymes which are resistant to the action of respiratory poisons may serve as an example.

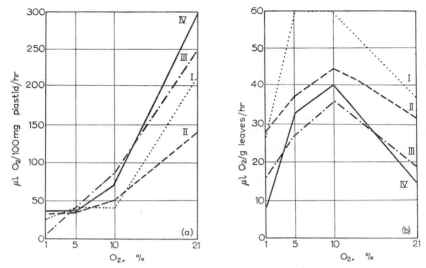

FIG. 4. Dependence of the activity of the cytochrome oxidase of barley leaves on partial pressure of oxygen and its connection with the localization of the enzyme in the cell.

(a) organoids. (b) homogenate. Age of plants in days, I—8, II—12, III—18, IV—22.

The diagram (Fig. 5) gives grounds for supposing that the biological significance of this changeover lies in its facilitating respiration of the fruit in falling air temperature, as the value of Q_{10} in the Fe- and Cu-proteins is considerably higher than that in the oxidases which are not susceptible to poisoning.

In the activation of 'cold-resistant enzymes' one may also include the adaptation to its purpose of the substitution of cytochrome oxidase by polyphenol oxidase which is seen during the process of ripening of apples [20].

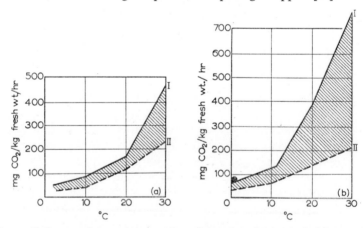

FIG. 5. Influence of temperature on the activity of respiration and of the respiratory enzymes of citrus fruits.

(a) Lemon (Novogruzinskiĭ). (b) Tangerine (Unshiu). I—Total respiration. II—Residual respiration. The hatched area represents the amount of respiration suppressed by sodium azide.

From the sketch which has been given above, which is far from being complete, it follows that in higher plants the oxidase enzymic system is constructed on the principle of multiplicity.

It is interesting to supplement the evidence from higher plants with material characterizing the oxidative system of animal organisms. What strikes the eye when one does so is the lack of uniformity of the pictures which are presented by different representatives of the animal world.

Those which are closest in this respect to the higher plants are those forms of animal which have not got a well developed blood-circulatory system or a constant body temperature. The systems catalysing the terminal stage of respiration in these organisms are also characterized by a multiplicity of components and a high lability, that is, they are inconstant. Thus, the respiration of the grasshopper embryo during the diapause is completely resistant to cyanide, while, in other phases of development, a considerable part of the respiration is suppressed by respiratory poisons [21]. Tyrosinase has been observed in the maggots of flies, in crustaceans, in molluscs and other animals. The blood of the crab, *Cancer pagarus*, contains a copper-containing protein with the properties of a pseudophenolase of the same type as catechol oxidase. In the prepupal and pupal stages of development of the meat fly there is a considerable rise in tyrosinase activity alongside a fall in the significance of cytochrome oxidase [22]. It is interesting that cytochrome oxidase has been shown to be present in the brains of all aquatic, cold-blooded vertebrates and some amphibia although cytochrome is practically absent from them, this being associated with a negligibly small activity in these animals of the cytochrome system as a whole [23, 24]. The formation of the full (true) cytochrome system in the brain cells is associated with a later stage in evolution. Most probably it was conditioned by the transition of animals to a terrestrial way of life.

At this time there occurred a diminution in the part played by anaerobic oxidative processes which were responsible for a substantial part of the energy metabolism of the brain in aquatic vertebrates, which developed under conditions in which oxygen was hard to obtain [25] (Tables 1 and 2).

TABLE I

*Respiration, anaerobic glycolysis and cytochrome oxidase
in the brains of vertebrates*

(average findings at 37·5 °C after Verzhbinskaya)

Object	Respiration Q_{O_2}	Anaerobic glycolysis Q_{CO_2}	Cytochrome oxidase Q_{O_2}
Lamprey .	—	—	16·5
Fishes .	3·8	18·8	44·5
Amphibians .	6·1	18·4	20·0
Reptiles .	8·7	16·6	67·3
Birds .	12·0	10·3	189·3
Mammals .	10·4	8·5	146·0

TABLE 2

The influence of the environmental conditions on the activity of cytochrome oxidase

(average findings after Verzhbinskaya)

Object	Av. value of Q_{10} at $16 \cdot 5$–$37 \cdot 5$ °C	Activity with a partial pressure of O_2 of 10–15 mm Hg as % of activity in air
Fishes . .	$1 \cdot 2$	109
Amphibians .	$1 \cdot 1$	97
Reptiles . .	$1 \cdot 9$	54
Birds . .	$2 \cdot 6$	34
Mammals . .	$2 \cdot 1$	40

Different classes of organism differ from one another, not only in the activity of their cytochrome oxidase, but also in its 'quality' which is expressed in an alteration in the dependence of the activity of the enzyme on temperature and partial pressure of oxygen.

A considerably higher temperature coefficient is characteristic of the cytochrome oxidase of terrestrial animals. The respiratory requirement of these animals increases markedly in oxygen.

It is well known that, in parallel with the increase in the complexity of the structure of the organism of animals, there occurred a stabilization of the condition of the environment of the internal tissues. Thus, mammals, which have highly developed nervous and blood-vascular systems, are characterized by constant body temperature and by the respiring cells being maintained at a constant partial pressure of oxygen. At the same time, one may note a certain simplification of the oxidative enzymic systems. Thus, in higher animals, especially in such specialized tissues as the brain and skeletal muscles, the predominant role in aerobic oxidation falls on the cytochrome system. It is interesting that, even within the confines of an animal organism, the individual organs and tissues, which are subject to specific conditions, possess certain peculiarities in the course of their oxido-reductive processes. As an example we may adduce the crystalline lens of the eye, which has no blood vessels. It is not cytochrome oxidase which plays the predominant part in the respiration of this tissue, but the direct oxidation of glucose [1].

From the evidence which has been brought forward it follows that the presence in green plants of complicated systems of oxidases made up of many components may be regarded as an important adaptive property which corresponds with the specific peculiarities of the structure of these organisms and the conditions of the medium in which they are accustomed to carry out their vital activities. To these peculiarities one must, to a certain degree, attribute the ability of green plants to exist under conditions of continually varying temperature, illumination, moisture etc.

We must remark that just such an expression of the principle of heterogeneity is found in the structure of the pigmentary apparatus of green plants. It is well known that chlorophylls, carotenoids and phycobilins enter into its composition while each of these groups, in its turn, is made up of a large number of representatives, differing from one another in their structural-chemical properties, absorption spectra, etc.

The complexity of the structure of the biologically active systems of green plants corresponds very well with the dynamic state and inconstancy of the conditions of their life.

REFERENCES

1. T. VON BRAND, *Anaerobiosis in Invertebrates*, Biodynamica, Normandy, Mo., 1946.
2. R. CLAUSON, *Ecology*, **15**, 139, 1934.
3. B. RUBIN & O. LUTIKOVA, *Biokhimiya*, **2**, 423, 1937.
   B. RUBIN, E. ARTSIKHOVSKAYA, N. SPIRIDONOVA & O. LUTIKOVA, *Biokhimiya*, **5**, 687, 1940.
   B. RUBIN, E. ARTSIKHOVSKAYA & O. LUTIKOVA, *Biokhimiya*, **10**, 54, 1945.
   N. SISAKYAN & A. KOBYAKOVA, *Biokhimiya*, **5**, 301, 1940.
   N. SISAKYAN & N. NUZHDIN, *Biokhimiya*, **9**, 104, 1944.
4. C. ANFINSEN & W. KIELLEY, *Ann. Rev. Plant Biochem.*, **23**, 17, 1954.
5. B. HORECKER, *Brewers Digest*, **28**, 56, 1953; A. BARKHASH & M. TIMOFEEVA, *Biokhimiya*, **20**, 623, 1955.
6. H. THEORELL, *Ark. Kemi. Min. Geol.*, **16**, 2, 1942.
7. K. KONDO & Y. MORITA, *Chem. Abstr.*, **47**, 3893, 1953.
8. M. JERMYN & R. THOMAS, *Bioch. J.*, **56**, 631, 1954; J. GILLESPIE, M. JERMYN & E. WOODS, *Nature, Lond.*, **169**, 487, 1952.
9. J. NELSON & C. DAWSON, *Advanc. Enzymol.*, **4**, 99, 1944.
10. W. GILLIGAN & E. REECE, *Canad. J. Microbiol.*, **1**, 2, 1954.
11. N. SISAKYAN & B. RUBIN, *Biokhimiya*, **9**, 307, 1944.
12. D. MIKHLIN & P. KOLESNIKOV, *Biokhimiya*, **12**, 452, 1947.
13. N. SISAKYAN & I. FILIPPOVICH, *Zh. obstch. Biol.*, **21**, 215, 1953.
14. W. JAMES, *Plant Respiration*, Oxford, 1953; *New Phytologist*, **54**, 1, 1955.
15. H. BEEVERS & M. GIBBS, *Nature, Lond.*, **173**, 640, 1954.
16. G. DUCET & A. ROSENBERG, *C. R. Soc. Biol.*, **229**, 391, 1949; *Bull. Soc. Chim. biol.*, **33**, 321, 1951.
17. N. SISAKYAN, *Fermentativnaya aktivnost protoplazmennykh struktur*, 5-e Bakhovskoe Chtenie. Izd. Akad. Nauk S.S.S.R., Moscow, 1951.
18. P. SALTMAN, *J. biol. Chem.*, **200**, 145, 1953.
19. B. RUBIN & M. LADYGINA, *Biokhimiya*, **21**, 347, 1956.
20. B. RUBIN, E. ARTSIKHOVSKAYA & T. IVANOVA, *Dokl. Akad. Nauk S.S.S.R.*, **59**, 1469, 1948.
21. J. BODINE & E. BOELL, *J. cell. comp. Physiol.*, **5**, 97, 1934.
22. P. KARLSON & E. WECKER, *Hoppe-Seyl Z.*, **300**, 42, 1955.
23. M. KRAHL et al., *J. gen. Physiol.*, **24**, 597, 1941.
24. J. FLEXNER et al., *J. cell. comp. Physiol.*, **18**, 55, 1941.
25. N. VERZHBINSKAYA, In Sbornik '*Biokhimiya Nervnoĭ Sistemy*', p. 193, Izd. Akad. Nauk Ukr.S.S.R., Kiev, 1954.

The Effect of Cysteine on the Methionine Content of the Animal and Plant Organism

SIMION OERIU

Dept. of Chemotherapy of the Academy of the Rumanian People's Republic and Dept. of Biochemistry of the Medicopharmaceutical Institute, Bucharest, Rumania

IN INVESTIGATIONS in the field of prophylaxis of the process of ageing and the prolongation of life C. I. Parhon, S. Oeriu & I. Tănase studied the content of sulphur-containing amino acids, in different conditions, in animals (rats) of different ages [12].

As sulphydryl groups have an important significance in oxido-reductive processes, in detoxication of the organism and in metabolic processes in general, we assumed that they also played a biological part in the process of ageing.

Our investigations showed that the methionine content of the serum of rats decreased with age while the cystine content increased [13].*

In order to observe the shifts in the oxido-reductive process in the cystine–cysteine system under the influence of methionine and cysteine, we determined the contents of methionine, cystine and cysteine in the serum of rats of different ages before and after the intramuscular administration of methionine or cysteine (50 mg/kg body weight daily for 16–20 days).

The administration of cysteine or methionine to young or adult rats led to an insignificant change in the methionine content. These findings confirm the results obtained by Arnstein & Crawhall [2] after the administration of cysteine labelled with ^{35}S to adult rats, and also the results of Stekol & Weiss [16] after the administration of cystine labelled with ^{35}S to young rats.

Old animals behave differently: the administration of cysteine, under the same conditions, leads to a marked increase (60–64%) in methionine. It may be supposed that the increase in the methionine in old animals after administration of cysteine is a very profound biological process, associated with the age of the animal.

The investigations of du Vigneaud [6] into the transformation of methionine into cysteine in growing rats to which, in the absence of cysteine from their diet, they administered, for 36 days in the food, methionine which, as well as being

---

* Methionine was determined by the method of Hess & Sullivan [8], cysteine + cystine by that of Wassel [19], cysteine and cystine were determined polarographically. For this purpose we used acid hydrolysis of the protein according to the method of Brdicka [3, 4] and Tropp [18].

labelled with the sulphur isotope [34]S, also contained the carbon isotope ^{13}C in the α and β positions in the carbon chain of the methionine, showed that in the cystine isolated from the hair of the rats there was absolutely no labelled carbon, while 80% of the sulphur of the cystine consisted of the isotopic sulphur of the methionine.

Du Vigneaud *et al.* [7] and Dyer & du Vigneaud [5] showed that the organism can synthesize the L-methionine required for growth from L- and DL-homocystine and homocysteine when there are adequate donors of methyl groups, choline and betaine in the diet.

Wood & Gutman [22] resolved *S*-benzyl-DL-homocysteine by isotopic labelling, it being an intermediate product in the synthesis of methionine. This confirms the mechanism of transformation of homocysteine into methionine *in vitro*.

Rose [14], White & Beach [20], Womack *et al.* [21] and Close [10] consider that the transformation of methionine into cysteine in the living organism is irreversible and that the requirements of the organism for methionine cannot be covered by cysteine.

Great interest attaches to the work of Horowitz [9] who discovered the ability of the mould *Neurospora crassa* to transform cysteine into methionine. Radioactive sulphur when administered to *Neurospora crassa* is incorporated into methionine.

TABLE I

The average content of methionine, cysteine and cystine in the serum of old rats, guinea pigs, rabbits and dogs treated with methionine and cysteine (50 mg/kg of body weight daily for 16 days; rabbits received 25 mg/kg body weight).

UNTREATED ANIMALS

Methionine	Cysteine (mg/100 ml serum)	Cystine
	RATS	
1·12 ($-0·05$; $+0·01$)	1·00 ($-0·1$; 0)	4·53 ($-0·1$; 0)
	GUINEA PIGS	
0·56 ($-0·02$; $+0·04$)	0·24 (0)	6·00 ($-0·12$; $+0·12$)
	RABBITS	
0·48 ($-0·03$; $+0·03$)	0·28 ($-0·08$; $+0·16$)	5·76 (0)
	DOGS	
0·50 ($-0·01$; $+0·15$)	0·36 (0)	6·27 ($-0·57$; $+0·27$)

TABLE I—*continued*

ANIMALS TREATED WITH METHIONINE

Methionine	Cysteine	Cystine
	RATS	
1·60	1·50	4·60
(−0·05; +0·20)	(−0·1; +0·1)	(−0·4; +0·4)
	GUINEA PIGS	
0·79	0·42	5·60
(−0·01; +0·03)	(−0·06; +0·06)	(−0·28; +0·56)
	RABBITS	
0·57	0·54	6·00
(−0·01; +0·03)	(−0·18; +0·18)	(−0·12; +0·24)
	DOGS	
0·53	0·48	5·58
(−0·01; +0·02)	(0)	(−0·30; +0·30)

ANIMALS TREATED WITH CYSTEINE

Methionine	Cysteine	Cystine
	RATS	
1·64	1·20	3·90
(−0·06; +0·02)	(0; +0·1)	(0; +0·1)
	GUINEA PIGS	
0·69	0·27	5·93
(−0·07; +0·18)	(−0·09; +0·15)	(−0·31; +0·29)
	RABBITS	
0·53	0·95	5·79
(−0·01; +0·02)	(−0·25; +0·13)	(−0·09; +0·03)
	DOGS	
0·79	0·57	6·81
(−0·08; +0·11)	(−0·63; +0·23)	(−0·39; +0·21)

Note: The figures in brackets give the difference between the mean and the maximum and minimum values.

Thus according to Braunshteïn [1] it has been established that this mould synthesizes methionine by means of a chain of reactions in the reverse direction to the formation of cysteine from methionine in animals.

The investigations of Shiota & Clark [17] deal with the metabolism of methionine in bacteria. They note the appearance of methionine in *Lactobacillus arabinosus* as a result of supplying L-cysteine or DL-homocysteine in a synthetic medium.

On giving cysteine labelled with ^{35}S to chick embryos Machlin, Struglia & Pearson [11] found 1·3% of the labelled sulphur in methionine and 49% in cysteine; on giving methionine labelled with ^{35}S they found 35% of the radioactive sulphur in methionine and 43% in cysteine.

In the work of Rose & Wixon [15] on the correlation between cysteine and methionine it was shown that, in man, after the administration of DL-cystine, the methionine requirement declines sharply (80–90%), which gives reason to believe in the formation of methionine by the agency of cysteine.

On the basis of the evidence of the current literature, as well as our own, we set ourselves the task of extending the study of the effects of methionine and cysteine on the metabolism of these sulphur-containing amino acids in other species of old animals as well, and also in the mould *Aspergillus niger*.

Table 1 gives the results of experiments on old rats, guinea pigs, rabbits and dogs.

Intramuscular administration of cysteine or methionine to rats, guinea pigs, rabbits* and dogs (50 mg/kg of body weight for 16 days) leads, in all the animals, to an increase in the methionine content.

As cysteine (cystine) enters into the composition of glutathione we determined the content of oxidized, reduced and ordinary glutathione† in rats of various ages after giving cysteine and methionine (50 mg/kg of body weight for 16 days) (Tables 2 and 3).

TABLE 2

Mean content of oxidized, reduced and ordinary glutathione in rats of various ages

Oxidized glutathione	Reduced glutathione (mg/100 ml blood)	Ordinary glutathione
YOUNG ANIMALS		
3·30 (−1·1; +0·8)	30·9 (−0·20; +0·3)	34·1 (−1·5; +1·0)
ADULT ANIMALS		
7·10 (−0·5; +0·7)	29·9 (−3·5; +1·2)	37·5 (−3·70; +1·9)
OLD ANIMALS		
7·65 (−0·45; +1·05)	28·8 (−0·20; +0·1)	36·5 (−0·3; +0·9)

Note: The figures in brackets show the derivation of maximal and minimal values from the mean.

* In rabbits there is an insignificant increase in the methionine content after giving cysteine. It must be borne in mind that, owing to their intolerance of the large dose of cysteine, these animals only received a half dose of 25 mg/kg of body weight.

† The oxidized, reduced and ordinary glutathione were determined by the method of Woodward & Fry [23].

TABLE 3

Mean content of oxidized, reduced and ordinary glutathione in the blood of old rats treated with methionine or cysteine (50 mg/kg of body weight daily for 16 days)

Oxidized glutathione	Reduced glutathione (mg/100 ml blood)	Ordinary glutathione
UNTREATED ANIMALS		
7·65 (−1·5; +0·45)	28·8 (−0·2; +0·1)	36·5 (−0·3; +0·9)
ANIMALS TREATED WITH METHIONINE		
7·11 (−0·99; +0·86)	28·3 (−2·32; +3·09)	35·5 (−2·34; +0·5)
ANIMALS TREATED WITH CYSTEINE		
5·88 (−1·69; +1·51)	34·2 (−0·8; +0·8)	40·1 (−0·87; +0·73)

Note: The figures in brackets show the deviation of the maximal and minimal values from the mean.

In animals which are not treated with methionine or cysteine the content of oxidized glutathione increases with age.

The administration of methionine to old animals leads to an insignificant decrease in the content of oxidized glutathione (from 7·65 to 7·11 mg/100 ml); the administration of cysteine leads to a considerable decrease in the content of oxidized glutathione (from 7·65 to 5·88 mg/100 ml).

In another series of experiments we aimed at studying the possibility of the transformation of cysteine into methionine in the plant organism *Aspergillus niger*.

The literature shows that this organism does not contain methionine.

Following the principle of the unity of the organism with the conditions of its existence, we changed the conditions of life of the mould by adding different amounts of cysteine and methionine to the nutrient medium.

We added methionine (0·5% and 2%) or cysteine (1%) to Kaufman's synthetic medium*, on which we cultivated *Aspergillus niger*, for 23 days.

Chromatographic determination of the amino acid composition of the *Aspergillus niger* gave the following results.† Methionine was absent from hydrolysates of the fungus grown on the basal medium, but present when methionine or cysteine had been added.

* We used Kaufman's synthetic medium: maltose 5 g, magnesium sulphate 0·1 g, calcium nitrate 0·5 g, potassium acid phosphate 0·25 g, distilled water to 1000 ml.

† We used the method of partition chromatography. Whatman No. 1 filter paper was used. A mixture of butanol, glacial acetic acid and water was used as the solvent. The solution was made to flow for 32 hours in one direction at room temperature (20–22 °C). The chromatogram was developed with a 0·2% solution of ninhydrin in butanol and then dried for 10 min at 110 °C.

CONCLUSIONS

1. The mean contents of methionine, cysteine and cystine in the serum, and of oxidized glutathione in the blood of rats changes with age. In old rats the methionine content is lower and that of cystine and oxidized glutathione is higher than in young ones.

2. Intramuscular administration of cysteine (50 mg/kg of body weight for 16 days) to old animals (rats, guinea pigs and dogs) leads to a considerable increase in the methionine content. It may be supposed that the increase in the methionine content after the administration of cysteine to old animals is a very profound biological process which may be associated with the age of the animal.

3. The addition of methionine or cysteine to the nutrient medium on which the mould *Aspergillus niger*, which contains no methionine, is cultivated, leads to the appearance of methionine in the composition of the mould as shown by chromatography.

4. The evidence obtained suggests that it would be worth studying the conversion of the sulphur-containing amino acids into one another in the ontogenesis and phylogenesis of organisms in relation to the physiological state of the animal and the conditions of its existence.

REFERENCES

1. A. E. BRAUNSHTEĬN, *Biokhimiya aminokislotnogo obmena*, Izd. med. Akad. Nauk S.S.S.R., Moscow, 1949.
2. H. R. V. ARNSTEIN & J. C. CRAWHALL, *Biochem. J.*, **55**, 280, 1953.
3. R. BRDICKA, *Coll. Czech. chem. Commun.* 1953 (3) 148.
4. R. BRDICKA, *Research, Lond.*, **1**, 25, 1947.
5. H. M. DYER & V. DU VIGNEAUD, *J. biol. Chem.*, **109**, 477, 1953.
6. V. DU VIGNEAUD, G. W. KLIMMER, J. R. RACHEL & M. KAHN, *J. biol. Chem.*, **155**, 645, 1944.
7. V. DU VIGNEAUD, H. M. DYER & J. HARMON, *J. biol. Chem.*, **101**, 719, 1933.
8. W. C. HESS & M. X. SULLIVAN, *J. biol. Chem.*, **151**, 635, 1943.
9. N. H. HOROWITZ, *J. biol. Chem.*, **171**, 225, 1947; *Fed. Proc.*, **6**, 262, 1947.
10. A. A. CLOSE & H. J. ALMQUIST, *J. biol. Chem.*, **138**, 407, 1941.
11. L. J. MACHLIN, L. S. STRUGLIA & P. B. PEARSON, *Arch. Biochem. Biophys.*, **59**, 326, 1955.
12. C. I. PARHON, S. OERIU & I. TĂNASE, *Bul. sti. (Sec. St. Med.) Acad. Repub. rom.*, **7**, (3), 884, 1955.
13. C. I. PARHON, S. OERIU & I. TĂNASE, *Bul. sti. (Sec. St. Med.) Acad. Repub. rom.*, **7**, (3), 891, 1955.
14. W. C. ROSE *et al.*, *J. biol. Chem.*, **114**, lxxxv, 1936.
15. W. C. ROSE & R. L. WIXON, *J. biol. Chem.*, **215**, 763, 1955.
16. J. A. STEKOL & J. A. WEISS, *Fed. Proc.*, **14**, 287, 1955.
17. SHIOTA TETSUA & F. M. CLARK, *J. Bact.*, **70**, 339, 1955.
18. E. TROPP, *Klin. Wschr.*, p. 405, 1938.
19. B. WASSEL, *J. biol. Chem.*, **140**, 323, 1941.
20. A. WHITE & E. F. BEACH, *J. biol. Chem.*, **122**, 210, 1938.
21. M. WOMACK, K. S. KEMMRER & W. C. ROSE, *J. biol. Chem.*, **121**, 403, 1937.
22. J. WOOD & H. R. GUTMAN, *J. biol. Chem.*, **179**, 535, 1949.
23. G. E. WOODWARD & E. S. FRY, *J. biol. Chem.*, **97**, 465, 1932.

Session VI   DISCUSSION

K. Mothes (Deutschland):

Ich möchte einige Bemerkungen zu den Vorträgen der Kollegen Braunstein, Florkin und Kretowitsch machen und etwas Allgemeines vorausschicken. Die Untersuchungen von Herrn Braunstein gehören nach meiner Meinung zum Bedeutendsten, das überhaupt in den letzten zwei Jahrzehnten in der ganzen Welt auf dem Gebiete des Stickstoff-Metabolismus geleistet worden ist. Sie erlauben uns eine einheitliche Betrachtung der Synthese der Aminosäuren in Tier und in Pflanze. Es erscheint mir sehr wichtig, daß auch hier diese merkwürdige Einheit des Lebens erschlossen worden ist. Diese Untersuchungen stellen eine konsequente Fortsetzung der Arbeiten des großen russischen Physiologen Prjanischnikow dar.

Nun komme ich zu speziellen Fragen.

1. Herr Kretowitsch hat in seinem interessanten Referat die Frage der Ammoniak-Entgiftung und Ammoniak-Speicherung angeschnitten und auf die Arbeiten von Ruhland und Wetzel hingewiesen, nach denen höhere Pflanzen Ammoniak speichern, wenn sie über große Mengen freier Säure verfügen: Säurepflanze = Ammoniakpflanze. Eigentlich müßte man sagen Ammoniumionpflanze, denn es ist entscheidend, daß diese Pflanze die Dissoziation der Ammoniumverbindungen so erhöhen, daß freies NH_3 praktisch nicht mehr vorhanden ist.

Gegen die Ruhland'sche Theorie hat Vickery Einwände erhoben. Er hat darauf hingewiesen, daß im Blatt vom Rhabarber (*Rheum*) hohe Säuregrade und außerdem Glutamin sich befinden.

Dieser Widerspruch ist aber nur ein scheinbarer. Ein Blatt ist nicht homogen, sondern es besteht aus biochemisch sehr differenten Geweben. Es zeigt sich, daß z.B. die Gefäßbündel aus dem Blattstiel von *Rheum* ein höheres pH haben und viel Glutamin, und daß das parenchymatöse Grundgewebe ein niederes pH hat und viel NH_4^+-Ion. Wenn man bei der Analyse alles vermischt, kann man keine sicheren Aussagen machen.

Es gibt aber auch echte Ammoniakpflanzen:

2. Butkewitsch hat zweierlei Schimmelpilze unterschieden. Die einen (*Aspergillus*) bilden beim Abbau des Peptons viel freie Säure (Oxalsäure), sie reichern NH_4^+-Ion an. Die anderen bilden keine Säure. Man sagt, sie bauen Pepton nur bis zu den Aminosäuren ab. Das ist aber unmöglich. Denn wenn ein Pilz allein von Pepton lebt, wächst und atmet, so müssen die Kohlenstoffketten zum Teil in CO_2 verwandelt werden. Diese Pilze bilden auch NH_3. Da aber ihr Milieu ein pH von 7 bis 9 hat, wird NH_3 gasförmig an die Atmosphäre abgegeben. Diese Pilze entsprechen in ihrem dissimilatorischen Eiweißstoffwechsel den Bakterien und vielen niederen im Wasser lebenden Tieren.

3. In vielen höheren Pflanzen ist Harnstoff gefunden worden. Meist ist er aber nicht frei vorhanden, sondern entsteht erst bei der Analyse durch Aufspaltung der Allantoin-säure.

4. Es gibt zahlreiche Pflanzen (Boraginaceae, *Acer*, *Platanus*, Leguminosae), die NH_3 dadurch entgiften, daß sie Allantoin bilden und in großen Mengen speichern. Füttert man solche Pflanzen mit NH_3, so entstehen zünächst große Mengen von Glutamin und erst allmählich Allantoin.

Allantoin entsteht leichter in der Folge eines endogenen Eiweißabbaus als aus exogenem NH_3. Es entsteht leichter in den Wurzeln als in den Blättern.

5. Ähnliches gilt für das Citrullin. Es ist die Hauptform der NH_3-Speicherung bei allen Betulaceen.

6. Manske fand in den Knollen von *Corydalis ochotensis* große Mengen von *N*-Acetylornithin. Das ist ein familienspezifischer Stoff, der in allen untersuchten Fumariaceen vorkommt. Er fehlt den nahe verwandten Papaveraceen oder kommt nur in geringen Mengen vor.

7. Es erscheint nicht ohne Bedeutung, daß die höhere Pflanze, sofern sie nicht viel freie Säure hat, neutrale Formen der NH_3-Speicherung bevorzugt: Glutamin, Asparagin, Allantoin, Citrullin, Acetylornithin.

8. Die Blätter aller Pflanzen, gleichgültig ob sie dem Glutamin-, Asparagin-, Allantoin-, Citrullin- oder Acetylornithin-Typ zugehören, bilden beim Eintauchen in NH_4^+-Lösungen sehr schnell fast ausschließlich Glutamin.

Diese Untersuchungen wurden mit Fräulein Dr. Engelbrecht, Herrn Dr. Reuter und Frl. Liß durchgeführt.

Pflanzenphysiologisches Institut der Universitaet,
Halle, Deutschland

A. Blagoveshchenskiǐ (U.S.S.R.):

The evolution of protein material undoubtedly determines the evolution of organisms. It is, therefore, one of the urgent tasks of biochemistry to establish the laws which connect the character of the protein substances with the organisms. It is important to establish which proteins are characteristic of the ancestral forms and which are characteristic of their successors; which processes of protein synthesis are essentially progressive in the evolving organism and which are in regression. First there must be closer contact with phylogenetical biologists and investigations must be carried out within the limits laid down by evolutionary series. In 1949 the excellent experimental findings of Danielsson appeared, showing that in the seeds of representatives of the family Leguminosae there are two globulins, vicilin, with molecular weight of 186,000, and legumin, with a molecular weight of 331,000. By analysing Danielsson's figures we have called attention to the fact that they contain a regularity which the author had not noticed, namely that the phylogenetically recent forms (*Acacia* in the Mimosoidae and *Pisum*, *Phaseolus* and *Trifolium* in the Papilionatae) there is a decisive predominance of vicilin, whereas, in the more archaic forms (*Arachis*, *Genista* and *Lathyrus* in the Papilionatae) legumin predominates. When we investigated the seeds of *Albizzia jalibrissin*, which belongs to the Mimosoidae, we found that 37% of the total quantity of protein is soluble in water and 9% is not soluble, either in water or in saline solutions but only in alkali. In more archaic, phylogenetically more ancient, forms (*Cercis siliquastrum*, *Sophora japonica*, *Maakia amurensis*, *Gleditschia triacanthus*) on the other hand, there were either no proteins extractable with water or saline solutions (*Cercis*) or else they were less in amount than those which were soluble in alkali.

By comparing the nature of the protein in the seeds with the phylogenesis of the plants concerned, it is easy to draw the conclusion that the proteins of evolutionarily recent forms are more soluble, harder to salt out and have a lower molecular weight than those of the more archaic, regressive forms which are becoming extinct. It is interesting that the recent investigations of I. D. Raacke (*Biochem. J.*, **66**, 101, 110, 113, 1957) have shown that this state of affairs is repeated in ontogenesis. During the ripening of peas, from the moment of fertilization to full ripeness, the content of water soluble albumins falls while that of vicilin rises and, at the very end of the process, that of legumin also rises. Such a process of change in the nature of the protein of the seed, with ontogenic and phylogenic ageing, is associated with a change in the ability of enzymes to lower the threshold of the reactions which they catalyse. This ability decreases in both cases.

N. S. Akulov (U.S.S.R.):

Darwinian Biological Evolution as a Higher Form of the General Evolution of Chain Processes in Nature

In his generally accepted theory A. I. Oparin has shown the part played by coacervates in the process of the emergence of life. It would, however, be incorrect to say that this theory gives a complete answer to the question of what life is and how it arose in nature. I must therefore point out that, in 1949, we published (*Dokl. Akad. Nauk S.S.S.R.*, Vol. **68**), work in which it was shown that any organism develops in accordance with the law of chain kinetics and the fundamental assumptions of the theory of the evolution of chain processes in nature.

This theory supplements and makes more precise the theory of coacervates. The synthesis of these two theories, it seems to us, gives a deeper and better developed answer to the question of what life is and how it arose. In the testimony of the professors of the Moscow State University very favourable mention is made of our theory of the evolution of chain processes in nature and their connection with biological processes. Oparin also gave a favourable account of my work and I value this most particularly. For example, he emphasizes the novelty of the conception of the alteration of chain chemical processes in the period preceding the origin of life.

Oparin agrees with us that, at this period, a very important part was played by reactions which proceeded via intermediate compounds (active products). By reacting with the starting products, these active products can give rise to final products and partially regain their own form (i.e. be regenerated). In this case the reactions which proceed via an intermediate compound assume the character of a cyclical chain reaction, at first of the radical, and then of a more complicated, prebiological type, but already with the participation of proteins. This seems to be the prototype of metabolism.

An extremely important peculiarity of such reactions is that, depending on the nature of the intermediate products, the reactions may be of a different nature, even though the starting products may be the same. As a result, such reactions may compete with one another in such a way that one or several reactions 'predominate' over the others, directing the process of chemical transformation along a path which is determined by the particular collection of intermediate products present. Owing to the cyclical nature which chain processes acquire in the course of time, there also occurs a transmission of the peculiarities and character of the process from cycle to cycle, so that this cyclical nature is the prototype of inheritance. Finally, under the influence of various conditions in the environment, in particular in the nature of the original nutrients, the character of the cycle can change. This corresponds to mutation.

Thus we have the fundamental elements required for the Darwinian evolution of chemical transformation in the pre-biological period.

We have given a detailed analysis of the consequences which flow from this concept and demonstrated the possibility of the origin of life, i.e. chain reactions accompanied by the growth and self-dispersal of colloidal protein systems with a monophasic or diphasic structure (nucleus and envelope).

In doing so we have given great attention to elucidating the effect of the environment on the nature of the processes which occur within these colloidal systems and have, with a fair degree of certainty, demonstrated the possibility of changes occurring within the nucleus when the conditions of the external environment change. Oparin emphasizes all this in his reviews. In his new and extremely interesting book he only gives a general favourable reference to our kinetic conception and makes some critical remarks in connection with the theory, but does not give even the shortest explanation of the essential nature of this theory, such as is necessary even for readers who know Russian. This gives rise to even greater difficulties for those who read Oparin's book in English, since work is criticized which is unknown to them and which is hard to find in literature outside this country. In his critical remarks Oparin wrongly states that we limit ourselves to the consideration of radical chain processes. This is in contradiction to what he has written in his own reviews. Other comments of a critical nature can also easily be refuted. Unfortunately we cannot deal in greater detail with the essential features of our theory. Under these circumstance it would be very important if we could find, before the end of this Symposium, some organizational possibility for assessing both of the two theories discussed and the connection between them.

G. A. KRITSKIĬ (U.S.S.R.):

I should like to make two comments on the problems under consideration.

1. The available evidence allows us to note that in processes of selection, except the

autocatalytic reactions discussed by Calvin, reactions are also reinforced by the inter-weaving of the catalytic or activizing effects of the products.

Thus, on the one hand, nucleic acids subserve the process of protein synthesis, while, on the other, proteins, in the form of the appropriate enzymes, catalyse the biosynthesis of nucleic acids.

Another example. The biosynthesis of nucleotides from their simple precursors leads to the formation of nucleotide coenzymes which take part in glycolytic and oxidative pro-cesses. On the other hand, as a result of glycolytic and oxidative processes, ribose-5-phosphate and pyrophosphate are formed and these take part in the biosynthesis of nucleo-tides from their simpler precursors.

2. In trying to find out the path of biosynthesis of proteins it would seem to be useful to take note of some analogies, namely those with the biosynthesis of polysaccharides and nucleic acids. It is well known that the synthesis of polysaccharides and nucleic acids is brought about by reversible reactions of phosphorolysis or pyrophosphorolysis. The reversible reactions of phosphorolysis of glycogen or pyrophosphorolysis of deoxy-ribonucleic acid may only lead to a lengthening of the already existing chain of the poly-mers (primers). An actual increase in the number of molecules of a polymer can obviously occur owing to the presence of a certain amount of hydrolytic enzymes which, in an orderly way and to a limited extent, divide up the extremely large molecules of the original polymer into a few smaller ones. With some changes, such a state of affairs may also occur in the process of the biosynthesis of proteins. As an example, we may take the formation, studied

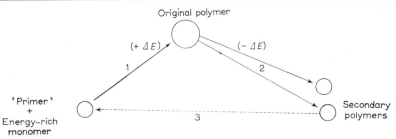

FIG. 1. General scheme of the biosynthesis of glycogen, ribonucleic acid, deoxyribonucleic acid and protein.

The process of formation of the original polymer takes place with the help of the 'primer' and with an increase in free energy, $(+\Delta E)$, while the process of breakdown of the original polymer into secondary polymers takes place without a 'primer' and with a decrease in free energy $(-\Delta E)$.

1. Retrophosphorolysis, retropyrophosphorolysis and other reactions of polymerization.
2. Partial hydrolysis.
3. The dotted line indicates that one of the products of the breakdown may be able to act as a 'primer'.

The enrichment of amino acids with energy in the biosynthesis of protein may occur by coupling of the carboxyl groups of amino acids with the phosphate groups of nucleotides.

by Northrop, of active proteolytic enzymes in the alimentary tract of animals from pro-enzymes by the proteolytic splitting of the proenzyme into the enzyme and an inactive polypeptide. The protein which is present on the surface of the nucleic acid might be the original high polymer.

It would seem that only one experimental fact contradicted this scheme, namely the fact that, according to the published evidence, the reaction of 'retrophosphorolysis' of ribonucleic acid takes place without a primer. However, as we showed about 10 years ago, it would appear that all preparations of native proteins and enzymes have in their com-position (perhaps in the form af adsorbed impurities) a nucleotide or nucleic acid pros-thetic group which could obviously serve, in this case, as a 'primer'.

Thus, we put forward the hypothesis that the process of biosynthesis of all polymers referred to consists of two stages; the process of polymerization of energy-rich monomers with the help of a 'primer' and the process of partial, limited hydrolytic splitting of the polymers which are formed in the first place (see Fig. 1). In this process the 'primer' often plays the part of a matrix.

The remark that the 'primer' may play the part of a matrix obviously requires clarification.

It is well known, for example, that the degree of branching of the chains of a polysaccharide synthesized by amylophosphorylase from glucose phosphate depends on the nature of the 'primer' (Kuzin). This is an experimental fact which shows the way in which there may develop, from one and the same monomer, high polymers which differ from one another in their structure.

Chairman: E. M. MAKOVSKIĬ

The Evolution of Metabolism
(continued)

Au Sujet du Passage de la vie Anaérobie à la vie Aérobie

E. AUBEL

Institut de Biologie Physico-chimique, Paris

Il est bien difficile de se représenter les formes vivantes primitives. Elles n'avaient certainement pas le degré de perfection que nous connaissons, même aux bactéries les moins évoluées, ce degré de perfection étant le fruit d'une évolution de millions d'années. Ce que nous pouvons penser c'est qu'elles existaient dans un milieu privé d'oxygène, renfermant des matières minérales et des substances organiques dont l'origine doit être cherchée dans ces réactions chimiques [5] sur lesquelles Oparine [1] a basé son explication matérialiste de l'apparition de la vie, et dont une synthèse partielle a été réalisée par Miller [4]. Ces formes primitives devaient avoir quelques ressemblances avec les formes anaérobies que nous connaissons, du moins quant aux procès fournissant l'énergie nécessaire au développement, au maintien et au fonctionnement des organismes. Ces procès sont d'origine fermentative et leur rendement est très inférieur à celui des procès respiratoires.

1. LES RÉACTIONS LIBÉRANT ET TRANSFÉRANT L'ÉNERGIE COMMUNES AUX ANAÉROBIES ET AUX AÉROBIES

Ce qui me semble important à noter c'est la similitude de tout un groupe de réactions intéressant le transfert de l'énergie que l'on trouve dans les deux groupes d'organismes anaérobies et aérobies et qui à cause de cela pourraient rappeler les réactions primitives.

Par exemple la formation de groupes phosphates forts sur lesquels Lipmann [6] a attiré l'attention se fait, pour une part, de façon analogue au cours du métabolisme des glucides chez tous les êtres vivants, parfois même de façon identique. En disant cela je pense au couplage, éclairci dans le laboratoire de Warburg [6], qui grâce à l'oxydation du phospho-3-glycéraldéhyde en acide 3-phosphoglycérique en présence de diphosphopyridine nucléotide (DPN), permet la formation d'une molécule de l'adénosine triphosphate (ATP) aux dépens d'une molécule de l'adénosine diphosphate (ADP) + 1 mol. de PO_4H_3. Ce couplage se rencontre aussi bien dans l'extrait musculaire, que dans le levure et vraisemblablement *Clostridium perfringens*. Il n'est pourtant pas absolument général; mais sa grande diffusion mérite qu'on y porte attention. Il en est de même de la formation d'une molécule d'ATP à partir d'une molécule d'ADP au cours de la transformation de l'acide phosphoenol-pyruvique en acide pyruvique. Un autre groupe de réactions paraît important en ce qui concerne la question qui nous occupe, elles concernent l'intervention du coenzyme A (CoA) découvert par Lipmann [6], en particulier la formation qu'il a décrit le premier d'acétyl coenzyme A (CoA) à partir de l'acide pyruvique. On la rencontre chez *Escherichia coli* qui est un anaérobie facultatif, chez *Clostridium butylicum* qui est un anaérobie strict, et dans le coeur de boeuf. Cette formation d'acétyl CoA s'accompagne d'une libération de CO_2 et d'hydrogène, qui fournit l'énergie nécessaire à la synthèse et peut exiger la participation du DPN qui est finalement réduit. Mais le sort de l'acétyl CoA diffère ensuit suivant qu'on a un microorganisme, aérobie ou anaérobie, ou un animal. Dans les microorganismes l'acétyl CoA sous l'action de la transacétylase donne de l'acétylphosphate riche en énergie et libère le CoA, l'acétylphosphate en présence d'ADP donnant par action de l'acétokinase de l'ATP et de l'acétate. Chez les animaux l'acétyl CoA rentre dans le cycle tricarboxylique de Krebs [6] et permet, grâce au mécanisme de la phosphorylation oxydative la formation de liaisons phosphoriques riches en énergie.

Ce type de chaînes de réactions qui ont un point de départ commun chez les anaérobies et les aérobies m'amène à signaler le rôle des flavoproteines, ces transporteurs qui à partir du diphosphopyridine nucléotide (DPN^+) ou du triphosphopyridine nucléotide (TPN^+) réduits à l'état de $DPNH + H^+$ et $TPNH + H^+$, transfèrent l'hydrogène et les électrons sur des accepteurs. Ces flavoprotéines existent universellement et, au départ, effectuent la même réaction; ce n'est qu'ensuite que la différenciation se produit chez les aérobies et les anaérobies: chez les aérobies l'accepteur final étant l'oxygène, chez les anaérobies l'accepteur final étant un composé moins réduit que le produit ultime de la fermentation ou simplement H^+ qui donne de l'hydrogène moléculaire qui se dégage.

A la faveur de ces exemples deux faits fondamentaux apparaissent, le rôle des liaisons phosphates élucidé par Lipmann [6] dans les transferts d'énergie, en particulier la position cruciale de l'adénosine triphosphate comme l'ont signalé Krebs & Kornberg [6], et le rôle des déshydrogénations bien connues depuis Wieland comme source d'énergie. On est conduit à penser qu'il s'agit là de mécanismes de base qui ont permis, eux, ou au moins des mécanismes analogues, aux organismes primitifs de se développer.

2. L'APPARITION D'OXYGÈNE LIBRE

Les procès fermentatifs anaérobies aboutissent à la formation de CO_2, et l'on peut admettre avec Oparine [1] & Urey [2] que c'est l'origine de l'apparition de ce gaz dans l'atmosphère. Ainsi, fut rendue possible la photosynthèse qui a permis la libération d'oxygène apparaissant à son tour comme gaz libre (Oparine [1], Urey [2]). La situation de la vie sur terre a été alors modifiée de façon radicale (Oparine [1]). L'apparition des organismes chlorophylliens a du être précédée par des formes voisines, possédant un pigment permettant la photosynthèse, mais incapables d'effectuer la photolyse de l'eau.

Ceci m'amène à attirer l'attention sur un groupe de bactéries qui pourrait

rappeler les formes de passage aux organismes capables d'effectuer la photosynthèse chlorophyllienne. Je songe aux bactéries pourpres du groupe des
Athiorhodacae qui réduisent photosynthétiquement le CO_2 en déshydrogénant
les composés organiques comme l'a montré Muller [7] et qui peuvent se développer sans air et surtout ces bactéries sulfureuses pourpres découvertes et étudiées
par van Niel [8], strictement anaérobies, croissant en milieu synthétique purement minéral et qui en présence de lumière réduisent le gaz carbonique en oxy-
dant H_2S. Dans tous les cas on n'observe pas de dégagement d'oxygène, ce qui
montre l'incapacité des microorganismes cités à effectuer la photolyse de l'eau.
Sans doute parce que la bactériochlorophylle des bactéries pourpres diffère
quelque peu de la chlorophylle dont pourtant elle est voisine. Et il faut arriver
aux êtres pourvus de chlorophylle pour observer le dégagement d'oxygène au
cours du procès de réduction du CO_2 grâce à la photolyse de l'eau.

On peut donc penser que des formes primitives anaérobies synthétisèrent un
pigment voisin de la chlorophylle qui leur permit de réduire photosynthétiquement le gaz carbonique grâce aux composés organiques du milieu.

Ensuite, certaines formes anaérobies acquièrent la possibilité d'utiliser uniquement des aliments minéraux pour leur croissance, et la réduction photosynthé-
tique du CO_2 fut effectuée grâce à l'hydrogène de divers composés minéraux,
en particulier H_2S. Ce furent les premiers autotrophes, qu'il ne faut pas con-
fondre avec les autotrophes utilisant l'oxydation de composés inorganiques par
l'oxygène de l'air et dépourvus de pigments. Ces dernières espèces en effet n'ont
pu apparaître qu'après les autotrophes pourvus de chlorophylle grâce à la transformation de la bactériochlorophylle en chlorophylle vraie.

3. LES CONSÉQUENCES DE L'APPARITION D'OXYGÈNE LIBRE

La présence d'oxygène libre dans l'atmosphère devait avoir une répercussion
considérable sur la vie des organismes. Et tout d'abord son action a dû se faire
sentir sur les anaérobies, seuls êtres existant alors. Au début ce gaz se trouvait
dilué dans l'atmosphère riche en hydrogène et en CO_2 où croissaient les anaérobies primitifs. Ceux-ci purent continuer à croître. En effet Aubel, Rosenberg &
Manago-Grunberg [10] ont montré que ces bactéries se défendent en créant
autour d'elles une zone réductrice formée d'H_2 et de métabolites réducteurs.

Si la quantité d'oxygène est relativement faible, d'une part l'oxygène est
réduit par l'hydrogène, d'autre part il reste encore suffisament d'hydrogène et
de métabolites nécessaires aux synthèses et la croissance se produit.

L'arrêt des cultures des bactéries anaérobies est déterminé par la compétition
entre l'O_2 et les produits du métabolisme bactérien, en particulier l'H_2.

Lorsque la teneur de l'atmosphère en O_2 fut suffisament élevée, les anaérobies
se réfugièrent dans des endroits où les procès fermentatifs permettaient de lutter
contre l'accès de ce gaz ou s'adaptèrent les uns comme les bactéries pourpres
étudiées par Stanier et G. Cohen-Bazire [17] qui grâce au développement des
caroténoïdes de la cellule se protègent contre l'oxygène, les autres en se transformant en anaérobies facultatifs.

Nous allons nous arrêter un instant sur ces dernières bactéries. Ce qui caractérise un système respiratoire complet, comme cela existe chez les êtres aérobies c'est d'une part l'existence d'un cycle tricarboxylique découvert par Krebs [6], avec l'équipement enzymatique qu'il comporte, d'autre part la catalyse du transfert de l'hydrogène et des électrons par le système des cytochromes sur l'oxygène lui-même activé par la cytochrome oxydase, tout ceci étant associé avec la création de liaisons phosphates riches. Ce sont les phosphorylations oxydatives qui, comme on le sait, diffèrent des phosphorylations anaérobies pa le découplage spécifique que provoquent certains inhibiteurs comme les nitrophénols ou l'azide. Chez les anaérobies facultatifs, depuis le travail fondamental de Keilin [9] était signalé le fait que dans beaucoup de bactéries les bandes del cytochromes réduits différaient de celles observées dans la levure et les tissus des mammifères, de nombreux auteurs ont étudié la distribution de ces pigments en particulier chez les anaérobies facultatifs. On a ainsi vu que certaines espèces sont complètement dépourvues de cytochrome, ce qui à ce point de vue les rapproche des anaérobies stricts. C'est le cas des ferments lactiques. Alors que d'autres comme *Pseudomonas fluorescens* possèdent les cytochrome *a*, *b*, *c*, et *d*. Et entre ces cas extrêmes on rencontre les intermédiaires.

Il y a en outre deux faits intéressants: le premier, c'est que pour une espèce déterminée de nombreux auteurs ont observé avec les conditions de culture des variations qualitatives ou quantitatives de la teneur en cytochromes, en particulier la tension en oxygène paraît souvent jouer un rôle important dans le phénomène. Une variabilité et une sorte d'instabilité caractérisent donc l'équipement cytochromique des bactéries. Mais il y a plus, et c'est ce second point que je veux signaler, Lucile Smith [9] a montré l'absence de cytochrome oxydase typique *c* dans les bactéries; on ne la voit apparaître que dans la levure qui possède un équipement complet analogue à celui des tissus animaux. C'est que, ainsi qu'il résulte des travaux de Chance [9] sur la cinétique de la photodissociation des composés oxycarbonés des oxydases des divers organismes, il n'y a pas une cytochrome oxydase, mais une famille d'enzymes respiratoires qui ont une fonction enzymatique commune, mais diffèrent par leur structure chimique et leur mode d'action.

En ce qui concerne la levure ou le muscle cardiaque les choses sont claires, le substrat qui s'oxyde est le cytochrome *c* et l'enzyme provoquant l'oxydation, la cytochrome *c* oxydase.

En ce qui concerne les bactéries, les substrats sont encore sujet à discussion.

Avant d'en terminer avec cette question des cytochromes il y a lieu de rappeler les experiences de B. Ephrussi & Slonimski [14] sur la levure de boulangerie qui ont montré que la formation de cytochrome avait un caractère adaptatif conditionné par la présence d'oxygène. Cultivée en anaérobiose en présence de glucose il n'y a pas de synthèse des cytochromes, la resynthèse induite se faisant en présence d'oxygène.

Tout ce que je viens de dire concerne le transfert de l'hydrogène sur l'oxygène. Il reste à voir ce qui concerne l'apparition du cycle tricarboxylique.

On sait que ce cycle exige pour s'accomplir une série de systèmes enzymatiques fonctionnant en chaîne: Le 'condensing enzyme', l'aconitase, l'isocitrique déshydrogénase, l'oxalosuccinique décarboxylase, la cétoglutarique déshydrogénase, la succinodéshydrogénase, la fumarase et la malicodéshydrogénase. Comme nous l'avons fait pour les cytochromes il est intéressant d'étudier la répartition de ces enzymes dans les différents groupes. Chez les anaérobies stricts, que ce soient les anaérobies glucidolytiques ou les anaérobies protidolytiques, on a en somme peu de renseignements. Ceux que l'on possède conduisent à penser que les enzymes du cycle de Krebs sont absents ou douteux, même ceux intéressant les acides dicarboxyliques en C_4.

Chez les anaérobies facultatifs les conditions de culture influent considérablement sur l'équipement enzymatique. Le cas de *Escherichia coli* à ce sujet est intéressant parce qu'il a été bien étudié. Aubel *et al.* [11] avaient constaté que ce bacille cultivé en milieu faiblement aéré (donc pratiquement en anaérobiose si l'on considère l'épaisseur du liquide de culture et l'importance du dégagement do CO_2 et H_2) ne présente pas une respiration véritable. Les bactéries mises en suspension dans un tampon glucosé consomment de l'oxygène et dégagent du CO_2, mais cette respiration n'est pas catalysée par les acides en C_4, elle n'est pas inhibée par l'azoture de sodium (inhibiteur du système cytochromique), mais l'est par l'acide monoiodacetique (inhibiteur de la fermentation). Les auteurs concluaient que dans le cas examine il ne s'agissait pas d'une respiration véritable, mais d'un mécanisme fermentatif fonctionnant en présence d'oxygène, qui fixait l'hydrogène transporté vraisemblablement par les flavines, puisque, si l'on bloquait la catalase par le cyanure on pouvait mettre en évidence H_2O_2. Mais d'autre part Madame Manago-Grunberg & Gunsalus [12] montraient que si le même *Escherichia coli* cultivé en anaérobiose ne possédait pas de 'condensing enzyme' et peu de succinodéshydrogénase, on rencontrait ces deux enzymes en quantités importantes chez les bactéries si on les cultivait en milieu fortement aéré. Ce fait très important conduisait à admettre que le cycle tricarboxylique avait chez *Escherichia coli* un caractère adaptatif, l'adaptation étant conditionnée par l'oxygène. Et de fait Aubel & Prieur [12] montraient le rôle catalytique de l'acide citrique dans la respiration de *Escherichia coli* en présence d'acétate pour les bactéries cultivées en milieu aéré et l'absence de catalyse pour les bactéries cultivées en anaérobioses. Englesberg et ses collaborateurs Gibor & Levy [13] ont mis en évidence chez un autre anaérobie facultatif, *Pasteurella pestis*, la synthèse induite des enzymes du cycle tricarboxylique par l'oxygène.

Ainsi ces microorganismes cultivés en anaérobiose ont un équipement enzymatique qui les rapproche des anaérobies stricts; mais par la faculté qu'ils ont de synthétiser en présence d'air les enzymes du cycle tricarboxylique ils se rapprochent des aérobies. S'agit-il là d'un procès général commun à toutes les bactéries anaérobies facultatives? Les données que nous possédons à l'heure actuelle ne permettent pas de répondre à la question.

On peut encore rapprocher de ces faits l'observation de Hirsch et Slonimski [18] sur la levure qui cultivée en anaérobiose renferme bien les enzymes du cycle de Krebs, mais en quantité beaucoup plus faible qu'en aérobiose.

Certains anaérobies facultatifs du groupe des *Pseudomonas*, et de nombreuses souches de *Escherichia coli* possèdent un cycle tricarboxylique modifié. A la suite de la découverte chez *Escherichia coli* par Wong & Ajl [15] d'une malate synthétase qui synthétise le malate à partir de l'acétate et du glyoxalate, Korn-berg & Krebs [15] ont montré qu'à partir de l'isocitrate le cycle présentait une variante, au lieu d'acétoglutarate, il se forme du glyoxalate + du succinate. Ce dernier s'accumule, et le glyoxalate s'unissant à de l'acétate forme du malate qui donne de l'oxaloacétate. Ce cycle qui diffère donc du cycle classique dont nous avons parlé, et qui explique la synthèse de certains composés, à partir de l'acétate chez certains microorganismes a été retrouvé dans les graines de ricin où il joue un rôle dans la conversion des graisses en glucides.

Il faut remarquer que si dans le cycle classique, l'acétate est complètement oxydé en CO_2 et H_2O, ce qui représente un véritable procès respiratoire, dans le cycle de Kornberg-Krebs, l'acétate n'est pas oxydé, mais condensé en acide succinique, qui sert de précurseur à la synthèse de constituants cellulaires, il ne s'agit donc, plus, là, d'un véritable procès respiratoire.

Puisque chez les anaérobies facultatifs, le cycle tricarboxylique lorsqu'il existe a son apparition conditionnée par la présence d'oxygène, on devrait s'attendre à le trouver constamment chez les aérobies stricts. En fait sa présence est quasi générale mais pas absolue. Ainsi dans les acétobacters, les groupes peroxydans et oxydans le possèdent, vraisemblablement aussi le groupe mes-oxydans mais pas le suboxydans. Là encore se maintient une certaine varia-bilité, moins grande que chez les bactéries anaérobies facultatives. Il faut arriver aux levures et aux organismes supérieurs pour avoir un équipement tricarboxylique constant.

Nous pouvons donc en résumé proposer l'enchaînement évolutif suivant:

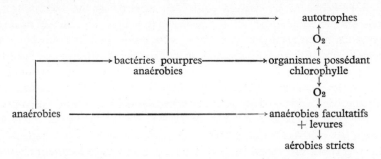

qui serait encore valable en ce qui concerne les phosphorylations oxydatives liées à la respiration. En effet si on a pu les mettre en évidence dans les hémolysats sanguins, les extraits de rein, de cerveau ou de coeur, ou de cellules de levure, dans les bactéries on a soit échoué, soit abouti à des résultats incertains. Pourtant Pinchot [16] chez *Alcaligenes faecalis*, aérobie strict, a pu les mettre en évidence.

Et ceci m'amène à parler des relations entre l'apparition de l'oxygène et le mode de dégradation oxydative du glucose ou plutôt du glucose-6-phosphate découvert par Warburg, Christian & Griese [6]. On sait grâce aux travaux de Dickens, Lipmann, Horecker, Racker [6] et d'autres que cette oxydation se fait suivant un cycle de 8 réactions centrées autour du ribose et aboutissant à la glycéraldehyde-3-phosphate en même temps que sont libérés du CO_2 et de l'hydrogène qui se fixe sur le TPN qui se transforme en TPNH + H^+. Ce cycle des pentoses phosphates se rencontre chez les animaux, les plantes et les microorganismes. Il n'existe pas chez les anaérobies stricts, mais on le rencontre parfois avec des variantes chez les anaérobies facultatifs (S. Cohen, Racker & Horecker [6]) et chez les aérobies. Il y a même des cas, par exemple celui de *Alcaligenes faecalis*, où ce mode d'oxydation du glucose a remplacé la dégradation fermentative.

CONCLUSIONS

La généralité des procès fermentatifs anaérobies permet de penser avec Haldane [3] qu'ils furent présents très tôt au cours de l'évolution de la matière vivante. On peut les considérer comme la base primitive des échanges de substances organiques fournissant l'énergie nécessaire à la vie. Plus tard ainsi que le dit Oparine [1], comme une superstructure greffée sur l'ancien mécanisme anaérobiotique, apparurent avec l'oxygène des systèmes permettant une utilisation meilleure de l'énergie libérable à partir des métabolites. Cette superstructure avait peut-être été préparée grâce à l'apparition d'un enzyme ou d'un système enzymatique permettant à partir du CO_2 alors seul présent dans l'atmosphère de se former un complexe du type de celui découvert par Ruben [7], réaction sombre qui constituerait pour certains le premier stade de la photosynthèse, et grâce aussi à l'acquisition par les bactéries pourpres qui vivaient dans des eaux sulfureuses de pigments permettant, en anaérobiose, la réduction du CO_2 par l'hydrogène sulfuré. Mais c'est l'apparition de la chlorophylle qui, permettant la photolyse de l'eau en libérant l'oxygène dans l'atmosphère, a bien été le saut qualitatif qui a modifié radicalement le procès d'utilisation de l'énergie des métabolites par les êtres vivants. On a vu que l'oxygène induit, chez certains microorganismes et la formation des enzymes du cycle tricarboxylique et la formation des cytochromes. On peut penser qu'il en est de même en ce qui concerne certains enzymes intéressant le cycle des pentoses chez les anaérobies facultatifs comme *Escherichia coli*. Mais cela est moins sûr, des expériences systématiques, de ce point de vue, n'ayant pas à ma connaissance été faites. Il serait intéressant à mon sens d'examiner ce problème comme cela a été fait pour les cytochromes ou les enzymes du cycle tricarboxylique. Cela permettrait de voir définitivement si, comme le pensent Krebs & Kornberg [6], le cycle des pentoses est apparu avant la photosynthèse ou s'il en est une conséquence.

L'argument que donnent ces auteurs est que la complexité des mécanismee biologiques a augmenté graduellement et que cela suggère l'apparition du cycle des pentoses avant la photosynthèse. Il suffirait en effet que se surajoute au cycle existant chez *Escherichia coli* peu de réactions complémentaires en particulier deux réactions, la transformation du ribose-5-phosphate en ribose 1 : 5-diphosphate et le clivage de ce dernier par CO_2 et H_2O pour donner deux molécules d'acide 3-phosphoglycérique. Il faudrait en outre ajouter la réaction propre au complexe photochimique. Mais l'aiguillage de la réaction à partir du glucose-6-phosphate vers l'acide 6-phosphogluconique exige la présence d'oxygène de même que la transformation de l'acide 6-phosphogluconique en ribulose-5-phosphate. En particulier la présence d'oxygène permet l'établissement d'un potentiel d'oxydoréduction égal ou supérieur à $E' = + 0,180$ v qui ainsi que

Engelhardt et Sakov l'ont établi supprime l'aiguillage vers le procès fermentatif du glucose. En outre, les anaérobies facultatifs comme *Escherichia coli* sont apparus et se sont adaptés évidemment après que l'oxygène eut été libéré dans l'atmosphère grâce à la photosynthèse, et à ma connaissance on ne trouve pas d'amorce du cycle des pentoses chez les anaérobies stricts. Tout ceci me conduit à penser qu'il s'agit d'un mécanisme apparu après la photosynthèse ou avec la photosynthèse.

BIBLIOGRAPHIE

1. A. I. OPARIN, *The Origin of Life*. Macmillan, New York (Republished by Dover Publications, 1953).
2. H. C. UREY, *The Planets*. Yale Univ. Press, New Haven, 1952.
3. J. B. S. HALDANE, The origin of life, *New Biology*, vol. 16. Penguin Books, London, 1954.
4. S. MILLER, *J. Amer. chem. Soc.*, **77**, 2351, 1955.
5. J. D. BERNAL, J. B. S. HALDANE, N. W. PIRIE & S. PRINGLE, *Une discussion sur l'origine de la vie*. Publication de l'Union rationaliste, Paris, 1955.
6. H. A. KREBS & H. L. KORNBERG, *Energy transformations in living matter*. Springer Verlag, Berlin, 1957.
7. E. RABINOWITCH, *Photosynthesis and Related Processes*. Interscience, New York, 1948.
8. C. B. VAN NIEL, *Cold Spr. Harb. Sym. quant. Biol.*, **3**, 138, 1935; *Bact. Rev.*, **8**, 1, 1944.
9. L. SMITH, *Bact. Rev.*, **18**, 106, 1954.
10. E. AUBEL, A. I. ROSENBERG & M. GRUNBERG, *Helv. chim. Acta*, **29**, 1267, 1945.
11. E. AUBEL, A. I. ROSENBERG & I. SZULMAJSTER, *Biochim. biophys. Acta*, **5**, 228, 1950.
12. E. AUBEL & P. PRIEUR, *C.R. Acad. Sci.*, Paris, **240**, 1945, 1955.
13. E. ENGLESBERG-LEVY, *J. Bact.*, **69**, 418, 1955.
14. B. EPHRUSSI & P. P. SLONIMSKI, *Biochim. biophys. Acta*, **6**, 256, 1950.
15. H. L. KORNBERG & H. A. KREBS, *Nature, Lond.*, **179**, 988, 1957.
16. G. B. PINCHOT, *J. biol. Chem.*, **205**, 65, 1953.
17. R. Y. STANIER & G. COHEN-BAZIRE, *Microbial Ecology*. Cambridge University Press, p. 56, 1957.
18. I. SLONIMSKI & H. HIRSCH, *C.R. Acad. Sci.*, Paris, **235**, 914, 1952.

Les compléments bibliographiques des auteurs cités dans le texte se trouvent dans les revues et dans les articles originaux référés ci-dessus.

Significance of Molecular Hydrogen Metabolism in the Transitionary Stage from Anaerobiosis to Aerobiosis

YOSHIHARU ODA

The Institute for Agricultural Research, Tohoku University, Sendai, Japan

INTRODUCTION

IT IS customary, when considering the chemical reactions which occur in living beings, to remark upon their versatility, their complexity, and that virtually all of them are catalytically induced by agents we call enzymes. As far as we know, enzymes are catalytic proteins.

To say that they are all proteins is perhaps a generalization, and some of them have now been isolated in the pure crystalline state. It has also been possible to build up trains or chains of enzyme reactions which reproduce *in vitro* some of the metabolic processes which occur in living beings.

But in the living beings, these enzyme systems do not function at random, but co-operate to bring about an organized chain of successive reactions, all directed to accomplishing the metabolic processes. It is fundamentally important to throw light on the organization and co-ordination of the enzyme systems in order to advance our understanding of this exceedingly dynamic aspect of the life process. But there has been a tendency that the organizing potentialities inherent in highly specific catalysts, enzymes, have not been adequately appraised in chemical thought.

We recently studied the problems of enzymic adaptation in micro-organisms to understand the dynamic mode and nature of enzyme systems in the living cells. In our studies [1, 2], it was found that control of events by intracellular enzymes in the living cell secures the status of the cell as a system which can maintain itself in dynamic equilibrium with its environment.

Here, the following question arises: how might the interrelated activity of enzyme systems with their environment—organization and co-ordination—have developed in the life process? In this connection, the activity of highly specific catalysts is a property left in the line of evolution and represents a notable device of Nature which has supported during the long course of biological evolution those dynamic manifestations which characterize living things. One of the basic problems of the activity of enzyme systems is the historical course of its development.

From the above standpoint, we have studied the significance of molecular hydrogen metabolism for comparative physiology for several years. A survey of the occurrence of hydrogen metabolism in micro-organisms discloses that the ability to evolve or utilize H_2 is not a restricted metabolic potentiality but rather that this type of activity is found in a large number of organisms of widely different physiological types. This fact does not only suggest that H_2 metabolism represents a fundamental aspect of microbial physiology, but that the deliberate study of it forms the basis for an approach to the comparative biochemistry of electron pathways.

In this report, the author will discuss particularly the significance of molecular hydrogen metabolism in the transitionary stage from anaerobiosis to aerobiosis.

STAGE OF ANAEROBIOSIS

The ability to evolve or utilize H_2—the reaction of hydrogenase system—appears to be mainly restricted to strict and facultative anaerobic micro-organisms. In the facultative anaerobes hydrogenase system occurs only in anaerobic culture conditions [3, 4]. Also in the photosynthetic micro-organisms such as green algae *Scenedesmus* [5], and *Rhodospirillum rubrum* [6], photochemical H_2 production occurs only after an extended dark anaerobic adapatation period. From these facts, it may be inferred that the ability to evolve or utilize H_2 has developed in the stage of anaerobic heterotrophy in which primitive living beings lived depending on the primary organic substances, produced in the regions of ancient sea physico-chemically, rather than by living beings. It is known that in this ancient stage, O_2 gas was not present in the atmosphere. Accordingly these primitive living beings could bring about energy-yielding reactions by anaerobic fermentations, and utilize the energy liberated from these processes for life processes.

A survey of the types of carbohydrate metabolism in present living beings shows their versatility and their complexity. It is now known that there are various types of fermentation processes such as lactic acid, alcohol, propionic acid, *Clostridium* type and *Escherichia-Salmonella* type of fermentations in reference to the varieties of end products shown in Scheme 1.

SCHEME 1

The versatility of fermentation types

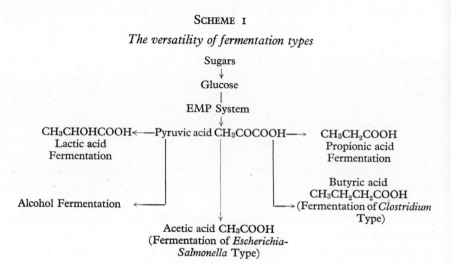

Sugars
↓
Glucose
|
EMP System
↓

CH₃CHOHCOOH ← Pyruvic acid CH₃COCOOH → CH₃CH₂COOH
Lactic acid   Propionic acid
Fermentation   Fermentation

                                    Butyric acid
                                    CH₃CH₂CH₂COOH
Alcohol Fermentation ←   → (Fermentation of *Clostridium*
                                           Type)
              Acetic acid CH₃COOH
         (Fermentation of *Escherichia-*
                Salmonella Type)

But the fact that the main path of those various types corresponds to the glycolytic system of Embden–Meyerhof–Parnas (EMP system) without exception indicates that each of them has been generated in close association with each other. This EMP system which is universally distributed in living cells is the fundamental metabolic system, forming the basis for development not only of the fermentation process but also of photosynthetic and respiratory processes. These observations indicate that though there are certain traits of similarity and a wide array of differences among metabolic systems, a fundamental unity exists in all life processes.

The primordial form of EMP system that may have been present in the more primitive living units is not found in the present living beings as a 'living fossil', and what type the primordial form may have been cannot now be speculated on and is unknown as far as we know. But when the various types of present fermentation processes are compared with each other, it is to a certain extent possible to speculate which type is original or derived—that is, primitive or recent.

Prof. Oparin considered instability, heterogeneity and low level of energy efficiency in the fermentation type as the reflection of its primitivity, the most primitive living things probably carrying out energy-yielding reaction by the *Clostridium* type of fermentation. And he concluded that alcohol or lactic acid fermentation is a more highly developed type than this.

An important process in the *Clostridium* type of fermentation is the so-called 'phosphoroclastic' reaction which occurs in saccharolytic clostridia [7, 8].

$$CH_3 \cdot CO \cdot COOH + H_3PO_4 \rightarrow (C)_3 \text{ compound} \rightarrow CH_3 \cdot CO \cdot OPO_3H_2 + CO_2 + H_2$$

In lactic acid or alcohol fermentation, electrons which are activated by dehydrogenation during the EMP process are transferred to pyruvate or acetaldehyde, that is, the intermediates in this process act as the ultimate acceptor and thus lactic acid or alcohol is produced. But on the other hand, in the clostridial type of fermentation, activated electrons are transferred to the hydrogenase system besides the intermediates as the ultimate acceptor and molecular hydrogen is evolved, being liberated by acetaldehyde dehydrogenation.

In homolactic acid fermentation, two molecules of high-energy phosphate are formed by the fermentation of one molecule of glucose, but in the clostridial type of fermentation one or more high-energy phosphates are formed in only the process of pyruvate decomposition. Therefore, the latter fermentation type is higher than the former in point of energy efficiency level.

The H_2-evolving reaction from pyruvate is inhibited by CN and CO radicals which are typical inhibitors of enzymes containing heavy metals as the active centre [9], but the CO inhibition cannot be reversed by light [10]. Furthermore, the author and colleagues [10] have recently demonstrated that the hydrogenase system may contain a metalloflavoprotein, which is not a typical haem protein. In the *Clostridium* type of fermentation, there is found an enzyme system containing heavy metal and more developed than that of homolactic acid fermentation. It is also very interesting that in the presence of metal-complexing agents such as cyanide, CO, the fermentation of glucose results mainly in lactic acid as opposed to the formation of H_2, CO_2 and volatile acids by uninhibited cells. The same result can also be achieved by controlling the metal nutrition of this organism; thus, cells from a medium rich in iron ferment glucose to C_2, CO_2 and volatile acids, while those from a medium deficient in iron carry out lactic acid fermentation. All these observations show that in some organisms of the clostridial group, butyric acid fermentation can potentially be switched back to the lactic acid fermentation by environmental conditions [9].

Thus, in opposition to Prof. Oparin's opinion, it may be inferred that homolactic acid fermentation is a more primitive one than the clostridial type of fermentation and that the latter has developed secondarily from the former, acquiring new metabolic systems additively. The new enzyme system that played the important role in this transition from the former to the latter was the hydrogenase system itself. Thus it follows that the fact that fermentation types containing the hydrogenase system were unstable and heterogeneous might be a factor in development of their versatility and their complexity inherent to the fermentation types in present living beings.

Next, the hydrogenase system has played an important role in raising the level of energy-yielding efficiency of fermentation types, by linking with pyridine nucleotide coenzyme systems (DPN, TPN) which were hydrogen carriers participating in the process of EMP system. The diverse types of fermentations that occur in present living beings have developed due to the fact that the electrons released in a series of dehydrogenation reactions could be transferred to a variety of intermediates and to the hydrogenase system as the ultimate acceptors, and that frequently several alternative routes were possible. In a number of fermentation processes, the end products are qualitatively or quantitatively related with the alternative paths of hydrogen transfer and their balance sheet. These facts are not only inherent in the strict anaerobes such as *Clostridium*, but also in facultative anaerobes such as the *coli-aerogenes* group, when they are adapted to anaerobic conditions, which are to be considered as a pre-stage in their evolutionary line.

From several points of view, it is convenient to consider the level of hydrogenase activity as the factor which controls the channelling of electrons into possible alternative routes in the stage of anaerobiosis. In this sense, the hydrogenase system can be considered as a substitute for cytochrome oxidases which have thus far not been detected in the strict anaerobes, and it is not only the actual controlling factor but a leaking system which enables the organism to discard excess electrons.

BIOLOGICAL REDUCTION

As the results of anaerobic fermentation by the primitive living beings, CO_2 and H_2 gases were evolved and gradually accumulated on the surface of the Earth. Thereupon, the living beings became able to acquire the new capacity of activating molecular hydrogen directly. In other words, the hydrogenase system which had been concerned solely with accommodating electrons during the fermentation process as molecular hydrogen, came to activate H_2 reversely and transfer it to various hydrogen acceptors, as the partial pressure of hydrogen in the environment gradually increased. Thus, the hydrogenase system came to play a new important role as reductant in biological reduction systems.

The hydrogenase system in some *Clostridium* spp. cannot utilize methylene blue as a hydrogen acceptor, but does utilize methylviologen having a low redox potential. But some of the strict anaerobes (*Micrococcus lactilyticus* [11]) and the facultative anaerobes (*coli-aerogenes* group) can utilize methylene blue as a hydrogen acceptor. Thus, the redox potential of the biological reduction system gradually shifted towards higher levels during the course of biological evolution.

A series of metabolic processes involving the hydrogenase system do not only liberate molecular hydrogen from carbohydrates and organic nitrogen compounds, but also can reduce various types of intermediates by activating molecular hydrogen that has been evolved during the fermentation process. Though it appears that there are various organic compounds from which molecular hydrogen is evolved in the fermentation process; the principle of the hydrogen-evolving processes is essentially the same mechanism that evolved molecular hydrogen from the C_2 compound, and it is fundamentally the H_2-evolving process from pyruvate in *Clostridium butyricum*, mentioned above.

Curiously, various types of organisms employ the same general mechanisms, the same pathways, and hence must have similar metabolic processes. In short, all life is alike in spite of differences which are 'in reality' minor, and at the same time each organism, or group of organisms, differs very markedly because the line of biological evolution has exploited diverse principles.

On the other hand CO_2, which was evolved with H_2 into the environment, enables the living beings to acquire the new ability to assimilate CO_2. Thus, the stage of heterotrophic CO_2 assimilation originated on the Earth. The process that was investigated in detail among the CO_2 assimilation processes of heterotrophs is the following reductive β-carboxylation.

$$\text{pyruvate} + CO_2 + \begin{matrix} \text{TPNH} \\ \text{or} \\ \text{DPNH} \end{matrix} \rightleftharpoons \text{malate} + \begin{matrix} \text{TPN} \\ \text{or} \\ \text{DPN} \end{matrix}$$

The equilibrium point of this reaction is far over to the left, and consequently it is necessary to reproduce DPNH (TPNH) by other processes in order to assimilate the CO_2 progressively in this reaction. It is apparent that this reaction may proceed *in vitro* by coupling the following reaction.

$$\text{DPN(TPN)} + \text{glucose 6-phosphate} \rightleftharpoons$$
$$\text{DPNH(TPNH)} + \text{gluconate 6-phosphate}$$

It is likely that reduction of the pyridine nucleotide coenzyme systems has an important significance for the mechanism of electron transport in all types of CO_2 reduction processes. From the existence of the hydrogen-evolving process as reductant it may be inferred that the generation of electrons (reducing power) occurs in a reaction characterized by a redox potential well below those of the pyridine nucleotide coenzyme systems, and that these coenzymes are probably not reduced by primary acts. In this connection, it is tempting to speculate that the carriers involved in the early stages of electron transport in CO_2 assimilation may be similar to those participating in the phosphoroclastic reaction of the clostridia and in decomposition of formate by the hydrogenlyase complex that will be discussed later.

While CO_2 and H_2 were evolved by the activities of anaerobic heterotrophs, N_2 gas and sulphate also gradually accumulated on the surface of the Earth, and the new ability of assimilating N_2 gas was born in the kingdom of living beings. But this ability may have developed in association with heterotrophic CO_2 assimilating process, and both processes may be essentially the same, in spite of the difference in the utilization of either CO_2 or H_2 as the ultimate hydrogen acceptor. Accordingly, it may be inferred that in the N_2 fixation process which occurs in some of the clostridia, the systems participating in the phosphoroclastic reaction also play the important role in electron transport.

As sulphate gradually accumulated and the new ability to activate molecular hydrogen developed, sulphate came to be reduced by molecular hydrogen in the environment and, as the results, sulphide and elementary sulphur gradually accumulated. Thus, the so-called stage of chemoreduction [12] came to develop on the Earth.

Furthermore, as heterotrophic CO_2 assimilation and chemical reduction proceeded actively, CO_2 began to be deficient in the atmosphere and its partial pressure became lower. Accordingly, the visible parts of the solar spectrum reached the surface of the Earth and made possible the appearance of the assimilative pigments which participate in the CO_2 assimilation by light in living beings. In this way the so-called stage of photoreduction [12], that is, the metabolic patterns of assimilation of CO_2 by utilizing radiant energy came to develop. As the living beings acquired these pigments and the capacity to react with light, photochemical processes appeared in the kingdom of living beings. Some living beings that lived in the stage of chemoreduction substituted some parts of their chemoreduction systems in CO_2 assimilation process for the photochemical reduction systems by acquiring new assimilative pigments. The photosynthetic reaction liberating oxygen is a process in association with photochemical reduction, and the former can be reversely transformed to the latter in proper conditions. Thus it may be inferred that photosynthesis developed on the basis of photochemical reduction. In the so-called 'photoheterotrophs' such as sulphur purple and nonsulphur purple bacteria, photochemical H_2 production appears only after an extended dark anaerobic adaptation period. In addition, a rapid production of H_2 by illumination occurs in the presence of suitable organic substrates, when the atmosphere surrounding the organisms does not contain O_2, N_2; it is also inhibited by NH_4^+ [6]. Furthermore, photosynthetic autotrophs such as Scenedesmus slowly produce H_2 in the dark and, at a relatively rapid rate, upon illumination. But this metabolic pattern also appears only after an extended dark anaerobic adaptation period. Once the organism is adapted, it is not only capable of photochemical H_2 production but can also reduce CO_2 with H_2 either photosynthetically or by a dark chemoautotrophic process, in which the energy for CO_2 assimilation is derived from the oxidation of H_2 with O_2. The latter type of oxidation is the energy source for growth of autotrophic hydrogen bacteria [15]. Frenkel & Rieger [13] have recently shown that numerous other species of green, blue-green, red and brown algae can utilize H_2 for the photochemical reduction of CO_2. As mentioned above, photosynthesis can be reversely transformed to photochemical reduction by adequate anaerobic conditions. From these observations photochemical reduction may be the more universal metabolic pattern and forms the basis of the photosynthetic process. Here again, the direct precursor of H_2 in the light-dependent process is unknown; it seems quite possible that water may not be the immediate source, but rather that H_2 is evolved from organic intermediates such as pyruvate by mechanisms similar to those operating in H_2-producing heterotrophs which was discussed before. The light dependency may, in a certain sense, be secondary, that is, light could be required for the generation of an organic precursor which is subsequently oxidized in a dark reaction, electrons being transferred to the hydrogenase system. With CO_2, however, H_2 is not utilized unless light of the proper wavelengths is supplied. When CO_2 is the ultimate oxidant, light may be obligatory for the generation of oxidized acceptors which are reduced by H_2 in subsequent dark reactions.

It is likely that photoproduction of H_2 has a fundamental significance for the mechanism of electron transport in all types of photosynthetic reactions. From the very existence of light-dependent H_2 evolution, it may be inferred that the photochemical generation of electrons, that is, reducing power, occurs in a reaction characterized by a redox potential well below those of the pyridine nucleotide coenzyme systems and that those coenzymes are probably not 'reduced' by primary acts.

Accordingly, it is tempting to speculate that the carriers involved in the early stage of electron transport in photosynthesis as well as in heterotrophic CO_2 reduction may be essentially similar to those participating in the phosphoroclastic reaction of *Clostridium* spp. and in decomposition of formate by the *coli-aerogenes* group.

Concerning the photochemical CO_2 assimilation, it is very interesting that the photosynthetic micro-organisms mostly have the ability of nitrogen fixation [6, 14]. These facts show that the N_2 reduction process has developed in connection with the CO_2 reduction process, and that both processes have been maintained without separation even in the transition from the utilization of chemical energy to that of radiant energy. Here again it is emphasized that a fundamental unity exists in all living forms, and life possesses its limitations as well as its organizing potentialities in biochemical planning.

Thus, the evolution of metabolic systems that originated from anaerobic heterotrophs has developed to the direction of autotrophy and it has led to the appearance of photosynthetic living beings that is, of free O_2.

The very appearance of free O_2 became the basis for the luxuriant development of aerobic living beings.

TRANSITIONARY STAGE
FROM ANAEROBIOSIS TO AEROBIOSIS

It is first emphasized that the activity of the hydrogenase system shows definite sensitivity and instability to O_2 [15, 16]. In a species of lactic acid bacteria, *Lactobacillus casei*, which is a typical anaerobic fermenter, the metabolic system is not influenced by the presence of O_2. Inversely, the metabolic systems of *Clostridium* and the *coli-aerogenes* group containing the hydrogenase system, are inactivated or fail to be formed, in the presence of O_2. In short, the fact that the hydrogenase system is very unstable and easily inactivated by O_2 shows that it has some reactivity or affinity for O_2. According to our experiments, the hydrogenase system in cell-free preparation from *E. coli* and *Azotobacter chroococcum* that is inactivated by O_2 is autocatalytically reactivated when left in a hydrogen atmosphere, but not in a nitrogen atmosphere. When at first inactivated by shaking with O_2 beyond the time of threshold, it is not reactivated again even in a hydrogen atmosphere. It may be inferred that the inactivation of the hydrogenase system by O_2 is not due to oxidation but to combination with O_2, that is, to oxygenation like that of haemoglobin [15].

The oxidation of H_2 with ferricyanide or methylene blue as the hydrogen acceptor by the hydrogenase system in cell-free preparations was inhibited by CO, but the inhibition cannot be reversed by light. HCN partially inhibits the oxidation of H_2 with the dye only after preincubation with O_2 but not in a hydrogen atmosphere.

Accordingly, it may be conceivable that in this system the typical iron porphyrin component is not involved, but a heavy-metal component is a cofactor. As mentioned above, a flavin component might be involved in this system as evidenced by the spectrum studies, and so the system may be probably a flavoprotein containing heavy metal as a cofactor.

Next, it is very important that even in the facultative anaerobes such as *E. coli* the synthesis of the hydrogenase system occurs only upon cultivation in anaerobic conditions. In this connection it should be noted that the system in the strict anaerobes, such as *Clostridium*, is extracted almost completely in the soluble cell-free system, but in the facultative anaerobes, *E. coli*, it is partially bound to the insoluble particles and partially in the soluble state.

After anaerobic dialysis against water this concentrated soluble cell-free system from *E. coli* is capable of decomposing formate only after a prolonged induction period. This induction phase is markedly shortened or abolished when the dialysed extract is preincubated with boiled preparations from *E. coli*, *Cl. butyricum*, yeast or pigeon liver. Among the variety of purified potential cofactor tested, only pyruvate, diacetyl and acetyl phosphate were found to spark decomposition of formate by dialysed extracts. Furthermore, under proper conditions small quantities of pyruvate, diacetyl or acetyl phosphate are also capable of sparking decomposition of formate by the 'dilute' (inactive) *E. coli* extract but only in the presence of *Cl. butyricum* extract. The clostridium extract, which does not metabolize formate, appears to be required for converting the added cofactor to the actual sparking intermediate. All of the above observations strongly suggest the participation of C_2 derivatives in the decomposition of formate to CO_2 and H_2. On the basis of the available facts, Barkulis & Gest [17] have proposed two alternative mechanisms for the decomposition of formate, both employing C_2 derivatives as electron carriers (Scheme 2).

SCHEME 2

*Possible mechanisms of formate decomposition to H_2 and CO_2
(from Barkulis & Gest [17])*

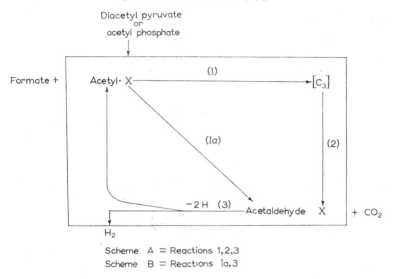

Scheme A = Reactions 1,2,3
Scheme B = Reactions Ia,3

According to scheme *A* (reaction 1, 2, 3), formate and an acetyl derivative are condensed to produce a C_3 compound, which is then decarboxylated yielding CO_2 and an acetaldehyde complex. The acetaldehyde compound is oxidized by transfer of electrons to the hydrogenase system, thereby leading to formation of H_2 and regeneration of acetyl X. This scheme implies that pyruvate decomposition to CO_2 and H_2 by *E. coli*, and *Cl. butyricum* may occur through the same pathway, that is, acetaldehyde-X $\rightleftharpoons$ acetyl-X. Scheme B postulates a direct dehydrogenation (decarboxylation) of formate with acetyl-X serving as the electron acceptor (reaction 1 a). Regeneration of acetyl-X and production of H_2 then occurs through reaction 3, as in scheme A. In short, the system in soluble cell-free preparation with hydrogenase system that degrades formate to CO_2 and H_2 is a primitive cyclic reaction where acetaldehyde-X $\rightleftharpoons$ acetyl-X is the basic catalytic mechanism, not metabolized and persisting as a more or less permanent part of the system.

In connection with reaction 3, in which acetaldehyde-X is oxidized to acetyl-X, the transfer of electrons to the hydrogenase system may not be obligatory. Thus, other oxidants such as methylene blue, or cytochrome system, could substitute for the hydrogenase pathway. Here, the system has exploited the appearance of a respiratory system such as the C_4-dicarboxylic acid system or the tricarboxylic acid cycle in the stage of aerobiosis through coupling with enzyme systems which condense the active C_2 derivative with various C compounds, and the cytochrome system in insoluble particulate particles.

On the other hand, the hydrogenase system bound to the particulate fraction became able to utilize various hydrogen acceptors such as O_2, NO_3^- in the oxidation of H_2 by linkage with the cytochrome system bound to the particles. The soluble hydrogenase system can utilize methylene blue as electron acceptor, but neither O_2 nor NO_3^-. It was originally suggested by Yamagata & Nakamura [18] that the reduction of acceptors by H_2 requires several carriers and enzymes, as indicated by the schematic sequence below.

$$H_2 \longrightarrow \text{Intermediary Carriers} \longrightarrow \text{Acceptors}$$

↓	↓	↓
Hydrogenase	X H_2	Specific Acceptor Enzymes

Thus, the hydrogenase system has developed to couple with enzyme systems bound to particulate particles, and particularly its linking with the cytochrome system has exploited the important principles of O_2 utilization, that is, the attainment of higher energy efficiency. Furthermore, it acquired the abilities to reduce fumarate, NO_3^-, SO_3, and O_2 as electron acceptors. In this way the development of special living beings possessing the particular systems which assimilate CO_2 chemoautotrophically by the energy liberated in the oxidation of H_2 with SO_3 or O_2 has occurred on the Earth.

But these mechanisms are essentially similar to those of photosynthetic reaction only with the exception of substitution of the oxidation of inorganic substances, for the photochemical reaction.

Accordingly, it may be inferred that various fermentation, photosynthetic, and respiratory processes were formed on the basis of the process of EMP system and are related to each other. And here, again, it is evident that there are certain types of similarity and a wide array of differences among organisms.

STAGE OF AEROBIOSIS

The best example of this type is the non-symbiotic N_2-fixing organism, *Azotobacter*. This strictly aerobic organism contains a powerful hydrogenase system which does not oxidize nor produce H_2 during normal metabolism. The system is formed particularly when *Azotobacter* is grown under conditions where it is restricted to use N_2 as the nitrogen source [19]. Cultivation in media containing ammonium salts or other fixed nitrogen compounds causes a marked depression of the hydrogenase system content. This observation suggests a close relationship between H_2 metabolism and N_2 fixation. A striking apparent contradiction is found in the competitive inhibition of N_2 fixation by H_2 in spite of the fact that the hydrogenase system is present only under N_2 fixing conditions [20]. There is clear-cut competitive inhibition in *Azotobacter* and symbiotic N-fixing organisms, but none with the anaerobic *Clostridia* and photosynthetic bacteria [6, 21]. In this connection, it is also important how the hydrogenase system which is inherently unstable to O_2 has developed to acquire stability against O_2 in aerobosis through the transitionary stage from anaerobiosis to aerobiosis.

To understand these problems the hydrogenase system from *Azotobacter* was compared with those from *Cl. pasteurianum* and *E. coli*. It appears from our studies that in the former practically all of the enzyme system is bound to the insoluble particulate fraction, being different from those systems in the latter organism. Spectroscopic studies of the particles have disclosed a new haemo-protein (cytochrome 552) with absorption peaks at 415 mμ (γ-band), 524 mμ (β-band), 552 mμ (α-band) in the reduced state, and absorption peaks at 390 mμ, 450 mμ characteristic for flavin in the oxidized state. This spectral change may conceivably be associated with the hydrogenase system itself, but more likely it is due to indirect reduction of a distantly related porphyrin enzyme. Thus the hydrogenase enzyme itself probably is a flavoprotein and may be able to oxidize H_2 with O_2 through a cytochrome system as intermediate hydrogen carrier. This oxidation of H_2 with O_2, that is the oxyhydrogen reaction, occurs actively only when the system is bound to the particles. It is very interesting that a partial pressure of over 5% O_2 in the atmosphere causes a marked depression in the oxyhydrogen reaction catalysed by the particulate system. This fact shows that the characters owing to which the hydrogenase system is essentially sensitive and unstable for O_2 have been maintained even when it has developed from anaerobiosis to aerobiosis.

But when the system becomes coupled with the succinic oxidase system in the particulate fraction, it is very stable for the partial pressure of O_2 in the atmosphere. From several points of view, it may be inferred that the hydro-genase system has differentiated morphologically from the soluble state to the particle-bound state, and functionally from a simple system to a complex one by coupling with other enzyme systems bound to particles in compliance with the environmental changes, that is, particularly with the appearance of O_2 on the Earth.

In this connection, in order to understand qualitative differences between the aerobic and anaerobic N_2-fixing bacteria in the interaction of N_2 reduction and hydrogenase system the following tentative mechanism can be proposed:

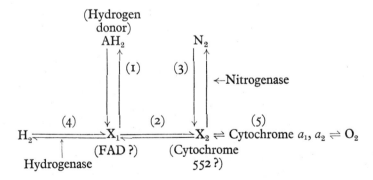

In the diagram, X_1 and X_2 are tentative components, which may take part in electron transport. Particularly X_1 is inferred to be also concerned with the

N_2-fixation mechanism. In anaerobic N_2-fixing bacteria such as *Cl. pasteurianum* O_2 cannot be utilized and so the maintenance of the reduced state for N_2 reduction, that is, the reduction of X_1, X_2, occurs by reactions (1), (4) of the diagram, resulting in the evolution of molecular hydrogen. The equilibrium of the hydrogenase system is far over to the side of H_2 evolution, and so there is no effect of H_2 on anaerobic N_2 fixation. On the contrary, in aerobic N_2-fixing bacteria such as *Azotobacter*, the reduced state for N_2 reduction is kept reversely by oxidative reactions (1), (2), (5) which onesidedly transfer electrons from hydrogen donors to O_2 through the powerful respiratory process characteristic of this microbe. It is very surprising that it has the most powerful respiration capacity in the kingdom of living beings, respiring 10 times as vigorously as ordinary microbes.

Accordingly, it may be inferred that the hydrogenase system is not directly concerned with nitrogen fixation, but may have the function of keeping other enzymes or intracellular hydrogen donors in the active reduced state. And its presence may indicate that X_1, X_2 are constantly kept in the reduced state. Therefore, in the presence of molecular hydrogen in the atmosphere, reaction (1) is depressed by the rapid proceeding of reactions (4), (2), (5), and N_2 fixation is inhibited by blocking of the acceptor system of the fixed nitrogen compound.

In this connection, it was actually demonstrated that even in the cells of *Azotobacter* grown in conditions excluding N_2 fixation, a complete synthesis of the hydrogenase system was observed upon anaerobic incubation in the proper conditions.

Thus, in aerobic *Azotobacter*, a striking contradiction is involved between the development of energy efficiencies by the utilization of O_2 and the difficulties in maintenance of reducing power for N_2 reduction. It is very interesting that the succinic oxidase system in *Azotobacter* has no cytochrome c–cytochrome c oxidase system and not the saturation point of O_2 pressure for its activity, differing from the system of the strict aerobes.

These facts show that *Azotobacter* may be closely related to the group of facultative anaerobes.

On the basis of the observations mentioned above, it is conceivable that the hydrogenase system has played an important role in the various biological reductions as the reductant of lowest potential in the stage of anaerobiosis.

But because of the remarked contradictions between the acquisition of potencies for O_2 utilization and the role of reducing agent in biological reductions the hydrogenase system could not universally be distributed among the strict aerobes, probably losing the specificities of H_2 evolution and activation inherent to this system in the line of biological evolution. But the flavoprotein that is inherent to the system has played a role for the appearance of the highly organized respiratory process as the electron-transporting system linking pyridine nucleotide coenzyme systems with the cytochrome system, and now does so as an important electron carrier in the present respiratory process.

In conclusion, in this report an attempt has been made to understand the significance of molecular hydrogen metabolism in the transitionary stage from anaerobiosis to aerobiosis in the line of biological evolution. This proposition should certainly serve as a sufficient challenge to provide further tests of the principle, and thus whatever their outcome, to advance our understanding of this exceedingly important aspect of life process.

Acknowledgment.—The author is indebted to his colleagues, Drs K. Obata, M. Yoneda, T. Masuda and M. Higuchi, for stimulating discussions which were very helpful in the development of this report.

REFERENCES

1. Y. ODA, *Biol. Sci. (Japan)*, **2**, 151, 1950.
2. Y. ODA, *Biol. Sci. (Japan)*, **3**, 26, 1951.
3. D. BILLEN & H. C. LICHSTEIN, *J. Bact.*, **61**, 515, 1951.
4. X. OBATA, M. YONEDA & Y. ODA. Unpublished.
5. H. GAFFRON & J. RUBIN, *J. gen. Physiol.*, **26**, 219, 1942.
6. H. GEST, *Bact. Rev.*, **15**, 183, 1951.
7. H. J. KOEPSELL & M. L. JOHNSON, *J. biol. Chem.*, **145**, 379, 1942.
8. J. WILSON, L. O. KRAMPITZ & C. H. WERKMAN, *Biochem. J.*, **42**, 598, 1948.
9. W. KEMPNER & F. KUBOWITZ, *Biochem. J.*, **265**, 245, 1933.
10. Y. ODA & T. MASUDA. Unpublished.
11. A. T. JOHNS, *J. gen. Microbiol.*, **5**, 326, 1951.
12. D. I. SAPOZHNIKOV, *Mikrobiologiya*, **20**, 439, 1951.
13. A. W. FRENKEL & C. RIEGER, *Nature, Lond.*, **167**, 1030, 1951.
14. E. S. LINDSTROM, S. M. LEWIS & M. J. FINSKY, *J. Bact.*, **61**, 481, 1951.
15. Y. ODA & T. MASUDA, *Symposium of Enzyme Chemistry (Japan)*, **10**, 69, 1954.
16. H. GUEST, *Phosphorus Metabolism* (Ed. by William D. McElroy and Bentley Glass), Vol. **2**, 552, 1952.
17. S. S. BARKULIS & H. GEST, *Biochim. biophys. Acta*, **11**, 306, 1953.
18. S. YAMAGATA & H. NAKAMARA, *Acta Phytochim.*, Tokyo, **10**, 297, 1956.
19. S. B. LEE & P. W. WILSON, *J. biol. Chem.*, **151**, 377, 1943.
20. O. WYSS & P. W. WILSON, *Proc. nat. Acad. Sci.*, Wash., **27**, 162, 1941.
21. E. D. ROSENBLUM & O. W. WILSON, *J. Bact.*, **59**, 83, 1950.

Development of the Mode of Action of the Photocatalytic System in Organisms

A. A. KRASNOVSKIĬ

A. N. Bakh Institute of Biochemistry, U.S.S.R. Academy of Sciences, Moscow

FORMATION OF PHOTOCATALYSTS

AT PRESENT most plausible are those hypotheses which attribute the metabolism of primary organisms to the assimilation of organic substances of abiogenic origin [1]. Such organic compounds are sufficiently stable in usual conditions; the activation of their transformation in living organisms could, in general, have been achieved catalytically or photochemically. However, 'light' activation is of advantage when there is need for energy 'storage', by conversion of the energy of light quanta into the potential chemical energy of photoproducts.

Processes thermodynamically spontaneous are efficiently activated catalytically; present-day heterotrophic organisms extensively activate substrates by catalysis. We may suppose that in utilizing energy-rich abiogenic organic compounds, primary organisms employed a simple catalytic mode of activation, the more so since they inevitably must have absorbed catalytically active substances from the environment. Probably the primary biocatalysts were complexes of amino acids, proteins, and porphyrins with metal ions or oxides, which are readily absorbed and bound by these substances. Complexes of metals with proteins, amino acids, and porphyrins could have ensured manifold 'dark' catalytic transformations of organic substances, without the aid of 'light' activation. This type of biocatalyst is still predominant in organisms: iron, copper, manganese, zinc, molybdenum, cobalt, and many other metals are essential components of enzymic systems.

Apart from the concentration of the elements and their compounds in the Earth's crust, several other factors were probably important in the 'selection' and absorption of inorganic compounds from the surrounding medium. Among these factors were: the solubility of the compounds of an element in the biosphere [2], its catalytic action in different complexes, the co-ordination number of bound metal atoms, etc.

It would be interesting to trace the possible stages in the formation of photocatalytically active pigments, and the changes in the mechanism of action of the pigment system in the course of evolution from primary heterotrophs to the autotrophic mode of life. But, unfortunately, in such an enquiry we cannot draw upon reliable palaeobotanic data; the most ancient known types of organ-

606

isms, photosynthetic bacteria and the blue-green algae, possess a fully developed pigment system containing chlorophylls, phycobilins and carotenoids.

Complex compounds of porphyrins are widespread among biocatalysts and pigments; the nature of the central metal atom is of great importance, determining many properties of the complex.

The most abundant elements in the Earth's crust [2] are: O (49·4%), Si (27·8%), Al (8·5%), Fe (5·0%), Ca (3·5%), K (2·5%), Na (2·6%), Mg (2%), and Ti (0·6%).

Porphyrins with Si, Al, or Ti in the centre of the molecule have not been found in organisms. One of the reasons for this is probably the low solubility of the compounds of these elements in the biosphere and, hence, the difficulty of their utilization by organisms.

Porphyrins containing potassium, sodium, or calcium undergo hydrolysis in aqueous media, the metal atom being replaced by atoms of hydrogen [3]; of the metals listed above, there remain, therefore, only Fe and Mg, porphyrin complexes of which are widespread in organisms.

The iron complexes possess diverse catalytic properties and a low photochemical activity; they do not exhibit fluorescence. Magnesium, hydrogen or zinc in the centre of the molecule give rise to complexes that are inactive catalytically, but extremely active photochemically, and exhibit bright fluorescence. Is there, however, really such a sharp distinction between the catalytically and photochemically active complexes? Probably there could have been transition types in the process of evolution from 'dark' to 'light' metabolism; this leads us to the question whether the activity of biocatalysts is affected by light. In other words, do biocatalytically active complexes also have a photosensitizing action?

Many biocatalysts are coloured compounds, i.e. they absorb light in the visible region of the spectrum. This applies to the porphyrin complexes, to flavins, and other compounds. The amount of biocatalysts in organisms is usually small, and they absorb only a small portion of the solar radiation falling upon the organism.

There is a vast but often contradictory literature about the effects of visible light on enzyme activity. Light has a particularly pronounced effect on the transformations of free flavins, which possess a bright fluorescence and photosensitizing action; however, the action of light on flavin–protein complexes in organisms requires further elucidation.

We have recently reported on the accelerating effect of visible light on the oxidation–reduction changes of cytochrome [4]. Earlier we found that light exerted an influence on reactions catalysed by crystalline analogues of the porphyrins, the phthalocyanins and their copper or magnesium complexes. These compounds have a catalytic effect on the oxidation of ascorbic acid and the decomposition of hydrogen peroxide in solution; illumination accelerates the catalytic reaction [5]. Illumination also accelerates the decomposition of hydrogen peroxide and the oxidation of fatty acids catalysed by TiO_2 [6]. The known biocatalysts are usually (with the exception of the flavins) rather poor photosensitizers; in a number of cases light can have an influence on their action, but there is no energy storage in the end products of the reaction.

The further development of photocatalytic systems made a specialization of functions necessary between biocatalysts (enzymes) and photosensitizers (pigments).

DEVELOPMENT OF THE PIGMENT SYSTEM

Unlike the biocatalysts, which act in very small amounts, pigments must be present in autotrophic organisms in much greater quantities so as to ensure sufficiently complete absorption of solar radiation by the organism, and the storage of light energy in the form of potential chemical energy of the reaction products.

A small amount of sensitizing pigment, comparable to the amount of enzymes, would suffice only if the sensitizing pigment initiated a thermodynamically spontaneous chain process, with the multiple utilization of light quantum energy to overcome potential barriers; however, we know of no types of metabolism utilizing chain processes: in all known types of metabolism multistage conjugated reactions are predominant.

The possible absorption of small quantities of porphyrins of abiogenic origin would not ensure any appreciable absorption of light by the organism. For the transition to autotrophy the organism would have to be able to synthesize pigments on a big scale. The vigorous biosynthesis of porphyrins, in turn, calls for an elaborate system of metabolism. These considerations are in accord with A. I. Oparin's ideas about photoautotrophy having arisen on the basis of a fully developed heterotrophic system of metabolism [1].

The primary photosensitizers could have been porphyrins formed in the line of biosynthesis of the iron-porphyrin biocatalysts. For instance, the most ancient type of photoautotrophs, the photosynthesizing bacteria, have been found to contain considerable amounts of free porphyrins [8] in addition to bacteriochlorophyll and iron porphyrins [7].

However, the simple porphyrins have an absorption spectrum which does not ensure sufficiently full utilization of the entire visible region of solar radiation. The long-wave absorption maximum of the porphyrins is at about 620 mμ; the value of the molar extinction coefficient (K_m) in this maximum, which determines the 'dyeing powers', i.e., the probability of absorption of light quanta, is low as compared with the K_m in the Soret band, situated at about 400 mμ. In the reducing medium of the ancient biosphere still devoid of free oxygen, there existed primordial photosynthetic bacteria. It is not surprising, therefore, that these organisms contain the most reduced form of porphyrin pigment, bacteriochlorophyll, with both the 'semi-isolated' double bonds hydrogenated. The absorption maximum of the bacteriochlorophyll thus formed lies in the near infrared region of the spectrum.

The possibility of such photoreduction of porphyrin is demonstrated by our model experiments in collaboration with K. K. Voĭnovskaya. It has been found that the porphyrins of bacteria [8] and haematoporphyrin [9], upon illumination without air in the presence of reducing agents, are indeed capable of forming photoproducts possessing the absorption spectrum of bacteriochlorin (with a maximum at about 750 mμ).

The subsequent evolution of pigments took the course of formation of chlorophyll as the 'main' pigment. The high concentration of chlorophyll in the granules of the plastids of present-day organisms ensures sufficiently complete absorption in the visible region of the solar spectrum.

The question arises as to what accounts for the widespread occurrence of magnesium complexes (chlorophyll), considering that metal-free porphyrins also have a photosensitizing action? Evidently we must take account of the following circumstances. The presence of a central magnesium atom possessing two co-ordination 'vacancies' enables the pigment to bind polar molecules, including molecules of water [10], and possibly accounts for the linking of the pigment with basic groups (histidine?) of a specific protein [11]. Apart from this, the magnesium atom influences the photochemical properties of the entire molecule, determining the higher activity of the pigment. Comparative investigation of the photochemical properties of chlorophyll and phaeophytin has shown that the photoreduced form of chlorophyll is more active than the corresponding form of phaeophytin [12].

The most ancient forms of photosynthetic organisms possess not only porphyrin pigments, but also a set of carotenoids and phycobilins. Degradation of porphyrins results in the formation of bile pigments; these, on combining with proteins, could have given rise to fluorescent phycobilins.

The route of carotenoid synthesis is quite different. The question as to whether the primary organisms could have possessed this type of pigment is still rather obscure. The study of the mechanism of its action seems to indicate that the porphyrins were an older type of sensitizers, moreover capable of photochemical electron transfer. In animal organisms, on the other hand, compounds of carotenoids with proteins became the prevailing photoreceptors.

MECHANISM OF PHOTOCATALYTIC ACTION

The light absorbed by pigments in photosynthetic organisms is used for an oxidation-reduction process opposing the thermodynamic potential gradient with 'storage' of energy in the reaction products. Studies from our laboratory (see [13]) revealed the mechanism of such processes in model systems; the photochemistry of pigments of photosynthetic organisms was studied in these experiments in its phylogenetic and comparative chemical aspects. Chlorophylls *a* and *b*, bacteriochlorophyll, protochlorophyll, porphyrins, phycobilins, phaeophytins, etc., as well as the synthetic analogues of these pigments, phthalocyanins, were studied.

Electron Transfer

When iron is replaced by magnesium, the porphyrins lose the ability to catalyse a dark electron transfer, but, upon illumination, acquire photocatalytic activity—the capacity for reversible photochemical acceptance of hydrogen (electrons) from donor molecules. This ability of chlorophyll and its analogues to undergo a reaction of reversible photoreduction was discovered by the author of the present paper in 1948 [13-14].

It is an essential feature of this reaction that part of the light quantum energy

39

absorbed by the pigment molecule is stored in the active photoproducts thus formed; when the light is switched off, the reaction proceeds in the backward direction, yielding the original pigment molecule. In this manner chlorophyll and its analogues can play the part of a photocatalyst, thermodynamically raising

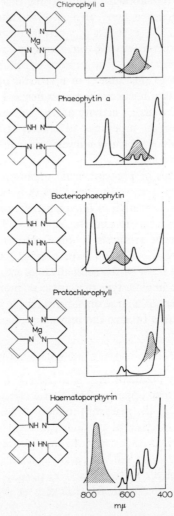

FIG. 1. Structure and absorption spectra of pigments before photoreduction and after the back-reaction in the dark.

Spectra of photoreduced forms are shaded (after illumination in pyridine with ascorbic acid, *in vacuo*).

the electron of the donor molecule 'uphill', which distinguishes the photo-catalytic action of the pigments from the 'dark' catalytic action of cytochromes which transfer electrons (in the thermodynamic sense) 'downhill'.

The reaction of photoreduction is observed in all pigments with a structure based upon a porphyrin- or azaporphyrin-ring system of conjugated double bonds with atoms of hydrogen, magnesium or zinc in the centre of the molecule. Iron complexes display little activity in reactions of this type. Detailed investigation of the mechanism of the reaction, carried out in our laboratory, revealed that the primary photo-act is an electron transfer from the donor molecule to the pigment molecule with the formation of a pair of ion radicals: $\cdot X \cdot + AH \rightarrow \cdot X^- + \cdot AH^+$. According to A. N. Terenin [15], it is most probable that the pigment molecule reacts in the biradical state. The properties of the primarily arising photoreduced form of chlorophyll and phaeophytin were extensively studied by V. B. Evstigneev & B. A. Gavrilova [12].

The subsequent uptake of a proton $\cdot X^- + \cdot AH^+ \rightarrow XH + \cdot A$ results in formation of more stable reduced types, the absorption spectra of which are shown for different pigments, in Fig. 1.

Investigations carried out in our laboratory have demonstrated that the sensitizing action of chlorophyll and its analogues is based on the reaction of

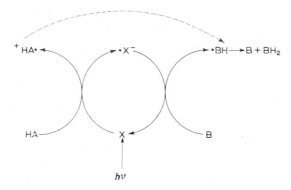

FIG. 2.—Electron transfer; – – –Proton transfer.

reversible photoreduction; the reduced form of pigment arising in the photo-act reacts in the dark stage of the reaction with the ultimate electron acceptor. (See [16 and 13].) The reversible transformations of the pigment molecule results in an electron transfer from the donor molecule to the acceptor molecule, with eventual regeneration of the molecule of the sensitizing pigment, as shown in simplified form in Fig. 2.

Work done in our laboratory has revealed that ascorbic acid, dihydroxymaleic acid, cysteine, hydrogen sulphide, hydroquinone, pyrocatechol and probably cytochrome (Fe^{++}) can act as hydrogen donors in reactions of this type; oxygen, quinones, cytochrome (Fe^{+++}), riboflavin, pyridine-nucleotides, and several dyes (thionine, safranine, phenol-indophenol, etc. [13]) can be used as acceptors of the electron (hydrogen) from the photo-reduced form of chlorophyll.

Porphyrin pigments are thus capable of transferring an electron from the donor molecule to the acceptor molecule either with energy storage $(+ \Delta F)$, or thermodynamically 'downhill' $(- \Delta F)$. In those cases where the final acceptor is atmospheric oxygen, the process results in sensitized oxidation of the hydrogen donor.

It should be pointed out that in recent spectroscopic investigations of living organisms it proved possible to detect the appearance of intermediate photo-products with an absorption maximum corresponding to the photo-reduced form of chlorophyll [17].

Unlike biocatalysts or enzymes, the chlorophyll pigments thus became able to effectuate a 'photochemical' electron transfer. This property appeared in organisms already endowed with a rather elaborate metabolic system. For the result of the photochemical process to be metabolically utilized it was necessary that this process be incorporated into the system of enzymic reactions; in this way could the wastage of light quantum energy by ineffective backreactions of the active photoproducts be prevented.

Energy Transfer

On absorbing a quantum of light, the pigment molecule passes into an excited state. A necessary condition for effective 'resonance' transfer of energy from an excited energy-donating molecule to an energy-acceptor molecule is an 'over-lapping' of the fluorescence spectrum of the donor molecule with the absorption spectrum of the acceptor molecule [18–19].

Since the fluorescence maximum of porphyrin pigments is situated in the red region of the spectrum, effective transfer of energy should be possible to a compound possessing an absorption band in the far-red region; in organisms, however, we know of no intermediate systems satisfying these requirements. In the course of evolution of the pigment system of organisms there could have arisen pigments whose fluorescence spectrum might have 'overlapped' the absorption region of porphyrin pigments. These requirements are satisfied by the phycobilins—phycocyanin and phycoerythrin—which have absorption peaks at 620 and 560–490 mμ, respectively. The work of several investigators on blue-green and red algae revealed the phenomenon of sensitized fluorescence of chloro-phyll upon excitation in the region of the absorption maximum of the phyco-bilins [20]. The light absorbed by these pigments is also used for photosynthesis. Similar phenomena were likewise observed with respect to the carotenoids of diatomaceous algae [21].

Energy can thus be transferred from the phycobilins and carotenoids to chloro-phyll, which is the final acceptor of energy and uses it 'chemically' by partici-pating in processes of photochemical electron transfer.

These conclusions are in accordance with the findings of our laboratory [22] concerning the photochemical properties of phycoerythrin isolated from the red algae *Callithamnion*. It was found that phycoerythrin, as distinct from chlorophyll, has a high photochemical stability, is incapable of reversible photoreduction, and does not have a photosensitizing effect in oxidation-reduction reactions.

A. N. Terenin and V. L. Ermolaev [23] discovered the phenomenon of sensi-tized phosphorescence, which indicates transfer of energy from the biradical state of the donor molecule, with concomitant transition of the acceptor mole-cule as well into a long-lived biradical state. Such a mechanism of energy transfer is also possible in photosynthetic organisms.

It is thus probable that porphyrin pigments were the primary participants in the phototransfer of electrons; subsequent evolution gave rise to the phycobilin pigments transferring the energy of light quanta to the primarily formed sensitizing porphyrins (or possibly to biocatalytic systems).

DEVELOPMENT OF CONJUGATION OF PIGMENT AND ENZYMIC SYSTEM

The excited pigment molecule can pass into the metastable state; in the absence of chemical interaction, the excitation energy of the molecule is rapidly degraded, finally to heat. If an elementary oxidation-reduction act is involved, the photoproducts thus formed (a pair of ion-radicals) can also undergo a backreaction, with wastage of energy. It is important that the active photoproducts can be utilized in the metabolic system before they become deprived of their energy in one way or another. It is therefore not enough for the organism to be endowed with a sensitizing pigment participating in the 'uphill' transfer of electrons; in addition to this conjugated biochemical systems must be available which utilize the active high-energy photoproducts. This is made clear by the following example. The introduction of porphyrins into organisms results in a photodynamic effect: it causes sensitized random oxidation of important metabolic hydrogen donors and finally causes severe disturbance of the vital functions. On the other hand, a sensitizing pigment in an organized living system with co-ordinated photochemical and enzymic processes has the opposite effect of maintaining normal metabolism (chlorophyll in the plants).

N. M. Sisakyan [24] has demonstrated that protoplasmatic structures containing pigments (chloroplasts) are the site of a variety of biocatalytic functions.

Just as in the case of sensitized reactions, here too there may be mechanisms of coupling based on the transfer of an electron and the transfer of energy from the excited sensitizer-pigment molecule.

Incorporation of Sensitizing Pigments into Systems of Biochemical Electron (Hydrogen) Transfer

In the course of reversible photochemical reduction the excited pigment molecule accepts an electron from the donor molecule and, in the dark act of the process, transfers this electron 'uphill', with the formation of a system possessing a higher reduction potential. Model experiments in our laboratory revealed that the molecules of porphyrin pigments upon illumination are capable of taking up electrons (hydrogen) from biochemically important compounds such as ascorbic acid, cysteine, polyphenols, and probably cytochromes.

Even the most ancient types of organisms probably possessed sulphur-containing amino acids and iron porphyrins, and it is therefore likely that these compounds interacted with pigment systems. Light energy 'storage' is possible if the photochemically mobilized electron is accepted by systems with a higher negative redox potential than that of the initial electron donor (up to $E_0 = -0.35$ V). We have demonstrated in 1948–1949 in collaboration with G. P. Brin, that flavins and pyridine-nucleotides can be used as such systems [25];

other investigators have shown that the reduced pyridine-nucleotides can be utilized in the system of biosynthetic reactions involved in carbon dioxide reduction [26].

A similar path of electron transfer is encountered in photosynthetic bacteria; here, however, an 'enzymic pretreatment' of the original hydrogen donors probably occurs before their interaction with the pigment molecules.

Back-reactions of Photoproducts: The Chemosynthetic Path of Coupling

After illuminating photosynthetic organisms for a certain period, Strehler & Arnold observed a faint afterglow, with a spectrum close to that of the fluorescence of chlorophyll [27]. This chemiluminescence is probably due to back-reactions of the active photoproducts. On the other hand, multistage reverse reactions of active photoproducts, proceeding with the participation of bio-catalytic systems, can give rise to biochemically important high-energy compounds utilized in the constructive metabolism of the organisms. The concept of a 'chemosynthetic path' of the utilization of active photoproducts is set forth in the latest reports of O. Warburg. 'Chemosynthetic' formation of high-energy phosphate compounds probably takes place as a result of the biochemical oxidation of active reduced compounds generated photochemically.

Uptake of inorganic phosphates upon illumination and the formation of adenosinetriphosphate has been observed in photosynthetic bacteria [28] and higher plants [29].

It has recently been established that isolated chloroplasts are also capable of such 'photosynthetic' phosphorylation [30]. The mechanism of this process evidently consists in the following. The initial electron (hydrogen) donors are photochemically generated reduced forms of pyridine-nucleotides or flavins; the final electron acceptor is not oxygen (as in ordinary oxidative phosphorylation) but rather a photochemically formed oxidizing agent, the nature of which has not yet been established; ascorbic acid, quinones and cytochromes [30] take part in this process as intermediate systems.

The anaerobic type of oxidoreductive coupled phosphorylation apparently is the older metabolic pattern; with the development of photosynthesis and of the aerobic mode of life, molecular oxygen came to be used as the ultimate electron (hydrogen) acceptor. The 'uphill' electron transfer due to the photochemical process thus ensures the generation of high-energy phosphate bonds.

Calvin and coworkers [31] have pointed out that the reaction cycle of carbon dioxide fixation and reduction is rendered possible by feeding energy into the system in the form of two types of active compounds, 'active hydrogen', probably in the form of reduced pyridine-nucleotides which ensure the reduction stage (phosphoglyceric acid → phosphoglyceric aldehyde), and the high-energy phosphate compounds required for the phosphorylation of intermediary products of the cycle.

The system of heterotrophic metabolism in ancient organisms which were not yet capable of light utilization apparently included the steps of catalytic electron transfer and 'anaerobic' oxidoreductive phosphorylation. The development of the pigment system had the result that the active products of the photoprocess were linked to formerly existing biocatalytic systems. The further development of catalytic pigment and systems led to the more rational utilization of light energy.

Energy Transfer

Within the frame of the present report it is impossible to dwell at length on the presumptive mechanisms of energy transfer in biological systems (see reviews [18, 19, and 32]). The following point, however, should be made. 'Resonance' transmission of energy from the chlorophyll excited molecule to enzyme systems requires definite conditions, discussed above. This mode of energy transfer to enzymic systems is not very plausible in the light of existing data, since the biocatalytic systems which probably take part in photosynthesis usually do not exhibit pronounced absorption maxima in the red region of the spectrum (with the exception of iron porphyrins). It is more probable that there is an energy transfer at the triplet state level, provided the conditions defined by Terenin & Ermolaev [23] are fulfilled. Such an energy transfer at the triplet state level may, in fact, be interpreted as the transfer of an unpaired electron in a conjugated system [41].

It seems probable that in ancient organisms conjugation was effected by the transfer of energy (electron) from magnesium porphyrins to iron porphyrins. In our model experiments we demonstrated the transformations of cytochrome *c* under the action of light absorbed by chlorophyll [33, 4].

DEVELOPMENT OF HYDROGEN (ELECTRON) DONOR UTILIZATION

Photosynthetic bacteria have not yet 'learned the trick' of liberating molecular oxygen from water, and utilize an energetically less expensive type of photosynthesis. Van Niel [34] has assumed that in all autotrophic organisms, including photosynthetic bacteria, there takes place photolysis of water ($HOH \rightarrow H + OH$). The initial hydrogen donor reacts with the OH radicals, while the (H) is used to reduce the carbon dioxide. In line with this view, it has been shown [35] that, regardless of the ΔF of the overall reaction (with different hydrogen donors), the quantum efficiency of bacterial photosynthesis is constant (roughly 8 $h\nu$ per CO_2 molecule). These results suggest that a uniform type of elementary photoprocesses is involved in bacterial photosynthesis, irrespective of the nature of the initial electron donor.

The work of our laboratory revealed that bacteriochlorophyll in solution can effect the photosensitized transfer of electrons from hydrogen sulphide or ascorbic acid to flavins and other hydrogen acceptors [36]. The participation of water in the photoprocess, in our opinion, stands in need of further substantiation. It appears more probable that photosynthetic bacteria utilize the electron of a donor molecule (e.g., SH', S_2O_3'', organic acids) and the protons (hydrogen ions) of water. The ability to 'take hold' of the electrons of water or OH'-ions only arose in the process of further evolution of the autotrophic organisms. It is reasonable to assume that the development of the ability to produce oxygen from water required the utilization of two quanta of light for the transfer of a single electron, i.e., the conjugation of two elementary photoprocesses to over-come the high energy barrier in the path of the transfer of a single electron (hydrogen) from water to carbon dioxide, whereas in bacterial photosynthesis one elementary photoprocess (using a single quantum of light) is sufficient for the transfer of a hydrogen atom from the hydrogen donor AH_2 to CO_2.

The two-stage electron transfer necessitated a more elaborate coupling with enzymic systems and the formation of a 'stock' of intermediate hydrogen donors.

One can envisage the development of the following stages: (1) transfer of an electron from water to an intermediate electron acceptor (e.g., cytochrome; polyphenols, dehydroascorbic acid, or disulphides), that is, the Hill reaction, (2) transfer of the electron from the reduced forms of these compounds to pyri-dine-nucleotides taking part in the reactions of carbon dioxide reduction (e.g., in the step phosphoglyceric acid → triosephosphate, according to the Calvin scheme). Above we have considered the 'short circuiting' of the second stage of hydrogen transfer by coupling with oxidative phosphorylation. The tentative nature of these suggestions is due to the fact that there is as yet no definite answer to the question as to whether the transfer of a single electron (hydrogen) in photosynthesis requires one or two quanta [19].

THE STATE OF PHOTOCATALYTIC PIGMENTS

As stated above, the utilization of solar energy by organisms necessitated the large-scale synthesis of pigments so as to absorb a considerable portion of the photochemically active part of the solar spectrum. Present-day organisms as a rule contain substantial amounts of pigments. *Chlorella*, for example, contains up to 5% of chlorophyll.

In a study of the process of accumulation of chlorophyll when aetiolated seedlings become green we observed in collaboration with L. M. Kosobutskaya the following picture of changes in the state of the chlorophyll [37]. Under the action of light, protochlorophyll is converted to the primary 'monomeric' form of chlorophyll, combined with proteins and lipids, which exhibits an absorption maximum at 670 mμ and has a low light stability. In the process of further formation and accumulation of chlorophyll in the granules, the absorption maximum gradually shifts to 678 mμ, which is characteristic of highly concen-trated, oriented and light-stable forms of chlorophyll. These observations are in keeping with the data obtained by T. N. Godnev and J. H. C. Smith [38].

By means of spectral methods we have studied the state of chlorophyll and bacteriochlorophyll in various organisms from the phylogenetic viewpoint, and arrived at the following conclusions. The peculiar absorption spectrum of bacteriochlorophyll in the cells of photosynthetic bacteria is due to aggregation, to the orderly packing of bacteriochlorophyll in the granules; the absorption spectrum of this pigment in solid films and colloid solutions corresponds to the spectra of living bacteria [39].

The chlorophyll in red and blue-green algae, and in green plants, is mainly in a highly concentrated, closely packed aggregated form. The 'monomeric' chlorophyll, associated with proteins and lipids, is in equilibrium with these forms. In the deep-sea red algae, *Phyllophora*, we were able to detect [40] three different types of chlorophyll packing in the granules (on the evidence of absorption spectra), with maxima at 690, 678 and 670 mμ.

The precise mechanism of participation of the different forms of pigment in the elementary photoprocess is not yet clear. The presence of orderly arranged forms of the pigments can result in electron migration at the triplet level state [41] to monomer forms, which may take a direct part in the photochemical reaction.

The further development of autotrophic organisms evidently proceeds along the lines of accumulation of large amounts of pigments absorbing practically the entire visible part of the solar spectrum.

The observations described above give support to the idea that the pigments of primitive organisms were in the 'monomeric' active state adsorbed on lipoproteins. With the development of the capacity of organisms for the biosynthesis and accumulation of pigments, orderly packing of the latter in highly concentrated state in granules began to predominate. The co-operation of pigments and enzymes in chloroplast structures necessitated the development of an elaborate organization, some of the features of which are visualized in modern electron-microscopic pictures of ultra-thin sections.

REFERENCES

1. A. I. OPARIN, *The Origin of Life on the Earth*.   Izd. Akad. Nauk S.S.S.R., Moscow-Leningrad, 1941.
2. A. P VINOGRADOV, Article 'Biogeokhimiya' in *Bol'shaya Sovetskaya Entsiklopediya*, vol. 5.
3. R. LEMBERG & I. W. LEGGE, *Hematin Compounds and Bile Pigments*. Interscience, New York, 1949.
4. A. A. KRASNOVSKIĬ & K. K. VOĬNOSKAYA, *Biofizika*, **1**, 120, 1956.
5. A. A. KRASNOVSKIĬ & G. P. BRIN, *Dokl. Akad. Nauk S.S.S.R.*, **53**, 447, 1946.
6. A. A. KRASNOVSKIĬ, Article in the collection *Electronic Phenomena in Catalysis and Adsorption*. Izd. Akad. Nauk S.S.S.R., Moscow, p. 40, 1955.
7. L. P. VERNON & M. D. KAMEN, *J. biol. Chem.*, **211**, 644, 1954.
8. J. LASCELLES, *Biochem. J.*, **55**, 4, 1953; K. K. VOIĬNOVSKAYA & A. A. KRASNOVSKIĬ, *Biokhimiya*, **20**, 123, 1955.
9. A. A. KRASNOVSKIĬ & K. K. VOIĬNOVSKAYA, *Dokl. Akad. Nauk S.S.S.R.*, **96**, 1209, 1954.
10. V. B. EVSTIGNEEV, V. A. GAVRILOVA & A. A. KRASNOVSKIĬ, *Dokl. Akad. Nauk S.S.S.R.*, **70**, 261, 1950.
11. A. A. KRASNOVSKIĬ & G. P. BRIN, *Dokl. Akad. Nauk S.S.S.R.*, **89**, 527, 1953.
12. V. B. EVSTIGNEEV & V. A. GAVRILOVA, *Dokl. Akad. Nauk S.S.S.R.*, **95**, 841, 1954; **96**, 1201, 1954; **103**, 97, 1955.
13. A. A. KRASNOVSKIĬ, *Zh. fiz. Khim.*, **30**, 968, 1956.
14. A. A. KRASNOVSKIĬ, *Dokl. Akad. Nauk S.S.S.R.*, **60**, 421, 1948.
15. A N. TERENIN, *The Photochemistry of dyes*, Izd. Akad. Nauk S.S.S.R., 1947; *Izv. Akad. Nauk S.S.S.R., Ser. biol.*, **3**, 369, 1947.
16. A. A. KRASNOVSKIĬ, Article in the collection *Problems of chemical kinetics, catalysis and reaction capacity*. Izd. Akad. Nauk S.S.S.R., p. 92, 1955.
17. L. M. N. DUYSENS, *Science*, **120**, 353, 1954; L. N. BELL, *Dokl. Akad. Nauk S.S.S.R.*, **107**, 329, 1956; B. L. STREHLER & V. H. LYNCH, *Science*, **123**, 462, 1956; J. V. COLEMAN, A. S. HOLT & E. RABINOWITCH, *Science*, **123**, 795, 1956.

18. A. N. TERENIN, *Usp. fiz. nauk*, **43**, 347, 1951.
19. E. RABINOWITCH, *Photosynthesis*, vol. II. Interscience, New York, p. 2, 1956.
20. R. VAN NORMAN, C. S. FRENCH & F. McDOWALL, *Plant Physiol.*, **23**, 455, 1948.
21. H. DUTTON, W. MANNING & R. DUGGAR, *J. Phys., Moscow*, **47**, 308, 1943.
22. A. A. KRASNOVSKIĬ, V. B. EVSTIGNEEV, G. P. BRIN & V. A. GAVRILOVA, *Dokl. Akad. Nauk S.S.S.R.*, **82**, 947, 1952.
23. A. N. TERENIN & V. L. ERMOLAEV, *Dokl. Akad. Nauk S.S.S.R.*, **85**, 547, 1952; *Trans. Faraday Soc.*, **52**, 1042, 1956.
24. N. M. SISAKYAN, *Enzymatic activity of protoplasmic structures*. Izd. Akad. Nauk S.S.S.R., Moscow, 1951; *Izv. Akad. Nauk S.S.S.R., Ser. biol.*, **5**, 32, **6**, 3, 1956.
25. A. A. KRASNOVSKIĬ & G. P. BRIN, *Dokl. Akad. Nauk S.S.S.R.*, **67**, 325, 1949; **87**, 109, 1952; A. A. KRASNOVSKIĬ, *Dokl. Akad. Nauk S.S.S.R.*, **61**, 91, 1948.
26. S. OCHOA, in *Currents in Biochemical Research* (ed. D. GREEN). Interscience, New York, 1946.
27. B. L. STREHLER & W. A. ARNOLD, *J. gen. Physiol.*, **34**, 809, 1951.
28. A. FRENKEL, *J. Amer. chem. Soc.*, **76**, 5568, 1954.
29. R. EMERSON, J. STAUFFER & W. UMBREIT, *Amer. J. Bot.*, **31**, 107, 1944; B. STREHLER, *Phosphate Metabolism*, vol. 2, 1952.
30. D. ARNON, *Science*, **122**, 9, 1955.
31. M. CALVIN, *Conférences et rapports; int. Congr. Biochem.* (No. 3). Liège, p. 211, 1956.
32. A. N. TERENIN & A. A. KRASNOVSKIĬ, *Usp. fiz. Nauk*, **37**, 65, 1949.
33. A. A. KRASNOVSKIĬ. *Dokl. Akad. Nauk S.S.S.R.*, **103**, 283, 1955.
34. C. B. VAN NIEL, *Photosynthesis in Plants*. Iowa State College Press, p. 437, 1949.
35. H. LARSEN, C. S. YOCUM & C. B. VAN NIEL, *J. gen. Physiol.*, **36**, 161, 1952.
36. A. A. KRASNOVSKIĬ, K. K. VOIĬNOVSKAYA, *Dokl. Akad. Nauk S.S.S.R.*, **81**, 879, 1951; **87**, 109, 1952.
37. A. A. KRASNOVSKIĬ & L. M. KOSOBUTSKAYA, *Dokl. Akad. Nauk S.S.S.R.*, **85**, 177, 1952; **91**, 343, 1953; L. M. VOROB'EVA & A. A. KRASNOVSKIĬ, *Biokhimiya*, **21**, 126, 1956.
38. J. H. C. SMITH et al., *Yearb. Carneg. Instn*, **52**, 149, 1953; T. N. GODNEV, *Izv. Akad. Nauk S.S.S.R., Ser. fiz.*, **20**, 557, 1956; T. N. GODNEV & N. S. SUDNIK, *Fiziol. Rastenii*, **3**, 352, 1956.
39. A. A. KRASNOVSKIĬ, L. M. KOSOBUTSKAYA & K. K. VOIĬNOSKAYA, *Dokl. Akad. Nauk S.S.S.R.*, **85**, 389, 1952; **92**, 1201, 1953.
40. A. A. KRASNOVSKIĬ, E. A. NESTEROVSKAYA & A. B. GOL'DENBERG, *Biofizika*, **1**, 328, 1956.
41. A. N. TERENIN, *Radiotekhnika i electronika*, **1**, 1127, 1956.

The Relation between Primitive and Present-day Photobiological Processes

C. REID

The University of British Columbia, Canada

THE PRIMITIVE photochemical processes which resulted in the syntheses of simple organic compounds on the Earth are not known. In view of the many possible routes it is unlikely that the pathway of molecular evolution, first random and later self-sustaining, that actually led to our present forms of life can ever be reproduced and we have no assurance that such a pathway is unique. However, the comparative ease with which an array of amino acids can be produced from the proposed primaeval atmospheric gases [1] makes it clear that we can follow the early stages of many such simple syntheses.

In setting up conditions for such experiments, the following postulates are fairly generally accepted [2]:

1. Little oxygen, and consequently no ozone layer was present in the atmosphere.

2. Solar energy extending to the neighbourhood of 2000 Å was consequently available. Since such energy is ample for the breaking of almost all chemical bonds, it is in view of the very high flux of solar radiation a more likely choice than atmospheric discharges as the energy source for the chosen process.

3. In the initially reducing atmosphere NH_3, CH_4 and water vapour probably predominated, with H_2 as a minor constituent; CO_2, intermediate oxidation products of methane, and oxygen appeared only at a later stage.

4. In view of the continuous 'trial and error' encounters which must have been necessary, and the hydrated nature of the present-day key biological substances, most of the processes probably occurred in the sea, although the possibility of atmospherically formed and subsequently dissolved primary substances cannot be ruled out.

5. In view of the number of features common to life as we now know it, a common origin is indicated. Any forms of life in which some of these features are absent must be considered as possible representatives of very primitive forms. This points to certain sulphur bacteria, in which sugars found in all other organisms are absent, as the most likely candidates.

GENERAL CONSIDERATION OF PHOTOPOLYMERIZATION

The continuous making and breaking of bonds under the influence of high-energy radiation provides a perfectly reasonable process for the formation of polymeric material. What such a process does not provide in its simple form is a mechanism for the stabilization of any of these polymers. Bonds are being continuously broken as well as formed, and unless the breaking process can be stopped or radicals stable against dissociation are formed, the equilibrium molecular weight must be expected to be rather low.

The stabilization mechanism thus appears as the key step which may have determined the mode of subsequent evolution, determining what kind of molecule may be expected to 'grow'.

Dissociation Prevented

In polyatomic systems, energy in excess of that required for bond breaking may be present for a finite time before the dissociation actually occurs. This time increases rapidly as the number of vibrational modes in which the energy may be accommodated is increased. If no means of disposing of the excess energy is available, dissociation must ultimately occur, but if some means of energy dissipation within the dissociation time is available, disruption will be prevented. Probably speaking this dissipation may occur in two ways:

(1) The molecule is fluorescent, rapidly re-emitting absorbed light and thus surviving until attacked chemically and increasing its molecular weight. To continue to invoke this process, as the molecule grows larger, means that where-ever in the molecule light is absorbed, the excitation energy must be transmitted to a luminescent group. Since we know that there are many more non-luminescent than luminescent groups among biologically important molecules, we arrive at the idea of a trap mechanism within the molecule, followed by a radiative process.

(2) The molecule is exceedingly well coupled to its environment, so that absorbed energy can be lost before dissociation. This is a well-known phenomenon in crystals—including molecular crystals—but again some molecule in the crystalline aggregate probably will be decomposed unless a 'trap' is provided. Dissipation as thermal energy within a crystal is also possible, though in molecular crystals this is usually too slow to prevent dissociation. A similar phenomenon may also occur for the case of a single molecule strongly absorbed on a suitable inorganic crystal, and such a heterogeneous system must be considered as a possibility.

Decomposition Occurs, followed by Recombination

This kind of mechanism is particularly suited to the condensed state and has been postulated to explain the results of many irradiation experiments. Two possibilities appear:

(a) Ions or radicals are formed, but are unable to move away from each other because of Coulomb attraction, strong absorption, or bulky neighbours (cage effect).

(b) Very long-living radicals are formed which can move apart, but which do not decompose into smaller fragments.

In both these cases excess energy may be dissipated at leisure as vibrational energy, and is followed by recombination in case (*a*) and either recombination or attack on some other molecule, resulting in increased molecular size, in case (*b*).

If we rule out the possibility of aromatic ions, since we suppose ourselves dealing with the pre-aromatic stage of synthesis, molecules containing —SH groups and —S—S— bonds are the most plausible choices for ion and radical formation respectively. Sulphur compounds could also very reasonably provide the traps required for the nondissociative step mentioned previously. We therefore look very carefully at the role of sulphur in present-day biology.

EVIDENCE FROM EXISTING BIOLOGICAL PROCESSES

The great importance of such sulphur-containing molecules as coenzyme A, glutathione and SH-enzymes is well known. The problem that confronts us is how to distinguish a primitive process from one of later development. The most reasonable approach appears to be:

Look for common features in natural processes still intimately connected with a light absorption or emission step.

Observe how organisms react to excessive amounts of radiation.

The processes which have so far been examined are set down below.

Photosynthesis

The generality of the photosynthetic process makes it clear that whereas it is not a primary process (the photosynthetic pigments themselves being more complex than the molecules being considered here, and anyway unable to survive irradiation with 2000 Å light), it does belong far back in the evolutionary sequence. It is therefore reassuring to find 6 : 8-dithio-octanoic acid postulated by Calvin and his co-workers [3] as the most likely electron-acceptor of the photoelectrons formed on irradiation of the chlorophyll grana.

$$
\begin{array}{c}
CH_2 \qquad\qquad COOH \\
\diagup \qquad\qquad \diagup \\
CH \qquad CH(CH_2)_4 \\
| \qquad\qquad | \\
S\text{——}S
\end{array}
\quad + 2e' \rightarrow \quad
\begin{array}{c}
CH_2 \qquad\qquad COOH \\
\diagup \qquad\qquad \diagup \\
CH_2 \qquad CH(CH_2)_4 \\
| \qquad\qquad | \\
S^- \qquad\quad S^-
\end{array}
$$

If Calvin's postulated mechanism is correct, the thioctic acid occupies a key position linking the photosynthesis with the Krebs cycle. This seems quite in keeping with the idea that sulphur occupied a key rôle in primitive bioenergetics.

The cytochrome system is not directly concerned with a photo-process, but in view of the structural similarity between the haem and chlorophyll molecules the confirmation of Theorell and his co-workers [4] that the haem is attached to its protein by two cysteine residues provides an interesting connection between the two systems.

Vision

Wald & Brown [5] found that the photobleaching of rhodopsin (the protein-retinene compound responsible for rod vision) liberated free SH-groups and that the resynthesis of rhodopsin from retinene and opsin could be inhibited if the —SH group of the opsin were first blocked with *p*-chloromercuribenzoate. It seems very probable therefore that after light absorption, which occurs in the retinene part of the molecule, there is an excited electron in the immediate vicinity of an SH group or a sulphur bond to the retinene itself. On the exposure of the eye to strong light, changes in retinal pH have been observed which may well result from a shift in the equilibrium

$$RSH \longrightarrow RS^- + H^+$$

which occurs when RSH is electronically excited. It seems clear that here again sulphur plays a key role at a point in the mechanism of vision very close to the photoabsorption step.

Phototropism

The struggle towards the light must have been one of the earliest survival mechanisms incorporated into living systems and phototropism is therefore relevant to our considerations.

The known 'auxins' are not sulphur-containing compounds. However, it has recently been shown [6] that the auxin naphthaleneacetic acid undergoes a specific reaction with the protein of an enzyme extract obtained from rapidly growing pea seedlings, but that the reaction is prevented if —SH groups in the enzyme are blocked. This work depends upon the interpretation of absorption spectrum changes of materials *in vitro*. If this intimate association between the auxin and —SH-containing molecules is confirmed, it provides more evidence that a general pattern of sulphur involvement in photoprocesses can be traced.

Bioluminescence

Only a very small proportion of living organisms show bioluminescence. In the cases so far investigated (bacteria such as *Photobacterium*, crustacea such as *Cypridina*, and the firefly, *Photinus pyralis*) the processes appear completely different from each other. These two facts suggest that bioluminescence is not part of the common evolutionary pattern, but has arisen accidentally in various quite unrelated species. If this view is correct, it is of much later origin than are the processes involving light absorption. This is consistent with the fact that no special rôle has yet been assigned to sulphur compounds in bioluminescence reactions, although in one case (firefly luciferin [7]) the presence of an —SH group has been suggested.

RADIATION DAMAGE

For several years it has been recognized that a number of substances can act as partial 'protectors' against radiation damage. Since radiation damage is usually of an oxidative nature, any added reducing material, and thus all organic matter, has some protective effect. Much the most efficient protectors are sulphur compounds [8]. It is of interest that free sulphur ranks with thiourea as one of the most efficient protective agents known. Protection measured in terms of retained activity of extracted enzymes, or of suspended living organisms show essentially the same results.

In contrast to this finding it is also well established that enzymes, the functional groups of which are thiol groups, are much more readily inactivated by radiation than are nonthiol enzymes [9]. A combination of the two observations suggests that a large proportion of the radiation is trapped by sulphur compounds. If they are essential groups, their efficient trapping power results in severe damage to the system under consideration, but if they are non-essential, as is the case for added protectors, they, instead of more important groups, are ruptured.

A very interesting indication of the rôle of sulphur compounds has come from the work of Gordy *et al.* [10]. Their technique was to subject various materials to X-irradiation, and then examine the electron paramagnetic resonance spectra resulting from any electron unpairing brought about by the X-irradiation.

They found the surprising result that all keratin-type proteins (present principally in outer 'protective' layers such as hair, feathers or scales and therefore subject to much radiation normally) showed a spectrum characteristic of only the cystine molecule, in spite of the fact that this amino acid represents only a few per cent of the total protein and therefore is responsible for only a few per cent of the total absorption of X-rays. Here is a clear case of trapping, this time probably via a 'hole' migration mechanism whereby electron loss from anywhere in the protein ends up as electron loss from the S—S group of cystine.

From all of the above considerations it seems reasonable to draw the conclusion that, although many different radiation-absorbing and utilizing molecules have been developed as life evolved the close connection of each of these with the cystine molecule or other reactive sulphur-containing system points to the latter as a component of the primitive photochemical process.

EXPERIMENTAL

Experiments were carried out using a General Electric 1000-w high-pressure arc (AH6 or BH6) as source of illumination. This arc emits about 5% of its energy as the (strongly self-reversed) 1849 Å line of Hg. Selection of a good arc is important because of absorption in the quartz capillary in some cases. For the same reason the 1849 Å line intensity falls in old lamps faster than does the general intensity. New arcs were used after about 40 hours of operation.

Two systems were employed. If material absorbing at 2537 Å or at longer wavelengths was present, a wide-angle grating monochromator was used with 2 mm slit width to isolate the 1849 Å line. Using this system only about 0·0005 w of 1849 Å light reached the sample. This was sufficient to detect, after 300 hours irradiation, amino acid formation from inorganic material, giving weak ninhydrin tests for alanine and glycine.

For most experiments there were no absorbers of 2537 Å present. In these cases direct irradiation of the surface of the liquid with the full arc was employed with an aperture $f = 1·5$. This gave about 0·1 w of 1849 Å light absorbed by the sample itself. This system had the advantage of giving more products in shorter times, but the disadvantage that absorption of infrared light by the glass vessel used resulted in warming up of the solutions. In these essentially preliminary investigations no attempt was made to control this factor.

Experiments were carried out on two kinds of system. In *the first* inorganic materials, of the kind expected to be present in the sea in the pre-oxygen era were irradiated in aqueous solutions in the presence of various homogeneous and heterogeneous catalysts which it was expected might significantly affect the amino acid yield. The aqueous solutions were desalted in ion-exchange columns (using A$_4$ Duolite resin for anions and Amberlite IR 120 for cations), taken to dryness, the products dissolved in alcohol and chromatographed on Whatman No. 1 paper, using butanol, acetic acid and water (4 : 1 : 5) as the usual eluting agent. Phenol-water and pyridine-methanol were used for confirmation in some cases.

In a *second* set of experiments the solutions were allowed to evaporate completely to dryness under irradiation, and irradiation continued for about 1 hour after liquid water had disappeared. This resulted in a considerable amount of polymeric material, which was estimated after dialysis in cellophan for 24 hours.

The substances investigated were methanol, formaldehyde, paraformaldehyde, ammonium carbonate, ammonium salts, free ammonia in basic solution, hydroxylamine, nitrites and nitrates. Many experiments were done both in air and in an atmosphere of CO_2, with CO_2 bubbling through the solution and filling the whole apparatus. Since the amino acid yields were always better under the latter conditions these are the ones reported. The concentrations of reactants were either 10% or, as in the case of paraformaldehyde, the maximum set by the solubility. Since the question of whether life began in concentrates of inorganic salts or in very dilute solution is unresolved, we saw no reason for working at very high dilutions.

Products

Apart from hexamethylenetetramine, which formed in large quantities at pH > 7·5 when formaldehyde and ammonia were present, and in smaller quantities when they were produced during the photoprocess, only glycine and formic acid were isolated (from the hydroxylamine-formaldehyde CO_2, in presence of Fe^{+++} system) in quantity large enough for positive identification (0·03% of CH_2O was converted to glycine). All other identifications are from R_F values and co-chromatography. So far we have concentrated on amino acids although some spots not due to amino acids are also present. Table 1 shows the substances so far identified. Table 2 gives the efficiency of the various substances, based on the intensity of the glycine spot.

TABLE 1.—*Products*

In alkaline soln.

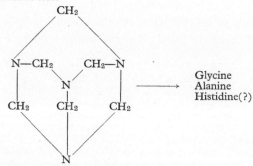

Hexamethylenetetramine

Glycine
Alanine
Histidine(?)

At pH 6

    Glycine
    Alanine
    Formic acid
    Glutamic acid?
    Leucine?

TABLE 2

Order of efficiency, based on glycine formation

Source of N

    H_2CO + Basic Soln. $NH_2OH > NO_2' > NH_3$
    H_2CO + Acidic Soln. $NH_2OH > NH_4^+ > NO_2' > NO_3'$

Source of C

    $HCOOH > (H_2CO)_n > H_2CO > CO_2 > CO_3''$
    (For polymer formation H_2CO best)

TABLE 3

Effect of catalysts

Catalyst	On glycine formation*			On polymer formation*		
	+	−	○	+	−	○
ZnO		ν		ν		
Cu^{++}			ν		ν	
Fe^{+++}	ν			ν		
Cystine		ν		ν		
Pinacyanol			ν			ν
Riboflavin	ν					ν
S			ν	ν		

* *Note*: + denotes quantity at least doubled; − denotes quantity at least halved; ○ denotes no effect.

In our attempts to find a system in which the amino acid yield was higher we tried 7 catalytic systems, 2 heterogeneous and 5 homogeneous. Their effects are listed in Table 3. A positive effect is recorded where the glycine spot is a factor of 2 more intense than the standard.

In the second kind of experiment we started out with amino acids, and attempted to elucidate the effect of further irradiation on them. To a considerable extent the simple amino acids break down to smaller molecules, glycine and alanine both giving easily detectable amounts of ammonia and CO_2.

However, glycine also gives one product in fairly large yield, moving with an R_F of about 0·37 in butanol-acetic acid which we first confused with alanine, but later showed by co-chromatography to be slightly slower. This substance still awaits final identification, but we suggest tentatively that it is glycylglycine. Its formation is increased in the presence of small amounts of riboflavin, but inhibited in the presence of cysteine.

The irradiation of cystine leads first to the formation of cysteine, and then to the formation of a great array of products. Among these some of the amino acids have been tentatively identified, but there are a great number of other types of chemical substance also present.

This result is interesting in view of the result reported by Fox recently of the thermal formation of a similar array of compounds from cystine.

This last result means that if there have been at any time conditions on the Earth under which comparatively large quantities of cysteine or cystine were formed, subsequent radiative or thermal transformations may have led to the production of a great array of small organic amino acids and other functional molecules close to each other. This is presumably the requirement if the very improbable association of a particular set of such molecules is to become significantly more probable.

REFERENCES

1. S. L. MILLER, *J. Amer. chem. Soc.*, **77**, 2351, 1955.
2. A. I. OPARIN. *The Origin of Life*, 2nd ed. Dover Publications, New York, 1953.
3. J. A. BARLTROP, P. M. MAYES & M. CALVIN, *J. Amer. chem. Soc.*, **76**, 4348, 1954.
4. H. THEORELL, *Currents in Biochemical Research* (Ed. D. E. GREEN). Interscience, New York, 1956, p. 275.
5. G. WALD & P. K. BROWN, *J. gen. Physiol.*, **35**, 797, 1951.
6. E. MARRE, *R.C. Accad. Lincei*, **18**, 88, 1955.
7. B. L. STREHLER, *The Luminescence of Biological Systems*. American Ass. Adv. Sci. Washington, 1955, p. 199.
8. W. M. DALE, *Discuss. Faraday Soc.*, 'Radiation Chemistry', 1952, p. 293.
9. E. S. G. BARRON, *Symposium on Radiobiology*. John Wiley, New York, 1952, p. 216.
10. W. GORDY, W. B. ARD & M. SHIELDS, *Proc. nat. Acad. Sci., Wash.*, **41**, 983, 1955.

The Evolution of Chemosynthesis

Yu. I. SOROKIN

'Borok' Biological Station, U.S.S.R. Academy of Sciences

AN EXTENSIVE body of factual material is already available on the morphology, physiology and systematics of chemoautotrophic organisms [1, 2]. But the views on the essence of chemoautotrophy are still controversial, as evidenced by the proceedings of the Fourth Conference on autotrophy in micro-organisms held by the British Society for General Microbiology. We believe that such a situation results from the absence of a consistent and well supported theory of the evolution of chemosynthesis. Many investigators—intentionally or otherwise—still attach paramount importance to insufficiently supported conceptions regarding the evolution of chemosynthetic organisms, considering them as the primary forms of life or, at any rate, as organisms with a 'special' primitive metabolism. The absence of any substantiated notions regarding the evolution of chemosynthesis accounts for the fact that some investigators, for example, artificially single out a group of 'anorgo-oxidants', believing them to be the real autotrophs [3]. Other authors generally consider it unnecessary to single out the chemosynthetic organism as a special physiological group of microbes [4–5]. According to Stephenson [2] chemosynthetic micro-organisms have not developed as advantageous methods of utilizing energy as green plants or heterotrophic bacteria. This, in her opinion, is the reason why the autotrophs are so rare in nature and the number of their forms is limited.

It follows from the above that one conception or another concerning the evolution of chemosynthetics will lead to their being considered either as rudimentary remnants of a group of primitive primary organisms which have persisted up to the present, or, on the contrary, as a highly perfected group of organisms of wide occurrence in nature. Hence the problem of evolution of chemosynthetics is an indispensable basis for all conceptions dealing with the essence of chemosynthesis and its importance in natural processes.

To-day there exist two principal viewpoints concerning the evolution of chemosynthesis. Some authors believe that chemoautotrophic bacteria could have been the 'pioneers of life', since they are capable of thriving in the absence of ready organic matter. In this case the primitiveness of their nutrient requirements is related to a primitive type of metabolism. The opinion that chemosynthetic microbes might be the first organisms that originated on the Earth was first voiced by Vinogradsky [6]. There is no doubt that it is precisely this idea about the primitive character of metabolism of chemosynthetic organisms that led him to define these organisms as 'anorgo-oxidants' incapable of assimilating organic matter [7]. Vinogradsky's views were supported by Osborn [8] in

his book on the origin of life and by Omelyanskiĭ [9] in his manual of microbiology. All these investigators considered the autotrophic type of metabolism
to be more ancient than the heterotrophic one. Similar views are to be found
even in quite recent publications. Thus Rabinowitch [10] in his book *Photosynthesis* holds the opinion that chemoautotrophic bacteria are of primary origin.
He believes that organic molecules, originating under the influence of ultraviolet rays or electric discharges, gave rise, in some way or other, to chemosynthetic organisms. These, in the author's opinion, utilized for chemosynthesis
the energy of oxidation of free hydrogen or hydrogen sulphide present in the
atmosphere at that time. Later, according to Rabinowitch, the evolutionary
development of chemosynthetic microbes led to the appearance of purple
bacteria, and further on of green plants which had come into being earlier than
heterotrophic bacteria.

Kermack & Lees [11] assert that chemoautotrophic bacteria, as organisms less
exacting with regard to the nutrient substrate, are, in the evolutionary aspect,
of more ancient origin than heterotrophic bacteria, the nutritional requirements
of the latter being more complex than those of autotrophic bacteria. The above-
mentioned authors founded their reasonings on the theory of evolution of
physiological functions put forward by Lvoff [12]. According to Lvoff, the
evolution of physiological functions proceeded not by their becoming more
complicated, but through a gradual limitation of the organism's capacity for the
synthesis of complex substances out of simple compounds. This resulted in a
complication and specialization of their food requirements. From the standpoint
of this theory, it naturally follows that autotrophic bacteria must have been the
primordial organisms. The inadequacy of such an anti-evolutionary 'theory of
evolution', and of the conclusions derived on its basis, is quite evident.

In a recently published monograph on the biochemistry of autotrophic bacteria Lees [13] again suggests that primordial organisms did not require ready
organic matter. In his opinion, these primary organisms might have been
organisms of the type of pigmented photosynthesizing sulphur bacteria. According to Lees, chemosynthetic microbes originated from photoautotrophic bacteria
through the loss by the latter of their photoactivating pigments. He believes that
it was sufficient for the primary organisms to possess a few enzymes to be capable
of utilizing the energy of light for assimilating CO_2. It is well known, however,
that the capturing of light energy, its transformation into chemical energy, the
formation of reducing agents and, finally, the fixation of CO_2 and its reduction
to organic matter are carried on in contemporary photoautotrophic organisms by
means of very elaborate biochemical mechanisms. The enzyme systems and
mechanisms of heterotrophic metabolism form the basis of all these processes.

Before the complex mechanisms of autotrophic nutrition appeared, the primordial living beings had doubtless passed a long period of evolution and gradual
increase in complexity on the basis of simpler metabolic reactions, utilizing ready
organic matter.

Another, more thoroughly substantiated viewpoint regarding the evolution of
chemosynthesis has been set forth by A. I. Oparin [14]. According to Oparin,
chemoautotrophic bacteria originated from heterotrophic forms, they appeared

later than photoautotrophic bacteria, since their coming into being is dependent on the accumulation of free oxygen in the atmosphere at the expense of photosynthesis. One of the chief arguments proving the secondary origin of autotrophic bacteria, as compared to heterotrophic ones, is that the capacity for building up their body entirely out of simple mineral compounds requires a more complex biochemical organization of the cell than does life involving the assimilation of ready organic matter [15, 16]. This assumption has been brilliantly confirmed in a great number of papers on the biochemistry of metabolism in chemoautotrophic bacteria [13, 17]. It was found that even the cells of the so-called 'obligatory' chemoautotrophs (sulphur bacteria, nitrifiers) do not differ, as regards the complexity of their biochemical organization, from the cells of the most highly perfected types of aerobic heterotrophic micro-organisms. The same amino acids enter into the composition of the protein of chemoautotrophic bacteria as into the composition of the protein of other living organisms [18]. All the water-soluble vitamins and other important biologically active compounds are found in their cells [3, 19]. It has been established by a number of investigations that the oxidation of mineral substances (NH_4^+, S and H_2) proceeds in the cells of chemosynthetics under the influence of the same enzymic systems which participate in the process of respiration in heterotrophic bacteria and in other more highly organized beings. Thus, cytochromes were found in the nitrifying microbe *Nitrosomonas* [20]. Pyridine dehydrogenases, cytochromes and even a glycolytic mechanism effecting the decomposition of intracellular reserve polysaccharide were found in the cells of another 'obligatory' chemosynthetic organism, *Thiobacillus thiooxidans* [3]. In hydrogen bacteria and sulphate-reducing bacteria the oxidation of hydrogen is carried on by the iron-containing enzyme, hydrogenase [2]. Other data, further, lead to the conclusion that a dicarboxylic acid system participates in the oxidative metabolism of chemoautotrophic bacteria [21].

The binding of the energy liberated in the course of oxidation of mineral substances in chemosynthesis and its utilization for synthetic processes proceeds in chemoautotrophic bacteria with the aid of the same biochemical mechanisms as in heterotrophic bacteria. The oxidation of mineral substances in chemosynthetic organisms occurs intracellularly and is associated with phosphorylation. In this case the oxidation energy is captured and bound as chemical-bond energy in phosphorus compounds. These may yield the energy concentrated in them for the assimilation of CO_2 in chemosynthesis. Such a mechanism was revealed in *Thiobacillus thiooxidans* [22], in hydrogen bacteria [23] and in sulphate-reducing bacteria [24]. Phosphorylation in chemoautotrophs proceeds with the aid of the system adenosine triphosphate $\rightleftarrows$ adenosine diphosphate [23, 35, 26].

The above-quoted data show that with regard to complexity of their biochemical organization, chemosynthesizing bacteria are not inferior to aerobic heterotrophs. It may be assumed that they even exceed the latter in this respect, since heterotrophic bacteria are devoid of the capacity for autotrophic nutrition, whereas most chemoautotrophic bacteria (and on the intracellular level probably all of them, owing to endogenous respiration) are capable of decomposing organic matter and feeding on it. Biochemical studies of chemosynthetic microbes have confirmed the principle of unity of the fundamental features inherent in the biochemical organization of living organisms, which forms the basis of comparative biochemistry [17, 27]. This unity of biochemical organization undoubtedly results from the fact that organisms with different types of metabolism originate from a common root, namely, from a heterotrophic one. The similarity of the most complex systems of biocatalysts in autotrophic and in heterotrophic organisms testifies to the fact that the former originated from heterotrophic organisms at an advanced stage of evolution of the latter, i.e. at the period when the fundamental metabolic mechanisms of primary heterotrophic organisms had already in the main been developed as we know them now. This is why autotrophic metabolism is chiefly based on the biochemical mechanisms of heterotrophic metabolism, including the mechanisms of oxidation, energy transfer and assimilation of CO_2 [10, 28].

The driving force of evolutionary development from heterotrophy to autotrophy was the competition for organic nutrient substrate, the tendency of individual groups of heterotrophic organisms to be freed from the necessity of obtaining energy and carbon only from organic matter. The competition for the organic substrate appears to have become particularly acute at the period of evolution of heterotrophic micro-organisms when these mineralized all the stores of primary organic matter of abiogenic origin, converting them to H_2, CH_4, H_2S and NH_3. The influence of this factor led some pigmented heterotrophic organisms to use their light-sensitive pigments for imparting by means of the energy of light a high reduction potential to the hydrogen of water and of some other compounds, and, in this way, to produce reducing agents of the type of reduced diphosphopyridine nucleotide. These reductants participated in the reduction of CO_2, and their oxidation provided energy. In this way there appeared the photoautotrophs, i.e. photosynthesizing bacteria and green plants.

Chemosynthetic organisms arose later than the photoautotrophs, when, as a result of photosynthesis, oxygen had appeared in the atmosphere. At any rate, there is very little probability that the chemoautotrophs were the precursors of photosynthetics assumed by van Niel [15] since, as will be seen below, they are akin to the aerobic forms of bacteria. Most likely these are two independent lines of development.

The results of research on the morphology of chemosynthetic organisms support the conclusion that the appearance of chemoautotrophic bacteria is the most recent stage in the evolution of micro-organisms. On the ground of morphological characteristics, the various types of chemosynthesizing bacteria may be placed in the following systematic groups [29]: the genus *Pseudomonas*, the family *Chlamydobacteriales*, and the class *Actinomycetes*. The following chemosynthetic organisms are related to the genus *Pseudomonas* in a number of features: the nitrifiers *Nitrosomonas*, *Nitrobacter*, the sulphur bacteria *Thiobacillus thiooxidans*, *Thiobacillus thioparus*, the hydrogen bacteria *Hydrogenomonas flava*, and others [30]. Most filamentous chemoautotrophic bacteria, such as the sulphur bacteria *Thiotrix* and iron bacteria of the genus *Leptotrix* are morphologically close to filamentous heterotrophic bacteria of the *Chlamydobacteriales* family [31, 32]. Unicellular iron bacteria of the genus *Galionella* are also classified by Bisset [30] as *Chlamydobacteriales*. Filamentous sulphur bacteria of the genus *Beggiatoa* are morphologically related to the blue-green algae *Oscillatoria* [33]. Finally, the autotrophic bacterium oxidizing carbon monoxide *Bacterium oligocarbophilum* belongs to the *Actinomycetes* [34].

It is thus evident that as regards their morphological characteristics chemosynthetic organisms belong to the most highly organized forms of micro-organisms. In fact, the bacterial forms of chemosynthetic microbes belong to the genus *Pseudomonas*, i.e. aerobic mobile bacteria known for their polyfermentative capacities. The organisms of the *Pseudomonas* group possess a powerful enzymic outfit which enables them to oxidize many organic substances hardly accessible for other bacteria, such as hydrocarbons and cyclic compounds. Undoubtedly this is the most elaborate and, from the evolutionary standpoint, the most recent group of bacteria among the *Eubacteriales*. Filamentous chemoautotrophic bacteria likewise belong to the higher representatives of micro-organisms with a complex life cycle.

Adaptation to autotrophic metabolism has occurred repeatedly in the various representatives of individual systematic groups of bacteria. This is borne out by the narrow specialization of chemoautotrophs belonging to different systematic groups in relation to the mineral substrate which serves as the source of energy for the particular organism.

Since the chemosynthetic bacteria emerged at advanced stages of the evolution of micro-organisms, there have persisted forms which are intermediate between autotrophic bacteria and heterotrophic ones. Thus, for instance, among the sulphur bacteria there are the so-called 'obligatory' autotrophs which cannot subsist without sulphur compounds and fail to assimilate organic matter [3]. But there are also 'optionally' autotrophic sulphur bacteria which can dispense with sulphur and assimilate organic substances [35]. Finally, there exist heterotrophic bacteria which oxidize sulphur compounds, but are incapable of effecting chemosynthesis [2, 35]. Among the obligatory heterotrophs there occur bacteria oxidizing ammonia [37]. Many heterotrophic bacteria inhabiting water basins catalyse the oxidation of ferrous iron into ferric iron and accumulate iron hydroxide in their cell walls [32]. Chemoautotrophic bacteria oxidizing hydrogen also readily assimilate organic matter, and the assimilation of organic matter may proceed in parallel with the oxidation of hydrogen [38]. The same phenomenon is also observed in desulphurizing bacteria, which may grow both autotrophically and heterotrophically [24, 39].

Photosynthesizing bacteria and green plants likewise readily assimilate organic matter and can thrive at the expense of heterotrophic metabolism. The capacity of autotrophic organisms for heterotrophic metabolism, as Oparin justly pointed out [14], is yet another proof of their secondary origin. The fact that the so-called 'strictly autotrophic' bacteria, such as sulphur-oxidizing bacteria and nitrifiers, fail to assimilate organic matter from the medium does not at all prove that they are incapable of oxidizing stored organic matter intracellularly by way of endogenous respiration. As a matter of fact, the available data prove that 'strict' autotrophs possess the capacity for endogenous respiration at the expense of oxidation of intracellular stores of organic matter [40, 41]. From our viewpoint, the utilization of organic matter from external sources is hindered in these organisms by special properties of their cellular membrane since 'strict auto-trophs' secrete highly acid products (HNO_3, H_2SO_4). According to some data, their cellular membrane possesses lipophilic properties [3] and appears to be impermeable for organic compounds.

As has been stated above, transition from heterotrophic metabolism to chemo-synthesis occurred repeatedly within various systematic groups of micro-organisms. The same may evidently be said about the photoautotrophic organisms. The very fact of repeated transition from heterotrophic to autotrophic nutrition signifies that the latter type of nutrition was an important advantage for the organisms. This advantage was that the organisms, in the case of such transition, obtained access to unlimited supplies of carbon for the building up of cellular substance. It is well known that heterotrophic bacteria can derive carbon for biosynthesis only by oxidative assimilation of a small part of the particular organic substrate on the oxidation of which they are specialized. It is also known that despite the extensive supplies of organic matter in the world there is a keen struggle between micro-organisms for the substrate. For instance, in silt deposits the organic matter of the bacteria themselves amounts to several per cent of the total quantity of organic matter of the silt. Therefore the liberation from the necessity of ensuring their anabolism by oxidative assimilation afforded to the chemoautotrophic bacteria a great advantage over heterotrophic organisms. This is confirmed by our experiments in which the rate of chemosynthesis in silt deposits has been estimated with the aid of ^{14}C [42]. We found that chemo-synthesis proceeds very intensively even in silt known to be rich in organic matter; up to 10% of the total mass of bacteria inhabiting the upper layer of the silt is renewed daily at the expense of chemosynthesis. These data refute the opinion that in conditions of abundance of organic matter chemoautotrophic bacteria feed heterotrophically, and that their capacity for chemosynthesis is a superfluous accessory function manifested only when they are cultivated on artificial nutrient media.

How can the biochemical evolution of chemosynthesis be pictured? It has apparently proceeded according to the scheme common to many other metabolic processes in micro-organisms. Owing to changed conditions of existence to which certain groups of micro-organisms were subjected, some function or other of their metabolism developed, became more complex and, rising to a quali-tatively higher level, became the chief function of their metabolism. The possi-bility of such an evolution of chemosynthetic organisms was provided by the fact that their predecessors were biochemically 'highly organized' microbes of the *Pseudomonas* type, endowed with a powerful enzyme outfit. All mineral substances the oxidation of which provides the source of energy for chemo-synthesis are products of life activity of these heterotrophic bacteria and in some way or other participate in their metabolism. It is therefore natural that enzyme systems capable of catalysing the transformation of the substances in some direction or other existed in the heterotrophic predecessors of chemo-synthetic bacteria. The direction of the reaction is of no particular importance, since all enzymic reactions are reversible.

In many heterotrophic bacteria there exist enzyme systems which activate molecular hydrogen and catalyse its liberation from organic compounds [43]. Most heterotrophic bacteria effect the transformation of the oxidized mineral compounds of sulphur into reduced ones by the formation of SH-groups from SO_4^{--}. The capacity of bacteria to reduce nitrogen in the form of NO_3^- to amino groups, and to produce ammonia, is almost universal. The process of oxidation of ferrous ions forms the basic enzymic reaction of biological oxidation. The metabolic formation of methane is inherent in some heterotrophic bacteria.

All these reactions, which are carried on by heterotrophic bacteria with the consumption of energy and reductants, when channelled in the reversed direction, will generate energy and reductants. Hence the reactions of constructive metabolism of heterotrophic bacteria could have been converted into those of energy metabolism of autotrophic bacteria. This may have been caused by the appearance of free oxygen in the atmosphere when large quantities of reduced products of anaerobic metabolism were present.

The capacity for assimilating CO_2 is likewise inherent in most heterotrophic micro-organisms [4]. However, in heterotrophic organisms the assimilation of CO_2 is not the main basis of carbon nutrition. The principal function of CO_2 assimilation by heterotrophic bacteria is associated with the synthesis of final products of oxidative and anaerobic fermentations. Since heterotrophic micro-organisms are less elaborate living systems than chemosynthetic organisms, they are devoid of certain mechanisms which enable chemoautotrophs to synthesize the substances of their body wholly from the carbon of CO_2.

Micro-organisms must have passed through the following stages in the course of transition from heterotrophic to autotrophic metabolism. At first, when getting into an environment characterized by an excess of a certain reduced mineral compound, the heterotrophic organisms acquired the capacity to oxidize it by means of the enzymes in their possession, and to utilize the energy of oxidation as an additional source of energy for constructive metabolism. Such organisms, existing under definite conditions, are already relatively independent from organic matter to meet their energy requirements. Therefore their evolution tends to develop further in these organisms the pre-existing function of heterotrophic assimilation of CO_2 so as to liberate the constructive metabolism likewise from the requirement for organic carbon. It is this evolutionary development in micro-organisms capable of oxidizing mineral substances (products of anaerobic metabolism of heterotrophs) of the capacity for heterotrophic assimilation of CO_2 that led to the appearance of chemoautotrophic bacteria.

After the discovery of the capacity of heterotrophic bacteria for assimilating CO_2, and of chemoautotrophs for assimilating organic substances, some investigators were inclined to deny the existence of chemoautotrophs as a separate physiological group of bacteria [4]. Umbreit thought it possible to include into the group of chemoautotrophic bacteria only two species of thiobacteria and two species of nitrifiers [3]. It is quite evident that this viewpoint is untenable. There is just as much sound reason to single out a physiological group of chemoautotrophic bacteria as there is for the group of photoautotrophic organisms. Representatives of both groups of bacteria can feed autotrophically. In this case the chemosynthetic organisms derive energy for CO_2 assimilation and reductants from the oxidation of mineral substances. The photosynthetic organisms obtain energy and reductants through photochemical decomposition of water or of certain mineral and organic compounds. The heterotrophic bacteria are not capable of thriving at the expense of the types of metabolism just mentioned.

The delimitation of each of these physiological groups of micro-organisms is also determined by the place they hold in the economics of Nature. The role of chemoautotrophic bacteria, in particular, consists in that they effect complete oxidation of the mineral products of anaerobic decomposition of organic compounds and, by utilization of the energy contained in these products, involve additional amounts of CO_2 in the process of synthesis of organic matter. Thus, chemosynthesis is not a parallel, but a subsequent process in relation to photosynthesis since in the final analysis the energy for chemosynthesis is derived from products of anaerobic decomposition of organic compounds built up in the process of photosynthesis.

Chemosynthesis plays an important part in the synthesis of organic matter in water basins, where it is connected with the anaerobic decomposition of organic matter in silt deposits [42, 44].

REFERENCES

1. S. I. Kuznetsov, *Mikrobiologiya*, **17**, 307, 1948.
2. M. Stephenson, *Bacterial Metabolism*. London–New York, 1939, 1951.
3. W. W. Umbreit, *Bact. Rev.*, **11**, 157, 1947.
4. C. H. Werkman & H. G. Wood, *Advanc. Enzymol.*, **2**, 135, 1942.
5. K. Y. Werkman, in *Bacterial Physiology* (Ed. by C. H. Werkman & P. Wilson). Academic Press, New York, No. 4, 1951.
6. S. N. Vinogradsky, *Ann. Inst. Pasteur*, **5**, 577, 1891.
7. S. N. Vinogradsky, *Zbl. Bakt.*, 2, Abt. **57**, 1, 1922.
8. H. Osborn, *The Origin and Evolution of Life*. London, 1918.
9. V. L. Omelyanskiĭ, *Principles of Microbiology*. Petrograd, Gosizdat, 1922.
10. E. Rabinowitch, *Photosynthesis*. 1951.
11. W. O. Kermack & H. Lees, *Science Progr.*, **40**, 44, 1952.
12. F. A. Lvoff, *L'Evolution physiologique*. Paris, 1944.
13. H. Lees, *Biochemistry of Autotrophic Bacteria*. London, 1955.
14. A. I. Oparin, *The Origin of Life on the Earth*. Akad. Nauk S.S.S.R., Moscow, 1941.
15. C. B. van Niel, in *Photosynthesis in Plants* (Ed. by Loomis). Iowa, 1949.
16. D. Foster, in *Physiology of Bacteria* (Ed. by C. H. Werkman). 1954.
17. Yu. I. Sorokin, *Mikrobiologiya*, **25**, 363, 1956.
18. I. D. Frantz, H. Feigelman, A. S. Werner & M. P. Smythe, *J. biol. Chem.*, **195**, 423, 1952.
19. D. Y. O'Kane, *J. Bact.*, **43**, 7, 1942.
20. H. A. Lees & R. Simpson, *Biochem. J.*, **59**, 1, 1955.
21. C. B. van Niel, *Physiol. Rev.*, **23**, 338, 1943.
22. W. Umbreit, *J. Bact.*, **67**, 387, 1954.
23. M. I. Belyaieva, *Uchennye. Zap. gosud. Univ.Kazan. Ser. biol.*, **114**, 3, 1954.
24. Yu. I. Sorokin, *Trudy Inst. Mikrobiol. Akad. Nauk S.S.S.R.*, **3**, 21, 1955.
25. I. A. Le Page & W. W. Umbreit, *J. biol. Chem.*, **148**, 255, 1943.
26. H. A. Barker & A. Kornberg, *J. Bact.*, **68**, 665, 1954.
27. A. J. Kluyver, *The Chemical Activities of Microorganisms*. London, 1931.
28. S. Ochoa, *Physiol. Rev.*, **31**, 56, 1951.
29. K. A. Bisset & J. B. Grace, in *Autotrophic Microorganisms*. 4th *Symp. Soc. Gen. Microbiol.* (London). Cambridge, 1954.
30. K. A. Bisset, *The Cytology and Life-history of Bacteria*. Edinburgh–London, 1955.

31. E. G. PRINGSHEIM, *Biol. Rev.*, **24**, 200, 1949.
32. E. G. PRINGSHEIM, *Proc. Roy. Soc.*, B. **223**, 453, 1949.
33. C. B. VAN NIEL, *Bact. Rev.*, **8**, 1, 1944.
34. K. LANTZSCH, *Zbl. Bakt.*, 2, Abt. **57**, 309, 1922.
35. R. L. STARKEY, *Soil Sci.*, **39**, 197, 1935.
36. R. L. STARKEY, *J. gen. Physiol.*, **18**, 325, 1935.
37. N. B. NECHAYEVA, *Mikrobiologiya*, 16, 418, 1947.
38. A. J. KLUYVER & A. MANTEN, *Leeuwenhoek ned. Tijdschr.*, **8**, 71, 1942.
39. YU. I. SOROKIN, *Dokl. Akad. Nauk S.S.S.R.*, **90**, 897, 1953.
40. H. BÖEMEKE, *Arch. Microbiol.*, **10**, 385, 1939.
41. K. C. VOGLER, *J. gen. Physiol.*, **25**, 617, 1942.
42. YU. I. SOROKIN, *Isotopes in Microbiology*. Izd. Akad. Nauk S.S.S.R., Moscow, 1955.
43. M. STEPHENSON, *Leeuwenhoek ned. Tijschr.*, **12**, 33, 1947.
44. YU. I. SOROKIN, *Mikrobiologiya*, **24**, 393, 1955.

Entstehung und Evolution der phototrophen Ernährungsweise

D. J. SAPOZHNIKOW

Botanisches Institut, Akademie der Wissenschaften UdSSR, Leningrad

A. I. OPARIN [1] hat eine konsequente Theorie der Entstehung des Lebens auf der Erde entwickelt. Nach dieser Theorie sind infolge eines sehr lange dauernden Evolutionsprozesses aus abiogen gebildeten organischen Stoffen die primären Lebewesen entstanden. Diese primären Lebewesen mußten die im umgebenden Medium gelösten organischen Stoffe assimilieren. Wir können mit A. I. Oparin annehmen, daß die primären Lebewesen anaerobe Heterotrophen gewesen sind. Die gegenwärtigen photosynthetisierenden Organismen sind aber aerobe Autotrophen.

Der Forscher, der den Weg nachweisen will, auf dem im Laufe der Evolution der Organismen die Photosynthese auftrat, sieht sich vor eine zweifache Aufgabe gestellt: einerseits muß gezeigt werden, wie die Autotrophie im allgemeinen und die Phototrophie insbesondere entstehen konnte, andererseits muß die Entestehung der Aerobiose erklärt werden.

Sapozhnikow [2] machte 1951 den Vorschlag auf eine Absolutisierung der Begriffe 'Autotrophie' und 'Heterotrophie' zu verzichten, und statt dessen den Begriff 'Grad der Autotrophie' einzuführen, in dem auch der Energiegehalt der assimilierten Stoffe mit einbegriffen ist. Vergleicht man zwei verschiedene Organismen nach dem Grad der Autotrophie, so hat man die Qualität und die Quantität der Elemente zu berücksichtigen, die in einer energieärmeren Form assimiliert werden.

Die Einführung energetischer Begriffe erscheint uns zweckmäßig, da der Stoffwechsel immer von Energieaustausch in den verschiedensten Formen begleitet wird. Von diesem Standpunkt betrachtet, waren die primären Organismen in höchstem Grade heterotroph, geschah doch ihr Stoffwechsel als Assimilation energiereicher Verbindungen. Dabei waren die Dissimilationsprodukte immer noch energiereiche Verbindungen, die sich in dieser Hinsicht nur wenig von den Anfangsstoffen des Assimilationsprozesses unterschieden.

In Verlauf der Evolution mußten die primären Heterotrophen die Fähigkeit erwerben, diese Dissimilationsprodukte weiter zu verwerten, d.h. organische Stoffe mit immer kleineren Vorräten an freier Energie; somit entwickelten sie sich zu Organismen mit niedrigerem Grad der Heterotrophie. Die Energiedifferenz zwischen dem Organismus und den von ihm unter den Bedingungen der Anaerobiose zu assimilierenden Stoffen mußte ihr Maximum erreichen, als durch die Entwicklung des Stoffwechsels die Assimilation von Kohlendioxyd möglich wurde, dieser am meisten mineralischen von allen organischen Verbindungen, und zugleich der 'energieärmsten' Kohlenstoffverbindung.

Einige Forscher ordnen die primären Lebewesen als 'Heterometatrophen' ein. Sie müssen organische Stoffe assimiliert haben, die Stickstoff, Phosphor, Schwefel und Eisen enthielten. Solche Verbindungen sind in der Regel Eiweißstoffe und Polypeptide. Ähnlich wie die Viren nach ihrer chemischen Zusammensetzung den Eiweißstoffen des Wirts sehr nahestehen, mußte auch das Nährsubstrat der primären Lebewesen nach Struktur und Zusammensetzung den Lebewesen selbst sehr nahe sein. Da der Unterschied zwischen dem primären assimilierenden Lebewesen und dem von ihm assimilierten Substrat sehr gering war, brauchten diese Lebewesen nicht über den komplizierten Fermentapparat zu verfügen, der den gegenwärtigen Organismen den Aufbau kompliziertester Verbindungen aus einfachsten anorganischen Substanzen ermöglicht; ein solcher Fermentapparat musste erst im Laufe des langwierigen Evolutionsprozesses entstehen.

Die primären Lebewesen konnten mit einem recht beschränkten Satz von Fermenten auskommen, und auch die Wirksamkeit dieser Fermente war höchst wahrscheinlich nicht sehr groß. Die Assimilation konnte als Hydratations-Reaktion erfolgen, oder durch hydrolytische Sprengung einer Bindung u.s.w. Infolge der mehrmaligen zyklischen Wiederholung des Assimilations-Dissimilationsprozesses erschienen in der 'werdenden' Biosphäre biogene Stoffe, die sich bereits stärker von denen der assimilierenden Lebewesen unterschieden. Für die Assimilation dieser einfacher gebauten organischen Stoffe wurde ein neuer Satz von Fermenten notwendig. Dies aber mußte unbedingt eine physiologische Komplizierung bewirken. ('Aromorphose' nach Sewertzow [3] oder 'Arochimose' nach Blagowestschenski [4].)

Die Erforschung der heutigen Mikroorganismen erleichtert uns das Verständnis des idioadaptiven Prozesses, der schließlich zur Assimilation von Kohlenstoffdioxyd (CO_2) geführt hat.

Die primären Organismen waren durch den höchsten Grad der Heterotrophie gekennzeichnet, ähnlich wie die heutigen Parasiten (pathogene Streptokokken, anaerobe Bazillen und Trypanosomen). Man könnte mit Jerusalimsky [5] sagen, sie seien vollkommen aminoheterotroph gewesen. Im Laufe der Evolution wuchs allmählich die Zahl der Aminosäuren, die von den Heterotrophen selbst synthesiert werden konnten. Gleichfalls nahm auch die Zahl der Wuchsstoffe (auxotrophe Gruppen) zu, die für die Organismen der archaischen Biosphäre entbehrlich wurden. Die von Jerusalimsky geprägten Bezeichungen benutzend, können wir sagen, daß mit der Zeit die Aminogramme und Auxogramme dieser Organismen kürzer wurden. Dies führte zur Entstehung von Organismen, die mit einem Minimum von Aminosäuren und Vitaminen (Auxogruppen) auskommen konnten, mit Hilfe deren sie instande waren, die notwendigen körpereigenen Stoffe zu synthesieren. Im weiteren Verlauf mußte dieser Prozeß notwendigerweise die nächste Etappe herbeiführen—namentlich die Entwicklung der Aminoautotrophie unter Beibehaltung von Wuchsstoffheterotrophie.

Unter den heutigen Mikroben begegnen wir dieser Ernährungsweise sehr häufig—bei Hefen, Bakterien der Buttersäure—Aceton-Äthanol—Propionsaüregärung und anderer Gärungen, sowie bei den meisten Fäulnisbakterien und bei parasitären Schimmelpilzen.

Die nächste Etappe—die 'Heteroautotrophie'—kennzeichnet sich durch Autotrophie gegenüber Aminosäuren und Vitaminen und durch die Fähigkeit, Stickstoff sowohl in Form von Ammoniak, als auch in Form von Nitraten zu assimilieren. Heutige Vertreter dieses Ernährungstyps sind: Pilze, Aktinomyceten, die meisten Mycobakterien, das Kolibakterium, die pigmentbildenden Bakterien, die Denitrifikanten, die freilebenden stickstoffbindenden Bakterien und einige hefeartige Organismen.

Der Abbau der abiogen synthetisierten organischen Stoffe führte schließlich zum Auftreten der energieärmsten Kohlenstoffverbindung—der Kohlensäure.

Mit dem Beginn der heterotrophen Assimilation von CO_2 ist der Kohlenstoff -Kreislaug enstanden. Im Azoikum migrierte das Kohlenstoffatom aus einfacher gebauten Verbindungen in immer kompliziertere. Mit der Entstehung des Lebens auf der Erde und dem Einsetzen des Stoffwechsels geriet die thermodynamische Stabilität der Kohlenstoff-Verbindungen ins Schwanken. Somit begann die biogene Migration des Kohlenstoffatoms in einfachere Stoffe, jedoch dürfte vom Auftreten eines Kohlenstoff-Kreislauf erst die Rede sein nach dem Zeitpunkt der Einbeziehung der am weitesten oxydierten stabilen Kohlenstoffverbindung—des Kohlendioxyds—in den Stoffwechsel.

Mit dem Beginn der heterotrophen Assimilation von CO_2 hat sich die Bilanz das Gaskreislaufs noch immer nicht verändert, da bei dieser Art der Assimilation von Kohlendioxyd die Menge des ausgeschiedenen CO_2 die des assimilierten etwas übertrifft.

Als Energiequelle für die heterotrophe Assimilation von CO_2 diente der Verbrauch von organischen Stoffen, somit mußte die nächste Etappe der Stoffwechsel-Evolution darin bestehen, daß das Kohlendioxyd unter anaeroben Bedingungen auf Kosten der Energie anorganischer Stoffe assimiliert wurde. Diesen Typ des Stoffwechsels hat der Verfasser als 'Chemoreduktion' bezeichnet [6].

Die Erforschung der heutigen Organismen erlaubt uns, mindestens drei quantitativ verschiedene Entwicklungsetappen beim Übergang von der heterotrophen CO_2-Assimilation zur Chemoreduktion zu erkennen.

Die 1. Etappe: allmählicher Übergang zu immer einfacheren Substanzen als Energiespender bei der Assimilation von CO_2; zur Zeit sind heterotrophe Organismen bekannt, die als einzige Energiequelle die Oxalsäure verwenden.

Die 2. Etappe: Ersatz einer Komponente des Redoxsystems durch eine anorganische Verbindung. Gegenwärtige Vertreter dieses Typs sind die sulfatreduzierenden Organismen.

Die 3. Etappe: Ersatz auch der zweiten Komponente durch eine anorganische Verbindung. Diese Ernährungsweise hat Pelsch [7] für das Wasserstoff-Schwefelbakterium nachgewiesen.

Infolge der Lebenstätigkeit von Organismen, deren Stoffwechsel auf Chemoreduktion beruhte, mußten im umgebenden Medium große Veränderungen eintreten. Erstens mußte in diesem Medium die Menge des CO_2 abnehmen, da infolge der Chemoreduktion die Assimilation von Kohlenstoffverbindungen deren Abbau mengenmäßig übertraf; zweitens mußte sich im Medium Schwefelwasserstoff anreichern.

Der allmähliche Rückgang der Konzentration des Kohlendioxyds in der Atmosphäre bewirkte eine Veränderung der spektralen Zusammensetzung der die Erdoberfläche erreichenden Strahlung. Der durch die Lebenstätigkeit chemoreduzierender Organismen verursachte Rückgang der Konzentration des Kohlendioxyds in der Atmosphäre mußte eine Abnahme der Wolkendecke zur Folge haben, und das bisher auf der Erde herrschende Zwielicht mußte dem hellen Lichte weichen.

Die nächsthöhere Stufe in der morpho-physiologischen Evolution sollte die Photoreduktion sein. Der Übergang von der Chemoreduktion zur Photoreduktion läßt sich ebenfalls in drei Etappen zerlegen.

Die 1. Etappe bestand wahrscheinlich in der Ausweitung des Bereichs der Redoxpotentiale, in dessen Grenzen der Stoffwechsel der chemoreduzierenden Organismen verlaufen konnte.

Die 2. Etappe muß mit der Entstehung von Farbstoffen begonnen haben, was die Verwendung der Lichtenergie für verschiedene Redoxreaktionen ermöglichte.

Die 3. Etappe besteht darin, daß in einer der zum Prozeß der Chemoreduktion gehörenden Reaktionen die chemische Energie durch Lichtsenergie ersetzt wurde, womit die Photoreduktion als solche beginnt.

Am Anfang der Epoche der Photoreduktion wirkte das umgebende Medium stark reduzierend, da infolge der Lebenstätigkeit der chemoreduzierenden Organismen auf der Erde große Mengen von Schwefelwasserstoff entstanden waren. Die Tätigkeit der photoreduzierenden Organismen wirkte in entgegengesetzter Richtung—der Schwefelwasserstoff wurde zu Schwefel oder Schwefelsäure oxydiert.

Die Lebenstätigkeit der photoreduzierenden Organismen löste einen großen Umschwung in dem umgebenden Medium aus. Allmählich entstanden Bedingungen, welche das Auftreten des aeroben Stoffweltyps begünstigten.

Wir haben somit den hypothetischen Weg verfolgt, den die Evolution der Ernährungstypen gehen mußte, um zur Autotrophie und namentlich zur Phototrophie zu gelangen: der Weg lag von den primären anaeroben Heterotrophen über die anaeroben Chemoautotrophen zu den anaeroben Photoautotrophen.

In der Epoche der Photoreduktion erreichte die Entwicklung des Lebens ein gewaltiges Ausmass, aber es handelte sich immer noch um Anaerobier. Die neuzeitlichen Formen der aeroben Organismen konnten nur mit dem Erscheinen von freiem molekularem Sauerstoff entstehen.

Geringfügige Mengen von freiem Sauerstoff konnten infolge der thermischen, elektrolytischen und photolytischen Spaltung von Wasser entstehen. Die thermische Zerlegung konnte bei Ausbrüchen von Vulkanen geschehen, die photo-chemische unter der Einwirkung der Ultraviolett-Strahlen, die elektrolytische — bei Gewitterentladungen. Es sei aber sogleich darauf hingewiesen, daß die hohe Temperatur, die elektrischen Entladungen und die Ultraviolett-Strahlen neben der Zerlegung des Wassers in Wasserstoff und Sauerstoff gleichzeitig die umgekehrte Reaktion, die Synthese von Wasser aus beiden Elementen, verursachen.

In der Epoche der Chemoreduktion enthielt das umgebende Medium große Mengen von Schwefelwasserstoff, durch welchen diese geringen Sauerstoffmengen gebunden wurden.

Nachdem die photoreduzierenden Organismen die Zufuhr von Schwefelwasserstoff in die unmittelbar über ihnen liegenden Mikrozonen, und somit auch in die Atmosphäre unmöglich gemacht hatten, entstanden auf der Erde allmählich die Voraussetzungen für die Aerobiose.

In der Reihe fortschreitender Anpassungen von der Photoreduktion zur Photosynthese lassen sich mehrere Etappen aufstellen.

Die 1. Etappe konnte in einer allmählichen Erhöhung des Redoxpotentials bestehen, bei welchem der Stoffwechsel dieser oder jener Lebewesen sich abspielte.

Die 2. Etappe ist die Entstehung und Vervollkommnung eisenhaltiger Fermentsysteme. Auf dieser Stufe konnte das dreiwertige Eisen-Ion die Rolle des terminalen Elektronen-Akzeptors spielen.

Die 3. Etappe ist das Ergebnis der weiteren Erhöhung des Redoxpotentials bis zur Einbeziehung des freien molekularen Sauerstoffs in den Stoffwechsel. Hier konnten Organismen mit photosynthetischem Stoffwechsel erscheinen.

Die Erforschung der am Stoffwechsel beteiligten Redoxsysteme zeigt, daß diese sich auf Grund der Höhe des Redoxpotentials in eine Reihe anordnen lassen. Ein besonderer Platz kommt in dieser Reihe dem Cytochromsystem zu. Das Potential des Cytochroms (0,69 v) unterscheidet sich von dem der Sauerstoff-Elektrode (1,23) um 0,54 v. Das Potential des Fe^{+++}/Fe^{++} Systems beträgt dagegen 0,75 v; der Unterschied gegenüber dem Cytochrom-System macht lediglich 0,06 v aus.

Dieser Umstand läßt uns annehmen, daß noch vor dem Beginn des Sauerstoff-Stoffwechsels den dreiwertigen Eisen-Ionen, oder Ferri-Ionen, im Stoffwechsel der archaischen Organismen eine große Rolle zukam.

Das Ferri-Ion konnte in der Epoche der Chemoreduktion nicht bestehen wegen der großen Schwefelwasserstoffmengen in der Biosphäre. Da die Photoreduktionsprozesse zu einer Erhöhung des Redoxpotentials führen, da also im Ergebnis dieser Prozesse Stoffe entstehen, deren Redoxpotential höher liegt, als das der Ausgangsstoffe, kann man sich leicht denken, daß die Evolution unter den photoreduzierenden Organismen solche hervorbrachte, deren Stoffwechsel bei allmählich ansteigendem Redoxpotential vor sich ging. So konnte das Ferri-Ion in Erscheinung treten. Die Beteiligung des Ferri-Ions am Stoffwechsel begünstigte die Entwicklung und Vervollkommnung der Cytochromoxydase-Systeme.

Für die Entstehung von Organismen mit photosynthetischem Stoffwechsel war die Ausbildung der Fähigkeit wesentlich, Sauerstoff als terminalen Elektronenakzeptor zu verwenden.

Mit der Entstehung von Aerobiern konnten auch photosynthetische Organismen entstehen. Dank dem Prozeß der Photosynthese nahm die Menge von Sauerstoff in der Biosphäre rapide zu. Bevor die Photosynthese begann, konnte auf der Erde Sauerstoff nur durch Faktoren freigemacht werden, die gleichzeitig auch seine Bindung bewirkten: durch hohe Temperatur, elektrische Entladungen und Ultraviolettstrahlen. Mit dem Beginn des photosynthetischen Stoffwechsels

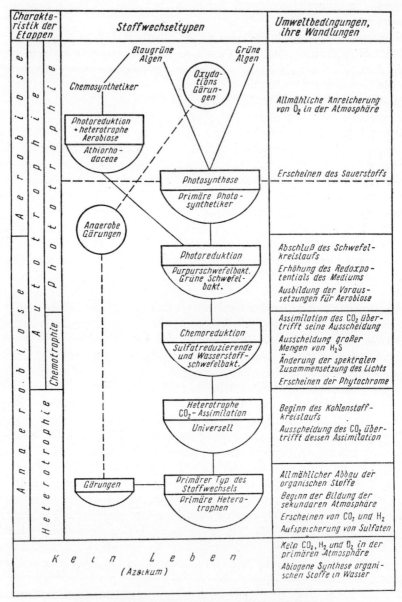

FIG. 1. Schema der Evolution der Stoffwechseltypen.

wurde Sauerstoff durch Prozesse in Freiheit gesetzt, die unter normaler Temperatur verliefen, wodurch Aufspeicherung des Sauerstoffs ermöglicht wurde.

Die Anreicherung von Sauerstoff in der Atmosphäre führte zur Entwicklung vielfältiger lebender Formen und zur Komplizierung der Stoffwechselprozesse. Das Leben eroberte das Festland.

Dem Aufsatz ist ein Schema beigelegt, das die Evolution der Stoffwechseltypen veranschaulicht, wie sie sich auf Grund der Analyse des uns zu Verfügung stehenden Materials darstellt (Fig. 1).

Das Schema gibt eine Reihe morphophysiologischer Komplizierungen wieder, von denen jede nächsthöhere auf der Grundlage der früheren entsteht. Auf diese Weise entsteht eine phylogenetische Reihe: primäre Heterotrophen, heterotrophe CO_2-Assimilatoren, chemoreduzierende Organismen, photoreduzierende Organismen und schließlich Photosynthetiker.

Jede Stufe dieser Reihe läßt sich durch experimentelle Angaben belegen, die uns die Erforschung neuzeitlicher Organismen liefert. Der Umfang dieses Aufsatzes hindert uns, mehr als auf eine dieser Etappen näher einzugehen, nämlich auf den Übergang von Photoreduktion zu Photosynthese. Die Photoreduktion verläuft anaerob, die Photosynthese jedoch ist ein aerober Prozess. Wir konnten nachweisen, daß an der Sauerstoff-Übertragung bei Photosynthetikern Carotenoide von epoxydem Typ beteiligt sind. Bei photoreduzierenden Organismen sind dagegen Epoxy-Carotenoide überhaupt nicht vorhanden.

In unseren Versuchen konnten wir feststellen, daß sich das Verhältnis Lutein/ Violaxanthin bei Einwirkung des Lichts auf Blätter verschiedener Pflanzen stark verändert. Aus den Ergebnissen dieser Versuche schließen wir, daß in den grünen Blättern ein Fermentsystem bestehen muß, welches das Verhältnis zwischen Lutein und Violaxanthin regelt. Dieses Fermentsystem bedarf zu seiner Funktion aerober Bedingungen.

Ein Vergleich des Fermentapparats der Purpurschwefelbakterien mit dem der höheren grünen Pflanzen ergibt, daß die photosynthesierenden Organismen zum Unterschied von den photoreduzierenden über einen Satz von Carotenoiden verfügen, der ihnen die Durchführung des aeroben Stoffwechsels ermöglicht. Unseres Erachtens ist dies mit ein Beweis für die Entstehung der Photosynthese aus der Photoreduktion.

LITERATURNACHWEIS

1. A. I. Oparin, *Entstehung des Lebens auf der Erde.* Izd. Akad. Nauk S.S.S.R., Moscow-Leningrad, 1941.
2. D. J. Saposhnikov, *Mikrobiologiya,* **20,** 438, 1951.
3. A. N. Sewerzow, *Ges. Werke,* Bd. 5, Izd. Akad. Nauk S.S.S.R., Moscow, 1949.
4. A. W. Blagowestschenski, *Biochemische Grundlagen des Evolutions-prozesses der Pflanzen.* Izd. Akad. Nauk S.S.S.R., Moscow, 1950.
5. N. D. Jerusalimsky, *Stickstoff und Vitamin-Ernährung der Mikroben.* Izd. Akad. Nauk S.S.S.R., Moscow, 1949.
6. D. J. Saposhnikov, *Sovetsk. Bot.,* **6–7,** 100, 1939.
7. A. D. Pelsch, *Trudy Solyanoĭ Laboratorii,* **14,** 5, 1937.

Die Grundetappen der Biogenese des Chlorophylls

T. N. GODNEV

Akademie der Wissenschaften BSSR, Minsk

AUF DIE genetische Verwandtschaft zwischen Chlorophyll und Hämin hat schon Nencki [1] hingewiesen. Hat man zu Ende des vorigen Jahrhunderts diese Verwandtschaft nur phylogenetisch betrachtet, wobei die Bildung des Chlorophylls als primär angesehen wurde, da die anfängliche Entstehung autotropher Organismen fast allgemeine Anerkennung besaß, so läßt sich gegenwärtig kaum darüber zweifeln, daß die zuerst auf Erden entstandenen Lebensformen Organismen mit heterotrophem Stoffwechsel waren. Das geht auch aus der Theorie von A. I. Oparin hervor [2].

Hieraus folgt, daß von den zwei wichtigsten Natur-Pigmenten das Häm wahrscheinlich das älteste ist.

Obwohl das Gesamtbild des Evolutionsprozesses auf Gesetzen der Paläontologie, vergleichender Anatomie und auf dem biogenetischen Gesetz beruht, so gibt die Paläontologie verhältnismäßig wenig in der Frage der Bildung und Evolution von Häm und Chlorophyll, weil diese Pigmente außerordentlich unstabil sind. Die Ergebnisse von Treibs [3] jedoch über die Auffindung von Porphyrinen in der Form von Vanadiensalzen in tiefen Erdschichten weisen auf eine noch ältere Bildung von hämähnlichen Verbindungen hin. Dafür spricht auch die Tatsache, daß bei primitiven Formen von Bakterien und Protozoa Fermente entdeckt wurden deren Agon den Metall-Protoporphyrinen identisch oder ähnlich ist.

Die Schule Hans Fischers [4] nimmt für die primitivste Form dieses Stoffes folgende Verbindung an : 1 : 3 : 5 : 8-Tetramethyl-4-Vinyl-Porphin-2-Formyl-6 : 7-Dipropionsäure.

Noch bevor es zur klaren Feststellung der Struktur oder bloß der Zusammensetzung des Chlorophyll-Moleküls kam, wurden wichtige Ergebnisse über den Bildungsprozeß des Chlorophylls in den Arbeiten von Preisser [5], Sachs [5] und besonders von Timirjasew [6], und in späterer Zeit von Monteverde & Ljubimenko [7] erzielt.

Die Feststellung der Strukturformel des Chlorophylls, anfänglich nur annähernd und später detailliert, machte die Aufstellung von Hypothesen über aufeinanderfolgende Bildungsphasen des Chlorophyll-Moleküls in lebenden Plastiden möglich, wobei man sich auf Beobachtungen über die Dynamik des Prozesses unter verschiedenen Bedingungen stützte.

In den Jahren 1926–1928 wurde vom Autor die Hypothese ausgesprochen über die Bildung von Pyrrol-Kernen zu Beginn des Prozesses und ihre nachfolgende Kondensierung in α-Form zu Leukoverbindungen, die dann durch Oxydierung zunächst zu Tetraoxyporphin und hierauf infolge Dehydrierung und Reduktion in Porphyrin umwandeln [8].

Die gleichzeitig von Euler vorgeschlagene Theorie über den Übergang der Carotinoidketten ins Porphyrinsystem durch Schließung des Ringes und Einführung von Stickstoffatomen, erklärte nicht die Lage von Substituenten im Porphyrinkern.

Schon die bloße Ähnlichkeit im Bau der Häm- und Chlorophyll-Moleküle wies auf die große Wahrscheinlichkeit ihrer gemeinschaftlichen Bildung hin. Die Methode der radioaktiven Atome ermöglichte es, im Laufe der letzten Jahre alle Grundstadien der Hämbildung völlig zu klären. Durch die Einführung stickstoffmarkierten Glycin (^{15}N) ins Blut gelang es Shemin und seinen Mitarbeitern [9] nachzuweisen, daß Stickstoff in alle vier Pyrrolkerne des Porphyrinsystems eindringt.

Die erwähnten Forscher [10] wie auch Neuberger [11], Cookson & Rimington [12], Falk & Dresel [13] führten in die Erythrocyten und in Hämolysate die wahrscheinlichen Vorläufer des Häms ein, welche in verschiedenen Stellungen markiert waren, und konnten die aufeinanderfolgende Überführung der Atome aus diesen Molekülen in die Häm-Moleküle verfolgen. Dies gelang infolge außerordentlich langsamer Aufspaltung des Häm-Moleküls und der Porphyrine bis zu Pyrrolkernen und nachfolgender Aufspaltung dieser Kerne bis zu den einfachsten Fragmenten, deren Radioaktivität einzeln gemessen wurde. Auf diesem Wege wurde das folgende Schema für die Bildung des Farbstoffes des Blutpigments entworfen. Azetat, durch Einschließung in den Tricarbonsäure-Cyclus, verwandelt sich in Succinyl—Koenzym A, und gibt mit Glycin Moleküle der Aminolävulinsäure (ALS). Zwei Moleküle dieser Säure bilden ein substituiertes Porphobilinogen—Pyrrol mit Essig-und Propionsäure in Stellungen 3 und 4 und mit Aminomethyl in Stellung 2

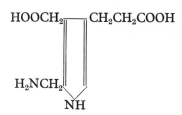

Porphobilinogen (PBG), wie experimentell festgestellt wurde, ist nicht nur im Blut, sondern auch in Hämolysaten und sogar in noch einfacheren Systemen fähig in Uroporphyrin I überzugehen und, was besonders interessant ist, sich in den dritten Isomer umzuwandeln, welcher den Grundbaustein der natürlichen Pigmente bildet. Gleichzeitig gelang es in einer Reihe von Laboratorien den genauen Charakter des Ferments festzustellen, welches die Umwandlung des ALS in PBG bewirkt. Wahrscheinlich erfolgt die Bildung der Porphyrine nach vorhergehender Bildung von Tripyrrylmethanen, welche infolge Zerfalls derartige Dipyrrylmethane geben, die ihrerseits fähig sind, sich in Porphyrine umzuwandeln. Uroporphyrin ergibt infolge Dehydrierung und Decarboxylierung mit höchster Wahrscheinlichkeit Protoporphyrin.

Nicht nur die Analogie im Bau des Chlorophylls und Häms, sondern auch experimentelle Befunde weisen darauf hin, daß die anfänglichen Stadien der Dunkelreaktionen der Chlorophyll-Molekülbildung zusammenfallen bis zum Protoporphyrin mit den oben angeführten Stadien der Hämbildung. Die Versuche von Granick [14] mit Bestrahlung von Chlorellazellen mit X-Strahlen oder Ultraviolettstrahlen führten zur Bildung von Mutanten in der Nachkommenschaft dieser bestrahlten Zellen, welche kein Chlorophyll enthalten, sondern an seiner Stelle Protoporphyrin, Magnesium-Protoporphyrin, Vinyl-Phäoporphyrin A_5 und andere Porphyrine anhäufen. Dies läßt sich leicht erklären durch die Annahme eines Abbruchs der Reaktionskette auf verschiedenen Stadien des Prozesses bis zum Porphyrin, das ein Zwischenglied sowohl bei der Bildung von Chlorophyll wie auch von Häm darstellt.

Alle diese Versuche geben jedoch keinen zweifellosen und endgültigen Nachweis. In der Pflanzenzelle gibt es immer Fermente, welche eine aktive Gruppe enthalten, die identisch ist mit dem Häm, oder ihm nahesteht; und wenn die Chlorophyll-Bildung auf etwas anderem Wege vor sich ginge, so würde seine Hemmung durch Röntgenstrahlen zu dem von Granick beobachteten Effekt führen. Immerhin erfährt die Identität der Bildungsprozesse von Häm und Chlorophyll stets mehr und mehr Bestätigung.

Bogorad & Granick [15] beobachteten die Bildung von Porphyrinen aus Porphobilinogen in Chlorellazellen, die durch Erfrierung und Auftauen getötet waren. Salomon, Altman & Della-Rosa [16] züchteten Chlorella in Kulturen, welche Glycin und Acetat, die in verschiedenen Stellungen markiert waren, enthielten, und zeigten, daß erste und zweite Kohlenstoffatom des Azetats und das zweite des Glycin in ungefähr der gleichen Proportion benützt werden, wie sie in der Biosynthese des Häms beobachtet wird.

Der Carboxyl-Kohlenstoff des Glykokolls ist jedoch in Chlorophyll a und b gleichfalls vertreten, während in der Biosynthese des Häms dieser Carboxyl-Kohlenstoff nicht benützt wird. Dieser Umstand könnte einen Einwand gegen die einheitliche Bildung beider Pigmente abgeben. Es ist jedoch eher damit zu rechnen, daß die Carboxylgruppe bloß indirekt am Prozeß teilnimmt. In einer mit A. A. Schlick zusammen ausgeführten Arbeit gelang es nachzuweisen, daß bei Einführung von im Carboxyl markiertem Azetat in die ethiolierten Zwiebelblätter und nachfolgender Belichtung Chlorophyll a und b eine bedeutende Aktivität zeigen (chromatographische Aufteilung), die in den beiden Fällen etwa die gleiche ist. In einem analogen, unter den gleichen Bedingungen ausgeführten Versuch mit Glycin wurde festgestellt, daß die spezifische Aktivität der Chlorophyll-Komponenten außerordentlich gering war: 26 mal niedriger als in Versuchen mit dem Carboxyl-Kohlenstoff des Azetats. Da nun in der Biosynthese des Häms und wahrscheinlich auch des Chlorophylls der Carboxyl-Kohlenstoff nur für die Bildung zweier Atome des Moleküls benutzt wird, so folgt, daß der Einbau der Carboxyl-Gruppe des Glycin nur ein Zehntel des Grammatoms darstellt, also ein verschwindend kleiner Wert ist, und daß also die Teilnahme dieses Carboxyls nur eine indirekte sein kann. Es ist möglich, daß das Glycin, zum Beispiel, sich in Azetat desaminiert und nur nachher in den Cyclus der pigmentbildenden Reaktionskette eintritt.

Woher kommt aber das Azetat im Organismus der Pflanzen? Der ganze Verlauf des Stoffwechsels im pflanzlichen wie im tierischen Organismus macht die Richtigkeit der Annahme wahrscheinlich, daß Monosen derartige Grundquellen sein könnten, wie es zum Beispiel der Fall ist bei der Umwandlung in Brenztraubensäure mit nachfolgender oxydierender Decarboxylierung in Azetyl-Koenzym A und späterem Eindringen in den Tricarbonsäure-Cyclus. Damit ließe sich denn auch die schon von Palladin [17] und anderen russischen Gelehrten gemachte Beobachtung erklären, daß die Bildung von Chlorophyll von Kohlehydraten günstig beinflußt wird.

In einer mit A. A. Schlick ausgeführten Arbeit [18] wurden Versuche angestellt über den Einbau von Kohlenstoff aus gleichmäßig markierter Glukose in das Chlorophyllmolekül. Die Glukose wurde in ethiolierte Zwiebelblätter eingeführt, worauf die Blätter so lange bestrahlt wurden, bis bedeutendes Ergrünen auftrat. Die extrahierten Pigmente zeigten nach chromatographischer Aufteilung sowohl im grünen Teil wie in den Carotenoiden eine Aktivität, welche ungefähr der Belichtungsdauer proportional war. Nach Aufspaltung des Chlorophylls mit Hilfe von Verseifung wurde festgestellt, daß die Aktivität des Phorbinteils und des Phytolrestes, sowie auch der Carotinoiden ihren Molekulargewichten proportional, also für ein Kohlenstoffatom die gleiche ist. Dieser Umstand wird gut durch die Annahme interpretiert, daß das Azetat in der Synthese des Phorbinteils des Chlorophylls denselben Anteil nimmt, wie in der Synthese des Häms, da ein derartiger Anteil des Azetats bei Carotenoiden und Phytol keinem Zweifel unterliegt.

All das erlaubt mit einem hohen Grad von Sicherheit die Reaktionsfolge im Bildungsprozeß des Chlorophylls in den Plastiden der Pflanzen folgendermaßen darzustellen. Bis zur Bildung des Protoporphyrins geht der Prozeß in der gleichen Weise vor sich, wie bei der Bildung des Häms, hierbei sind Glukose und andere Monosen eine der Hauptquellen der Kohlenstoffatome in seinem Molekül, welche für die Anfangsbildung des Azetats und möglicherweise eines bedeutenden Teils des Glykokolls benützt werden.

Da in den Versuchen von Granick mit Mutanten-Auswüchsen aus bestrahlten Chlorellazellen das Vorhandensein von Magnesium Protoporphyrin und Vinyl-Phäoporphyrin A_5 festgestellt wurde, so kann man den wohlbegründeten Schluß ziehen, daß diese Stoffe sich aufeinanderfolgend aus Protoporphyrin bilden:

$$\text{Fe} \cdots \text{Häm}$$
$$\uparrow$$
$$\text{Protoporphyrin}$$
$$\downarrow$$
$$\text{Mg} \cdots \text{Magnesium-Protoporphyrin} \rightarrow \text{Mg—Vinyl-Phäopor-}$$
$$\text{phyrin A} \rightarrow \text{Protochlorophyll} \rightarrow \text{Chlorophyll } a.$$

Wenn die Teilnahme von Glycin, Acetat, Succinat (Succinyl Koenzym A), δ-Aminolävulinsäure und Porphobilinogen als unmittelbare Vorläufer des Häms und Chlorophylls keinem Zweifel unterliegt und immer mehr Bestätigung findet, so steht die Frage der Teilnahme des Porphyrins unter Zweifel und muß von Neuem geprüft werden.

Versuche mit Einführung von ^{14}C-markierten Porphyrinen in Erythrozyten-Hämolysate oder direkt ins Blut der Tiere gaben ungenaue oder negative Resultate. Die Aktivität des gebildeten Häms sowie auch anderer Porphyrine, deren Bildung aus dem eingeführten markierten Porphyrin erwartet wurde, war unbedeutend. Sie war um ein Mehrfaches niedriger als jene, welche unter analogen Bedingungen bei Einführung markierter unzweifelhafter Vorläufer des Häms beobachtet wurde. Eine Ausnahme wären wohl die Versuche Salomons und anderer mit Einführung markierten Uroporphyrins in die Zellen des Knochenmarks, in welchem sich markiertes Häm bildete. Die aktivität war jedoch auch hier nicht groß. Versuche von Dresel & Falk [19] mit isotoper Verdünnung deuten wie die vorherigen auch nur auf eine indirekte Teilnahme der Porphyrine in der Biosynthese von Häm hin. Die Einführung von nichtmarkierten Porphyrinen in Hämolysate, welche markiertes Glycin enthielten, hatte fast keinen Einfluß auf die Aktivität des gebildeten Häms (mit Ausnahme des dritten Uroporphyrins, welches die Aktivität des synthesierten Häms etwas verminderte). Dagegen verursachte die Einführung von tatsächlichen Vorläufern in unmarkiertem Zustand in ein solches System einen starken Rückgang der Aktivität sowohl des Häms wie der Porphyrine. Die Autoren kommen zu dem ohne weiteres wahrscheinlich erscheinenden Schluß, daß die Porphyrine nicht echte Vorläufer, sondern nur Nebenprodukte dieser echten Vorläufer sind und geben folgendes Schema:

$$
\begin{array}{ccccccc}
& & (COOH)_8 & (COOH)_7 & & (COOH)_4 & (COOH)_2 \\
& & \uparrow & \uparrow & & \uparrow & \uparrow \\
ALA \longrightarrow PBG \longrightarrow & x & \longrightarrow x & \longrightarrow x & \longrightarrow x & \longrightarrow H\ddot{a}m \\
& & \downarrow & & & \downarrow & \downarrow \\
& & \text{Uropor-} & & & \text{Kopropor-} & \text{Protopor-} \\
& & \text{phyrin III} & & & \text{phyrin III} & \text{phyrin}
\end{array}
$$

Wir haben schon in unserer zusammen mit A. A. Schlick gemachten Mitteilung darauf hingewiesen, daß der Übergang von Porphobilinogen in Porphyrine oder ihre Modifikationen—echte Zwischenprodukte in der Kette der Biosynthese—besonders wenig ausgearbeitet ist und Unklarheiten aufweist. Schon vor vielen Jahren hatte der Autor darauf hingewiesen, daß die Bildung der Porphyrine voraussichtlich über eine vorläufige Bildung von Leukoverbindungen von sich geht und zwar nach dem Schema:

Wir möchten mit großer Genugtuung feststellen, daß solche hervorragende Forscher wie Shemin, Rimington und Cookson die Bildung von Leukoverbindungen auf dem Wege der Umwandlung des Porphobilinogens in Porphyrin für wahrscheinlich halten; im übrigen gibt es hierfür auch experimentelle Befunde durch Untersuchung der Reaktionskinetik in Abhängigkeit von der Aeration.

Uroporphyrin wandelt sich mittels Dehydrierung und Decarboxylierung in Protoporphyrin III um, möglicherweise über das Stadium von Koproporphyrin III. Es ist jedoch wahrscheinlicher, das auch die weitere Umwandlung auf dem Niveau der reduzierten Leukoverbindungen vor sich geht, d.h. die Leukoverbindung des Uroporphyrins wandelt sich in Koproporphyrinogen und das

Letztere in Protoporphyrinogen um, das sich infolge Oxydierung mit Einbau von Eisen in Hämin umwandelt.

Wir halten es für wahrscheinlich, daß auch die schrittweise Bildung des Chlorophyllmoleküls auf dem Niveau von Leukoverbindungen bis zur Bildung des Leukoprotochlorophylls vor sich geht. Versuche über die Reduktion des Protochlorophylls und seine Reoxydation sind daher, unseres Erachtens, von Interesse.

Die Reduktion im Pyridin mit Hilfe von Zink und Essigsäure führte zur völligen Entfärbung des Pigments, aber nach erfolgter Reoxydation hatten wir ein Pigment, dessen Spektrum dem des Protochlorophylls ähnlich ist.

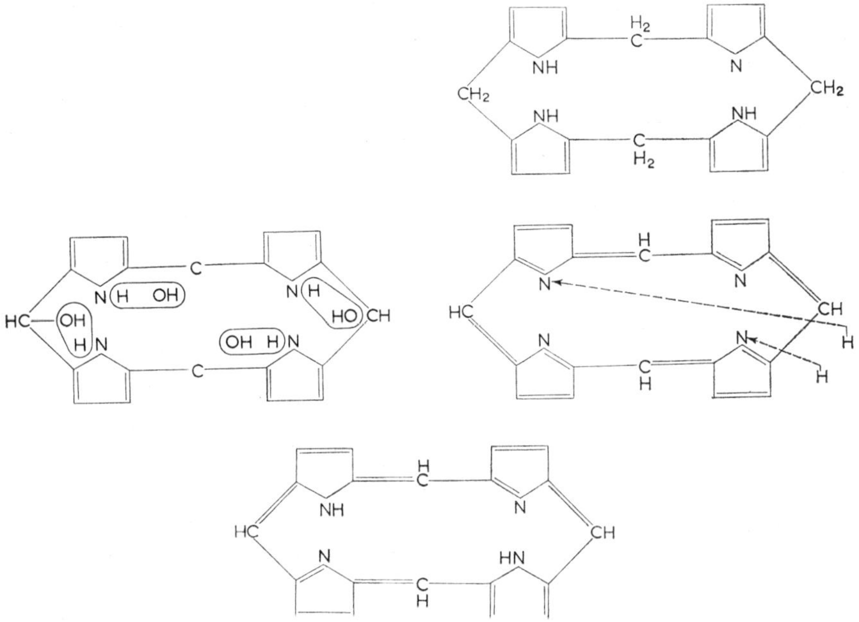

FIG. 1. Schema der Porphyrinsynthese.

Wenn noch bis vor kurzer Zeit der Übergang des Protochlorophylls in Chlorophyll als eine Folge der Hydrierung der 7–8 Doppelbindung des Protochlorophylls gedacht wurde, so ist man seither zu der Auffassung gelangt, daß sich diese Reaktion einen in zwei Stadien vor sich gehenden Zerfall darstellt.

Nach einer vorläufigen Mitteilung von Wolff & Preiss [20] ist das Protochlorophyll nicht ein Phytoläther des Magnesiumsalzes des Vinyl-Phäoporphyrin A_5, sondern ein Magnesiumsalz des Vinyl-Phäoporphyrins A_5. Im ersten Moment der Belichtung erfolgt eine Verbindung des Wasserstoffs an der Doppelbindung 7–8 und es bildet sich Chlorophyll *a*. Hierauf unter der Wirkung von Chlorophyllase erfolgt die Addition des Phytols.

Unsere vorläufigen Versuche bestätigen diese Ergebnisse. Bei Belichtung bei *ca.* 0° im Verlaufe einer halben Stunde bildete sich in ethiolierten Ausläufern Pigment, das aus einer 0,02 N alkalischen Ätherlösung extrahiert wurde und ein dem Chlorophyllid sehr ähnliches Spektrum besaß.

In den Arbeiten von Krassnovsky und Smith wurde nachgewiesen, daß in lebenden Plastiden Protochlorophyll und Chlorophyll zu einem Komplex verbunden sind, wobei die Moleküle dieses Komplexes Monomere darstellen. Auf Grund der Ergebnisse von Wolff und von uns soll daher im Anfangsstadium, vor der Wirkung von Chlorophyllase auf Chlorophyll, ein einfaches Monomer entstehen, welches nur aus dem Chlorophyllid-Molekül und Eiweiß besteht. Da das Chlorophyllid-Molekül hydrophil ist und, wie man annehmen kann, keinen Komplex mit Lipoiden bildet, so folgt daraus, daß der Komplex wahrscheinlich erst nach der Eindringung von Phytol entsteht.

Unsere Versuche über die Wechselwirking des Chlorophyllids a mit Protamin führten zur Bildung eines Produktes, dessen Spektrum demjenigen entsprach, welches Krassnovsky und Kossobutzkaja sowie Smith in den ersten Augenblicken der Chlorophyllbildung aus Protochlorophyll beobachten konnten. Der Gesamtprozeß der Chlorophyllbildung läßt sich nun durch folgendes Schema darstellen:

Der Prozeß der Biosynthese des Häms und des Chlorophylls ist so geartet, daß kein Zweifel besteht über die Gleichheit der Anfangsstadien in der Bildung beider Pigmente bis zum Protoporphyrin und bis zur sekundären Bildung des Chlorophylls aus ihm. Da nun die Grundzüge der Evolution in der Ontogenese und Phylogenese wenn auch nicht identisch so doch äußerst ähnlich sind, so kann man annehmen, daß die Aufdeckung der Grundetappen der Biosynthese des Chlorophylls zu wertvollen Hinweisen über seine Entstehungsgeschichte führen wird in jenen ersten einfachsten photosynthesierenden Organismen, mit denen die Entwicklung der Pflanzenwelt anfängt.

Die Biosynthese des Chlorophylls geht also unseren Vorstellungen entsprechend nach folgendem Schema vor sich:

Die aktive Form des Azetats, das sich hauptsächlich aus Monosen bildet, dringt in den Dreicarbonsäurecyclus ein und gibt Succinyl—S—Co A.

1. Monosen → Brenztraubensäure (oxydierende Decarboxylierung) → Acetyl —S—Co A → Citronensäure (oxydierende Decarboxylierung) → Succinyl—S— Co A.

2. Succinyl—S—CoA gibt in Wechselwirkung mit Glycin δ-Aminolävulinsäure.

3. Zwei Moleküle δ-Aminolävulinsäure bilden auf Grund der Knorr-Reaktion Porphobilinogen (2-Aminomethyl-3-Carboxymethyl-4-Carboxyäthyl-Pyrrol).

4. Porphobilinogen unterliegt der Desaminierung in der Aminomethylgruppe und der Oxydierung mit der Bildung des entsprechenden Alpha-Pyrrolaldehyds.

5. Die Wechselwirkung des Alpha-Pyrrolaldehyds mit zwei Molekülen Porphobilinogen ergibt Tripyrryl-methan mit den Resten von Essig—und Propionsaure in β-Stellungen.

6. Tripyrrylmethan gibt zwei Dipyrrylmethane mit bestimmter Reihenfolge der Reste von Essig- und Propionsäure in β-β' Stellungen.

7. Die Kondensierung dieser Methane nach Abspaltung der Aminomethylgruppe im ersten führt zur Bildung von Leuko-Uroporphyrin.

8. Die Decarboxylierung der Essigrests, sowie die Decarboxylierung und Dehydrierung der Propionreste in 2 : 4-Stellung ergibt Leuko-Protoporphyrin,

das sich infolge Eindringens von Magnesium in Leuko-Magnesium-Protopor-phyrin umwandelt.

9. Die Abspaltung zweier Wasserstoff-Atome: des einen vom γ-Methylen und des anderen im Propionrest (in 6-Stellung) und ihre Uebertragung zur Vinylgruppe (in Stellung 2) des Magnesium proto-Porphyrinogens ergibt Leuko-Vinyl-Phäoporphyrin A_5.

10. Das Eindringen von Methylalkohol ins Carboxyl (in der Stellung 10) ergibt die Leukoform des Protochlorophylls, das sich zu Protochlorophyll oxydiert.

11. Die Hydrogenisierung der Verbindung 7,8 ergibt Chlorophyllid A.

12. Durch Einwirkung von Chlorophyllase in Gegenwart von Phytol ver-wandelt sich das Chlorophyllid *a* in Chlorophyll *a*.

LITERATUR

1. M. NENTSKIĬ (NENCKI), *Arkh. biol. Nauk,* **5,** 301, 1897.
2. A. I. OPARIN, *Die Entstehung des Lebens auf der Erde.* Izd. Akad. Nauk. S.S.S.R., Moscow, 1957.
3, 4. H. FISCHER & H. ORTH, *Chemie des Pyrrols,* Bd. 2, Teil 2, Acad. Verlag, Leipzig, 1937.
5. F. CZAPEK, *Biochemie der Pflanzen.* Bd. 1, Springer, Berlin, 1922.
6. K. A. TIMIRYAZEV, *Gesamt. Werke.* Bd. 2, Selkhozgiz, Moscow, 1937.
7. N. A. MONTEVERDE & W. N. LUBIMENKO, *Izv. S-Pb. Bot. Sada,* **9,** 2, 27, 1909.
8. T. N. GODNEV, *Izv. Ivanovo-Voznes. Politekhn. Inst.,* **2,** 123, 1928.
9. D. SHEMIN & D. RITTENBERG, *J. biol. Chem.,* **166,** 621, 1946.
10. D. SHEMIN, Reports on *Int. Conf. Peaceful Uses Atomic Energy,* Geneva, 1955.
11. A. NEUBERGER & J. J. SCOTT, *Nature, Lond.,* **172,** 1093, 1953.
12. J. COOKSON & C. RIMINGTON, *Biochem. J.,* **57,** 476, 1954.
13. J. E. FALK & E. DRESEL, *Nature, Lond.,* **172,** 292, 1953.
14. S. GRANICK, *Ann. Rev. Plant Physiol.,* **2,** 115, 1951.
15. L. BOGORAD & S. GRANICK, *J. biol. Chem.,* **202,** 793, 1953.
16. K. SALOMON, K. ALTMAN & R. DELLA-ROSA, *Fed. Proc.,* **9,** 222, 1950; *J. biol. Chem.,* **202,** 171, 1953.
17. V. PALLADIN, *Trudy Obshchestva Isp. Prirody, Kharkov,* **26,** 67, 1891.
18. T. N. GODNEV & A. SHLYK, *Dokl. Akad. Nauk S.S.S.R.,* **94,** 301, 1954.
19. E. DRESEL & J. E. FALK, *Biochem. J.,* **64,** 388, 1956.
20. I. B. WOLFF & L. PRICE, *Plant Physiol.,* **31,** Suppl., 1956.

Thermal Factors in Archaeometabolism

S. SCHER

Department of Botany, Rutgers University, New Brunswick, New Jersey, U.S.A.*

ONE OF the more formidable problems of comparative biochemistry is to determine the nature of the first enzymes in primitive metabolic systems. Tracing the course of complex enzyme systems in present-day organisms to their beginnings poses several interesting questions. Do present-day forms contain primitive enzymes? Bernal [1] has suggested that everything an organism contains is evidence of its predecessors; and to get significant information we must draw deductions from the chemical structure of actual organisms. If we were to look for archaic enzymes in present-day organisms how would we recognize them? To put this question in another form, what would be the best criteria for primitive versus advanced or recent enzymes? According to Oparin [2], the primitive pattern of metabolism has been masked by a superstructure of supporting or alternate pathways. How then are we to differentiate the first enzymes from those which have developed later in the course of evolution?

If we take as postulates that life arose in thermal waters and that the evolution from heterotrophy to autotrophy was paralleled by a gradual decrease in environmental temperature, then thermal factors may provide clues to the nature of primitive metabolic systems.

In support of a thermal origin of life, Copeland [3] has provided taxonomic evidence which suggests that the thermophilic blue-green algae are a vestige of a primordial thermal flora, and that the thermophilic forms have given rise to the mesophilic forms. All of the orders, most of the families and the majority of the important genera of the blue-green algae include thermal species. Their notable incidence in thermal habitats suggests the probability of the origin of living organisms in general in thermal waters.

Haldane [4] postulated that the most primitive metabolic systems were heterotrophic, with little or no synthetic ability. The metabolic activity of such a unit was at first completely dependent upon its environment. Fox [5] has found that heat-induced anabolic reactions follow the same sequence, and produce the same intermediates as occur in present-day living systems. In addition, Abelson [6] has demonstrated the stability of certain amino acids at temperatures above those in thermal waters.

If biochemistry recapitulates pyrochemistry, as suggested by Fox, then it may be assumed that with the cooling of the Earth, the efficiency of pyrosynthesis would be reduced. This would result in the depletion of one or more inter-

---

* Present address: Hopkins Marine Station of Stanford University, Pacific Grove, California.

mediates in a thermal-reaction sequence. With each drop in temperature, a selective advantage would be enjoyed by a unit which could catalyse the synthesis of such intermediates from available precursors. As the stepwise evolution of synthetic ability followed the course suggested by Horowitz [7], chemical catalysis would replace heat-driven reaction. Although the efficiency of chemical catalysis may have been low at first, Calvin [8] has described how inorganic ions may have evolved into chelates and metal-containing enzymes with high efficiency.

If enzymes are substitutes for heat, then we should look for such evidence in thermophiles. Indeed, Harvey [9] has noted that, like most anaerobes, hot-spring algae lack catalase. At the high temperatures at which they live, the decomposition of hydrogen peroxide proceeds rapidly enough by itself.

The thermal limit of present-day blue-green algae and bacteria suggests that early enzymes may have originated at temperatures above 85 °C. The persistence of thermotolerant enzymes in present-day mesophiles as well as thermophiles attests to the primitiveness of this characteristic. If efficiency at high temperatures can be considered a primitive trait, then enzymes which have evolved comparatively recently are probably less efficient at high temperatures. If evolution proceeded from higher to lower environmental temperatures, can we recapitulate biochemical evolution by reversing the thermal arrow? Can we attempt to distinguish between archaic and recent metabolic pathways by using elevated temperature as a tool for probing into enzyme evolution?

We have been studying the enhanced nutritional requirements of a variety of protista (including algae, bacteria, protozoa as well as yeast), grown at incubator temperatures above their usual optimum. Heightened temperature, by fraying the biochemical fabric of the organism, brings to light otherwise poorly accessible metabolic chains. The appearance of substrates as temperature factors for photosynthetic forms such as *Ochromonas* and *Euglena* supports the idea of reduced biosynthetic ability of a primitive thermotolerant heterotroph. In addition increased requirements of metals and chelating agents in both photosynthetic and non-photosynthetic forms are reminiscent of a stage in Calvin's chemical evolution. Finally, since these experiments are carried out in synthetic media, the specific requirements of protista under thermal stress may shed light on the contribution of abiogenic synthesis to the primitive environment.

In summary, temperature factors appear to provide clues—could we but interpret them—to archaeometabolism, if we assume a thermal origin of life and an early evolutionary tendency from heterotrophy to autotrophy.

REFERENCES

1. J. D. BERNAL, *The Physical Basis of Life*. Routledge & Kegan Paul, London, 1951.
2. A. I. OPARIN, *The Origin of Life on the Earth*. Oliver & Boyd, London, 1957.
3. J. J. COPELAND, *Ann. N.Y. Acad. Sci.*, **36**, 1, 1936.
4. J. B. S. HALDANE, *The Origin of Life*. Rationalist Annual, 1929.
5. S. W. FOX et al. *Ann. N.Y. Acad. Sci.*, **69**, 328, 1957.
6. P. H. ABELSON, *Ann. N.Y. Acad. Sci.*, **69**, 276, 1957.
7. N. H. HOROWITZ, *Proc. nat. Acad. Sci., Wash.*, **31**, 153, 1945.
8. M. CALVIN, *Amer. Sci.*, **44**, 248, 1956.
9. R. B. HARVEY, *Science*, **60**, 481, 1924.

Session VII   **DISCUSSION**

Prof. M. Calvin (U.S.A.), as president of the closing session, gave a short resume of the basic problems which had been considered in the previous sessions and invited the participants in the Symposium to contribute to a general discussion on the whole programme of the Symposium.

The following took part in the general discussion: S. Fox (U.S.A.), S. Scher (U.S.A.), J. D. Bernal (Great Britain), D. I. Sapozhnikov (U.S.S.R.), K. Mothes (German Democratic Republic), E. Chargaff (U.S.A.), G. Schramm (Federal German Republic), K. Felix (Federal German Republic), A. M. Goldovskiĭ (U.S.S.R.), T. N. Godnev (U.S.S.R.), M. Calvin (U.S.A.), A. E. Braunshteĭn (U.S.S.R.), A. G. Pasynskiĭ (U.S.S.R.), S. Miller (U.S.A.), N. Horowitz (U.S.A.), L. Pauling (U.S.A.), A. I. Oparin (U.S.S.R.) and M. Florkin (Belgium). Below is a transcript of the contributions.

The contributors unanimously remarked on the extreme interest of the Symposium and the outstanding importance of Academician A. I. Oparin's theory which provides the possibility of proceeding to the formulation and solution of a number of questions concerned with the problem of the origin of life on the Earth. They thanked the International Union of Biochemistry, the Academy of Sciences of the U.S.S.R. and the Organizing Committee for calling the Symposium, for its good organization and for the hospitality extended to the foreign visitors.

S. Fox: It is necessary to stress the possible part played by a high environmental temperature in facilitating the process of autotrophic synthesis in the earliest living systems. In this connection we should direct attention to the importance of the investigations of the biochemical processes in contemporary thermophilic organisms inhabiting hot springs.

At the beginning of this month I visited Cerro Pietro, a volcanic region in Mexico, and was struck by the similarity of the flora of the hot springs there to that of the hot springs in the Yellowstone Park. Dr Scher informed me that the same is true of those in New Zealand. At the present moment I cannot yet tell what is the significance of this parallelism, but I expect that it is great and I hope that the biochemistry and biology of the organisms of hot springs will receive thorough study. Further details are given in an article in *J. chem. Educ.*, **34**, 472, 1957.

S. Scher: I listened with interest to Prof. Fox's remarks. It must be pointed out that a medium with a high osmotic pressure is more effective for supporting life at high temperatures.

J. D. Bernal: We have more or less reached agreement about the formation of the first organic compounds on the Earth and the conditions under which anaerobic and aerobic metabolism arose. But the intermediate stages between these two are still poorly studied and neither the chemical nor biochemical laws applying to them are known.

In giving a definition of life we must take into account whether the medium in which separate components interacted could promote the origin of metabolism and also whether coacervate drops (of the type discussed by Oparin) favourable to metabolic processes could develop within this medium.

The models which have been discussed here (gelatin and gum arabic) were not made with substances which could have been primary in the process of emergence of life, such as, for instance, polysaccharides. It would be a good thing if further investigations could be carried out using these substances.

D. I. Sapozhnikov: I cannot agree with the opinion that autotrophic organisms were primary. The idea that life first arose in hot springs was first put forward by V. L. Komarov

652

in 1936. While studying the flora in Kamchatka he found a rich microflora in hot springs at a temperature of 70° C.

It is, however, hard to believe that the first organisms could have had such a collection of enzymes as to enable them to assimilate simple mineral compounds.

K. MOTHES: Chemists and physicists have a different approach to the problem of the origin of life from that of biologists. In regarding life the biologist first sees its tremendous multiformity, the complexity of the organization of plants and animals, of organisms large and small. This being so, it is remarkable, and by no means self-evident, that, from a chemical point of view, the organization of all these organisms is essentially similar.

It follows that, in its development, life has proceeded along paths which are, from a chemical point of view, very close to one another. I consider that this is a very important point which biologists cannot ignore. Certainly the chemists, who have understood life better, will tell us that life is by no means so perfect as it is said to be, that life, in its contemporary form is not, so to speak, optimal. It only appears so near to perfection because everything which has developed during the past thousands of millions of years and has not been so well adapted to the conditions it met, has ceased to exist and does not come to our observation.

E. CHARGAFF: At first I did not intend to speak in this discussion but I already feel obliged to take part in it. I think that, having heard the truly passionate appeal of the biologists, the biochemist should raise his humble voice. If we look at what is now called comparative biochemistry we must conclude that it is essentially a catalogue of our ignorance. If the biochemist arrives at the amazing discovery that many enzymic systems and many components of cells are present and active in organisms separated widely from one another, is not the reason for this the fact that the biochemist only finds what he is looking for? For example, if we suspect or even believe that some nucleoproteins are in some way associated with the carrying or the transfer of hereditary characteristics, it is really surprising that the tables of nucleic acids in our books cover less than 100 organisms which have been studied. There is not the slightest reason to suppose that the billions and trillions of, as yet, unknown compounds have a similar composition.

G. SCHRAMM: Much has been said at this Symposium about the synthetic processes which are necessary for the formation of natural substances and highly developed organisms, but it seems to me that the processes of breakdown and degradation are also important for the development of living materials. It is now well known that selection is possible only when the individuals which have been formed disappear, to give place to ones which are better adapted.

I suggest that we ought to give deeper consideration to the question of how the systems, which were formed as a result of synthesis, were broken down to make way for further development.

K. FELIX: Dr. Mothes has already pointed out the similarity between the chemical composition of different organisms. This fact is often emphasized nowadays. We study processes in very simple organisms and find confirmation of them in more highly organized organisms. The difference between the different organisms consists in the quantitative composition of substances and their spatial arrangements and the temporal sequences of the reactions. This side of the question is, however, stil unknown to us.

The following example will serve to illustrate the importance of the quantitative relationships. People are distinguished from one another by their blood groups. These blood groups, so far as we can judge from our investigations, differ only insignificantly from one another in their composition; the difference consists only in the quantitative relationship between the components.

A. M. GOLDOVSKIĬ: The fact that contemporary organisms, independently of their degree of complexity, are essentially built up of substances belonging to the same chemical groups (proteins, carbohydrates, lipids, isoprene compounds and a few cyclic compounds) may be explained by assuming that substances of any particular group can take part in the common plan of chemical construction by fulfilling several functions in the complicated organism in question. Thus, different physical and chemical properties of substances of the particular group are used during the course of evolution. The substances are used in all sorts of ways to participate in the structure of the tissues and organs and to carry out functions of various kinds. Thus, for example, in the case of fats, various of their functions are based on physical properties such as their relatively low thermal conductivity, their specific gravity of less than one, their liquid state and their lubricating properties and on chemical properties such as their ability to produce a considerable amount of energy and water on oxidation.

Thus, as the complexity of structure and number of functions of organisms increased during the course of evolution, the use of substances belonging to any particular group extended to an ever-increasing number of fields (within each organism).

M. CALVIN: Being a cross between a biologist and a biochemist I should like to confirm and amplify the suggestion put forward by Prof. Bernal on behalf of another department of science. I should like to direct the attention of physical chemists and organic chemists to a large field of which we have absolutely no understanding, namely to the behaviour of coacervated colloids.

It is not a question of simply taking any mixture of polymers and seeing whether a coacervate can be made from it. I am speaking of a detailed understanding of the physico-chemical nature of the phenomenon. It is necessary to find out what molecular forces take part in the separation of a second phase out from a very dilute solution of substances of high molecular weight, how these new phases change the physical and chemical properties of the small molecules within the coacervates, how they affect the interaction of these molecules with one another and with the larger molecules associated with this new phase.

A. E. BRAUNSHTEĬN: I must comment on the inconsistency of the attempts of some scientists to identify the transition from non-living material to life with the appearance of particular, extremely complicated, forms of organic compounds, as if their molecules were endowed with the property of 'life' by virtue of their having particular physical and chemical characteristics. The ability of protein molecules, under certain conditions, to incorporate or even exchange individual amino acid residues is just as decisive as the importance of nucleic acids as a factor determining the specific direction of the biosynthesis of proteins, they are necessary prerequisites if proteins and nucleic acids are to be able to form the major components of multimolecular living systems. These characteristics do not, however, give any reason for considering molecules of protein or desoxyribose nucleic acid in the isolated state as 'living molecules'.

The transition to life only occurs when these compounds and many other substances are unified into complicated systems with an internal organization, capable of growth and of specific self-reproduction by means of an exchange of substances with the external environment. I should like to emphasize that there is one gap to be found in the programme of our Symposium. Although we have listened to a number of communications on the original conditions for the synthesis of amino acids and polypeptides, no new material has been laid before the Symposium concerning the conditions for the abiogenic synthesis of carbohydrates, especially of complicated carbohydrates, or concerning the possibilities for the synthesis of organic phosphorus compounds, in particular nucleotides. It is, at present, more difficult for us to imagine clearly how nucleotides or polymers of nucleic acid could have been formed abiogenically, than it is for us to imagine the formation of polymers such as proteins. Strictly speaking, we have no more experimental evidence for the direct synthesis of carbohydrates than Butlerov's model involving the condensation of formaldehyde.

I call upon those who are interested in this problem to take up the making of models in the field of the biosynthesis of organic phosphorus compounds, especially macroergic compounds and polymers which could lead to the synthesis of nucleic acids from inorganic polyphosphates. We should then be able to reopen the discussion on a more precise basis.

A. G. PASYNSKIĬ: If our respected Chairman is, as he puts it, a cross between a biologist and a biochemist, then I should like to intervene as a cross between a physical chemist and a biochemist. It seems to me that the study of the growth of complexity of substances in the course of evolution, which has made such great advances during the past years, is only one aspect of the evolutionary process. At the same time as the increase in complexity of substances there have arisen definite relationships, definite networks of reactions between these substances—an increase in complexity, not merely of the substances, but also of the network of chemical reactions. Nevertheless, this aspect of the matter has so far been quite insufficiently studied. The difficulty, which has been formulated in to-day's discussion, in understanding how a more or less uniform collection of substances could account for the evolution and development of the extreme variety of living creatures, may be explained, to a considerable extent, by the fact that the combination of these substances, the spatial arrangement and sequence of these reactions in time, can be infinitely various in a collection of very similar and uniform substances. I should like to remind you of Prof. Hinshelwood's formulation that in the cell there is a collection of more or less constant structures, while, at the same time, there is an extreme variety in the quantitative relationships between them.

I believe that for further symposia we shall want, not only an extension of our information on the conditions of formation of carbohydrates, nucleoproteins and other substances, but also of that concerning the basic laws governing the networks of chemical reactions in the open systems which led directly to the formation of life.

S. MILLER: I should like to take up the question of the origin of life at high temperatures. Life is in general characterized by lability to heating. The organic compounds of which the living organism is made up, nucleic acids, sugars, polysaccharides and proteins, are also characterized by lability to heating. When organic substances were heated under geological conditions they were heated for a very long time. It is hard to understand how the complexes of living structures of which living organisms must have been made up could have survived for long geological periods under conditions of high temperatures.

The hypothesis that the chemistry of the time before the beginning of life must have been similar to contemporary biochemistry is a great simplification of the reactions which took place in the earliest stages. I should like to emphasize that this hypothesis is not inevitable. Chemical processes occurring before and after the formation of enzymes must have been very different from one another both qualitatively and quantitatively. Let us consider, for example, the transamination of oxaloacetic acid with the formation of aspartic acid. In the absence of a sufficiently active catalyst to speed up the reaction, aspartic acid will, in general, not be formed because oxaloacetic acid is spontaneously decarboxylated at an appreciable rate. Thus, in the presence of a catalyst, aspartic acid is formed while, in the absence of a sufficiently active catalyst, it is not formed at all. I think that this example supports the idea that there was a qualitative difference in chemistry before and after the origin of enzymes.

K. MOTHES: So far as we know the conditions for the existence of living things at, for example, 85 °C are not limited by the fact that nucleic acids and proteins are denatured at high temperatures, but by the fact that, in hot springs, all metabolism becomes extremely difficult. Theoretically one may imagine that life has many forms which differ among other things in their response to a rise in temperature, and it cannot be affirmed categorically that life is necessarily characterized by being associated with a material which is denatured within the range 50–60 °C.

L. PAULING: I suggest that consideration of the question of the nature of proteins could be continued. In particular, I think it would be good if the question were more fully clarified from a theoretical point of view.

We know that, in general, proteins are molecules which can be denatured by various means, among them heating. It is certainly hard to construct a protein which will serve as an enzyme and yet will not be denatured by the temperature of the body. Let us suppose that we have an organism which produces proteins which are stable at one particular temperature. If the body temperature then falls and remains low for long enough, then the organism may change, mutating in such a way that its proteins are stable at the new lower temperature and unstable at the former temperature.

This would not involve any increase in complexity of the organism in the new conditions. I think therefore that, owing to the nature of protein molecules, there is nothing surprising in the fact that many proteins are stable at body temperature and even at a somewhat higher temperature, and that there are organisms which exist at high temperatures. Obviously these living things have learned to produce proteins which are stable at a high temperatures.

J. D. BERNAL: I only want to touch upon a question raised by Prof. Pauling. The rearrangement of proteins at the onset of denaturation depends essentially on the length of the chain. Calculations carried out in our Laboratory show that the character of the forces of the bonds in ordinary proteins corresponds well with what is known of the process of denaturation. Clearly, the smaller the protein molecule and the shorter its chain, the greater will be its stability. Such stable proteins are in fact known, for example insulin and ribonuclease. It seems to me that this argues in favour of, rather than against, the hypothesis that life arose at a high temperature, as short protein molecules must, naturally, have come before longer ones. It is therefore quite possible that the modifications suggested by Prof. Pauling consisted simply in lengthening of the shorter proteins as it was no longer useful for them to be short and thermostable.

My second remark concerns Prof. Calvin's contribution. Some types of coacervate can be studied quantitatively. These are coacervates in which the particles are long and straight and are arranged parallel to and equidistant from one another. Such an arrangement was first observed in the tobacco mosaic virus, but it has no connection with life, for Rizzatti has recently shown that very similar coacervates, with the particles parallel to one another, may be obtained with soap solutions.

A. I. OPARIN: Our Symposium is drawing to a close. I cannot speak for the other participants in our conference, but it seems to me that this arouses complicated, even mixed feelings in me. Of course we are all a bit tired by the glittering, many-coloured rainbow of the flow of ideas and facts which has passed before us, by the abundance of scientific achievement which we have witnessed. But still, in spite of this, I am sorry that our exchange of opinions is being brought to an end, as I believe that it has been very fruitful for the scientific solution of the problem of the origin of life. I hope that this is only a temporary break and that, in another place and at another time, this exchange of opinions will be renewed.

As Prof. Pauling rightly pointed out, one great advantage of our gathering is that we have not had to vote and we did not try to convert others to our opinions. Even if we sometimes could not reach an agreement and often differed in our opinions, all these disagreements, and even quarrels, have been useful for the rapid progress of knowledge.

A difference of opinion cannot be settled by conversations, only by experimental work; it therefore stimulates investigation. I consider that the most important result of the Symposium is that it displayed to each experimental scientist a number of problems, the solution of which requires the work of physicists, astronomers, geologists, chemists and biologists of various specialities.

Each of them, if only he is seriously interested in the solution of the problem of the origin of life, will find that progress in his field will contribute to the solution of the problem in which we are all interested.

Whether this progress is achieved by the syntheses of Miller or by Akabori's theory, by the remarkable investigations of the structure of proteins of Pauling or Bernal or the brilliant studies of nucleic acids and viruses of Chargaff, Fraenkel-Conrat and Schramm or by studying the origin of enzymes or open systems in pre-cellular structures, it will be equally encouraging as it will bring us nearer to a rapid solution of the problem which, as this Symposium has shown, is of great interest to us all.

Therefore, it seems to me that we should take measures, so that the richness of knowledge which has been assembled in this room may be made accessible and be available to wide circles of scientists.

Allow me to express my deep gratitude to all those who have participated in the Symposium and to wish them a pleasant journey to their own countries and success in their scientific work.

Furthermore, a number of contributors have remarked on the desirability of publishing a complete collection of the work of the Symposium, and also of calling, in the future, further international gatherings on the problem of the origin of life, chemical and biochemical evolution and related questions.

Resolutions to this effect, put forward by A. I. Oparin, M. Florkin and M. Calvin, were adopted by the meeting.

In declaring the Symposium closed, Prof. M. Calvin (U.S.A.) expressed the hope that the exchange of opinions and ideas which had taken place would be embodied in new experiments which, in their turn, would lead to new ideas. In the name of the participants in the Symposium Prof. Calvin expressed his hearty thanks to Acad. A. I. Oparin and the Organizing Committee which had organized the Symposium and made it so interesting and profitable.

Author Index

ABELSON, P. H. 133, 134, 135, 227, 241, 254, 650, 651
ABRAHAM, E. P. 260, 262
ACKERMAN, D. 103, 105
ACKERMAN, J. 103, 105
ADA, G. J. 407, 416
ADAMS, M. E. 559, 561
ADEL, A. 19, 22
ADELBERG 535
ADEMBRI, G. 160, 167
ADLER 373
ADLER, E. 546, 553
AHRENS, L. H. 24
AKABORI, S. 164, 168, 174, 175, 182, 183, 189, 196, 224, 229, 241, 254, 292, 656
AKIMOWA, L. 231, 240
AKULOV, N. S. 579
ALDERTON, W. 432, 436
ALEKSANDROV 495
ALEXANDER 318
ALEXANDER, J. 216, 223
ALLAN, D. W. 12, 15, 115
ALLEN, D. 220
ALLEN, M. B. 413, 417
ALLFREY, V. G. 335, 337, 343, 358, 359, 360, 363, 364, 365, 367, 404, 416, 464
ALLISON 222
ALLOWAY 318
ALMQUIST, H. J. 573, 577
ALPATOV, V. V. 115, 176, 178, 179
ALTMAN, K. 644, 649
AMMIARD, G. 99, 104
AMMON, K. 159, 167
ANDERSON, L. 98, 104
ANDERSON, R. A. 224, 225, 229
ANDERSON, R. B. 131, 135
ANDERSON, W. T. 101, 105
ANDO, T. 251, 255
ANDREEVA, G. A. 404, 416
ANDREJEW, J. 139
ANFINSEN, C. B. 244, 254, 289, 376, 397, 399, 564, 571
ANKER, H. S. 455, 459
ANSON 219
APT, L. 246, 255
ARD, W. B. 623, 625
ARISTOTLE 315
ARKHANGELSKIĬ, A. D. 85
ARNET, L. 467, 468, 469
ARNOLD, W. A. 614, 618
ARNON, D. I. 80, 83, 413, 417, 614, 618
ARNSTEIN, H. R. V. 144, 145, 150, 572, 577

ARRHENIUS, S. 16, 22
ARTSIKHOVSKAYA, E. 567, 568, 571
ASEEVA, K. B. 547, 554
ATKINSON, H. J. 224, 229
AUBEL, E. 585, 587, 589, 592
AVERY, O. T. 318, 320
AXELROD, B. 411, 417
AZARKH, R. M. 144, 145, 150, 535, 536, 537, 543

BAALSRUD, K. S. 520, 526
BAHADUR, K. 140, 145, 150, 151, 157, 171, 185, 294, 544
BAILAR, J. C. 161, 168
BAILEY, J. M. 293, 294
BAKER, W. 161, 167
BALANDIN, A. A. 161, 168
BALBI 286, 288
BALDWIN, E. 539, 543
BALDWIN, J. 107, 109
BALDWIN, K. B. 11, 15
BALE, W. F. 336, 343
BALESCU, R. 422, 425, 427
BALLOU, G. 471, 479
BALLOU, J. E. 336, 343
BALY, E. C. C. 140, 150
BANDURCKI, R. S. 411, 417
BANERJEE, B. 160, 167
BARBU, E. 46, 53, 323, 327, 331
BARGHOORN 34
BARKASH, A. 564, 571
BARKER, H. A. 336, 343, 628, 633
BARKULIS, S. S. 601, 605
BARLTROP, J. A. 621, 625
BARNER, H. D. 363, 367
BARRON, E. S. G. 623, 625
BARRY, J. M. 336, 343
BARTH, H. 145, 150
BASTIAN 76
BASTIN 85
BASYNSKII 43
BAUER, D. J. 342, 343
VON BAUEYER, A. 141, 150
BAXENDALE, J. H. 270, 274
BEACH, E. F. 573, 577
BEADLE, G. W. 248, 255, 260, 262
BECQUEREL, H. 101, 105
BEERS, R. F. 348, 357
BEEVERS, H. 566, 571
BEIJERINCK, M. W. 520, 526
BEKINA, R. M. 411, 415, 416, 417

BELCHRADEK, J. 490
BELIKHOV, D. V. 84, 93
BELL, L. N. 612, 617
BELL, P. H. 243, 254
BELOV 115
BELOZERSKIĬ, A. N. 322, 323, 327, 328, 329, 330, 331, 349, 356, 357, 374, 375, 377, 381, 434, 436
BELYAIEVA, M. I. 628, 633
BENNHOLD, H. 246, 254
BENOIT, J. 291
BENSON, A. A. 256, 262
BEREDJIK, N. 96, 104
BEREZOVSKAYA, N. N. 536, 543
BERG, L. S. 169, 170, 179
BERG, R. L. 169, 496
BERGEY 327,
BERGMANN, M. 231, 240
BERGMANN, W. 508, 509, 515
BERKOWITZ, J. 131, 135
BERLINGOZZI, S. 160, 167
BERNAL, J. D. 16, 22, 38, 46, 53, 116, 117, 123, 135, 169, 182, 189, 196, 282, 283, 284, 285, 288, 290, 339, 343, 369, 374, 385, 389, 398, 399, 492, 500, 585, 592, 650, 651, 652, 655, 656
BERNHEIM, F. 202, 206
BERNHEIM, M. L. C. 202, 206
BERNHEIMER, A. W. 348, 356
BERTALANFFY, L. V. 334, 340, 343, 437, 440
BERTHELOT, D. 139
BERTHELOT, M. 85
BERTRAND, G. 99, 104
BESSMAN, M. J. 345, 356
BETTI, M. 104, 105
BEUTHE 172
BEZINGER, E. N. 407, 409, 410, 411, 416, 417
BIEDERMANN, W. 263, 274
BILLEN, D. 594, 605
BIRCH 115
BIRCH, F. 25, 37
BIRD 375
BIRYUSOVA, V. I. 404, 416
BISSET, K. A. 629, 630, 633
BLAGOWESTSCHENSKI, A. W. 579, 636, 641
BLISS 514
BLOCK, H. 226, 230
BLOKHINA, V. P. 444
BLUM, H. F. 256, 262
BOATO, G. 72, 73, 75
BODINE, J. 569, 571
BOELL, E. 569, 571
BÖEMEKE, H. 630, 634
BÖESEKEN, J. 99, 104
BOGDANOV, G. A. 270
BOGORAD, L. 644, 649
BONINO, G. B. 160, 167
BONNER, J. 411, 417
BOOIJ, H. 471, 479

BORDET, J. 318, 320
BORSOOK, H. 363, 365, 367, 433, 436
BOSWORTH, R. C. L. 488, 490
BOULANGER 540
BOURLAND, E. 224, 229
BOVER, P. 471, 479
BOWEN 23
BOWNE, S. W. 226, 230
BRACHET, J. 298, 302, 309, 311, 344, 353, 356, 357, 361, 362, 363, 364, 365, 367, 377, 380, 463, 464
BRADLEY, W. 160, 167
BRAGG, Sir L. 397, 398, 399
BRANN, I. 199, 206
BRAUN, E. 102, 105
BRAUNSTEĬN, A. E. 118, 144, 145, 150, 527, 528, 529, 531, 534, 535, 536, 538, 540, 541, 543, 574, 577, 578, 654
BRDICKA, R. 572, 577
BREDIG, G. 102, 105, 163, 164, 168, 263, 270, 274
BREINL, F. 216, 223
BREMNER, J. M. 224, 229
BRESLER, E. S. 189, 196
BRESLER, S. E. 47, 53, 289, 290, 356, 357, 376, 378
BRICAS, E. 226, 227, 228, 229
BRIGGS, R. 362, 367
BRIN, G. P. 409, 411, 416, 607, 609, 612, 613, 617, 618
BROD, I. O. 86, 87, 91, 93, 94
BRODA, E. 334, 335, 336, 342, 343, 487
BRODSKIĬ, K. A. 175, 178
BRODSKIĬ, V. 494, 496
BROSER, W. 263, 274
BROWN 375
BROWN, H. 27, 37, 73, 75, 228, 230, 231, 240
BROWN, P. K. 621, 625
BROWN, R. A. 243, 254
BROWN, R. H. 107, 108, 109
BROWN, R. R. 253, 255
BRUCKNER 226
BRUMBERG, E. M. 493
BRUMMOND, D. O. 348, 357
BRUNEL, A. 551, 554
VON BRUNN-LEUBE, I. 307, 311
BRUTON, O. 246, 255
BRUZAU, M. 99, 104
BUCHANAN, C. 159, 167
BUCHANAN, J. M. 542, 543
BUDDINGTON 27
BUDOVSKIĬ, E. I. 165, 168, 176, 179
BULEN, W. A. 125, 135
BULLARD, Sir E. C. 25, 37
BULLEN, K. E. 27, 70, 75
BUNDEL, A. A. 546, 547, 548, 553, 554
BUNGENBERG DE JONG, H. G. 441, 443, 467, 468, 469, 471, 479, 493, 494
BURMA, P. 160, 167
BURNS, R. H. 224, 229

BURRELL, R. C. 125, 135
BURRIS, R. N. 535, 552, 554
BURTON, A. 445, 451, 454
BUTLEROW 222, 654
BUTLIN, K. R. 559, 561
BYK, A. 101, 105
BYSTROVA, M. 472, 479

CACCIOLA, A. R. 243, 254
CAHEN, L. 33, 37
CALDWELL, P. C. 440, 443
CALVIN, M. 44, 207, 256, 262, 266, 274, 317, 320, 487, 581, 614, 618, 621, 625, 651, 652, 654, 656
CALZAVARA, E. 99, 104
CAMIEN, M. N. 226, 230
CAMPBELL, D. H. 216, 223
CAPELLE, G. 551
CARASSITI, V. 160, 167
CARESS, A. 131, 135
CARLISLE, C. H. 397, 399
CÂRSTEANU, M. 466, 469
CASPAR, D. L. D. 48, 53, 390, 399
CASPERSON, T. 363, 365, 367
CASTERMAN, C. 364, 367
CEDRANGOLO, F. 281, 282, 284, 285, 286, 288, 536, 543
CHABEREK, S. 266, 267, 269, 274
CHAMBERLAIN, J. W. 19, 22
CHAMBERLIN, R. T. 27, 57, 66, 73, 75, 171
CHAMOVA, K. G. 411, 417
CHANCE, B. 269
CHANTRENNE, H. 356, 357, 362, 365, 367, 407, 416
CHANUTIN, A. 202, 206
CHAPEVILLE, F. 560, 561
CHARGAFF, E. 297, 298, 300, 301, 302, 322, 323, 331, 335, 343, 377, 470, 478, 653, 656
CHAYEN, R. 356, 357
CHAYEN, S. 356, 357
CHENERY, E. M. 80, 83
CHENG, P. Y. 396, 399
CHEPINOGA, O. P. 470, 471, 478, 479
CHERYNAK, M. S. 407, 416
CHEVRÈMONT, M. 364, 365, 367
CHEVRÈMONT-COMHAIRE, S. 364, 365, 367
CHIBNALL, A. C. 409, 410, 416, 548, 554
CHILD, R. B. 243, 254
CHRISTIANSEN 426
CHUPKA, W. A. 131, 135
CIERESZKO, L. S. 226, 230
CLAPP, F. G. 88, 93
CLARK, F. M. 574, 577
CLARK, H. E. 548, 554
CLARK, L. C. 127, 135
CLARKE, H. T. 224, 229
CLAUSON, R. 563, 571
CLELAND, K. W. 441, 443
CLEMO, G. R. 101, 105

CLOSE, A. A. 573, 577
CLOSS, K. 160, 167
COHEN, A. 139
COHEN, E. 89, 93
COHEN, H. L. 162, 168
COHEN, J. B. 141, 150
COHEN, P. 535
COHEN, S. S. 363, 367
COHEN-BAZIRE, G. 587, 592
COHN, M. 203, 206, 336, 343
COLEMAN, J. V. 612, 617
COLOMBO, U. 159, 167
COLTER, J. S. 375, 553, 554
COMANDON, J. 362, 367
COMFORT 510
COMMONER, B. 285, 288, 496
COOKSON, J. 643, 646, 649
COOPER, H. C. 158, 167
COPELAND, J. J. 650, 651
COREY, R. B. 175, 217, 220, 222, 223
COSTE, E. 85
COTTON, A. 101, 105
COURTNEY, R. 266, 267, 269, 274
COUSIN, D. 434, 436
COX, H. R. 243, 254
CRAIG, H. 82, 83
CRAIG, L. C. 229, 230
CRAMER, F. 160, 161, 167
CRAMPTON, C. F. 248, 255, 301, 302
CRAWHALL, J. C. 572, 577
CRICK, F. H. C. 217, 223, 397, 398, 399, 437, 439, 442
CUMMINS, C. S. 227, 230
CURIE, P. 101, 105
CURTI, R. 159, 167
CURTISS, R. 99, 104
CUTTER, V. M. 262, 267
CZAPEK, F. 642, 649

DALE, W. M. 622, 625
DALGLIESH, C. E. 160, 167
DALY 23
DALY, M. M. 364, 367
DANIELLI, J. F. 441, 443
DANIELSSON 579
DANJON, A. 19, 22
DARMOIS, E. 100, 105
DARWIN, C. 40, 117, 229, 256, 262, 369, 370
DARWIN, F. 141, 150
DAS, N. 546, 553
DAUBRÉE 23
DAVIDSON, J. N. 335, 343
DAVIES, B. D. 528, 534, 543
DAVIES, D. R. 352, 357
DAVIES, D. S. 243, 254
DAVIS, B. 471, 479
DAVIS, B. D. 195, 196
DAVIS, M. C. 243, 254
DAVIS, S. B. 243, 254

DAVSON, H. 441, 443
DAWSON 318
DAWSON, C. 565, 571
DAWSON, H. M. 99, 104
DAYTON, B. B. 131, 135
DEAN, A. 444, 454, 490
DEBOER, Z. C. 159, 167
DEBORIN, G. A. 467, 469, 470, 472, 475, 479, 492, 494, 499, 500
DE DONDER 487, 490
DEFAY, R. 422, 427
DE GROOT, S. R. 340, 343
DEICHMILLER, M. P. 335, 343
DEKEN-GRENSON, M. 404, 416
DE LA VERGNE, L. 336, 343
DELBRÜCK, M. 216, 223
DELLA-ROSA, R. 644, 649
DELLWEG, H. 332, 333
DEMEREC 497
DE MOSS, J. A. 365, 367
DENBIGH, K. G. 444, 445, 451, 454
DENT, C. E. 160, 167
DERRIEN, Y. 245, 254
DERVICHIAN, D. F. 470, 479
DERYAGIN, B. V. 392, 399
DESNUELLE, P. 247, 255, 492
DEUTSCH, T. 542, 543
DE VRIES, T. 159, 167
DEWEY, D. L. 195, 196, 224, 229
DHAR, N. R. 133, 135, 141, 150
DIACONO, G. 245, 254
DISKINA, B. S. 485, 498
DIXON, F. J. 335, 343
DIXON, M. 440, 443
DOBBERT, N. N. 226, 230
DOLLFUS, A. 19, 21, 22
DOMARADSKIĬ 538
DONE, J. 551, 554
DONIGER, R. 301, 302
DONN, B. 71, 75
DORNO, C. 176, 178
DOTY, P. 345, 353, 356
DOUDOROFF, M. 336, 343
DOUNCE, A. L. 356, 357, 377, 439, 442
DREIDING, R. 175, 178
DRESEL, E. 643, 646, 649
DRIKOS, G. 104, 105
DROUGININE, G. 100, 105
DUBININ, N. P. 108, 109
DUBOS, R. 471, 479
DUCET, G. 566, 571
DUGGAR, R. 612, 618
DUKYANOVA, N. P. 409, 411, 416
DUNHAM, T. 21, 22
DUNN, M. S. 226, 230
DUNNEBACKE, T. H. 321
DUSCHINSKY, R. 100, 105
DUTTA, S. K. 323, 331
DUTTON, H. 612, 618
DU VIGNEAUD, V. 572, 573, 577
DUYSENS, L. M. N. 612, 617

DYER, H. M. 573, 577

EACLE, A. S. 99, 104
EASTY, G. C. 160, 167
EDSALL, J. T. 400, 415
EFIMOCHKINA, E. F. 536, 540, 542
EGAMI, F. 348, 356, 545, 553, 555, 557, 558, 561
EHRENSVÄRD, G. 528, 543
EIGNER, E. A. 243, 254
ELLFOLK, N. 547, 554
ELLIOT, D. F. 243, 244, 254
ELODY, P. 542, 543
EL'PINER, I. E. 172
ELSDEN, S. R. 521, 526, 559, 561
ELSMORE, B. 107, 109
ELSON, D. 300, 301, 302, 323, 331
EMELÉUS, H. J. 137, 139
EMERSON, R. 614, 618
EMMETT, P. H. 159, 167
EMPEDOCLES 368
ENGELBRECHT, L. 484, 551, 554, 579
ENGELHARDT 592
ENGELS, F. 78, 373, 378, 485
ENGLER, R. 310, 312
ENGLERT, M. 243, 254
ENGLESBERG-LEVY, E. 589, 592
ENGLISH, J. P. 243, 254
EPHRUSSI, B. 588, 592
EPHRUSSI-TAYLOR 318
ERLENMEYER, E. 99, 104
ERLENMEYER, H. 163, 168
ERMOLAEV, V. L. 612, 615, 618
ERNSTER, L. 400, 415
EULER 535
EULER, H. 546, 553
EULER VON 643
EVANS, Jr., E. A. 144, 145, 150
EVREINOVA, T. N. 428, 429, 436, 466, 469, 493, 494
EVSTIGNEEV, V. B. 409, 411, 416, 609, 611, 612, 617, 618
EVSTIGNEEVA, Z. G. 548, 554
EYRING, H. 409, 416, 485, 486, 487

FABER, J. G. 159, 167
FAIRHURST, A. S. 535, 543, 547, 554
FALK, J. E. 643, 646, 649
FALTINGS, K. 136, 137, 139
FANKUCHEN, I. 392, 394, 399
FARKAS, A. 336, 343
FARKAS, L. 336, 343
FEDOTINA, V. 496
FEIGELMAN, H. 227, 230, 628, 633
FELIX, B. 99, 104
FELIX, K. 224, 229, 241, 248, 250, 255, 282, 292, 653
FELSENFELD, G. 352, 357
FERNANDEZ-MORAN, H. 311, 312

FERREIRA, R. C. 100, 105
FESENKOV, V. G. 9, 10, 15, 54, 55, 56, 65, 68, 69, 75, 84, 93, 113, 114, 119
FEUGHELMAN, M. 398, 399
FEVOLD, J. 432, 436
FICQ, A. 362, 363, 367
FILIPCHENKO 381
FILIPPOVICH, I. I. 405, 411, 416, 417, 566, 571
FINCHAM 535
FINN, B. M. 243, 254
FINSKY, M. J. 599, 605
FISCHER, E. 99, 104
FISCHER, H. 250, 255, 642, 649
FISCHGOLD, H. 159, 167
FISKE, P. S. 163, 168
FLEMING, W. H. 18, 22, 34, 37
FLEXNER, J. 569, 571
FLING, M. 145, 150
FLORKIN, M. 503, 578
FLOYD, C. S. 202, 206
FOGG, G. E. 409, 416
FOGH, J. 321
FOLKES 462
FOLKES, B. F. 409, 410, 416
FOLKES, J. P. 335, 344, 356, 364, 365, 367, 406, 415
DE FONBRUNE, P. 362, 367
FOSSE, R. 551, 554
FOSTER, D. 628, 633
FOSTER, J. W. 226, 229
FOWDEN, L. 409, 410, 416, 551, 554
FOX 625
FOX, H. M. 506, 515
FOX, S. W. 184, 256, 259, 260, 261, 262, 492, 650, 651, 652
FRAENKEL-CONRAT, H. 231, 240, 285, 288, 289, 303, 304, 305, 306, 309, 310, 311, 312, 319, 320, 344, 356, 364, 367, 370, 371, 372, 373, 375, 376, 379, 495, 496, 656
FRANK, G. M. 491
FRANKLIN, R. 48, 53
FRANKLIN, R. E. 310, 312, 390, 391, 398, 399
FRANTZ, I. D. 227, 230, 628, 633
FRANZ, J. 134, 135
FREDBERG, F. 406, 416
FREEMAN, B. 362, 367
FRENCH, C. S. 612, 618
FRENKEL-CONRAT 289
FRENKEL, A. 614, 618
FRENKEL, A. W. 599, 605
FRENKEL, YA. N. 488, 490
FRESCO, J. R. 345, 353, 356
FREUDENBERG, K. 99, 104
FREUNDLER, J. 104, 105
FREY-WYSSLING, A. 441, 443
FRISCH-NIGGEMEYER 396, 399
FROMAGEOT, C. 226, 227, 228, 229, 548, 554

FROMAGEOT, F. 560, 561
FROST, A. V. 90, 93
FRY, E. S. 575, 577
FUJII 409, 416
FUJII, Y. 183
FUJISAWA, Y. J. 160, 167
FUJISE, S. 163, 168
FUJIWARA, T. 224, 229, 409, 410, 416
FURBERG, S. 398, 399

GAFFRON, H. 594, 605
GALAEV, YU V. 226, 229
GALAKTIONOVA, N. M. 111
GALE, E. F. 335, 343, 344, 356, 364, 365, 367, 406, 415, 433, 434, 436, 462
GAMOW, G. 377
GARIBYANTS, A. A. 109
GARRISON, W. M. 133, 135, 256, 262
GARŹO, T. 455, 459
GAUDECHON, H. 139
GAUSS 422
GAUZE, G. F. 177, 179, 291
GAVRILOVA, L. P. 330, 331
GAVRILOVA, V. A. 409, 411, 416, 609, 611, 612, 617
GAWRILOW, N. 231, 240
GERANSON 13
GERASSIMOVA-NAVASHINA 170
GEIJER, P. 34, 37
GEL'MAN, N. S. 413, 417, 430, 431, 432, 435, 436, 466, 469, 475, 479
GERNEZ 98, 104
GERSHGORIN, S. A. 493
GERSTNER, F. 164, 168, 272, 274
GEST, H. 594, 598, 599, 601, 602, 605
GEYER, V. 159, 167
GHEORGHE, V. 466, 469
GHOSH, J. G. 164, 168
GIBBS, M. 566, 571
GIERER, A. 303, 304, 306, 309, 310, 311, 312, 319, 321, 344, 356, 364, 366, 367
GIGGER, R. P. 226, 227, 230
GILLESPIE, J. 565, 571
GILLIGAN, W. 565, 571
GINOZA, W. 310, 312
GINZBURG-KARAGICHEVA, T. L. 85
GIRI, K. V. 224, 229
GISH, D. T. 228, 230
GITLIN, D. 246, 255
GLANSDORFF, P. 421, 427
GLASS, H. B. 528, 529, 534, 535, 542, 543
GLIKINA 289
GLOCKLER, G. 133, 135
GNICHTEL, H. 263, 274
GODCHOT, M. 99, 104
GODNEV, T. N. 616, 618, 642, 644, 645, 646, 649
GOLDACRE, R. J. 391, 399
GOL'DENBERG, A. B. 617, 618
GOL'DIN, M. I. 496

GOL'DOVSKIĬ 185
GOLDOVSKII, A. M. 293, 294, 653
GOLDSCHMIDT 115
GOLDSCHMIDT, S. 158, 167
GOLDSCHMIDT, V. M. 14, 15, 23, 37, 79, 83
GOLDSTEIN, L. 365, 367
GOLUMBIC, E. 131, 135
GOMILEVSKAYA, N. A. 409, 411, 416
GOODY, R. M. 21, 22
GORBACHEVA, L. 472, 479
GORDY, W. 623, 625
GOUDOT, A. 269, 274
GRACE, J. B. 629, 633
GRAHAM, S. H. 159, 167
GRANDJEAN, J. 21, 22
GRANICK 212
GRANICK, S. 644, 645, 649
GRANT 34
GRAYTON, L. K. 13, 15
GREEN, C. 301, 302
GREEN, D. 400, 415
GREEN, H. 455, 459
GREENBERG, D. 406, 416
GREENHILL, A. W. 548, 554
GRIFFITH, F. 318, 321
GRIGNARD, V. 98, 104
GRINBERG, I. V. 92, 94
GROBBELAAR, N. 228, 230
GROMOVA, I. I. 138, 139
GROSS, J. 363, 365, 367
GROSSBERG, A. L. 218, 223
GROTE 139
GROTH, W. 131, 135, 136, 137, 138, 139
GRUBEŠOVA, M. 471, 479
GRUBHOFER, W. 159, 167
GRUNBERG, M. 587, 592
GRUNBERG-MANAGO, M. 344, 345, 346, 347, 348, 349, 350, 352, 353, 355, 356, 357, 366, 367, 377, 378
GRÜNER 34
GUBKIN, I. M. 85, 93, 119
GUEST, H. 600, 605
GUEX-HOLZER, S. 227, 230
GÜNTHER, G. 546, 553
GUREVICH, L. E. 70, 75
GURVICH, A. A. 185
GURWITSCH, A. 145, 146, 147, 148, 150
GURWITSCH, L. 145, 150
GUSTAFSON, R. 266, 267, 269, 274
GUSTAFSON, T. 300, 302, 323, 331
GUTENBERG, B. 37
GUTMAN, H. R. 573, 577
GUYE, C. E. 283

HAAKH, H. 105
HALDANE, J. B. S. 16, 22, 46, 53, 76, 83, 169, 282, 283, 284, 285, 288, 334, 342, 386, 399, 437, 440, 442, 585, 591, 592, 650, 651
HALDEMAN, R. G. 159, 167

HALL, J. 385
HALPERN, P. E. 226, 227, 230
HALVORSON, H. A. 363, 367
HALVORSON, H. O. 226, 230
HAMILTON 422
HAMILTON, J. G. 133, 135, 256, 262
HAMILTON, P. B. 224, 225, 229
HÄMMERLING, J. 362, 367
HANAFUSA 190
HANSHOFF, G. 260, 262
HARADA, K. 259
HARDIN, G. 141, 150
HARMON, J. 573, 577
HARRIES, J. O. 101, 105
HARRIS, H. 227, 230
HARRIS, S. I. 247, 255
HART, R. G. 309, 311, 347, 356
HARTECK, P. 136, 137, 139
HARVEY, R. B. 651
HASHIMOTO, C. 251, 255
HASLEWOOD, G. A. D. 509, 515
HASS, H. B. 159, 167
HASSID, W. Z. 336, 343
HASTINGS, A. B. 506
HAUDUROY 495
HAUGAARD, E. S. 231, 240
HAUGAARD, N. 231, 240
HAUROWITZ, F. 216, 223, 248, 255, 440, 443
HAVINGA, E. 99, 104
HAWORTH, R. D. 224, 229
HAWORTH, W. N. 293, 294
HAYASHI, T. 471, 479
HAZARD, C. 107, 109
HEATH, R. L. 293, 294
HEGGIE, D. 104, 105
HEGGIE, R. 101, 104, 105
HEIDELBERGER, M. 506
HEIDER, R. L. 132, 135
HEMS, R. 349, 357
HENDERSON 39, 385
HENDERSON, G. M. 160, 161, 167
HENGLIN 172
HENLE, F. 105
HEPPEL, L. A. 350, 357
HERRIOTT, R. 473, 479
HERTZ 422
HERZBERG, G. 19, 22
HESS, W. C. 127, 135, 572, 577
HEVESY, G. DE 334, 343
HEYMAN, H. 546, 553
HICKS, M. 445, 451, 454
HIGUCHI, M. 605
HILDITCH, T. P. 82, 83
HILL, A. V. 335, 343
HILL, D. W. 98, 104
HILZ, H. 560, 561
HINSHELWOOD, C. 338, 343, 440, 442, 443, 444, 454, 487, 490
HIRS, C. H. W. 237, 240, 290
HIRSCH, C. G. 455, 459

HIRSCH, H. 589, 592
HIRSCH, M. 434, 436
HOAGLAND, M. B. 365, 366, 367, 376, 377
HOARE, D. S. 226, 229
HOCKENHULL, D. J. 560, 561
HODGE, A. J. 386, 399
HOFFMANN, A. 159, 167
HOFFMANN-OSTENHOF, O. 197, 206, 290, 291, 338, 339, 343, 369
HOFMAN, T. 227, 230
HOFMANN, A. 226, 229
HOGNESS, D. S. 336, 343
HOLDEN, J. T. 226, 230
HOLDEN, M. 354 (Pl. IV), 357
HOLDSWORTH, E. S. 224, 229
HOLLAND, W. 268, 274
HOLMES, A. 33, 37
HOLMES, E. 14, 15
HOLT, A. S. 612, 617
HOLYK 24
HOLZAPFEL, L. 161, 168
HOMEYER, P. G. 259, 262
HORECKER, B. 564, 571
HORIUTI, J. 336, 343
HORN, M. J. 224, 229
HOROWITZ, N. H. 40, 53, 106, 107, 117, 118, 145, 150, 209, 248, 255, 378, 573, 577, 651
HOTCHKISS 318
HOTCHKISS, B. R. D. 298, 302, 332, 333
HOWARD, K. S. 243, 254
HOYLE, F. 71, 74, 75
HÜCKEL, W. 99, 104
HUFFMAN, H. M. 257, 262
HUGHES, E. W. 220
HUISMAN, T. H. J. 246, 254
HULTIN, T. 363, 367
HUMPHREY, J. H. 335, 336, 343
HUXLEY 76
HUXLEY, H. E. 311, 312, 386, 394, 399
HYYTIANEN, H. 266, 267, 269, 274

IKAWA, M. 216, 223, 227, 230, 529, 543
IKEDA, C. 216, 223
INGELMAN, B. 308, 311
INGERSOLL, A. V. 98, 104
INGRAM, V. M. 246
IOFFE 290
IOFFE, K. G. 379, 380
IORDACHE, C. 466, 469
ĬORDANOV, ZH. 491
ISELIN, B. 243, 244, 254
ISHII, S. 251, 255
ISHIMOTO, M. 558, 559, 561
ITANO, H. A. 220, 223
IVANKO, S. H. 405, 416
IVANOVA, T. 568, 571
IVANOVICS 226
IVANOVSKIĬ 314
IVASHCHENKO, G. 472, 479

IWAI, K. 251, 255
IZUMI, Y. 183

JACHERTS, D. 332, 333
JACKSON, D. S. 131, 135
JACKSON, I. 363, 367
JACOB, E. 407, 416
JACOBS, J. A. 12, 15, 115
JAEGER, F. M. 99, 101, 104, 105
JAENICKE, F. 134, 135
JAFFE, H. 159, 167
DE JAGER, C. 136, 139
JAKOVLEVA, A. V. 138, 139
JAMES, W. 566, 571
JAMIN 101, 105
JAMISON, M. 159, 167
JANEWAY, C. 246, 255
JEAN, G. 506
JEANS, Sir J. 16, 17, 20, 68
JEENER, R. 310, 312, 342, 343, 364, 367, 407, 416
JEFFREYS, H. 13, 15, 27
JENKINS, L. T. 226, 230
JERMYN, M. 565, 571
JERUSALIMSKY, N. D. 528, 543, 636, 641
JOHNS, A. T. 597, 605
JOHNSON, J. E. 184, 261, 262
JOHNSON, M. 159, 167
JOHNSON, M. L. 595, 605
JOLY, M. 46, 53
JOLY, R. 99, 104
JONES, A. S. 323, 331
JONES, D. B. 224, 229
JONES, T. C. 514, 515
DE JONG, B. 284
JONSEIS, J. H. P. 246, 254
JORDAN, P. 216, 223
JUCKER, H. 136, 139
JUNGFLEISH, E. 98, 99, 104
JUNQUEIRA, L. C. U. 455, 459

KAHN, J. R. 243, 244, 254
KAHN, M. 572, 577
KALINA, G. P. 484, 495
KALNITSKY 290
KAMEN, M. D. 559, 561, 608, 617
KAPLANSKIĬ, S. YA. 536, 543
KAPPELER, H. 243, 244, 254
KARAGUNIS, G. 104, 105, 159, 167
KARLSON, P. 569, 571
KARUSH, F. 160, 167
KASPERSON 494
KASSPAROV, K. 138, 139
KATCHALSKI, E. 258, 259, 262, 377
KATSOYANNIS, P. G. 228, 230
KAY, E. R. M. 356, 357, 377
KEARNS, C. W. 202, 206
KEIL, B. 238, 239, 240

KELLER, E. B. 363, 364, 365, 367, 403, 404, 415
KELLNER, W. 224, 229
KEMMRER, K. S. 573, 577
KEMPNER, W. 595, 596, 605
KEMPPI, A. 553, 554
KENDREW, J. C. 397, 399
KERMACK, W. O. 627, 633
KERNBAUM, M. 139
KHADZHIOLOV 491
KHESIN, R. B. 376, 404, 407, 415, 435, 436, 460, 498
KHLOPIN, V. G. 55, 65
KHMELEVSKAYA, L. V. 90, 93, 110
KHOLODNYĬ 169
KIELLEY, W. 564, 571
KIMURA, M. 251, 255
KING, E. J. 176, 178
KING, H. K. 547, 554
KING, J. 362, 367
KING, T. P. 229, 230
KIPPING, F. S. 98, 104
KIRKWOOD, J. G. 145, 150, 392, 399
KISCH, B. 202, 206
KISS, A. 270, 274
KISTIAKOWSKY, G. B. 131, 135
KITAI, R. 228, 230, 231, 240, 241, 254
KITSENKO, L. S. 271
KIVKUTSAN, F. P. 410, 417
KI YONG LEE 323, 327, 331
KIZEL, A. R. 177, 179
KLABUNOVSKIĬ, E. I. 95, 100, 101, 105, 158, 160, 161, 162, 164, 165, 167, 168, 174, 175, 176, 179, 183
KLIENEBERGER-NOBEL 485
KLIMMER, G. W. 572, 577
KLINGENBERG 499
KLOTZ, J. 470, 479
KLUBOV, V. A. 87, 93
KLUG, A. 310, 312, 390, 399
KLUYVER, A. J. 256, 262, 516, 525, 629, 630, 633, 634
KLYUGE, I. V. 540, 541, 543
KNIGHT, A. 315
KNOPF, E. 101, 105
KOBAYASHI, M. 161, 168
KOBYAKOVA, A. M. 404, 416, 563, 571
KOBOSEV, N. I. 266, 270, 274
KOENYVES, J. 259, 260, 262
KOEPSELL, H. J. 595, 605
KOFER, M. 100, 105
KOGL, F. 159, 167
KOLESNIKOV, P. 565, 571
KOMAROV, V. L. 652
KONDO, K. 565, 571
KONDRAT'EVA, E. N. 521, 526
KONIKOVA, A. S. 116, 226, 229, 230, 275, 277, 278, 279, 280, 378
KORNBERG, A. 107, 341, 343, 345, 347, 348, 356, 585, 586, 588, 589, 590, 591, 592, 628, 633

KÖRNER, W. 99, 104
KOROBKOV, I. L. 179
KOROLEV, N. V. 493
DE KOROSI, K. 145, 146, 150
KORPUSOVA, R. D. 269, 271, 274
KOSHLAND 291
KOSOBUTSKAYA, L. M. 616, 618
KOSSEL, A. 281, 286, 288
KOSSEL, H. 429, 436
KOSSOBUTSKAJA 648
KOSTER, H. 202, 206
KOTAKE, H. 160, 167
KOVACS, J. 259, 260, 262
KOVAGVA, E. B. 411, 417
KOYAMA, J. 558, 559, 561
KOZHEVNIKOV, A. V. 179, 181
KOZLOVSKAYA, S. V. 70, 75
KOZYREV, N. A. 11, 19, 22
KRAHL, M. 569, 571
KRAMER, M. 458, 459
KRAMPITZ, L. O. 595, 605
KRASNOVSKIĬ, A. A. 114, 409, 411, 416, 606, 607, 608, 609, 611, 612, 613, 615, 616, 617, 618, 648
KRASNOVSKIĬ, V. I. 44
KRAUSE, H. 335, 343
KRAVTSOV, A. 118
KREBS, H. 160, 167, 281, 286, 288
KREBS, H. A. 144, 150, 199, 206, 341, 343, 349, 357, 585, 586, 588, 589, 590, 591, 592
KREKELS, A. 250, 255
KREMS, A. Y. 88, 93
KRETOVICH, V. L. 536, 543, 544, 546, 547, 548, 553, 554, 578
KREUZER, L. 250, 255
KRIK (CRICK) F. 160, 167
KRITSKIĬ, G. A. 580
KRITSMAN, M. G. 144, 150, 226, 229, 275, 277, 278, 279, 280, 535, 543
KROIT 494
KROPOTKIN, P. N. 13, 15, 74, 75, 84, 86, 91, 93, 179, 180, 181
KUBOWITZ, F. 595, 596
KUDLAI, D. G. 328, 329, 331
KUDRYAVTSEV, A. M. 494
KUDRYAVTSEV, N. A. 86, 88, 93, 181
KUDRYAVTSEVA, N. A. 179, 181
KUEBLER, I. R. 161, 168
KUHN 96
KUHN, C. 99, 104
KUHN, R. 199, 206
KUHN, W. 101, 102, 103, 105, 160, 167
KUIPER, G. P. 9, 15, 17, 19, 21, 22, 57, 60, 63, 66, 67, 68, 69, 73, 75
KULP, J. L. 73, 75
KUNITZ, M. 473, 479
KURATA, Y. 558, 561
KUVAEVA, E. G. 409, 416
KUZIN 582
KUZNETSOV, S. I. 626, 633

LADYGINA, M. 567, 571
LAIDLAW 374
LAMBERTON, A. H. 159, 167
LAMBOOY, J. P. 160, 167
LANDES, K. L. 86, 93 •
LANDMAN, O. E. 364, 365, 367
LANDSTEINER, K. 216, 224, 228, 229, 230
LANGENBECK, W. 263, 274
LANGENBECK, W. 198, 206, 336, 343
LANKESTER, R. 506
LANTZSCH, K. 630, 634
LAPPIN, G. R. 127, 135
LARINOVA, G. 428
LARSEN, H. 615, 618
LASCELLES, J. 608, 617
LASKOWSKI, M. 492
LATMANISOWA, L. W. 145, 146, 150
LAURENT, G. 546, 554
LAUTSCH, W. 263, 274
LAWRENCE, N. L. 226, 230
LEBEDINSKIĬ, A. I. 70, 75, 113
LE BEL, J. A. 101, 105
LE CLERK, J. 363, 364, 367
LECOMTE DU NOÜY 283, 288
LEDERBERG 495
LEDERBERG, J. 319, 321
LEDERER, E. 270, 274
LEDOUX, L. 364, 365, 367
LEE, S. B. 602, 605
LEES, H. 627, 628, 633
LEES, H. A. 628, 633
LEGGE, I. W. 607, 617
LEHMAN, I. R. 345, 356
LEIDY 318
LEIGHTON, P. A. 133, 135, 136, 139
LELOIR 330
LEMBERG, R. 607, 617
LEMMLEĬN, G. G. 97, 176, 178
LEONARD, R. O. 224, 229
LE PAGE, J. A. 628, 633
LEPESHINSKAYA, O. B. 484
LERNER, A. B. 247, 255
LEROY, P. 291
LEVENE 322
LEVIN, B. J. 70, 75
LEVIN, B. YU. 67, 69, 70, 73, 75
LEVINSON, V. G. 91, 94
LEVY, H. B. 333
LEWIS, S. M. 599, 605
LICHSTEIN, H. C. 594, 605
LIDA, K. 558, 561
LIND, S. C. 133, 135
LINDBERG, O. 400, 415
LINDSTROM, E. S. 599, 605
LINDERSTRØM-LANG 289, 397, 399
LINK, T. A. 74, 75
LINNAEUS, C. 76
LIPKIN, D. L. 163, 168
LIPMANN, F. 44, 53, 560, 561
LIPPINCOTT, Y. 285, 288
LIPSHITZ, R. 300, 301, 302

LISSITZKY, S. 546, 554
LITTAUER, U. Z. 347, 348, 356
LITTLEFIELD, J. W. 363, 365, 367
LOEB, W. 151, 157
LODOCHNIKOV, V. N. 70, 75
LOMBARD, A. 300, 302
LOVERN, J. A. 82, 83
LOW, E. M. 224, 229
LUBIMENKO, W. N. 642, 649
LUCAS, F. 379, 380
LUCCHI, E. 104, 105
LUCK, J. 471, 479
LUDWIG, W. 175, 178
LUGG, J. W. H. 409, 410, 416
LUMRY, R. 409, 416
LUTHER, R. 101, 105
LUTIKOVA, O. 563, 571
LVOFF, F. A. 627, 633
LWOFF 318
LWOFF, A. 81, 83
LYELL 38, 41
LYNCH, V. H. 612, 617
LYOT 84
LYOT, B. 20, 22
LYUBIMOVA, E. A. 12, 15, 24, 37
LYUBIMOVA, H. A. 114

MCCARTY, M. 318, 320
MCCOLLOUGH, T. P. 19, 22
MACDERMOTT, E. 86, 93
MCDERMOTT, W. 471, 479
MCDOWALL, F. 612, 618
MCELROY, W. D. 528, 529, 534, 535, 542, 543
MCFARLANE, A. S. 335, 336, 343
MACGILLIVRAY, R. 224, 229
MACGREGOR 34
MACGREGOR, A. 19, 22
MCKENZIE, A. 98, 101, 104, 105
MACLEOD, C. M. 318, 320
MACNAMARA, J. 18, 22, 34, 37
MACNEICE, L. 83
MCOMIE, J. F. 161, 167
MCQUILLEN 495
MACHLIN, L. J. 575, 577
MACHT, D. J. 101, 105
MACOVSCHI, E. 466, 467, 469, 494
MAGNITSKIĬ 115
MAHLER, H. R. 199, 206
MAITLAND, P. 163, 168
MAKIVSKIĬ, E. M. 292
MÁLEK, I. 368
MANDEL'SHTAM 486
MANNING, W. 612, 618
MANTEN, A. 630, 634
MARCO POLO 80
MARKOV 171, 486
MARMUR, J. 434, 436
MARQUENNE, L. 99, 104
MARRE, E. 622, 625

MARTELL, A. 266, 267, 269, 274
MARTHIN, H. 160, 167
MARTIN, A. J. P. 226, 229
MARTIN, E. M. 407, 416
MARTIN, H. 224, 229
MASEVICH, A. G. 10, 15
MASON, B. 73, 75
MASON, M. 160, 167
MÄSTAR, P. 239, 240
MASUDA, T. 595, 599, 600, 605
MATHÉ, J. 224, 229
MATHIEU, J. P. 100, 105
MATTERN 316
MATTHEWS, D. M. 160, 167
MAURER, P. H. 335, 343
MAURER, W. 335, 343
MAYER, C. H. 19, 22
MAYER, A. W. 243, 254
MAYES, P. M. 621, 625
MAZIA, D. 362, 367
MAZUR, A. 202, 206, 224, 229
MEEDOM, B. 231, 240
MEGGY, A. B. 258, 262
MEI CHIO CHEN 136, 139
MEISENHELDER, J. H. 243, 254
MEISTER, A. 534, 535, 538, 543
MELIK-SARKISYAN, S. S. 144, 150, 407, 416
MELOVN, B. 239, 240
MEMPELL 497
MENDELEEV, D. I. 85
MENKE, W. 407, 416
MENOZZI, A. 99, 104
MENZEL, D. H. 19, 20, 22
MERRIFIELD, R. B. 231, 240, 359
MESSINEVA, M. A. 179, 181
METZLER, D. 529, 531, 543
METZNER, H. 411, 417
METZNER, M. 411, 417
MEYER, J. 101, 105
MICHURIN 381
MIGRDICHIAN, V. 131, 135
MII, S. 347, 356
MIKHLIN, D. 565, 571
MIKHLIN, D. M. 545, 553
MILAS, N. A. 131, 135
MILLER, E. C. 253, 255
MILLER, J. A. 253, 255
MILLER, L. L. 336, 343
MILLER, S. L. 17, 43, 61, 66, 83, 123, 124, 129, 135, 151, 154, 155, 156, 157, 171, 172, 183, 184, 189, 196, 241, 254, 256, 262, 282, 288, 294, 308, 311, 544, 585, 592, 619, 625, 655, 656
MILLERD, A. 411, 417
MILLS, W. H. 163, 168
MINAGAWA, T. 224, 229
MINARD, G. 548, 554
MINEEVA, L. 330, 331
MIRSKY, A. E. 219, 335, 337, 343, 358, 359, 360, 363, 364, 365, 367, 404, 416, 464

MISANI, F. 301, 302
MITARBEITER 291
MITCHELL 500
MITCHELL, P. 437, 441, 443
MITCHELL, S. 101, 105
MITRA, S. K. 56, 65
MOISSAN, H. 85
MOLISCH, H. 521, 526
MONOD, J. 203, 206, 336, 343, 441, 443
MONTEVERDE, N. A. 642, 649
MOORE 87, 290
MOORE, D. H. 470, 478
MOORE, P. 11, 15
MOORE, S. 125, 135, 237, 240, 409, 417
MORITA, Y. 565, 571
MORREFIELD, H. 202, 206
MORRISON, D. C. 133, 135, 256, 262
MORSE, L. M. 336, 343
MORTON, R. K. 407, 416
MOSOLOVA, I. M. 411, 415, 416, 417
MOTHES, K. 480, 550, 551, 554, 578, 653, 655
MOULD, D. L. 293, 294
MOUNTER, L. A. 202, 206
MOURGUE, M. 506
MOYER 375
MOYLE, J. 441, 443
MUDD, S. 216, 223
MUELER, G. 89, 93
MULLER 317, 318, 380
MÜLLER, F. H. 517, 519, 526
MUELLER, G. 72, 74, 75, 80, 83
MULVANIA 286, 288

NAGAI, Y. 558, 559, 561
NAKAMURA, N. 160, 167, 602, 605
NASONOV 495
NASONOV, D. N. 467, 469
NASTYUKOVA, O. K. 176, 179
NATTA, G. 104, 105, 175
NECHAYEVA, N. B. 630, 634
NEEDHAM, J. 76, 539, 543
NEIDIG, B. A. 127, 135
NEIL, J. M. 506
NEISH, A. S. 407, 416
NELSON, J. 565, 571
NENTSKII, M. 642, 649
NESTEROVSKAYA, E. A. 617, 618
NESTYUK, M. N. 428, 429, 436, 466, 469
NETTER 487
NEUBERG, C. 99, 104
NEUBERGER, A. 144, 145, 150, 336, 343, 643, 649
NEUIMIN, H. 136, 138, 139
NICHOLSON, S. B. 19, 22
NICKOLAEV, L. A. 273
NIDZYAN, E. I. 356, 357, 377
NIEMANN, C. 231, 240
NIKLAS, A. 335, 343
NIKOLAIDIS, P. 159, 167

NIKOLAEV, L. A. 263, 264, 269, 270, 271, 274
NIKOPULOS, A. 101, 105
NISMAN, B. 434, 436
NIWA, M. 557, 561
NORRISH, K. 392, 399
NOTHROP, D. 460, 473, 479, 492, 581
NOVELLI, G. D. 365, 367
NOYES, W. A. 133, 135
NUZHDIN, N. 563, 571
NUZHDIN, N. I. 380

OBATA, K. 605
OBATA, X. 594, 605
OBRUCHEV, V. A. 13, 15
OBRYADSHIKOV, S. N. 90, 93
OCHOA, S. 48, 53, 305, 346, 347, 348, 349, 350, 352, 356, 357, 359, 360, 366, 367, 377, 400, 415, 434, 436, 614, 618, 629, 633
ÖDA, Y. 593, 594, 595, 599, 600, 605
ODINTSOVA, M. S. 407, 416
OERIU, S. 291, 572, 577
OGNEV, B. V. 175, 178
OHARA, M. 558, 561
OHMURA, T. 411, 417
OKAMOTO, H. 348, 356
O'KANE, D. 434, 436
O'KANE, D. Y. 628, 633
OKAWA, K. 191, 196
OLENICHEVA 538
OLITSKY, P. K. 286, 288
OLIVARD, J. 531, 543
OMELYANSKIĬ, V. L. 626, 633
ONO, H. 224, 229
ONSAGER, L. 423, 427, 485
OOMACHI, K. 558, 561
OORT, J. 107, 109
OPARIN, A. I. 16, 22, 47, 53, 54, 55, 57, 61, 65, 76, 84, 93, 101, 105, 107, 119, 123, 132, 135, 141, 150, 151, 157, 174, 175, 189, 196, 197, 206, 207, 241, 254, 256, 262, 281, 284, 288, 294, 307, 317, 321, 334, 336, 339, 342, 343, 368, 369, 380, 381, 400, 413, 415, 417, 428, 429, 431, 432, 435, 436, 441, 443, 444, 454, 466, 467, 469, 470, 475, 479, 484, 491, 493, 494, 495, 498, 528, 543, 555, 561, 579, 580, 585, 586, 591, 592, 595, 596, 606, 608, 617, 619, 625, 627, 633, 635, 641, 642, 649, 650, 651, 652, 656
ÖPIK, E. 12, 15
OPPENHEIMER, F. 136, 139
ORECHOWITSCH, W. N. 336, 343
ORLOV, E. 152, 157
ORTH, H. 642, 649
ORTIZ, P. J. 346, 347, 349, 350, 352, 356, 366, 367
OSAWA, S. 358, 359, 360, 363, 365, 367, 404, 416

OSBORN, H. 626, 633
OSGAN, M. 96, 104
OSHIMA, Y. 224, 229
OSIPOVA, O. P. 407, 408, 411, 416
OSNITSKAYA, L. K. 90, 93
OSTEUX 540
OSTROMYSLENSKIĬ, I. 99, 100, 104, 105
OVERBEEK, J. TH. G. 392, 399
OZAWA, H. 245, 254, 508, 515

PADOA, M. 104, 105
PAGE, F. 445, 451, 454
PALADINI, A. 229, 230
PALEUS, S. 242, 254
PALIT, C. C. 133, 135
PALLADIN, V. 645, 649
PARDEE, A. B. 344, 356, 363, 367
PARHON, C. I. 572, 577
PARKER, B. N. 86, 88, 93
PARKER, D. I. 224, 229
PARLIN, R. B. 133, 135
PARTHIER 484
PASTEUR, L. 76, 82, 95, 96, 97, 100, 101, 105
PASYNSKIĬ, A. G. 151, 171, 172, 174, 184, 241, 254, 290, 444, 445, 451, 453, 454, 486, 500, 654
PATIL, K. M. 332, 333
PATRIKEEV, V. V. 100, 101, 105, 161, 168, 175, 176, 179
PATTERSON, T. S. 159, 167
PAULING, L. 47, 53, 119, 175, 182, 215, 216, 217, 218, 219, 220, 221, 222, 223, 245, 292, 437, 496, 497, 655, 656
PAVLOV, A. P. 13, 15
PAVLOVSKAYA, T. E. 43, 151, 171, 172, 184, 241, 254, 294
PAVLOVSKIĬ, E. N. 369
PAVLOVSKIĬ, I. 471, 479
PAYYNSKIĬ, A. J. 294
PEACOCK, D. H. 224, 229
PEARLMAN, G. 289
PEARSON, P. B. 575, 577
PEART, W. S. 243, 244, 254
PEAT, S. 293, 294
PEDERSEN, K. O. 506
PEIVE, A. V. 91, 93
PELSCH, A. D. 638, 641
PENDL, I. 224, 229
PEREVOSHCHIKOVA, K. A. 404, 416
PERL, K. 455, 459
PERRONE, J. C. 336, 343
PERRY, J. J. 226, 229
PERUTZ, M. 397, 398, 399
PETERS, T. 455, 459
PETRASHKAĬTE, S. K. 435, 436
PETRZILKA, T. 226, 229
PETTIT, E. 19, 22
PFAHL, D. 333
PFLEIDERER, G. 134, 135

PIKE, R. W. 93
PINCHOT, G. B. 590, 592
PIRAK, J. 104, 105
PIRIE, N. W. 16, 22, 45, 47, 53, 76, 78, 79, 82, 83, 117, 169, 282, 283, 284, 285, 288, 334, 336, 343, 354 (Pl. 4), 357, 370, 372, 585, 592
PLAUT, G. W. E. 345, 356
PLAUT, W. 365, 367
PLESHKOV, B. P. 405, 416
PLYSHEVSKAYA, E. G. 404, 416
PODISKO, V. S. 96, 104
POLANYI, M. 336, 343
POLLARD, J. K. 224, 228, 229, 230
POLLOCK, M. R. 203, 206
POLONOVSKY, J. 471, 479
POLOTSKIĬ 172
POMERANTSEVA 497
PONDER, E. 471, 479
PONOMAREV, A. A. 165, 168
POOLE, J. H. J. 16, 22, 30, 37, 57, 66
POPE, W. J. 98, 104
PORFIR'EV, V. D. 74, 75
PORFIRIEV, V. B. 92, 94
PORTER, J. R. 528, 543
POSTGATE, J. 557, 558, 561
POTAPOV, L. I. 92, 94, 99, 104
POTAPOV, V. M. 159, 167
POUCHET 76
POWELL, H. M. 161, 167
POWELL, J. F. 226, 229
POWERS, S. 88, 93
DE PRAILAUNE, S. 227, 230
PRELOG, V. 159, 160, 163, 167, 168
PRENDEL, R. 89, 93
PRESCOTT, D. M. 362, 367
PRESSMAN, D. 216, 218, 223
PRETEL-MARTINEZ, A. 323, 330
PRETORIAN, C. 466, 469
PRICE, C. C. 96, 104
PRICE, L. 647, 648, 649
PRIESTLEY, L. H. 141, 145, 150
PRIEUR, P. 589, 592
PRIGOGINE, I. 340, 343, 418, 419, 421, 427, 444, 454, 485, 486, 487, 490, 500
PRINGLE, J. 282, 283, 284, 285, 288
PRINGLE, J. W. S. 45, 46, 53, 441, 443
PRINGLE, S. 585, 592
PRINGSHEIM, E. G. 629, 634
PRYANISHNIKOV, D. N. 548, 554
PTUITI, A. 99, 104
PUCHER, G. W. 548, 554
PUISEUX, P. 11, 15
PURDIE, T. 99, 104
PUTNAM, F. 470, 479
PUTNAM, F. W. 283, 284, 285, 288

QUASTEL, J. H. 547, 553, 554, 556, 561

RAACKE, I. D. 579

RABINOWITCH, E. 133, 135, 587, 591, 592, 612, 615, 617, 618, 627, 629, 633
RACHEL, J. R. 572, 577
RACKER 210
RADCHENKO, O. A. 90, 91, 92, 93, 94
RADHAKRISHNAN, A. N. 224, 229
RADIN, N. S. 227, 230
RAGETLI, H. W. J. 409, 410, 416
RAHN, O. 145, 146, 147, 150
RAM, A. 141, 150
RAMASWAMY, A. S. 224, 229
RAMSEY, W. H. 70, 75
RAMSPERGER, H. C. 141, 145, 150
RANDALL, J. T. 398, 399
RANGANAYAKI, S. 140, 145, 150, 151, 157
RANKAMA, K. 34, 37, 57, 58, 66, 84, 93
RAS, R. 146, 148, 150
RASCHE, R. 160, 167
RATNER, S. 539, 540, 542, 543
RATYNSKIĬ, V. M. 31, 37
RAYLEIGH 30, 37
READ, J. 98, 104
REDDI, K. K. 323, 331
REDFIELD, R. R. 244, 254
REDI 76
REECE, E. 565, 571
REICHARD, P. 260, 262
REID 44
REID, C. 183, 619
REINER, J. M. 437, 442
RENSE, W. A. 131, 135
RESTLE, H. 307, 308, 311
REUTER 579
REVELL, S. H. 364, 365, 367
RICH, A. 345, 347, 352, 356, 357, 398, 399
RICH, J. 48, 53
RICK, W. 251
RICKENBERG, H. V. 442, 443
RIDEAL, SIR E. K. 131, 135, 136, 139
RIEGER, C. 599, 605
RIMINGTON, C. 643, 646, 649
RINIKER, B. 243, 244, 254
RINNE, F. 398, 399
RITCHIE, P. D. 100, 105
RITTEL, W. 243, 244, 254
RITTENBERG, D. 144, 150, 334, 341, 343, 643, 649
RIVERS, T. M. 321
RIZZATTI 656
ROASIO, G. 100, 105
ROBERT, L. 471, 479
ROBERTS, E. R. 278, 280, 356, 357
ROBERTS, J. 92
ROCHE, J. 245, 254, 506
ROGERS 290
ROKA 374
ROKA, L. 241, 248, 254, 282, 285, 288
ROLLEFSON, G. K. 133, 135
RONDONI, P. 285, 288
RONOV, A. B. 31, 37
ROQUES, M. 245, 254

Rose, J. 434, 436
Rose, W. C. 573, 575, 577
Rosenberg, A. 298, 302, 566, 571
Rosenberg, A. I. 587, 589, 592
Rosenberg, T. 441, 443
Rosenblum, E. D. 552, 554, 602, 605
Rosenthaler, J. 100, 105
Rossolimo, O. K. 116
Rost, F. 164, 168
Rothschild, H. A. 455, 459
Rubey 115
Rouyer, M. 224, 229
Rovery, M. 247, 255
Roy, D. K. 224, 229
Rozenzweig, B. 467, 469
Rubey, W. W. 30, 37, 57, 66, 73, 75, 78, 83, 84, 93, 134, 135
Rubin, B. 562, 563, 565, 567, 568, 571
Rubin, B. A. 294
Rubin, J. 594, 605
Rubina 377
Rudolph, L. 164, 168
Ruff, O. 99, 104
Ruhland, W. 520, 525, 551, 554
Rule, H. G. 160, 161, 167
Russell, R. D. 29, 37
Ryle, A. P. 231, 240, 241, 254
Ryle, M. 107, 109
Rysselberge, C. v. 310, 312
Ryzhkov, V. 373

Sakamoto, Y. 224, 229
Sakan, T. 160, 167
Sakov 592
Sakurai, S. 183
Salkind, S. 145, 146, 148, 150
Salle, A. J. 226, 230
Salmenoja, E. 553
Salomon, K. 644, 649
Saltman, P. 566, 571
Salton 495
Samarina, O. P. 226, 229, 278, 279, 280
Sanger 286, 290
Sanger, F. 228, 230, 231, 240, 241, 254
Santamaria, L. 140, 150
Santoro, A. 160, 167
Sapozhnikov, D. 183
Sapozhnikov, D. I. 555, 561, 598, 605, 635, 637, 641, 652
Sarys, H. 545, 553
Sasaki, H. 163, 168
Sastry, D. S. 160, 167
Satake, K. 224, 229, 245, 254, 508, 515
Sato, R. 557, 561
Schachman, H. 315
Schäfer 375
Schaffer, F. L. 316, 321
Scharfe 136, 139
Scher, S. 650, 652
Schiedt, U. 308, 311

Schiff, H. I. 131, 135
Schleith, L. 159, 167
Schlenk, W. 161, 168
Schlick, A. A. 644, 645, 646, 649
Schmidt 114, 115
Schmidt, C. L. A. 144, 150
Schmidt, O. Yu. 23, 54, 65, 68, 69, 71, 75, 91
Schneider, W. C. 400, 415
Schönfellinger, H. 342, 343
Schoenheimer 534
Schoenheimer, L. 334, 340, 343
Schoenheimer, R. 144, 150
Schramm, G. 248, 255, 303, 304, 306, 307, 309, 310, 311, 312, 319, 321, 344, 356, 364, 366, 367, 370, 371, 373, 374, 375, 376, 379, 495, 496, 653, 656
Schröeder, I. 333
Schroeder, W. A. 220
Schrödinger, E. 380, 437, 438, 439, 442
Schröer, E. 159, 167
Schulman, M. P. 532, 543
Schulz, G. V. 307, 311, 334, 340, 341, 342
Schulz, S. 471, 479
Schumacher, G. 309, 311
Schwab, G. M. 97, 164, 168
Schweitzer, G. K. 161, 168
Schwerdt, C. E. 316, 321
Schwyzer, R. 229, 230, 243, 244, 254
Scott, J. J. 643, 649
Seifert, H. 161, 168
Seifriz, W. 490
Senez, J. C. 559, 561
Senoh, S. 160, 167
Serchi, G. 160, 167
Severtsov 292
Sewell, C. E. 547, 554
Sewerzow, A. N. 636, 641
Shakeshaft, J. 107, 109
Shakespeare, N. E. 243, 254
Shankman, S. 226, 230
Shapiro, H. S. 301, 302
Shaposhnikov, V. N. 516, 525, 526
Shaw, J. T. B. 379, 380
Shemin 646
Shemin, D. 144, 150, 643, 649
Shemyakin, M. M. 529, 531, 543
Shepherd, C. J. 335
Shepherd, R. G. 243, 254
Sheshina, L. S. 90, 93
Shibanova, O. 472, 479
Shields, M. 623, 625
Shifrin, K. S. 171
Shillibeer, H. A. 29, 37
Shiota, T. 574, 577
Shipitsyna, G. K. 224, 229
Shiraki, M. 559, 561
Shklovskiĭ, I. S. 65, 69, 75, 107, 108, 109, 113, 114
Shorland, F. B. 82, 83

SHPITAL'SKIĬ, E. I. 270
SHUBERT, T. A. 428, 429, 436, 466, 469
SHUBNIKOV, A. V. 96, 104, 175, 178
SHUGAYEVA, N. V. 323, 327, 331
SHUĬKIN, N. I. 161, 168
SHUMWAY, N. P. 243, 244, 254
SIA 318
SIEBER, P. 229, 230
SIEGEL, A. 310, 312
SIEGEL, J. M. 521, 526
SIEKEVITZ, P. 403, 404, 415, 498
SIMMS, E. S. 345, 356
SIMPSON, R. 628, 633
SINGER, B. 303, 306, 309, 310, 312
SINGER, M. F. 352, 357
SINGER, S. J. 220, 223
SINSHEIMER, R. L. 107
SISAKYAN, N. M. 400, 404, 405, 407, 409,
    410, 411, 415, 416, 417, 462, 563, 565,
    566, 567, 571, 613, 618
SKAVRONSKAYA, A. G. 329, 331
SKEGGS, L. T. 243, 244, 254
SLACK, H. G. 336, 343
SLATER, E. C. 441, 443
SLAVIK, K. 470, 479, 499
SLICHTER, L. B. 24, 37
SLONIMSKI, P. P. 588, 589, 592
SLOTIN, L. 144, 145, 150
SMELLIE, R. M. S. 349, 357
SMETANA, R. 471, 479, 499
SMILLIE, R. M. 411, 417
SMIRNOV, B. P. 407, 416
SMIRNOV, L. A. 176, 179
SMIRNOVA, A. YA. 184
SMITH, J. D. 350, 357
SMITH, J. H. C. 616, 618, 648
SMITH, J. O. 347, 356
SMITH, L. 588, 592
SMITH, L. F. 231, 240, 241, 254
SMITH, P. W. 91, 94
SMITH, S. G. 379, 380
SMORODINTSEV, A. A. 371, 372
SMYTH, D. H. 160, 167
SMYTHE, M. P. 227, 230, 628, 633
SNELL, E. E. 226, 227, 230, 529, 531, 535,
    543
SOKOL, F. 492
SOKOLOFF, V. 91, 93
SOKOLOV, N. D. 119
SOKOLOV, N. V. 72, 75
SOKOLOV, V. A. 54, 57, 62, 63, 66, 86,
    90, 92, 93, 94
SOKOL'SKAYA, A. V. 172
SORET, C. 99, 104
ŠORM, F. 232, 237, 238, 239, 240, 290,
    471, 479, 499
SOROKIN, YU. I. 44, 520, 526, 626, 628,
    629, 630, 633, 634
SOWDEN, F. J. 224, 229
SPALLANZANI 76
SPARNAAY, M. J. 392, 399

SPENCER, H. 77
SPIEGELMAN, S. 203, 206, 344, 356, 363,
    364, 365, 367, 437, 442, 471, 479
SPIKES, J. D. 409, 416
SPIRIDONOVA, N. 563, 571
SPIRIN, A. S. 322, 323, 327, 328, 329,
    330, 331
SPITKOVSKIĬ, D. 476, 479
SPITKOVSKIĬ, D. M. 375
SPITZER 12
SPROSTON, T. 224, 229
SPURR, J. 11, 15
STACEY, M. 323, 331
STADNIKOV, G. L. 85
STAEHELIN 305, 495
STAEHELIN, M. 348, 357
STAHL, L. E. 131, 135
STANIER, R. Y. 203, 206, 587, 592
STANKJEWIECZ, A. 164, 168
STANLEY 371, 372, 496
STANLEY, W. M. 313, 321
STARKEY, R. L. 630, 634
STAUB 376
STAUDINGER 307
STAUFFER, J. 614, 618
STEIN, J. M. 224, 229
STEIN, W. H. 125, 135, 237, 240, 290
STEINER, A. B. 136, 139
STEKOL, J. A. 144, 145, 150, 572, 577
STEPHENSON, M. 556, 561, 626, 628, 630,
    632, 633, 634
STEPHENSON, M. L. 342, 343
STERN, H. 335, 337, 343
STERN, W. 409, 417
STERNBURG, J. 202, 206
STETTIN, M. R. 144, 150
STEVENS, C. M. 226, 227, 230
STEWARD, F. C. 228, 229
STEWART, T. D. 163, 168
STOANAKER, R. M. 19, 22
STOCK, L. W. 100, 105
STOLL, A. 159, 167, 226, 229
STORCH, H. H. 131, 135
STRAUB, F. B. 48, 53, 455, 458, 459, 462,
    492
STRAUSS, E. 202, 206
STRECKER, H. J. 547, 554
STREHLER, B. L. 612, 614, 617, 618, 622,
    625
STRUGLIA, L. S. 575, 577
SUDNIK, N. S. 616, 618
SUESS, H. 137, 139
SUKHAREVA, B. S. 279, 280
SULLIVAN, M. X. 572, 577
SUSS, E. 23, 74
SUTHERLAND 101, 105
SUYAMA, T. 558, 561
SVEDBERG, T. 506
SWALLOW, D. L. 260, 262
SYCHEV, A. P. 271
SYNGE, R. L. M. 224, 226, 227, 228, 229,

230, 281, 288, 290, 293, 294
SZABÓ, M. T. 455, 459
SZÖRENYI, E. T. 542, 543
SZULMAJSTER, I. 589, 592

TAKAHARA, S. 246, 254
TAKAHASHI, H. 557, 561
TAKASHIMA, S. 409, 416
TALBOTT, C. K. 161, 168
TALMAGE, D. W. 335, 343
TAMURA, T. 251, 255
TĂNASE, I. 572, 577
TANASESCU, I. 292
TANIGUCHI, S. 545, 553, 557, 558, 561
TARNANEN, J. 547, 554
TARVER, H. 335, 336, 343
TAYLOR, H. A. 136, 139
TAYLOR, H. S. 131, 135
TEAS, H. J. 145, 150
TENNEY, L. 101, 104, 105
TERENIN 43, 169
TERENIN, A. 136, 138, 139
TERENIN, A. N. 136, 138, 139, 611, 612, 615, 617, 618
TERENT'EV, A. P. 95, 99, 100, 104, 105, 159, 164, 165, 167, 168, 174, 176, 179
TETSUA, S. 574, 577
THANEREY, J. 108, 109
THEORELL, H. 564, 565, 571, 621, 625
THIMANN, K. V. 342, 343
THODE, H. G. 18, 22, 34, 37
THOMAS, M. 559, 561
THOMAS, R. 565, 571
THOMPSON, E. O. P. 231, 240
THOMPSON, R. C. 336, 343
THOMSON, J. 107, 109
TIAN, A. 139
TIMIRYAZEV, K. A. 642, 649
TIMOFEEVA, I. V. 407, 411, 416
TIMOFEEVA, M. 564, 571
TIMOFEEV-RISOVSKIĬ 497
TINYAKOV 497
TODD 377
TODOROV, K. D. 101, 105
TOMCSIK, J. 227, 230
TOMPSETT, R. 471, 479
TONGUR 492, 494
TONGUR, V. S. 375, 497, 499
TRASK, P. D. 85
TREBST, A. 332, 333
TRELEASE, S. F. 224, 229
TRENT, L. W. 301, 302
TRINCHER, K. S. 487
TRISTRAM 290
TROPP, E. 572, 577
TROSHIN, A. S. 467, 468, 469
TSUCHIDA, R. 101, 105, 161, 168
TUPPY, H. 231, 240, 242, 254
TURNER, E. 159, 167
TURING, A. M. 437, 442

TUTTLE, O. F. 13, 15
TYLER 34
TYMAKAV, V. D. 328, 329, 331
TYNDALL 76, 117

ULLMAN, A. 455, 459
UMBREIT, W. 434, 436, 614, 618, 626, 628, 630, 632, 633
UREY, H. 11, 15, 16, 17, 22, 23, 24, 37, 57, 65, 68, 69, 70, 71, 75, 91, 114, 123, 131, 132, 134, 135, 170, 171, 282, 586, 592
URYSON, S. I. 407, 416
USHER, F. L. 141, 145, 150
USPENSKIĬ, V. A. 86, 91, 94
USSING, H. H. 335, 343, 441, 443

VANDERHAEGHE, F. 362, 365, 367
VAN DER SCHAAF, P. C. 246, 254
VAN DER SCHEER, J. 243, 254
VANĚČEK, J. 239, 240
VAN HELMONT 76
VAN NIEL, C. B. 212, 256, 262, 517, 518, 521, 525, 587, 592, 615, 618, 628, 629, 630, 633, 634
VAN NORMAN, R. 612, 618
VAN ORSTRAND, C. E. 86, 93
VAN RYSSELBERGHE 487, 490
VAN SLYKE, D. D. 506
VAN'T HOFF 99, 101, 104, 158, 166
VAN TUYL, F. M. 86, 88, 93
VANYUSHIN, B. F. 323, 327, 331
VARNER, J. E. 125, 135
VASU, S. 466, 469
VECHER, A. S. 407, 416
VEGOTSKY, A. 184, 259, 260, 261, 262
VELLUZ, L. 99, 104
VENDRELY, C. 291
VENDRELY, R. 291
VERHOEVEN, W. 556, 561
VERHOGEN 115
VERNADSKIĬ 169, 170
VERNADSKII, V. I. 23, 89, 90, 93, 175, 176, 177, 178, 179, 181
VERNON, L. P. 559, 561, 608, 617
VER VIEBE, W. A. 86, 87, 93
VERZHBINSKAYA, N. 569, 571
VIAME, J. M. 418, 427
VIAMES 487
VICKERY 534, 578
VICKERY, H. B. 548, 554
VIELES, P. 99, 104
DU VIGNEAUD, V. 228, 230, 243, 254
VILLANO 286, 288
VIL'YAMS 169
VINOGRADOV, A. P. 23, 29, 30, 31, 33, 37, 69, 73, 115, 606, 617
VINOGRADSKY, S. N. 626, 633
VINSON, E. 202, 206

VIRTANEN, A. I. 228, 230, 534, 535, 545, 547, 553, 554
VISCHER, E. 301, 302
VOGLER, K. 100, 105
VOGLER, K. C. 630, 634
VOĬNOSKAYA, K. K. 607, 608, 615, 616, 617, 618
VOL'KENSHTEIN, M. 174
VOL'KENSHTEĬN, M. V. 485
VOLTERRA, V. 425, 427
VON BRAND, T. 563, 570, 571
VON PRZYLECKI, S. 471, 479
VOROB'EVA, L. M. 616, 618
VOROBIEV, V. I. 494
VYSOTSKIĬ, I. V. 90, 93

WACKER, A. 332, 333
WAHL, R. 323, 327, 331
WALD, G. 513, 515, 621, 625
WALEY, S. G. 226, 230
WALKER, A. C. 144, 150
WALKER, J. 152, 157
WALL, J. S. 126, 135
WALLACE 76
WALLACE, A. R. 370
WALLACE, W. M. 116
WALRAVEN, T. 107, 109
WALSH, D. 108, 109
WALTERS, R. F. 88, 93
WANG, T. 496
WARBURG, O. 133, 135, 263, 274, 614
WARD, H. 432, 436
WARNER, R. C. 345, 347, 352, 356
WASSEL, B. 572, 577
WASSINK, E. C. 409, 410, 416
WATSON, J. D. 217, 223, 437, 439, 442
WAUGH, D. F. 389, 399, 470, 478
WEBB, J. M. 333
WEBSTER, G. S. 404, 405, 416
WECKER 375
WECKER, E. 569, 571
WEGLER, R. 162, 163, 168
WEIBULL 495
WEICHERT, R. 160, 167
WEISS, I. 269, 274
WEISS, J. A. 572, 577
WEISS, K. W. 144, 145, 150
WEISS, S. 144, 145, 150
WEISSMAN, G. S. 224, 229
WELLS, I. C. 220, 223
WERKMAN, C. H. 144, 145, 150, 595, 605, 626, 632, 633
WERKMAN, K. Y. 626, 632, 633
WERNER, A. 99, 104
WERNER, A. S. 227, 230, 628, 633
WESSEL, G. 80, 83
WESTERBACK, S. 266, 267, 269, 274
WETZEL, K. 551, 554
WEYGAND, F. 332, 333
WEYSSENHOFF, H. V. 138, 139

WHATLEY, F. R. 413, 417
WHELAN, W. J. 293, 294
WHETMAN, M. D. 556, 561
WHIPPLE, F. H. 19, 20, 22
WHIPPLE, G. H. 336, 343
WHITE, A. 573, 577
WHITE, C. D. 85
WIAME, J. M. 340, 343, 535, 543
WIELAND, P. 160, 167
WIELAND, T. 134, 135
WILDE, K. A. 133, 135
WILDMAN, S. G. 310, 312
WILHELM, M. 163, 168
WILKENS, H. 11, 15
WILKINS, M. H. 398, 399
WILLIAMS 375
WILLIAMS, R. 285, 288
WILLIAMS, R. C. 303, 306, 309, 310, 312, 315, 320, 344, 356, 364, 367
WILLSTÄTTER, R. 159, 167
WILSON 115
WILSON, O. W. 602, 605
WILSON, P. W. 551, 552, 554, 595, 602, 605
WILSON, S. D. 243, 254
WILSON, S. W. 362, 367
WINDSOR, E. 224, 229
WINKLER, C. A. 131, 135
WINNICK 460
WINNICK, T. 406, 416
WISME 500
WISNIEWSKI, J. 353, 357
WISSMANN, H. 307, 311
WIXON, R. L. 575, 577
WOLF, M. 409, 416
WOLFF, I. B. 647, 648, 649
WOLFF, L. K. 146, 148, 150
WOMACK, M. 573, 577
WOOD, H. G. 144, 145, 150, 626, 632, 633
WOOD, J. 573, 577
WOOD, T. 278, 280
WOODS, E. 565, 571
WOODWARD, G. E. 575, 577
WOOLF, B. 547, 554
WOOLLEY, D. M. 231, 240
WOOLNOUGH, W. G. 88, 93
WORK, E. 195, 196, 224, 229
WRIGHT, G. F. 162, 167
WUITS, H. 163, 168
WÜSTINGER, G. 342, 343
WYROUBOFF, G. 99, 104
WYSS, O. 602, 605

YAGI, T. 559, 561
YAKABSON, L. M. 226, 229
YAKOVLEVA, V. I. 546, 553
YAMAGATA, S. 557, 561, 602, 605
YATES, W. F. 132, 135
YATKAR, S. K. 160, 167

Yemm, E. W. 409, 410, 416, 550, 554
Yeremenko, N. A. 86, 87, 93
Yocum, C. S. 615, 618
Yoneda, M. 594, 605
Yonge 510
Yoshida 374
Yoshihara, S. 224, 229
Yudkin, J. 336, 343
Yuile, C. L. 336, 343
Yushina, V. V. 271, 273, 274
Yyshepan, E. D. 226, 230

Zadorozhnyĭ, I. 23, 37
Zahn, R. K. 252, 255
Zaĭtseva, G. N. 323, 330, 331
Zamecnik 376
Zamecnik, O. C. 403, 415

Zamecnik, P. C. 342, 343, 363, 364, 365, 367
Zbarskiĭ, I. B. 404, 407, 416
Zechmeister, L. 159, 167
Zelenkova, V. V. 165, 168
Zelinskiĭ, N. D. 99, 104
Zelitch, I. 552, 554
Zeller, E. A. 511, 515
Zhukova, I. 431, 432, 435, 436
Zhukova, I. G. 413, 417, 466, 469
Ziff, M. 470, 478
Zil'ber, L. A. 372
Zillig, W. 309, 310, 311, 312
Zinder, N. D. 319, 321
Zitcer, E. M. 321
Zolkover, A. M. 404, 416
Zubovskaya, A. M. 497
Zwolinski, B. T. 133, 135
Zykov, S. I. 23, 37

43

Subject Index

Acer. Platanus 578
Acetabularia 361–362, 365
Acetic acid, formed by electrical discharge 125
Acetylorthrinine 578
Achatinella mustelina 177
Acipenser sturio 249
Acoustic energy, in initiation of chemical processes 172–173
Actinomyces globisporis streptomycini 325, 326
Actinomycetes 629, 630
Acyl-coenzyme A 401
Adenine, effect on proteinases 471
  in bacteria 324, 325, 328
  inhibition of by ribonucleic acid 471
Adenosine diphosphate 347, 348, 349, 354, 355
Adenosine monophosphate 346, 347, 349, 354, 355
  in protein synthesis 365, 366
Adenosine triphosphate 349, 355, 585
  in protein biosynthesis 462
  in protein synthesis 364
  in the incorporation of amino acids into proteins 279
  synthesis of 358, 359–360
Adenylic acid 324, 326, 328, 351, 359
  abiogenic synthesis of 149
Adolase, effect of deoxyribonucleic acid 471
Aerobacter aerogenes 325, 326, 332
Aerobiosis, evolution from anaerobiosis 585–592
  transition from anaerobiosis, hydrogen metabolism in 593–604
Age, effect on cysteine content, 572
Aggravation, theory of 266
Alanine, composition of 249
  deamination of 540, 541
  in assimilation of ammonia 547
  in bacteria 226
  in plants 410
  in protein synthesis 219
  peptide bonds in 233
  synthesis of 144, 193, 536, 548, 624
  by electrical discharge 125, 128, 130, 155, 156, 282
  by ultraviolet light 138, 153, 154
  in *B. subtilis* 547
β-Alanine, formed by spark discharge 125, 128, 129, 130

Alanyglycine, formation of 257
Alcaligenes faecalis 348, 590, 591
  dioxyribonucleic acid composition of 325, 326
  ribonucleic acid composition of, 326
Alcohol fermentation 595
Aldehyde oxidase 564
Aldehydes, formed by electrical discharge 127, 129, 130
  formed by ultraviolet light 131, 132, 137
  hydrolysis of 128–130
Aldolase 289
Algae 616–617, 651
  amino acid composition of 410
  on primaeval earth 34
  photocatalysis in 612
  proteins in 409
Allantoic acid 551, 578
Allantoin 512, 551, 578
Alpha-particles, chemical effects of 57, 58
Aluminium 80
Amide groups, structure of 221
Amide N, in plants 410
Aminoacetonitrile, formation of 189
  polymerization of 189
Amino acids, abiogenic synthesis of 140–149
  action of pyridoxal enzymes on 531–532
  amylase synthesised from 461
  and synthesis of chlorophyll 643, 644, 645
  assimilation of ammonia and 547, 548, 549
  biosynthesis of 528
  composition of 249
  deamination of 539–542
  D-forms 226
  effect of light on *dextro*- 97
  formation of in fore-protein 192–195
  in *Aspergillus niger* 577
  in bacteria 225–228
  in collagen 236
  in corticotropin 235, 236
  in cytochrome *c* 242
  in fibroin 236
  in fossils 241
  in haemoglobin 245, 508
  in hypertensin 243–244
  in insulin 235, 236, 242, 290
  in intermedin 247
  in peptides 235, 236

Amino acids—*continued*
  in proteins 224–225, 227–228, 235, 409–411
  in protein synthesis 219, 377, 464
  in shells of molluscs 178
  in silk fibroin 290
  incorporation of 432
  incorporation of into proteins of biological systems 276, 277–280
  occurrence in Nature 224–229
  organisation into proteins 282, 283, 285
  original formation of 151–157
  peptide bonds in 233
  peptides formed from 257
  sequences of, in proteins 379–380
  stereoisomers of in protoplasm 292
  Strecker synthesis of 129, 131–132
  synthesis of 44, 45, 51, 184, 185, 189, 256, 462
    ammonia in 534–539
    by electrical discharge 61, 77, 125, 128–130, 151–157, 256, 282
    by light 140–149
    by radiation 623–625
    by ultraviolet light 138, 151–157, 183
    effect of fluorocitrate on 537
    effect of Vitamin B_6 deficiency of 536, 537
  thermal treatment of forming peptides 257–260
  transformations of 529, 530
Amino acid derivatives, polymerization of 96
Amino acid oxidase, in synthesis of co-carboxylase 286–287
α-Aminoadipic acid, in maize 225
Amino-butyric acid, synthesis of by electrical discharge 125, 128, 156, 282
α-Amino*iso*butyric acid 225
Aminonitriles, hydrolysis of 128, 130
α-Aminosuccinaldehydic acid 145
Ammonia, activated by ultraviolet light 136, 137
  assimilation of 534, 544–553
  excretion of 539
  fixation in plants 548
  formation of by supersonic vibrations 172, 173
  in formation of amino acids 534–539
  in nitrogen metabolism 527
  in primitive oceans 183
  on planets 71
  organic compounds formed from 123, 138, 151, 154
Ammonium compounds, in volcanos 30, 41
Amoeba 361
Amylase, formation of 455–457
  in coacervates, 429–430
  in microsomes 456
  pancreatic 460

Anaerobiosis, evolution to aerobiosis 585–592
  hydrogen metabolism in 593–604
Analogy 505–506
Angiotensin 243–244
Animal metabolism, cytochrome oxidase in 569–570
Animal world, symmetry and asymmetry in 175–178
Animals, respiration in 563, 569, 570
Annelida, blood pigments in 505
  lipids in 508
  sterols in 509
Anthraxolites, composition of 92, Fig. 3
Antibodies, manufacture of 216, 218
Antipodes, spontaneous crystallization of 98–100
Aplexa hypnorum 178
Archaean era, petroleum in 85
Archaeozoic, solar radiation during 177
Archeogastropoda 177
Arginine, composition of 249
  in plants 410
  peptide bonds in 233
  synthesis of 145, 195
  synthesis of by light 142
Argon, from radioactive decay 29
Arthropoda, sterols in 509
Arum family 564
Ascorbic acid, oxidation of 445–453
Ascorbic oxidase 564
Asparagine 548
  in protein synthesis 538–539
  nitrogen in 550, 551, 552
Aspartase, forming aspartic acid 534
Aspartic acid, amide structure for peptides formed from 260
  composition of 249
  deamination of 540, 541
  in bacteria 226, 227
  in haemoglobin 508
  in plants 410
  peptide bonds in 233
  synthesis of 144, 192, 534, 536, 547
    by electrical discharge 125, 156, 282
    by light 142
  thermal treatment of 259
  transformation of 529, 530
Aspergillus niger 575, 576
Asphalts, composition of 92, Fig. 3
Asymmetric adsorption, resolution of racemates by 158–161
Asymmetric catalysis 97, 158–166, 174, 183
Asymmetric synthesis 96, 174–175
  absolute 158–166
  absolute under influence of circularly polarized light 101–103
  of organic compounds 114
  photochemical 100–101
  photochemical absolute 103

Asymmetry, in living material 182
Asymmetry of organic substances 174–175
Athiorhodaceae 521, 522
Atmosphere 133, 134, 169
    carbon dioxide in 57, 59, 60, 61, 62, 64,
        73, 77–78, 84, 109–110, 134
    formation of 73, 77
    helium in 57–58, 63
    hydrogen in 62, 63–64, 109, 110, 114
    methane in 57, 59, 60, 61, 62, 63, 64, 65
    nitrogen in 57, 59, 61, 64, 84, 134
    of Jupiter 10
    of Mars 11, 12, 21–22, 113
    of primaeval Earth 41, 52, 109, 123, 124
    of Uranus 10
    of Venus 19–21, 84
    oxygen in 77, 84, 109, 170, 587, 600
    role of radiation in formation of 170–171
    water in 57, 84, 109, 110, 134
Autocatalysis 209
Autoduplication 284–285
Autosynthesis 284–285
Autotrophic bacteria 227
Autotrophy, degrees of 635
Azotobacter 544, 602, 603, 604
    ribonucleic acid content of 323, 324, 345
Azotobacter agile deoxyribonucleic acid
        content of 323, 324, 325
    ribonucleic acid content of 323, 324, 325,
        326
Azotobacter chroococcum 600
    deoxyribonucleic acid composition of
        325
    ribonucleic acid composition of 326
Azotobacter vinelandii 345, 347, 349, 350,
        351, 355, 552
    deoxyribonucleic acid composition of
        325
    nucleic acids in 300
    ribonucleic acid composition of 326

Bacillus brevis, tyrosines in 228
Bacillus cereus 458
Bacillus firmus 332
Bacillus megatherium 364, 471
Bacillus mycoides 115, 176, 177, 292
Bacillus prodigious 332
Bacillus pycnoticus 520
Bacillus spp. 226
Bacillus subtilis 332, 535, 547
    amino acids in 227
Bacillus terminalis 226
Bacteria 503–504
    amino acids in 225–228
    anaerobiosis and aerobiosis in 585–586
    cellulase in 565
    chemoautotrophic 626
    chemosynthesis in 626–633
    cytochrome in 588
    deoxyribonucleic acid in 332

    enzymes in 345, 354, 632
    filterable forms of 495
    hydrogen donor utilization in 615–616
    lysogenic 318
    nitrate reduction by 556–560
    nitrogen metabolism in 544, 551, 552
    nucleic acids in, species specificity
        322–330, 332–333
    photosynthesis in 521–522
    protein synthesis in cells of 406
    respiration in 589
    sulphur 586, 628, 629, 630, 632
    photosynthesis in 518–519
Bacteriochlorophyll, 608, 615, 616
Bacteriophaeophytin 610
Bacterium enteriditis Breslau, deoxyribo-
        nucleic acid composition of 328, 329
    ribonucleic acid composition of 328, 329
Bacterium ologcarbophilum 630
Balsaminaceae 116
Barium, in choroid 80
Barley, amino acid composition of 410
Basalts, chemical analysis of 28
Beggiatoa 630
Begoniaceae 116
Bentonite clays, cryohydric forces in 393
S-Benzylcysteine, formation of 191–192
Biochemical constituents, evolution of
        504–510
Biochemical convergence 507
Biochemical evolution, and biosphere
        503–514
Biochemical parallelism 506
Biochemical processes in simple structures
        428–436
Biochemical systems, evolution of 510–514
Biogemetic law 259
Biological and chemical change 335–336
Biological reduction, and hydrogenase
        systems 596–599
Biological structures, scale of structural
        units in 385–399
    stages of aggregation in 395
Biology, entropy in 487–490
    thermodynamics in 485–490, 500
Bioluminescence 622
Biopoesis 116, 117
    biochemical aspects of 39
    conditions for 169–171
    major problems of 52
    stages of 38–53, 386
    structural units in 385–399
Biosphere, age of 37
    extension of and biochemical evolution
        503–514
    indications for early 32–35
    origin of 23–37
Bitumin, composition of 92, Fig. 3
    formation of 112
    in sedimentary and metamorphic rocks
        111–112

Blood 507
Blood pigments 505
Bombyx mori 379
Brain, energy metabolism in 569
  oxidative processes in 569
Broad beans 405, 408
Bromine, use of by eobionts 80
Bromuracil 332, 333
Brucella abortus 325, 326
Butter yellow 353
Butyryl-coenzyme A dehydrogenase 564

Callithamnion 612
Callithamnion rybosum 409, 410
Calothrix 544
Carbohydrate metabolism, in plants 564
  types of 594
Carbohydrates, breakdown of 564
  synthesis of 654
Carboligase 162, 166
Carbon, in meteorites 72, 73
  relationship with germanium 80
Carbonaceous chondrites 72
Carbon compounds, chemosynthesis of
    519–520
  photosynthesis of 516–518
Carbon dioxide, assimilation of 629, 632,
    637
  fixation of 614
  formation of 118, 171
  from volcanoes 60, 64
  in atmosphere 57, 59, 60, 61, 62, 64,
    73, 77–78, 84, 109, 110, 134
  in meteorites 71
  in primaeval atmosphere 31, 41
  on Mars 21, 22, 71, 113
  on Venus 19, 71
  organic compounds formed from 133
  partial pressures in tissues 563
  photochemical production of 599
  production by anaerobes 597, 598–599
Carbon monoxide, activated by ultraviolet
    light 136, 137
  effect of ultraviolet light on 131
  formation of 118, 125
  in atmosphere 134, 184
  organic compounds formed from 151,
    155
Carelozoon jatulica 34
Carotenoids 643, 645
  of diatoms 612
Carotenoid synthesis 609
Catalase, activity of copper resembling
    264–267, 270
  incorporation into coacervates 430–431
Catalase-like catalysts 264–267, 270
Catalysis 336, 339, 581
  asymmetric 161–166, 174, 183
  development of 207–210
  inorganic 198

in sedimentary formations 180–181
in the formation of enzymes 198, 201
multiplet theory of 162
photo 606–616
Cell(s), ammonia in 547, 548
  biochemical events in 432
  biochemical function of, structural ele-
    ments of 400–415
  changes in biochemical function 402–
    409
  chemical composition of units of 407
  correlation of structure and function 401
  differences in composition of animal and
    plant 407
  digestion in 510–511
  egg 491
  energy metabolism of 413
  enzyme activity in 411–413, 444–445
  formation of first 261
  glycolytic system in 413
  importance of deoxyribonucleic acid in
    290
  nucleus of 402
    in protein biosynthesis 462–463
  nucleotides in 359
  organoids of 400, 401
  origin of 50, 52
  plant, structure of 404
  protein synthesis in 460–465
  reproduction of 485
  requirements of 297–298
  specificity of 289, 290
  structure and biochemical functions in
    411–414
  structure of and protein synthesis 460–
    465
Cell lethals 463
Cell membranes, development of 340
  origin of 49
Cellulase, in bacteria 565
Cellulose, composition of 92, Fig. 3
Cephalopoda, sterols in 509
Chain processes in Nature 579
Clay, biogenesis in 182
Chelation 531
Chemical and biological exchange 335–336
Chemical diversity of the origin of life
    76–83
Chemiluminescence 614
Chemosynthesis, evolution of 614, 626–
    633
  in bacteria 626–633
  of carbon compounds 519–520
  oxidation in 628
Chemosynthetic microbes 626
Chlamydobacteriales 629, 630
Chlorella 644
Chlorella ellipsoidea 225
Chlorine, in meteorites 72
  use of by eobionts 80
Chlorobium 559

Chlorocruorin 505
Chlorophyll 586, 587, 591, 609, 610, 616
  biogenesis of 642–649
  relationship with haem 212
  sensitizing action of 611
  synthesis of 212
Chlorophyll-protein complex 409
Chloroplasts 213
  enzymes in 411–412
  incorporation of radioactive glycine into 406
  ribonucleic acid content of 408
Cholesterol, in various animal phyla 509
Chondrites, chemical elements in 28
  radioactivity in 24
Chordata, lipids and sterols in 508, 509
Chromatium vinosum 522
Chromium, in blood 80
Chromosomes 337
Chymotrypsin 289, 492
  artificial nucleoproteins made with 499
  effect of ribonucleic acid 471
  proteolytic activity associated with 498–499
Chymotrypsinogen 237, 238
Citrulline 542, 551, 578
Citrus fruits, metabolism in 565, 566
Clostridium 544, 561, 594, 595, 596, 600, 602
Clostridium butylicum 586
Clostridium kluyverii 348
Clostridium pasteurianum 551, 552
Clostridium perfringens 585, 325, 326
Clostridium butylicum 597
Clostridium welchi 557–558
Clupea harengus 249
Coacervates 441, 484, 491, 493–494, 579–580, 652, 654, 656
  enzymes in 429–431
  formation of 493–494
  lipoproteins in formation of 471
  long range forces in 393
  nucleic acids in 493–494
  preparation of 428–429
  relationship with enzymes 466–469
  sorption of enzymes by 467
Coal, composition of 92, Fig. 3
Cocarboxylase, synthesis of 286
Coelenterata, lipids and sterols in 508, 509
Coenzyme A 586, 643
Cold resistant enzymes 567
Coli-aerogenes group 596, 597, 600
Collagen 336
  amino acids in 236
  formation of 47
Collenia Walcotta 34
Complex compounds, activation of by adsorption 272–273
  aggravation theory of 266
  entropy differences in formation of 272
  enzyme models and 263–274
  hydrogen peroxide in 264, 270
  in relation to enzymes 263–274

Condensing enzymes 588
Configuration 396
Convergence, biochemical 507
Copper, catalytic activity of, energy involved 271
  oxidase activity of 269
Copper compounds, catalase-like activity of 264–267
Corals, amino acids in 225
Corticosteroids 514
Corticotropin 246
  amino acids in 235, 236, 243
Corycium 79
Corydalis ochotensis 578
Corynebacterium 332
Corynebacterium diphtheriae 225–226, 325, 326
Cosmic rays, influence on origin of life 107–108, 114
Coupling, chemosynthetic path of 614
Coupling mechanisms 441–442
Coxsackie virus 316
Crab nebula 107–108
Crossopterygian fish, amino acids in 227
Crustacea, lipids in 508
Cryohydric forces 392, 393
Cyclophorase 411–413
Cypridina 622
Cysteine, effect on synthesis of glutathione 575
  effect of on methionine 572–577
  in *neurospora crassa* 573, 574
  transformation of to methionine 573
Cystine, compounds formed from 625
  in plants 410
  peptide bonds in 233
Cytidine diphosphate 347
Cytidine monophosphate 346
Cytidine triphosphate 354
Cytidylic acid, in bacteria 324, 326, 328
Cytochrome 603
  effect of light on 607
  evolution of 559–560
  in bacteria 588
  in microbes 628
  in nitrate reduction 557, 558, 559
Cytochrome *c*, amino acids in 242
  in different species 242
Cytochrome oxidase 565–566
  affinity for oxygen 564, 567
  effect of environment on 570
  in animal metabolism 569–570
  in plant metabolism 564, 566, 567, 568
Cytochrome–oxidase system 462
Cytoplasm 359, 463
Cytosine, in bacteria 324, 325, 328

DDT 202
Decarboxylase 166
Dehydrogenases, models of 273

Deoxyribonucleic acid 352, 353, 581
  and hereditary changes in ducks 291
  artificial nucleoproteins made with 499
  complexes formed with 493–494
  effect on adolase 471
  effect on enolase 471
  effect on enzymes 476–478
  genetic role of 107, 117, 118, 381
  in adenosine triphosphate synthesis 358, 359
  in *Azotobacter agile* 323, 324, 325
  in bacteria 318, 319, 322, 323–330, 332–333
  in enzyme formation 458, 463
  in *Escherichia coli* 323, 324, 325
  in protein synthesis 363–366
  in replication of proteins 351–352
  in the dynamic state 336, 337
  protolytic activity associated with 498
  replication of 439–440
  specificity of 332–333
  structure of 217, 398
  substitutes for 359
Desoxyribose nucleic acid, formation of 47, 48, 49, 50, 51
Desulfovibria 556, 557, 558, 559
Devonian, organic catalysis in 180
Devonian beds, bituminous substances in 111–112
Diaminopimelic acid, formation of 195
  in bacteria and algae 225–226
Diaminosuberic acid, in bacteria 226
Diatoms, hydroxyproline in 225
Dichapetalium 80
Digestion, intracellular 510–511
p-Dimethylaminoazobenzol 353
Diphosphopyridine nucleotide 585
  in fermentation 596, 597
  reduction of 597
Dissociation, in photopolymerization 620
Dissymmetry, in origin of living material 95–104
  in primaeval protoplasm 96–98
  of living organisms 115
DNA viruses, origin of 49, 50
Dogs, cystine and methionine in 573–574
Drosophila, 'maternal effect' in 463
  mutation in 497
Ducks, deoxyribonucleic acid in 291
Dunites 23
  chemical analysis of 28
Dynamic state 368
  behaviour of 334–335
  chemical and biological exchange 335–336
  extent of 336–337
  origin of 334–342
  thermodynamic aspects 424

Earth, atmosphere of 16–19, 133, 134
  evolution of 54–65
  primary state 29–31
  core of 70
  crust of, at present time 23–24
    cold theory of 27–29
    composition of 33–35
    formation of 25–26, 33
    organic matter in 91–93
    thickness of 26–27
  formation of 9–14, 54–65, 67, 114
    from cold material 67–75
  geological condition of primaeval 84–85
  heat of 12–14, 16, 24–25, 31
  hot theory of formation 26–27
  loss of mass of 9–12, 13
  primaeval state of 9–14, 73, 113–114
    formation of organic compounds in 123–125
  radioactivity in primaeval 55, 57, 64, 73
  temperature of primaeval 55–56, 59, 60, 67, 73, 109, 110, 114
Earth–moon system 9–14
Echinodermata, lipids and sterols in 508, 509
  parallelism in 506
Egg albumin, amino acids in 236
  protein complex formed from 472
Egg cells, yolk globules 491
Egg protein 336
Electrical discharge, amino acids formed by 61, 77, 125, 128–130, 151–157, 256, 282
  organic compounds formed by 154–157
Electron transfer, in photocatalysis 609–612, 613, 615
Embden–Meyerhof-Parnas system 594, 595, 596
Energy transfer, in biological systems 615
  in photocatalysis 612–613, 615
Enolase, effect of deoxyribonucleic acid 471
Enterococcus stei 332–333
Entropy 438, 500
  in a closed system 487–490
  in biological systems 418–420
Enzymes 48, 79, 593
  action of in sedimentary formations 180–181
  activating effect of 185
  activity of 293
  activity of in proteins 289
  and protein complexes 472–473
  asymmetric action of 161–165
  bacterial 345, 354
  chemical models of 161–166
  classification 199–200
  cold-resistant 567
  complex compounds in relation to 263–274
  condensing 588
  conjugation with pigment systems 613–615

Enzymes—*continued*
control of by genes 248
cyclophorase system in 411–413
definition of 197
effect of light on 607
effect of nucleic acids on 475–478
evolution of 207–214
flavine 563, 564
fore runners of 198–204
formation of 43–44, 45, 458
  catalysis in 198, 201
  in nucleus 463–464
genetic fixation of 204–205
importance of 161
inactivation of 466
in amino acid biosynthesis 529, 530
in bacteria 632
in coacervates 429–431
in plant metabolism 563
in nitrate reduction 555, 560
in nitrogen metabolism 545
in protein biosynthesis 434–436
in sulphate reduction 555, 560
in uricolysis 512
in viruses 197
induced 203
models of and complex compounds 263–274
nitrogen fixation with 560
origin of 197, 206, 291, 339–341, 650, 651
originally formed, genetic fixing of 204
oxidation of ascorbic acid by 447–450
pyridoxal 529, 530
  effect on amino acids 531–532
  in porphyrin biogenesis 532–534
relationship with coacervates 466–469
relationship with genes 463
sorption of by coacervates 467
synthesis of ribopolynucleotides 344–356
Enzymic activity, in protein synthesis 377
of proteins 369
Enzymic coupling 441
Enzymic reactions in open systems 444–454
Enzymoids, synthesis of 147
Eobients 78
Ergosterol, complexes formed from 472, 473–475
Erwinia carotovora 325, 326
Escherichia coli 210, 332, 347, 348, 458, 556, 586, 589, 600, 601
  deoxyribonucleic acid content of 323, 324, 325, 326, 328, 329, 332–333
  nucleic acids in 300
  ribonucleic acid content of 323, 324, 325, 326, 329
Esterase 166
Etiolated plants, structural elements of cells of 404

Evolution 79, 82, 369
accelerating the tempo of 496–497
heteromorphic 507
of biochemical constituents 504–510
of biochemical systems 510–514
of chain processes 579–580
of chemosynthesis 614, 626–633
of metabolism, in microorganisms 516–525
of oxidative systems 562–571
organic molecular, order of formation of 42
rate of in Man 223
thermodynamic aspects of 418–427

Feed-back 492
Fermentation processes 594–596, 597
Fibroin, amino acids in 236
Fischer-Tropsch reaction 131
Flavine enzymes 563, 564, 565–566
Flavoproteins 560, 564, 565, 586
Fluctids 438
Fluctoid 438
Fluorine, in metabolism 80
Fluorocitrate, effect on amino acid synthesis 536, 537
Forces, types of interparticulate 392, 393, 394
Fore-protein, origin of 189–195
Formaldehyde, amino acids formed from 151
  formation of by electrical discharge 184
  by supersonic vibrations 173
  in ocean 183
Formamide, formed by ultraviolet light 137
Formate decomposition 600–601
Formic acid, synthesis of 125, 132, 624
Fossils, amino acids in 80, 227, 241
Fructicicola lantzi 178
Fusus antiquus 177

β-Galactosidase, formation of 458
Galaxies, supernovae in 108
Galionella 629
Gallus domesticus 249
Gas deposits, space distribution of 86–87
Gases, activated by supersonic vibrations 172, 173
  activated by ultraviolet light 136, 137
  formation of, in primaeval earth 57–61, 62, 64
Gelatine, amino acids in 236
Genes 463
  chemical nature of 107
  duplication of 217, 218
  nature of 313–320
  relationship with enzymes 463
  relationship with viruses 317, 319, 372, 373

Genetics, in origin of life 380–381
Germanium, relationship with carbon 80
Gilsonites, composition of 92, Fig. 3
Globia 336
γ-Globulin, amino acids in 236
Glucose, in plant metabolism 566
  nitrate reduction by 556
  oxidation of 590
Glutamic acid, amination of 547
  composition of 249
  in bacteria 226
  in nitrogen metabolism 546
  in plants 410
  synthesis of 144, 145, 195, 535
    by electrical discharge 125, 156
    by light 142
    by ultraviolet light 153, 154
  thermal treatment of 259
  transformation of 529, 530
Glutamine 578
  in protein synthesis 538–539
  nitrogen in 549, 550, 551, 552
  peptide bonds in 233
  synthesis of 548, 549
Glutathione, content of 575–576
Gluten, structure of 500
Glycine 644
  composition of 249
  deamination of 540, 541
  in haemoglobin 508
  in plants 410
  in protein synthesis 219
  peptide bonds in 233
  synthesis of 144, 151, 193, 624
    by electrical discharge 125, 128, 130, 156, 282
    by light 141
    by ultraviolet light 138, 153, 154
  transformation of 529, 530
Glycylglycine, formation of 257
Glycogen 581
Glycolic acid, formed by electrical discharge 125, 128, 130
Glycolysis 566, 569
  in animal metabolism 569
  in plants 566, 570
Glycolytic system 413
Glyoxylase 207
Glyoxylic acid, catalysis with 432
Golgi bodies, formation of 49, 50
Grahamites, composition of 92, Fig. 3
Gramicidin, amino acids in 236
Gramicidin S 229
Granites, chemical analysis of 28
Graphite, composition of 92, Fig. 3
Grass, amino acids in proteins of 410
Guanine, in bacteria 324, 325, 328
Guanosine diphosphate 347, 354
Guanosine monophosphate 347
Guanosine triphosphate 354
Guanylic acid, in bacteria 324, 326, 328

Guinea-pigs, cysteine and methionine in 573–574

Haem 642, 643, 645–646
  relationship with chlorophyll 212
Haematoporphyrin 610
Haemoglobin(s) 505, 507
  abnormal 222
  amino acids in 221, 222, 239
  amino acid sequences in 508
  in various species 506
  molecular weights of 508
  peptides in 239
  sickle cell 245
  species differences in 228, 244–245
  structure of 220
Haemophilia 246
Helices, formation of 391
Helium, from radioactive decay 29
  geochemical origin of 89–90
  in atmosphere 57, 58, 63
Hen, cytochrome *c* in 242
  hypertensin in 243–244
Heterotrophic photoassimilation 521–525
Heterotrophs, primaeval 209
Hexamethylenetetramine 183
Hippuric acid, formation of 257
Histidine, composition of 249
  in plants 410
  peptide bonds in 233
  synthesis of 143, 145, 193
Histone, protamine conversion in 252–253
Homogeny 506
Homolactic acid fermentation 595, 596
Homopolar forces 393
Homoserine, synthesis of by light 141
Horse, cytochrome *c* in 242
Horse radish 564
  peroxidase prepared from 445
Hot springs, flora of 652, 653, 655
Humins, in plants 410
Hydrocarbons, associated with oil 89, 90
  formation of 59, 65, 110, 111, 118
  in Devonian rocks 112
  in meteorites 72, 73
  in primaeval Earth 74
  vertical range of 87–89, 91
Hydrocyanic acid, formation of 173
Hydroformalation 131
Hydrogen, effect of supersonic vibrations on 172, 173
  escape of 213
  escape of from Earth 9, 17
  escape of from Mars 21
  escape of from Venus 20
  formation of 59, 118
  formation of organic compounds from 123
  geochemical origin of 89–90
  in atmosphere 62, 63–64, 109, 110, 114, 134

Hydrogen—*continued*
  in meteorites 71
  in primaeval atmosphere 114
  isotopic exchange of 335
  molecular, metabolism of 593–604
  organic compounds formed from 154–156
  photochemical production of 598–599
  production by anaerobes 597, 598–599
Hydrogen cyanide, formation of 172
  by ultraviolet light 131
  by electrical discharge 127, 130
Hydrogen donor utilization 611, 615–616
Hydrogen metabolism, in transitionary state between anaerobiosis and aerobiosis 593–604
Hydrogen peroxide, decomposition of 264, 270
  energy of activation 271
Hydrogen transfer, and porphyrin pigments 613
Hydrogenase 335
Hydrogenase systems, biological reduction and 596–599
  effect of oxygen on 600, 602
  in micro-organisms 594
  in transition from anaerobiosis to aerobiosis 600–601
Hydrogenomonas flava 629
Hydrolases 565
α-Hydroxybutyric acid, formation of, by electrical discharge 125, 128, 130
Hydroxyglutamic acid, synthesis of by light 142
Hydroxylamine 183, 545
Hydroxynitriles, hydrolysis of 128–130
L-Hydroxyproline, in animals 225
Hyoscyamus niger 480
Hypertensin 243–244

Iminodiacetic acid, formed by electrical discharge 125, 128
Imino-acetic-propionic acid, formed by electrical discharge 125, 128
Immunological specificity 216
Impsonites 92, Fig. 3
Inactis 34
Inclusion complexes, optical resolution by 160–161
Inert gases, in earth's atmosphere 9, 26, 29, 56, 61
  on Jupiter 11
Inosine diphosphate 345, 346, 354
Inosine monophosphate 346
Insecta, lipids in 508
  uricolysis in 513
Insulin, amino acids in 235, 236, 290
  fibrous-globular transition in 389
  species differences in 228, 241
  structure of 397

Intermedin 246
Invertase-protein complex 414
Iodine, effect of supersonic vibrations on 172
  in metabolism 81
Iodoacetate, effect on tobacco mosaic virus 305
Iron, catalytic properties of 207–209, 211
Iron ores, in the early biosphere 33–34
Iron porphyrin 210
Irradiation, influence on origin of life 107–108
Irreversible processes, thermodynamics of 418–427
*iso*Leucine, composition of 249
  in plants 410
  peptide bonds in 233
  synthesis of 193, 194
    by light 144
    by ultraviolet light 153, 154
Isology 504–505
Isonicotinylhydrazide, effect of transamination 536, 537

Jupiter, angular momentum of satellites 10
  atmosphere of 10
  composition of 10
  methane and ammonia in 71

Ketoaldomutase 162, 166
Klebsiella pneumoniae 332

Lactic acid, fermentation 595
Lactobacillus 226
Lactobacillus acidophilus 332
Lactobacillus arabinosus 332–333, 574
Lactobacillus casei 600
Lactobacillus leichmannii 332, 333
Lactobacillus plantarum 332–333
Lagoons, origin of life in 171
Lamprey, metabolism of 569
Lanthionine, in locusts 225
Leaf, ageing and regeneration of 480–484
Legumes, amino acids in proteins of 410
Legumin 579
Leguminosae 579
Leptotrix 629
Leucine, deamination of 540
  in haemoglobin 508
  in plants 410
  peptide bonds in 233
  reduction of 547
  synthesis of 193, 194
    by light 143
Leuconostoc 226
Leuconostoc citrovorum 332–333
Leucoplasts, transition to chloroplasts 404
Leucylglycine, formation of 257

Life, definition of 40, 78, 106, 116, 117, 118, 361–363, 368, 373, 378, 380
  dissymmetric sequence as a factor in 103–104
  dynamic state in 334–342
  geological conditions for appearance of 84–94
  metastable state in 337–339
  nature of 313–326
  non-cellular forms of 484
  on Mars 22, 113
  on Venus 20
  origin of on earth, *See* Origin of life on earth
  precellular forms of 484
  qualitative specificity of 380–381
Light, effect on enzymes 607
  formation of organic compounds by 140–149
Lignites, composition of 92, Fig. 3
Limnaea stagnalis 178
Linkage 388
Lipid membranes 441
Lipids 491
  in cells, 289, 290, 407
  in different species 508
  origin of 49–51, 52
Lipoproteins, role of in formation of co-acervates 471
  structure of 500
Liver, nitrogen metabolism in 541–542
  proteins in 337, 464
Living material, asymmetry in 182
Living organisms, duplication of molecules in 215–223
Long range forces 392, 393
Lonistes 177
Luciferin 622
Lysine, biosynthesis of 528, 530
  composition of 249
  in plants 410
  peptide bonds in 233
  synthesis of 145, 195
    by electrical discharge 156
    by light 142
Lysogeny 318–319
Lysozyme, activity of 431–432
  amino acids in 234, 235, 236

Macromolecules 486
Magma 109–110
Magnesium, in chlorophyll 213
Malaria 222
Malthes, composition of 92, Fig. 3
Maple-sap peptides 225
Mars, atmosphere of 11, 12, 21–22, 113
  biochemistry of 228
  carbon dioxide on 113
  composition of 70
  life on 22, 113

  oxygen on 132
  water on 113
Melampyrum nemorosum 496
Membranes, development of 340
  effect of in enzymic oxidation of ascorbic acid 452
  formation of 437–442
Mercury, composition of 70
  oxygen on 132
Mesogastropoda 177
Mesozoic reptiles 108
Metabolism, as criterion of life 106
  at different oxygen pressures 569–570
  effect of temperature on 569–570, 650–651, 652
  evolution of, in microorganisms 516–525
    nitrate reduction in 555–561
    sulphate reduction in 555–561
  in autotrophs 629, 630
  in simple proteins 275–280
  origin of 497
  transition from heterotrophic to auto-trophic 626–633, 650, 651, 652
Metal complexes, catalytic properties of 263
  role of oxygen in formation of 265
Metals, effect on tobacco mosaic virus 305
Metastable state 337–339
Meteorites 69, 71
  carbon in 72, 73
  chlorine in 72
  composition of 28
  gases contained in 71
  hydrocarbons in 72, 73
  nitrogen in 30
  radioactivity in 24
Methane, activated by ultraviolet light 136, 137
  formation of 84, 92, 110
  geochemical origin of 89–90
  in atmosphere 57, 59, 60, 61, 62, 63, 64, 65, 73–74
  in meteorites 71
  in oil fields 86, 88
  in primary atmosphere of Earth 30
  non-organic origin of 118–119
  on planets 71
  organic compounds formed from 123, 138, 151, 154
Methionine, effect of cysteine on 572–577
  effect on glutathione synthesis 575
  in plants 410
  peptide bonds in 233
  synthesis of 573
    by *neurospora crassa* 573, 574
N-Methylalanine, formed by electrical dis-charge 125
Methylglutamine 551
Methylurea, formed by electrical discharge 125
Micrococcus lactilyticus 597

Micrococcus lysodeikticus 348, 430, 431
Micrococcus pyogenes 332–333
Microorganisms, hydrogen metabolism in 593–594
Microsomes 363, 402
  biochemical activity in 415
  chemical composition of 407
  synthesis of amylase in 456, 457, 461
Milk protein 336
Minerals, in the body 334
Mineral world, relation with organic world 184–185
Mitochondria 49, 50, 213, 363, 402
  biochemical activity in 414
  chemical composition of 407
  protein synthesis in 497–498
  role of in protein biosynthesis 462
  synthesis of amylase in 457, 461
Mitogenetic radiations 145–148, 185
Mohorovičič discontinuity 23
Molecular structure 389, 390, 391, 392
Molecules, duplication of, in living organisms 215–223
Mollusca, digestion in 510
  lipids and sterols in 50, 509
  parallelism in 506
Molybdenum oxide, organic compounds formed from 140
Moon, angular momentum of 10
  composition of 70
  density of 70
  origin of craters 11
Moon–earth system 9–14
Motility 491–492
Mud, biogenesis in 182
Multiplet theory of catalysis 162
Multivariance of chemical reactions 293–294
Muscle, structure of 386–387
Mustard gas 353
Mustelus canis 507
Mutation 439, 497
  as criterion of life 106, 118
  in cell 463
  in proteins 353–354
Mycobacterium tuberculosis 325, 326, 471
Myoglobin, structure of 397
Myokinase 377
Myosin, hydrolysis of 277, 278
Myriapoda, lipids in 508

Nemathelminthes, lipids in 508
Neptune, ammonia in 71
  methane in 71
Nerve fibres, excitation of 492
Neurospora 145, 560
Neurospora crassa 573
Nickel-iron 70
Nicotiana sylvestris 480
Nitrate, biological reduction of 555–561

oxidation by 556
reduction by bacteria 556–560
  by glucose 556
  phosphate incorporation of 557, 558, 559
transformation of 545
Nitrides, in the primary atmosphere of Earth 29
Nitriles, hydrolysis of 128–130, 132
Nitrobacter 629
Nitrogen, activated by ultraviolet light 137
  autotrophic assimilation of 544–553
  dissimilation of 539–542
  effect of supersonic vibrations 172, 173
  effect of ultraviolet on 131
  formation of, by spark discharge 123
  formation of organic compounds by electrical discharge 126
  from volcanic activity 60, 64
  geochemical origin of 89–90
  in amino acids 547–551
  in asparagine 550, 551, 552
  in atmosphere 29, 57, 59, 61, 64, 78, 84, 109, 134
  in glutamine 549, 550, 551, 552
  in meteorites 30
  in plants 410
  in synthesis of amino acids 534–539
Nitrogen fixation 544–545, 551–552, 560, 602–604
Nitrogen metabolism 527–543, 544–553
  enzymes in 545
  in bacteria 544, 551, 552
Nitrogenous nutrition 527–528
Nitrosomonas 227, 628, 629
Norleucine, synthesis of by light 143
Nostocaceae 544
Nuclear transplantation 362
Nucleic acids 440, 653
  amounts of in cell units 407
  and protein synthesis 363–366
  and the origin of proteins 361–367, 374, 375
  as carriers of biological information 297–302
  diversity of 300–301
  effect on enzymic activity 476–478
  evolution of 358–360
  formation of 46–48, 51, 149, 394, 395
  formation of bonds with proteins 492–493
  genetic role of 107
  in bacteria, species specificity 322–330
  in cells 289, 290
  in coacervates 493–494
  in formation of proteins 282–283, 285
  in protein synthesis 219
  in tobacco mosaic virus 303–306, 319
  in viruses 371, 372, 373, 375
  infective from tobacco mosaic virus 303–306
  invariability of 300

Nucleic acids—*continued*
  irradiation of 145–146
  possessing virus-like activity 320
  regularity of 301
  species specificity of 322–330, 332–333
  structure of 222, 304, 395–396, 398
Nuceloproteids 116
Nucleoproteins, artificial 485
  as living organisms 315, 316
  deoxyribonucleic acid in synthesis of 375–376
  formation of 498–499
  nature of bond in 493
  structure of 398
Nucleotides 44, 51, 581
Nucleus, biochemical activity in 414
  chemical composition of 407
  of cell 362
  protein synthesis in 464
Nutrition, nitrogenous 527–528

Oceans 13, 14, 110
  amino acids on shores of primaeval 97
  endergonic reactions in primitive 42
  exergonic reactions in primitive 41–42
  formation of 73, 77
  organic compounds in 130
  origin of life in 169
  primary state of 31–32
Oil, space distribution of 86–87
  See also Petroleum
Oil fields, geological description of 88
Open systems, thermodynamics of 444–454
Optical activity, in racemates 158–161
  of organic substances 95–96
  origin of 184
Optical resolution, by inclusion complexes 160–161
Orchidaceae 116
Organic acids, formation of 72
Organic compounds, assymmetric synthesis of 114
  asymmetry of 174–175
  formation of 67–75
    by spark discharge 123
    by ultraviolet light 131–132, 136–139
    from carbon dioxide 133
    on primitive Earth 123–135
    role of acoustic energy 172–173
    under oxydizing conditions 133
  optically active 95–96
  preliminary to protoplasm 140–150
  primary synthesis of 109–110
Organic molecular evolution, order of
  formation of 42
Organic world, relation with mineral
  world 184–185
Origin of life on earth, and primitive
  planetary atmospheres 16–22
  chemical diversity and 76–83

conditions for 169–171
  earliest appearance of 34–35
  effect of temperature 650–651, 652
  influence of cosmic rays 107–108, 114
  influence of irradiation 107–108
  influence of ultraviolet light 124, 136–139
  multivariance of chemical reactions 293–294
  role of dissymmetry 95–104
  thermal theory of 256–261
  thermodynamic considerations of 418–420
Ornithine, synthesis of 142, 144, 194
Ornithine cycle 540, 541
Oscillatoria 409, 630
Ox, cytochrome *c* in 242
  hypertensin in 243–244
  insulin in 242
  vasopressin in 243
Oxidase-like activity, of copper 271
Oxidases 562, 564, 565, 570
Oxidation, in chemosynthesis 628
Oxidative phosphorylation, involvement of
  iron in 209
Oxidative systems, comparison of 652–571
Oxides, formation of 59
Oxoglutaric acid 538
Oxygen, activated by ultraviolet light 136,
  137
  appearance of free 586–587
    consequences of 587–591
  dependence of cytochrome oxidase on
  567
  effect on cytochrome oxidase 568
  effect on hydrogenase system 600
  first appearance in Earth's atmosphere
  18–19, 44
  formation of 59, 61, 62, 64, 77, 118
  in atmosphere 77, 84, 109, 170, 587, 600
  in formation of complex compounds 265
  in tissues 563
  liberation of in photosynthesis 212
  metabolism at different pressures of
  569–570
  on Mars 21
  oxidation by 556
  partial pressures in tissues 563
  transport of 505
Oxyminaline 225
Oxynitrilase 162, 166
Oxytocin, amino acids in 236, 243
Ozone, formation of 62, 213
Ozone screen 170, 183

Palaeozoic, solar radiation during 177
Pancreas, amylase formed from 455–457,
  460
Papain, effect on coacervates 467
Paraformaldehyde, organic compounds
  formed from 140, 146

Parallelism 506
Pasteur effect 95–96
Pasteurella pestis 599
Pasteurella tularensis 325, 326
Partula saturnalis 177
Peas, cyclophorase activity in 412
Peat, composition of 92, Fig. 3
Penicillin 471
Penicillinase 458, 462
Pentose cycle 591
Pepsin 289
  complexes formed from 475
  effect on coacervates 468
Peptide bonds 221
Peptides, abiogenic synthesis of 145
  amino acids in 224, 235
  formation of 51, 257
  thermal pathways of formation of 258
Peroxidase 564, 565
  in oxidation of ascorbic acid 445–453
Petroleum, *See also* Oil
  as source of life 84
  formation of 74, 119, 179–180
    asymmetric catalysts in 97
    inorganic 85–86, 112
    organic theory 91–93
    thermal conditions 90–91
  geochemical associates of 89–90
  in Archaean era 85
  optical activity of 177
  vertical range of 87–89
Petroleum bacteria 85, 179
Petroleum beds, formation of 71
Phaeophytin 610
Phenylalanine, deamination of 540
  in bacteria 226
  in plants 410
  peptide bonds in 233
  synthesis of 193
    by ultraviolet light 153, 154
  transformation of 529, 530
Phosphates, assimilation of by protoplasts 433–434
  chemosynthetic production of 614
  importance of in origin of life 44, 47, 51
  incorporation in nitrate reduction 557, 558, 559
Phosphoric esters, as criterion of life 78
Phosphorolysis 581
Phosphorus anhydride, in atmosphere 109
Phosphorylase 335, 336
Phosphorylation, photosynthetic 413
Photinus pyralis 622
Photoassimilation, heterotrophic 521–525
Photobacterium 622
Photobiological processes, relation between primitive and present day 619–625
Photocatalysis, back-reactions in 614
  development of 606–616
    electron transfer in 609–612, 613, 615
    energy transfer in 612–613, 615

mechanism of 609–613
Photochemical absolute asymmetric synthesis 103
Photochemical asymmetric synthesis 100–101, 102
Photopolymerization 619–621
Photosynthesis 62, 64, 404, 409, 587, 619–625, 630
  by ultraviolet light 136–139
  development of 210–214
  evolution of 44–45, 51, 52
  evolution of enzymes and 207–214
  in bacteria 521–522
  of carbon compounds 516–518
Photosynthetic phosphorylation 413
Phototrophic nutrition, origin of 635–640
Phototropism 622
Phycobilins 409, 612
Phycocyanin 409, 410, 612
Phycoerythrin 409, 410, 612
Phyllophora 617
Piezo effect 95
Pig, corticotropin in 243
  cytochrome *c* in 242
  insulin in 242
  oxytocin in 243
  vasopressin in 243
Pigment, development of 608–609
  in photosynthesis 621
Pigment systems, and hydrogen transfer 613
  conjugation with enzymes 613–615
Planets, atmospheres of, and origin of life 16–22
  biochemistry of 228
  life on 370
  origin of 67, 113
Planorbis 177
Plant cells, biochemical structure and function 404–407
  chemical composition of 407
  enzyme system in 411–413
Plant metabolism 645
  cytochrome oxidase in 564, 566, 567, 568
  enzymes in 563
  glucose in 566
Plants, ammonia fixation in 548
  carbohydrate metabolism in 564
  cyclophorase activity in 411
  oxidase enzymic system in 564–569
  oxidases in 565, 566
  photochemical apparatus in 210, 212
  respiration in 562, 563, 564, 568
  symmetry and asymmetry in 175–178
Plastids 49, 50, 402, 403
  biochemical activity in 415
  chemical composition of 407
  invertase-protein complex in 414
  proteins in 409
  structure of 500

Pneumococcus, transformation of 318
Polarized fluorescence 95
Polarized light, absolute asymmetrical synthesis in 101–103
photosynthetic influence of 176
Poliomyelitis virus 316
Polydehydroalanine, amino acids formed from 192–193
Polyglycine, action of aldehydes on 292
condensation of aldehydes with 190–191
formation of 189–190
Polymerization 439
Polymers 103
configuration of 396
formation of 46–48, 51, 52, 394, 395, 396
isotactic and syndiatactic 174, 175
structure of 394–396
Poly-metaphosphate 44
Polynucleotide phosphorylase 345–352
stereochemistry of 346
Polynucleotides, biosynthesis of 349
role of in cell 358, 359, 360
Polypeptide chains, configuration of 396–397
synthesis of 218, 219, 220–221, 292
Polypeptides, in origin of enzymes 201
Polyphenol oxidase 564, 565, 566, 567
Polyphosphates, significance of 374, 375
Porifera, lipids and sterols in 508, 509
Porphobilinogen 643
Porphyra tenera 409, 410
Porphyrin complexes 607
Porphyrins 644, 646
biosynthesis of 532, 534, 608
in formation of petroleum 90–91
in photocatalysis 609–612
in photosynthesis 213
photoreduction of 608, 609–611
synthesis of 647
Potassium, radioactive 115
Potato 565, 566
phosphorylase in 293
ribonucleic acid changes in 408
Pre-Cambrian 76
geological formations in 119
Pre-Cambrian strata, bituminous substances in 111
Prolactin 514
Proline, composition of 249
in plants 410
peptide bonds in 233
synthesis of 144
by light 141
Propionic acid, formed by electrical discharge 125, 128
Prosobranchia 177
Protamines 250
Proteases, effect of ribonucleic acid 471
Proteinases, inhibition of by ribonucleic acid 471

Protein(s), amino acids in 224–225, 227–228, 235, 409–411
amino acids in synthesis of 219
amino acid sequences in 379–380
as criterion of life 78
association with lipids and nucleic acids 500
catalytic structure 290–291
configuration of 396
continuity of 241–254
crystallization of 398
interparticulate forces in 393
effect of temperature on 655–656
egg 336
enzyme activity in 289, 369
evolution of 579
fibrous-globular transition in 389
folding of chains in 397
formation of bonds with nucleic acids 492–493
importance of in asymmetric adsorption 160
in cells 289, 290
in cell units 407
incorporation of amino acids into 276, 277–280
in seeds 579
interaction of 472
interactions of molecules in 492
irradiation of 148–149
isomerism in 492
liver 337
metabolic processes in simple 275–280
microheterogeneity of 470
milk 336
molecular structure of 286
mutation in 352–354
origin of 200, 201, 202, 281–288, 294, 369, 455–459
and nucleic acids 361–367, 374, 375
reduplication of 248, 284–285
relationship with deoxyribonucleic acid 375–376
replication of 219, 248, 439–440
deoxyribonucleic acid in 351–352
reproduction of 248–250
role of nucleic acids in formation of 282, 283, 285
serum 337
structure of 389, 397
peptide bonds in 233
similarities in 231–240
species differences 241–248
structure and function of 289
synthesis of 44, 46–48, 51, 52, 184–185, 247–248, 256, 275, 376, 379–380, 394, 395, 403–407, 432–433, 434, 455–459, 581
adenosine monophosphate in 365, 366
adenosine triphosphate in 365
cell structure and 460–465

Protein(s)—*continued*
  deoxyribonucleic acid in 363–366
  enzymic activity in 377, 379
  from amino acids 464
  from inactive precursors 247–248
  in bacterial cells 406
  in mitochondria 497–498
  in pancreatic amylase 455–456
  nucleic acids in 219, 363–366
  ribonucleic acid in 363–367, 376, 377,
    379
  role of chloroplasts 404–405
  role of coacervates 468
  role of mitochondria 462
Protein complexes, and enzymes 472–473
  as biochemically active systems 470–478
  fibrillar, formation of 494–495
  formation of 470
  formed from egg albumin 472
Protein enzymes 563
Protein–lipid complexes 472
Protein–sterol complexes 472
Protein structures, catalytic 290–291
Proteus morganii 325, 327
Proteus vulgaris 325, 326, 327
Protochlorophyll 610
Protoplanets 67, 68, 109
Protoplasm 400
  amino acids in 292
  compounds preliminary to 140–150
  optical activity of 115, 291–292
  primaeval, dissymmetry in 96–98
Protoplasts 432
  assimilation of phosphate into 433–434
  protein nitrogen in 435
  respiration of 432, 433
Protozoa, lipids in 508
Psalliota campestris 564
Pseudomonas 629, 630, 631
Pseudomonas aeruginosa 325, 326, 332
Pseudomonas fluorescens 588
Pseudomonas saccharophila 336
Purine bases, in bacteria 324, 325, 328
Purine nucleotides, in bacteria 324, 326,
    328
Purines, formation of 51
Pyridine, reduction of 647
Pyrimidine bases, in bacteria 324, 325, 328
Pyrimidine nucleotides, in bacteria 324,
    326, 328
Pyridoxal enzymes 529
  effect on amino acids 531–532
  in porphyrin biogenesis 532–534
Pyrophosphate 185
  effect on ribonucleic acid in tobacco
    mosaic virus 305
Pyrosynthesis 650
Pyruvate, amination of 536

Quartz, absolute asymmetric syntheses on
    161, 164, 165
  as catalyst for asymmetric syntheses 97
  asymmetric catalysis with 174
  dissymmetry in 176

Rabbits, cystine and methionine in 573–
    574
Racemates, asymmetrical decomposition of
    101
  resolution of 174–175
    by asymmetric adsorption 158–161
Radiation, effect on amino acids 145–149
  in formation of atmosphere 170–171
Radiation damage, protective agents 622–
    623
Radioactive heating 12, 24, 27, 35, 115
Radioactivity, in primaeval earth 12, 55,
    57, 64, 73, 115
Rats, methionine and cystine in 573–574
Reductase 162, 166
Reproduction, as criterion of life 106, 118
Reptiles, in Mesozoic age 108
Resonance, theory of 221–222
Respiration 562–563
  evolution of 557, 559–560
  in bacteria 589
  in plants 562, 563, 564, 568
Retinene 621
Retinin 513
Rhodopseudomonas 544
Rhodopseudomonas gelatinosa 521
Rhodopsin 513, 621
Rhodospirrillum 544
Rhodospirillum rubrum 594
Ribonuclease 289, 290
  action of enzymes 347
  effect on amylase 455
  in protein synthesis 364
Ribonucleic acid, as substitute for deoxy-
    ribonucleic acid 359
  biosynthesis of 581
  changes in plants 408
  combination with urease 499
  effect on chymotrypsin 471
  effect on proteinases 471
  in *Azotobacter agile* 323, 324, 325
  in bacteria 322, 323–330
  in enzyme formation 458
  in *Escherichia coli* 323, 324, 325
  in protein synthesis 363–367, 376, 377,
    379, 461
  in silk fibroin 379–380
  in tobacco mosaic virus 304, 350–351,
    495, 496
  instability of 304–305
  stereochemistry of 352
  synthesis of 48, 50, 362
Ribopolynucleotides, enzymic synthesis of
    344–356
Ring formation, in complex compounds
    266

Rubiacae 544

Sabellaria 505
Saccharomyces carlsbergensis 332
Saccharomyces globosus 435
Salmin, amino acids in 236
Salma fontinalis 249
Salmo irideus 249
Salmo lacustris 249
Salmo salar 249
Salmo trutta 249
Salmonella, transduction in 319
Salmonella enteritidis 332–333
Salmonella paratyphii 332
Salmonella schottmülleri 332
Salmonella typhimurium 325, 326
Salmonella typhosa 325, 326, 327
Salt, in body fluids and oceans 169–170
Sandal leaves, hydroxyproline in 225
Sapropelite substances, composition of 92, Fig. 3
Sarcina lutea 325, 326
Sarcosine, formed by electrical discharge 125, 130
  in groundnuts 225
Saturn, methane and ammonia on 71
Scenedesmus 594, 598
Seaweeds, proteins in 225
Sedimentary formations, enzyme activity in 180–181
Selenium 80, 225
Serine, composition of 249
  in haemoglobin 508
  in plants 410
  peptide bonds in 233
  synthesis of 144
    by light 141
    by ultraviolet light 153, 154
  transformation of 529, 530
Serum, cysteine content of 573–574
  methionine content of 573–574
Serum albumin, digestion of by trypsin 473–475, 476, 477
  proteolysis of 473, 474–475, 476, 477
Serum proteins 337
Sheep, corticotropin in 243
  insulin in 242
Shigella dysenteriae, deoxyribonucleic acid composition of 325, 327
  ribonucleic acid composition of 326
Shungite, composition of 92, Fig. 3
Silk fibroin 395
  amino acids in 290, 379–380
Snakes, evolution of venom apparatus 511
Soaps, interparticulate forces in 393
Soils and bogs, gases from 62
Solids, classification of 438–439
Specialisation, in evolution of biochemical systems 510–513, 514

Specificity 220
Spinach, amino acid composition of 410
Spindle, in mitosis 362
Spirorbis borealis 505
Spirorbis corrugatus 505
Spirorbis militaris 506
Sponges, proteins in 225
Spontaneous crystallization, in an optically active solvent 98
  initiation of by crystals 98
  of antipodes 96, 98–100
Spontaneous generation, chemical theory of 256–261
Staphylococci 335, 462
Staphylococcus aureus 348, 350, 434
Staphylococcus pyogenes aureus 325, 326
Starch, effect of amylase on 430
  in coacervates 429
Stars, binary 10
Statids 438
Stenoglossa 177
Sterols 51, 509
Strecker synthesis, of amino acids 129, 131–132
Streptococci 226
Streptococcus faecalis 332–333
Streptococcus haemolyticus 348
Streptococcus pyogenes 332
Streptolysin 348
Structural units in biopoesis 385–399
Structure, complimentariness of 216
  motility in 491
  origin of 497
Succinic acid, formation of by electrical discharge 125, 129–130
Sugar beet, chloroplasts of 402
  proteins in 409
Sugars, origin of 43, 45, 51, 52
  synthesis of 184
Sulfomonas denitrificans 520
Sulphate, biological reduction of 555–561
  oxidation by 556
  reduction, in bacteria 560
Sulphur, in primary atmosphere of earth 30
Sulphur bacteria 516, 628, 629, 630, 632
  photosynthesis in 518–519
Sulphur compounds, as radiation protective agents 622–623
  importance in photosynthesis 621, 622
  in primary oceans 32
  in sedimentary rocks 34–35
Sun flower, ribonucleic acid changes in 408
Supernovae 107–108
Supersonic vibrations, chemical reactions due to 172–173
Synaeresis 182

Tactoids 394

Temperature, effect on early forms of metabolism 650–651, 652
  effect on metabolism 569–570
  effect on plant respiration 568
  of primaeval Earth 109, 110, 114
  origin of life at high 655
Template hypotheses 439
Tertiary period, enzyme activity during 181
  flora and fauna 116
  formation of organisms during 178
Thermal reactions, of amino acids 256–261
Thermodynamics, of irreversible reactions 418–427, 485–490, 500
  of open systems 444–454
Thermophilic organisms 652
Thiobacillus 210
Thiobacillus denitrificans 520
Thiobacillus thiooxidans 227, 628, 629
Thiobacillus thioparus 629
Thiotrix 629
Threonine, composition of 249
  in plants 410
  peptide bonds in 233
  synthesis of 143, 145
Thymine, in bacteria 324, 325, 328
Thyroid gland, proteins in 225
Tipula virus 393
Tobacco, protein in cells of 405
Tobacco mosaic virus 286, 314, 342, 370–371, 372, 378, 495, 496
  effect of iodoacetate on 305
  effect of metals on 305
  infective nucleic acid from 303–306
  long range forces in 393
  ribonucleic acid in 350–351, 408
Tomato bushy stunt virus 390
Torulopsis utilis, amino acids in 227
Transamination 535–539
Transduction 318–319, 371, 372
Triboluminescence 95
Tricarboxylic acid cycle 588, 589, 590
Triphosphopyridine nucleotide 586
  in fermentation 596, 597
  reduction of 590–591, 597
Trypsin 492
  complexes formed from 473
  digestion of serum albumin by 473–475, 476, 477
  proteolytic activity of 473–475, 476, 477
Trypsinogen 237, 238
Tryptophan, deamination of 540
  formation of 193
  in plants 410
  peptide bonds in 233
Tunicates, vanadium in 79, 80
Turnip yellow virus 390
Tyrocidin, amino acids in 235, 236
Tyrosinase 566, 569
Tyrosine, formation of 193
  in bacteria 228

  in plants 410
  in the thyroid 225
  peptide bonds in 233

Ultraviolet light, activating gases 136, 137
  amino acids formed by 151–157
  chemical action of 96
  effect on origin of life 124, 136–139
  organic compounds formed by 131–132, 136–139
  photosynthesis by 136–139
  screening of by ozone layer 183
Uniformitarian principle 38, 76–77
Uranus, ammonia on 71
  atmosphere of 10
  composition of 10
  methane on 71
Urea 578
  biosynthesis of 540, 541
  formed by electrical discharge 125
Urease, combination with ribonucleic acid 499
Urechis caupo 507
Uricolysis, enzymes in 512
Uridine diphosphate 347, 348, 349, 354
Uridine monophosphate 346, 347, 349
Uridine triphosphate 354
Uridylic acid, in bacteria 324, 326, 328
Uridylitic acid 351
Uroporphyrins 646

Vaccinia 315
Valine, composition of 249
  in haemoglobin 508
  in plants 410
  peptide bonds in 233
  reduction of 547
  synthesis of 193, 194
    by light 144
    by ultraviolet light 153, 154
Vanadium, in tunicates 79
Vasopressin, amino acids in 235, 242
  species differences in 228, 243
Venoms, evolution of 511
Venus, atmosphere of 19–21, 84
  composition of 70
  oxygen on 132
Vibrio spp. 226
Vicilin 579
Vigna sesquipedalis 558
Virus(es) 341–342, 371, 372, 373
  enzymes in 197
  growth of 286
  nature of 313–320
  nucleic acids in 371, 372, 373, 375
  nucleoproteins in 493
  origin of 284, 285
  protein synthesis in 364

Virus(es)—*continued*
  relationship with genes 317, 319, 371, 373
  shell of 390
  size of 314
  tobacco mosaic, *See* Tobacco mosaic virus
  transformation of types 318
Vision 621
Vitamin A 513
Vitamin B_1, in synthesis of cocarboxylase 286, 287
Vitamin B_6, effect on transamination 536, 537
Volcanic activity 55, 56, 60, 109
  gases produced by 60, 64, 73
Volcanos 11–12, 13, 27
  composition of gases from 29
  in origin of moon's craters 11

Water, activated by ultraviolet light 136, 137
  effect of supersonic vibrations 172, 173

importance of in origin of life 169–170
  in atmosphere 57, 84, 109, 110, 134
  on Mars 21, 113
  organic compounds formed from 126, 138
Water vapour, escape of 12–13, 14
  in primary atmosphere of earth 31
  on Venus 19, 20
Wheat, cytochrome oxidase in 565
Wood, composition of 92, Fig. 3

Xanthine oxidase 471, 564

Yeast, enzymic synthesis in 345
  nitrogen metabolism in 548
  ribonucleic acid in 377, 379

Zone melting 28
Zwitterions, interparticulate forces in 393
Zymogen granules 456, 457